The Good Food Guide *1991*

The Good Food Guide *1991*

Edited by Tom Jaine

Published by Consumers' Association
and Hodder & Stoughton

Which? Books are commissioned and researched by
The Association for Consumer Research and published by
Consumers' Association,
2 Marylebone Road, London NW1 4DX and
Hodder and Stoughton,
47 Bedford Square, London WC1B 3DP

Special thanks for this year's *Guide* to Michael Frith for
the cover illustration, Mon Mohan for the cover design, Tim Higgins
for the typography. The Maps are by Bartholomew,
A Division of Harper Collins Publishers

British Library Cataloguing in Publication Data
Jaine, Tom
    The good food guide
    1991
I. Restaurants, lunch rooms, etc.–
    Great Britain – Directories
    I. Title   II. Consumers' Association
    647'.9541'05   TX 10.G7
ISBN 0-340-52816-8

Photoset in Linotron Meridien Medium
by Tradespools Ltd, Frome, Somerset
Printed and bound in The Netherlands
by Rotatie Boekendruk B.V., Krommenie

Contents

Restaurants

Features

So, have restaurants improved?

It is almost 40 years since the first, pocket-sized edition of *The Good Food Guide*, edited by Raymond Postgate, appeared in 1951. Is everyone agreed that the restaurants of Great Britain are better now? Would Raymond Postgate think his battle won? Many would think not.

A restaurateur of long-standing, having opened his premises in 1952, the second year of *The Good Food Guide*, reflected this year that in those days his greengrocers were providing matchless quality (even if not flown in from the tropics); that the baker was producing bread to the restaurant's own recipe, as enjoyable as any eaten today (if less internationally voguish); that the butchers knew their meat, knew how to kill it, hang it and cut it up; that fish could be ordered from Billingsgate as they went to bed at 2am and be with them (by train) at 7am; and that a network of gardeners, farmers, shooters and trappers could be constructed as easily then as now. There was not the knowingness that we encounter today; restaurants were not switched on to the latest rave of California; nor did they try to ape the dairy practices of the Auvergne. That is what we have gained after forty years of consumption, of benefiting from the information explosion.

Sophistication is more widely spread and the number of restaurants is greater, but I would suggest they are not, overall, better. Things that irritated Postgate still needle us today. Humbug is as rife as it ever was; so, too, is processed food, even if it is harder to detect. The fast-food revolution has flavourised cheap eating, but it rarely tastes better – and costs a lot more. Most significantly, Britain still has great wastes where good food is hard to find.

The Guide's intentions have not changed: to signal good food wherever it may be had, to foster the appreciation of good food and to draw from the real experiences of paying customers. Over the years, a system has been constructed: people who buy and use the *Guide* are automatically members of the Good Food Club; they submit, in their thousands, reports on delights and disasters in restaurants across the land. These reports are read by me, invariably acknowledged or answered, and filed for action towards the next edition. If a place is new, or a candidate for re-entry in the *Guide*, we send at least one inspector; if complaints are received about an established business already in the book, we send inspectors again. No place appears as a main entry without inspection.

Who are our inspectors? They are customers like the rest of us, who have been particularly assiduous in sending us reports, with whom, therefore, we have built up a rapport; people whose judgement we trust and whose comments we understand. They are not usually catering professionals, simply very experienced customers; most cook at home and know their onions from their shallots. The cost of their inspection meals, always conducted anonymously, are borne by the *Guide*.

The system, which has served us well, only prospers if people keep writing to us. This year the number of letters has increased and we thank you for them. The more we have, the better our intelligence and the more shades of opinion we can build into our reports.

A misapprehension common among the subjects of this *Guide* – the chefs and restaurateurs – is that the bulk of our post is carping and critical. They tend to assume that if a dissatisfied customer storms out of the restaurant swearing vengeance through our agency, he will send off darts of opprobrium as soon as he gets home. We do get that sort of letter but we are as able as anyone to allow fair play to balance its more extreme sentiments. Most of our correspondence is affirmative, urging the claims of this or that restaurant. Letters may express support with qualifications, but they are constructive.

A pre-occupation of commentators on last year's edition was our enthusiasm for bread, some ridiculing us for spending more than a few phrases on one chef's production. How can one of the most basic foodstuffs be a matter for ridicule? If every restaurant were able to bake a matchless loaf (or buy it) and if every diner knew one when they saw one, cooking would be better throughout the country. As it is, we accept mediocrity and congratulate anyone who bakes it themselves, no matter what it tastes like.

Money, heroes and villains

Inflation is still with us and a major topic of discussion has been the cost of eating out in 1990. There is a whole series of myths surrounding this, as well as hard fact. Some of them are addressed by Tim Hart in a feature towards the end of the book. The nub of the problem is that the fixed costs of owning and running a restaurant have squeezed the profit margins far more severely than any food price or staff wages increase. Because most restaurants in Britain are floated on a raft of borrowed capital, they are very susceptible to interest rate changes, made worse by new arrangements in local taxation. As property prices have risen, over the last ten years, too many restaurateurs have needed a capital larger than their business could support. Sale values, as the market turns down, only make matters worse.

Customers are feeling the pinch just as much, as mortgage payments take up more of their income. A falling income from a declining customer base is difficult to counteract. One way is to put up prices, and risk alienating the ever-decreasing number of clients. Not every proprietor has the courage or ability to break out of the vortex.

Within this picture of gloom there are heroes and villains. Heroes are those who have tried for a formula other than the luxury restaurant with expensive draped tablecloths and many staff. Many have explored the concept of the brasserie, cooking slightly less elaborate dishes, offering fewer frills, charging a price that can be afforded by many. Others have revived the British café, sometimes with a vegetarian bias, or sought to cook good food within the context of a pub, both operations encouraging less formal eating and a faster throughput of customers – essential if margins are to be kept tight.

The villains are the big corporations that carry on producing mediocre food in fancifully luxurious surroundings at ludicrous prices. Others who deserve short shrift from the consumer are the restaurants who charge an arm and a leg, yet do not manage to maintain reasonable consistency. A bill of £100 or more for two people should guarantee at least that. Were an outfitter to supply a suit with gaping seams, he would remedy the deficiency. It is not enough to merely shrug and admit to having 'a bad night'.

One reason why British catering has been through some lengthy bad patches is that the biggest investment of bricks and mortar and money has been in pubs. These have concentrated on liquid, not solid refreshment, and for the most part are owned by multiples which were, until recently, uninterested in food. The natural spot for a light meal in almost any street, town or village should be a pub. Yet for decades they were innocent of anything more enterprising than packet crisps and pasties.

The shake-up in pub ownership that might have put hundreds more into private ownership is still in progress. It has not been as thorough-going as it could have been and the emergence of mini-chains of themed restaurants using processed food is not encouraging. None the less, pubs are still the brave frontier for restaurateurs: income assured from bars, rapid turnover of customers, a sense of serving the local community. When we asked our inspectors for nominations for good pub food, the litany of 'good for a pub' or 'not bad but not *Good Food Guide* standard' was monotonous. Low standards in popular catering continue to persist: custard powder, stock cubes, frozen this and canned that are fine for pubs, runs the argument, just as sliced bread is all right for sandwiches. Well, it isn't.

How fresh is fresh?

1990 saw the continuation of problems associated with the safety of our food supply. As if salmonella in eggs and chicken were not enough, BSE and pollution of shellfish from algae off the north-east coast of England and Scotland were two major issues concerning the safety of the food supply, compounded by moves at government level to allow irradiation of raw foods. All these have heightened awareness of the potential danger of food processing.

Cooks and chefs are at the end of the food chain, much as any private household, but they have buying power and their opinions and preferences have the weight of professional experience. We can look to the best of them to search out wholesome ingredients and condemn bad practice. The *Guide* identifies and applauds restaurants that show determination in offering organic vegetables and fruit and the manifold produce of the individuals and small businesses who consciously distance themselves from factory farming and intensive arable husbandry, preferring to devote their energies to growing food with *taste*. Many of those businesses, indeed, survive only on restaurant custom.

It would be comforting to think that all restaurants in the *Guide* pursue enlightened buying policies. Perhaps one day it will come to this. However, the absence of any rules of disclosure and rather foggy laws about misleading descriptions leave menus a minefield for the interested customer. 'Fresh orange juice' still comes out of a packet so-labelled in too many hotels and restaurants; 'fresh tomato soup' is still made with tinned tomatoes, too.

In 1945, it was obvious when peas had come out of a tin. In 1990, the *sous-vide* duck breast in cherry sauce may fool the world, especially if it comes with the implied assurance of a chef in his whites and the panoply of a fancy restaurant. While the deception works a few times, even the most imperceptive may begin to realise that the dish lacks taste and texture, especially when brought up short by the real thing from a decent kitchen. The proposed amendments to the Food Labelling Regulations (issued as the *Guide* was about to go to press) are encouraging signs that, for irradiated foods at least, there is growing recognition of the consumer's right to information, even at the dining table. It is intended that restaurants, take-aways and other food retailers should disclose when ingredients have been subjected to irradiation and that this information should be shown on a 'menu, notice, ticket or label that is readily discernible by an intending purchaser at the place where he chooses the food.' This will perhaps change our perception of honest menu-writing. Why, after all, should restaurateurs be allowed to hide the origins and preprocessing of any foodstuffs offered for sale?

Tips, smoke and muzak

While some are enraptured by the variety of experience open to them in British restaurants, there are not a few who would wish it to be more predictable. Questions abound: what sort of food does the restaurant serve? will your meal be ruined by cigar-smoke-drift? will your ears be assaulted by pop songs, Viennese waltzes, or Bach on automatic replay? what should you wear? do you have to tip? whom do you have to tip? The list could go on. It's not surprising that both restaurateur and customers would like to see some clear lead being given. Restaurateurs want to avoid complaint and warring factions; customers want to eat with no insidious doubt or distasteful intrusion. Compromise seems far away and unlikely to occur without external encouragement. For this reason, we urged last year that tipping should be regulated out of existence, just as this year we would urge the same with smoking in restaurant.

No one really likes tips, even serving-staff. As the world becomes more complicated, cash loses its charm. As one family man, head-waiter in a super-deluxe hotel, observed, 'Tips don't help you get a mortgage.' For the young and unattached who make up the bulk of the labour force, cash supplements may be welcome but what hope does this industry have to improve labour recruitment if it continues to rely on them? Doubts may also be raised about the true destination of a tip. Does it go to the staff? Is it taxed? What about the service charge? There are plenty of instances of waiters having their wages paid out of the percentage supplement. In other instances the tips may be funnelled into the owners' holiday fund. None of this is healthy; nor is the practice of leaving the credit card total empty, despite the fact that service has already been included. Many restaurateurs say they would like to improve matters but are inhibited by competition. Catering is highly price-sensitive, so there may be some validity in their claim. There is no reason why eating in a restaurant should not be a simple commercial transaction and maybe we need to think more effectively of how to ensure this. It did not, after all, take the government long to sort out the matter of including V A T on menu prices.

Smoking in restaurants is a similar topic: customers and proprietors would equally like to see it regulated. No chef enjoys the sight of a diner taking the last puff of a king-size over a plate of sweetbreads with tarragon and chives, any more than the neighbours of our addict relish the cedary bouquet of Latour '62 mixed with the wastes of a smouldering butt. Dr Johnson observed in 1705 that the habit of smoking was on the wane: 'To be sure, it is a shocking thing, blowing smoke out of our mouths into other people's mouths, eyes and noses.' Well, he was wise, but he was wrong in his forecast. The question of smoking excites too many passions, growing every year, for it to be ignored by the community at large. There is no reason why smoking in public places should not be banned. Smokers and non-smokers alike, whenever they are polled, seem to welcome the prospect. All manner of praise should go to those restaurants which manage to control it of their own accord, but we should also spare a little sympathy for some who feel they cannot. An interesting case was brought in a small claims court this year, after a customer left a restaurant without paying, because he has been asked to stop smoking. There were no signs forbidding it in the restaurant itself, but the proprietor and the other customers that night did not wish him to continue. The proprietor won her claim (for non-payment and lost profit) because, the registrar said, there is *no presumption that you may smoke* in a restaurant. If you are asked to desist by the owner, you should obey.

Aural pollution is different, but no less pernicious. We signal in the *Guide* places that do play music, but next year we will positively seek out and notify you of those where you can eat to the sole accompaniment of champing, movement of glass and cutlery and the happy sound of conversation. It has to be agreed that a country restaurant occupied on a winter's night by a handful of couples, married for 40 years, may benefit from a spot of Vivaldi, otherwise there is that terrible spiral of whispering – softer and yet softer – as eavesdroppers are identified and avoided. Yet restaurants are insensitive to the distress that music can cause, particularly when they repeat the second movement of Grieg's piano concerto for the fourth time of an evening.

These aspects of dining out have all turned on the restaurateur: on the treatment, as well as the food, he or she dishes out to customers. There is traffic in the reverse direction. Some of the rights and obligations of customers are set out in our brief legal appendix, but one in particular needs to be stressed: turning up at a restaurant where you have booked a table. 'No-shows' have caused consternation for many years, especially when margins are tight. The contract implicit in a table reservation is enforceable in law; the producer is entitled to the lost profit if the table cannot be re-let. Many restaurants are turning to the hotels' ploy of asking for a credit card number when the booking is made, ensuring automatic deduction of the lost profit (but only that, please) if no one turns up. One cannot but regret the procedure: it is untidy, potentially troublesome – yet, so they claim, mightily effective. Such mutual distrust can be avoided only by proper behaviour.

Drinking matters

As each entry in this *Guide* gives details about the restaurant and the cooking, so it also mentions wine. We dish out awards – a glass or a bottle – for good lists worth investigating and for outstanding lists almost worth a visit for themselves alone. Serving wine is almost axiomatic in any restaurant, though visitors to Chinese, Indian or Thai establishments may prefer other drinks. Many people, however, do not drink alcohol or prefer it in small quantities. Neither party gets much joy from the condition of tap water, or the paucity of half-bottles on too many wine lists.

We all object when the perceived value of a commodity bears no relation to its end-costs. Mineral water and wine are prime examples of this in restaurants. The restaurant answer is that each customer must deliver a certain gross revenue and its apportionment through the meal 'experience' is unimportant. Rather than load it all on to the food, put some on to ancillaries. The same argument is deployed on the wine list as a whole. Flat percentages are levied on wines costing £100 as well as those at £7. This makes good wine seriously expensive and helps few people. The idea of a reduced percentage as the value creeps up needs to be encouraged. Although the overall standard of wine lists has improved greatly in the past decade it still leaves much to be desired. There is no need to stock or sell bad or uninteresting wines. All it needs is thought and enthusiasm – and a good supplier – to convert a list of two dozen boring old Beaujolais, Anjou rosés, cooking claret and token Spaniard into a fistful of treasures (costing no more, save in effort). Positive efforts are visible in London, but the message still needs to be rammed home. Restaurants need to consult range of price as well as fair margins. It is of little comfort if all the bottles cost £50, even if that is auction or retail price with no profit. There is just as much fun to be had from things under £15, and often as much quality. See page 000 for a list of bottles that restaurateurs would do well to stock, and that consumers can look for. Many wine lists could be improved with some effort, even when the cellar is a good one. Muddle, different vintages brought to table, and lack of advice are endemic. Far be it that we should encourage flatulent paeans to each bottle, but intelligent arrangement and head notes can only promote enjoyment.

Value judgements

The *Guide* comes under attack for its coverage from inside and outside London. On the one hand, dwellers in the capital maintain that it discriminates against many passable London restaurants and over-values some in the counties; on the other, there are those who live in provincial centres, often light of *Guide* entries, who say we are toffee-nosed and can't recognise good when we see it. Guides do apply relative as well as absolute values. A restaurant in London might in some senses be a good one in Staffordshire yet remain very undistinguished by contrast to its metropolitan neighbour. A good restaurant in Northumberland might not be highly regarded in the South East. That there is a difference between regions is inescapable, but we often make that plain and we set the best in a national context. The same set of criticisms, and rejoinders, might be made with regard to cost. Evidently a place that charges £5 operates according to a different set of rules (though not values) to one that sees £50 as the norm. Context is important and it would be foolish to ignore it.

Tom Jaine

The top-rated restaurants

Mark 5 for cooking

London

Chez Nico, W1
Le Gavroche, W1
Tante Claire, SW3

England

Le Manoir aux Quat'Saisons,
    Great Milton
L'Ortolan, Shinfield

Scotland

Altnaharrie Inn, Ullapool
Peat Inn, Peat Inn

Mark 4 for cooking

London

Alastair Little, W1
L'Arlequin, SW8
Bibendum, SW3
Capital Hotel, SW3
Cavaliers, SW8
Clarke's, W8
Connaught, W1
Four Seasons, Inn on the Park, W1
Harvey's, SW17
Oak Room, Meridien Piccadilly
    Hotel, W1
Le Soufflé, Inter-Continental Hotel,
    W1
Sutherlands, W1

England

Adlard's, Norwich
Box Tree, Ilkley
Carved Angel, Dartmouth
Castle Hotel, Taunton
Chez Nous, Plymouth
Croque-en-Bouche, Malvern Wells
Gidleigh Park, Chagford
Lettonie, Bristol

Manleys, Storrington
Marryat Room, Chewton Glen
    Hotel, New Milton
McCoy's, Staddlebridge
Miller Howe, Windermere
Morels, Haslemere
Oakes, Stroud
Old Manor House, Romsey
Old Vicarage, Ridgeway
Poussin, Brockenhurst
Redmond's, Cleeve Hill
Restaurant 19, Belvedere Hotel,
    Bradford
Seafood Restaurant, Padstow
Sharrow Bay, Ullswater
Waterside Inn, Bray
Winteringham Fields,
    Winteringham

Scotland

Airds Hotel, Port Appin
Kinnaird House, Dunkeld
La Potinière, Gullane

Wales

Plas Bodegroes, Pwllheli
Walnut Tree Inn, Llandewi Skirrid

15

Restaurants with outstanding wine cellars

marked in the text with a 🍾

London
Au Jardin des Gourmets, W1
Bibendum, SW3
Capital Hotel, SW3
Gilbert's, SW7
Leith's, W11
Mijanou, SW1
190 Queensgate, SW7
Pollyanna's, SW11

England
Bell, Aston Clinton
Brookdale House, North Huish
Carved Angel, Dartmouth
Cobwebs, Leck
Corse Lawn House Hotel, Corse
   Lawn
Croque-en-Bouche, Malvern Wells
Dundas Arms, Kintbury
Epworth Tap, Epworth
Fountain House, East Bergholt
French Partridge, Horton
George, Stamford
Gidleigh Park, Chagford
Gravetye Manor, East Grinstead
Harvey's Cathedral Restaurant,
   Lincoln
Hope End, Ledbury
Lake Isle, Uppingham

Manor, Chadlington
Old Manor House, Romsey
Old Vicarage, Ridgeway
Redmonds, Cleeve Hill
Röser's, St Leonard's
Sir Charles Napier Inn, Chinnor
Le Talbooth, Dedham
Tarts, Bath
Thornbury Castle, Thornbury
The Three Lions, Stuckton
Village Restaurant, Ramsbottom
White Horse, Inn, Chilgrove
White Moss House, Grasmere

Scotland
Airds Hotel, Port Appin
Ard-Na-Coille Hotel, Newtonmore
Cellar, Anstruther
Champany Inn, Linlithgow
Cross, Kingussie
Knipoch Hotel, Oban
Peat Inn, Peat Inn
La Potinière, Gullane
Ubiquitous Chip, Glasgow

Wales
Meadowsweet Hotel, Llanrwst
Plas Bodegroes, Pwllheli
Walnut Tree Inn, Llandewi Skirrid

County restaurants of the year

Our indulgence. The restaurants listed below are not invariably the best (highest rated) in their respective counties, but they are the ones that have caught the eye this year, engendered most excitement, or generally seemed laudable enterprises. Not all counties have an award winner.

England

Avon Lettonie, Bristol

Berkshire Waterside Inn, Bray

Buckinghamshire Pebbles, Aylesbury

Cambridgeshire Midsummer House, Cambridge

Cheshire Arkle, Chester Grosvenor Hotel, Chester

Cornwall Well House, St Keyne

Cumbria Sharrow Bay, Ullswater

Derbyshire Fischer's at Baslow Hall, Baslow

Devon Table, Babbacombe

Dorset Bridge House, Beaminster

East Sussex Little Byres, Dallington

Essex Dickens, Wetherfield

Gloucestershire Epicurean, Stow-on-the-Wold

Greater Manchester Quan Ju De, Manchester

Hampshire Dew Pond, Old Burghclere

Hereford & Worcester Hope End, Ledbury

Hertfordshire Mims, Barnet

Humberside Epworth Tap, Epworth

Kent Eastwell Manor, Boughton Lees

Lancashire Cobwebs, Leck

Leicestershire Hambleton Hall, Hambleton

Lincolnshire Black Swan, Beckington

Merseyside Rondelle, Birkenhead

Norfolk Moorings, Wells-next-the-Sea

North Yorkshire McCoy's, Staddlebridge

Northamptonshire Roundhouse, Roade

Northumberland Funnywayt'-mekalivin, Berwick-upon-Tweed

Nottinghamshire Les Artistes Gourmands, Nottingham

Oxfordshire Le Manoir aux Quat' Saisons, Great Milton

Shropshire Country Friends, Dorrington

Somerset Ston Easton, Ston Easton Park

South Yorkshire Greenhead House, Sheffield

Suffolk Martha's Vineyard, Nayland

Surrey Le Berger, Bramley

Warwickshire Restaurant Bosquet, Kenilworth

West Midlands Nuthurst Grange, Hockley Heath

West Sussex Manleys, Storrington

West Yorkshire Paris, Leeds

Wiltshire Lucknam Park, Colerne

COUNTY RESTAURANTS OF THE YEAR

Scotland
Central Braeval Old Mill, Aberfoyle
Fife Ostlers Close, Cupar
Grampian Silver Darling, Aberdeen
Highland Ard-Na-Coille, Newtonmore
Lothian Martins, Edinburgh
Strathclyde October, Glasgow
Tayside Kinnaird House, Dunkeld

Wales
Clwyd Starlings Castle, Chirk
Dyfed Harbour Lights, Porthgain
Gwynedd Old Rectory, Llansanffraid Glan Conwy
South Glamorgan Egerton Grey County House, Porthkerry
West Glamorgan Keenans, Swansea

How to use this *Guide*

All the entries in this year's *Guide* have been rewritten between April and August. The information on which they are based is from reports sent in by readers over the last year and confirmed by anonymous inspection. No entry is based on a single nomination. In every case readers and inspectors have been prepared to endorse the quality of the cooking, the dining-room and the value for money.

The rating system grades restaurants, on the basis of their cooking only, from 1 to 5. This takes no account of elegance, ambience, service or value. The marks take into account the perception of the *Guide* and its reporters, and signify the following:

1 **Competent cooking** Restaurants that achieve a satisfactory standard, endorsed by readers as worthy of the *Guide*.

2 **Good cooking** Restaurants that produce good food in most departments, though some inconsistencies may have been noted. They please most readers much of the time.

3 **Very good cooking** The kitchen achieves consistent quality, rarely disappointing in any department. Seldom faulted by *Guide* reporters.

4 **Excellent cooking** Restaurants with a high level of ambition and achievement. Generally, they delight.

5 **The best** These may excite debate, not as to whether the cooking is good, but whether it is better than their peers'.

The *Guide* office is reliant on proprietors for price information. Each year owners are asked to mark on a questionnaire the cost, for autumn of that year, of any set meals, and also the lowest and highest à la carte prices for each course. Our computer then adds the quoted price for coffee, service, and half a bottle of house wine per head. For à la carte prices it calculates the strict average cost. In practice, however, most people do not eat an 'average' meal, but may have drinks before the meal, drink a more expensive wine, and choose at least some top-flight dishes. The result can be a bill much higher than expected. Also, prices are likely to rise during the currency of the *Guide*.

To try and satisfy everyone, the *Guide* continues, in the prices below the entry, to give the average cost of three-course meals as calculated by computer and double-checked. However, above the entry, the cost quoted gives the lowest such price, and the highest such price inflated by 20 per cent to bring some realism to bear on the likely upper limit.

How to read a *Guide* entry

CANTERBURY Kent [1]   map 3 [2]

▲ *Mary's Kitchen* [3] ▮ ♟ [4]

16 Elwood Avenue, Canterbury CT41 4RX [5]
CANTERBURY (0227) 7770666 [6]   COOKING 2 [8]
behind Scala Cinema [7]   COST £19−£24 [9]

(main text) [10]   CELLARMAN'S CHOICE [11]

CHEF: Mary Smith   PROPRIETORS: Mary and David Smith [12]
OPEN: Mon to Sat [13]
CLOSED: Aug [14]
MEALS: 12 to 2, 7 to 9 [15]
PRICES: £13 (£19), Set D £15 (£20), Snacks from £1.50. [16] Service 10% [17]
CARDS: Access, Amex, Diners, Visa [18]
SEATS: 72. 4 tables outside. Private parties: 26 main room, 10 private room. [19] Car-park, 40 places. Vegetarian meals. [20] Children's helpings. No children under 10. [21] Jacket and tie preferred. [22] No-smoking area. [23] Wheelchair access (2 steps; also WC). [24] Music. [25] One sitting [26]
ACCOMMODATION: 14 rooms, all with bath/shower. B&B £20 to £40. [27] No pets. [28]
Afternoon teas. [29] Garden. Swimming-pool. Tennis [*Which? Hotel Guide*] [30]

---

1 The town and county (in the London section, restaurants are listed alphabetically by name rather than geographically).

2 The map number. The maps are at the end of the *Guide*.

3 The name of the restaurant. ▲ by the name denotes that it offers accommodation too.

4 ♟ denotes a wine list that is good, well above the ordinary. The symbol ▮ indicates a truly outstanding wine list.

5 The restaurant's address, with post code whenever possible.

6 The restaurant's telephone number, including its STD code.

7 Any special directions in case the restaurant is difficult to find.

8 The *Guide*'s mark, out of five, for cooking quality, ranging from 1 for competent cooking to 5 for the best. See page 19 or the inside of the front cover for a full explanation.

9   This is the price range for three-course meals, based on our computer's calculation of an average three-course meal, including coffee, wine and service, according to prices provided by the proprietor. The top figure, however, has been inflated by 20 per cent to reflect (i) that many readers do not eat an 'average' meal and are therefore shocked when, with extra drinks and some top-range dishes, the bill rises well beyond the average price, and (ii) likely price rises that will come into play during the life of the *Guide*.

10   The text is based on reports sent in by readers during the last *Guide* year, confirmed by commissioned, anonymous inspections.

11   Most entries conclude with a CELLARMAN'S CHOICE . This is a wine, usually more expensive than the house wine, that the restaurateur assures us will be in stock during 1991, and recommends as suitable for the kind of food served, if you do not want to order the house wine.

12   The names of the chef and the owner, so that any change in management will be instantly detectable.

13   The days of the week the restaurant is open.

14   Annual closures.

15   The times of first and last orders for meals. It is always advisable to book before going to a restaurant. If you book and then cannot go, please remember to phone the restaurant to cancel.

16   These are average prices for three-course meals, giving the à la carte price and variations for set lunch (L) and dinner (D) where applicable. The initial price represents the prices on the main menu; the second price, in brackets, is the real cost when the extras of house wine, coffee and service (at 10% unless otherwise specified) have been added.

17   This indicates that a fixed service charge will be added to the bill. Where service is included in the menu prices this is specified. When service is not mentioned, it is at the discretion of the customer.

18   The credit cards accepted by the restaurant.

19   Not all restaurants will take private parties. The maximum number of people in a party is given.

20   Many restaurants claim to cater for vegetarians but do not include suitable dishes on their menus as a matter of course. It is always advisable to explain, when booking, if you do not eat meat.

21   Some restaurants and hotels are not keen on children. Where it says children welcome or children's helpings, this indicates that they don't mind. Any limitations on age are specified.

22   Jackets and ties are compulsory in very few restaurants and this is specified; otherwise it means the proprietor prefers smart dress.

23   Any no-smoking arrangements as given to us by the restaurants.

24   Wheelchair access means that the proprietor has confirmed that the entrance is 33 inches wide and passages four feet across. Where there are steps it will say so. If it says 'also WC', then the owner has told us that the toilet facilities are suitable for disabled people. The *Guide* relies on proprietors giving accurate information on wheelchair access. If you find the details in the *Guide* are inaccurate, please tell us.

25   If a restaurant plays music, this is specified.

26   The restaurant serves a single sitting at a specific time.

27   The price for rooms as given to us by the hotels. The first price is for one person in a single room, the second is the upper price for two people in a double room.

28   Some hotels will not take pets; others prefer to be asked. It is best to check.

29   Teas are served to non-residents.

30   [*Which? Hotel Guide*] denotes that this establishment is also listed in the 1991 edition of our new, sister guide to over 700 hotels in Britain.

London

Alastair Little

map 14

49 Frith Street, W1V 5TE
071-734 5183

COOKING 4
COST £49

Halfway up Frith Street, the plain shop front patterned only by venetian blinds
is broached to reveal an interior of no more adornment. Bare black tables, board
floor and simple chairs fill the room as far as a plunging spiral staircase to one
side and an open doorway to the kitchen to the other. Only some large loud
paintings give colour – that is, except the customers who are usually animated,
and the staff who exude an accessible big city cool. Alastair Little and Juliet
Peston change the menu at every meal, not root and branch, but if they run out
of turbot, say, they replace it with whatever is the best buy that day. A printed
menu set in stone can curdle the brain. This immediacy means that few dishes
stay the same, even though the repertoire is obviously repeating. Customers
and staff are kept on their toes. Even a basic such as fish soup may be
'traditionally brick coloured one day, with a coarse texture; velvety smooth
with chunks of fish another; a delicate consommé with hints of sweetness with
a glistening selection of scallops, fish fillets and mussels a third.' There are two
underlying themes binding the variety together: Japanese sushi and Italian
vegetable cookery and materials. Sushi, from the chef on duty in the basement
bar, is produced for its own sake – be warned of the explosive heat of the
wasabi (horseradish) – and serves as inspiration for other raw food
combinations. The Japanese influence merges with California in the enjoyment
of chillies and other hot seasoning. A salad of lobster tails surrounds a heap of
couscous done to the right tenderness and moistness, a deep-coloured sauce of
tomato, pimento, chilli and garlic giving sweetness and heat. A sashimi of
scallops sits atop a pile of cooked spinach. These dishes might be found on the
Pacific Rim. Italy is the second pole: bruschetta, crostini, risotto, asparagus
with parmesan and olive oil, vitello tonnato or quail with polenta, mushrooms
and deep-fried sage. To these sources is joined a delight in relishes, another
New World tendency. Griddled escalope of salmon with pablano and black-
bean relish and coriander sauce is an example from a summer menu, which
substituted tuna the next day. The range of dishes has summer and winter
sides: *pot-au-feu* or meats wrapped in ham and cabbage appear more regularly
in the cold along with, perhaps, a long-cooked ox-tail, not perfectly trimmed,
that would feed a giant for a day, with an exactly seasoned swede purée to
lighten the blow. Among the dishes that get repeated mention are crostini, 'a
signature dish of stunning colour: eight piles of marinated vegetables like
small mountains of emeralds, rubies and onyxes'; wild mushroom risotto;

focaccia with ceps, mascarpone and white truffles; very fine gravlax; lobster and hake with aïoli; grouse on foie gras and a croûton to soak up the juices; carpaccio with rocket and artichoke hearts with truffle oil; partridge with braised cabbage; bream (inadequately scaled) with scallop sauce; salt cod with a pimento sauce. Desserts sometimes come as an anticlimax to all that colour and bravura, but please with such as chocolate mousse cake with vanilla ice-cream and Bourbon sauce; good sorbets; or crème brûlée with fantastic raspberries. There is no point in saying it is all marvellous because an identifiable fraction think it is not. There are those who cannot abide the noise and bareness of it, at the price; others find the service too distant and at times unfamiliar with the menu. There are nights when it does not gel – the dish was too little practised, the seasoning omitted, a basic of preparation elided. More thoughtfully, some find the conjunction of barely cooked elements seriously at odds with classic ideas on Western cookery, their disparity overshadowing any enjoyment. The wine list consists of two dozen whites and two dozen reds of which half are French. It changes too frequently to make recommendations, but the choice is invariably interesting and makes room for geographical oddities, even if none for rare and old treasures. House wine is £12 for a Côtes de Buzet or a Muscadet-sur-lie. Go down that spiral staircase to reach the small dug-out bar – surely it must have been a Soho gambling den – where a short menu of sushi, sashimi and other first courses from the menu upstairs are served. It might be expensive as a snack but imaginative and worthwhile as a light meal. No booking down below and no credit cards anywhere. This is one 'famous' restaurant where 'I can eat in my scruffy jeans when I've finished work at 10pm' or 'go back in and ask for some water for the car radiator without embarrassment.' It's just a place, run by people, and happens to serve very fine food.

CHEFS: Alastair Little and Juliet Peston   PROPRIETORS: Mercedes Andre-Vega, Kirsten Pedersen and Alastair Little
OPEN: Mon to Sat, exc Sat L
CLOSED: bank hols
MEALS: restaurant 12.30 to 2.30, 7.30 to 11.30; bar 12 to 2.30, 6 to 11.30
PRICES: £30 (£41), snacks in the bar from £4
SEATS: 38. Private parties: 8 main room. Vegetarian meals. Children's helpings. Wheelchair access (2 steps)

Al Hamra   map 13

31–33 Shepherd Market, W1Y 7RJ   COOKING 2
071-493 1954 and 6934   COST £25–£36

A well-staffed restaurant with an authentic air which gets very busy at night. It is almost best at lunchtime, especially outside in hot weather. The menu changes not a lot from year to year, save prices, and the meze are the thing. Charcoal-grilled main dishes are numerous but the palate may enjoy the greater variety of the first courses. There are daily specials that involve braising, such as 'labban immo', lamb cooked in yoghurt, or 'kibbeh labanieh with shish barak', cracked wheat and minced lamb cooked in yoghurt, with pasta parcels of lamb and onion. A cover charge is justified by the small greengrocer's stall and olives that are parked on your table to while away the time before the meal. Meze that have been approved include 'sanbousak', deep-fried pastry turnovers filled with lamb, onions and pine nuts; 'moutabel', aubergine with sesame and oil and lemon; 'foul moukala', fried broad beans with garlic and coriander; and 'sojuk sadah', hot Armenian sausages with a fried egg if you want. Breads are good. Drink mineral water. Service is still very patchy, partly due to press of business.

CHEF: Hassan Mardani   PROPRIETORS: R. Nabulsi and H. Fansa
OPEN: all week
CLOSED: 25 Dec and 1 Jan
MEALS: noon to midnight
PRICES: £12 (£25), Set L £15 (£25) to £18 (£28), Set D £15 (£25) to £20 (£30). Cover £1.75
CARDS: Access, Amex, Diners, Visa
SEATS: 73. 4 tables outside. Private parties: 80 main room. Vegetarian meals. Children's helpings. Wheelchair access. Music

Andrew Edmunds
map 13

46 Lexington Street, W1R 3LH   COOKING 1
071-437 5708   COST £23

Young staff, young crowd, old house. It can be a happy place to have a meal: the wine list is very good and the food is good in parts. A superlative cullen skink may be balanced by decidedly below-par grilled sardines. 'Tataki beef' shows wider horizons than used to be the case. The owner once described himself as serving 'clubby food'. It is a 'clubby' place and much loved by 'members'. It does not help to increase 'membership' to berate publicly someone who elects not to leave the 'optional service charge'. For this reason alone, the pressure on businesses to make them change such practice is justified. On Saturdays and Sundays, the restaurant is open non-stop from 12.30 to 10.45. Wines change frequently. House wine: £6.95.

CHEF: Paul Croal   PROPRIETORS: Andrew and Bryony Edmunds
OPEN: all week
CLOSED: 24 Dec to 3 Jan
MEALS: 12.30 to 2.45, 6.30 to 10.45
PRICES: £12 (£19)
CARDS: Access, Visa
SEATS: 48. 2 tables outside. Private parties: 30 private room. Vegetarian meals. Children welcome. No pipes in dining-room

Anna's Place
map 11

90 Mildmay Park, N1 4PR   COOKING 2
071-249 9379   COST £23

It's so popular, and so is its owner, that people cry 'shame!' that Anna Hegarty goes on holiday. Her relaxation is well deserved, though some couples – forced to co-operate with two inflexible sittings on busy nights – wish her restaurant were a little less popular. The place has cluttered charm, the owner and staff much character. The cooking is Swedish and famous for its gravlax. There are modern touches along the lines of chicken breast stuffed with leek, cheese and peanuts served with ratatouille, or cinnamon pears with an apricot sauce. The style is quite direct: marinated herring; a red venison with a horseradish cream; smoked mackerel salad; or lingonberry parfait. It is wholesome and conspicuously fair value. This carries over into the short carefully chosen wine list, and there is Swedish beer and schnapps. House wine: £6.15.

CHEFS: Ross Mason and Craigh McKechnie   PROPRIETOR: Anna Hegarty
OPEN: Tue to Sat
CLOSED: 2 weeks at Christmas and Easter
MEALS: 12.15 to 2.30, 7.15 to 10.30
PRICES: £14 (£19). Service 10%
SEATS: 52. 5 tables outside. Private parties: 10 garden room. Vegetarian meals. Children's helpings. Wheelchair access. Music

L'Arlequin

map 10

123 Queenstown Road, SW8 3RH   COOKING 4
071-622 0555   COST £23–£56

One reader manages a lunch here at regular intervals with half a bottle of wine and it rarely comes to more than £60 for two. As many of the dinner menu dishes will find their way on to the lunch offerings, this may be a relative bargain, just as in so many London restaurants. With fine cooking, plenty of space and light in quietly elegant rooms on the Queenstown Road, and usually good service, the questions are best reserved for the value of the evening meal. The *carte* is short with seven choices supplemented by daily fish and perhaps one or two extras. Choice is further restricted in first courses because one of them is Beluga caviare at £40, a reasonable possibility for very few. The cooking is very refined, though there is normally at least one dish that shows earthiness, whether it be stuffed cabbage *à l'ancienne*; scallops with robust tomato sauce, basil and garlic; ox cheek braised with an onion confit; or lambs' tongues with lentils. This refinement has more often this year been characterised as occasional dullness, understatement to a fault, or lack of sufficient distinction to place it firmly above other kitchens. It is none the less cooking of great skill and capable of giving great pleasure: from the amuse-gueule of tiny mushroom tart and baby fish mousseline and the crusty but flavourful bread rolls to a superb squab pigeon from Bresse cooked with cherries and served with mushroom and leek raviolis that succeeds in letting the pigeon flavour through, yet affords subtle combination when eaten with the ravioli or with the bed of spinach on which the dismembered bird is laid. Sauces may sometimes lack elaboration, as in a fillet of beef with bone marrow where the red wine sauce 'was almost evanescent in flavour and added nothing save lubrication.' Judgement is apparent in a pair of courgette flowers, one stuffed with a courgette mousse on a hollandaise, the other with a feather-light salmon mousse on a fresh tomato sauce. 'The one was strong and smooth, the courgette mousse as resonant as guacamole and the sauces had the right degree of acid to offset the unctuousness of their vehicles.' Vegetables have not impressed beyond accurate cooking, and the parsimonious portions of potatoes – usually a made dish such as rösti, dauphinoise or lyonnaise – have been noted. Desserts are classical: a chaud-froid of raspberries; marquise served in thin, not thick, slices; very good crème brûlée; an orange, banana and grapefruit terrine; and vibrant sorbets, even of kiwi-fruit. They please mightily but do not surprise. Service is not always as knowledgeable, or as comprehensible, as it should be; it is not satisfactory that staff do not know what they are serving. The wine list is comparatively short and suffers from the need to load up with prestige bottles within limited space. This makes for a strange price spread: there are four clarets at £20 or less, one at £27.50, then 12 between £45 and £210. In defence, it is one of the few London places of this calibre that still has bottles priced in single figures, and there is real choice among decent bottles below £15.

CHEFS/PROPRIETORS: Mr and Mrs Christian Delteil
OPEN: Mon to Fri
CLOSED: 1 week winter, 3 weeks Aug
MEALS: 12.30 to 2, 7.30 to 10.30
PRICES: £42 (£47), Set L £18.50 (£23). Service inc
CARDS: Access, Amex, Diners, Visa
SEATS: 45. Children welcome. Smart dress preferred. No pipes in dining-room. Wheelchair access (also WC). Air-conditioned

▲ Auberge de Provence, St James's Court Hotel

map 11

51 Buckingham Gate, SW1E 6AF
071-821 1899

COOKING 3
COST £27–£74

The decoration of this artfully designed restaurant may not prepare some people for a very expensive meal. Hard surfaces, Provençal-style chairs and Artexed walls smack of taverna and trattoria, even if in their native province they might simply be a natural reaction to the heat and dust beyond the windows. The Auberge has continued to be a branch of L'Oustau de Baumanière, with new chef Olivier Massart coming from its platoons to do his London posting. The Provençal tilt of the long menu is emphatically modern. None of your simple pissaladières, aïoli garni or bouillabaisses here. A summer meal began with ravioli of scallops and micro-chopped ratatouille in a dill cream; a feuilleté of asparagus with a fresh coriander mousseline; and a liver mousse with scallops arranged round it. Main courses were tiny medallions of lamb stuffed with vegetables and laid on a light vegetable-based sauce; and a large piece of sea bass on a bed of tomato, with four steamed slices of aubergine, the sauce being aromatic virgin oil and basil. Desserts come from a trolley, just like the very fine range of cheese, but they are buttressed by a list of hot or composed dishes left for the kitchen to prepare. Crêpes soufflés Baumanière get rave comments, as do three mousses glacées with their sauces. The trolley does not always get the same support. The level of achievement at present seems very high. House wines are £9.50 and front a list supplied by L'Oustau itself of mainly French wines.

'We've completely refurbished the ground floor and banished the loathed woodchip and Dralon to the scrapheap. We've also made the restaurant itself non-smoking now - a move which has met with more approval than we anticipated from our customers.'
Gloucestershire restaurateur

LONDON

CHEF: Olivier Massart   PROPRIETORS: TAJ International Hotels
OPEN: Mon to Sat, exc Sat L
MEALS: 12.30 to 2.30, 7.30 to 11
PRICES: £31 (£45), Set L £19.50 (£27) to £25 (£33), Set D £30 (£40) to £50 (£62)
CARDS: Access, Amex, Diners, Visa
SEATS: 80. Private parties: 40 main room. Vegetarian meals. Children welcome. Smart dress
preferred. Music. Air-conditioned
ACCOMMODATION: 390 rooms, all with bath/shower. Rooms for disabled. Lift. B&B £142 to
£174. Baby facilities. Afternoon teas. Garden. Sauna. Air-conditioning. TV. Phone

Au Bois St Jean   map 11

122 St John's Wood High Street, NW8 7SG   COOKING 1
071-722 0400   COST £15–£34

Jean Claude Broussely remains as chef though the ownership of this basement
restaurant has changed. The policy, however, has not: it is still a Gallic
neighbourhood place with a French staff and French cooking at affordable
prices. Some redecorating and upgrading has been done. The regular menu is
on expected lines: snails, fish soup, garlic mushrooms, duck with prunes and
honey, rack of lamb, steak au poivre, nougat glacé, tarte Tatin, chocolate
mousses. Daily specials may strike a little further afield – chilled cucumber
soup with basil, guinea-fowl in a vol-au-vent case with prawns – but the
essence is indeed in its predictability, down to the set price (bar supplements).
People like this, and regulars find it an acceptable version of French country
cooking, just the thing for a leisurely Sunday lunch. The wine list has grown
somewhat in new hands but is still entirely French and rather dependent on
wines from the big houses. The growth area has been in fancier bottles, at a
price. House wine: £7.45.

CHEF: Jean Claude Broussely   PROPRIETORS: Bestmill Ltd
OPEN: all week D, Sat L
MEALS: 12 to 2.30, 7 to 11.30
PRICES: Set L £9 (£15) to £20.25 (£28), Set D £16.75 (£24) to £20.25 (£28)
CARDS: Access, Amex, Diners, Visa
SEATS: 65. Private parties: 20 main room, 25 private room. Vegetarian meals. Children's
helpings (L only). Smart dress preferred. Music

Au Jardin des Gourmets   map 14

5 Greek Street, W1V 5LA   COOKING 3
071-437 1816   COST £26–£44

A long established Soho fixture, the restaurant has recently been extended by
half: a good example of invisible mending. The result upstairs is a series of
private rooms for hire; downstairs there are now smoking and non-smoking
sections. The curved mirrors and green banquettes lay claim to a vaguely 1930s
inspiration but the effect is more late 1970s. This has been faithfully
reproduced in the new dining-room. Most striking are the owner's collection of
pictures crammed on to available wall space. Service is relaxed but efficient.
The good-value set-price menu at £16.50 offers three starters and three mains
and is written in French; the extensive *carte* is in French and English. Chef

28

Nicolas Picolet now seems to be in his stride after a shaky start. His cooking betrays the influence of Paul Bocuse, with whom he worked for a couple of years. A gazpacho aux langoustines was reported as having 'vibrant flavour' but the tomato and garlic overpowered the crustaceans. Warm scallop and potato salad emerged as 'fine slivers of sweet, intensely flavoured scallops on a bed of thinly sliced potatoes, pan-fried to pre-caramelisation.' Sea bass, sauce vierge, achieves unusual equilibrium, the fish matched by a chervil, fennel, chive, onion and basil vinaigrette. Bresse pigeon has distinctive flavour. Apple tart with tarragon is another less than common combination. Cheeses from Harvey and Brockless are French and well kept. Chocolates are also fresh. The wine list is a balancing act of intelligence and fairness. With many decent bottles below £10, the range extends through a catalogue of internationally renowned growers – Heitz in California, Vega Sicilia in Spain and Dom. de Trévallon in Provence – to good-value older clarets such as Ch. Cissac 1970 at £29.50, the first of a run of 12 from that year. Half-bottles are well provided. A model of charity in presentation, it is altogether a drinker-friendly list.

CHEF: Nicolas Picolet   PROPRIETORS: Au Jardin des Gourmets Ltd
OPEN: Mon to Sat, exc Sat L
MEALS: 12.30 to 2.30, 6.15 to 11.15 (11.30 Sat)
PRICES: £25 (£37), Set L and D £17.50 (£26). Service 15%
CARDS: Access, Amex, Diners, Visa
SEATS: 150. Private parties: 50 private rooms. Children's helpings on request. Separate smoking area. Wheelchair access. Air-conditioned

Bahn Thai

map 14

21A Frith Street, W1V 5TS   COOKING 2
071-437 8504   COST £28

Enthusiasts breathed a sigh of relief when Philip Harris announced that Bahn Thai was not going to close. This Soho restaurant is still the benchmark for Thai cooking in Britain and it continues to offer challenging, authentic food with only the occasional disappointment. Readers always have plenty to say, and there has been the usual abundant crop of recommended dishes. The menu is long and wide ranging, but everything is accurately described. Excellent starters have included spring rolls with plum sauce; satay with a perfectly balanced peanut sauce; and grilled king prawns with tamarind sauce. Elsewhere on the menu, fish dishes bring in most reports: steamed mussels with lemon grass; squid with yellow beans and spring onions; and crispy fried pomfret coated with chilli and tamarind sauce have all been good. 'Deceptively hot' green papaya salad comes with sun-dried shrimps or with salted baby crabs roughly crushed into pieces (one of the restaurant's most prized specialities). The cooking needs balance, contrast and complexity to succeed and the Bahn Thai gets full marks on all levels. Consider a chicken curry, creamy at first, then followed by 'a forearm smash of heat' and backed up by the sweetness and texture of baby Thai aubergines. Glutinous rice, noodles and stir-fried vegetables are generally up to the mark. The home-made ice-creams are memorable. While there is plenty of praise for the cooking, readers are less happy with the decor and service. The restaurant, especially the downstairs room, has always been cramped, but recently it has taken a turn for the worse.

There are complaints about scruffiness, dusty fittings, stained tablecloths and unhelpful, off-hand service. Now that closure is no longer threatened, perhaps these details will be dealt with. 'Thai food offers a formidable challenge,' says a note on the wine list. Intelligent selection combined with very fair prices for central London encourage up-take of the challenge. The list reads well, with good clear descriptions and special sections devoted to Sauvignon and Gewürztraminers which suit the food admirably. Otherwise there is Thai beer and chrysanthemum tea. House French £6.95.

CHEF: Penn Squires   PROPRIETORS: Bahn Thai plc
OPEN: all week
CLOSED: some bank hols, some days at Christmas and Easter
MEALS: 12 to 2.45, 6 to 11.15 (12.30 to 2.30, 6.30 to 10.30 Sun)
PRICES: £16 (£23). Cover 75p (D only). Service 12.5%
CARDS: Access, Amex, Visa
SEATS: 100. Private parties: 25 main room, 35, 50 private rooms. Vegetarian meals. Children welcome. No cigars/pipes in dining-room. Wheelchair access (also WC). Music. Air-conditioned

Bambaya   map 10

1 Park Road, N8 8TE   COOKING 1
081-348 5609   COST £22

Rosamund Grant's co-operative takes in more cuisines than just Caribbean, drawing on the southern United States and Africa for inspiration and working them into her own interpretation. The dining-room is cool and understated with a raised platform on one side; it gives the impression of space and calmness. The food is spicy, but not as hot as might be expected, and its fire is tamed by generous use of coconut. Dishes that have pleased have included 'Stamp and Go', torpedoes of salt-fish deep fried, served with a warm chutney; sobito, a creamy chowder that tasted like a Mediterranean fish soup with coconut, with generous chunks of fish; 'run-down fish', pomfret in a coconut sauce; a mild Louisiana king-prawn creole. Rice and peas, and good salads mean that vegetarians have a look in. The ice-creams, of which one is coconut, are very rich. Anyone with a liking for coconut will be happy here.

CHEFS: Rosamund Grant and Jenny Agada   PROPRIETORS: Bambaya Restaurant Ltd
OPEN: Tue to Sun, D only
CLOSED: bank hols
MEALS: 6.30 to 11 (10.30 Sun)
PRICES: £11 (£18). Cover 50p
CARDS: Access, Amex, Visa
SEATS: 45. Private parties: 45 main room. Vegetarian meals. Children's helpings. Wheelchair access. Music. Air-conditioned

The Guide *office can quickly spot when a restaurateur is encouraging customers to write recommending inclusion - and sadly, several restaurants have been doing this in 1990. Such reports do not further a restaurant's cause. Please tell us if a restaurateur invites you to write to the* Guide.

La Bastide

map 14

50 Greek Street, W1V 5LQ
071-734 3300

COOKING 1
COST £28–£41

A bastide was a fortified town in medieval Gascony. Its role was both to hold
the frontier line against incursion and to extend the benefits and influence of
one side to the other, by means of concentrated settlement. Thus, into a fine
Georgian house in Greek Street have been poured the benefits of French
cooking: a bastion against England. Its commanding officer is Nicolas
Blacklock who has taken upon himself the role of apostle, cooking both a
general *carte* and a monthly French regional menu that serves as an exposition
of good old French values. Casseroles are not ignored, offal is enjoyed, and
while the *carte* explores modern variations such as courgette flowers stuffed
with a lobster mousse, the regional menu goes for (Burgundian in this case)
oeufs en meurette, quenelles de brochet à la lie de bourgogne, coq au vin, côte
de veau à la dijonnaise. The setting, English historical domestic, is enjoyable;
the price is not high for London; the service is French and sometimes fitful; the
food is likewise. While some reports speak glowingly of escalope of veal with
limes, carré d'agneau on a bed of spinach, onion soup, sorbets or a gratin of
apples with calvados, others have suggested that leaden duck and poor cooking
are no way to extend benefits. The carefully chosen wine list has equally
Francophile tendencies; prices for Central London are very fair. A good range
takes in most French regions, but nothing beyond the hexagon. There are some
mature clarets, a nice range of Beaujolais and strong representation from the
south-west. Half-bottles of white number three, but there are a few more reds.
The list of armagnacs is remarkable.

CHEF: Nicolas Blacklock   PROPRIETORS: Nicolas Blacklock and Susan Warwick
OPEN: Mon to Sat, exc Sat L
CLOSED: bank hols
MEALS: 12.30 to 2.30, 6 to 11.30
PRICES: £22 (£34), Set L and D £18.50 (£28) to £21 (£31)
CARDS: Access, Amex, Diners, Visa
SEATS: 45. 3 tables outside. Private parties: 60 main room, 75 private room. No children
under 11. Air-conditioned

Bedlington Café

map 10

24 Fauconberg Road, W4 3JY
081-994 1965

COOKING 1
COST £13

In a parade of small shops in residential Chiswick, the restaurant has a decor
like a thousand and one English cafés: lino floor, Formica-topped tables, Coke
machine. The difference is the food during the evenings, which is Thai. Good,
fresh ingredients are in absolute evidence and, apart from one complaint for
'tough, bland beef', the major gripe is 'dinky' portions. Spring rolls with
pancake-like wrapping, 'quite a change from the crispy, splintery version'
were ultra fresh with good dips. Baby squid was 'out of this world, the subtlety
of flavour fit for the gods.' Chicken and coconut soup with coriander and
lemongrass was labelled as classic. The beef in sweet basil, though less classic,
was delicate with the herb doing its job admirably. Bananas in coconut make a

31

good, simple rounding off. Popularity, close-packed tables and the sense of pleasure in a bargain mean that sometimes it gets too noisy and too smoky. It's unlicensed, with a small corkage; credit cards are not accepted. The Priyanus have recently opened a marginally smarter branch in Chiswick (see Topsy-Tasty).

CHEF: Mrs P. Priyanu   PROPRIETORS: Mr and Mrs Priyanu
OPEN: Mon to Sat
MEALS: 12 to 2, 6.30 to 9.30
PRICES: £7 (£11). Unlicensed, but bring your own: corkage 50p
SEATS: 30. Private parties: 30 main room. Vegetarian meals. Children's helpings.
No-smoking area. Wheelchair access (1 step)

Beotys
map 14

| 79 St Martin's Lane, WC2N 4AA | COOKING 1 |
| 071-836 8768 and 8548 | COST £37 |

A comforting fixture in the West End's mutating landscape, the Frangos family's comfortable and efficiently run restaurant even predates *The Mousetrap*. Despite Victorian-style furnishings and a *carte* that's partly continental, its heart is in Greece. An inspector was impressed with the quality of ingredients. Crevettes 'Theodore' (shrimps, mushrooms and tomatoes in sherry sauce) is a worthy alternative to taramosalata as a first course. There's well-made kleftiko, and lots of it, and pepper steak was cooked to perfection on a spirit stove in the centre of the room. Moussaka comes with mushrooms instead of potatoes but is none the worse for that. The dessert trolley proffers profiteroles and crème caramel, for instance, as well as laudable baklava and even better lokmades dumplings in syrup. Even the Turkish delight draws raves, but coffee could be better. Largely frequented by business folk, but it is 'a sound bet for a meal before or after the theatre'. There's a handful of Greek and Cypriot wines on the adequate list of 90. House wine is £8.

CHEF: E. Gallant   PROPRIETORS: The Frangos family
OPEN: all week
CLOSED: Christmas, Easter, bank hols
MEALS: 12.15 to 3, 5.30 to 11.30
PRICES: £20 (£31). Cover £1
CARDS: Access, Amex, Diners, Visa
SEATS: 80. Private parties: 14 main room, 40 private room. Children's helpings. Smart dress preferred. No pipes in dining-room. Wheelchair access (also WC). Air-conditioned

Bibendum ▮
map 12

Michelin House, 81 Fulham Road,	
SW3 6RD	COOKING 4
071-581 5817	COST £33–£65

When the Michelin Tyre Company forsook the pavements of Brompton for the meadows and hillocks of Harrow, it left behind this old garage. Sir Terence Conran and his allies have converted part of it to less industrial use: oyster bar, restaurant and furnishing showrooms. Of a summer evening, a 2CV van is parked in the piazzetta or forecourt and swains returning home from pastures

32

in the City can pick up a few oysters from it for supper. On the first floor, Simon Hopkinson cooks in what, for many, is the most enjoyable restaurant in London. The dining-room is large and airy: the windows allow light to stream through stained and engraved glazing, dappling many heads bent over their grilled calf's liver, salsa and avocado. The flowing covers to the chairs (changing colours with the seasons – or the dry cleaners) afford softness where the light and the building's geometry might have promoted harshness. There are two menus on offer. At lunch there is a prix fixe with perhaps eight options at each course; at dinner the choice doubles and turns à la carte. The most adventurous dishes are on the longer menu. Simon Hopkinson has continued to pursue his aim of delivering flavour without unnecessary trivialisation, mobilising classic (rich) sauces – a mint béarnaise, hollandaise, choron, mayonnaise – as well as the gamut of Mediterranean taste enhancers and accompaniments – pesto, ratatouille, capers, lemon-scented olive oil (the taste novelty of the Tuscan year), rouille. Some more modern items may crop up – coriander dressing, salsa – but this is not 'modern' cooking in the style of California or New South Wales. Rather, is it a hybrid of sound northern bourgeois cooking, the products of better French bistros and brasseries and our own preoccupation with capturing the taste and robustness of the warmer climes of the Mediterranean. Thus, when a reader complained that the sauce for his bourride of sea bass overwhelmed the flavour of the fish itself – 'might as well serve polystyrene' – he was correct yet missed the possible intention of that pungently garlicked and chillified sauce. The menu changes often enough, but some signature dishes might include risottos (primavera, saffron, truffle); tomato and pesto tart; Piedmontese peppers; a gratin of smoked haddock; fried fish (sole or plaice) with chips and a tartare; grilled calf's kidney and black pudding; roast beef and Yorkshire pudding; crème brûlée; steamed ginger pudding and custard; lemon tart; caramel ice cream; fine sorbets; a chocolate Pithiviers. Vegetables are extra and simple; some say it's a lot to pay for a little. Mashed potatoes are delectably oily; chips are among the best to be had. The cheeseboard seems largely French, in good condition when reported on but, again, expensive unless a half pound can be consumed. Nice mixed olives come at the beginning of the meal, truffles at the end.

There is an underlying simplicity to all the output of this kitchen. Things are what they say they are on the menu (no nouvelle jokes), and they turn up on the plate in recognisable shapes and sizes (though portions of some richer items can be disconcertingly large). This directness wins friends but also leaves a few who wonder if the effort was worth it. The great problems at Bibendum are popularity and the pressure of seven-day business. So many people press at the door that it may engender peremptoriness from the staff; the long working week seems to be the logical explanation of the fluctuating reports received by the *Guide*. One day, two inspectors were lunching there independently (their parties occupying, in aggregate, more than a dozen seats). Comparison of their reports shows how a kitchen under pressure can fail to deliver the goods – and, unfortunately, everyone had to pay the same. Money does get in the way of people's judgement, for the bills are never low. If discretion is exercised, then lunch can be no more expensive than many other West End places – many cooking vastly inferior food – but beware the wine list! It may be well-chosen and encyclopaedic but, one German visitor observed, 'there is little choice under £55.' An exaggeration, perhaps, but when people's bills are examined, it is the wine that proves their undoing. For value and fair quality, drink from the house wines, all available from £9.90, in 'Le Pot' (46cl) and by the glass; or try the Italians. Although there are still grumbles about service, it has greatly improved this year and children are nicely treated. But don't try taking photographs or proffering Amex cards.

CHEFS: Simon Hopkinson and Henry Harris   PROPRIETORS: Paul Hamlyn, Sir Terence Conran and Simon Hopkinson
OPEN: all week
CLOSED: Christmas and Easter
MEALS: 12.30 to 2.30 (3 Sat and Sun), 7 to 11.30 (10.30 Sun)
PRICES: £30 (£45), Set L £21.50 (£33) to £23.50 (£35), Set D £30 (£42) to £40 (£54). Service 15%
CARDS: Access, Visa
SEATS: 74. Children's helpings. No children under 5. No pipes in dining-room. Wheelchair access. Air-conditioned

▲ *Blakes Hotel*   map 12

33 Roland Gardens, SW7 3PF   COOKING 3
071-370 6701   COST £35−£85

Blakes did not figure in the 1990 *Guide* because the chef changed in the course of the year and what little comment we received was negative. Perhaps people do not dare admit to going here: it has an enticingly decadent feel, and it is punishingly expensive. If you cross the threshold on Roland Gardens, you will pass through an Indian-imperial-traveller-style lobby and descend to a black and white grotto of a restaurant. Here you may linger on divans in a side room or proceed straight to table. Black has been used to marvellous effect: it has richness and mystery and sets off the golds, crimsons, whites and crystal-sparkle of other furnishings and table settings. The whole operation avoids glitz, however; the staff are knowledgeable and attentive and the food is intended to be serious. David Wilson has cooked here long enough to know the Blakes' style of creative eclectism crossed with techniques of display that remind one of photographs from the now defunct *A la Carte* magazine. That is the sense in which it is dated, but it is often carried on with assurance. The menu is long and studded with some jewels of the caviare sort but it boldly mixes east and west − miso consommé, sashimi, teriyaki, Szechuan duck, and chicken tikka sit alongside baked sea bass, rack of lamb, smoked salmon and carpaccio. Portions are foolishly generous (perhaps to justify the prices) and indulge in wild display: there was enough fresh saffron on a langoustine bombe wrapped with sole with a saffron and lobster sauce to set up a market stall for a week. Many of the offerings have real flavour. Scallops were steamed with a seasoning of cumin and came with a pile of fried seaweed. The turmeric in the sauce could have been cooked longer to lose its ponderous harshness but the combination was impressive. A first course of a pavé of herring and eel was set in a crystal slice of jelly wrapped with nori-nori. In the dead centre of the slice was Japanese horseradish, thunderously hot. The pure fish taste of the jelly gave a clean base on which to build contrasts of taste and texture among its components. Much of the rest of the output of this kitchen is in this mode. Sometimes the balance fails, or the conception, as in the austere Szechuan duck, does not seem to match expectation. It is a pity that nights of total culinary disappointment are also reported. Among desserts, soufflés and ice-creams seem especially good. The wine list is short and carefully chosen but dear.

CHEF: David Wilson PROPRIETOR: Anouska Hempel Weinberg
OPEN: all week
CLOSED: 25 and 26 Dec
MEALS: 12.30 to 2.30, 7.30 to 11.30
PRICES: £48 (£71), Set L £28.50 (£35). Service 15% alc
CARDS: Access, Amex, Diners, Visa
SEATS: 36. Private parties: 8 main room, 12 private room. Vegetarian meals. Children's helpings on request. Smart dress preferred. No cigars in dining-room. Music. Air-conditioned
ACCOMMODATION: 52 rooms, all with bath/shower. Lift. B&B £127.50 to £185. Baby facilities. Afternoon teas. Air-conditioning. TV. Phone. [*Which? Hotel Guide*]

Bloom's
map 11

90 Whitechapel High Street, E1 7RA COOKING 1
071-247 6001 COST £19

Bloom's and nearby Aldgate East underground station are reassuring fixtures in the ever-transmogrifying East End. The former's decor is 1940s with waiters to match. Prices, handwritten on the plasticised menu, change but the Kosher cooking hardly a jot. Generous bowlfuls of soup served with a stack of white bread set the tone. Home-style barley, pea, carrot and butter-bean, and beetroot bortsch and potato were pleasant and hearty. Accompaniments – potato latkes, tzimmas, dumplings and dill pickles, for example – get more praise than the sometimes poorly cooked meat dishes. Lovers of light pastry should end with a hot clove-laced apple strudel. House wine is £7.20.

CHEF: Peter Nicholas PROPRIETORS: The Bloom Family
OPEN: Sun to Fri, exc Fri D
CLOSED: Jewish hols and 25 Dec
MEALS: 11.30am to 9.30pm (3pm Fri, 2pm Fri in winter)
PRICES: £9 (£16)
CARDS: Access, Amex, Visa
SEATS: 160. Private parties: 140 main room. Car-park, 100 places. Children's helpings. Wheelchair access. Air-conditioned

Blue Elephant
map 10

4–5 Fulham Broadway, SW6 1AA COOKING 1
071-385 6595 COST £32–£42

The most glamorously promoted and opulently staged Thai cooking in London. The restaurant has been lavishly extended with a series of authentic Thai 'houses' on different levels, approached via a bridge over a lily pond. Diners are surrounded by luxuriant jungle greenery, exotic orchids and waterfalls. The kitchen tries hard to keep pace, and each chef has special skills and responsibilities for different dishes and styles of cooking – curries, stir-frying, soups and salads. Some of the results have been excellent – but highly priced:

menam chicken soups with coconut, lemon grass and kaffir lime leaves (marred only by tough, woody lemon grass stalks); massaman – a Muslim lamb dish with a lightly spiced coconut based sauce; prawn curry; and 'emerald chicken' wrapped in green leaves have all been well-reported. Also a salad of exotic fruit and 'jasmin cake' – which might be called a Thai version of cream caramel – have been good finishes. Against this there have been complaints about the quality of raw materials, including 'disgusting little scallops', and 'the toughest crabmeat I have ever eaten'. Dishes that once would have contained no dairy products now taste as if cow's milk, as well as coconut milk, is being introduced. The increase in seating has not been matched by very much more kitchen space. Reports say the consequence is that the edge has often gone from the cooking. Service is generally pleasant, but can be slow, and expansion has affected efficiency. On a bad day your dishes may end up on the wrong table, not just in front of the wrong member of your party. To drink, there are cocktails and Thai beer; wines show intelligent selection but, after a reasonable start, prices climb steeply. House French: £7.95. CELLARMAN'S CHOICE: Pouilly Fumé, Serge Dagueneau 1988, £15.95.

CHEFS: Thaviseuth Pouthavong and Rungsan Mulijan PROPRIETORS: Blue Elephant Ltd
OPEN: all week, exc Sat L
CLOSED: 25 and 26 Dec
MEALS: 12 to 2.30, 7 to 11.30 (10.30 Sun)
PRICES: £21 (£35). Set L and D £22 (£32). Cover £1.50. Service 15%
CARDS: Access, Amex, Diners, Visa
SEATS: 250. Private parties: 250 main room. Vegetarian meals. Children welcome. Smart dress preferred. Wheelchair access (2 steps; also WC). Music. Air-conditioned

Blue Nile map 11

341A Harrow Road, W9 3RA COOKING 1
071-286 5129 COST £17–£22

Proclaiming itself as 'Ethiopia in the Year 2000', the restaurant – out in the westerly territory of Harrow Road – offers a rare taste of authentic East African cooking. The menu defines the cuisine in plain language: 'Wats' are hot; 'alechas' are not. Newcomers will do best by staying with the set meals, for otherwise the menu runs into uncharted territory: kitfo 'crack' crucial combi is the Ethiopian version of steak tartare served with a jug of 'crucial brew', 'strong, dark, and deadly'. Dishes are normally eaten with the fingers, helped along by injera, the classic Ethiopian sour-dough flat bread, which is regarded as naturally antibiotic. As an alternative to the crucial brew, there is Quti – Ethiopian tea 'made from coffee leaves'. An 'optional' surcharge of 50p per person goes towards African Village Projects, a charity devoted to funding a tree nursery and reforestation projects in the country. Ethiopian honey wine heads a rudimentary list.

The 1992 Guide will be published before Christmas 1991. Reports on meals are most welcome at any time of the year, but are extremely valuable in the spring. Send them to The Good Food Guide, FREEPOST, 2 Marylebone Road, London NW1 1YN. No stamp is needed if posted in the UK.

CHEF/PROPRIETOR: Elsa Wubneh
OPEN: all week, D only
MEALS: 6.30 to 11.30
PRICES: £12 (£18), Set D (for 2) £28 (£34)
CARDS: Access, Amex, Visa
SEATS: 50. 2 tables outside. Private parties: 70 main room, 70 private room. Vegetarian meals. Children's helpings. Wheelchair access. Music

Bombay Brasserie

map 12

140 Gloucester Road, SW7 4QH

COOKING 1

071-370 4040

COST £18–£34

The cavernous restaurant, preceded by a large bar, holds more people than most in London. The glass roof, swirling ceiling fans and general colour scheme was likened by one observer to the old Raffles in Singapore, and there is careful attention to creating the image of the late-lamented empire. This may be punctured by the pianist/vocalist whose efforts garner constant comment, but will be reinforced once more by the giant menu that in fact contains a smaller number of dishes than many Indian restaurants. These concentrate on Bombay and the Punjab, taking in specialities of several cultures that inhabit or influence the two regions. Goan prawn curry, Parsi kid gosht, a Kashmiri hot mirchi korma are examples. At least three first courses and three vegetable dishes have been dropped from last year's repertoire, leaving the menu more formulaic. Sometimes the cooking is spot on: the house thali was 'small but good'; the chicken makhali as 'good as any in India'; the vegetarian thali a good combination of tastes and textures; nans and particularly lemon rice often enjoyed. Main dishes are automatically served with potatoes, a vegetable and lentils, which goes some way to justify the high prices. There is often too long a gap between delivery of stage one and two. The overall verdict is mixed. The prices don't help, nor do the frequent delays in service. This is exacerbated by the distance from which you have to summon a waiter in so large a place, though no one ever accuses the staff of bad spirit, just of not being there. This may lead to cold food, another common grouse. None the less, the atmosphere is enjoyed, often displacing the food in the memory.

CHEFS: S. Rao and Udit Sarkhel   PROPRIETORS: TAJ International Hotels
OPEN: all week
MEALS: 12.30 to 3, 7.30 to 12
PRICES: £19 (£28), Set L buffet £12.95 (£17). Minimum £18. Service inc
CARDS: Access, Visa
SEATS: 175. 25 tables outside. Vegetarian meals. Children's helpings. Music

Boyd's ♟

map 11

135 Kensington Church Street, W8 7LP

COOKING 3

071-727 5452

COST £21–£42

A lot has changed at Boyd's. The entire restaurant has been renovated, with the rather formal reception being replaced by a dresser and a bar. The intention is to create more warmth and informality. There is a short set menu with no more than six choices at each stage (fewer at lunchtime) and the style is up-to-the-minute metropolitan. Chargrilled dishes, oriental influences, ravioli and Italian salads show that Boyd Gilmour is moving with the trends. 'A classy menu superbly executed' is one view, although others feel it is sometimes too rarefied and elaborate. However, the balance is firmly in its favour. Excellent reports have appeared of ravioli filled with spinach, roasted peppers, ricotta and pine kernels; monkfish marinated in lime juice and thyme, layered between summer leaves with a mint and sour cream dressing; and sauté calf's liver with a sage and potato pancake. Others have enjoyed salmon roulade with dill sauce, 'superb' fillet of beef with foie gras and saddle of rabbit served on a bed of savoy cabbage flavoured with rosemary. There is no fading towards the end of the meal: a trio of fruit sorbets; dark and white chocolate terrine with vanilla crème anglaise; and charentais melon filled with raspberries and glazed with Champagne sabayon have all been good. Service is fast. An intelligent and robust wine list offers the world's best and, for this address, prices are not excessive. House wines from £8.75.

CHEF/PROPRIETOR: Boyd Gilmour
OPEN: Mon to Fri
CLOSED: bank hols, 1 week at Christmas
MEALS: 12.30 to 2.30, 7.30 to 10.30
PRICES: Set L £14 (£21) to £17.50 (£25), Set D £21.50 (£30) to £27.50 (£35)
CARDS: Access, Amex, Visa
SEATS: 40. Private parties: 40 main room. Children welcome

Burt's ♣   map 14

42 Dean Street, W1V 5AP   COOKING 2
071-734 3339 and 439 0972   COST £25−£41

Hailed as the thinking person's (or at least Soho's) answer to vegetarian restaurants when it opened over a year ago, Burt's has become metamorphic. It is still the classiest London restaurant specialising in vegetable main dishes and fish. And it still pulls off the trick of beguiling carnivores by offering a menu jammed with dishes like tapenade of red mullet with potato and fennel rösti or salmon escalope with sauté shellfish and grapes beurre noisette or even aubergine sausages with spinach and creamed turnips. This isn't wimp's food. Chef Andrew Magson and his new cohort Hugh Tiley aim high. The results can be mighty: a robust demi-vegetarian cuisine big on flavours. As Burt's novelty value diminished, a more solid and natural audience developed, potentially the fastest growing that a trend-setting restaurant could want – vegetarians, demi-vegetarians, would-be vegetarians and refugees from the year's food scares. But just as the mood shifts, and as if to be perverse, more *meat* has crept into the menu. Although still a restaurant with a mission, the segregation of meat is gone. Suggestions are no longer tucked behind a flap in the menu as if liable to offend. Of the score of dinner dishes, only eight are marked with a V for vegetarian. Now there is ballotine of rabbit with wild mushroom and artichoke and confit of spiced duckling with mixed lentils, and rosemary vinaigrette to start and breast of chicken stuffed with black pudding, and apple brandy sauce to follow. There is a vegetarian menu in a new ghetto of its own but the good-value, three-course, pre-theatre menu remains. Although the intentions are clearly cookery with flavour as well as style, the two are not invariably achieved. The vegetarian dishes have sometimes lacked punch or simple taste; the result is then over-complicated muddle. Or they may be treated brutally, as were the celeriac spring rolls with oriental vegetables with an excess of soy in the butter sauce. On a good day, however, this may be a kitchen that delivers what it promises. The colour scheme is now apricot and pale blue and still seems chilly: sparse verging on severe. Service ranges from meticulous to somnolent. Sometimes when a restaurant actually has enough waiters they become so interested in each other's company that a fist waving a credit card becomes invisible. If you still can't contain your curiosity as to Burt's identity, ask a waiter for the printed sheet entitled 'All about Burt'. Burt Shevelove wrote the hit musical *A Funny Thing Happened on the Way to the Forum*. It doesn't say whether he was a vegetarian. The wine list is excellent, encompassing whites from Nelson, New Zealand and Long Island, New York, and reds from the Jura and the Loire. House white is £9.30; house red, £7.85.

CHEFS: Andrew Magson and Hugh Tiley   PROPRIETORS: P. Ward and John-Jacques Kaeser
OPEN: Mon to Sat, exc Sat L
MEALS: 12.30 to 2.30, 5.30 to 11.30
PRICES: £23 (£34), Set D £17.75 (£25). Service 15%
CARDS: Access, Amex, Diners, Visa
SEATS: 60. Private parties: 100 main room, 35 private room. Vegetarian meals. Children welcome. Smart dress preferred. Wheelchair access (also WC). Music. Air-conditioned

Bu San
map 10

43 Holloway Road, N7 8JP
071-607 8264

COOKING 1
COST £11–£26

A few minutes' walk from Highbury and Islington station, and almost hidden among clothes shops and estate agents which have seen better days, Bu San seems destined to see some very good days and evenings. Once inside, the noisy, traffic-clogged Holloway Road seems so far away that you may as well be in Korea. Part of the white walls of this front room of a terraced house are hung with Korean plates and a huge wooden fork. No forks on the small, shining stripped pine tables though. Only metal chopsticks and a spoon on a chopstick rest, and a vase of flowers. To say it is intimate is understating the effect of six tables positioned close together. They are filled with locals, Far Easterners and local Far Easterners. Proprietors Young Hyung Lee and Tea Sun Lee and their staff are from Korea. Service loses nothing in translation although a few descriptions might. Pa Jeon is explained as 'Korean deep pan pizza mixed with meat, oyster, spring onion and covered with egg'. Dishes come out of the kitchen one by one and some are cooked at the table on a gas burner. 'The marinade is sweet, the beef tender and tasty,' reports one reader. Some specialities can be modified to suit western palates if the chef is given early warning. Vegetables, fish and seafood are fresh and cooked with a light touch. Kimchee, spicy Korean pickled vegetables, are much in evidence and presentation of almost all dishes is striking and elaborate. Saké is served hot in the traditional way. House wine: £7.50 and £8.50.

Report forms are at the back of the book; write a letter if you prefer.

CHEF: Young Hyung Lee   PROPRIETORS: Young Hyung Lee and Tea Sun Lee
OPEN: all week, exc Sun L and Mon L
CLOSED: 2 days at Christmas, 1 Jan
MEALS: 12 to 3, 6 to 11
PRICES: £12 (£21), Set L £5.50 (£11) to £5.90 (£12), Set D £8.90 (£15) to £16.50 (£22)
SEATS: 26. Private parties: 31 main room. Vegetarian meals. Children's helpings. Music

Le Cadre

map 10

10 Priory Road, N8 7RD
081-348 0606

COOKING 2
COST £19–£36

The frame is French: pavement eating under a large awning in a row of shops
in the shadow of Alexandra Palace. The decor and menu design, the close-
packed tables and the waiters all spell Gallic. Daniel Delagarde cooks in
French too, but with a fruity tang: duck with raspberries, shallots and
pineapple; fillets of sole on a passion-fruit sauce; pigeon with rhubarb.
Sweetness from Banyuls wine, blackcurrants or honey is another constant
strain. He is accurate and not all experimental, witness the endives with
lardons and pine kernels; good soups, for instance carrot and rice or celeriac
and olives; braised dishes like skirt of beef with shallots; and modern classics
such as salmon with saffron. Desserts are not ignored: pear tart with a liquorice
sauce or white chocolate mousse with strawberry coulis show the same modern
tilt. Prices are not high and service is emphatically included. David
Misselbrook expresses regret that legislation was not made more stringent to
clean up the whole service charge imbroglio. The wine list is very short but the
choices are good. The price range has taken in more expensive bottles than last
year so it does not have the air of value for quality that it seemed to at first.
However, prices are still by no means excessive. The caricatures on the menu of
debonair smokers may be a true indication of the atmosphere on a busy night.
House wine: £9.50. CELLARMAN'S CHOICE: Ch. des Jacques, Chardonnay 1987,
£15.50; Brouilly, Ch. Thivin 1988, £15.

CHEF: Daniel Delagarde   PROPRIETORS: David Misselbrook and Marie Fedyk
OPEN: Mon to Sat, exc Sat L
CLOSED: 2 weeks in Aug, 25 to 30 Dec, bank hols
MEALS: 12 to 2.30, 7 to 10.30
PRICES: £23 (£30), Set L £12.50 (£19) to £15.50 (£22), Set D £17.50 (£24). Service inc
CARDS: Access, Amex, Visa
SEATS: 40. 12 tables outside. Private parties: 50 main room. Children welcome. Wheelchair
access. Music

Café du Marché

map 11

22 Charterhouse Square, EC1M 6AH
071-608 1609

COOKING 1
COST £34

Tucked down a passageway beyond Smithfield market – 'outside an air of
Victorian London; downstairs a contrived rustic jazz club (even the air-
conditioning is pine clad); upstairs a pleasantly converted loft' – the restaurant
is consistently popular with the residents of the nearby Barbican and City
workers. There is a set-price menu of everyone's idea of French country

cooking: salade lyonnaise, soupe de poissons, moules à l'ail, casserole de lapin aux nouilles, navarin d'agneau, côte de porc aux pruneaux, crème caramel, tarte aux fruits, and so on. This is backed up by a short, well-chosen wine list that goes further afield than any French person would deign. The menu upstairs in Le Grenier du Café is the same price but with greater emphasis on grills. It is open only for dinner from Tuesday to Friday. The atmosphere is lively and enjoyable, though the erratic service can shorten tempers. Good reports have been had of cold basil and tomato soup; artichoke heart with seafood in a cheese sauce; pheasant and pistachio terrine; decent grills of chicken or a large côte de boeuf béarnaise; poached salmon with tomato and mint sauce; and the crème caramel. Many, however, judge the cooking rather approximately French, especially the pastry work, and the flavours equally approximate. Stews, which should be a strong point, are not. 'The pianist has perked up no end with the company of a double bassist. They played modern jazz standards well.' Care has gone into the short wine list which has some exceptional names at reasonable prices: Chave Hermitage Blanc, Lignier Morey St Denis. House wines are either *ordinaire* or *supérieur*. The latter, at £11, may be a good Côtes du Rhône and a Jurançon. The former are much cheaper, but appreciated.

CHEFS: Simon Cottard, Rupert Pitt and Ewan Yapp   PROPRIETOR: C. K. Graham-Wood
OPEN: Mon to Sat, exc Sat L
MEALS: 12 to 2.30, 6 to 10
PRICES: Set L and D £17.50 (£28). Service 15%
CARDS: Access, Visa
SEATS: 50. Private parties: 50 main room. Children's helpings. No children under 2.
No pipes in dining-room. Music

Café Flo
map 11

205 Haverstock Hill, NW3 4QG
071-435 6744

COOKING 1
COST £10-£24

Considering the rate at which this unpretentious but somewhat contrived café/ brasserie is propagating, Café Spurt would be more like it. There are now four Café Flos. This, the original one, actually faces its cousin, Flo's Bar and Grill, which also has outside tables but a less strategic vantage point for ogling queues at the nearby Screen on the Hill. Simple wooden tables, large posters, shelves lined with cookery and wine books, and a long bar are the informal setting for the short menu of modern and provincial French dishes. These are cooked with varying accuracy. Daily specials are marked on the blackboard. Light or small dishes, such as warm onion tart, frisée salad with bacon, croûtons and soft boiled egg, and ham, salami or cheese baguettes can be mixed and matched. Main dishes might be 'generous and tasty' aubergine stuffed with rice and nuts with spicy tomato sauce, or roast poussin with roast potatoes. Everyone seems to devour basketfuls of the freshly baked French bread. Good desserts include dark and white chocolate cake. 'L'Idée Flo' is an inexpensive set two-course meal with two choices, steak and chips being one. The two- or three-course set lunch on Sunday is also good value. No one can accuse service of being professional and cinema-goers should plan for delays. Of the four establishments, Café Flo at 51 St Martin's Lane, WC2 (071-836 8289) also deserves a mention. Prices, comfort and warm welcome compare

41

favourably with other theatre-land cafés, as does the food that might be chicken liver salad, minced steak with french fries, 'not chips', good mixed salad, and a delicious cream/meringue/coffee concoction. The wine list is short but intelligent. House French: £6.75. CELLARMAN'S CHOICE: Orlando Semillon Chardonnay, Jacob's Creek 1989, £8.95; Orlando Shiraz, Jacob's Creek 1989, £8.95.

CHEF: Stephen Bullock   PROPRIETOR: Russel Joffe
OPEN: all week
MEALS: 12 to 3, (3.30 Sat, 3,45 Sun), 6(6.30 Sat, 6.45 Sun) to 11.30 (11 Sun)
PRICES: £13 (£20), Set L and D £5.95 (£10)
CARDS: Access, Visa
SEATS: 38. 6 tables outside. Private parties: 8 main room. Vegetarian meals. Children welcome. Wheelchair access. Music

Canal Brasserie

map 11

Canalot Studios,
222 Kensal Road, W10 5BN
081-960 2732

COOKING 1
COST £23

Canalot Studio events give it a boost and other custom manages to find its way to this brasserie in a warehouse. It's on the south side of the canal that laps its outer wall, and not easy to get to except for neighbours. Art on the wall gives it some interest, people are cheerful and the somewhat shortened menu delivers creditable soups, game and fresh fish, such as excellent squid with garlic on a fashionable salad with cherry tomatoes; old-fashioned salmon hollandaise; or scallops in puff pastry. Outside seating has been increased for any hot weather that may come. There is a short but decent wine list with some half-bottles. House wine: £6.25. Cider from Normandy is £2.95.

CHEF: Nicholas Anderson   PROPRIETORS: Antony and Alexandra Harris
OPEN: all week, exc Sat L and Sun D
MEALS: 12 to 3.30, 6 to 10.30
PRICES: £12 (£19)
CARDS: Access, Visa
SEATS: 60. 15 tables outside. Vegetarian meals. Children's helpings. No smoking in dining-room. Music. Air-conditioned

▲ Capital Hotel ▮

map 12

Basil Street, SW3 1AT
071-589 5171

COOKING 4
COST £25–£54

This small yet luxurious hotel is 'within falling distance' of Harrods. Philip Britten cooks classically inspired food of restrained precision. He is neither silly nor showy, perhaps to be likened to a tortoise, working gradually to demonstrate the innate quality of his materials, rather than a more modish chef's hare, rushing hither and yon scattering inventions across his menu that show off his mastery of technique. The frame to his work is a small dining-room, slightly awkward in shape, in a wholly refurbished hotel that has shed its image of silvered modernism in favour of repro-French woodwork, festoon curtains and a blush pink colour scheme. Some can find this room constraining to happy sociability, others deem it at its most pleasant at lunchtime. All agree to the quality of the table settings and purpose-made French china. At night a *carte* of maybe a dozen choices, changed with the seasons, is supplemented by a six-course gastronomic set meal, an innovation this year. At lunch there are two short set-price menus. There is acclaim for their value in general, exemplified by a pre-Glyndebourne visit that yielded smoked salmon with asparagus and scrambled eggs; roast lamb on an eloquent garlic sauce, and a prune and armagnac ice-cream touched with maple syrup. The bill included coffee, petits fours and mineral water – more economic than the reader who insists he was charged for tap water. Good value excites favourable reaction but at dinner such reaction must depend on quality alone. Many are not disappointed: a composed salad of artichoke, pink grapefruit, small beans and mixed leaves; salmon fried to crisp the skin, on a thyme butter sauce, with little piles of broccoli, asparagus and green beans; cod (Philip Britten is fond of cod) on a Champagne sauce sprinkled with caviare, accompanied by shredded courgettes and carrots; breast of chicken braised in vin jaune and cream with morels and grapes; magical soufflés (one party of four, having ordered differently all through the meal, all plumped for the hot lemon soufflé with lemon sauce and were not disappointed); fine tarte Tatin 'crumbling gently under the fork'; and good cheeses, including a Boulette d'Avesnes, though Ryvita, Carr's water biscuits and Jacob's tired cream crackers hardly did it justice. This very steady quality is spoiled by examples of excess age in a gateau of foie gras, oversweetness in some of the sauces and the lack of definition that a discreet kitchen style may fall victim to. There are also niggles with the service – too much hauteur and surprising patches of ignorance for such a place. The wine list always prompts comment, usually for the prices. In fact, it is not far adrift from other West End places and a close search will yield affordable and good bottles. There is a short list of bottles under £16 on the front page. The range of French classic wines, especially claret, is exemplary for its maturity and choice of properties, though burgundies are a conservative collection. The extra-France page is so expensive and often so young as to be pointless: best not to explore.

CHEF: Philip Britten   PROPRIETOR: David Levin
OPEN: all week
MEALS: 12.30 to 2.30, 7 to 11
PRICES: £37 (£45), Set L £18.50 (£25) to £21.50 (£28). Set D £38.50 (£45). Minimum £25. Service inc
CARDS: Access, Amex, Carte Blanche, Diners, Visa
SEATS: 35. Private parties: 6 main room, 4 and 24 private rooms. Car-park, 12 places. Vegetarian meals. Children's helpings. No children under 4. Smart dress preferred. No pipes in dining-room. Wheelchair access (3 steps; also WC). Air-conditioned
ACCOMMODATION: 48 rooms, all with bath/shower. Rooms for disabled. Lift. B&B £157.50 to £190. Deposit: one night charge. Baby facilities. Pets welcome with prior notice. Afternoon teas. Air-conditioning. TV. Phone

---

All details are as accurate as possible at the time of going to press, but chefs and owners often change, and it is wise to check by telephone before making a special journey. Many readers have been disappointed when set-price bargain meals are no longer available. Ask when booking.

Le Caprice

map 13

Arlington House
Arlington Street, SW1A 1RT   COOKING 3
071-629 2239   COST £36

When Charles Fontaine, who used to work here, opened the Quality Chop
House (see entry), one had the vision of several Caprice clones across London.
No bad thing, for the food is stylish, quality control stringent and service
prompt and effective. No place can hope to replicate the smartness of the
Caprice, and all would envy its press of business – book in advance. The
character of the *carte* is now familiar: standards such as egg Benedict, salmon
fishcake, steak tartare, scrambled eggs and smoked salmon line up with
vegetable crudités with three dips, grilled baby squid with marinated peppers,
a large and luscious panaché of mushrooms, North African paella – a spicy
shellfish assortment with couscous and cracked wheat – or baked cod with a
vinegar dressing and mashed potatoes with chopped olives. The menu is
addressed exactly to the profile of the restaurant's clientele, and of course
there's no need to eat a full meal. That there is skill in the kitchen is seen from
something as simple as egg Benedict: the bun is fairly characterless but has
retained its toasted crunch, the egg is exactly poached and the hollandaise is
purposely bland – to accompany the first-rate gammon that has more flavour
than most served in the capital at any lunchtime. There is satisfaction in
watching the barman – worth sitting at the bar just for this – producing a
Bloody Mary while driving the coffee machine, talking over the next order
with the waiter and seeing to his own customers. The wine list, as couth as the
restaurant, is brief but there is absolutely nothing amiss. Alsace from Rolly
Gassmann, the excellent Dom. le Couroulu Vacqueyras, Gevrey-Chambertin
from Rousseau and Sandford Pinot Noir show the quality. Half-bottles abound,
prices are surprisingly reasonable and the spread, from house Trebbiano at
£6.50 to £95 for 1975 Pauillac, is sensibly encompassing. CELLARMAN'S
CHOICE: Crozes-Hermitage, les Pontaux 1988, Fayolle, £15.50; Sangioveto del
Borgo, 1985, Citterio, £10.75.

CHEF: Mark Hix   PROPRIETORS: C.J. Corbin and J.R.B. King
OPEN: all week
MEALS: 12 to 3, 6 to 12
PRICES: £20 (£30). Cover £1.50
CARDS: Access, Amex, Diners, Visa
SEATS: 70. No children under 5. Wheelchair access. Music. Air-conditioned

Carraro's

map 10

32 Queenstown Road, SW8 3RX   COOKING 1
071-720 5986 and 7079   COST £18–£34

This is a deceptively large restaurant in three rooms, with a tinkling piano in
the evenings, at the Clapham end of Queenstown Road. It has some intention
of cooking north Italian food and can indeed produce a lip-sticking bean soup
as well as passable prawn, cuttlefish and mussel risotto, bresaola and squid in
its own ink. Lunchtime is its best showcase with a fair value short choice at a
low set price that includes more than mere trattoria fare, for example a good

hare casserole or lemon sole wrapped round tagliolini with a hollandaise glaze. Tiramisu leads the desserts, but the crespelle with a coffee filling and caramel sauce can be toothsome. A la carte prices seem reasonable, but add vegetables and a stiff cover charge. The set-price dinner is at the same reasonable price as lunch. Cooking can fall down badly. There is an all-Italian wine list with upper-crust Antinori, Loredan and Biondi Santi and half a dozen Italian sparklers. House Valpolicella, £9.05, and Soave, £7.60. CELLARMAN'S CHOICE: Prust Grigio Collio 1988, Comini, £14.20; Chianti Classico 'Granaio' 1985, Melini £14.50.

CHEF: Jairo Carvajal   PROPRIETOR: Gian Franco Carraro
OPEN: Mon to Sat, exc Sat L
MEALS: 12 to 2.30, 7 to 11.30
PRICES: £18 (£28), Set L and D £11.95 (£19). Cover £1.50
CARDS: Access, Amex, Visa
SEATS: 90. Private parties: 100 main room, 20 private room. Vegetarian meals. Children's helpings. No-smoking area. Music. Air-conditioned

---

Cavaliers ♥   map 10

129 Queenstown Road, SW8 3RH   COOKING 4
071-720 6960   COST £25–£54

A dark blue frontage now greets arrivals on Queenstown Road, and shipshape it looks. Confidence may falter when they find that a bell has to be rung to gain entry, and it is round the side to boot. Morale can be further sapped at the first hurdle of dress: 'I tried my best for "smartness". I have a suit for my travels, but it lives in a suit carrier and probably looks like it. Perhaps I looked the worse for wear with five days of stubble. The head waiter just looked at me for several seconds.' The threshold crossed, further redecoration is in evidence: the sponged yellow walls, cheerful swagged curtains and comfortable chairs sit well in a room with enough variety of shape and openings to keep the curious amused, even if they force long circuits of approach on the waiting staff. The practical works have done David Cavalier a lot of good. The cooking appears less cluttered and in some respects more confident. There remain elements of borrowing from current masters which have the effect, on the observer, of detracting from his clear ability to stand on his own: a delectable plate of 'oysters Muscovite' with caviare, cucumber 'tagliatelle', spinach and a sabayon, served warm, is a case in point. His menu, too, has gone like others towards a fashionable reticence: 'scallops tart, lemon oil; infusion Agnès Sorel; veal kidney, celery *jus*; duck, four ways' it reads, making enquiry virtually obligatory – though the explanation is full and instructive. The greater simplicity is revealed by a lightening of what frills and gewgaws there are: no more enriching with a spot of hollandaise; using pasta tortellini rather than pastry; not so much foie gras or other rich offal for the sake of it, though it does still occur, for instance in the deeply flavoured roast pigeon (more gamey than most) that is flanked by a pair of sweetbread tortellini. Arrangement of dishes is resolutely vertical – even salads tower – so that pigeon, split and opened out, sat on a galette of potato, itself supported by a layer of cabbage. The topmost tier, covering even the pigeon, consisted of the thinnest celeriac crisps. Flavours can be exquisitely handled: 'infusion Agnès Sorel' is a light egg liaison of the consommé made from soaking and poaching morels. The funghi are stuffed with chicken, and more varieties still are in the soup when it is served. Thin flat noodles give a little bulk against which to appreciate the clear yet modulated tastes of each element. David Cavalier is not afraid of presenting materials in relative simplicity: John Dory is steamed (and is a trifle dry), given a medley of small vegetables, and served with a plain light butter sauce. Noodles again provide the bulk. 'Duck four ways' is the signature dish at the moment, and it certainly provides the variety he eschews elsewhere: the breast sauté; the leg in confit; a piece of pig's trotter stuffed with sweetbreads ('he must have been a funny specimen,' was one amateur zoologist's comment); some foie gras de canard with spinach. 'The confit was particularly good, small enough in the context,' and the sweetbreads, with some wild mushrooms, were also greatly favoured. Desserts carry on the good work: they are great on presentation (sugar cases obligatory and several tottering pillars of ice-cream confirm the love of the vertical), but also good on taste and technique, as in a hot ginger soufflé with an orange sorbet and caramel sauce; a thin mille-feuille of raspberries slightly enriched with syrup and raspberry mousse, and a fine lemon parfait as tart as it was bittersweet from a swift caramelisation to the surface. Cheeses are English and from James of Beckenham; the bread rolls are very crusty and use good flavourful flour; the pasta amuse-gueule, tarts and tuiles with the coffee are all of a piece. The restaurant, intent on working the furrow of haute cuisine, does it with an involvement that is meritorious and with few solecisms. It is also fair value for London particularly when the excellent service and surroundings are taken into account. Since the set price does not include dessert, however, and miniatures with coffee are extras as well, the cost can spiral. There is a cheaper, very much shorter, lunch menu. The carefully chosen wine list has a page of 'world' wines but is otherwise French, as is the sommelier. There are good half-bottles. An interesting section of old Vouvrays and a dozen red Loires (including some mature) help keep the price range lower than in similar places. CELLARMAN'S CHOICE: Vouvray 1985, Brédif, £16.90; Taltarni Shiraz 1982, £13.20.

CHEF: David Cavalier PROPRIETORS: David and Susan Cavalier
OPEN: Tue to Sat
MEALS: 12.15 to 2, 7.15 to 10.30 (11 if busy)
PRICES: Set L £16.50 (£25), Set D £26 (£45)
CARDS: Access, Amex, Diners, Visa
SEATS: 50. Private parties: 50 main room. No children under 10. Smart dress preferred. Air-conditioned

Chanterelle
map 12

119 Old Brompton Road, SW7 3RN
071-373 5522 and 7390

COOKING 1
COST £13—£25

This inviting, dark, embracing room with fairly close-set tables has been likened to a pair of old slippers one is reluctant to throw away, so long has it provided a fair service as *restaurant du quartier* towards the western end of Old Brompton Road. There are moments through the year when irritation surfaces at the service: dour, surly and miserable are three epithets. Perhaps even old slippers pinch swollen feet. Usually, however, the sense is of a place that discharges its task amicably, professionally and without charging too much. Food is offered at a set price, cheaper at lunchtime, and the repertoire may include potato salad with venison sausage; whole roast partridge; mussel and saffron tart; salmon and sorrel sauce; pigeon breast and pink grapefruit; chocolate cake with caramel fudge; rhubarb and ginger fool; or fresh figs and cream. Sunday lunch is roast. Unfortunately, poor food at any price is no bargain and there have been times when the cooking is seriously awry. The wine list is a short canter through 30 French items, fairly priced and nearly all in half-bottles. House French: £6.40.

CHEF/PROPRIETOR: Fergus Provan
OPEN: all week
CLOSED: 4 days at Christmas
MEALS: 12 to 2.30, 7 to 11.30
PRICES: Set L £8.50 (£13), Set D £16 (£21). Service charge 12.5% for parties of 6 or more
CARDS: Access, Amex, Diners, Visa
SEATS: 45. 2 tables outside. Private parties: 15 main room. Children welcome. Wheelchair access

▲ *Chelsea Room,*
Hyatt Carlton Tower

map 12

2 Cadogan Place, SW1 9PY   COOKING 3
071-235 5411   COST £26–£70

This long suite of rooms with a conservatory, sited over the front door of the Hyatt Carlton Tower, affords views of the treetops of Cadogan Square or equally large vistas of carpets, pastel colours and other colours. Most tables are set in their own grounds. The menu, itself as large as a small front lawn, looks as if it were written by a disciplined Cocteau, but there is not much of the surreal about it – except perhaps a dish of turbot, salmon and foie gras (best left to the Futurists). Bernard Gaume has pitched the food exactly to modern conservatives: mild flavoured, light, and harbouring pleasing combinations but no shockingly pronounced flavours. The cooking is done with skill but sometimes is of moderate taste. Materials such as Parma ham, foie gras, scallops, venison, and vegetables, are among the best available in London: this is one of the restaurant's qualities. Ingredients can be correctly combined – a loin of lamb roasted with herbs could not be faulted, loin of venison with blackcurrant sauce and chestnuts had remarkable taste and texture, the sauce carefully balancing the gamey flavours. They can also be insipid. Thus scallops were precisely cooked, just crisped in butter but melting within, but the basil (winter grown), tomato (hot-house) and saffron cream sauce had little flavour. Correctness also may give way to speed or convenience. A classic diplomat pudding should be layers of fruits, raisins and kirsch biscuits, not a creamed rice mould with jelly and a few odd bits, as was sold under this name. There is a massive dessert trolley, better dressed than in most hotels, and hot desserts too, though they may not be offered to late diners. This denial is so tactfully handled that it is not usually noticed, as the staff show their long training in customer management. Paramedical training in dealing with shock, rather than tact, could be needed when approaching a customer with the wine list. The Sancerre is as expensive as any in London and house Champagne is £31. There are two wines under £20: a Beaujolais and a Pinot Blanc d'Alsace. It is a shame. There is not a non-French wine on the list. At lunch, a half-bottle of house wine is included on the set menu, a welcome concession.

CHEF: Bernard Gaume   PROPRIETORS: Hyatt Hotels Ltd
OPEN: all week
MEALS: 12.30 to 2.45 (2.30 Sun), 7 to 10.45 (10.30 Sun)
PRICES: £40 (£58), Set L £23.50 (£26)
CARDS: Access, Amex, Diners, Visa
SEATS: 60. Private parties: 30 main room, 35 private room. Car-park. Children welcome. Smart dress preferred at D. Wheelchair access. Music. Air-conditioned
ACCOMMODATION: 224 rooms, all with bath/shower. Lift. B&B £150 to £210. Baby facilities. Afternoon teas. Garden. Sauna. Tennis. Air-conditioning. TV. Phone. Confirm by 6

Cherry Orchard

map 10

241–245 Globe Road, E2 0JD   COOKING 1
081-980 6678   COST £9–£18

Mushroom moussaka, tofu Stroganoff and nut roast – the offerings on one night's menu – sound as if the whole carnivorous repertoire might one day be converted to vegetarian principles in this longstanding co-operative (10 years old in June 1990). From counter service at lunch it converts to waitresses and candlesticks at dinner and is very moderate in price at both. If occasionally the flavours seem vapid, they are not always so: witness a reader's vegetable stir-fry with pilau rice and peanut sauce or cauliflower and lentil gratin. There are lots of salads and substantial puddings. A vast range of teas replaces a wine list, but you can bring your own wine and pay a small corkage.

CHEFS: Jamie Lemone and Sheena Marsh   PROPRIETORS: Pure Land Co-operative
OPEN: Tue to Sat
CLOSED: 1 week at Christmas
MEALS: 12 to 3, 6 to 10.30
PRICES: L £6 (£9), D £9 (£15). Service 10% for parties of 6 or more. Unlicensed, but bring your own: corkage £1
CARDS: Access, Visa
SEATS: 54. 6 tables outside. Private parties: 25 main room. Vegetarian meals. Children's helpings. No smoking. Wheelchair access (1 step). Music

Chez Liline

map 10

101 Stroud Green Road, N4 3PX   COOKING 2
071-263 6550   COST £34

This is the sort of place one likes to have 'discovered'. It's useful that the rating is for cooking only, as the surroundings are none too brilliant, but fish is the thing, prices are very reasonable and the two sittings at weekends testify that N4 has taken Liline's to its heart. 'Crowded, tables very close, which did not matter as people chatted to each other; only problem two smokers who seemed immune to protests. We both had scallops with oyster mushrooms, followed by sea bass, one with herbs – especially coriander – the other with cream and peppercorns.' The menu does not change much. The dishes to go for are the simple ones, as more complex offerings may show lack of care. Sweet dishes are not a strong point but the portions of fish are so generous that dessert is hardly necessary. Liline Ng Yu Tin makes the point that all the fish is fresh and is not taken off the bone or otherwise prepared until ordered. As the restaurant is Mauritian, the emphasis is on shellfish and warm water sea fish such as bourgeois, vacqua and capitain. Salmon figures strongly but northern species such as sole, turbot or halibut do not. Flavouring is southern too: a strong French influence is shown with garlic and saffron, and much ginger, soy, coriander and chilli make a bow to South-east Asia. This strong mixture can sometimes result in everything tasting uniform, so try to choose very dissimilar methods of saucing or preparation. The wine list is excellent, not overpriced, and has improved in range over the year. House French: £6.95. CELLARMAN'S CHOICE: Pouilly Fumé 1988, £12.50; Chablis 1988, Dom. Servin, £13.75.

CHEF: Mario Ho Wing Cheong   PROPRIETOR: Liline Ng Yu Tin
OPEN: Mon to Sat
MEALS: 12 to 2.30, 6.30 to 11
PRICES: £19 (£28). Minimum £8.50
CARD: Visa
SEATS: 52. Private parties: 52 main room. Vegetarian meals. Children's helpings
on request. Music

Chez Moi

map 10

1 Addison Avenue, W11 4QS   COOKING 3
071-603 8267   COST £19–£35

Chez Moi is a warm red with lots of mirrors and an air of permanence, though one reader commented that it looked 'fairly gloomy, with statues in strange places'. That same person's father visits no more than once a year, but the staff never fail to recognise him. Traditional values have it in the comments: 'classic, but nothing wrong with that' and Richard Walton continues to mine an oriental vein of tikkas, satays and masalas at lunchtimes while producing his famous lamb dishes – with garlic and mint, with an apricot sauce, or devilled – or modern affairs like calves' sweatbreads with chanterelles and raspberry vinegar for the à la carte dinners. First courses may include goats' cheese with basil and pine nuts under a puff pastry cover which may have looked approximate but was in fact exactly cooked, or refuge can be taken with repeated successes such as snails in a tart with vermouth, tomatoes, herbs and cream, or tartare of raw salmon. The cooking and the welcome have the quality of consistency but evidently the spirit of enquiry and improvement has not died. The wine list is a sound canter through classic France with a very good show of Bordeaux at prices in line with most places of this standard; New World regions are barely mentioned but four good Californians fly the flag. House wines start at £6.75.

The Guide *office can quickly spot when a restaurateur is encouraging customers to write recommending inclusion - and sadly, several restaurants have been doing this in 1990. Such reports do not further a restaurant's cause. Please tell us if a restaurateur invites you to write to the* Guide.

CHEF: Richard Walton   PROPRIETORS: Richard Walton and Colin Smith
OPEN: Mon to Sat, exc Sat L
CLOSED: bank hols, Christmas to New Year
MEALS: 12.30 to 2, D 7 to 11
PRICES: £20 (£29), Set L £13.50 (£19)
CARDS: Access, Amex, Diners, Visa
SEATS: 45. Children's helpings. No pipes in dining-room. Wheelchair access.
Air-conditioned

Chez Nico ♥   map 13

35 Great Portland Street, W1N 5DD   COOKING 5
071-436 8846   COST £40–£73

Walking up Great Portland Street at night, one sees Chez Nico as a black hole.
The blinds seal any escape of light. Once the door is opened, the brightness
dazzles the eyes. It is rather refreshing to be able to see the food you are to eat,
and be free of the dimming of the lights – a lumen or two every 15 minutes
progressively from 9.30 – that is irritatingly practised in so many London
restaurants. However, that aspect will never place Chez Nico high in the rating
of places for a lovers' tryst, unless they love their stomachs more. Food is the
main subject here. There is no preliminary zone for waiting or drinking – go to
the table and get on with it. That table may be in the main body of the room or
tucked round the corner in a small extension, a favoured spot to put early
comers. Space – physical, aural, and olfactory if you are non-smokers – is
slightly cramped. Service is as keen as mustard. People have exposed
weaknesses of information, but not of willingness. It is less smooth than in
many places of this ilk, but it does seem prepared to please. If the rendering of
Reynolds's *Simplicity* on the menu cover is a coded statement, it is not really
borne out by the cooking. There is a lot of choice, though expressed in French
alone. Explanations have to be sought, as well as recitation of the daily fish
dishes, not listed. There are times through the year when choice may be limited
by repetition. One reader noticed how wild mushrooms crowded into every
dish that she wanted to eat, yet she did not eat wild mushrooms. Another
found, after close questioning, because the menu itself did not let on in French
or English, that foie gras cropped up a great deal. This may have the important
consequence of enriching a meal too much, even if you do like foie gras. A third
commented that mashed potato appeared not only with her sea bass, but
seemed to be on every plate around her. The flavours mobilised are often
strong. Sometimes everything seems to have a fashionable southern tilt to it:
saddle of lamb with aubergines and couscous and little blobs of pesto; a
saffroned ragout of fish and shellfish; or red mullet atop a layer of kidney
potatoes and browned onions with a pimento and chilli sauce. Another month,
however, the emphasis is on the classic tastes of the north: duck with honey
and pepper; shin of veal 'jardinière'; squab pigeon with lentils. Comments on
the product of either school show Nico Ladenis master of both. Four griddled
scallops are arranged on a bed of steamed white cabbage with an orange lobster
sauce; 'the flavour contrasts of each element made this truly memorable'.
Scallops are Nico Ladenis' forte. The largest scallop possible is grilled with
garlic and served in a filo basket on a leek purée. There is a well-balanced
butter sauce, perhaps of leeks, white wine and fish stock, and on the side of the

plate is a filo parcel containing a baked clove of garlic. Simpler dishes also show technical competence: salmon is cooked for the briefest of times and served with a chive cream sauce, 'perhaps with fish stock and vermouth to extend the richness'; tender and thin ravioli contain very plump langoustines in what may be a salmon mousse, with a light langoustine sauce, just flashed under the grill.

The kitchen has often been accused of trying to combine too many elements. Most dispute among readers occurs when complexity results in discord. Thus one criticised a rack of lamb with rosemary sauce for its accompaniment of figs (too sweet) and pine kernels (absolutely unnecessary), making an assemblage rather like a rough provincial chef's, not sure of the impact of one thing on another. Sweetness, particularly in sauces, is another element in the debate. Les petits 'Rossini' is a variation on the classic: beef, two slices of foie gras, a generous amount of truffles, spinach, sauté potatoes and a crust under the beef to soak up the sauce. However, it may be argued that the sweetness of the sauce failed to counteract the palpable richness of the centrepiece. But all these cavils may be quieted in a dish of fillet of veal, cooked to just pink, then sliced on to a bed of mashed potato with olive oil. At the top of the plate was a galette of overlapping discs of turnip, 'each exposed edge caramelised to the same mathematical degree', and some turned vegetables poached in veal stock. The sauce was almost sticky but in fact a finely judged veal and madeira reduction, 'beautifully clear and shining'. The meat was 'the finest I have tasted all year. The combination could be a tedious flop in lesser hands, tasting of nothing. Surrounded by a tumultuous welter of flavours, it was not swamped.' Desserts are always numerous and people give up the need for decision by opting for the grand selection. Old favourites have a long life: lemon tart is still good but the pastry is still thick; marquise is rich and soft; bavarois au kirsch makes a boring flavour something special; terrine of fruits with a raspberry coulis is heavenly and refreshing. Some have felt that more adventure is needed in the sweet repertoire; others that the petits fours are so generous one is safe leaving dessert for another time. Bread has changed this year to a French or Italian hard-crusted roll made with only a little yeast. Some may like it. Cheese is excellent, though quantities may outface. The meal is a set price. The economic pressures of the year have resulted in supplements (for foie gras, lobster, veal and beef) appearing for the first time. These make meals even more expensive and will cause trouble in the end. Perhaps a move to à la carte pricing is inevitable. At lunch there are two menus: one short and 'cheap', the other longer and as dear as dinner. When reservations are expressed, they often come from people who have had the cheaper menu.

The wine list is not cheap by any standards. That is its greatest fault. It has a fine selection of Bordeaux, Burgundy and Rhône, with special sections on Ch. Palmer, d'Yquem and Pomerol. Without being too long, it gives fair balance of age and commune. The provincial French and New World coverage is more summary. Thus, white Rhônes consist of five examples of Condrieu – great, but the starting price is £60. Halves are decent and have just enough range. The wines are well chosen and advice is given freely by the young wine waiters. Occasionally this may be inaccurate as to fact, but they do know which bottles are drinking well.

Nico Ladenis has another restaurant, in Victoria: Very Simply Nico, 48A Rochester Row, SW1P 1JU (071-630 8061). This would have an entry all to itself had there not been a complete change of team in the kitchen and refurbishment in the restaurant, not completed until after we went to press. Very Simply Nico was intended to offer plain food cooked well at a single inclusive price. The intention remains, though it is expected that the menu will have less emphasis on old favourites, such as steak and chips or crème brûlée. Andrew Jeffs, the chef, comes from the Great Portland Street kitchen and the price at the re-opening was £21 for three courses.

CHEFS: Nico Ladenis and Paul Flynn   PROPRIETORS: Nico and Dinah-Jane Ladenis
OPEN: Mon to Fri
MEALS: 12 to 2.15, 7 to 11
PRICES: Set L £27 (£40) and £40 (£61), Set D £40 (£61). Service inc
CARDS: Access, Visa
SEATS: 48. Private parties: 48 main room, 12 private room. No children under 5. Smart dress preferred. No pipes in dining-room. Wheelchair access (1 step). Air-conditioned

Chiang Mai
map 14

48 Frith Street, W1V 5TE
COOKING 1
071-437 7444
COST £18–£30

This simple, clean restaurant survives not only on the fickle Soho scene but despite burgeoning competition from new Thai establishments elsewhere in London. The menu, written in Thai and English, explains that northern Thai cuisine is appreciated 'for its rich and spicy flavours'. There are plenty of those with over 100 savoury dishes listed. Northern Thai cooking also has fewer stir-fried and more long-cooked dishes in its repertoire. Sometimes the latter lack sufficient distinction to make the effort worthwhile. Portions can be small. 'Starters are the best', reports one reader, commending the spicy sausages. Singha Thai beer is appropriate. House French is £6.50.

CHEF/PROPRIETOR: Vatcharin Bhumichitr
OPEN: all week
MEALS: 12 to 3, 6 to 11.30
PRICES: £12 (£18), Set L and D £15.60 (£22) to £18.75 (£25)
CARDS: Access, Amex, Visa
SEATS: 60. Private parties: 12 main room, 20 and 25 private rooms. Vegetarian meals. Children welcome. Music

Chinon
map 10

25 Richmond Way, W14 0AS
COOKING 3
071-602 4082
COST £24–£43

A reader wanted to nominate this 'Shepherds Bush Restaurant of the Year'. His reasons were the evident fervour about raw materials; the sensible concentration on cooking a few things well and so not running too long a menu; and the fresh approach to dishes that rarely tips into overstatement or excess. The restaurant is small, a converted shop, the kitchen half-screened from the tables by a piece of black lacquered chinoiserie, predominant pink giving the room warmth, pictures lending it interest. The character or style of cooking that has led to favourable comment is shown in a first course of scallops, seared on a hot surface and sweetly juicy inside, arranged around a central mound of strips of crinkle-cut courgettes enclosing chopped tomato flesh and salmon roe. The light dressing, aromatic with cooking *jus*, tomato liquid and olive oil, was exactly seasoned: a dish of well-bought ingredients and restrained composition. Similarly, very good fresh puff pastry was piled with white crab meat surrounded by a halo of samphire, giving the necessary briny bite to the shellfish, all sitting on a saffron sauce. 'It had a brightness about it that shouted "just made".' Main courses have shown less piercing simplicity, which is the way with main courses, perhaps, where the necessity of vegetables and 'finish' may introduce too many elements. Thus a noisette of lamb wrapped in caul fat (which added texture and earthy flavour to the meat) is served with a tower of vegetables in strands, a fried cake of potato, a few oyster mushrooms in a nutmeg and cream sauce topped with a button onion, and some radishes. A plate of salmon and sole came with roasted red pepper and a saffron sauce plus another tower of vegetables, but no potatoes. The end of the meal is largely without choice. Before dessert, a plate of cheese is made up for each order, seven or eight sorts, plus fruit, from the butcher's block by the front door. Dessert is no-choice, too: a plate with half a dozen different items: a spearmint sorbet, an apple sorbet with a spun sugar cape, lemon tart, a mousse, and a brandy-snap basket with soft fruits. The short wine list, largely French, shows as much care in buying as does the food. Half-bottles are in evidence.

CHEFS/PROPRIETORS: Barbara Deane and Jonathan Hayes
OPEN: Tue to Sat, exc Sat L
CLOSED: most bank hols
MEALS: 12 to 2, 7 to 10 (11 Fri and Sat)
PRICES: £25 (£36), Set D £15 (£24). Service 12%
CARDS: Access, Amex, Visa
SEATS: 21. Private parties: 30 main room. Smart dress preferred

Christian's

map 10

1 Station Parade,
Burlington Lane, W4 3HD
081-995 0382 and 0208

COOKING 1
COST £31

Christian Gustin has sold Le Bistro, his second restaurant (in Barnes): 'staffing and running two establishments whilst still doing the cooking is totally impossible.' This is a familiar cry from many small restaurateurs willing to expand yet unable to delegate their personalities – which are often the reason for success anyway. Contraction has caused a decorative rush of blood to the head with a new front and a set of tables in a 'terrace' passage to one side of the kitchen. Diners can monitor the progress of their meal if they peek over the high counter dividing the kitchen from the restaurant. The repertoire is modern without going overboard: mousse of artichoke hearts with red pepper coulis; goats' cheese soufflé; vegetarian stuffed aubergine; leg of lamb with garlic and shallots; pork with ginger and honey; and a set of desserts recited to you at the table including chocolate terrine and greengage tart à l'ancienne. Execution is fair, without great finesse of flavour or, sometimes, kitchen skills. A greengage tart without sugar is not much of a sweet; burnt garlic and shallots don't help a light lamb gravy support leg of lamb. The place is rescued by its pleasantness:

Christian and his ebullient staff of women are a pleasure. A good neighbourhood spot. The short, intelligent wine list is fairly priced, entirely French and includes a good Sancerre, Ch. de Maimbray. House wine is £6.25.

CHEF/PROPRIETOR: Christian Gustin
OPEN: Tue to Sat, exc Sat L
CLOSED: bank hols
MEALS: 12.30 to 2, 7.30 to 10.45
PRICES: £19 (£26). Service 12%
SEATS: 40. 4 tables outside. Private parties: 8 main room. Vegetarian meals. No cigars/pipes in dining-room. Wheelchair access

Chuen Cheng Ku

map 14

17 Wardour Street, W1V 3HD
071-437 1398

COOKING 1
COST £10–£41

Reports have not been encouraging about the standard fare, little better than average and served with a certain grimness and haste. The recommendation is for the dim-sum at lunch. The trolleys come trundling around and although the waitress may be unable to explain the contents, they are good: whelks, char-siu stuffed buns, yam fritters, fragrant rice, spare ribs, and sucking pig have been enjoyed. You have to know the system. The place is enormous and not always welcoming. The long menu has some interesting, less familiar dishes but their fair price may be their strongest recommendation. Fair prices also characterise the short wine list. House wine: £6.30.

CHEF: Yat Au   PROPRIETORS: Choi and Kam Au
OPEN: all week
MEALS: 11am to midnight (11.30pm Sun)
PRICES: £13 (£22), Set L £6 (£10) to £15 (£19), Set D £9 (£13) to £30 (£34). Service inc
CARDS: Access, Amex, Diners, Visa
SEATS: 400. Private parties: 150 main room, 50 and 80 private rooms. Vegetarian meals. Children welcome. Wheelchair access. Music

Cibo

map 10

3 Russell Gardens, W14 8WZ
071-371 6271 and 2085

COOKING 2
COST £37

Russell Gardens might almost be the boundary of chic, before the railway tracks and the bulk of Olympia on the nether side. This new Italian restaurant made a good first impression and appears set for a fair run even though its predecessors on the site changed not annually but by the season. Decoration is clean yet busy with many pictures, objets and three-dimensional constructs, including a pair of arms and hands hanging centre-stage in some gesture of supplication. The layout of the restaurant – three open-ended zones with a bar at the hub – is satisfactorily varied to the eye and absorbs well a happy and expansive clientele. The cooking is linked to the River Café and Orso (see entries), or perhaps Alastair Little or Rowley Leigh in their Italian modes. It is no Britalian trattoria, but rather an exercise in Italian home-cooking with an emphasis on the charcoal grill. Parma ham and melon is not in evidence, but sauté radicchio and endive with goats' cheese and olive oil is. This has made it justifiably popular at a time when olive oil (and truffle oil for the determinedly trendy), grilled foods, vibrant colour and an apparent simplicity are more in favour than cream, butter or lard. Meals may start well with antipasto arranged on gaily polychrome pottery; these, however, can look better than they taste. The fast-changing menu runs to maybe a dozen choices in each course but readers stress that it may not always be necessary to launch into full-scale exploration of the options, particularly at lunch. A spinach broth followed by another first course of pigeon breast with artichokes on a piece of toasted bread made a particularly satisfying midday meal. The grill plays its part, offering baby squid with tomato and chilli; Parma ham with mozzarella; a daily selection of grilled shellfish or fish; a veal chop *alle erbe*; and a lamb steak cut from the leg served with sauté of peppers (this last sadly chosen and poorly grilled on one occasion). Longer and wetter cooking occurs, too, with good soups; cotechino sausage with lentils and polenta; a giant fish stew; several pasta dishes, a couple of risottos and well-received potato gnocchi with tomato and mozzarella. Portions are generous. Vegetables have been praised for accuracy of cooking and intelligent seasoning: endive, spinach, French beans, even red cabbage. Service appears invariably enthusiastic and pleasant – 'they seem to enjoy their job'. Coffee is good. Three Champagnes apart, wines are resolutely and enthusiastically Italian. Listed by price, those not initiated into the vagaries and particularities of Italy are not helped, but can feel confident for the bottles are from good, modern wine-makers throughout. Prices are fair, so experiment is possible. The Italian refusal to use half-bottles is necessarily reflected. House wine: £6.75.

CHEF: Claudio Pecorari   PROPRIETOR: Gino Taddei
OPEN: all week, exc sun D
CLOSED: bank hols, 2 weeks Aug
MEALS: 12 to 2.30, 7 to 11
PRICES: £23 (£31). Service 12.5% for parties of 5 or more
CARDS: Access, Amex, Diners, Visa
SEATS: 55. Private parties: 60 main room. Children's helpings. Music

Ciboure

map 11

21 Eccleston Street, SW1 9LX
071-730 2505

COOKING 2
COST £23–£34

Geographically, Ciboure is on the Biscay coast in the border country between France and Spain. In British restaurant terms it is a neighbourhood eating place on the fringes of Belgravia not far from Victoria Station. In the evening this area 'feels like a resort town out of season'. Inside it is sparse and modish – a wall-to-ceiling mirror near the bar, low spotlights, arch-backed black aluminium chairs. The menu is short and modern with distinct French overtones and an almost obsessive fondness for mushrooms and spinach. Fungi are everywhere. A selection, including morels and girolles, accompanies pungent slices of smoked goose breast with the appearance and texture of Parma ham; they also garnish a hot timbale of leeks. As for spinach, a ball of perfectly cooked leaves and a handful of minute baby turnips are served with fanned slices of roast rabbit. Paired with couscous, it sits alongside grilled pigeon breasts. The two signature ingredients come together in a dish of roast fillet of English lamb –

generous, well-cooked slices of meat arranged over a mound of deep green spinach and cultivated mushrooms with a very light drizzle of pale brown sauce. In theory, vegetables are matched with individual dishes, although there's a suggestion that orders can be mixed up in the kitchen – which defeats the point. Desserts are Gallic: a 'deeply classical' version of *île flottante* with hazelnut praline; big slices of tarte Tatin embellished with blobs of whipped cream. While Melanie Dixon runs the kitchen, proprietor Jean Louis Journade ensures that service is efficient and professional. There is a good deal of flair and imagination, but minor details can irritate: 'appalling' French bread, careless seasoning and an obligatory 15 per cent service charge 'for your convenience'. The wine list has been pared down to the French essentials, including some good properties. House wine £8. CELLARMAN'S CHOICE: Mâcon Aze, Dom. des Teppes de Chatenay 1988, £13.20.

CHEF: Melanie Dixon   PROPRIETOR: Jean Louis Journade
OPEN: Mon to Fri
CLOSED: 3 weeks Aug
MEALS: 12 to 2.30, 7 to 11
PRICES: £19 (£28), Set L £14.50 (£23), Set D £16 (£25) to £17.50 (£26). Service 15%
CARDS: Access, Amex, Diners, Visa
SEATS: 36. Children welcome. No cigars/pipes in dining-room. Wheelchair access. Air-conditioned

Clarke's ▼

map 11

124 Kensington Church Street, W8 4BH   COOKING 4
071-221 9225   COST £22−£41

This popular restaurant towards the northern end of Kensington Church Street is among the few in London offering a no-choice menu at dinner. The menu is set a week ahead so serious problems can be negotiated in advance. Lunch is a short menu of three options, and the popular dishes disappear early, but it is very fairly priced and many prefer the format. The restaurant is quite plain and small at street level (next door to the shop where you can buy cheeses and breads and cakes, baked on the premises), but is larger, charming and airy in the basement where cooking and eating shake hands. Sally Clarke herself will be at the stove at lunchtime: people talk wonderingly of her precision timing while juggling many a conversation across the divide. At night she dresses in mufti and rules the front of house. Adoption of this formula is bound to impose limitations of material and style to preserve its acceptability. Offal, casseroles and long-cooked items appear but rarely: meals are rarely over-rich and there is a fresh delicacy of flavour. Such cooking relies on perfect materials for its eloquence and exact timing for success. Above all, there is a homogeneity of approach so that regulars are not disconcerted by great swings of style or experiment that might, elsewhere, be accommodated in a small corner of the menu. There is development, for one reader has remarked on how she is 'mining a rich Italian vein this year'. The hallmarks may be char-grilling; sauces that are perforce not made from pan juices, that do not use deep reductions or too much butter or cream but are relishes, vegetable based or light oil dressings or emulsions; vegetables often having equal weight with the meat or fish, as in a dish of grilled loin of pork with a sauce of apple, prunes and sage, accompanied by a paper package of root vegetables and a pile of rocket leaves – unfortunate that the pork was not of sufficiently good quality to support this assemblage. A better instance was grilled scallops with an olive and sun-dried tomato relish, on one side a pile of wild rice with slippery fresh spinach and green spring onion and on the other a slab of aubergine topped with half a grilled baby radicchio spread with an intense herby paste. 'These were the finest scallops I've eaten in Europe, three plump monsters timed to the second, pure succulence. The relish was outrageous – all that strength and oiliness as a foil to the fish.' If those are some main courses, then beginnings of clam and parsley risotto with 'moist, rich rice grains bursting with stock', or warm boiled Jersey Royal potatoes dressed with oil, chervil and parsley accompanied by a few leaves and a great dollop of crème fraîche, keep the standard high. So do desserts like bananas wrapped in crisp filo with an orange caramel sauce, fine chocolate cake (alone worth a visit) with brandied cherries in a kirsch cream (cry, cry Black Forest), or a dish of fruits poached with vanilla syrup and served with vanilla ice-cream in which one may learn the positive value of vanilla while regretting the vapidity of imported spring fruits. Baking of bread, biscuits and other things is done here with enthusiasm and success; just as is working through the vegetable kingdom for new combinations to set off the much plainer meats: basil and lentils, potato and spring onion champ (a Lancashire dish), skewered new potatoes grilled with aïoli, or green beans, wild mushrooms and hazelnuts. Sally Clarke does not often go to the sweet side of taste when balancing her savoury dishes, rather will she mobilise bitter leaves: this is refreshing. Nor does she, as do many Californian cooks with whom she is bracketed, indulge the chilli for that sad uniformity of flavour that spoils much New World cooking. Because of the simplicity of the no-choice menu at night, the waiting staff have little to do save ferry materials hither and yon and keep tables topped up. This they do well though occasionally there are murmurs of brusqueness and ignorance of the ingredients. They also have to deliver wine from a list that changes often and is well chosen. As if to deny still further that Californian description, most wines are French, though the American section is always worth a look. A dozen wines available by the glass heads the list; this is a good indicator of the quality and catholicity of the remainder. This is not a blockbuster list, just over a hundred wines, but anything can be ordered confidently and at fair prices.

CHEF/PROPRIETOR: Sally Clarke
OPEN: Mon to Fri
CLOSED: 2 weeks Aug, 10 days Christmas, 4 days Easter, bank hols
MEALS: 12.30 to 2, 7.30 to 11
PRICES: Set L £18 (£22) to £20 (£24), Set D £30 (£34). Service inc
CARDS: Access, Visa
SEATS: 90. Private parties: 8 main room. Children welcome. Wheelchair access. Air-conditioned

Several sharp operators have tried to extort money from restaurateurs on the promise of an entry in a guide book that has never appeared. The Good Food Guide *makes no charge for inclusion and does not offer certificates of any kind.*

▲ *Connaught*   map 13

Carlos Place, W1Y 6AL   COOKING 4
071-499 7070   COST £37–£79

First-time visitors may treat a tour of the ground floor as if to a historic house:
the Connaught preserves in an aspic as finely crafted as any round a terrine de
foie gras the niceties of old-fashioned hotels, though buffeted by the winds of
tourism and big business. The dining-room has qualities matched nowhere
else: 'the pleasure of being there begins as you sit down; the comfort of the
chairs, the size of the tables and perfect ratio of chairs, tables and serving
paraphernalia to the available space, plus the impression that the polished
panels of the walls owe their chestnut gleam to a strapping such as given by a
groom to his favourite stallion, that the cut-glass screens, goblets and
silverware have been rendered speckless by paranormal dusters, and that the
spotless white linen has been dealt with in a celestial laundry. None of this is
to be sneezed at.' The art of waiting is taken to extremes. 'Two thick slices of
terrine de foie gras were cut, brought to me for approval, then taken away to be
adorned with diced port jelly decorated by a criss-cross of truffle.' Calf's liver is
cooked thick, brought to the table, acknowledged, removed to be cut into thin
slices, then reconstituted into its original shape. All dishes are handled,
reverently, several times before they finally hit the table. As many people go to
the Connaught to experience British plain cooking done well, as do to try the
many examples on the long and hard-to-decipher menu of classical haute
cuisine. The British side – mixed grill, kidneys and bacon, roast beef – is often
carried off with style and accuracy, though more complicated examples may
result in error. 'Roast woodcock had splendid breadcrumbs and bread sauce
but was overcooked to an unappetising degree. The wild duck, shown whole,
then presented as slivers of breast alone, tasted as though it had been reheated;
its garnish, a preserved peach ornamented by angelica leaves and a glacé
cherry, was decidedly downmarket.' Classical cooking, seen in soft poached
eggs on a jelly with shreds of ham (oeufs en gelée Stendhal), or croustade of
quails' eggs Maintenon; or salmon and sorrel 'Jean Troisgros', are more
exciting statements of a demanding art. Even so at one meal the rack of lamb
with a pastry crust and a stuffing of mushrooms and artichoke mousseline
(carré d'agneau de Kent forestière) was overcooked and the béarnaise with a
fillet steak oversalted. Rice or bread-and-butter puddings are available and
there is a sweets trolley. These misgivings do not entirely detract from the
achievement of a remarkable restaurant which most people find invigorating as
an experience, though some may think it intimidating. There is much good
cooking, sometimes the best of its kind, though the numbers involved mean
that slip-ups may occur. The wine list has been overtaken by the numerous big
hotel cellars in London that offer a wider range for not much more money. The
clarets are a fine set, few younger than 1981, many dating back to the 1960s.
The burgundies also have enviable breadth, of age as well as commune, but the
shippers tend to the old fashioned. Other regions get cursory, dismissive
treatment and countries other than Italy, which is favoured with good growers
as well as older vintages, and Germany, are totally ignored. It will not be long
before it becomes a poor list, except for Champagnes and vintage port.

CHEF: Michel Bourdin   PROPRIETORS: Savoy Hotel plc
OPEN: Restaurant all week, Grill Room Mon to Fri
CLOSED: Grill Room weekends and bank hols
MEALS: 12.30 to 2, 6 to 10.15
PRICES: £46 (£65), Set L £24.45 (£37) to £50.30 (£66), Set D £26.50 (£39) to £50.30 (£66).
Minimum £25. Service 15%
CARD: Access
SEATS: 115. Private parties: 20 private room. No children under 6. Smart dress preferred.
No pipes in dining-room. Wheelchair access (also WC). Air-conditioned
ACCOMMODATION: 90 rooms, all with bath/shower. Rooms for disabled. Lift. Rooms £150
to £195. Afternoon teas (priority to residents). TV. Phone

Connolly's   map 10

| 162 Lower Richmond Road, SW15 1LY | COOKING 1 |
| 081-788 3844 | COST £17–£30 |

Eamonn Connolly cooks at this popular small restaurant – almost too popular
for efficiency – and his sister superintends the customers. A *carte* of eight dishes
in each course is both supplemented and rendered less dear by the option of a
set-price menu. Cooking is 'modern British' in as much as it is difficult
otherwise to characterise pheasant with kümmel and artichokes; a chicken
salad with pickled bananas; or salmon and cod with basil and orange sauce.
These have pleased, while ox-tail rillettes, salad of mozzarella and avocado,
and a vegetarian dish of lasagne have not. The cooking, while adventurous, is
also up and down. There is a decent short wine list, not too highly priced.
House French: £7.50.

CHEF: Eamonn Connolly   PROPRIETORS: Kate Connolly and Eamonn Connolly
OPEN: all week, exc Sun D
CLOSED: bank hols
MEALS: 12 to 2.30 (12.30 to 4 Sun), 7 to 10.30
PRICES: £16 (£25), Set L and D £11.95 (£17)
CARDS: Access, Visa
SEATS: 40. 6 tables outside. Private parties: 40 main room. Vegetarian meals. Children's
helpings (Sun L only). Wheelchair access (1 step to rest). Music

Cork & Bottle ♥   map 14

| 44–46 Cranbourn Street, WC2H 7AN | COOKING 1 |
| 071-734 7807 | COST £20 |

Cork & Bottle, Shampers in Kingly Street, W1, and Methuselah's in Victoria
Street, SW1, are wine bars owned by Don Hewitson, a high-profile and
intelligent enthusiast of wines, particularly those from his native Australia
(although he says he is beginning to be a little disappointed in the whites). The
food continues to rely on Pavlova, 'the best we eat anywhere', raised cheese
and ham pie, 'feather-light pastry, a perfect gastronomic marriage', and
standbys like garlic mushrooms 'faultlessly executed'. Perhaps such eloquence
is encouraged by reasonable prices. Not everything is perfection, but the food
does a very decent job as sensible accompaniment to the great wines. Would
that all wine bars were like this.

CHEF: Louis Eghan PROPRIETOR: Don Hewitson
OPEN: all week, exc Sun L
MEALS: 11 to 3, 5.30 to 11 (10.30 Sun)
PRICES: £9 (£17)
CARDS: Access, Amex, Diners, Visa
SEATS: 60. Private parties: 20 main room, 20 private room. Vegetarian meals. Children
restricted. Music. Air-conditioned. Self-service

La Croisette

map 11

168 Ifield Road, SW10 9AF   COOKING 2
071-373 3694   COST £27–£35

The original of Pierre Martin's fleet of fish restaurants, La Croisette is tucked
down spiral stairs in a basement and offers a large range of fish, simply cooked
but carefully bought from northern France, Scotland and Ireland. Menus from
one branch to another are the same. Fruits de mer are the consistent favourite
and the *carte* reflects this by being weighted firmly towards shellfish, the white
fish taking its place among the daily specials. Ambience and service are
unreservedly French. House wine from Provence: £8.50.

CHEF: Robin Bertrand PROPRIETOR: Pierre Martin
OPEN: Tue to Sun, exc Tue L
CLOSED: 25 Dec
MEALS: 12.30 to 2.30, 7.30 to 11.30
PRICES: £18 (£27), Set L and D £25 (£35). Cover £1. Service 15%
CARDS: Access, Amex, Diners, Visa
SEATS: 55. 3 tables outside. Private parties: 10 main room. Children welcome. Smart dress
preferred. No pipes in dining-room. Music

Crowthers

map 10

481 Upper Richmond Road West,
SW14 7PU   COOKING 2
081-876 6372   COST £21–£34

The location, in a shopping parade on the South Circular, is dull, which
perhaps is why the small shop conversion, fairly tight packed if busy, retreats
to Laura Ashley nostalgia to shut out the reality. The menu offers a short
modern choice at a set price: timbale of carrot with orange and cardamom,
tortellini of seafood; spinach and ricotta gnocchi; calf's liver with sage and
onion; salmon in pastry with a sole and pistachio mousseline; pork in filo with
garlic and juniper. The repertoire sticks within well-practised bounds,
obviously enjoying pastry work and baking, quite skilled but not always
exciting if repeated visits are made. Service has been criticised for being slow
and for lacking warmth or enthusiasm. The need to survive as a neighbourhood
restaurant, albeit at £30 a head, means that being neighbourly would help. The
wine list is short, not greedily priced, well chosen, with equal New World
representation but with only two halves of dry white wine on offer. House
wines: £8 and £10.50. CELLARMAN'S CHOICE: Gigondas, Grand Montmirail
1985, £13.50; Basedow Semillon 1988, £13.25.

CHEF: Philip Crowther PROPRIETORS: Philip and Shirley Crowther
OPEN: Mon to Sat, exc Mon and Sat L
MEALS: 12 to 2, 7 to 10
PRICES: Set L £15 (£21), Set D £21 (£28)
CARDS: Access, Amex, Visa
SEATS: 32. Private parties: 32 main room. Children welcome. Wheelchair access.
Air-conditioned

Diwana Bhel Poori   map 11

121 Drummond Street, NW1 2HL   COOKING 1
071-387 5556   COST £5−£12

Drummond Street, between Hampstead Road and Euston Station, is a Little
India, full of Indian grocers, Islamic video shops, halal butchers, sweet centres
and, above all, vegetarian restaurants. Diwana set the pace in the 1970s and
regulars have bemoaned its absence from recent editions of the *Guide*. Despite
some refurbishment, this is still a café with hard seats, queues, no bookings,
and a bustling atmosphere. One reader favours the scheme of ordering a
selection of starters − bite-sized onion bhajias served with tomato and chilli
sauce on the side, bhel-poori, aloo papri chat and samosa. Then he by-passes
the main course and moves straight to the sweets − in particular the excellent
kulfi ice-creams. The only weakness seems to be the breads. The waiters work
fast and the food is a testament to its Gujerat source. Unlicensed, but there is
lassi, fruit juice or mango milk shake; otherwise bring your own wine, free of a
corkage charge. There is a sister restaurant at 50 Westbourne Grove, W2.

CHEF: Abdul Kabir PROPRIETORS: The Patel family
OPEN: all week
CLOSED: 25 Dec
MEALS: noon to 11.30
PRICES: £7 (£10), Set L and D £3.50 (£5) to £5 (£6). Unlicensed, bring your own: no corkage
CARDS: Access, Amex, Diners, Visa
SEATS: 72. Vegetarian meals. Children welcome. Wheelchair access (1 step). Music

La Dordogne   map 10

5 Devonshire Road, W4 2EU   COOKING 2
081-747 1836   COST £34

Dark green inside and out, the Dordogne continues as steadily as its formulaic
menu, though daily adding oysters and lobsters to its repertoire of Anglo-
French, rather than regional south-western food. Fillets of sole with passion-
fruit sauce, lamb with mint and honey, and duck with raspberries or grapefruit
have less to do with the Dordogne than first courses of foie gras and confit of
duck. People generally enjoy the French atmosphere and service − though it
may be too slick one day, 'just off the boat for the holidays' another. The
cooking eschews brilliance but rarely displays serious faults, making the
restaurant a sound neighbourhood option. If visits are too frequent, however, it
would be easy to tire of a choice that hardly changes from month to month,

Report forms are at the back of the book; write a letter if you prefer.

except in detail. Reports have spoken well of a salad of fresh and smoked duck; a mille-feuille of scallops and vegetables in a lobster sauce; magret of duck with grapefruit sauce; fillet of beef with Cahors red wine sauce; and a domino of white and dark chocolate with peppermint sauce. Worth noting on the wine list are the half dozen 'exclusives' from Bergerac and Cahors. House Bergerac is £7.40.

CHEF: Jean-Claude Paillard   PROPRIETOR: Rachel Bitton
OPEN: all week, exc Sat and Sun L
MEALS: 12 to 2.30, 7 to 11
PRICES: £18 (£28). Cover £1. Service 10%
CARDS: Access, Amex, Visa
SEATS: 80. 6 tables outside. Private parties: 20 and 38 private rooms. Children restricted. Smart dress preferred. Wheelchair access. Music

Dragon Inn

map 11

63 Westbourne Grove, W2 4UA   COOKING 1
071-792 9185 and 229 8806   COST £16–£30

The decor is smart but one reader was underwhelmed with his stir-fried prawns with straw mushrooms, carrots and spring onions. He thought the blubber with duck and a few slices of pig's intestine (for once, undyed) in chilli sauce a competent rendering, however. Garlic-laden stewed mutton and dried bean curd in a typical Cantonese hot-pot was excellent. Service is scrutable. The dim-sum are well-reputed and offer a fair range. The menu has good sections of one-plate dishes, and a certain number of tripe and offal dishes. Drink tea or lager. A sister restaurant is at 12 Gerrard Street, W1.

CHEF: Sham Yau Wong   PROPRIETORS: Hareleap Projects Ltd
OPEN: all week
MEALS: noon to 11.45
PRICES: £13 (£25), Set L and D £10 (£16) to £16.50 (£23). Service 10%
CARDS: Access, Amex, Visa
SEATS: 75. Private parties: 60 main room. Vegetarian meals. Children's helpings. Smart dress preferred. Music. Air-conditioned

Dragon's Nest

map 14

58–60 Shaftesbury Avenue, W1V 7DE   COOKING 2
071-437 3119   COST £20–£34

Opinion is still divided about the merits of this prettily decorated restaurant full of bevelled mirrors and Chinese wall-paintings. But the overall consensus is that high-class Szechuan-style food is to be had, although even loyal followers have to admit that dishes have lost some of their original dazzle. The menu comes as a little book with parchment pages. A glance shows the bias of the cuisine: lots of hot garlic sauces, chillies, dried red pepper and even fermented rice wine as elemental flavourings. Some dishes are unique to the Dragon's Nest, in particular the vegetable dumplings and Shanghai dumplings in a basket, which the chef learned at a famous restaurant in Taipei. These may well be the highlights of the menu. The recommendations are impressive:

appetisers such as smoked fish; cold brisket of beef; kidneys with chilli sauce; bon-bon chicken with sesame paste. From other parts of the menu there are good reports of crispy chicken with hot garlic sauce; yellow fish in sweet-and-sour sauce; and sizzling squid with mange-tout and mushrooms. General Tsang's chicken is 'a great shock to the taste buds'. Some dishes seem like perfectly formed nouvelle miniatures: tiny spring rolls 'the size of one's little finger,' bowls of clear, clean-tasting wun tun soup with some cabbage and four pasta shapes each with a prawn inside. At the other end of the scale, readers have mentioned overbearingly rich and heavy platefuls: even the much-lauded aubergines with yellow-bean sauce can be too daunting for some appetites. When the restaurant disappoints it is often because the food does not live up to people's expectations, but clearly there are real inconsistencies which need to be ironed out. More worrying is the steady stream of complaints about the service. One cynical view is that 'it is geared to the tourist market where they are not expecting the customers to return.' Others have found the waiters 'surly to the point of rudeness' and 'indifferent'. Prices are now higher and the value, compared to other Soho stalwarts, has been questioned. The wine list is short and adequate. House wine: £7.80.

CHEF: M. Chang PROPRIETOR: P. Lam
OPEN: all week
CLOSED: Christmas
MEALS: noon to 2.45, 5 to 11.15
PRICES: £16 (£28), Set D £13 (£20) to £18 (£26). Minimum £10. Service 12.5%
CARDS: Access, Amex, Diners, Visa
SEATS: 150. Private parties: 70 main room; 40 private room. Music. Air-conditioned

▲ *Dukes Hotel*

map 13

St James's Place, SW1A 1NY
071-491 4840

COOKING 2
COST £28–£77

At this price, it should be good, though reports are more along the lines of 'satisfactory'. The hotel prides itself on its discretion – so discreet that many of the windows, dining-room and bedrooms look on to inner courts or ventilation shafts – and its prices indicate a desire for exclusivity. The bar strikes a clubland note of leather and panelling while the dining-room has a more designer approach, apparently dominated by hats: large ones on pictures of fin-de-siècle ladies, pseudo-hats, complete with ribbon bows, enveloping cheeses. Tony Marshall cooks a discreet menu: flavours, such as elderflower wine, ginger, or coriander, are there but it takes a fine palate to appreciate them through the butter or cream that is often their vehicle. Reports speak well of beef with foie gras and madeira sauce and the joint from the trolley. Desserts are on a trolley, too, and acceptable. The wine list harbours many fine bottles, but the prices – Muscadet at £14.50 – remind the drinker how costly maintaining a hotel in this area must be. Clarets are the strongest suit, but red burgundies are also well chosen. A half-bottle of Bollinger will cost more here than a whole bottle at Jemima's in west Wales (see entry under Haverfordwest). Who is to measure the degree of enjoyment? House wine is £10.75, but virtually nothing else is below £15.

CHEF: Tony Marshall   PROPRIETORS: Cunard Hotels & Leisure Plc
OPEN: all week, exc Sat L
MEALS: 12.30 to 2.30, 6 (7 Sun) to 10
PRICES: £33 (£48), Set L £17.50 (£28) to £50 (£64), Set D £22 (£33) to £50 (£64). Licensed,
also bring your own: corkage £10
CARDS: Access, Amex, Diners, Visa
SEATS: 50. Private parties: 45 main room, 12 private room. Vegetarian meals. Children
welcome. Smart dress preferred. Wheelchair access (also WC)
ACCOMMODATION: 62 rooms, all with bath/shower. Rooms for disabled. Lift. B&B £165 to
£195. Afternoon teas. TV. Phone

Efes Kebab House
map 13

80 Great Titchfield Street, W1P 7AF   COOKING 1
071-636 1953   COST £17−£23

The rollicking atmosphere keeps the holiday spirit ticking on through the
colder months; meze and charcoal-grilled main courses − 'enormous portions,
beautifully cooked, at very reasonable prices' − are adequately rounded off by
sticky pastries. Another view is that it is 'uneven, but fun'. The cooking is not
always as evocative and aromatic as the menu may imply: fresh chicken with
special walnut sauce was tasteless shredded chicken with barely detectable
walnut flavour; 'plakiler', dry beans, were just boring; vine leaves and peppers
with rice stuffing 'samey'. But all might be forgiven for the excellent pitta, the
grilled chicken marinated in garlic, and the 'gorgeous' baklava. House wines
may not be so brilliant, but there are a dozen Turkish fruit liqueurs for the
brave and beer from Ephesus for the thirsty. People do comment less happily
on the crowding together of tables for two, the smoky atmosphere and the
somewhat hustling service. This fault is compounded by bills that are not
itemised. There is now an Efes Kebab House II at 175−177 Great Portland
Street, W1N 5FD (071-436 0600) which is more spacious and has received
recommendation.

CHEFS/PROPRIETORS: K. Akkus and I. Akbas
OPEN: Mon to Sat
MEALS: Noon to 11.30
PRICES: £10 (£17), Set L and D £14 (£19) to £15 (£20). Cover 60p. Minimum £6
CARDS: Access, Amex, Visa
SEATS: 150. Private parties: 70 main room. Vegetarian meals. Children welcome.
Air-conditioned

Eleven Park Walk
map 12

11 Park Walk, SW10   COOKING 1
071-352 3449 and 8249   COST £36

Not as studied as L'Incontro or Santini (see entries), nor as expensive, this
Italian restaurant pleases with its plants a-million, mirrors, cane and bamboo
chairs and general air of bustle. Certainly the ambience, even more than the
food, suggests those busy Roman trattoria, accessible to every generation and
supervised by quick-witted waiters as anxious to supply your needs as they are
to ply the peppermill. The menu is neither resolutely trendy, nor old-

fashioned. It includes some regional dishes like osso buco, bagna cauda and
bollito misto as well as restaurant standards such as chicken cacciatore,
calamari fritti and Parma ham. Duck with blackcurrants, maybe a famous
Italian dish to come, is recommended. Cooking can be accurate, particularly
fish according to one report, the osso buco according to another, yet it may also
suffer from English approximation. The bagna cauda was a tepid, rather than a
hot bath. A fair rendering of tiramisu made up for a Park Walk Special that was
nothing more than a mix of fruits in a cocktail glass. In all, an enjoyable place.
The wine list is full of good Italian bottles, all given proper details, unlike the
menu. The menu sent to the *Guide* failed to mention the cover charge or the
service charge of 15 per cent. House wine: £7. CELLARMAN'S CHOICE: Pinot
Grigio 1988, Gianni Vescovo, £13; Chianti, San Lorenzo 1986, Ama di Gaiole,
£28.

CHEF: Giancarlo Moeri   PROPRIETORS: S. Livesi, G. Movio, F. Zanallato and C. Pulze
OPEN: Mon to Sat
MEALS: 12.30 to 3, 7 to 12
PRICES: £20 (£30). Cover £1. Service 15%
CARDS: Access, Amex, Visa
SEATS: 100. Private parties: 100 main room. Vegetarian meals. Children's helpings.
Wheelchair access (1 step). Music. Air-conditioned

Emile's
map 10

144 Wandsworth Bridge Road, SW6 2UH   COOKING 1
071-736 2418   COST £18–£22

The gentrification of this leafy stretch of Wandsworth Bridge Road has moved
into a new phase. Shops selling reproduction pine furniture, toys and
children's clothes share the space with bar/brasseries, pasta joints and bistros.
Emile's is on the site of the old Filling Station Bistro. The exterior may look
uninviting with some neglected pub benches and timber-slated blinds, but
inside it is cosy and quite classy. The cheerful ground floor feels like an old-
style neighbourhood bistro with white cloths and candles on the tables.
Downstairs is a quarry-tiled basement with painted brick walls. Diners sit
cheek by jowl and the piped music never stops. The place works to a simple
but commendable formula of simple dishes backed up by 'gutsy sauces', all at a
price that suggests 'good old-fashioned value for money'. A short set menu on
the blackboard at £12 is supplemented by a *carte*. There has been a good crop of
recommended dishes, including a 'refreshing' red pepper, tomato and basil
mousse; avocado with smoked salmon and clams, breast of duck glazed with
plum and fresh ginger served with a cherry apple and cider sauce; and chicken
stuffed with apricots, onions and cheese. In addition there are plain chargrills,
and readers have also mentioned the quality of the beef Wellington. Sweets are
competent rather than inspiring. Service usually copes well. The short wine list
is reasonable as far as it goes, with a broad selection of a few bottles from
different regions and countries. House French is £6. There is a branch at
96 Felsham Road, SW15 1DQ (081-789 3323).

See the back of the Guide *for an index of restaurants listed.*

CHEF: Andrew Sherlock   PROPRIETORS: Emil Fahmy and Andrew Sherlock
OPEN: Mon to Sat, D only
CLOSED: bank hols, 25 Dec, 1 Jan
MEALS: 7.30 to 11
PRICES: £12 (£18), Set D £12 (£18)
CARDS: Access, Visa
SEATS: 60. 12 tables outside. Private parties: 42 private room. Vegetarian meals. Children
welcome. Wheelchair access (1 step)

L'Escargot Doré

map 11

2–4 Thackeray Street, W8 8ET
071-937 8508

COOKING 2
COST £22–£43

This snail lives underground, in the basement of a smart shop front on a small
street tucked one block south of Kensington High Street. The arrival of chef
Hervé Pronzato has added lustre to its shell even if the dining-room,
fortunately air-conditioned, is quite close set for comfortable appreciation of
the substantial cooking. The *carte* has a section on snails: three dishes, one
standard with garlic butter, one in mushrooms and the third with goats' cheese
in tomatoes. Although these have been approved, particularly those with
mushrooms, more satisfaction has been voiced for feuilleté of asparagus with
poached quails' eggs on a cream and chive sauce; light pasta with smoked
salmon and a peppered cream sauce; rack of lamb roasted in sea salt with a
gratin of fennel that had been braised in cream then browned under the grill;
and fillet of beef in a first-class truffle and celeriac sauce with a fondue of
shallots and onion. Chips were served with the latter, but good chips. The
regular appearance of cream may be noted. This is no new-wave warm-
vinaigrette-and-lentil cooking, witness a whole roast calf's kidney with a side
dish of pasta and foie gras. The sure touch of the savoury dishes is sometimes
lacking from the desserts, even classics like crème brûlée or tarte Tatin, which
the chef's formal training might have drummed into him. Service is the good
old-fashioned sort, headed by the proprietor. The wine list is short and almost
entirely French save for a handful of Spanish bottles. Prices, generally high, can
be kept down by choosing from the front page of French country wines, or the
house Duboeuf at £8.

CHEF: Hervé Pronzato   PROPRIETORS: Mr and Mrs Sanchez
OPEN: Mon to Sat, exc Sat L
CLOSED: 25 Dec and bank hols, last 2 weeks Aug
MEALS: 12 to 2.30, 6.30 to 11.30
PRICES: £24 (£36), Set L and D £13.50 (£22). Cover £1.30
CARDS: Access, Amex, Diners, Visa
SEATS: 65. Private parties: 45 main room, 14 and 24 private rooms. Children's helpings.
Smart dress preferred. Separate smoking area. Wheelchair access. Music. Air-conditioned

*All details are as accurate as possible at the time of going to press, but chefs and owners
often change, and it is wise to check by telephone before making a special journey. Many
readers have been disappointed when set-price bargain meals are no longer available. Ask
when booking.*

Faulkner's
map 11

424–426 Kingsland Road, E8 4AT
071-254 6152

COOKING 1
COST £16

If the menu doesn't vary, neither does the high standard. Here are fish and chips as they ought to be: big pieces of fish, from halibut to Dover sole to plaice, on or off the bone, with big chips and a big smile. The fish is fresh, not frozen, and therefore depends on what the boats bring in. There are no West End conceits, such as Champagne at £50 a bottle, just East End common sense and reasonable prices – plus jellied eels for authenticity. Tea and coffee are at old-fashioned prices. There are five inexpensive wines, all white, though customers can bring their own and the corkage charge is not applied to reds. House French: £4.70.

CHEF: Michael Webber   PROPRIETORS: John Faulkner and Mark Farrell
OPEN: Mon to Sat
CLOSED: bank hols, 1 week Christmas to New Year
MEALS: 12 to 2, 5 (4.30 Fri) to 10 (11.30am to 10 Sat)
PRICES: £9 (£13). Minimum £2.50. Licensed, also bring your own: corkage £2 on white wine only
SEATS: 65. Children welcome. No-smoking area. Music. Air-conditioned

La Fin de la Chasse
map 11

176 Stoke Newington Church Street,
N16 0JL
071-254 5975

COOKING 1
COST £17–£32

A hanging fox over the street front marks the spot where some people have found fair cooking in Stoke Newington. The restaurant is long and thin, going back to a garden with outside tables for fine days: 'Except for the tablecloths it would not look out of place on the Left Bank.' A short *carte* is changed every six weeks but it is supplemented by half a dozen daily items and a fixed-price set menu that people reckon fair value. The cooking is not the bistro mixture of casseroles and provincial French recipes, but rather a modern méli-mélo of spicy foods and Anglo-European restaurant cooking familiar to many English people. Examples are spiced vegetables in a filo pastry purse; chicken rillette with Stilton and salad; salmon marinated in whisky; best end of lamb with poached pears; and breast of duck with a pile of bean sprouts, peppers, onions and cream sauce spiked with cumin. Vegetables and potatoes are charged as extras. Standards of cooking are fair but uneven. One meal yielded good spiced duck and decent bread. There is a propensity to give two or more sauces to a dish – a tricolour of pepper sauces with a duck terrine, for example. The wine list may be short but it is full of well-chosen bottles including CELLARMAN'S CHOICE: Ch. Rahoul, Graves 1981 £20.25; Bourgogne Aligoté 1986, Tollot-Beaut, £13.50. There are no half-bottles. House wine is £7.25.

Consumers' Association is planning to publish Out to Eat, *a new guide to budget eating out in restaurants, pubs, cafés, brasseries and so on. Please send reports and recommendations to Out to Eat, FREEPOST, 2 Marylebone Road, London NW1 1YN.*

CHEF: Sharon Hickey   PROPRIETORS: Robbie and Carol Richards
OPEN: Tue to Sat
CLOSED: 1 week at Christmas
MEALS: 12.30 to 2, 7 to 10.30
PRICES: £19 (£27), Set L £10.50 (£17) to £12.50 (£19), Set D £13.50 (£20). Cover £1.
Service 10%
CARDS: Access, Amex, Diners, Visa
SEATS: 40. 5 tables outside. Private parties: 14 main room. Vegetarian meals. Children's
helpings. No-smoking area. Wheelchair access (1 step). Music

Fleet Tandoori
map 11

104 Fleet Road, NW3 2QX
071-485 6402

COOKING 1
COST £18

An empire that began with this unpretentious little restaurant has recently
expanded to three, the latest off Kingsway (see Saheli Brasserie). The
Hampstead branch is well placed for eating after a walk on the Heath, and
recent reports confirm that the kitchen is still turning out satisfying curries such
as meat dhansak, and tandoori dishes such as chicken tikka. One reader
especially liked the lamb pasanda and chicken bhuna. Drink lager or lassi.
House French: £4.95.

CHEF/PROPRIETOR: Abdur Rahman Khan
OPEN: all week
MEALS: 12 to 2.30, 6 to 11.30 (noon to 11.30 Sun)
PRICES: £8 (£15). Service 10%
CARDS: Access, Amex, Diners, Visa
SEATS: 52. Private parties: 35 main room, 18 private room. Vegetarian meals. Children's
helpings. Wheelchair access

Florians
map 10

4 Topsfield Parade,
Middle Lane, N8 8RP
081-348 8348

COOKING 1
COST £23

Crouch End rides on the Italian new wave with this restaurant behind a wine
bar. The owners learned the trade of popular catering at Café Flo and Le
Bistroquet and their chef is English. It is a very London cocktail even if the
repertoire is Italian regional: olive oil, grills, and alternatives to the endless
veal and pizzaiola dishes of yore. The wine bar will serve Italian snacks, but
the pocket will not be seriously lightened by eating a full meal in one of the
two dining-rooms, all bare brick, greys, blues and gardenia. Polenta crops up
almost more often than rice: with grilled calf's liver; with home-made plain,
garlic or fennel sausages; with rabbit braised with orange and thyme; or as a
pudding laced with chocolate and shaped into a loaf and cooked in milk. The
menu of perhaps nine dishes at each course has hardly one old-style cliché on
it, though the lack of flavour detected in the potato gnocchi in a gorgonzola
sauce or the saffron ravioli with spinach and seafood tossed in a lemon and
sage butter may presage the arrival, almost instantaneously, of newer clichés.
Dishes that have, by contrast, pleased early visitors are quail roasted with sage

and pancetta served on a risotto; marinated grilled chicken with a rocket salad; chargrilled vegetables first drizzled with virgin oil, then served with lemon and a salsa verde; a decent tiramisu, not too sweet; and a 'salami' of dark and white chocolate. Service is cheerful and laidback. The wine list alone is worth a visit: only 30 wines but good ones, all Italian, and cheap. New-wave makers are stocked as well as good traditional sources. Note the Marsala from Bartoli, and Vernaccia di Oristano, a Sardinian fortified aperitif. Prices for both wine and food are refreshing for London and may reconcile many to uneven performance.

CHEF: David Craig   PROPRIETORS: Franco Papa and Arnie Onisto
OPEN: all week
CLOSED: bank hols
MEALS: 12 to 3 (3.30 Sun), 7 to 11 (10.30 Sun)
PRICES: £15 (£19). Minimum £10 in restaurant. Service inc
CARDS: Access, Visa
SEATS: 70. 4 tables outside. Private parties: 35 main room, 18 and 35 private rooms.
Vegetarian meals. Children's helpings on request. Music

▲ Four Seasons, Inn on the Park

map 13

Hamilton Place, Park Lane, W1A 1AZ   COOKING 4
071-499 0888   COST £27−£58

The hotel is as weird as ever − dripping chandeliers, fake woodwork in a modern setting − but the restaurant has been redecorated and is more satisfactory than hitherto, if you like luxury and can take the air-conditioning. The scheme looks French and connects more clearly with the trees growing beyond the massive window on to Park Lane; colours are blue-green and pink, the motif roses in an arbour. This, along with new china, allows Bruno Loubet a distinct arena for his cooking, which deserves it. The multitude of staff are indeed obliging: one reader who lunches with her mother every four weeks speaks highly of their courteous treatment of women. And there is an attempt to make this luxury accessible. The set-price lunch is all-in, down to a cheese course, coffee, petits fours and service. Take care, however, what you drink. Bruno Loubet offers a long *carte*, a five-course chef's surprise menu and the shorter prix fixe at lunch. Some of the dishes are marked as being 'nutritionally balanced, reduced in calories, cholesterol, sodium and have low fat levels'. On a trial of some of these dishes, one reader was moved to wonder just how 'light' was her 'pigeon de nid grillé aux petites céréales et quenelles de foie'. However, it was quite superb in flavour, the mixed sprouting grains combined with the spinach to afford bulk without excess texture, and the simple *jus* that lubricated the whole had sufficient presence to give variety to the carefully dismembered pigeon. 'Pigeon on a bed of its breakfast' might be another way of describing it. Another part of the menu is devoted to *la cuisine du terroir*. M Loubet, who comes from south-western France, seems to define this as 'classical bourgeois cooking with modern touches, and the emphasis on the flavour of fresh produce'. A wide definition indeed, and one that is reinforced by techniques such as braising as opposed to steaming. What it does not seem to mean is a variant on regional cooking: it is 'earthy' rather than 'of a particular bit of earth'. However, 'quenelles of pike and ragout of frogs' legs with a watercress cream' does not sound very earthy to many readers. A willingness to experiment with flavours that were once thought too common or strong runs all through the menu. Thus a wing of skate was taken off the bone and sandwiched between some creamed cabbage of triumphantly mild and sweet flavour. Over the whole was strewn diced tomato and fried tarragon leaves. The sauce was a light tomato and sea urchin decoction, with enough edge to it to counterpoint the rich fish. There were boiled potatoes, it was unfortunate that one had been prepared too long before. Another fish dish that exemplifies the kitchen's tendency is a first course of home-smoked salmon sitting on mashed potato and a lubrication of veal gravy. This reminded one of nothing more than a northern dish of cod cooked in bacon fat and was indeed sustaining. The salmon was moist and had been smoked on a domestic hot-smoker. By the finish, potato, cooking fat and veal gravy and all made it difficult to remember that you were eating fish. Desserts, which come on a trolley at lunch, continue the vein of serious thought. An orange plate contained a fantastic orange crème brûlée, a rather dry orange madeleine and an orange and cardamom ice-cream where the back-taste of spice wafted the consumer to memories of Baalbek in happier times. Even standards such as îles flottantes or apple tart with a raspberry sorbet, are worth exploring. What should not be missed are the petits fours glacés served with coffee at dinner: small globes of chocolate enrobing piercing sorbets. Pure passion there! Of all the hotels in London, this is perhaps the front runner. Not surprisingly, it's full much of the time. The wine waiter is full of enthusiasm and, though French, is happy to discuss the New World bottles and the good range of Spanish wines on his long list – which offer glimpses of value in an otherwise darkening sky. The house of Louis Jadot has a spotlight section of older burgundy vintages and there are plenty of half bottles. For moderate drinkers there is an excellent selection of wines by the glass. The range of classics is indeed impressive, but they are at a full mark up of three times wholesale (if not retail) price. That makes Sancerre £22 and Muscadet £17.50. Bordeaux is more interesting than burgundy, Jadot apart, but who wants to pay £280 for a Ch. Latour 1970 when it can be bought for under £100 in a shop? The very rich will doubtless enjoy the flight of eleven vintages of Latour.

CHEF: Bruno Loubet   PROPRIETORS: Inn on the Park
OPEN: all week
MEALS: 12.30 to 3, 7 to 10.30
PRICES: £40 (£48), Set L £20.50 (£27) to £23 (£30), Set D £38 (£45). Service inc
CARDS: Access, Amex, Carte Blanche, Diners, Visa
SEATS: 62. Private parties: 10 main room. Car-park, 85 places. No children under 5. Smart dress preferred. No pipes in dining-room. Wheelchair access (also WC). Music. Air-conditioned
ACCOMMODATION: 228 rooms, all with bath/shower. Rooms for disabled. Lift. B&B £224.25 to £247.25. Baby facilities. Afternoon teas. Air-conditioning. TV. Phone. Confirm at least 48 hours ahead

The Guide *office can quickly spot when a restaurateur is encouraging customers to write recommending inclusion - and sadly, several restaurants have been doing this in 1990. Such reports do not further a restaurant's cause. Please tell us if a restaurateur invites you to write to the* Guide.

Frith's ♟   map 14

14 Frith Street, W1V 5TS   COOKING 2
071-439 3370 and 734 7535   COST £41

There is much of a New World feel to Frith's, even if Carla Tomasi comes from
southern Italy. The wine list shows a refreshing neglect of French bottles; the
restaurant has a cool style that smacks of California, as does the waiting; the
menu is like a Sydney brasserie's – no sauces but salsa, southern flavours and
vegetables, olive oil and salads; and there is even an oriental influence, as in
Thai fishcakes with cucumber and coriander. Now Carla Tomasi has opened a
vegetarian café on the lower ground floor as she takes some of the tendencies
latent in the cooking to their conclusion. Spring rolls of raddichio and
mozzarella with three salse; asparagus, spinach and parmesan fritatta with
relishes; grilled sourdough bread with roasted new season's garlic, extra virgin
olive oil, basil and a spring salad with fennel are some of the dishes available.
This welcome development, in many instances only small variations of dishes
already prepared for the main restaurant, explores the contribution of
Mediterranean cooking to vegetarian gourmandise, whereas many mainstream
vegetarian places now seem to pursue the oriental line. The café is considerably
cheaper too. The restaurant's menu adds meat and fish to the equation, but is
devoted to lighter cooking: 'We have been using non-stick pans for years,
adding olive oil only after the food is cooked.' Small wonder, then, that a menu
may divide equally between fish and meat, that the meats are rabbit, chicken
and lamb and that there is little offal, luxury items, or long-cooked enriched
casseroles. Whereas the objects of the cooking seem wholly admirable, there
are occasions when the performance during the last year has fallen short of
intentions. Take one instance: after a good correctly seasoned vegetable soup
came ravioli that were tough and undercooked; spring rolls that had been
baked rather than fried, and so were enrobed with a dry carapace; chicken with
little character accompanied by poorly prepared leeks and lacklustre
vegetables; and a slate of desserts that seemed dominated by chocolate. In
contrast was the satisfactory meal that began with mussels in a risotto scented
with ginger and air-dried beef with radicchio and a walnut dressing. There
followed grilled tuna with a spicy parsley and anchovy sauce and simple veal
with lime and rosemary, rounded off by a chocolate and cinnamon ice-cream on
one side and nut and toffee on the other. There are lots of outside tables in an
attractive yard full of plants, including herbs; quiet and sunny on good days.
The wine list continues to be a fine short selection of Italian, Spanish, and New
World bottles. It is only a couple of dozen bins, but they change often and few
cost more than £15. Every item is worth exploring, though the writing is so
nearly illegible you may need an interpreter and some have found that asking
for an equivalent of, say, Chablis, does not always produce the desired result.
House wines are £8.50 and £9.

The 1992 Guide *will be published before Christmas 1991. Reports on meals are most
welcome at any time of the year, but are extremely valuable in the spring. Send them to*
The Good Food Guide, *FREEPOST, 2 Marylebone Road, London NW1 1YN. No stamp
is needed if posted in the UK.*

CHEF/PROPRIETOR: Carla Tomasi
OPEN: Mon to Sat, exc Sun L
CLOSED: bank hols, 25 Dec to 2 Jan, 5 days at Easter
MEALS: 12.30 to 2.30, 7.30 to 11.15
PRICES: £23 (£34). Licensed, also bring your own: no corkage
CARDS: Access, Visa
SEATS: 81. 16 tables outside. Private parties: 40 main room. Vegetarian meals. Children's helpings. No cigars/pipes in dining-room. Wheelchair access. Air-conditioned

Fung Shing   map 14

15 Lisle Street, WC2H 7BE   COOKING 3
071-437 1539   COST £20–£48

The restaurant has a well-used air, short of dowdy, that speaks volumes for the constant tramp of feet across the threshold. Here is good cooking, largely Cantonese, and many visit and revisit for it has the quality of consistency. The menu is long, with the most interesting dishes in the 'Special' section, though all are worthy of attention. Lovers of the Chinese predilection for texture will be as satisfied (for instance, with crispy fried intestine) as those who desire the flavour preeminent in steamed scallops with garlic and soy sauce, baked prawns with chilli and salt, fried eel with garlic and clay-pot of duck with yams, or those who clamour for both at once, found most satisfactory in deep-fried soft-shell crab with chilli and salt or roasted duck Cantonese style. The ground-floor room is more pleasant; on occasion the smaller first-floor space can be too easily dominated if there is a noisy, extrovert group. Service is generally free of the abruptness sometimes encountered in like restaurants. The wine list is short but well supplied with decent bottles, even if the descriptions stop short of maker's names. Tea there is aplenty. Except for a few items, such as mineral water, the quality/value equation of the restaurant is sensational. House French is £7.50.

CHEF: Fu Kwun   PROPRIETORS: Traceflow Ltd
OPEN: all week
MEALS: noon to 11.45
PRICES: £25 (£35), Set L £15 (£20) to £20 (£25), Set D £15 (£25) to £35 (£40). Minimum £8.50. Service inc
CARDS: Access, Amex, Diners, Visa
SEATS: 85. Private parties: 50 main room, 30 private room. Children welcome. Music. Air-conditioned

Galicia   map 11

323 Portobello Road, W10 5SY   COOKING 1
081-969 3539   COST £10–£28

One of the more authentic tapas bars, perhaps because of its location near the Spanish school, in an Iberian enclave. The long narrow bar fronts a set of tables on the ground floor and there is an overflow gallery upstairs. True to its name, dishes from the north-west of Spain are the most interesting: anchovies in a garlic vinaigrette; turbot and sole a la plancha (griddled); pulpo (octopus) a la Gallega, served on a wooden plate with rock salt and pimentos. A brimming paella brings back the memory of Spain. 'The place has a very Spanish feel: noisy and animated, men at the bar, people still coming in well after 11 in the evening.' There are seven Galician wines and three times as many of Rioja. They are not expensive. House Rioja is £6.

CHEF: Mr Ramon PROPRIETORS: E. Lage and J. Nieto
OPEN: Tue to Sun
CLOSED: 25 Dec, Aug
MEALS: 12 to 3, 7 to 11.30
PRICES: £15 (£23), Set L £6 (£10)
CARDS: Access, Diners, Visa
SEATS: 48. Private parties: 35 main room. Children welcome. Music

Ganpath   map 11

372 Grays Inn Road, WC1 8BB   COOKING 1
071-278 1938   COST £7–£14

'Summary: a useful haven in an urban desert,' wrote a visitor from the north-east. More regular customers, denizens of the desert itself, speak of the Ganpath as a place for 'spicy, succulent, traditional non-meat food from Southern India. There is none of the cloying, oily or fatty presentation that often gives a disturbing aftertaste. The surroundings, slightly improved in the last year, are still pretty basic, but there is genuinely attentive service. The best onion bhaji in town, and they will make a variant to order that incorporates ferocious green chillies.' Others have commented that the vadas (lentil doughnuts) are not at all greasy; the marsala dosa exquisite, light, crisp and tasty; the tikkas good and sag gosht leaves texture in the spinach and life in the lamb. Value is very fair. Kingfisher is on draught.

CHEF: S. Rajah PROPRIETOR: R. Sivanantham
OPEN: all week, exc Sun L
CLOSED: bank hols, 25 and 26 Dec
MEALS: 12 to 3, 6 to 12
PRICES: £6 (£12), Set L £4.95 (£7). Service inc set only, alc 10%
CARDS: Access, Visa
SEATS: 50. Private parties: 60 main room. Vegetarian meals. Children's helpings. No-smoking area. Wheelchair access. Music

La Gaulette   map 13

53 Cleveland Street, W1P 5PQ   COOKING 2
071-580 7608 and 323 4210   COST £24–£43

This is the junior but more central branch of Chez Liline in Stroud Green Road (see entry). Comparing the two restaurants reveals similarities rather than differences. Sylvain Ho Wing Cheong's migration into town has ensured this. London's second Mauritian fish eatery is a piscatorial paradise. Huge slabs of vara vara, vacqua and yellow fin bream, not to mention red snapper, dorade or wild salmon, are served à la creole, with garlic and spring onion, with herbs, or with saffron. The menu changes daily and seasonally according to what is available at Billingsgate market and from specialist suppliers. The cooking style amounts to a French-Chinese hybrid which the chef calls Mauritian.

Downstairs is a cheaper wine bar, where some of the same dishes are available. Service has been categorised as 'attentive but relaxed'. Seating is cramped and some wines are overpriced. House French: £8.25 and £9.95.

CHEF: Sylvain Ho Wing Cheong PROPRIETORS: Mr & Mrs Sylvain Ho Wing Cheong
OPEN: Mon to Sat, exc Sat D
CLOSED: bank hol Mons
MEALS: 12 to 3, 6.30 to 11.30
PRICES: £26 (£36), Set L £17.95 (£24)
CARDS: Access, Amex, Diners, Visa
SEATS: 70. Private parties: 40 main room, 30 private room. Vegetarian meals. Children welcome. Music

Le Gavroche ♥   map 13

43 Upper Brook Street, W1Y 1PF   COOKING 5
071-408 0881   COST £31–£78

The entrance from this Mayfair street of discreet flats, houses and offices is as sombre as the rule that jackets should be worn at all times. The stairs lead you down to a large basement, all air-conditioning and leather. The colours are muted; the atmosphere neutrally tasteful. The circus comes from the innumerable waiters, 'I swear there were seven in attendance at a single table,' and the sight of other people spending their money. Unless given the menu as the host, no whisper of prices will ever be heard. The *carte* is long, in French, and bolstered by a *menu exceptionnel* and daily extras. At lunch there is a short set menu, always considered good value. The minimum charge in the evening is £45. The *carte* seems to develop at snail's pace. More than half its three dozen items appear almost fixtures. There is not much indication of adventure, rather the elaboration of a repertoire fixed by a consensus of the ancients, even if each dish has 'the hallmark of our interpretation'. Its single most identified characteristic is that it is rich. The consequence to the uninitiated may be that the meal becomes less rather than more enjoyable as it progresses, and that some dishes are perceived to be absolutely right but in fact little better than many other good cooks may achieve at half the price. Thus cotelettes d'agneau au vinaigre d'estragon at £23.50 were perfectly cooked, the lamb of exquisite quality, with a rich, deep-tasting sauce, and surrounded by turned roasted potatoes, crisp courgettes and crunchy carrots glazed with butter, but 'it lacked the essential quality of originality.' This was present in scallops sauté with spices, however. The shellfish was seared outside, succulent right through, on a sauce with soy and spices and accompanied by thin julienne of deep-fried crisp vegetables. The combination worked wonders in terms of texture and taste. Le Gavroche has never been unwilling to face up to making long-cooked dishes objects of desire. Since the days of pot-au-feu Albert, the restaurant has taught the British that stews are not just for bistros: thus a daily dish of ox-tail formed into a round on deep dark juices with root vegetables and mashed potatoes, or the farmhouse chicken en cocotte with lentils and thyme, or daube de boeuf à la bourgeoise, are definitive statements of this sort of cooking with touches of presentation and service to lift the mind out of its rut so as to be ready to appreciate the deep flavours. A pause for cheese would bring for selection three great panniers – goats', hard and soft. The Gavroche has long been valued for its sweet course, with sablé aux fraises, hot soufflés and orange and grapefruit gateau with Champagne being as famous as soufflé suissesse or smoked salmon Claudine. The hot soufflés, perhaps raspberry, or spiced with a chocolate sauce, are very expert, 'peeping like a cottage loaf over the tin, still wobbling; it swayed perceptibly and inflated as the dark sauce displaced it.' More important, the sweetness was judged finely. At this same meal, the impact of the sablé was lessened by the use of unripe fruit, a rare failing in the buying. The waiting staff and the mechanics of the meal sometimes obtrude. It is suggested that coffee be taken in the large sitting-out zone; the table is re-let within minutes. Haste is not imposed but pace may be apparent. The weight of staff numbers sometimes promotes a sense of impersonality. This is a very fine restaurant that aims to be 'hors classe' in its approach. We are meant to accept what it does as the best, but we can't ignore that much more interesting things may be underway at other people's stoves. It doesn't help, either, if there are errors in the well-oiled machinery: a mousseline of lobster with double salting; an 'assiette du boucher' with undercooked veal; an unsatisfactory mustard sauce with the lamb, and the lamb itself 'soggy' from incorrect cooking. The wine list is magisterial: long pages of clarets supported by ample burgundies and a fair selection of French regional wines. Prices are, of course, high. To illustrate, at a time when Ch. Léoville-las-Cases 1970 could be obtained from the Wine Society at £35, it is listed here at £167. The magnificent choice thus makes dispiriting reading unless money is an incidental. There is, however, a generous number of half-bottles and there are wines at the lower end of the price range. Although the menus and invoices are very clear that prices include service, readers are enraged that here, of all places, the credit card slip is never closed. As meals are too expensive to pay for by cheque, and not many of us carry the odd £200 in cash, it is likely that the card will be the most frequent means of settling the bill. Perhaps the restaurant should learn to settle it completely.

CHEFS: Albert Roux and Michel Roux Junior   PROPRIETORS: Le Gavroche Ltd
OPEN: Mon to Fri
CLOSED: 23 Dec to 2 Jan
MEALS: 12 to 2, 7 to 11
PRICES: £53 (£65), Set L £22.50 (£31), Set D £50 (£62). Minimum £45 at D. Service inc
CARDS: Access, Amex, Carte Blanche, Diners, Visa
SEATS: 60. Private parties: 10 main room, 20 private room. No children under 5. Smart dress preferred. No cigars/pipes in dining-room. Air-conditioned

Gavvers
map 12

61–63 Lower Sloane Street, SW1W 8DH   COOKING 2
071-730 5983   COST £16–£32

'I doubt you could buy a lunch of such good value elsewhere in SW1,' commented a happy reader about the set-price lunch. The same thought has been echoed by dinner visitors who find the inclusive formula – one price from Kir to coffee – fairly executed and not padded out by unforeseen details. After some ups and downs, Gavvers' fortunes are now apparently stabilised with the arrival of Chris Sellors from the Waterside Inn (see entry, Bray). Both the lunch and dinner menus are short and generally rehearse mid-Channel recipes with no strong affiliation to provincial French bourgeois cooking. Neither do they espouse the cause of adventurous modernism. To add the touch of authentic France, there are evening recommendations by the brothers Roux which include dishes like jambon persillé and poulet grandmère. The cooking has been more consistent, but falls down on details. A good duck terrine studded with pistachios showed true Roux pedigree but came with a Cumberland sauce that had more Worcestershire in it than Lake District; gazpacho was fairly flavoured but was an emulsified cream – filling rather than refreshing; chicken on a celeriac rémoulade with salty wild mushrooms was a slightly unsatisfactory mixture of hot and cold. The best thing was exactly cooked salmon with Champagne sauce and nicely timed vegetables. Service has also had a welcome injection of new blood, though general attention has been known to waver, perhaps through tedium at a quiet meal. Orange juice may still taste tinny. Given a basic level of expertise, which is usually achieved, the problem lies in management. This year it was solved. If you don't drink the house wine, the list is short and dear.

CHEF: Chris Sellors PROPRIETORS: Roux Restaurants Ltd
OPEN: Mon to Sat, exc Sat L
CLOSED: bank hols
MEALS: 12 to 2.30, 7 to 11
PRICES: Set L £11.50 (£16) to £13.50 (£18), Set D £22 (£27) to £27.50 (£27.50). Service inc
CARDS: Access, Amex, Diners, Visa
SEATS: 80. Children welcome. Wheelchair access. Air-conditioned

Gay Hussar
map 14

2 Greek Street, W1V 6NB   COOKING 2
071-437 0973   COST £19–£37

Even though there has been time for bad habits to emerge since absorption into new ownership, there is still little criticism that 'things are not how they were.' A remarkable achievement. People should visit the restaurant to see how old Soho used to look (even though there is some 'redecoration'). How can so many people be shoe-horned into rooms of red-plush, deep banquettes, dark wood and cream paint, and still feel comfortable? You will need to book lunch well ahead and the set-price daytime meal remains a bargain even though there are more supplements than formerly. The central European food – and this kitchen takes the whole of *mitteleuropa* for its inspiration – is deceptive. It looks as heavy as lead, especially when traditionally ornamented and served as it is here. It sounds even heavier. Yet it eats light, the flavours often having a sharp edge that aids digestion. The restaurant still attracts loyal regulars. A recent report was from one who had been 20 times in 18 months. His comments were that the bortsch, bean soup, goose and pork pâté, fish salad, Bulgar salad, vegetables and sausage still continue to please, as do the fish and roast meats. Another remarked how buttery was the texture of his rib of beef, taken with savoy cabbage, and a third reaffirmed the value of the strongly smoked goose breast with scholet ('pungent' smoked baked beans and grains). Invariably there are some red fruits. The poppy seed strudel is well loved, as is the liptoi, home-made cream cheese, by aficionados. Portions are giant: you need two plates for the wiener schnitzel. Sometimes the goulash and braised dishes may

LONDON

remind of school dinners, if the seasoning has not been as apt as usual.
Upstairs, 'Albert's domaine' is smaller than down, conversations ready to be
eavesdropped. Some people prefer it. Over the last three years both menu and
wine list have shrunk a little, no bad thing necessarily, though clarets have
suffered. The Hungarian and other Eastern European wines still give best value
for this cooking. House wine: £7.20 and £7.30.

CHEF: Laslo Holecz   PROPRIETORS: Magyar Restaurant Ltd
OPEN: Mon to Sat
MEALS: 12.30 to 2.30, 5.30 to 11
PRICES: £20 (£31), Set L £13.50 (£19)
SEATS: 70. Private parties: 20 main room, 12 private room. Children's helpings (L only).
Smart dress preferred. Wheelchair access. Air-conditioned

Gilbert's 🍴

2 Exhibition Road, SW7 2HF
071-589 8947

map 12

COOKING 2
COST £11–£31

There are not many restaurants in central London with wine lists of this calibre
at such reasonable prices. Together with Ann Wregg's thoughtful hospitality, it
compensates for the slightly uncomfortable seating. Menus are priced
according to the number of courses consumed, starting from a base of one for
£6.50 at lunchtime. Choice is from a slate of five or six dishes at each course.
The style combines the modern, like baked herb bread with goats' cheese and
sun-dried tomatoes, with the French provincial classics, such as pork with
prunes or fish stew with aïoli, with pages from our British heritage cookbook
containing tipsy cake, marbled veal with Cumberland sauce or warm rhubarb
and orange sponge. A meal of gratin of smoked haddock with a nice touch of
leeks and a seductively rich sauce, followed by well hung and well timed roast
pheasant with apples and calvados, excellent vegetables and a veritably 'boozy'
(so called) trifle impressed for its generous flavours, just as others have enjoyed
the details of good bread and cheese, olives with a hot brioche to accompany
aperitifs, and good fudge with the coffee. Local shopping is first-rate. The wine
list shows knowledge, enthusiasm and a line to the best shippers. No
concentration here on France, with New World favourites like Stag's Leap,
Cloudy Bay, Petaluma, or Chilean Santa Rita Valley Cabernet Sauvignon being
accorded their place. The list arranged by grape type, with a fine wine
appendix and a commendable selection of halves. The notes are enjoyable too.
It is one of the most accessible of the shorter 'fashionable' modern lists. House
wines include a Montepulciano d'Abruzzo and a Sicilian Cellano at £7.50.
CELLARMAN'S CHOICE: Jurançon sec, Dom. Cauhapé 1988, £13.90; Pinot Noir-
Trousseau, Côtes de Jura 1985, Boilley, £12.10.

CHEFS: Julia Chalkley and Sue Breen   PROPRIETORS: Julia Chalkley and Ann Wregg
OPEN: Mon to Sat, exc Mon and Sat L
MEALS: 12.30 to 2, 7 to 10.15 (bookings up to 10.45 by arrangement)
PRICES: Set L £6.50 (£11) to £13 (£18), Set D £16.50 (£22) to £19.50 (£26)
CARDS: Access, Amex, Visa
SEATS: 32. 2 tables outside. Wheelchair access (2 steps). Air-conditioned

Gopal's of Soho

map 14

12 Bateman Street, W1V 5TD
071-434 1621 and 0840

COOKING 2
COST £14–£25

Since N.P. Pittal, known to his friends as Gopal, opened his classy little restaurant in Soho, reports have been virtually unanimous about the high quality of the cooking. Even so, the feeling is that the last *Guide's* rating was a touch too enthusiastic. Dish names and spellings may look unfamiliar, but menu descriptions are accurate, and the kitchen delivers. Not surprisingly many ideas have been inherited and adapted from Gopal's early days at Lal Qila and Red Fort. A healthy list of recommended dishes includes patties (potato cakes stuffed with lentils and chillies served with a tamarind-based sauce); fish steaks served on the bone with coconut rice; karai lamb; and fresh bhindis cooked with spices. Highly praised specialities have ranged from unusual dum ka murg (chicken steamed in a sealed pot with Hyderabi herbs and spices) to prawns cooked with spring onions. There are also good reports of the thalis, which are in a different league from the tit-bits offered in many restaurants. The hallmarks of Gopal's cooking are the freshness of the ingredients and the strident flavours, 'free from the blurring effect you get in the ordinary Indian restaurant'. Every dish has his own stamp. Service is efficient, careful and agreeable. Kingfisher beer suits the food, but there are some run-of-the-mill wines. House French: £6.75.

CHEF/PROPRIETOR: N.P. Pittal
OPEN: all week
CLOSED: 25 and 26 Dec
MEALS: 12 to 3.15, 6 to 11.45
PRICES: £12 (£21), Set L and D £8.50 (£14) to £14.50 (£21). Minimum £8.50
CARDS: Access, Amex, Diners, Visa
SEATS: 48. Private parties: 50 main room. Vegetarian meals. Children's helpings.
Wheelchair access (1 step). Music. Air-conditioned

Grahame's Seafare

map 13

38 Poland Street, W1V 3DA
071-437 3788 and 0975

COOKING 1
COST £24

It is wise to book for lunch, especially on Fridays, at this Kosher fish restaurant – hence the matzo flour, the fish fried in oil or grilled or steamed, and butter or milk used only on request, at extra charge. Salmon, sole, halibut, plaice or haddock are on offer, with half a dozen sauced dishes. The product is fresh, the cooking accurate, the trimmings as expected. Chips are nicely thin cut but not always as crisp as they could be. The ambience is a time warp, with its dark green banquettes, slightly crowded seating, and amiable well-established service. Though the pace moves along smartly, there are plenty of people sitting over their Muscadet come the end of the session, and no hassling to hurry anyone up. Tea is strong but there are half a dozen lowly priced white wines, four in half-bottles, from £6.50.

PROPRIETOR: Chetin Esmet
OPEN: Mon to Sat
CLOSED: 25 Dec, Jewish New Year
MEALS: 12 to 2.45, 5.30 to 9 (8 Fri and Sat)
PRICES: £13 (£20)
CARDS: Access, Amex, Visa
SEATS: 85. Private parties: 30 main room. Children's helpings. Wheelchair access (also WC). Air-conditioned

Great Nepalese

map 11

48 Eversholt Street, NW1 1DA   COOKING 2
071-388 6737   COST £13–£17

By the side of Euston Station, this is well used by travellers and Shaw theatregoers, but it is more than just a waiting room with food, and has its loyal regulars. Stubbornly old wave, and rough around the edges, it is nevertheless warm and cheerful after its redecoration, and cooking is up to the mark. Moist chicken tikka is cut in chunks big enough to benefit from charring in the tandoor, mutton is cooked a dozen ways, spinach is favourably reported, and coriander pickle is stunningly good. There are plenty of vegetarian dishes as well as plain and peshwari nan, puffy and fresh. Masco bara, a black lentil bread, is served with meat or curry sauce as a first course. Service is all smiles and prompt action. Kingfisher at £1.30 is more expensive than draught lager. Lassi £1.25, house Italian £5.25.

CHEF: Ishad Ali   PROPRIETOR: Gopal Manandhar
OPEN: all week
CLOSED: 25 and 26 Dec
MEALS: 12 to 2.45, 6 to 11.45
PRICES: £10 (£17), Set L and D £8.50 (£13). Minimum £4.75. Service 10%
CARDS: Access, Amex, Carte Blanche, Diners, Visa
SEATS: 48. Private parties: 34 main room. Vegetarian meals. Children's helpings. Music

Greig's

map 10

5 White Hart Lane, SW13 OPX   COOKING 2
081-876 3335   COST £19–£31

This White Hart Lane is near the Bank of England's sports ground in Barnes, not the home of Tottenham Hotspurs. An active clerk or teller might be pleased to find this restaurant, a new arrival in 1989. Malcolm Greig intends to run an 'English' restaurant, though 'modern British' would be the more recognisable cant term. Although the menu is spelled as if the printing was done in some other EC member state, the wish for solidarity with that British tendency shines through, from a filo parcel of seasonal vegetables to a hot steamed syrup pudding. The small, pleasantly spare, apricot-coloured dining-room offers two set-price menus that include a first and main course and coffee but not dessert, for which you must pay extra. The range of tastes in the sauces runs an English gamut: Stilton, lime, saffron, watercress and chive. The style of presentation is markedly picture-book. This may sometimes overshadow the eating process, as when a red herring tart with whisky cream seemed devoid of adequate whisky

LONDON

but was buttressed by a billowing pile of mustard and cress. Flavours, however, have been enjoyed: a pike terrine given point and nice balance by slivers of anchovy; a harmonious combination of guinea-fowl, slices of pear and a lime sauce; a well-judged and upstanding herb and green peppercorn crust to lamb cutlets. The wine list shows signs of nervous beginnings: not all the vintages are just the ticket, but experience may build up the portfolio. In all, the place, the service and the welcome are a happy addition to Barnes' charms. House French: £7.25, CELLARMAN'S CHOICE: Breaky Bottom 1989, £8.75, Ch. Rauzan-Gassies 1978, £28.95.

CHEF: Malcolm Douglas   PROPRIETORS: Malcolm and Carolyn Greig
OPEN: Tue to Sun, exc Sat L and Sun D
CLOSED: 25 Dec to 1 Jan
MEALS: 12 to 2.30 (3.30 Sun), 7 (6 Sun) to 11
PRICES: £18 (£26), Set Sun L £13.50 (£19), Set D £13.95 (£19) to £16.95 (£23)
CARDS: Access, Amex, Diners, Visa
SEATS: 35. 2 tables outside. Private parties: 40 main room, 25 private room. Vegetarian meals. Children's helpings (Sun L only). No pipes in dining-room. Wheelchair access (3 steps)

Guernica

map 13

21A Foley Street, W1P 7lA
071-580 0623

COOKING 1
COST £21–£35

The arresting black and white awning is at the Middlesex Hospital end of Foley Street: the last outpost, or first warning, of the rag-trade and media mix to the west. Black and white continues, with pink, in the restaurant itself: a colour scheme that needs high maintenance for its full impact. Though Basque, the restaurant is in tune with the tapas bars that succeeded wine bars as smart watering holes. Basque specialities there are aplenty: tuna, potato and capsicum soup; squid in its own ink; hake with garlic and parsley; tuna with tomatoes and capsicums; or duck with a mild pimento. This list indicates the strength of the restaurant in fish, which is sometimes of high quality and delicately cooked. Others have reported meals that are grossly portioned (you will never starve here), approximately cooked and of indifferent flavour. Some of the excitement of the first year or two has fled. This is not to deny that the staff treat you very kindly. There is a short and good Spanish wine list, much of it Rioja, as well as the King of Spain's favourite white, Yuntero from La Mancha, which also happens to be the cheapest. In Spanish tradition, there is no mention of vintages, but with the rigorous classification of Reservas and so on, and with the respective ageing requirement, who is to say the year is important? House wine: £7.50. As we went to press, ownership changed, though the chef remained. More reports, please.

CHEF: José Ramon   PROPRIETORS: Post Drive Ltd
OPEN: Mon to Sat, exc Sat L
CLOSED: Christmas to New Year, Easter, last 2 weeks of Aug
MEALS: 12 to 2.45, 7 to 10.45
PRICES: £22 (£29), Set L and D £14 (£21). Cover £1.30. Service 10% on parties of 6 to 10
CARDS: Access, Amex, Diners, Visa
SEATS: 40. Private parties: 40 main room. Vegetarian meals on request. Children welcome. Music. Air-conditioned

80

Harveys

map 10

2 Bellevue Road, SW17 7EG
081-672 0114 and 0115

COOKING 4
COST £47–£70

On the edge of Wandsworth Common, quite unassuming from the outside, the restaurant has overtones of a film set in its plasterwork and weird pictures of disembodied hands. An American likened it to a railroad car diner, but she was probably used to more spacious surroundings for such good, expensive cooking. The fixed-price dinner is now £42, up from £15.50 in 1987. 'At this rate it will have priced itself beyond my reach by next year, but I would not begrudge the price,' wrote one financial masochist who singled out the sauces in his meal of oysters with tagliatelle; seafood ragout with leeks and truffles; ravioli of sweetbreads; pigeon with morels, ceps, lentils and spinach; lamb wrapped round veal kidney with a tarragon sauce; and dessert plate of three lemon dishes. From this list it may be deduced that the repertoire evolves more slowly than the prices, but the dishes are elaborated with such care that people find repeated visits still satisfy. The care does not always extend to the menu itself, so salmon with basil turned up as salmon with chives; 'the waiter agreed there seemed to be no basil, but had no explanation.' Another case was rabbit that unexpectedly came with langoustines and seafood sauce. As one of the party was allergic to shellfish, it would have helped if the menu had explained the dish fully. Another consistent problem is the lack of adequate vegetables. Perhaps the same reader experienced a night of forgetfulness, but he had no *amuse-gueule* such as he had hitherto enjoyed, and his main courses were quite bereft of vegetables. Often something is built in to the design of the dish, but it hardly gives relief to what is otherwise a giant slab of protein. Sometimes lunch is a meal to try new dishes. One spring day yielded sauté foie gras on a potato galette with Sauternes sauce and baby onions; ravioli of langoustines with asparagus, white truffle oil and strips of fried leek; pigeon *en vessie* with madeira cream sauce, morels and lentils; saddle of rabbit with endives and a soy-based sauce; tarte Tatin and a two-tone chocolate slice. A meal of such assurance can be undercut by a cheaper one from the set-price lunch menu, where the turbot with mustard sauce was undercooked and the chocolate had not been properly folded into the egg white for the hot soufflé. Perhaps Marco Pierre White was not there that day, for his craft still dominates the kitchen, though he has been seen less in the restaurant of late. Where his writ may not always rule is in the pâtisserie, for some have detected less satisfactory pastrywork even though the composed desserts – the pyramid of hazelnut ice, the lemon plate, the peach melba – have continued to gain applause. In general, this kitchen's flavours run deep and true, and gain in intensity through long practice and careful development. There has been some toying with further combinations of fish and meat, as in the rabbit above, and seen too in the dish of foie gras and scallops that comes with a Sauternes sauce. The service has been praised this year. It is not always sophisticated but it is not of the irascible nature that made a tale to be told with gusto by those who suffered it. It may still be slow. The wine waiter has been singled out for his knowledge and enthusiasm. It is a pity his wares, though of faultless origin, are so

Report forms are at the back of the book; write a letter if you prefer.

expensive. There are barely bottles below £20. The philosophy of charging what the market will bear has many advocates, but it is a pity to see such skill and so many hopes retreat behind its plutocratic barricades.

CHEF/PROPRIETOR: Marco Pierre White
OPEN: Mon to Sat
MEALS: 12.30 to 2, 7.30 to 11.15
PRICES: Set L £29 (£47), Set D £42 (£58)
CARDS: Access, Visa
SEATS: 45. No children under 16. No pipes in dining-room. Air-conditioned

Hiders
map 10

755 Fulham Road, SW6 5UU
071-736 2331

COOKING 2
COST £21−£30

'Hiders is so well hidden we walked past it twice,' wrote one party who was relieved to find it in the end because it appeared to fulfil its promise: not too high in price for sensitive cooking that is often good and rarely less than acceptable. At lunch there is a *carte*, at dinner three set-price meals that indulge in a few more substantial dishes. What pleased a reader was the simplicity of the cooking: fillets of plaice in fresh breadcrumbs and *fines herbes*, deep fried and served with tartare and chips; a cucumber mousse with enough sweetness to cut the cucumber's edge of bitterness; a straightforward salad with Roquefort dressing − which at night becomes a 'rendezvous of lettuces topped with pine kernels and cherry tomatoes with haricots verts and vinaigrette.' Modish ideas are there in sufficiency for the modish inhabitants of Fulham: lentil *farce* for a chicken breast, crème fraîche sauce with lemon, vermouth and fennel seeds for salmon, but nothing is done to excess. Desserts keep up the standard: a praline ice-cream with coffee bean sauce and a trio of white, bitter and milk chocolate mousses both surprised with their strength of flavour. The wine list is written down one margin of the menu. It is perforce basic, and has little detail, but is priced tolerably. House wine: £6.95.

CHEFS: Paul Duvall and Andrew George   PROPRIETORS: Richard and Hilary Griggs
OPEN: Mon to Sat, exc Sat L
CLOSED: bank hols
MEALS: 12.30 to 2.30, 7.30 to 11.30
PRICES: £17 (£23), Set D £14.95 (£21) to £19 (£25). Service 12.5%
CARD: Access, Visa
SEATS: 70. Private parties: 40 main room. Children welcome. Wheelchair access

Hilaire
map 12

68 Old Brompton Road, SW7 3LQ
071-584 8993

COOKING 3
COST £21−£46

Chef Bryan Webb has struck out on his own and is now the proprietor of this apparently small restaurant; a second dining-room is downstairs. Columns lend grandeur at one end, while sitting at the window tables at the other make some people feel like shop goods. The cooking takes a modern view of flavourings as in langoustine with spicy carrot and coriander salad; oysters au gratin with laverbread and Stilton; asparagus with balsamic vinegar and

Parmesan from a long and daily changing list of first courses. Seafood with coriander and ginger; turbot with dill and mustard sauce; veal chops with chicory; or more orthodox duck with blackcurrants are indicative of the main courses. A daily menu should mean that materials do not need to repose in a fridge so long as to kill all flavour, as happened with a mille-feuille of foie gras and artichokes, themselves discoloured. However, the general tone of reports has been very positive for dishes such as griddled scallops with a vegetable relish and rocket, though the butter sauce that came with them was over-rich; rabbit with wild rice, celeriac chips and wild mushrooms; and calf's liver with chicory and peppercorns. Chocolate marquise and a gratin of strawberries and raspberries have also pleased. A visitor from out of town found it lower key than he was expecting, with the flavours less surprising. He also watched his bill, starting from an apparently reasonable base of £23.50 for two courses, rise alarmingly as the bare bones of the meal were fleshed out. The wine list is not too long and gives some very good choices from around the world. It lists them in terms of colour and weight and, though the prices are West End, at least it gives equal position to Jean Léon or Te Mata Estate and the classic French wines. There are only a handful below £15. House wine: £9.75. CELLARMAN'S CHOICE: Rothbury Estate Chardonnay 1988, £15.50 Châteauneuf-du-Pape, Clos des Papes 1986, £24.

CHEF/PROPRIETOR: Bryan Webb
OPEN: all week, exc Sat L and Sun D
MEALS: 12.30 to 2.30, 7 to 11.30
PRICES: Set L £14.50 (£21) to £18 (£25), Set D £23.50 (£33) to £28 (£38)
CARDS: Access, Amex, Diners, Visa
SEATS: 50. Private parties: 8 main room. Children's helpings. Air-conditioned

Honeymoon   map 10

33–35 Park Road, N8 8TE   COOKING 1
081-341 5113   COST £15–£23

Few newlyweds spend their honeymoon in Crouch End, though more may now be tempted to venture from their suites for food which appears to be consistently good. This is a smiling, even joyous, Peking and Szechuan restaurant. The manager claims he will surprise birthday celebrants, and presumably honeymooners, by playing his violin. Look for the 'horrendous' purple and yellow neon sign over the tinted-glass gameshow-style frontage: the gameshow-style logo features a pair of conjoined hearts. The passion is more restrained in the inside decoration. Walls are rag-rolled in united pinks and blues. Tables are well spaced and dressed with two layers of linen. Chairs are comfy. The menu is concise and easily digestible. House specials are crispy Szechuan lamb 'incandescent with garlic' and aromatic duck. One reader reported 'this was beautifully done. The meat was deftly shredded with a fork and spoon at the table by a youthful waiter who, with impressive care, separated every last fragment of bone from the mound of carved meat.' Overall, the cooking 'shows evidence of freshness'. MSG is restricted to a 'minimum'. The brief wine list features Shao Hsing rice wine, saké and Tiger beer. House French is £5.50. CELLARMAN'S CHOICE: Great Wall Chinese, £7; Chablis, £12.50.

LONDON

CHEF: Philip Chan   PROPRIETORS: K.K Chan and Andy Fung
OPEN: all week
CLOSED: 25 and 26 Dec
MEALS: 12 to 2.30, 6 to 11.30
PRICES: £11 (£19), Set L and D £10 (£15) to £13 (£18). Service 10%
CARDS: Access, Amex, Diners, Visa
SEATS: 90. Private parties: 60 main room, 30 and 40 private rooms. Vegetarian meals.
Children welcome. Wheelchair access (1 step). Music. Air-conditioned

Ikkyu
map 13

67 Tottenham Court Road, W1P 9PA   COOKING 2
071-636 9280   COST £10–£24

At lunchtime this lively, crowded basement a couple of doors from Goodge
Street tube station continues to offer some of the best-value Japanese food in
the West End. The mood is casual but the pace can be hectic. Lunches centre on
set meals of sashimi, grilled fish, deep-fried dishes and teriyaki, backed up by
the Japanese gastronomic trinity – miso soup, rice and pickled vegetables. In
the evening the menu opens out, but the style remains robust and generous,
with echoes of home cooking in the hot-pots, noodle dishes and soups. Reports
have mentioned the range of skewered grilled dishes (taking in squid with
okra, asparagus with bacon and grilled chicken offal); salad of four seaweeds
with contrasting colours and textures, and rice cake roasted with a soy-based
sauce. Fried pork with slender green Japanese leeks is a best seller. It can get
hot, claustrophobic and chaotic at night, especially sitting at the curved bar.
Customers may be outnumbered by legions of cooks and waiters, few of whom
speak English, and there may be problems with the bill. To drink there is green
tea (served without charge), saké or Japanese Kirin beer. A sister restaurant,
Arisugawa, opened in the summer at 27 Percy Street, as we went to press.

CHEF: M. Suzuki   PROPRIETOR: M. Kawaguchi
OPEN: all week, exc Sat and Sun L, Sat D
MEALS: 12.30 to 2.30, 6 to 10.15
PRICES: £15 (£20), Set L and D £5.60 (£10) to £6.90 (£12). Service 10%
CARDS: Access, Amex, Diners, Visa
SEATS: 65. Private parties: 65 main room, 12 private room. Vegetarian meals with prior
notice. Children welcome. Music. Air-conditioned

L'Incontro ▼
map 12

87 Pimlico Road, SW1W 8PH   COOKING 2
071-730 6327   COST £21–£53

A modern front on the Pimlico Road opposite the erstwhile dictator of fashion,
Casa Pupo: the 1980s outstare the 1960s. The mirrored room – a bar at the
front, a wall of wine at the back – is a lively variation on grey; only the 1980s
could make grey lively. The customers are irrepressibly stylish. L'Incontro, like
its sister restaurant Santini (see entry), serves Venetian food though the
vegetables stay English. There is a long *carte* and, at lunchtime, a shorter and
better-value set-price affair. The only certainty here is that a meal will be
expensive … but all that style! Some dishes are done well: the Venetian bean

soup, a lip-sticking stock with deep flavours, is first rate and unexpectedly of a peasant nature; a fair hand with calf's liver and calves' kidneys; some well grilled fish and shellfish, as in a mixed plate of monkfish, langoustines and salmon, or langoustines served plainly with lime. Italians have reported favourably on the risotto. Ambitions are high, but execution may be less consistent: a sea bass (of medium quality) was overcooked, untidily filleted and served with a mild balsamic vinegar sauce; lamb chops with an agrodolce sauce were so badly burned as to taint everything on the plate; a mozzarella salad seemed innocent of any intervention by cooks whatsoever, perhaps it was rushed in from a sandwich bar. These dishes were at one meal alone. This is the place to try Italian wines but don't bother to look for half-bottles. There is a marvellous balance of Barolo with some age – Monfortino 1974 – with some new-fangled styles of Mascarello, and an impressive range of chiantis. France makes a respectable if brief show with Branaire-Ducru 1976 to Puligny Montrachet 1986. Cheap and cheerful Asti Spumante at a high and gloomy cost warns that prices are not generous. House Italian: £12. CELLARMAN'S CHOICE: Terre Bianche 1988, £14.50; Venègazzu 1985, £15.50.

CHEFS: D. Minuzzo and I. Santin   PROPRIETOR: G. Santin
OPEN: all week
MEALS: 12.30 to 2.30 (1 to 3.30 Sun), 7 to 11.30 (10.30 Sun)
PRICES: £30 (£44), Set L £14.50 (£21). Cover £1.50. Service 12%, inc Set L
CARDS: Access, Amex, Diners, Visa
SEATS: 65. Private parties: 30 private room. Vegetarian meals. Children's helpings.
Wheelchair access. Music. Air-conditioned

Ivy
map 13

1 West Street, WC2H 9NE
071-836 4751

COOKING 2
COST £40

The appearance of what is virtually Caprice Mark II in the heart of London's theatreland must be good news. Jeremy King and Christopher Corbin have taken over one of Covent Garden's classic venues, across the road from the perennial *Mousetrap*. For years this curious place looked for all the world like a 1940s Hollywood set for an Elizabethan drama, with its leather benches, oak panelling and mullioned stained glass windows. In its new incarnation it has been subjected to designer overkill as if to shake off all the cobwebs of the past. A huge modern painting dominates the scene with its own version of technicolour, and young waiters with designer haircuts and black shirts move around smoothly. The menu has all the hallmarks of the original Caprice (see entry): an eclectic assortment of urbane specialities with a global flavour: bang bang chicken, prosciutto with balsamic vinegar, grilled polenta, braised ox-tail, coq au vin. Readers have enjoyed soft, fat shiitake mushrooms sauté with bordelaise sauce; terrine of foie gras with toasted brioche; and roast Gressingham duck with braised red cabbage. Salmon fishcakes – a Caprice classic – are served here with an all-enveloping sorrel sauce. In general, few dishes startle the taste buds, but there is much to please. As the kitchen settles, perhaps the chef will be bold enough to stamp his own style on the menu. On Sunday there is a brunch of Bucks fizz, bagels and blueberry muffins in addition to the standard menu. The short wine list is headed by Europe, followed by also-rans from the New World. There are some interesting bottles to be found and most are reasonably priced. House French is £6.50.

CHEFS: Tony Howorth and Nevil Wilkins PROPRIETORS: Jeremy King and Christopher Corbin
OPEN: all week
MEALS: 12 to 3, 5.30 to 12
PRICES: £23 (£33). Cover £1.50
CARDS: Access, Amex, Diners, Visa
SEATS: 110. Private parties: 8 main room, 20 and 50 private rooms. No children under 5. Wheelchair access. Air-conditioned

Jade Garden
map 14

15 Wardour Street, W1V 3HA
071-437 5065

COOKING 2
COST £13–£31

One overview of Soho's Cantonese restaurants is that they have sharpened their decor, raised prices, reduced portions and broadened their menus into areas that they are not always equipped to handle. Given these parameters, the Jade Garden seems to hold up well. The decor has been given a face lift with lots of reddish wood, a spiral staircase leading to the balcony section, and gold reliefs of Chinese warriors. The menu is strong on seafood, with dishes ranging from stewed eel with roast pork and deep-fried squid to steamed crab. Otherwise there are soups and one-plate noodle and rice dishes for a quick, reasonably priced meal. A specialist menu written in Chinese has more esoteric items along the lines of crunchy shredded sea blubber with shredded duck, and roast quail with garlic and spiced salt. Orange segments arrive at the end of the meal. Dim-sum Sunday lunches draw the crowds, so go early. Wines are rudimentary but fairly priced and the house wine matches the food. House wine: £6.50

CHEF: Raymond Bignold PROPRIETORS: L.S. and P.W. Man
OPEN: all week
CLOSED: 25 and 26 Dec
MEALS: noon (11.30am Sat and Sun) to 11.30
PRICES: £14 (£26), Set L and D £8 (£13) to £15 (£20)
CARDS: Access, Amex, Visa
SEATS: 160. Private parties: 70 main room, 70 private room. Children welcome. Wheelchair access (1 step). Air-conditioned

Jason Court
map 13

Jason Court, 76 Wigmore Street,
W1H 9DQ
071-224 2992

COOKING 2
COST £27–£44

This is nearly a very good restaurant. It certainly has style. A broad stair from a court off Wigmore Street takes you, encouragingly for once, to a large and airy basement. The roughcast stucco and blue ceiling beams and archways everywhere may seem over-artful but the space has coolth and is comfortable. Service, too, is very willing and competent and the idea of serving a British nouvelle menu cooked by Shaun Thomson, long the chief harbinger of a British revival, seems a fair one. Menus include cabbie claw a (a Scottish dish based on steamed cod), potted eel, Mendip snails, fried elvers, rabbit eger-douce (a medieval dish cooked in honey and whisky), trifle and summer pudding. Presentation is as nouvelle as it can be. Some of this has been very positively reported: clay-pot guinea-fowl stuffed with watercress and celery cooked with madeira and served with an onion sauce; potted shrimps with smoked salmon on a watercress salad; steamed lobster with shellfish and vegetables; an apple tansy; a soufflé omelette with caramelised cider sauce, 'the best sweet I've ever eaten.' Other comments have agreed that the ideas are all there but the actual execution, or the buying, leaves some significant detail unattended – for instance, tenderness or sufficient cooking. There seems to be a need to concentrate on technique and bringing out the best of the flavours. Credit card bills are not left open. The wine list is less elaborate than it was and it may benefit from this, for the selection intelligently provides real choices. The range allows for cheaper drinking and does not climb too steep a slope of cost. The main French run is supplemented by inexpensive New World wines from Geoffrey Roberts. There are four English bottles to complement the food. House wine from Duboeuf is £7.50. CELLARMAN'S CHOICE: St Aubin 1986, Prudhon, £17.50; Rully 1988, O. Leflaive, £15.

CHEF/PROPRIETOR: Shaun Thomson
OPEN: Mon to Fri
CLOSED: bank hols
MEALS: 12 to 2.30, 7 to 10.30
PRICES: £25 (£37), Set L £18 (£27). Service 12.5%
CARDS: Access, Amex, Diners, Visa
SEATS: 70. Private parties: 70 main room, 14 private room. Vegetarian meals. Children welcome. No-smoking area. Air-conditioned

Joe's Café

map 12

126 Draycott Avenue, SW3 3AH
071-225 2217

COOKING 1
COST £37

A small front, a big behind: all in black and white and hard surfaces at fashionable Brompton Cross. This is itself of course, a fashionable spot, owned by the designer Joseph Ettedgui. You can clothe yourself or furnish your house from his shops nearby. It's cheaper, though more transitory, to eat his food. This, however, is not as distinctive as his designs. It is modern brasserie fare – eggs Benedict, black and white noodles, carpaccio, Porkinsons bangers and mash, crème brûlée – done with unattractive cupidity: cover charge, high minimum, 15 per cent service. The standards are acceptable but many will not think the price worth it unless interested in the anthropology of the West End. Places of this ilk, calling themselves cafés, should provide all-day food and refreshment, but what happens when a passerby goes in hoping for a snack at the bar at 6pm? Not possible ... must sit at a table ... twenty minutes waiting for two smoked salmon ... a Campari ... eating ... a bill for £27! Try for a coffee on a hot summer night at a few minutes after ten. The bar is empty, the restaurant full, the staff cleaning glasses. Not possible. No coffee without a full meal. Madness. The bar is open for drinks from 6pm to 9pm on weekdays. There is breakfast from 10.30am to lunchtime on Saturday. And Sunday offers up a brunch menu rather than lunch. So perhaps some glimmering is dawning that English cities need adaptability. There is a short wine list on which prices start at around £12 for a Chinon, but house wine is £9.80.

CHEF: James Waters   PROPRIETORS: Joseph Ltd
OPEN: all week, exc Sun D
CLOSED: 25 Dec and 1 Jan
MEALS: 12 (11 Sun) to 3.30, 7.30 to 11.30
PRICES: £18 (£31). Cover £1. Minimum £5.50. Service 15%
CARDS: Access, Amex, Carte Blanche, Diners, Visa
SEATS: 95. 2 tables outside. Private parties: 25 main room. Vegetarian meals. Children's helpings. Wheelchair access. Music. Air-conditioned

Kalamaras

map 11

76–78 Inverness Mews, W2 3JQ
071-727 9122

COOKING 2
COST £19–£24

Loud were the howls of outrage at our description of the waitresses here as matronly and Greek who ignore pushy customers: 'the only matrons I have seen have been eating at table, and the staff never ignore customers, busy or not,' wrote one in strong defence. And even though these same waitresses interpret the wholly Greek menu with ease and speed for non-Greek speakers, they are, according to another who listed their origins in tedious detail, of every nationality but Greek. The basement is dark, low ceilinged and hot on summer nights especially when crowded. Chairs are uncomfortable but the food is authentically Greek, as opposed to Greek-Cypriot, though a Spanish chef has been sighted. There is a tendency towards seafood and time-consuming dishes connected with home cooking rather than a lot of grilled dishes – the easy option taken by most other like restaurants in this country. Recommendations have been made for tsirosalata – salted and sun-dried anchovies filleted, cooked briefly over an open flame and served with olive oil and lemon; dolmades, which one Greek cook felt were a little meaty and bland, needing more herbs and rice; grilled octopus; fritters of salt cod which, like the squid, could have had less batter; and horta or greens, a salad of cooked Swiss chard with oil and lemon. Roasted meats can be dry from long heating, but where else in London can you buy large grilled fresh Dover sole for £6.20 as was reported by one very happy man? This is a very cheerful place that replicates the atmosphere of the taverna as well as any in London. There is a Micro Kalamaras at number 66. It is also well liked but is not licensed. The wines served in Macro are Greek but do not go so far as to include the exciting new Greek producers that are beginning to appear on shippers' list. House wine from £6.20.

The Guide *is totally independent, accepts no free hospitality, and survives on the number of copies sold each year.*

CHEF/PROPRIETOR: Stelios Platonos
OPEN: Mon to Sat, D only
CLOSED: bank hols
MEALS: 7 to 12
PRICES: £11 (£20), Set D £14 (£19). Cover £1. Service 10%
CARDS: Access, Amex, Diners, Visa
SEATS: 96. Private parties: 16 and 28 private rooms. Vegetarian meals. Children's helpings.
Wheelchair access. Music. Air-conditioned

Keats
map 11

3A Downshire Hill, NW3 1NR
071-435 3544

COOKING 3
COST £20–£46

A Hampstead institution has been designer-revamped to look like a Victorian
library, with the creamy brown paint on the tall panelled walls cracking to
reveal red underneath. Wonderfully theatrical or over-contrived? It's
comfortable, at least, and since its recent change of ownership and acquisition
by Roy Ackerman's umbrella organisation, the Restaurant Partnership, the
food has inspired waxings poetical. (Other associations with the poet himself
are weak, though he lived one street away.) 'An absolutely impeccable
meal … uncomplicated, very delicate, fresh-tasting food – genuinely French.'
The menu, a longish *carte* plus a commendable value set dinner and even better
value set lunch (no choice in either), doesn't vary much and indulges in
occasional clichés such as black truffles and madeira sauce. Although there may
be few fireworks, Herbert Berger skilfully integrates his ingredients to deliver
clean, true flavours. Particularly fine were mignons of veal, which were not
lost in their regalia of fresh gooseliver topping, bed of savoy cabbage, and
Sauternes-spiked juices. Wild mushroom and parsley soup with a cheese
soufflé lid, balanced and creamy, was more than just a good idea. One very fine,
slightly pink, lamb's kidney on lightly oiled, multi-coloured leaves, rang true,
and a medley of seafood that included salmon and red mullet was nicely set off
by its saffron cream sauce. Lighter dishes have an upbeat bounce, as in
'delightfully fresh' sea bass and red mullet ('cooked spot-on') or a rocket salad
dressed with olive oil, 'old' vinegar and garlic. Vegetables and salads,
inexpensive extras on the *carte*, are further reason to trust the kitchen, as are the
home-made bread rolls that might be black, walnut or wholemeal as well as
white. Desserts have included caramel mousseline with mango compote and
lime, and iced Irish coffee soufflé with whisky sauce. A very competent hot
apple and almond Pithiviers with blackberry coulis, sampled in spring, was
presented artistically, and had beautiful pastry and lovely apple flavour.
Espresso is good quality. Service is discreet, professional and semi-formal.
Good growers and fine properties are scattered through the wine list, which is
dominated by claret, but with little below £15 and the mark-up stretching
prices rapidly, this is not the place for good-value drinking.

The Guide *office can quickly spot when a restaurateur is encouraging customers to write
recommending inclusion - and sadly, several restaurants have been doing this in 1990.
Such reports do not further a restaurant's cause. Please tell us if a restaurateur invites you
to write to the* Guide.

CHEF: Herbert Berger PROPRIETORS: The Restaurant Partnership
OPEN: Tue to Sat
MEALS: 12.30 to 2.30, 7.30 to 10
PRICES: £30 (£38), Set L £15.50 (£20), Set D £21 (£26) to £28 (£33). Service inc
CARDS: Access, Amex, Visa
SEATS: 36. Private parties: 40 main room. Children's helpings. Smart dress preferred.
No pipes in dining-room

Kensington Place ▼   map 11

201 Kensington Church Street, W8 7lX   COOKING 3
071-727 3184   COST £19–£34

In the home strait of Kensington Church Street as it crests up to Notting Hill
Gate is a glazed frontage to a scene of intense animation: people at table, others
rushing hither and yon, still more milling about a curving bar. The decoration
is hard edged, though never rectilinear, softened by a mural of some riparian
idyll. Lighting is strong and sound can practically be *seen* to bounce off the
surfaces: 'A few acoustic tiles would be very cheap and would only be noticed
by the absence of treble.' 'The staff are very willing to do your bidding but have
some difficulty hearing it.' The setting excites some barbed comments:
'Howling draught, like Paddington Station'; 'like a recycled '50s carpet
showroom', are but two. Others just like the lure of success, the buzz of
togetherness, and the good food. It is often likened to a brasserie; this it is not.
You can neither visit nor drink without a meal. It is not a pausing place, though
London needs more pausing places that are not pubs or cafés. Rowley Leigh's
cooking, from a long menu with many daily extras, is inventive and moderately
priced. He may offer foie gras and oysters, but the style is neither aristocratic
nor overladen with chef's conceits. Sauces there are, but in the modern manner.
As in the United States, for instance, they are not the centrepiece they may
appear to be in more traditional restaurant cookery. There are standard items –
chicken and goats' cheese mousse with olives, lemon tart and the steamed
puddings get repeated mentions – but the kitchen is firmly wedded to the
market and presents a kaleidoscopic selection from day to day. Examples of
success run to a long list but may include scallops (or cod) with rocket; several
soups, including mussel and parsley, but not cauliflower, which had lost its
original flavour to that of boiled socks; oysters with wild rice and cucumbers;
hake with more wild rice; chicken breast with truffle oil; partridge with
cabbage (very good, this, presented beautifully and not buried in old brassica
flavour); a good cheeseboard; and sweets like chocolate marjolaine, tarte Tatin
or wild strawberry cake. An affection for trendy ingredients, perhaps truffle oil,
may overestimate their ability to deliver flavour without more thought to the
vehicle. When on form, this is estimable craft put to good use with lots of ideas
and a sense of happy invention. It is unfortunate that off-days are recorded too
often to ignore. Perhaps the strain of seven-day working is too much, or the
press of business is too heavy. The consequence may be cold food, a failure to
hit the sweet spot of taste, or incompetence in the cooking. The no-nonsense
wine list is wide in range. Such impeccable choices as Paillard Champagne,
Montagny from Vachet, Heitz Zinfandel and Juillot Mercurey show a sharp eye
for quality. This is matched by friendly pricing. House French: £8.25.

CELLARMAN'S CHOICE: Reuilly 1985, £12; Pinot Noir de Bourgogne 1986, Rossignol, £14.75.

CHEF: Rowley Leigh   PROPRIETORS: N. Smallwood and S. Slater
OPEN: all week
MEALS: 12 to 11.45 (10.15 Sun)
PRICES: £21 (£28), Set L £12.50 (£19)
CARDS: Access, Visa
SEATS: 90. Private parties: 90 main room. Children's helpings. Music. Air-conditioned

Khun Akorn
map 11

136 Brompton Road, SW3 1HY
071-225 2688

COOKING 1
COST £15–£35

The avowed aim of this extremely elegant restaurant is to market Thai cooking to the up-market clientele of Knightsbridge, using tourism and tropicana as its major selling points. The menu has been deliberately designed to look like a holiday brochure, with technicolour photographs of Thai landscapes and luxury hotels owned by the restaurant's parent company. Despite the exotic overtones, the list of dishes makes familiar reading, with few items not found elsewhere. Both the spicy tom yam kung soup and fishcakes have been acceptable; other recommendations have included prawns in coconut gravy flavoured with chilli and coriander; fried chicken with chilli and cashew-nuts; and chandburi king prawn noodles topped with a paper-thin omelette. Roast duck curry has been 'superlative', and spinach has been cooked to perfection with ginger and garlic. A la carte prices are on the high side, but then this is Knightsbridge. Set dinners will be arranged on request. A branch was due to open in Earls Court in October 1990, as we went to press. The high mark-ups extend to the standard wine list. House wine: £8.80 and £9.

CHEFS: Mr Boontavee and Mr Dusit   PROPRIETOR: Khun Akorn
OPEN: all week
CLOSED: 25 and 26 Dec, 1 Jan
MEALS: 12 to 3 (2.30 Sun), 6.30 to 11 (10.30 Sun)
PRICES: £15 (£29), Set L £9.50 (£15)
CARDS: Access, Amex, Visa
SEATS: 60. Private parties: 90 main room. Vegetarian meals. Children's helpings on request. Music. Air-conditioned

Lal Qila
map 13

117 Tottenham Court Road, W1P 9H1
071-387 4570

COOKING 1
COST £17–£28

One of the earliest smart Indian restaurants in the capital, this holds its position by amiable, informed service – though it can be over-attentive one moment, neglectful the next – comfortable surroundings and occasionally excellent cooking. Tandoori dishes are among the most successful: the quail has been well seasoned and the fish cooked accurately. Vegetables appear a strong point, including the aloo chat, spiced potatoes in a sour sauce; the aloo gobi, potatoes and cauliflower; and the spinach. Nans and basmati rice are good. Less acceptable have been prawns curled as tight as a hiding snail and as dry as sawdust, and seasoning as undifferentiated as in the humblest curry shop of yesteryear. The Sunday set lunch is a buffet, as much as you can eat, and includes a sweet. The brief wine list lacks details but prices are not unreasonable. House French: £7.50.

CHEF: Ayub Ali   PROPRIETORS: Enamul Haque, Abul Kalam and Ayub Ali
OPEN: all week
MEALS: 12 to 3, 6 to 11.15
PRICES: £12 (£23), Set Sun L £9.95 (£17). Service 15%
CARDS: Access, Amex, Diners, Visa
SEATS: 80. Private parties: 40 main room. Vegetarian meals. Children's helpings. Smart dress preferred. Music. Wheelchair access (1 step). Air-conditioned

Langan's Brasserie
map 13

Stratton Street, W1X 5SD
071-493 6437

COOKING 2
COST £34

'Visiting to celebrate a friend's birthday, it proved itself to be the stylish place expected and remembered from the past. The food was far more realistic than my usual places and the price was good value for Mayfair for a meal that neither failed nor excelled.' It is interesting how often the past figures in people's accounts of this large restaurant on two giant floors, just off Piccadilly. Of course it looks old, some of the menu offers establishment food not far adrift from places like the Connaught, and it came into its own in the glorious youth of all those besuited customers that fill it at lunch: a recipe for nostalgia. The skills are managerial in that large numbers of people are kept happy and satisfied; the food achieves a standard; the menu is a happy mix of the familiar and the new or of the mundane and the luxurious; and the service is committed enough to make it enjoyable. 'The food was good, the service friendly, and I relieved myself next to a celebrity in the gents,' was another reaction that sums up other attractions of the place. 'The chicken was perfectly pleasant, only slightly inferior to the kind of thing my mum does so well.' Everyone should still go to Langan's – it's an education.

CHEFS: Richard Shepherd, Dennis Mynott and Roy Smith   PROPRIETORS: Michael Caine and Richard Shepherd
OPEN: Mon to Sat, exc Sat L
MEALS: 12.30 to 3, 7 to 11.45 (8 to 12.45 Sat)
PRICES: £20 (£28) Cover £1. Service 12.5%
CARDS: Access, Amex, Diners, Visa
SEATS: 200. Private parties: 12 main room. Vegetarian meals. Children's helpings. Wheelchair access (1 step). Music. Air-conditioned

Launceston Place
map 12

1A Launceston Place, W8 5RL
071-937 6912

COOKING 2
COST £18–£34

The corner of Kensington occupied by Launceston Place has a village air, promoted by a shop called 'Frog Hollow', flowering trees in gardens and on pavements, and narrow carriageways. The microblinds of the restaurant may shut out the world at large, but decoration within – comfortable, with plenty of paintings and mirrors – is of a piece with the location. The menu is at once fashionable and reassuring: grilled squid and rocket salad, navarin of lamb; vinaigrette of smoked eel; calf's liver with onion marmalade; chicken liver salad with olive; red mullet with bordelaise sauce are some of the opposing components. At lunchtime and during the first hour of the evening there is an inexpensive set-price menu. The execution of these dishes can be very accurate: lightly grilled vegetables with pesto; squid with blackened pasta; tagliatelle with girolles; simply grilled Dover sole; and desserts such as pineapple fritters, a compote of plums and cinnamon, and bread-and-butter pudding are favourably reported. However, there are lunches and dinners when the performance is less than satisfactory and when business is too brisk to allow lingering over coffee or satisfactory service. The catalogue of miscreance stretches long, though not so long as that of virtue. It is a pity more consistency cannot be achieved. The wine list is concise and offers a fair range for all purses. Indeed, its selection is almost more interesting in the lower than the upper price bracket. House wines: £7.50 and £8.50. CELLARMAN'S CHOICE: Vacqueyras, Dom. les Garrigues 1985, £12.50; Monthélie 1983 Denis Boussey, £18.50.

CHEF: Charles Mumford   PROPRIETORS: Nick Smallwood and Simon Slater
OPEN: all week, exc Sat L and Sun D
MEALS: 12.30 to 2.30, 7 to 11.30
PRICES: £19 (£28), Set L and D (till 8pm) £11.50 (£18) to £13.75 (£20)
CARDS: Access, Visa
SEATS: 55. Private parties: 25 main room, 14 private room. Vegetarian meals. Children's helpings (L only). No pipes in dining-room. Wheelchair access. Air-conditioned

Laurent   map 11

428 Finchley Road, NW2 2HY   COOKING 1
071-794 3603   COST £20

There is only one first course at Laurent's: brik à l'oeuf (crispy egg-filled pancake); there are only three main courses: three sorts of couscous, one of them vegetarian; and there are only four desserts: ice-creams, sorbets, crème caramel and crêpes Suzette. It makes for a simple life and should mean that everything is perfect. Well, it isn't always: the crêpes Suzettes are really Cointreau pancakes but the price hints at that; the brochette served with the 'couscous royal' may be approximately cooked; the brik is sometimes approximately seasoned. Yet the couscous itself is first rate, the broths enjoyable indeed and the merguez (sausage) well spiced. Traditional harissa hot sauce comes with every order and will fortify the wilting. The crème caramel is the apple of any sweet-tooth's eye. This couscous house feels like the real thing: plenty of francophone customers, whitewashed walls, checked tablecloths, candles and plenty of Moroccan or Algerian wine. House French: £6.50.

All letters to the Guide *are acknowledged with an update on latest sales, closures, chef changes and so on.*

CHEF/PROPRIETOR: Laurent Farrugia
OPEN: Mon to Sat
CLOSED: first 3 weeks Aug
MEALS: 12 to 2, 6 to 10.30
PRICES: £11 (£17). Minimum £5.75
CARDS: Access, Visa
SEATS: 36. Private parties: 50 main room. Vegetarian meals. Children's helpings

Left Bank
map 11

88 Ifield Road, SW10 9AD
071-352 0970

COOKING 1
COST £21–£32

Parties may interrupt quieter conversations in this neighbourhood bistro-cum-restaurant (Chelsea's bistro nowadays is the rest of the world's restaurant). The staff, however, is anxious to please and the cooking may satisfy. Broccoli soup, Rosslare oysters, Bayonne ham and avocado, quail salad, calf's liver with a herbed gravy, fish in a feuilleté with a white wine sauce, chocolate mousse and lemon tart – some are well done, others may lack sufficient flavour, but the standard is quite adequate. It might be said that the whole place depends on France for inspiration and style, but nothing could be further from the truth. For one thing, it might not last long in Paris or Brussels at these prices; for another, it is in fact the quintessential West London 'bistro'. Wines are all French with decent vintages and fair prices. Bordeaux are particularly strong with a good spread of bourgeois growths through a scattering of better known names.

CHEF: John Beaumont   PROPRIETORS: Fernando Peire and Keith Wormleighton
OPEN: Mon to Sat, Sun L
MEALS: 12 to 2.30, 7 to 11.30
PRICES: £17 (£27), Set D £15 (£21)
CARDS: Access, Amex, Visa
SEATS: 95. 2 tables outside. Private parties: 14 to 50 main room, 30 private room. Children's helpings. Wheelchair access. Music. Air-conditioned

Leith's ▮
map 11

92 Kensington Park Road, W11 2PN
071-229 4481

COOKING 3
COST £29–£55

Leith's stands majestically in a Notting Hill terrace, its dining-rooms fashioned to appear like a courtyard with false windows on the walls and a night sky of spotlights twinkling above. It has many of the attributes of a long-established place: a certain independence and 'character' on the part of the staff, which may be evinced by an unacceptable level of noise coming from the kitchen or by old-school service, and not always the best sort. Thomas Alf has ceded the kitchen to his deputy Alex Floyd, but the main lines of style and content are preserved. There are two menus, one for vegetarians, one for omnivores. The price of each is set according to the number of courses taken. Fixed points are trolleys for hors d'oeuvre, cheese and sweets, and certain long-popular dishes like Leith's duckling and chargrilled beef. Seasonal dishes are of the likes of black risotto with squid and wild mushrooms; charred fillet of salmon with chilli and sesame sauce; or lamb with lentils, beans and rosemary. Vegetarian cooking is often praised for exactness of flavour and execution, for example in a red pepper mousse with a fragrant warm vinaigrette where the mousse was given a nice crunch by dice of three peppers, onions, carrots and olives. The hors d'oeuvre trolley may turn up before contemplation of the menu is complete. Some find its wares old-fashioned, preferring to order a hot first course such as the well-textured crab and sea trout mousse with a glazed sabayon, but others enjoy the simple pleasures of Caesar salad, a good chicken terrine or avocado mousse. Although many have noted decent rounded tastes in hearty dishes such as a venison and boar casserole, it has also been noted that a perfectly cooked fillet of salmon basted in sesame oil that purported to have a chilli and sesame sauce seemed quite innocent of chilli. The style of cooking is not assertive, occasionally to a fault. Cheeses are British, often good, and desserts run round on a trolley, except for soufflés. Eating lemon tart and a moderate bread-and-butter pudding cold from the trolley had one reader questioning the policy: 'even tepid or lukewarm, their flavours would sparkle instead of tasting flat.' Like all trolleys it's great on a good day but seems hackneyed and lack-lustre on a bad one – or to a bad-tempered customer. Coffee comes with good petits fours, including mint ice-cream encased in a globe of chocolate. The restaurant gets solid support from the business and diplomatic community; it also pleases visitors to London impressed by its air of established competence; it can grate with a younger, more metropolitan constituency who tangle occasionally with the waiters and who may question the value. The wine list occupies much of manager Nick Tarayan's working life. It improves. There is a fine range of classics, especially 1970s clarets, but expertly reinforced by New World and new European selections. Prices are not high for the expensive bottles and across-the-board percentage mark-ups are not in evidence. Some recompense is sought from stiff mark-ups on cheaper wines so the base price is fairly high, but then Leith's usually works out very expensively. Makers of high quality abound: Charles Dupuy from Sancerre, Umani Ronchi's Verdicchio from the Marches, Petaluma from South Australia, Frog's Leap from Napa, Jean Clerget, Roland Rapet and Fontaine-Gagnard from Burgundy and some good bourgeois châteaux as well as Bordeaux names everyone knows. House French: £12.95.

CHEF: Alex Floyd   PROPRIETORS: Leith's Restaurant Ltd and Prue Leith
OPEN: all week, D only
CLOSED: 3 or 4 days at Christmas, 2 days at Aug bank hol
MEALS: 7.30 to 11.30
PRICES: Set D £22 (£29) to £39.50 (£46). Service inc
CARDS: Access, Amex, Diners, Visa
SEATS: 85. Private parties: 24 main room, 10, 24 and 36 private rooms. Vegetarian meals. Children welcome. Wheelchair access (3 steps). Air-conditioned

Ley-On's

map 14

56–58 Wardour Street, W1V 3HN

071-437 6465

COOKING 1

COST £16–£38

Ley-On's is part of old Soho. In 1926 the original building was taken over and turned into a chop-suey house, making it one of the longest surviving Chinese restaurants in central London. Although it stands only a hundred yards from the heart of Chinatown and the pandemonium of the Wong Kei, the atmosphere – and the high prices – could not be more different. At lunchtime it can be fun when a cosmopolitan crowd arrives for dim-sum (served from 11.30am to 4.30pm); otherwise the cavernous dining-room feels like a becalmed 1950s ballroom in Shanghai, with its greenery, huge Chinese prints, green pillars and marble slabs. The long menu has a daunting collection of regional dishes, peasant specialities and strange ingredients: stuffed scallops with mango and yam croquette; 'treasured calamari in a jar'; casserole of chicken with cockles; minced pork with salted egg. Sometimes the results can be totally unconvincing. It seems that the kitchen works best, with more familiar items such as hot-and-sour soup, paper-wrapped chicken with coriander, and hot-pot of eel and roast belly pork with garlic. Sago pudding in coconut cream with chunks of melon makes a refreshing sweet. To drink there is Tiger beer or Chinese Tsing Tao, as well as saké and wine. House French: £7.80.

CHEF: S.M. Ng   PROPRIETORS: S.K. Leung and S.M. Ng
OPEN: all week
MEALS: 11.30 to 4.45, 6 to 11
PRICES: £15 (£26), Set L and D £10.90 (£16) to £25 (£32)
CARDS: Access, Amex, Diners, Visa
SEATS: 330. Private parties: 300 main room. Children welcome. Music. Air-conditioned

Los Remos

map 11

38A Southwick Street, W2 1JQ

071-723 5056 and 706 1870

COOKING 1

COST £17–£33

Roberto Lopez has pitched his Spanish restaurant within walking distance of Paddington Station. Most hungry travellers head for the happy atmosphere and good value of the basement tapas bar, with its short menu of authentic snacks. Patatas bravas (potatoes in spicy sauce), seafood salad, and choquinos (baby squid) have all been reported with enthusiasm. Octopus with oil and paprika is a best seller. The ground-floor dining-room specialises in grilled meat and fish. Three Champagnes apart, wines are Spanish, very well chosen, and presented clearly and proudly. Riojas, white and red, get a fine showing. House Rioja: £6.50. CELLARMAN'S CHOICE: Marqués de Cáceres Crianza 1985, £8.95.

CHEF/PROPRIETOR: Roberto Lopez
OPEN: all week
MEALS: 12 to 3, 7 to 11 (10.30 Sun)
PRICES: £13 (£22), Set L £10 (£17) to £18 (£26), Set D £12 (£19) to £19.50 (£27). Cover £1
Service 10%
CARDS: Access, Amex, Carte Blanche, Diners, Visa
SEATS: 70. Private parties: 70 main room. Children's helpings. Music. Air-conditioned

Lou Pescadou

map 11

241 Old Brompton Road, SW5 9HP
071-370 1057

COOKING 1
COST £30

The faded charm and the no-booking policy may be part of the attraction of this cut-price fish restaurant (the cheapest of Pierre Martin's flotilla). The short menu relies on regular supplies of admirably fresh fish shipped over from Britanny. Plaice, skate, turbot, red mullet and oysters all make an appearance; there have also been good reports of John Dory, monkfish in cream sauce, and salt cod with tarragon. There is no great difficulty in producing dishes like these, but they are excellent of their kind. Bolstering the fish are pizzas, salads and omelettes, plus steaks for meat eaters. There is plenty of calvados in the tarte aux pommes. 'Unpretentious and satisfying', is a popular view. The attitude of the waiters and the patron has not impressed, provoking even pacific humans. This group needs to review its customer relations. House wine: £7.80.

CHEF: David Laurent   PROPRIETORS: Oakhelm Ltd
OPEN: all week
CLOSED: 2 weeks at Christmas
MEALS: 12 to 3, 7 to 12
PRICES: £17 (£25). Cover £1. Service 15%
CARDS: Access, Amex, Diners, Visa
SEATS: 60. 8 tables outside. Private parties: 20 main room. Vegetarian meals. Children's helpings. Wheelchair access (1 step)

Mandalay

map 10

100 Greenwich South Street, SE10 8UN
081-691 0443

COOKING 2
COST £16−£28

This is unique both as one of the few entries in the south-eastern quarter of London and for the Burmese food. Curiosity about Burma is amply repaid by Gerald Andrews' enthusiasm for the subject. He is of part Burmese parentage so has imbibed the lore at first hand, and is missionary in his zeal. The menu is divided into starters; one-plate meals that consist of meat or noodles in a soup; curries that need to be accompanied by a soup, a vegetable or a relish such as fish paste with dried prawns, chillies and garlic; and sweets that include a fragrant mango ice-cream, sweet rice with palm sugar and semolina cake with almonds. Dominant flavours come from onion oil, fish sauce, tamarind, tomato, garlic, coriander (fresh and ground) and, of course, chillies, though this cuisine is not overly hot. Consult the staff if you need advice. The one-plate meals of molinga (rice noodles in a fishy soup with onions in batter and lots of green coriander) and pun-ta-hkaw-swe (egg noodles with chicken slices, with raw onions and sliced egg yolk in a coconut-flavoured soup that's spicy but not chilli-hot) have been well liked, but there are meatier dishes such as duck hsi-byan, consisting of marinated duck in casserole with ginger, garlic, onion and tomato; this can be dunked in a tomato soup, again with lots of coriander. The stir-fried cabbage gives crunch to the meal. Beer is probably the best drink with this food, but Gerald Andrews will recommend a light white wine that's not expensive. House Spanish: £6.50.

CHEF/PROPRIETOR: Gerald Andrews
OPEN: Tue to Sat, D only and Sun L
MEALS: 12.30 to 3.30, 7 to 10.30
PRICES: £15 (£23), Set Sun L £9.50 (£16)
CARDS: Access, Amex, Diners, Visa
SEATS: 58. Private parties: 26 main room, 26 private room. Vegetarian meals.
Children welcome

Mandarin Kitchen
map 11

14–16 Queensway, W2 3RX   COOKING 2
071-727 9012 and 9468   COST £13–£26

Regulars reckon that this long-established Cantonese restaurant opposite
Queensway Skating Rink has moved up a gear of late, and now serves some of
the best food in the area. There are tanks of live fish on display and the menu is
dominated by seafood. Highlights have included fresh lobster steamed on a
bed of soft noodles, and crabmeat with king prawns in a 'first-class' creamy
sauce, although deep-fried soft-shelled crab with garlic and peppercorns
doesn't come up to versions elsewhere. The rest of the menu has less sparkle,
running from crispy duck to chicken in yellow-bean sauce. Chinese greens
with oyster sauce have plenty of crunch. House French: £6.50.

CHEFS: Fong Ho and Kwong Wing Man   PROPRIETORS: Stephen and Helen Cheung
OPEN: all week
MEALS: noon to 11.30
PRICES: £14 (£22), Set L and D £8.90 (£13). Minimum £7. Service inc
CARDS: Access, Amex, Diners, Visa
SEATS: 110. Private parties: 110 main room. Vegetarian meals. Children welcome.
Wheelchair access. Music. Air-conditioned

Mandeer
map 13

21 Hanway Place, W1P 9DG   COOKING 1
071-323 0660   COST £7–£27

No flock wallpaper in either the cellar dining-room or the Ravi Shankar Hall of
this Indian vegetarian restaurant just behind Tottenham Court Road. Rather, a
space as authentically Indian as the food. This is served on metal plates and
trays and takes in half a dozen thalis as well as some dishes such as aravi leaves
layered with chickpea paste; masala dosa filled with potato and onion with a
coconut chutney and a nicely spicy sambhar; Bombay aloo; or paneer korma, a
cheese dish, aromatic rather than hot, which is enriched with cream. Onion
bhajis and potato and aubergine bhajis are also approved, though sev usher –
dried yellow peas cooked sweet and sour, with vermicelli – was on one
occasion badly undercooked. Shrikhand – yoghurt whipped with sugar,
saffron and cardamom – and Himalayan apricots with rosewater are just two of
a strong suit of desserts, which also take in Loseley Park ice-creams. There are
lots of fruit juices and a short wine list including some organic wines, Mas de
Gourgonnier among them. The self-service lunch is excellent value. House Ch.
des Hautes Combes (organic) is £6.25.

CHEF: Mr Daudbhai PROPRIETORS: Mr and Mrs Patel
OPEN: Mon to Sat
CLOSED: bank hols
MEALS: 12 to 3, 6 to 10
PRICES: £13 (£22), Set L £3 (£7) to £5 (£10), Set D £6 (£11) to £9.75 (£15). Minimum £5.
Service 10%
CARDS: Access, Amex, Diners, Visa
SEATS: 75. Private parties: 100 main room. Vegetarian meals. Children's helpings.
No-smoking area. Music. Self-service at L

▲ *Manzi's* map 14

| 1–2 Leicester Street, WC2H 7BL | COOKING 1 |
| 071-734 0224 | COST £37 |

This is in 'the old style' and it is a nostalgic haunt for faithful regulars. The
Manzi family has been in residence since 1928. Little changes. Not
surprisingly, this provokes mixed reactions. 'A great place to have lunch or
dinner on a day out in London,' says one reader. 'Very simple. Good grilled or
fried fish and chips. Sit downstairs and you are fed and watered without any
frills,' comments another. On the other side of the coin, diners have found
pieces of squid in their scampi, and have been put off by being cramped in a
corner when there were plenty of empty tables, as well as by the service. A so-
called kiwi-fruit sorbet tasted of gooseberry: 'You may be right,' replied the
waiter. No doubt the love/hate relationship will continue. The wine list may be
worth a look, but the best advice is to drink the house white at £7.20.

CHEF: Vincenzo Frappola PROPRIETORS: The Manzi family
OPEN: all week, exc Sun L
CLOSED: 25 Dec
MEALS: 12 to 2.30, 5.30 to 11.30 (6 to 10.30 Sun)
PRICES: £22 (£31). Cover £1.30
CARDS: Access, Amex, Diners, Visa
SEATS: 160. Private parties: 17 main room, 45 private room. No children under 7
ACCOMMODATION: 16 rooms, all with bath/shower. Lift. B&B £35 to £55. Deposit: £10.
Confirm by noon

Maroush III map 11

| 62 Seymour Street, W1H 5AF | COOKING 2 |
| 071-724 5024 | COST £30 |

As we go to press, the Maroush empire is in the throes of refurbishment at its
main branch at 21 Edgware Road, but it has taken over this former fish
restaurant on Seymour Street for its third establishment. The decoration,
cleaned up but not altered from its earlier existence, is lush and classical, not
especially Middle Eastern unless you take a Hellenistic view. From the large
basket of vegetables and fresh pitta bread brought to the table at the outset, the
bread then never stinted, the meal takes an optimistic turn, fuelled most
satisfactorily from the long list of meze. These include a tabouleh light of
bulgar and high in parsley and mint; warm ful medames; a moussaka of
aubergines and chickpeas; good bazinjau rahib (grilled aubergines); excellent,

oily hummus, not too peppery; and well-cooked lamb's brains. Basturma has been overly strong. Service is attentive. Portions are big. The Lebanese coffee with cardamom is excellent.

CHEF: F. Ladkani   PROPRIETOR: M. Abouzaki
OPEN: all week
CLOSED: 25 Dec
MEALS: noon to midnight
PRICES: £14 (£25). Cover £1.50
CARDS: Access, Amex, Diners, Visa
SEATS: 60. 5 tables outside. Private parties: 60 main room. Vegetarian meals. Children welcome. Music. Air-conditioned

Martin's
map 11

239 Baker Street, NW1 6XE
071-935 3130 and 0997

COOKING 2
COST £26–£40

A smart, urbane restaurant with a pink and peach colour scheme and a conservatory skylight dominating the main dining-room at the back. The fashionable, modern food is in keeping. Lunch is a fixed-price menu, dinner is a *carte*, and there are daily specials: warm duck salad with foie gras; ravioli filled with crab and langoustines; and medallions of beef with a confit of garlic and shallots show the style. Occasional vegetarian dishes echo the same themes: artichoke hearts are filled with wild mushrooms and served on a saffron risotto. Plain meat and fish grills provide some lighter dishes – the salmon has been well reported. To finish there is a trio of sorbets, a hot soufflé and a 'delicious' white and dark chocolate truffle cake. Most of the farmhouse cheeses are unpasteurised. Wines are treated intelligently; growers are good, prices are fair, presentation is clear. A model list of its type. House wines: £9.75 and £12.75.

CHEF: Brendan McGee   PROPRIETOR: Martin Coldicott
OPEN: Mon to Sat, exc Sat L
MEALS: 12 to 2.30, 6 (7 Sat) to 10.30
PRICES: £24 (£33), Set L £17.50 (£26), to £21 (£30). Service 15%
CARDS: Access, Amex, Diners, Visa
SEATS: 60. Private parties: 16 private room. Children welcome. Smart dress preferred. Wheelchair access (1 step). Music. Air-conditioned

Mekong
map 11

46 Churton Street, SW1V 2LP
071-834 6896

COOKING 1
COST £16–£25

It styles itself a Vietnamese bistro, but the snug, simply furnished ground and downstairs rooms seem to have a more general oriental feel. The menu, which includes three set meals, follows suit, drawing mainly on regional and regulation Chinese. Spiced fish balls with French beans and garlic and Vietnamese spring roll are recommended specialities. The most successful Chinese dishes include garlic-laden bird's nest with prawns, sizzling mixed seafood platter, and 'quite superb' crab claw wrapped with minced prawn, all from the seafood banquet. Oil and salt occasionally overpower, and some

dishes simply lack flavour. Service is relaxed. Drink saké or tea. House
French: £5.90.

CHEFS: Vinh Thap Tran and T.Y. Cheung   PROPRIETOR: Howard Tso
OPEN: all week
CLOSED: 25 and 26 Dec, Easter Sun and Mon
MEALS: 12 to 2.30, 6 to 11.30
PRICES: £11 (£20), Set L and D £12 (£16) to £16 (£21). Service 10%
CARDS: Access, Visa
SEATS: 50. Private parties: 24 main room, 14 private room. Children welcome. Wheelchair
access. Music

Melati

map 14

21 Great Windmill Street, W1V 7PH   COOKING 1
071-437 2745   COST £21

Three floors of stripped pine and 120 seats often packed to bursting means that
a large constituency perceives value, cheerfulness and fair cooking of
Malaysian/Indonesian food. An habitué claims quarterly visits for a 'best meal'
of lumpia, spring roll with chicken and shrimp; sup sayur, hot-and-sour
vegetable soup; rendang, the Indonesian spiced beef and coconut masterpiece;
and ayarn masak jeruk, chicken in a lemon sauce 'for my tender-palated wife'.
For, as another remarks, 'they make few concessions to westerners here.' Mee
hoon goreng, rice noodles with chicken, shrimps and vegetables, makes a good
one-plate meal for lunch and tahu telor, beancurd omelette, is an option for
vegetarians. The list of sweets – sago, coconut milk, palm syrup and tropical
fruits in abundance – is long. Indonesian (Bintang) and Singaporean (Tiger)
beers are served. House French: £6.55.

CHEFS: S. Alamsjah and H. Hasyim   PROPRIETORS: M.C.W. Ong and S. Alamsjah
OPEN: all week
CLOSED: 25 Dec
MEALS: noon to 11.30 (12.30 Fri and Sat)
PRICES: £11 (£20), Set L and D £38 for two (£42). Service charge of 10% for parties
of 6 or more
CARDS: Access, Amex, Diners, Visa
SEATS: 120. Private parties: 50 main room. Vegetarian meals. Children welcome.
Wheelchair access. Music. Air-conditioned

Meson Don Felipe

map 11

53 The Cut, SE1 8LF   COOKING 1
071-928 3237   COST £22

The best tapas bars are high on atmosphere, and this red brick building
opposite the Young Vic is no exception. One regular describes the scene: 'The
doors open and in the people fall. From then on it is full. Those from outside
push to get in, and vice versa. The largest concentration of people is by the
door; if you happen to sit there you can almost get squashed. It is lively and
there are always Champagne corks popping. You feel you are eating in a
foreign country.' The atmosphere can range from 'excellent to terrifying'. It may
be chaotic and frenetic, with dim lights, dark red colour schemes and 'a layout

101

perversely designed to cause the maximum inconvenience to staff and customers', but the food is good and wholesome. The long menu is dominated by fish and vegetable dishes, including grilled sardines; squid cooked in its own ink; substantial tortilla; and mushrooms stuffed with chorizo. Skewered, marinated pork with tomato sauce and saffron rice has been an enjoyably spicy meat dish; otherwise there are meatballs, lambs' kidneys in sherry; and chicken with oil and garlic. A good way is to order a selection of tapas – from £2 to £3.75 each – and salad, skip the sweets and bypass the coffee. The list of 50 wines centres on Spain and provides excellent drinking from the major growing regions. There are half a dozen good sherries by the glass and decent half-bottles. House Ochoa: £6.25. CELLARMAN'S CHOICE: Yllera, Ribero del Duero 1983, £12.50.

CHEF: Juan Arteaga PROPRIETORS: Philip and Ana Diment
OPEN: Mon to Sat, exc Sat L
MEALS: 12 to 3, 5.30 to 11
PRICES: £12 (£18). Service 10%
CARDS: Access, Visa
SEATS: 50. Private parties: 10 main room. Vegetarian meals. Children's helpings.
Wheelchair access (also WC). Music at D

Le Mesurier

map 11

113 Old Street, EC1V 9JR   COOKING 2
071-251 8117   COST £35

Old Street is not a pretty sight, though the small terrace next to the church is some sign of what it was once like. On the ground floor, Gillian Enthoven has a tiny restaurant which she opens at lunch. In the evenings, she will cook for pre-booked parties of 15 to 24 people. The restaurant is small and spare and white, tables quite close set, old posters on the walls. The menu is not long: three choices at each course of modern cooking encompassing dishes such as wild mushrooms in a puff pastry tart; Stilton and apple soup; saddle of hare with grapes; monkfish with peppers, tomatoes and onions; a soufflé omelette of caramel and orange; and more puff pastry, this time filled with caramel pears, with a pistachio sauce. Pastry work and soufflés continue to be good, on some days heralded by the miniature pizzas and cheese pastries served as *bonnes bouches* to start. The retreat to one meal a day has turned the style closer to that of a talented private cook and has reduced the number of slip-ups that come from over-extending energies and staff. However, a meal in the summer that began with great promise went sharply downhill: a simple rabbit salad with fine-judged vinaigrette and a 'soup' of Gewürztraminer with oyster mushrooms and asparagus that was light yet sustaining in just the way required of it, went on to charred and dry noisettes of lamb, entirely bereft of juice or gravy, with passable mint béarnaise. An escalope of salmon on a bed of spinach and sorrel with a fresh tomato sauce should have been good but failed to make its mark in terms of flavour. Cheeses were of moderate condition and a dessert of a peach in nutty caramel was amateur. People speak highly of the evening dinners for parties. These can be a set menu or à la carte as at lunch. Twenty wines, mainly from Corney & Barrow, are cheap for London though the food cost is not. House wine from Lebègue is £8 and CELLARMAN'S

CHOICE: Muscadet, Clos de Beauregard 1987, £9 and Chablis, Domaine St Louis 1987, £14.

CHEF/PROPRIETOR: Gillian Enthoven
OPEN: Mon to Fri L (D by arrangement for minimum of 15)
CLOSED: 3 weeks Aug, 1 week after Christmas
MEALS: 12 to 3, 6 to 11
PRICES: £20 (£29). Service 12.5%
CARDS: Access, Amex, Visa
SEATS: 24. Private parties: 24 main room. Children's helpings. No children under 5. Wheelchair access

Mijanou ▮ map 12

143 Ebury Street, SW1W 9QN   COOKING 3
071-730 4099   COST £25–£56

Ring the bell to enter this apparently tiny restaurant. The first room might be a fortune-teller's parlour of deep colours pressing in – but light is visible across a balustrade to the kitchen where Sonia Blech rules. It is through her kingdom that you are led to outside tables when the weather is clement, or past it to take the stairs to the lower, (non-smoking) room that gives the illusion of space by means of a wall of mirrors. Sonia Blech has been mining a vein of cross-fertilisation in the kitchen for these last four or five years, blending clear clean tastes from herbs, spices and broths with earthier flavours of peasant dishes and the weight and substance of classical cooking. Hence a dish such as a cassoulet of pheasant, 'the epitome of hearty food done very well', may co-exist with a 'marmite des pêcheurs' of several sorts of fish and shellfish cooked with noodles and vegetables in a broth perfumed with lemon grass and coriander, or a first course of marinated fish with a coriander and ginger dressing, and rice spiked with horseradish just to emphasise the Japanese note. These were on the short lunch menu in the winter. Pastry is important to her cooking: billowing Pithiviers may be filled with turnip and fennel for a vegetarian dish, found on a separate vegetarian menu. Calf's offal is presented in puff pastry with a shallot and horseradish sauce; leek tart, a standby of the bourgeois repertoire, has delicate flavour, exquisite texture and the thinnest of crusts. Sweet-and-sour was noticed as a significant taste element in the last *Guide*. It may still figure, for example in a carpaccio of duck with melon and a sweet hazelnut dressing, but it does not strike so forcibly from this year's crop of reports. Fruit is not involved in as many savoury dishes. So strong is the following for this restaurant that the repertoire moves by evolution rather than revolution. No more so than among the desserts. People still speak highly of 'Arlequinade', a plate of sorbets with fruits liberally disposed about; a strong prune and armagnac fromage blanc 'ice-cream', and crêpes soufflés filled with strawberry mousse. Cheeses and petits fours are good. The major criticism has been the vegetable cookery: though showing invention, it has sometimes not been accurate in timing and execution. The wine list is a paragon of intelligent modern choices with enough to suit every pocket and an expert in Neville Blech. 'Too good to choose from,' said one who willingly surrendered the privilege to the host. House wines are Sirius 1986, from Sichel in Bordeaux at £13, a Marcilly 1985 at £16, or a Bourgogne Aligoté 1988 from Rollin at £13.50.

The evolution of Mijanou's very personal style leaves some people wondering how it will progress from here. If it remains immutable it pleases those who enjoy the comfort of the familiar. It is a dilemma with no easy resolution.

CHEF: Sonia Blech   PROPRIETORS: Neville and Sonia Blech
OPEN: Mon to Fri
MEALS: 12.30 to 2, 7.30 to 11
PRICES: Set L £16.50 (£25) to £29.50 (£40), Set D £25 (£35) to £36 (£47)
SEATS: 30. 4 tables outside. Private parties: 24 main room. Vegetarian meals. Children welcome. No smoking in one dining-room

Ming
map 14

35–36 Greek Street, W1V 5lN   COOKING 2
071-437 0292 and 734 2721   COST £16–£26

A new chef has moved in, but the inventive thrust of the menu at this Soho street corner restaurant remains. The inspiration is the cuisine of the great Ming dynasty that refined Chinese civilisation in the seventeenth century. The imperial court kitchens of Peking drew from every province and region of China, and Ming's menu follows suit. From Szechuan there is shredded beef with chilli sauce and dry-cooked beans, from Hunan comes hot and sour Dongan chicken, and from Tibet there is garlic lamb with chilli and peanuts. Jellyfish with shredded chicken, fried beef with coriander and onion pancakes, and twice-cooked Gansu duck pointed up with star anise overshadow the likes of sesame prawn toasts and sizzling beef with black-bean sauce. Seasonal menus add even more possibilities: from June to August there might be whole steamed pomfret or the king prawn speciality 'gamla daxia' – 'for prawn lovers, the head juice is the best part,' says the menu. For theatregoers' convenience, there is a pre-theatre menu from 5 to 7 pm at a moderate price and including a glass of house wine. Some have found the pale blue dining-room lacking in ambience, but service is 'disarmingly charming'. Owner Christine Yau no longer opens on Sunday because she missed a regular weekend walk. House French: £6.90.

CHEF: Hong Ching Wong   PROPRIETORS: Christine and May Yau
OPEN: Mon to Sat
MEALS: noon to 11.45
PRICES: £14 (£22), Set L and D £10 (£16) to £15 (£21). Minimum £6. Service 10%
CARDS: Access, Amex, Diners, Visa
SEATS: 80. Private parties: 56 main room; 24 private room. Vegetarian meals. Children welcome. No-smoking area. Wheelchair access. Music. Air-conditioned

Mr Kong
map 14

21 Lisle Street, WC2H 7BA   COOKING 2
071-437 7341   COST £13–£23

The queues indicate the popularity of this restaurant, double its apparent size thanks to the basement, though the claustrophobic may prefer to stay above ground. The cuisine is Cantonese, but is especially noteworthy for offering Hakka or East River cooking – an ethnic variation of Cantonese that arose after the southwards migration of northern peoples at the end of the Sung dynasty. Hakka specialities include roasted salt chicken, its flesh gently permeated with salt and ginger; fried stuffed bean curd; fried pig's intestine; and belly-pork braised with salted preserved cabbage. Other dishes have been warmly recommended, such as sesame prawn toasts, 'luscious' scallops, venison marinated in ginger, fried duck with bitter melon, crab in black-bean sauce, and special law hoh, casseroled vegetables. The service is speedy and amiable.

CHEFS: K. Kong and Y.W No   PROPRIETORS: K. Kong, Y.W. No, M. Lee and W. Lee
OPEN: all week
CLOSED: 4 days at Christmas
MEALS: noon to 1.45am
PRICES: £9 (£17), Set D £8.25 (£13) to £17 (£19). Minimum £7 after 8pm
CARDS: Access, Amex, Diners, Visa
SEATS: 150. Private parties: 80 main room, 40 private room. Vegetarian meals with prior notice. Children welcome. Wheelchair access. Air-conditioned

Miyama
map 13

38 Clarges Street, W1Y 7PJ   COOKING 1
071-499 2443   COST £17–£52

Eight set-lunch menus are the best bet for value at this calming, white-painted Japanese restaurant hung with 'disturbingly good' mirrors. Trellises separate groups of tables where diners can work their way through well-liked sashimi, teriyaki and miso soup. Service is attentive. Alternatively, watch the chef at work in the teppan-yaki bars, where seafood, meat and vegetables are grilled to order before your eyes. There is beer and saké, but green tea is served automatically at no charge.

CHEFS: F. Miyama and T. Miyama   PROPRIETORS: F. Miyama, T. Miura and Y. Ishibashi
OPEN: Mon to Sat, exc Sat L
MEALS: 12.30 to 2.30, 6.30 to 10.30
PRICES: £19 (£33), Set L £9 (£17) to £12 (£20), Set D £28 (£39) to £32 (£44). Service 15%
CARDS: Access, Amex, Diners, Visa
SEATS: 75. Private parties: 30 main room, 8 and 12 private rooms. Children's helpings (L only). Smart dress preferred. Wheelchair access (1 step; also WC). Music. Air-conditioned

Monkeys
map 12

1 Cale Street, Chelsea Green, SW3 3QT   COOKING 2
071-352 4711   COST £15–£47

Chelsea Green may not be as large as a village green in the country, but there is enough mix in the shops, from posh to serviceable, for it to feel like a neighbourhood, complete with pub and restaurant. Go up the steps to Monkeys and enter a pine-panelled space made larger and lighter by smoked-glass mirrors. It is an exceedingly pleasant place to sit and is a model of the Chelsea neighbourhood restaurant offering good mainstream Anglo-French cooking and professional service that is neither fussy nor casual. House wine: £8. More reports, please.

CHEF: Tom Benham   PROPRIETORS: Tom and Brigitte Benham
OPEN: Mon to Fri
CLOSED: 2 weeks at Easter, 3 weeks Aug
MEALS: 12.30 to 2.30, 7.30 to 11
PRICES: £30 (£39), Set L £10 (£15) to £15 (£21), Set D £17.50 (£24) to £27.50 (£35).
Minimum £16.50 at D
CARDS: Access, Visa
SEATS: 45. Private parties: 50 main room, 10 private room. Vegetarian meals with prior
notice. Children welcome. No pipes in dining-room. Air-conditioned

Mon Petit Plaisir map 11

| 33C Holland Street, W8 4LX | COOKING 2 |
| 071-937 3224 | COST £18–£30 |

Tucked down a narrow street, offering a simple French menu and a blackboard
of daily specials in an 'authentic' French setting of bistro chairs and tables and
lots of pictures, maps, objets d'art and objets trouvés on the walls. Outside is a
tiny terrace for high summer. Mon Petit Plaisir probably gives bigger pleasure
than its senior partner in Monmouth Street. It's expensive for simple food, but
cheap for the area, and it does well what it sets out to do. The repertoire takes in
snails with garlic, Pacific prawns with Ricard, rack of lamb, chicken with
ginger, entrecôte sauce Choron and simple desserts. This is not home cooking
and no long-cooked dishes are to be had but performance is consistent. Service
is cheerful. The main menu has shifted from set price only to à la carte,
although there is a set lunch and dinner as well. It now states that prices
include service. House wine: £7.20. There is French beer and a small wine list
of fair bottles.

CHEF: Pascal Onnée   PROPRIETOR: Alain Lhermitte
OPEN: Mon to Sat, exc Sat L
MEALS: 12 to 2.15, 7 to 10.30
PRICES: £19 (£25), Set L and D £12.95 (£18). Service inc
CARDS: Access, Amex, Diners, Visa
SEATS: 36. 4 tables outside. Private parties: 20 main room. Children's helpings

Mon Plaisir map 14

| 21 Monmouth Street, WC2H 9DD | COOKING 1 |
| 071-836 7243 | COST £13–£31 |

'I was last there 15 or 20 years ago. It must have changed, but it really did seem
the same. Smoked chicken salad, gratifying; delicate bream with piquant
cream sauce; excellent fresh vegetables; French apple tart, not as good as my
wife's but tasty nonetheless.' The changes, over so long a period, include
another dining-room, but the main intent remains constant: serving gutsy
French food in pleasantly French surroundings, with an emphasis on cheaper
table d'hôtes at lunch and before the theatre. Pre-theatre dinners include three
courses, wine, coffee and service and are first-rate value. The problems arise
from the press of too much custom, sometimes causing abrupt service and
approximate cooking, and too high a price-to-value ratio once you move off the
prix fixe and into the à la carte. Onion soup with a good stock flavour; rillettes

de porc with toasted brioche; roulades of smoked salmon filled with cream cheese and with a tomato sauce; fillet steaks (though the other cuts of steak, and of lamb, have sometimes been tough); and some good moist salmon have all been approved. Vegetables are often thought a less wise choice than salad, though the gratin dauphinois and the chips have pleased. Raspberry tart and marquise au chocolat are popular desserts, and cheeses are well chosen. Standards are very mixed but in the right mood, at the right time, the restaurant fills a very exact and desirable need. There is a good steady range of French wines and house French is £7.20.

CHEF: Michel Dubarbier PROPRIETOR: Alain Lhermitte
OPEN: Mon to Sat, exc Sat L
MEALS: 12 to 2.30, 6 to 11.15
PRICES: £18 (£26), Set L £12.95 (£20), Set pre-theatre D £12.95. Service 12.5%
CARDS: Access, Amex, Diners, Visa
SEATS: 95. Private parties: 26 main room, 30 private room. Children's helpings. Wheelchair access. Music

Le Muscadet

map 11

25 Paddington Street, W1M 3RF
071-935 2883

COOKING 2
COST £32

Le Muscadet is not exactly comfortable: it goes in for bistro tables and chairs, at bistro spacing, in a simple shop conversion with a bar at the back and a blackboard on the wall – and it levers people into impossible tables because they want to eat there and the staff want to oblige. So the great majority are pleased. The recitation by the proprietor of the chalked-up menu is done with gusto and will doubtless excite anticipation. Portions are large and the cooking by an English chef is acceptably French in style. Beef with shallots and red wine was cooked soft, and a giant supreme of duck was served with an old-fashioned and comforting sauce of white wine, grapes and cream. There was also cream with lots of mussels and with the kidneys with mustard: but then, this is *cuisine bourgeoise*. The cheeses are excellent, well kept, well explained and generous of portion. Coffee is strong. The wine list is summary, French, yet affordable – house Muscadet is £8.10. The staff rush about and when it gets late and it's time to go home, the music is deafening. A most enjoyable experience. Hélas, in France it would cost half as much – or be twice as good.

CHEF: Donald Smith PROPRIETOR: François Bessunnard
OPEN: Mon to Sat, exc Sat L
MEALS: 12.30 to 2.30, 7.30 to 10.45 (10 Sat)
PRICES: £19 (£27). Service 12.5%
CARDS: Access, Visa
SEATS: 35. Private parties: 40 main room. Children welcome. Smart dress preferred. Wheelchair access. Music. Air-conditioned

The 1992 Guide will be published before Christmas 1991. Reports on meals are most welcome at any time of the year, but are extremely valuable in the spring. Send them to The Good Food Guide, *FREEPOST, 2 Marylebone Road, London NW1 1YN. No stamp is needed if posted in the UK.*

Museum Street Café

map 13

47 Museum Street, WC1A 1LY
071-405 3211

COOKING 3
COST £15-£24

There are not many London folk who try the small country restaurant approach, as do Gail Koerber and Mark Nathan in their first business: little choice, no frills, no staff, low prices, full house and ... the jackpot! It is harder in London, if only because of overheads, but they are already seeking larger premises. Their first months have seen many return to eat their Anglo-American cooking and baking for its value and flavour, as well as to enjoy their quiet charm and evident enthusiasm. There is but a room with a kitchen behind, and it's a simple café by day, a restaurant by night. The daytime operation should not be disregarded. It has developed from the soup and foccaccia of early days and now may offer sandwiches on home-made bread, chargrilled chicken, burger or salmon with herbs and olive oil, tarte Tatin, Neal's Yard cheeses. In particular it gives local workers and residents a change from the snack bars endemic in the area. Dinner is a weekly menu at a fixed price with two choices in each course. There are two main cooking implements: a bread oven and a grill. Chargrilling is inescapable: salmon with ginger and black pepper; chicken, first marinated in red wine, with blanched garlic butter; halibut with lemon and caper butter. Braised or sauté foods are also offered, however: osso buco with plenty of marrow; sauté John Dory with onion compote or relish. Criticisms are that potatoes are often absent and that the overall effect can be dry, especially if the dessert chosen is a baked one. Set against these small points the value, the keenness to use the best ingredients, and the will to explore flavour in an interesting but not silly way. The bread and pizzas, predictably, are wonderful. City economics are such that the place will probably have to change. It is hoped that it will not be too radical a shift. Do not expect comfort or wine, but it is no problem to bring your own bottle. If you plan to bring children in the evening, check beforehand.

CHEFS: Gail Koerber and Mark Nathan   PROPRIETOR: Mark Nathan
OPEN: Mon to Fri
MEALS: 12.30 to 2.45, 7.30 to 9 (9.45 Fri)
PRICES: £11 (£15), Set D £17.50 (£20). Unlicensed, but bring your own: no corkage
SEATS: 22. Private parties: 22 main room. Vegetarian meals L, with prior notice D.
Children's helpings at L. Children restricted at D. No-smoking area. Music at L

Nakano

map 12

11 Beauchamp Place, SW3 1NQ
071-581 3837

COOKING 2
COST £19-£43

A new breed of Japanese restaurant is emerging in London. The genre caters deliberately for Westerners but offers dishes that go far beyond sushi and sukiyaki into traditional specialities normally reserved for the knowledgeable. This is a welcome trend. Nakano looks positively down-market, almost canteen-like, with a noisy quarry-tiled floor, bleak white walls and yellow tablecloths, yet it is in fashionable up-market Beauchamp Place. It attracts a lively cosmopolitan crowd – shirt-sleeved Japanese businessmen, Western families with children, couples and friends. The menu is impressive even by

Japanese standards: the usual set meals, grilled dishes, sashimi and tempura are supplemented by a prodigious list of 51 'side dishes' of the kind you might find in a Japanese drinking house rather than in a grand restaurant. In England most are extremely rare: salmon head grilled with salt; raw tuna with grated yam; lightly fried beef with *ponzu* vinegar; crab's gut. An inspector discovered many delights on the menu: grilled salmon skin topped with *momiji oroshi* (chilli and white radish grated together) served in an irregular porcelain dish; deep-fried soft-shelled crab claws beautifully served on a paper origami crane in a decorative wicker basket; simmered taro potatoes, 'deliciously sweet and gooey' with snow peas served in a large stemmed black porcelain dish with a lid. Another surprise was *nasu dengaku*, a rare example of Japanese home cooking in the form of half a grilled aubergine spread with salty miso sauce and sprinkled with sesame seeds. In familiar territory, there is good quality sushi and cold buckwheat noodles with a separate jug of sauce made from a chilled mixture of soy and mirin. Service could be improved, but it is worth putting up with the brusque welcome for the chance of sampling such unusual dishes. As well as tea and saké, there is a short list of mainly French wines. House Muscadet: £12.

CHEF: Mr Kikuchi   PROPRIETORS: Meadowdown Ltd
OPEN: Tue to Sun, exc Sun L
CLOSED: bank hols, 1 week at Aug bank hol, 25 Dec, 1 Jan
MEALS: 12.30 to 2.30, 6.30 to 11
PRICES: £19 (£29), Set L £10.50 (£19) to £17.50 (£27), Set D £25 (£36). Minimum £20 at D .
Service 15%
CARDS: Access, Amex, Diners, Visa
SEATS: 30. Private parties: 30 main room. Vegetarian meals. Children's helpings on request.
Music. Air-conditioned

Neal Street Restaurant
map 14

26 Neal Street, WC2 9PH
071-836 8368

COOKING 2
COST £56

The long room stretches back from the street; pass the bar into a cool though noisy space enlivened with good art, still bought with gusto by the owner, Antonio Carluccio, man of many mushroom hunts. The restaurant is ostensibly Italian and some things seem genuinely so, but it is not the place in London to research authentic Italian cookery. The speciality here is indubitably funghi; the time to visit is the autumn when you will see what England can offer to the alert of eye in the woods and vales once thought to yield up only great plate mushrooms. Wild mushroom soup; tagliolini with mushrooms; honey fungus cooked in oil; rabbit with oyster mushrooms; even a tiramisu with a soused chanterelle on the top are some of the good dishes encountered. Alternatively, the unfortunate may find this woody cornucopia ruined – improperly sauté, laden with fat, even flavourless. Other aspects of the cooking may please, for example black pasta with seafood, a scallop chowder, or a duck with mango, but then dishes will appear that too closely resemble 'restaurant' cooking: how to ruin an exercise in freshness and simplicity by cooking an *aïoli garni* with floury cream sauce and strange piped moulds of chillified aïoli. Details, too, could be better when the price is considered: oiled butter, acidulated dressing, poor sauté potatoes, overcooked vegetables. The place, especially at lunch, is fairly humming with London life and made the more pleasant by the passage of Sr Carluccio among the tables: it does have atmosphere. Top clarets at corresponding prices are possibly better passed by in favour of the fine Italians – Tignanello 1983, Barolo from Pio Cesare – or even the sprinkling of non-European bottles at reasonable prices. House Italian: £8 to £8.80.

CHEF: M. Santiago Gonzalez   PROPRIETOR: Antonio Carluccio
OPEN: Mon to Fri
CLOSED: Christmas to New Year, bank hols
MEALS: 12.30 to 2.30, 7.30 to 11
PRICES: £33 (£47). Service 15%
CARDS: Access, Amex, Visa
SEATS: 65. Private parties: 24 private room. Vegetarian meals. Children's helpings. Wheelchair access. Air-conditioned

Neshiko

map 11

265 Upper Street, N1 2UQ
071-359 9977

COOKING 2
COST £17–£74

Though most customers make for the cramped ground-floor dining-room with its sushi bar, the basement is much more spacious and, being Japanese, is not oppressively decorated. Not only is the atmosphere less formal and stuffy than many Japanese restaurants, but there is a chance to try dishes that are usually only found on the Japanese-language menus, or to be had in Japanese homes. These include *nameko oreshi*, small mushrooms with grated white radish, and *ika natto*, raw squid with fermented soya beans. The menu also offers the standard dishes and the standard arrangement of set meals, though another novelty is roast duck with plum sauce. Surprisingly, there is a charge for the usually free green tea. Objections to this may be minimised by the fact that the restaurant is not generally as expensive as many of its competitors, and that it makes a genuine and enthusiastic effort to explain Japanese cooking to Westerners. The standard of cooking is very adequate, though the sushi was not all of an equal consistency. When preparing eel on rice, the chef had commendably used fresh English eel rather than frozen Japanese, but it was not absolutely successful because the English variety is too tough and too oily. The wine list is better and cheaper than is often the case. The £70 kaiseki menu must be ordered three days in advance.

CHEF: A. Ujihara   PROPRIETORS: Kawab Ltd
OPEN: all week, exc Sat L and Sun L
CLOSED: Christmas to New Year
MEALS: 12 to 2.30, 6 to 12 (11 Sun)
PRICES: £17 (£26), Set L £8.50 (£17), Set D £10 (£18) to £50 (£62). Service 10%
CARDS: Access, Amex, Diners, Visa
SEATS: 55. Private parties: 30 main room, 25 private room. Vegetarian meals. Children welcome. Wheelchair access. Music

See the inside of the front cover for an explanation of the 1 to 5 rating system recognising cooking standards.

New World

map 14

Gerrard Place, W1V 7LL
071-734 0677 and 0396

COOKING 1
COST £7–£41

'I love dim-sum. This is the place in London for it and today it was on form. The snails in black-bean sauce were a trifle over-vinegared, but tangy chicken feet, contrasting pork with mushrooms and the depth and range of flavours generally make this a better bet than most; cheaper too.' Not everyone agrees. Some find that this vast two-storeyed emporium needs a face-lift, that the contents of the trolleys are long past their best at a late lunch, and that the food is not remarkable if you don't have dim-sum because there is too much flavour enhancer. But the trolley women are obliging to a fault and have the stamina of marathon-runners. They will prepare some things there and then – noodle soup with barbecued pork, for example, which was thought the best thing on an otherwise lacklustre day – and they will help you choose what they think best at the moment. As with so many big places like this, it is 'best if you adopt a positive attitude to each trolley that passes; in view of the modest price, you can't go far wrong.' There is a longer wine list than often encountered; house French is £6.05.

CHEFS: L. Diep, T. W. Man and R. Wong PROPRIETORS: New World Restaurant
OPEN: all week
MEALS: 11am to 11.45pm (11pm Sun)
PRICES: £13 (£20), Set L £3 (£7) to £8 (£12), Set D £6 (£10) to £30 (£34) Service inc
CARDS: Access, Amex, Diners, Visa
SEATS: 600. Private parties: 200 main room, 20, 80 and 100 private rooms. Vegetarian meals. Children welcome. Wheelchair access (also WC). Music. Air -conditioned

Nichol's

map 11

75 Fairfax Road, NW6 4NN
071-624 3880

COOKING 2
COST £24–£31

In a shopping parade on a western foothill of Swiss Cottage, Nichol's achieves a sense of space by cool decoration rather than complex geometry. David Nichol cooks in a cool manner, too. Although a gratin of aubergines may be as substantial and as simple as weekend home-cooking, his set pieces – duck with soy, ginger and honey; ox tongue with a piquant sauce; or salmon with a fennel butter sauce – will be more subtle, if not attenuated, in their flavours. Details, such as the cucumber with dill in a sharp aspic to accompany the leek and smoked haddock tartlet, can be well thought out and the dauphinois potatoes and other vegetables well judged. Desserts are adequate even if a chocolate mousse cake was undistinguished and a summer pudding in November is anticipating the Greenhouse Effect by a generation. Susan Nichol is a good hostess. Perhaps the restaurant needs the push of popularity to make the flavours and techniques stand out more assertively and to convince it to use better butter and coffee. All choices in each course are the same price on the à la carte. The wines are nicely chosen (though few halves) with some good bottles from the Southern Hemisphere (whence come the owners) including the elegant Wynn's Cabernet Sauvignon and Castle Hill Sauvignon Blanc from Te Mata Estate. Three Alsace, a Jadot Chambertin and the Rioja Contino Reserva

show a sure footing in Europe also. House wine is £8.50. CELLARMAN'S
CHOICE: Elston Chardonnay, Te Mata 1988, £18.95; Cabernet Sauvignon,
Matua Valley 1987, £16.50.

CHEF: David Nichol   PROPRIETORS: Susan and David Nichol
OPEN: all week, exc Sat L and Sun D
MEALS: 12 to 3, 7 to 10
PRICES: £19 (£26), Set L £16 (£24), Set D £19 (£26). Service 10%
CARDS: Access, Amex, Visa
SEATS: 45. 3 tables outside. Vegetarian meals. Children's helpings. Wheelchair access.
Music. Air-conditioned

Ninety Park Lane

map 13

90 Park Lane, W1A 3AA
071-409 1290

COOKING 3
COST £31–£77

Louis Outhier, the vaunted French chef with a taste for experiment and a touch
of spice, is consultant here. A protégé is chef. The restaurant is exceptionally
expensive, even with a cheaper set-price lunch, and it must be questionable
whether such consultancies result in pleasure for the consumer. The restaurant
now has a separate entrance and separate identity to the hotel itself. Entry from
the permanent traffic jam of Park Lane takes you into a low, long space, heavily
panelled and upholstered, where the loudest sound is the air-conditioning.
This results in a very cold climate and a noise similar to a jet-engine test bed.
Sofas as seats for dining were pioneered here. They are good for a loll, but
sometimes do not provide the right angle of attack for eating. One reader got
hiccups from the bodily contortions occasioned by these couches. The menu,
priced only for the person paying, begins with the 'Louis Outhier' suggestion
at £55. This should be a warning. The rest of the long *carte* describes some
interesting ideas, the best involving use of spices or oriental influences. A meal
in the summer included a Thai chicken and coconut milk soup and a tartare of
tuna for the Eastern elements, and a medley of fish with a wine and herb sauce
and 'brochettes' of scallops and turbot, where the skewers were thin spears of
asparagus, for more orthodox European wine cookery. An amuse-gueule was a
fried scallop of remarkable taste and texture on a gentle saffron sauce. The
cooking showed great technical skill, with light flavours. Thus the soup may
not have satisfied a Thai, but could please and interest a Western novice. The
medley of fish was also very even tasting; some first-rate, basil-scented noodles
as accompaniment were almost the greatest success. The tartare of tuna was
cleverly arranged and more 'natural' tasting than many which are overloaded
with cream, herbs and lemon. It borrowed from the Mediterranean for three
olive oil-based emulsions. The restaurant's invention fails when desserts are
wheeled out on the giant cakestand. These can hardly be Outhier-inspired, and
can be lacklustre in the extreme. Cheeses may not be any more exciting, with
crackers and stale walnut bread. Coffee and petits fours are acceptable. The
wine list compounds the food cost. It is long, remarkable in its way, and dear.
When a bottle is ordered, they may bring a different year to that listed, not tell
you they have, then admit to the act while stating, contrary to every printed
opinion, that the substitute is better. At such prices, this is not on. Service is
otherwise solicitous and anxious to get it right. House wines: £12.50 and

£19.50. Accommodation details are not included this year as the restaurant is now being run as a separate operation.

CHEF: Hervé Guillaume   PROPRIETORS: Trusthouse Forte Ltd
OPEN: Mon to Sat, exc Sat L
MEALS: 12 to 2.30, 7 to 10.30
PRICES: £50 (£60), Set L £25 (£31), Set D £35 (£41) to £57.50 (£64). Service inc
CARDS: Access, Amex, Carte Blanche, Diners, Visa
SEATS: 70. Private parties: 80 main room. Vegetarian meals. No children under 6. Smart dress preferred. No-smoking area. Wheelchair access (2 steps;also WC). Music. Air-conditioned

Ninjin   map 13

244 Great Portland Street, W1N 5HF   COOKING 1
071-388 4657   COST £13–£41

In a basement beneath a Japanese supermarket, this is a place for inexpensive lunches, the price depending on which main course is selected. Thus a tempura lunch will start with a selection of raw fish, then the tempura of large prawns with aubergine, green pepper and onion in the lightest batter, miso soup, rice and pickled radish, then half an orange for dessert. The à la carte menu includes pork cutlets Japanese style, cheese-filled potato croquettes, and potato salad Japanese style, spiked with onion and cucumber, as east compromises with west. Also on the menu are yakitori (a separate yakitori counter is planned), prawn dumplings, and aubergine fried, then topped with miso-paste. This fair range of dishes has none the less decreased in interest and variety since the last *Guide*. Complimentary green tea is served constantly.

CHEF: Mr Funakoshi   PROPRIETORS: Ninjin Ltd
OPEN: Mon to Sat, exc Sat D
MEALS: 12 to 2, 6 to 10
PRICES: £17 (£24), Set L £6.90 (£13) to £12 (£19), Set D £26 (£34)
CARDS: Access, Amex, Diners, Visa
SEATS: 50. Private parties: 10 main room. No children under 5. Music. Air -conditioned

▲ Nontas   map 11

16 Camden High Street, NW1 0JH   COOKING 1
071-387 4579   COST £17

Nontas and Helen Vassilakas' long-standing taverna almost qualifies as chic at this yet to be gentrified end of Camden High Street. An inspector liked the rustic white stucco and dark wood, with bar and snackery next door, and also complimented the friendly service. The *carte* does not venture beyond the expected, including meze which are still good value. Taramosalata is correctly salted (and not garishly pink), fried squid are tender though their batter is a little soft and oily, and tomato and rice soup is pleasantly simple. There are fish as well as meat kebabs, and herbs are well judged. Rice is nice, desserts pedestrian. House wine is £5.70, and there's also Ch. Carras, Greece's answer to Bordeaux.

LONDON

CHEF: Nontas Vassilakas   PROPRIETORS: Nontas and Helen Vassilakas
OPEN: Mon to Sat
MEALS: 12 to 2.45, 6 to 11.30 (snacks 8.30am to 11.30pm)
PRICES: £8 (£14). Service 10% for parties of more than 6
CARDS: Access, Amex, Diners, Visa
SEATS: 50. 10 tables outside. Private parties: 25 main room. Children welcome. Wheelchair
access. Music
ACCOMMODATION: 12 rooms, all with bath/shower. B&B £32 to £49. No children under 12.
Afternoon teas. Garden. TV. Phone. Doors close at 12.30

▲ Oak Room,
Le Meridien Piccadilly Hotel ♀   map 13

Piccadilly, W1V 0BH   COOKING 4
071-734 8000   COST £30−£65

'I had forgotten that there was such a thing as light oak; I had expected it to be
dark and sombre.' Almost without exception, the ambience and surroundings
of this enormous but spacious restaurant within the Meridien Piccadilly are
liked. One grouse is the efficiency of the air-conditioning, the other is the
pianist − victimisation, perhaps, but the sight of David Chambers doing his
chef's rounds, with much respectful inclination of heads, to bursts of *Puttin' on
the Ritz* seemed inapposite. Space, peace, good service and outstanding food
make good ingredients for any hotel, particularly when allied to lunchtime
economy. Another feature guaranteed to endear customers is the
complimentary dish brought before the meal. 'We were initially presented
with what appeared to be two cups of black coffee. As I was about to point out
the obvious error, it was announced as langoustine consommé with diced
scallops.' Another amuse-gueule at the Oak Room, an intense tomato soup
with diced truffles, shows the quality of care and willingness to spend. Menu
structure is complicated because of the need to accommodate and show off the
work of two chefs: Michel Lorain of Côtes St-Jacques at Joigny in Burgundy is
the consultant and David Chambers is the executant. Menus feature 'cuisine
traditionelle' and 'cuisine créative', the product of Lorain's fertile invention,
while David Chambers prepares a weekly and a daily menu. 'Créative' seems
to result in the mixing of meat and fish (lobster with a meat stock garlic sauce
or crayfish and foie gras with fresh noodles), the use of spices (turbot with
ginger, pigeon with couscous and spiced aubergines), of blue cheese (lamb
with creamed potatoes, flavoured with Roquefort) or producing 'old-fashioned'
meats such as rabbit. 'Traditionelle' reads somewhat more like the usual
mobilising of truffles, foie gras and caviare. A David Chambers menu conjures
up the extremely simple and fresh. Many of the dishes are merely highlighted
with herb sauces. It is not, at first sight, a daunting style of cooking. The level of
success must be measured by the recommendations received by the *Guide*, and
it is clear that many dishes command respect: oysters with a julienne of carrot
and leek and a Champagne sauce are accompanied by little croûtons topped
with caviare; game consommé is poured over strips of venison and quails'
eggs; a simple salad of red mullet, mange-tout and lemon dressing; steamed
salmon with a basil butter sauce; turbot stuffed with salmon mousse (that day's
'roast of the day') with a light saffron sauce; cassolette of scallops and

114

langoustines in a lobster sauce; squab with a truffle *jus*. Vegetables, always hot, have been better reported this year. When the final stages of the meal approach, the waiting staff takes over and trolleys begin their rounds: the cheese trolley is first rate, a wonderful selection of goats' cheese, for example, and well-informed waiters handle it. The dessert trolley has nearly all that might be desired and the quality of, for example, the chocolate bavarois with a bitter cocoa top was irreproachable. The waiters feather the sauces with furrowed brow. The long set dinner may take a very long time indeed with waits en route making the food cooler than it ought to be but generally the service is of a high standard and few instances of prevarication or superciliousness have been described. When one reader experienced a muddle over the wine order, the situation was not handled well, but the list deserves some attention as long as price is not a consideration and French wine is preferred. Except for a range of Californian, there is little from outside France. The price range is what might be expected for such a place, though it is not as expensive as some. There is adequate choice for all the French classic regions, although it requires close study to sort out the halves from the wholes and to make sure of the price to avoid spending £100 by mistake. Arrangement of the list seems to lack logic, while being detailed. House wine: £13. CELLARMAN'S CHOICE: Meursault 1986, Limozin, £41; Ch. Haut-Bages-Averous 1979, £34. In the same hotel is the Terrace Room on the top floor: a giant balcony-cum-greenhouse that accommodates a few hundred people at a time and feeds them well enough. Reports for this have been much more mixed than for the Oak Room. Although under the same direction, it has a more difficult task in pleasing so many people all the time. The menu makes a point of offering dishes with reduced fat content.

CHEF: David Chambers PROPRIETORS: Meridien Hotels
OPEN: Mon to Sat, exc Sat L
MEALS: 12 to 2.30, 7 to 10.30
PRICES: £34 (£47), Set L £21 (£30), Set D £40 (£51) to £43 (£54)
CARDS: Access, Amex, Diners, Visa
SEATS: 50. Private parties: 10 main room. Children welcome. Smart dress preferred.
No pipes in dining-room. Wheelchair access (also WC). Music. Air-conditioned
ACCOMMODATION: 284 rooms, all with bath/shower. Rooms for disabled. Lift. B&B
£201.25 to £224.25. Baby facilities. Afternoon teas. Swimming-pool. Sauna. Snooker.
Air-conditioning. TV. Phone. Confirm 24 hours ahead

Odette's ▼ map 11

130 Regent's Park Road, NW1 8XL   COOKING 2
071-586 5486   COST £37

A pretty restaurant taking in the pavement, a gilt-edged mirrored room with pictures further back, and a top-lit conservatory for the illusion of outside eating without the raindrops. Wayne Bosworth has left (see the Charnwood Hotel, Sheffield) and John McManus is in charge of a menu that reads in the same vein, if not identical recipes, as his predecessor's. Seriously modern cooking is proclaimed as soon as the bread basket arrives, full of surprising flavours like rolls with sultanas and pieces of ginger. It is further confirmed by a good jellied rabbit consommé studded with small pieces of meat. Rabbit

appears on the main *carte* with its legs stuffed with mushrooms, on a gin sauce.
Also offered have been salt cod and mussels with cumin; pigeon with green
lentils and bacon; a panaché of lamb's offal; a plate of calf's kidneys and liver
plus a béarnaise; or escalope of salmon smoked over apple and cinnamon tea,
served on chicory with a warm vinaigrette. The cooking is more assured than
hitherto so that first courses of foie gras on a warm new potato and truffle salad
(warm new potatoes is now a mark of ultra-fashionability in London) and a
terrine of crisp spring vegetables and salmon wrapped in sole fillets with a
gazpacho sauce were acceptable. The foie gras leaked its fat, and the terrine
looked good but was fairly light on flavour. Better was a Gressingham duck
with its leg stuffed with wild mushrooms and a chicken mousse. The tastes
asserted themselves to give character while the duck was appreciated for itself.
Another main course of grilled poussin on basmati rice with coriander lacked
determination on the grill, and though the rice was pleasing, lacked any relish
or sauce to make the whole cohere. Desserts such as a red fruit crème brûlée
and a not very sharp lemon tart show fair pastry work and confident flavours.
The wine list is concise, not expensive and chosen from the best, or most
modish, growers. It does not help with so short, but not meagre, a choice that
each wine of a party's selection was not the vintage advertised on the list. But
Rolly Gassman, Henry Natter, J. Guindon, Prudhon, Bernard Legland, Collard,
and Saintsbury are fine names and affordable. House wine: £7.95.

CHEF: John McManus PROPRIETOR: Simone Green
OPEN: Mon to Sat, exc Sat L
CLOSED: last 2 weeks Aug
MEALS: 12.30 to 2.30, 7.30 to 11
PRICES: £22 (£31). Service 12.5%
CARDS: Access, Amex, Diners, Visa
SEATS: 55. Private parties: 8 and 28 private rooms. Children welcome

190 Queensgate ▮   map 12

190 Queen's Gate, SW7 5EU   COOKING 3
071-581 5666   COST £21–£53

'Are you in the club?' asked the receptionist of a woman enquiring about a
table in this grand Kensington house. She referred to the club for restaurateurs
and catering professionals. Non-members are able to dine, too, but a £2.50
surcharge is made. The ground floor is a pastiche of a gentleman's club; the
restaurant in the basement is overblown Second Empire complete with
mustard marbled panelling, sculptures, modern paintings and bagnio tenting.
It is fun in the evening, less so at lunch. There are two qualities that mark out
Antony Worrall-Thompson's management. First is the excellent, non-fusty,
service that increases everyone's enjoyment. Second is the adaptable and
inventive style of his menu. It is long and takes in new-wave Italian cooking,
complete with bruschetta and virgin oils; New World cooking, the chargrill to
the fore; and the nostalgic school of *cuisine du terroir* which affects love of stews,
offal and pulses. He also piles layer upon layer. This is never light cooking.
Three of his signature dishes are: avocado guacamole with a tartare of salmon
and a hot crab pancake; sea bass with a fish mousse on a bed of sprouting
wheatgrass with globe artichokes in olive oil; two poached figs, one cooked in

raspberries and red wine, the other with honey and fennel, with a vanilla ice-cream. Even the 'executive lunch' will be 'confit of Toulouse sausages, fried apples and mashed potato'. This cooking has pleased; it may leave even the fittest gasping for breath on the pavement, but it does address the problem of flavour. Not invariably is it correct: a 'tarte Tatin' of chicory with foie gras, served with a glass of the sweet Pineau de Charentes, was expected to use the bitterness of the chicory to cut the beautifully cooked foie gras. In the event it was so caramelised with sugar that 'I could have poured cream on it and had it for pudding.' Something of the same imbalance is seen in a salmon steak au poivre on a red wine sauce. The fish had no chance. The warm rock oysters sitting on wild rice with a rich sabayon and a blade of chive across the top were much better. A main course of best end of lamb roasted and served with a potato and lentil galette on which nestled a kidney was satisfactory, save for its lack of balancing green vegetable. Such a vegetable did come with a ballotine of chicken sliced round a central langoustine set in a chicken mousse, leeks and two sauces, of saffron and caviare. Red peppers were used for floral decoration. No reader has had the stomach for figs, but the chocolate selection and a grand plate of desserts have been enjoyed; crème brûlée seems a strong point. The rule, however, is cooking with great style, matched by an excellent wine list and wine service. This is not so highly priced as many in the West End and its range is considerate of those with less than £15 to spend on wine. Halves there are and Italy, Spain and the New World are heavily represented with very fashionable growers.

CHEFS: Antony Worrall-Thompson and Sebastian Snow   PROPRIETORS: 190 Queensgate plc
OPEN: Mon to Sat, exc Sat L
CLOSED: Christmas to New Year
MEALS: 12 to 3.30, 7 to 11.30
PRICES: £20 (£28), Set L £11.50 (£21) to £22.50 (£33), Set D £32.50 (£44). Non-member charge £2.50
CARDS: Access, Amex, Diners, Visa
SEATS: 45. Private parties: 20 main room, 32 private room. Vegetarian meals on request. Children welcome. No pipes in dining-room. Music. Air-conditioned

192 ♥   map 11

192 Kensington Park Road, W11 2ES   COOKING 2
071-229 0482   COST £30

Every night of the week may now be spent propping up the bulging bar of this abidingly popular spot, though you'll have to sleep through Monday lunch if you want to spend the days there too. The place attracts friends and regulars. The menus for the two meals of the day are similar, though lunch may have slightly fewer main dishes, but prices are not high for London and there is no pressure to spend unduly. The style is resolutely modern – it almost pioneered it – Italian influenced with a Californian hot-climate emphasis on grills, tomatoes, oil and salads. Typical dishes are squid with chilli and lemon dressing; wild mushroom and chicken focaccia with baby artichokes; lamb brochette with tandoori spices and cucumber raita; a duo of fish with a tarragon butter sauce or on a baby corn salad with aïoli; veal with salsa verde and polenta; and desserts like chocolate brownies; various tarts, a mousse cake and home-made ice-creams. Coffee is good. Standards overall are steady but capable of collapse as in so many places with lots of seats and good-quality food at reasonable prices: scrambled egg was sent out on totally blackened toast; calf's liver was overcooked, untrimmed, and much too greasy; vegetables were losing their flavour. Satisfaction is normally higher than that. Service is very willing. The wines are exemplary, and not dear. The world is its oyster for five dozen choices, each one of which could be justified: look for the Leflaives, the Muscat de Beaumes de Venise, the Pokolbin and the Chileans. Many wines are available by a large as well as standard glass. House French: £7.25. CELLARMAN'S CHOICE: Ch. Thieuley 1988, £9.25; Côtes du Rhône 1985, Guigal, £11.75.

CHEF: Maddalena Bonino   PROPRIETORS: Anthony Mackintosh, Michael Chassay and John Armit
OPEN: all week, exc Mon L
MEALS: 12.30 to 3 (1 to 3.30 Sun), 5.30 to 12 (7 to 11 Sun)
PRICES: £17 (£25)
CARDS: Access, Amex, Visa
SEATS: 75. Private parties: 10 main room, 30 private room. Children's helpings.
No cigars/pipes in dining-room. Wheelchair access. Music. Air-conditioned

---

Orso ♥   map 14

| 27 Wellington Street, WC2E 7DA | COOKING 2 |
| 071-240 5269 | COST £35 |

A large basement restaurant reached from an undistinguished entrance just south of Covent Garden. Its location and opening times make it very useful for fitting round a visit to opera or theatre. However, if you want to dine leisurely and book a table at 8.30, you are likely to be told that it will be needed again at 10.30. Although the decoration has been likened to a 'large overheated public lavatory' – coincidentally the red wine, stored just off the main room, appeared to have suffered from this constant 'supra-chambré' temperature – it is the bustling resort of many smart people from the district. It offers a fast-changing menu of colourful and varied Italian food: antipasti of lots of vegetables and amusing leaves; thin-crusted pizzas; half a dozen pasta dishes more interesting than anything served 20 years ago when carbonara was pretty daring; eight or nine main dishes including a couple of fish (bass, swordfish, monkfish or mullet more than flat fish), a couple of calf's offal such as liver with thyme and balsamic vinegar or kidneys with wild mushrooms; some excellent vegetables; and a few desserts and cheese dishes. Orso was a pioneer in popularising this vibrant and expressive cookery punctuated by strong flavours, quite different from those favoured by the cold north. The menu still holds out the promise of warmth and delectation though the execution has been open to much more criticism since the last *Guide*. This is not just the consequence of popularity – to which may be ascribed many of the brushes with the waiting staff over the same period – but a reflection of bland uniformity in elements such as bresaola, the tomato sauce with crespelle or rigatoni that were not 'superlativi' to the customer who felt they had been kept hot for too long. Cooking and buying, too, can be inaccurate: underseasoned veal escalopes with too-dominant sage; Dover sole that tasted past its prime; spinach and ricotta ravioli tough and inedible. Coffee and bread are good. The wine list is a roll call of the best modern Italian names, Lungarotti, Mastroberardino, Jermann, Capezanna, Gasparini. Commendably, older wines, Rubesco 1979, Barbaresco 1982, at affordable prices are scattered through the list. House wine is £8 a litre.

CHEF: Martin Wilson   PROPRIETORS: Orso Restaurants Ltd
OPEN: all week
CLOSED: 25 and 26 Dec
MEALS: noon to midnight
PRICES: £19 (£29)
SEATS: 110. Vegetarian meals. Children welcome

Pagu Dinai
map 10

690 Fulham Road, SW6 5SA   COOKING 1
071-736 1195   COST £19–£30

Plain white brickwork and a splendid open coal fire make the unpretentious setting for unpretentious Italian cooking with a tilt towards Sardinia. Soupy fish stew, Sardinian-style unleavened bread, sea bream with capers or lamb with garlic and capers have survived a change of ownership (the chef remains), though more general Italian dishes have been introduced. Although readers speak well of the attention and cheerfulness of the staff, they also note that the cooking may lack generosity: that tomato and basil sauce with gnocchi was good but insufficient for the bulky and chewy semolina or that a crust of almond and garlic on lemon sole was meagre and tasted of little. There are two dozen Italian wines, about half of them Sardinian, and a few of them good names from the mainland; but they are given rudimentary descriptions on the list. Such a range will be hard to come by elsewhere, and prices are fair. One glass of wine is included in the set lunch.

CHEF: Giovanni Branco   PROPRIETORS: Franco Santoro and Lello Demartino
OPEN: all week
CLOSED: 25 and 26 Dec, Easter Sun and Mon, Aug bank hol
MEALS: 12 to 2.45, 7 to 11.45
PRICES: £15 (£25), Set L £11 (£19) to £15 (£23). Cover £1
CARDS: Access, Amex, Diners, Visa
SEATS: 60. Private parties: 30 main room, 20 private room. Vegetarian meals. Children welcome. Smart dress preferred. Wheelchair access (1 step)

Il Passetto
map 13

230 Shaftesbury Avenue, WC2H 8EG   COOKING 1
071-836 9391 and 379 7962   COST £30

Jesus Sanchez' old-school 'ristorante' has see-sawed in and out of the *Guide* for the last decade, but remains a fixture of the West End scene at the New Oxford Street end of Shaftesbury Avenue. The long narrow room is cramped, noisy and frenetic: it's rather like a rush-hour train carriage as trolleys of fresh fish, antipasti and sweets are trundled along the corridor between the tables. Some readers are addicted to the place; others find it erratic, uncomfortable, even dull. The cooking is certainly closer to all-purpose, hybrid Continental than authentic Italian, but there's no arguing with the freshness of the ingredients or the quality of most of the home-made dishes. Ravioli with spinach and ricotta is spot-on and pointed up with sage leaves; calf's liver is timed to perfection; and breast of chicken stuffed with garlic and butter 'shows up the processed version, with juicy flesh that picks up the garlic flavour'. Order the excellent mushrooms sauté in garlic and white wine if they are on offer. Vegetables are simple and flavoursome, which is more than can be said for some of the sweets. Ebullient waiters play their part with lots of flamboyant 'buona seras' and 'grazies'. The wine list is adequate and mostly Italian. House wine: £6.95.

CHEF: Jesus Sanchez PROPRIETORS: Domenico Forcina and Jesus Sanchez
OPEN: Mon to Sat, exc Sat L
CLOSED: bank hols
MEALS: 12 to 3, 6 to 11.30
PRICES: £17 (£25). Cover £1. Service 10%
CARDS: Access, Amex, Diners, Visa
SEATS: 46. Private parties: 55 main room. Vegetarian meals. Children welcome. Wheelchair access. Music. Air-conditioned

Pizzeria Castello

map 11

20 Walworth Road, SE1 6SP
071-703 2556

COOKING 1
COST £13

The setting is hardly an estate agent's – or anyone else's – dream: an unpromising building opposite the shopping centre on the Newington Butts roundabout. And yet, Pizzeria Castello has acquired an enviable reputation. Like the Pollo in Old Compton Street, it has been 'discovered' and has moved into popular mythology, although sceptics are still bemused by the fact that it is often cited as serving among the best pizzas in town. But there is no arguing with the popular vote, or with the entrenched queues – even at 6.30 on a Thursday evening. A regular fan sums up its attractions: 'Highly recommended, just for being fed when you are hungry. House wine, a pizza, a fiver a head.' The pizzas are freshly cooked in a big oven by the entrance and dauntingly piled with all kinds of toppings. They steal the show, but the back-up is impressive: gargantuan antipasti, ample pasta dishes, garlic bread and sweets from the trolley have all been mentioned. Service is fast but indifferent. House wine: £4.90.

CHEF: Cicero Calogero PROPRIETORS: Renzo Meda and Antonio Proietti
OPEN: Mon to Sat, exc Sat L
MEALS: noon (5 Sat) to 11
PRICES: £7 (£11)
CARDS: Access, Visa
SEATS: 180. Private parties: 30 main room. Vegetarian meals. Children's helpings on request. Wheelchair access (also WC). Music. Air-conditioned

The Guide is totally independent, accepts no free hospitality, and survives on the number of copies sold each year.

Pizzeria Condotti
map 13

4 Mill Street, W1R 9TE
071-499 1308

COOKING 1
COST £18

A debonair aristocrat that is linked to the Pizza Express chain. It makes most other pizzerias look as flat and limp as their pre-cooked creations. Original works by Allen Jones, Paolozzi, Joe Tilson, Apicella and yet others line the walls. The pizza bases are light and crisp and their standard is consistent. Salads such as tuna and bean show similar care, and service is friendly and usually brisk. Drink Nastro Azzurro Italian beer, or the good house Chianti at £6.75.

CHEFS: Mahmoud Eskendry and Nacevr Hammami   PROPRIETORS: Enzo Apicella and Peter Boizot
OPEN: Mon to Sat
MEALS: 11.30am to midnight
PRICES: £9 (£15). Service 12.5% for parties of 6 or more
CARDS: Access, Amex, Diners, Visa
SEATS: 130. Private parties: 70 main room, 50 private room. Vegetarian meals. Wheelchair access (2 steps). Air-conditioned

Pollyanna's ▮
map 10

2 Battersea Rise, SW11 1ED
071-228 0316

COOKING 2
COST £23–£38

The first house on Battersea Rise after Clapham Common, it looks more like a fashionable art gallery than a restaurant. The dining-room is on the mezzanine level, hidden from pavement inspection by a modern art screen and reached by a short flight of steps from the front door. Inside, the long space is broken up by pools of light, broad blocks of light and shade created by clever paintwork. This feeling of ultimate trendiness very assuredly handled is carried through to the menus and food. It is humanised by the relaxed yet effective service from Norman Price and his staff. Richard Aldridge's food has more than a whiff of the nouvelle cuisine of an earlier tide of taste and arrangement on the plate confirms this. A seasonal *carte* is reinforced by a short list of daily specials and on Sundays there is a less expensive menu including at least three roasts and more traditional cooking. While the intentions are excellent, the execution has sometimes missed the marks of accurate cooking, proper sauce construction and correct tasting. One reader suggested the menu may be too long. Meals have included smoked haddock soup; a round snuff-box of filo filled with scallops and a curry cream sauce; a salad of smoked duck with a strawberry vinaigrette; artichoke hearts with wild mushrooms in a pastry wrapping with a tomato beurre blanc; brill on a sardine mousse with two sauces, one of green and one of red peppers; red mullet with a scallop mousse and saffron sauce; and a fricassee of lamb fillets and kidneys on a mustard sauce. Desserts include that stalwart of English country restaurants, banoffi pie, as well as bread-and-butter pudding or an apple tart cooked to order. The wines to go with this may sometimes cry out for simpler fare, without strident tastes or seasoning, for the choices are impressive in every way. Nothing beyond France is included, but age as well as breeding is given its chance particularly in clarets and white burgundies; the notes are helpful and Norman Price knows what he sells.

There are properties not given such an outing elsewhere in England: Ch. Trimoulet, St Emilion in six vintages, Dom. de Chevalier in four, Rullys and Mercureys from Jacqueson and Protheau, as well as some interesting petits châteaux. House wine from £9.50. CELLARMAN'S CHOICE: St Aubin, le Charmois 1988, Leflaive, £24.50; Cornas 1980, Jaboulet, £22.50.

CHEF: Richard Aldridge   PROPRIETOR: Norman Price
OPEN: Mon to Sat, D only and Sun L
CLOSED: 4 days at Christmas
MEALS: 1 to 3, 7 to 12
PRICES: £21 (£32), Set Sun L £14.95 (£23). Service 10%
CARD: Access, Visa
SEATS: 35. Private parties: 20 main room, 35 private room. Vegetarian meals. Children's helpings. Music. Air-conditioned

Poons   map 14

4 Leicester Street, WC2H 7BL   COOKING 2
071-437 1528   COST £10–£21

Soho Chinatown is a major tourist attraction and the name of Poons is well known to visitors. Wind-dried foods are the speciality and the restaurant window is hung with flattened ducks that look like edible frisbees, two kinds of sausage, black belly bacon and various types of offal. The long menu of around two hundred dishes is dominated by hard-core Cantonese specialities: one-plate rice, noodle and soup dishes, roast and barbecued meats, and authentic hot-pots such as braised lamb with bean stick, eel with crispy pork, and duck's feet with abalone. Fish is a strong point. Readers have liked the wan-tun soup; steamed pork with shrimp paste; and 'superb quality' fried sliced duck with ginger and pineapple. The dining-room is usually crowded and turnover is fast, but service is neither as frenetic or brusque as might be expected. It is good value, and amongst the cheapest venues in Chinatown. Tea is free. House French: £5.70.

CHEF/PROPRIETOR: W. N. Poon
OPEN: Mon to Sat
CLOSED: 25 Dec
MEALS: noon to 11.30
PRICES: £9 (£18), Set L £5.50 (£10) to £6.50 (£11), Set D £6.50 (£11) to £11 (£16)
SEATS: 100. Private parties: 30 main room. Children welcome. Air-conditioned

Poons at Whiteleys   map 11

Queensway, W2 4YN   COOKING 1
071-792 2884   COST £19–£31

There are essentially two ways to approach dinner here: instantly forget that you have ascended escalators in the atrium of a shopping centre, turn your back to the glass doors fronting the 'food boulevard' and gaze at the room and the view out of the windows. Or sit anywhere and glory that you are in Britain's classiest new-age shopping entrepôt. The restaurant, with a name familiar from Soho and Covent Garden, is faintly glitzy: brass, chrome, mirrors and plants. Service is unsmiling though professional. The menu is solid 'British

Cantonese' but there are a few Szechuan and even satay diversions. Whatever you choose, portions are generous. Among the starters, hap yak soon requires some dexterity: iceberg lettuce leaves will have to be wrapped around a mixture of minced wind-dried bacon, bamboo shoots and mushrooms. Crab-meat and crisp soup is much easier to eat and is made with good stock. Fried oysters with spring onions arrives with unadvertised ginger but the oysters are plump and fresh. Cantonese roast duck in prepared soy sauce is 'tender not fatty and replete with flavour'. Braised aubergines in hot chilli sauce were 'not hot in the spicy sense but had good texture' and smoked fish Cantonese style is reported as restrained and delicate. This seems to be a place where quality raw materials are cooked with minimum fuss. The set-price dim-sum offering of five mixed items is available from noon to 5 for £5.65 per head and is good value indeed. The wine list is expensive with a fair Californian and Australian bias. Beers come from China, Czechoslovakia and most everywhere else. The best is Australian Coopers. House wine: £8 and £9.

CHEF: Mr Wong   PROPRIETOR: Peter Poon
OPEN: all week
CLOSED: 25 Dec
MEALS: noon to midnight
PRICES: £16 (£26), Set D £12 (£19)
SEATS: 100. Private parties: 100 main room. Children welcome. No smoking in dining-room. Music. Air-conditioned

Quality Chop House

map 11

94 Farringdon Road, EC1R 3EA
071-837 5093

COOKING 2
COST £28

'Progressive Working Class Caterer' is on the masthead of the menu, as well as etched on the window glass of this revived café at Mount Pleasant. Post Office sorting workers can still get a 'Noted Cup of Tea' (another message on the window) during the breakfast hours from 7 to 9.30am, when they might be joined by journalists and sub-editors from newspaper offices nearby. As the day progresses, the clientele changes, for this is no ordinary café. However, it is close enough to the real thing for one reader to recognise his own grandmother's café from the days when raisins had to be stoned for the spotted dick and dinners cost sixpence. At the back is a vertiginous staircase, now a dumping ground for odd bottles and staff supplies, that shoots up to what had once been the living quarters. The Chop House itself is all stained pine and cream Lincrusta, contrasting strongly with the stainless steel kitchen at the end of the central aisle dividing the rows of booths formed by benches for seating. These are famously uncomfortable. Each table is for six (or four if you book), so people are expected to share. At the ends of the tables, wall brackets support a sacred group of ketchup and malt vinegar bottles, but no salt (and it is not needed, says a reader). The nostalgia is arch but carried through to the cooking and the pricing, respectively less modern and more reasonable than may be anticipated. If you are expecting the Caprice further east because Charles Fontaine was chef there, you would be only partially satisfied. Asparagus hollandaise, celeriac rémoulade, scrambled eggs with mushrooms, Caesar salad, eggs Benedict, corn beef hash, sausage (veal) and mash, black pudding and apple compote, salmon fishcake, calf's liver and ribeye steak are the staples of a menu that incorporates daily changes. These may alter the detail but never the drift of the kitchen. The grill and the fryer are much in evidence: even the mushrooms were deep-fried for the accurately scrambled eggs of one reader. The fish, the calf's liver, the spring chicken and the steaks see the grill; many dishes come with good chips; the mash with the sausages is also recommended. Materials are decent and tastes simple, but may be delivered in giant quantity: the steak hanging over the edge of the plate, the liver invisible beneath a mountain of chips. The staff is a model of relaxed amiability and good at handling the varied bunch that come through the door. Coffee is strong; desserts are less impressive; no credit cards. There are good beers and half a dozen wines, all decent, none dear.

CHEF/PROPRIETOR: Charles Fontaine
OPEN: all week, exc Sat L
MEALS: 12 to 3, 6.30 to 11.30
PRICES: £15 (£23)
SEATS: 48. Children's helpings. Wheelchair access

Ragam

map 13

57 Cleveland Street, W1P 5PQ   COOKING 1
071-636 9098   COST £14

Unusual food from the Kerala coast of Southern India is available only a short walk from the Goodge Street tube station. Some dishes are sweet, like kalan, a curry with yoghurt, mango and coconut. Others are delicately spiced: sambhar, curry of lentils, vegetables and tamarind juice. Many are pancake-shaped: masala dosai, stuffed with potatoes and fried onions; uthappam, laden with onions, green chillies and tomatoes. This last one is hot, so ask for the coconut chutney. Both the staff and the menu are helpful and there is plenty for vegetarians. No frills decor and very good value. House wine is Italian at £5.

CHEFS: J. Dharmaseelan and Mojid Ullah   PROPRIETORS: J. Dharmaseelan, T. Haridas and S. Pillai
OPEN: all week
MEALS: 12 to 3, 6 to 11.30
PRICES: £7 (£12), Minimum £4. Service 10%. Licensed, also bring your own: corkage £1.50
CARDS: Access, Amex, Diners, Visa
SEATS: 34. Private parties: 34 main room, 25 private room. Vegetarian meals. Children's helpings. Wheelchair access (also WC). Music. Air-conditioned

Rani

map 10

7 Long Lane, N3 2PR
081-349 4386 and 2636   COOKING 2
off Ballards Lane   COST £13–£28

Red is the colour of this family-owned Indian vegetarian restaurant. It runs through the modern bright lit frontage, the venetian blinds, the carpeting and the paintwork. The dining-room has tripled in size and the furniture is Habitat style. This is one of the most authentic restaurants of its kind in the capital, thanks largely to the fact that the owner's wife and mother do most of the cooking. The details are worth a mention of their own: five home-made chutneys and pickles (including green chilli, date and coconut); excellent breads, notably bhatoora and thapla flavoured with fenugreek, and an enterprising range of vegetable dishes, ranging from black-eyed bean curry to extraordinary sounding banana methi. These are backed up by masala dosa, papi chat, bhel pooris, and bhajias. Each day there are specials: on Friday, for example you will find deep-fried kachori and tindora curry (baby cucumbers with potatoes in a yoghurt-based sauce). To finish there are home-made sweets such as rich shrikhand, plain or with fresh fruit, ras malai and carrot halva, as well as Loseley ice-creams. Flavours are fresh and distinctive with no hint of commercial boosters, service is of a high order, and the value for money is still excellent, although prices have crept up slightly. The restaurant has a strict code: 'No service charge and gratuities accepted. Any change left behind will be donated to charities.' To date more than £4,500 has been passed on. 'The scheme has restored dignity to my profession,' says Jyotindra Pattni. Excellent lassi and Indian lager to drink.

CHEFS: Kundan Pattni and Sheila Pattni   PROPRIETOR: Jyotindra Pattni
OPEN: Tue to Sun, exc Tue L and Sat L
CLOSED: 25 Dec
MEALS: 12.30 to 2, 6 to 10.30
PRICES: £15 (£21), Set L £7 (£13) to £17 (£23), Set D £12 (£18) to £17 (£23). Minimum £7 weekdays, £10 Sat
CARDS: Access, Visa
SEATS: 90. Vegetarian meals. Children's helpings. No children under 6. No-smoking area. Music

Rebato's
map 10

169 South Lambeth Road, SW8 1XW   COOKING 1
071-735 6388   COST £19

Behind a modest shop front is London's best-loved Spanish eating place. Sit in the front bar area with a glass of wine and a selection of tapas – grilled sardines, Spanish tripe, anchovies in vinegar, tortilla – or make your way to the main restaurant at the back. The dining-room is all colour and light, with blue and yellow tiles on the floor and cleverly placed mirrors and skylights. There are flowers everywhere. The atmosphere is frenetic as Spanish locals swap stories with holidaymakers, media types and office workers. Many seem to smoke and take photos. It is invariably loud, the noise often drowning out the musicians who struggle on bravely in one corner of the room. There are no pretensions about this place, no precious garnishes gilding the atmosphere or the food. The kitchen delivers good, honest stuff and plenty of it. Grills and fish dishes are the highlights – regulars have praised the grilled sole, lamb cutlets with garlic mayonnaise and specials such as skate and black butter. Before these hefty main courses, there is excellent fish soup, a thick brew richly flavoured with stock and shells, soft roe on toast, and calamares Romana. By-pass the sweet trolley and the cheese. There are very reasonably priced Riojas and other well chosen, mostly Spanish wines, but most drink the range of house Torres (£5.95). Empty bottles are waved in the air, refills arrive, all is well.

CHEF: Edwardo Carvalho   PROPRIETORS: Tino and Shelia Rebato
OPEN: Mon to Sat, exc Sat L
MEALS: 12 to 2.30, 7 to 11
PRICES: Tapas from £1.90 (£5), Set L and D £10.75 (£16)
CARDS: Access, Amex, Diners, Visa
SEATS: 60. Private parties: 70 main room. Children welcome. Wheelchair access. Music.
Air-conditioned

River Café ▼   map 10

Thames Wharf, Rainville Road, W6 9HA   COOKING 3
071-385 3344(am), 381 8824(pm)   COST £40

'Isn't this how eating places should be? A simple but welcoming atmosphere,
nice staff and caring service and a good standard of straightforward cuisine.
Langoustine with penne in a spicy sauce, excellent grilled sardines with chips
and a green salad, followed by a chocolate cake and a lemon and almond tart,
all was acceptably pleasing.' Thus reported one who was able to take this café
as he found it. Others, who have to book four weeks in advance because its
'straightforward cuisine' is both popular and fashionable, may set their sights
and expectations higher, and thus subvert the original intentions of the hard-
working founders, to a degree at least. The café is on the ground floor of
warehouses converted to studios by the architect Richard Rogers. Its view
across the open Thames to Harrods' repository, good at any time of the year, is
best appreciated when weather permits use of tables on the terrace. Finding it
is not easy as it is tucked behind an impenetrable barrier of one-way streets
between Fulham Palace Road and the river, sometimes defeating even taxi
drivers. The cooking has continued to delight Londoners; competition and
imitation has not yet matched its standards. It leans heavily on north Italian
cooking both for materials and methods, and it follows the American example
of converting this into an acceptable form for restaurants. Much of the meat and
fish is chargrilled, as are the peppers and aubergines. Flavours are simple and
direct, in that ingredients such as olive oil or sun-dried tomatoes are the sauces
or accompaniments, and are not integrated into some confection as they would
be in classical cooking. This may make for a fairly gaunt style. It is filled out in
some dishes of rustic origin, soups, stews and roasts that are perhaps the most
individual contribution of the River Café to London's eating out: a mixture of
chicory, pancetta, Parmesan and parsley baked in the oven, 'the bitterness of
one, rich savouriness of the ham, sharp stickiness of the cheese and the relief of
the parsley all did their bit'; bollito misto with salsa verde; or quail roasted
with wild mushrooms after marinating in grappa and thyme, served with
polenta. Desserts do not continue the uniformly Italian theme, but they are
satisfactory: the previously mentioned chocolate cake and lemon tart being
regularly on the card. Coffee is powerful. One party found it unnerving to be
moved out at 11.08pm, their meal having got off to a late start, and the café can
suffer from the consequences of popularity: too much noise, too many people,
cool food, and occasional upsets. But the sheer number must be some measure
of success in deploying the kitchen's chosen flavours, colours and ingredients.
The wine list has a few French half-bottles, but all the wholes are Italian and
finely chosen indeed. Italian wine shipping to London has taken a great turn

for the better in the last four years and this range of good and fashionable makers reflects the improvement. It makes a change to see a list of reds that does not mention Antinori once, good though he may be.

CHEFS: Rose Gray and Ruthie Rogers   PROPRIETORS: Richard and Ruthie Rogers and Rose Gray
OPEN: all week, exc Mon L, Sat D and Sun D
CLOSED: 1 week at Easter, 1 week at Christmas
MEALS: 12.30 to 3.30, 7.30 to 9.30
PRICES: £25 (£33)
CARDS: Access, Visa
SEATS: 60. 8 tables outside. Private parties: 60 main room. Vegetarian meals. Children's helpings (L only). Wheelchair access (also WC). Air-conditioned

Rotisserie
map 10

56 Uxbridge Road, W12 8LP
081-743 3028

COOKING 1
COST £15–£28

The bridge masquerading as a train at the east end of Shepherd's Bush is the marker for this effective concept restaurant that stretches long and narrow from its unremarkable front. The grill is in full view and contributes its aroma to the anticipation. The menu barely changes, the theme is set firm, and even the appendages such as warm chicken liver salad, Merguez lamb sausages (spicy), asparagus, gravlax or ravioli of spinach with cream and Parmesan continue their reliable way. Grills are straightforward: beef, trout, veal, and liver. Salmon, chicken, duck, lamb or rib of beef is cooked on the spit roast. Chips, dauphinois potatoes or salads can be had. Puddings are simple, coffee is espresso. Service is usually cheerful and fast. The wine list is just what is needed: short, catholic and cheap. It's a concept that works.

CHEF: Emanuel Schandorf   PROPRIETOR: Karen Doherty
OPEN: Mon to Sat, exc Sat L
MEALS: 12 to 3, 6.30 (7 Sat) to 11 (11.30 Fri and Sat)
PRICES: £12 (£19), Set L £10 (£15) to £15 (£20), Set D £14 (£19) to £18 (£23). Cover 50p. Minimum £6 at L. Service 10% for parties of 6 or more
CARDS: Access, Visa
SEATS: 76. Vegetarian meals. Children welcome. Wheelchair access. Music

Royal China
map 10

3 Chelverton Road, SW15 1RN
081-788 0907

COOKING 2
COST £28–£41

The first impact is stunning: black enamelled walls are decorated with waves and birds, Perspex-edged pillars support art deco wall-lights, the black ceiling is divided into squares by gold coloured lines. 'It is like diving into a massive enamelled oriental cabinet.' This restaurant has the buzz of success; it is also a bolt-hole for off-duty restaurateurs who come for the style of the place and its original, complex menu. House specialities have impressed: 'golden scallops' are sandwiched between slices of cucumber and deep fried; little Peking-style dumplings are served in chilli oil, and 'frilly' squid balls are deep fried. Other highlights for an inspection meal have included double-cooked Szechuan pork; stir-fried 'embroidery chicken' in an edible basket; 'simple but perfect' slices of courgettes, cooked almost like Japanese tempura. Lobster is cooked six different ways, and the Peking duck does justice to the genre. Service is smooth and skilful. The wine list offers good value and is notable for its clarets and wayward descriptions. There is also something called Captain Morgon – 'presumably a rather rum Beaujolais'. House French: £7.50.

CHEFS: C.Y. Man and K.K. Chan   PROPRIETORS: Alan Poon, K.K. Poon, C.Y. Man and M. Man
OPEN: all week
CLOSED: 25 and 26 Dec
MEALS: 12 to 2.30, 6.30 to 11
PRICES: £18 (£30), Set D £20 (£28) to £26 (£34)
CARDS: Access, Amex, Diners, Visa
SEATS: 70. Private parties: 70 main room. Children welcome. Smart dress preferred. Wheelchair access. Music. Air-conditioned

RSJ ♥

map 11

13A Coin Street, SE1 8YQ
071-928 4554 and 9768

COOKING 2
COST £19–£32

One of the few restaurants to take its name from construction material: RSJ is hard-hat argot for 'rolled steel joist'. Diners can inspect the RSJ of their choice by gazing towards the restaurant ceiling. This sort of let-it-all-hang-out interior decoration, as well as the fashion of referring to things by their initials, was popular when the first place setting was laid 10 years ago. On the bill is the proclamation, 'the restaurant on the South Bank'. Back in 1980 it seemed to be the *only* restaurant on the South Bank. It is still popular with the London Weekend Television folk in the neighbourhood. There is nothing historic about the food, although prices are old-fashioned. The choice is threefold: a good-value, set-price two-course menu, an even better-value set-price three-course menu, or the *carte*. One report has noted that 'menu descriptions are a little over the top'. It is more that they are just overlong: langoustine and écrevisse tart is 'a short paste tart, filled with spinach and sorrel, topped with hot langoustine and crayfish and served with a shellfish sauce and glazed'. Sometimes the menu writers forget to talk to the kitchen, as one diner discovered when she ordered a dish that promised asparagus but turned up wild mushrooms. Service is relaxed. A veritable catalogue of wines from the Loire includes elderly but far from fading sweet whites. At such modest prices, how can they be resisted? And the reds of Bourgueil, Chinou and Anjou even include mature wines. Sidelines though other regions may be, quality is maintained with excellent properties throughout. Even if left staggering himself, one reader judged RSJ as 'always good fun'. House wine from Anjou is £8.75.
CELLARMAN'S CHOICE: St Nicholas-de-Bourgueil, Cuvée Prestige 1986, £13.75; Bourgueil, Vieilles Vignes, Pierre Breton, £13.95.

Consumers' Association is planning to publish Out to Eat, *a new guide to budget eating out in restaurants, pubs, cafés, brasseries and so on. Please send reports and recommendations to Out to Eat, FREEPOST, 2 Marylebone Road, London NW1 1YN.*

CHEF: Ian Stabler PROPRIETOR: Nigel Wilkinson
OPEN: Mon to Sat, exc Sat L
CLOSED: 3 days at Christmas
MEALS: 12 to 2, 6 to 11
PRICES: £19 (£27), Set L £13.25 (£19) to £14.75 (£21), Set D for 2 £29.50 (£37) to £32.50
(£41). Service 10%
CARDS: Access, Amex, Visa
SEATS: 60. Private parties: 40 main room, 20 private room. Children's helpings on request.
Music. Air-conditioned

Rue St Jacques   map 13

5 Charlotte Street, W1P 1HD   COOKING 3
071-637 0222   COST £32–£56

Gunther Schlender's cooking is always fashionable, often rich, often clever,
sometimes mistaken. Similarly, the restaurant itself is resolutely fashionable
and rich in its strong, enclosing colours, cleverly modulated by the use of
smooth grey in the bar and passage zone, and sometimes mistaken in its
avaricious pricing. There are two set-price long menus, one for the daytime,
one for the night, with a wide choice of dishes. Lunches are consciously lighter:
an escalope of salmon in a vegetable vinaigrette as opposed to a roll of fresh
and smoked salmon on a bed of lentils with a smoked salmon sauce in the
evening. The cooking is luxurious and cosseting, rather like the service. Sauces
are described as 'bright yellow and shiny, looking like the essence of butter
and egg yolk plus, in this case, herbs'. This was an accompaniment to a timbale
of fish with garlic snails; the fish mousse was light and true flavoured, even if
the diners were unsure about the snails: 'I was sure they were mushrooms, my
hostess (who was French) that they were English snails.' The next course in
this meal had the same golden-hued sauce: a panaché of fish laid out like fabric
samples: two white, a pink salmon, a darker red mullet, and a scallop in the
centre on top of emerald green spinach, 'good enough to overcome my
prejudice'. The impact was spoiled by the vegetables, inapposite for the food, 'a
wet scoop of swede purée, a cauliflower floret with cream sauce, potatoes dyed
bright yellow on the outside, and a mange-tout or three'. Gunther Schlender
has confirmed his drift away from the outré combinations of earlier years and
his cuisine is very much in the neo-classical mode, evinced in dishes like lamb
with diced vegetables and a tomato sauce; venison with green peppercorns and
mushrooms and more vegetables; veal with morels and cream; or turbot with a
'spaghetti' of vegetables and a butter sauce. The hallmark is those sauces, and
whether called 'light' or no, they have an emollient richness that stops people
in their tracks. If cheese and coffee is taken with the set menu, the price nudges
£50 when the 15 per cent service is added. The cooking has to be very exact to
justify this, yet reports imply that it is not always so. The wine list is shorter
this year. Neither Alsace, Loire nor white burgundy stocks are as interesting as
they were and depletion has had its effect elsewhere. Prices can be very
punishing, and the range of cheaper bottles has diminished. Even though some
old clarets (a strength) have come down in price, can this justify charging £45
(plus 15 per cent service) for a Coulée de Serrant 1986 from Savennières? At the
time of writing it was available from Yapp Brothers for no more than £14 a

bottle. House wines: £10 and £11. CELLARMAN'S CHOICE: Champagne NV, Pommery, £25; Chablis 1987, Regnard, £16.50.

CHEF: Gunther Schlender   PROPRIETORS: Jessop and Boyce Restaurants Ltd and
Gunther Schlender
OPEN: Mon to Sat, exc Sat L
CLOSED: Christmas, Easter, bank hols
MEALS: 12.30 to 2.30, 7.30 to 11
PRICES: Set L £23 (£32), Set D £33 (£47). Service 15%
CARDS: Access, Amex, Diners, Visa
SEATS: 70. Private parties: 30 main room, 12, 14 and 24 private rooms. Children's helpings.
No pipes in dining-room. Wheelchair access (1 step). Music. Air-conditioned

Sabras   map 10

| 263 Willesden High Road, NW10 2RX | COOKING 1 |
| 081-459 0340 | COST £10−£24 |

Over the years Sabras has developed from a neighbourhood café into a well-respected vegetarian restaurant. The decor is modern and the tables are closely packed. The extended menu still deals in authentic Gujerati and South Indian cooking, with fresh flavours, vivid spicing and consistency right across the range. Fried bateta vadas, patras and steam-cooked khamans (square pieces of spongy, savoury cake made from grain flour, lentils and yoghurt) are well-reported Gujerati snacks. From Bombay's Chowpatty Beach come puris, and the South is represented by a range of dosas (stuffed ground rice pancakes which are brightened up with a spicy sambhar and coconut chutney). The Hyderabad version is spiced with black pepper and cumin and stuffed with potatoes, onions, cashews and coconut. Vegetable dishes include rarities such as ravaiga, baby aubergines stuffed with bananas and potatoes. Refreshing yoghurt-based kadhi is an apt accompaniment and there is a decent range of rice and breads. The restaurant now has a bar stocked with beers and lagers from around the world, as well as a few basic wines − or drink lassi or spiced tea. House French: £5.50.

CHEFS/PROPRIETORS: Hemant and Nalinee Desai
OPEN: Tue to Sun
MEALS: 12.30 to 3, 6 to 10 (1 to 10 Sat and Sun)
PRICES: £8 (£17), Set L £5 (£10) to £10 (£15), Set D £10 (£15) to £15 (£20). Service 10%
CARDS: Access, Visa
SEATS: 32. Private parties: 32 main room. Vegetarian meals. Children welcome. Separate
smoking area. Wheelchair access. Music

Saheli Brasserie   map 14

| 35 Great Queen Street, WC2B 5TB | COOKING 1 |
| 071-405 2238 and 430 9963 | COST £12−£24 |

The latest branch of the Fleet Tandoori chain (see entry) is a shade more up-market than its relatives. 'Saheli' means 'lady friends' and the long narrow dining-room makes a pleasant place to meet, with its pastel colour schemes and caned chairs. The tag 'brasserie' has been adopted by many new Indian restaurants, although it normally implies no more than an in-vogue designer approach to decor. There are few food surprises here. The menu is a recognisable mix of familiar tandooris and curries with a North Indian bias; one feature is a fish thali and pomfret appears from time to time. At its best the kitchen can deliver subtly flavoured dishes, with good all-round spicing and a noticeable lack of excess oil. Successes have included karahi kebab kyberi, sag paneer and mushroom bhaji. Some of the side dishes and accompaniments are less impressive. The restaurant stands between Kingsway and Covent Garden and provides a set lunch, handy for office workers, as well as an early evening menu for theatregoers. The wine list is mainly French with a few representatives from the New World; otherwise there is Kingfisher beer and some jazzy cocktails. House wine: £6.95.

CHEFS: Mohammed Hanif and Abdul Rahman Khan PROPRIETORS: Saheli Brasserie Ltd
OPEN: Mon to Sat
CLOSED: 25 Dec
MEALS: 12 to 3, 5.30 to 11.30
PRICES: £11 (£20), Set L £8 (£12), Set pre-theatre D £8.50 (£13). Service 12.5%
CARDS: Access, Amex, Diners, Visa
SEATS: 64. Private parties: 50 main room, 30 private room. Car-park. Vegetarian meals. Children's helpings. No-smoking area. Wheelchair access (also WC). Music. Air-conditioned

St Quentin   map 12

243 Brompton Road, SW3 2EP   COOKING 1
071-581 5131   COST £20–£37

The restaurant manages to serve the local community, particularly because its set menus are fair value for these parts. It also acts as a useful staging post if on an expedition to Knightsbridge shops or South Kensington museums. The hours are convenient and the comfort welcome. It is resolutely French, although the chef is now an Englishman, and the repertoire signals not so much *cuisine bourgeoise* as modern restaurant fare common enough across the continent: seafood in pastry with Thai herbs; salmon in aspic; sea bass roasted in olive oil with scallops; sweetbreads with a piquant sauce; pigeon with foie gras and cabbage. Cabbage is as popular here as in other kitchens, one set meal offering seafood with sauerkraut or confit of duck with red and white cabbage. After good beginnings, meals can lose their way in the rush and hurry, so not all reports show equal satisfaction. Tales of muddled bills, incorrectly delivered meals, a 'service charge of 12.5 per cent which is at the discretion of the customer' (a complicated piece of double-speak if ever there was one), and inefficient service do abound and vitiate what should be a resounding success. House wine is £7.60.

CHEF: Stephen Witney PROPRIETORS: St Quentin Ltd
OPEN: all week
MEALS: 12 to 3 (4 Sat), 7 to 12 (11.30 Sun)
PRICES: £20 (£31), Set L £11.90 (£20), Set D £14.90 (£23). Cover £1.30. Service 12.5%
CARDS: Access, Amex, Diners, Visa
SEATS: 85. Private parties: 25 private room. Children welcome. Wheelchair access. Air-conditioned

San Martino

map 12

103 Walton Street, SW3 2HP
071-589 3833 and 1356

COOKING 1
COST £37

Compared to its sleek and fashionable neighbours, the San Martino always looked a little behind the times. It promoted regional flavours (Tuscan, in particular) and good ingredients, however, and has now converted to the new-wave look as well with clean lines, cool colours and not a wax-covered Chianti bottle in sight. Lighting by little black-shaded halogen lamps hanging low over pink-clothed tables is effective. Seating is cheek by designer-stubble jowl, it can get very noisy, and Signor Martinucci is apt to snap at customers as well as staff, many of the latter his relatives. Overbooking, an ever-increasing cover charge, and uncompleted credit card slips after a 15 per cent service charge is added to the bill, do not endear. The *carte*, rarely changing but supplemented by a good number of semi-seasonal extras and embellished throughout with 'superb' this and 'fantastic' that, is more appealing. The food has had a mixed press since the last *Guide*, losing it a mark, but on balance is still deserving. Fresh papaya with white crab meat and delicate fried baby squid are two well-handled first courses. Porcini crop up through the seasons, with fresh tagliatelle, perhaps, or in a creamed sauce with tender pigeon breast. Salads, created in full view by la signora, and vegetables, are deserving extras. Desserts, placed on the table for perusal, always include bowls of fresh fruit, as well as tiramisu, perhaps, or an excellent rich crème caramel. Pastry cornetto with fresh fruit in its custard filling was a welcome variation. Negative comments cite gristly tournedos, involtini 'rather like a school meatball', and overcooked pasta. Service, considering the constraints of space and demand, is admirable. The wine list is a scrapbook of Italian labels pasted in, fancy and plain. Growers are good and prices are not excessive. House Chianti is £7.15.
CELLARMAN'S CHOICE: Dolcetto d'Alba, £15.

CHEFS: Costanzo Martinucci, Alfonso Cestaro and Fernando Da Costa Lima
PROPRIETOR: Costanzo Martinucci
OPEN: Mon to Sat
MEALS: 12 to 2.45, 7 to 11.30
PRICES: £21 (£31). Cover £1.90. Minimum £8.50. Service 15%
CARDS: Access, Amex, Diners, Visa
SEATS: 48. Private parties: 65 main room, 24 private room. Vegetarian meals. Children's helpings. Wheelchair access (1 step). Air-conditioned

Santini ♟

map 11

29 Ebury Street, SW1W 0NX
071-730 4094 and 8275

COOKING 2
COST £24–£48

The probable reason for using this restaurant is that it is smart. It is certainly expensive, yet tables are close set and it will be noisy when full. The main *carte* stays the same from year to year and is neither particularly regional (Santini has Venetian connections) nor especially striking: all that changes is the price, often up by between 15 and 20 per cent. The best cooking is in the daily specials, the cheapest in the set-price lunch menu. These will include good pasta, polenta and wild mushroom dishes, and dishes where the regional affiliation comes out more strongly, such as calamari veneziana, risottos, or whole sea bass. Like its sister restaurant L'Incontro (see entry), the wine list has a fine range of Italian bottles, at a price. Barolos and north Italian whites are impressive though the list shows as little development as the menu. Most people must drink the house Valpolicella and Soave at £11.50. CELLARMAN'S CHOICE: Cervaro della Sala Marchesi Antinori 1986, £29.50; Bertucchi bianco Imperiale, £19.50.

CHEFS: G. Santin and G. Rosselli   PROPRIETOR: G. Santin
OPEN: all week, exc Sat L and Sun L
CLOSED: bank hols
MEALS: 12.30 to 2.30, 7 to 11.30
PRICES: £28 (£40), Set L £14.50 (£24). Cover £1.50. Service 12%
CARDS: Access, Amex, Diners, Visa
SEATS: 65. Private parties: 25 main room. Vegetarian meals. Children welcome. Wheelchair access. Air-conditioned

---

▲ Savoy Grill and River Restaurant

map 14

Strand, WC2R 0EU   COOKING 3
071-836 4343   COST £33–£70

The River Restaurant is deep in the hotel with views over the river and the South Bank that are worth the bother to get a window table. There is also Upstairs, the Savoy's oyster and seafood bar. Mythology has it that the Grill's tables are carefully allocated to the rich and famous. Charts have even been produced in Sunday newspapers to reveal the lineaments of power and influence. David Sharland has taken over the job of chef at the Grill, Alan Hill having migrated northwards. The menu has kept the same pattern, though there are a greater number of choices to each course. It still has the week's rota of daily dishes, from steak and kidney pie to salmon coulibiac. One difference is that it changes more frequently than before. The kitchen lightens the traditional British repertoire with neo-classical dishes that take in modern developments: ravioli of truffle-scented vegetables; sea bass with fennel butter; turbot with a red wine truffle sauce; chicken with wild mushrooms, pine kernels and bacon. It is punishingly expensive and neither so wonderfully British as the Connaught nor so culinarily exciting as newer and brighter London hotels. The waiters are old-school and spoken of with awe. The sommelier is informed, enthusiastic and doesn't mind if you spend £15 or £50. The River Restaurant is especially enjoyed at lunch, when there is a set-price menu that is not too expensive. It offers sound cooking of a wholly classical cast, although a sign of the times is the vegetarian 'menu du régime naturel' that is offered at the same price. As can happen in very large places, service that is usually praised for high training and smoothness may fall down if the customer does not obey the rigid unwritten rules. The wine list has some comfort in a couple of Chileans, and it extends to other New World producers and to Italian and Spanish makers. It is not so elaborate a collection as is now found in the gourmet restaurants of the West End hotels, but neither the River Restaurant nor the Grill Room aims to dazzle in that way.

CHEFS: Anton Edelmann (River Restaurant) and David Sharland (Grill)
PROPRIETORS: Savoy Hotel plc
OPEN: Grill Mon to Sat, exc Sat L; River Restaurant all week
CLOSED: Grill Aug
MEALS: Grill 12.30 to 2.30, 6 to 11.15; River Restaurant 12.30 to 2.30, 7.30 to 11.30
(10.30 Sun)
PRICES: Grill £31 (£48), Set pre-theatre D £24 (£33); River Restaurant £39 (£58), Set L
£23.75 (£36), Set D £28.75 (£42) to £39.85 (£50)
CARDS: Access, Amex, Carte Blanche, Diners, Visa
SEATS: Grill 80, River Restaurant 150. Private parties: Grill 10, River Restaurant 30 main
room. Car-park, 30 places. Vegetarian meals. Children restricted. Smart dress preferred.
No pipes in dining-room. Wheelchair access. Music/dancing River Restaurant.
Air-conditioned
ACCOMMODATION: 202 rooms, all with bath/shower. Rooms for disabled. Lift. B&B £155 to
£180. Baby facilities. Afternoon teas. Air-conditioning. TV. Phone. Confirm by 6
[*Which? Hotel Guide*]

7 Pond Street

map 11

7 Pond Street, NW3 2PW
071-435 1541

COOKING 1
COST £26

Sandy Anderson, late of Quincy's in Finchley Road, has opened this wine bar/
café/restaurant opposite the Royal Free Hospital. The snacks in the wine bar
are variously reported and this entry relates to the restaurant, open for fewer
hours than the all-day café. On offer is a fast-changing choice numbering
maybe a dozen, priced at London brasserie levels. Recommendations have
included a warm salad of foie gras with a nutty vinaigrette; fish soup with
aïoli; calf's liver with a mushroom, mustard and sesame sauce; guinea-fowl
with lardons and a clear reduction parsley sauce; a Dover sole with a lime
beurre blanc. Rack of lamb with garlic was bland, rather like the modish
vegetables. The end of the meal was acceptable. There is change afoot. Reports
of the early months were encouraging, but business was not. In sensible
response, the choice has been cut down. The wine list is short but good with
fashionable bottles. It may be because of persistence in offering a 1985
Muscadet from Bonhomme that two bottles in succession were out of
condition. Prices are not high and growers like Parent, Javillier, Brown Bros,
and Zind-Humbrecht are encouraging. More reports, please.

CHEFS: Sandy Anderson and Ian Ramsay   PROPRIETOR: Sandy Anderson
OPEN: all week, D only and Sun L
MEALS: 12 to 3, 7 to 11
PRICES: £15 (£22)
CARDS: Access, Visa
SEATS: 60. Private parties: 80 main room. Vegetarian meals. Children's helpings.
No-smoking area. Music. Air-conditioned

The Guide *is totally independent, accepts no free hospitality, and survives on the number
of copies sold each year.*

All letters to the Guide *are acknowledged with an update on latest sales, closures, chef
changes and so on.*

Si Chuen

map 14

56 Old Compton Street, W1V 5PN
071-437 2069

COOKING 1
COST £13–£36

Devotees of the Dragon Gate welcomed its new incarnation (with plush decor
and a new name) in Old Compton Street. That was in 1986. At first Si Chuen
showed all the intensity of the Gerrard Street original and its commitment to
authentic Szechuan cooking. Since then it has changed complexion: many of
the classic specialities, such as tripe with chilli and 'ants climbing a tree' have
disappeared, and the menu has been invaded by a standard repertoire of
Cantonese and Pekinese favourites. Most readers now mention these familiar
items, such as hot-and-sour soup; chicken with cashew nuts and chilli; and
fried mixed vegetables. But it is possible to eat adventurously because the
kitchen can still deliver tea-smoked duck; fish-fragrant aubergines with
shredded pork; and pelmeni with hot pepper sauce and garlic. Dishes rarely
disappoint and the service is excellent. House wine: £6.50

CHEF: Ping Tzue   PROPRIETORS: A.Y.C. Cheung and C.M. Liew
OPEN: Mon to Sat
CLOSED: Christmas
MEALS: noon to 11.30
PRICES: £18 (£30), Set D £8.50 (£13) to £13 (£18)
CARDS: Access, Amex, Diners, Visa
SEATS: 70. Private parties: 30 main room. Vegetarian meals. Children's helpings.
Wheelchair access (3 steps). Music

Singapore Garden Mayfair

map 14

85 Piccadilly, W1V 9HD
071-491 2222

COOKING 1
COST £19–£37

A newish branch of the Swiss Cottage original (see entry) in the heart of
Mayfair, virtually opposite the Ritz. Inside it is classy, modern and luxurious
with two dining areas, a black marble floor, black chairs and exotic plants
everywhere. The cooking centres on Singapore with a shy borrowing from the
cuisines of China and Malaysia, and an inspector's visit showed food of a
sound quality. Vegetarian spring rolls with extremely delicate pastry,
authentically dry beef rendang, mee goreng and a creamy, coconut-based
vegetable curry served in a earthenware pot were all excellent. Others have
approved of the fiery prawn sambal and sizzling scallops with black-bean
sauce. Chilli lobster is the house speciality. To finish there's a dramatic
gimmick: chocolate truffles brought in a silver container filled with dry ice. Hot
towels come at the beginning and end of the meal. The set lunch and dinner
menus include tea at no extra charge. Prices are not cheap, but most reckon that
they are reasonable for the area; less acceptable is the £1 cover charge, plus 15
per cent service and a blank space at the bottom of the credit charge slip. The
wine list has some decent bottles but prices climb steeply. House wine is £8;
Tiger beer is perhaps more appropriate.

The Guide always appreciates hearing about changes of chef or owner.

CHEF: Toh Kok Sum PROPRIETORS: Stephen Lim, David Tsai and Thomas Wong
OPEN: all week
CLOSED: Christmas week
MEALS: 12 to 2.45, 6.30 to 11.30 (11 Sun)
PRICES: £16 (£31), Set L £9.80 (£19), Set D £18 (£29). Cover £1. Minimum £10. Service 15%
CARDS: Access, Amex, Diners, Visa
SEATS: 90. Private parties: 80 main room, 10 private room. Children welcome. Music.
Air-conditioned

Singapore Garden Restaurant

map 11

83–83A Fairfax Road, NW6 4DY
071-328 5314

COOKING 1
COST £18–£28

As the name implies, the restaurant serves a cross-section of Chinese and
Malaysian/Singaporean dishes behind its venetian blinds. The Malaysian
dishes are the best bet, though flavour enhancers are sometimes used as
liberally as they are in South-East Asia. Fish seems to be another strong suit,
and readers applaud the friendly service. Recommendations have been for the
tenderised satay; fried kway tiow (rice sticks with prawns); prawn sambal;
'reasonably authentic' noodle dishes; and fine sago pudding. Seasonings are
westernised and have sometimes lacked the fragrance of lemon grass and the
fire of the chilli encountered in the Straits. House wine is £6.65, but Tiger beer
is better.

CHEF: Mrs S. Lim PROPRIETORS: The Lim family
OPEN: all week
MEALS: 12 to 2.45, 6 to 10.45 (11.15 Fri and Sat)
PRICES: £12 (£23), Set D £13 (£18). Minimum £8 at D. Service 12.5%
CARDS: Access, Amex, Diners, Visa
SEATS: 100. Private parties: 60 main room, 60 private room. Children welcome. Music. Air-
conditioned

Sonny's

map 10

94 Church Road, SW13 0DQ
081-748 0393

COOKING 2
COST £15–£22

After broaching the grey front pass through the bar, where the quietest tables
are, to the large split-level dining-room. In full cry, Barnes can be noisy, so the
best tables are by the windows looking on to the small garden. Pictures relieve
the monotony of the walls. The menu works to a satisfactory formula in which
the food is not overdressed. Many of the tastes are up-front and the chargrill is
favoured for main courses. The place succeeds through speed, economy and
palatability, and there has been a steady flow of good reports. As well as the
carte, there is a very short set-price meal of two courses and coffee offering good
value for London. Dishes that have been mentioned include warm salad of
quail, redcurrants and bacon, merguez sausages and a cucumber raita;
asparagus with virgin oil and Parmesan; grilled tuna and maître d'hotel butter;
chargrilled breasts of pigeon, quite firm but not overcooked, with a sweet wine
sauce; chicken with watercress sauce; coeur à la crème with orange and
grapefruit; pear with praline meringue. The cooking has been simple but

accurate. Vegetables cost extra but portions are generous and the cooking acceptable; one purée is always included. Salads, including a good Caesar, are also extra. Service may be overtaken by numbers but the kitchen produces at speed and the staff normally smile. Good cafetière coffee. A short fashionable wine list, acceptably priced, includes a Basedow Shiraz, Ch. Pichon-Longueville-Lalande, João Pires Moscato, Petaluma Chardonnay, and Roulot's Passetoutgrain rosé. House wine is £6.50. CELLARMAN'S CHOICE: Gamay de Touraine La Chamoise 1989 £11.95; Castle Hill, Te Mata Sauvignon Blanc 1988, £15.50.

CHEFS: Ellie Link and Stephen Baker   PROPRIETOR: Rebecca Mascarenhas
OPEN: all week, exc Sat L
CLOSED: 1 week at Christmas
MEALS: 12.30 to 2.30, 7.30 to 11
PRICES: £14 (£22), Set L and D £10.50 (£15)
CARDS: Access, Diners, Visa
SEATS: 70. Private parties: 70 main room. Children welcome. Wheelchair access

Soong Szechuan Restaurant   map 11

| 45A South End Road, NW3 2BQ | COOKING 1 |
| 071-794 2461 | COST £21–£34 |

The consensus is that this is a cut above the average for suburban Chinese restaurants. Hanging flower baskets and pictures set the scene, and the menu puts its faith in the lively, chilli-hot cuisine of Szechuan. 'General chicken' cooked with peanuts and peppers impressed one newcomer; otherwise the menu takes in sauté prawns and scallops with Szechuan peppercorns; crispy shredded beef with chilli; and hot and sour pork fillets. Specialities from Peking and Hunan also feature and readers have liked the sesame prawn toasts, sizzling lamb with spring onions and diced chicken with almonds and hoisin sauce. Service is charming and prices are reasonable. House wine: £5.

CHEF: V.T. On   PROPRIETOR: Soong Yap
OPEN: all week
CLOSED: bank hols, 24 to 26 Dec
MEALS: 12 to 2.30, 6 to 11 (10.30 Sun)
PRICES: £19 (£28), Set D £16.90 (£21) to £23.90 (£28). Service inc
CARDS: Access, Amex, Diners, Visa
SEATS: 85. Private parties: 100 main room. Children's helpings on request. Music.
Air-conditioned

▲ Le Soufflé,
Inter-Continental Hotel   map 12

| 1 Hamilton Place, W1V 0QY | COOKING 4 |
| 071-409 3131 | COST £35–£64 |

The dining-room and bar together form a huge rectangle, divided from each other by a central wall on the long axis. In the bar a pianist and his drum machine plays resolutely, dispensing cheer or melancholy to the single guests or couples in sofas and armchairs. Escape to the restaurant and the greens and aquamarines may waft you in imagination on to the cruise ship it resembles.

All the waiters have name tags, they are irrepressibly keen, and the seats are comfy. Peter Kromberg is a very skilled chef. The menu is among the most modern in London, the food often light, and the execution can be without fault. Many of the sauces are vinaigrette based, there is a willingness to use vegetables or potatoes in the construction of the dish to vary and lighten its impact and there are, of course, the soufflés from which the restaurant takes its name. Although the dinner *carte* and gastronomic menu are as expensive as any in the clutch of Park Lane hotels, the short menu at lunch may be reckoned a fair price, especially as there is no stinting on the luxuries. A modern and successful dish entailed slicing escalopes from across the body of a small turbot, cooking them for the briefest possible time, laying them on a bed of spinach and interlayering them with red and green lentils, then dressing them with fresh coriander vinaigrette. This was sensitively handled and had a very fine contrast of flavour and texture. The menu persists in overloading its choice with luxury items, the climax of which must be a salad of lobster in caviare butter, an oyster in its own jelly, Maryland crab fritter on a mustard sauce and a slice of foie gras on dandelion leaves. It also keeps abreast of the latest developments in the grocery trade: a wild mushroom salad is dressed with a citrus and pistachio nut oil vinaigrette, one of a range of novelty oils that have been seen in the last year or two. Luxury does not bite so deep into the main courses and so saves them from excess richness: turbot and salmon layered with potato on a sorrel sauce; squab with a 'choucroûte' of turnips; or lamb with a vegetable ragout and spinach keep their feet on the ground. The end of the meal should be reserved for a soufflé, which comes in a handsome silver pot and is usually well executed, though sometimes there is too much butter left from lining the dish. The cheese trolley will amaze more for its mechanics than for its choice, and the wine list may cause worry because of its prices. There are a couple of items at £13 or £15 at the beginning of each section, and there are a decent number of halves, but to explore the strongest suit, old clarets, you will need serious money. The range outside France is not interesting and the range of makers in France could be more lively; choice of burgundies is conservative. House wine: £15.

CHEF: Peter Kromberg   PROPRIETORS: Inter-Continental Hotels Corporation
OPEN: all week, exc Sat L
MEALS: 12 to 3.30, 7 to 11
PRICES: £37 (£53), Set L £24 (£35), Set D £40 (£52)
CARDS: Access, Amex, Carte Blanche, Diners, Visa
SEATS: 80. Private parties: 10 main room. Car-park, 100 places. Children welcome. Smart dress preferred. Wheelchair access (also WC). Music. Air-conditioned
ACCOMMODATION: 490 rooms, all with bath/shower. Rooms for disabled. Lift. B&B £224 to £241. Baby facilities. Afternoon teas. Sauna. Air-conditioning. TV. Phone

Soulard   map 11

113 Mortimer Road, N1 4JY   COOKING 2
071-254 1314   COST £18–£24

'It looks as if it once was a bicycle repair shop, ironmonger's or draper's attending to the needs of the houses about', but it brings France to Islington – 'just like Dordogne, especially with all the British voices.' Philippe Soulard worked among the bright lights of West End French catering before setting up on his own. The *carte* of six choices is supplemented by a blackboard of specials. A tarte aux poireaux of firm buttery pastry, with depth and weight to the filling and decent dressing for the lollo rosso on one side, was how one diner started; another with garlic mushrooms – 'garlic, mushrooms, garlic and garlic', in the form of a confit of new season's cloves, as soft as could be. A main course of escalope de veau normande, with calvados and onions, had sauce a mite thin but the meat was good, as it was in the saddle of lamb grilled to char the outside. The lamb came with a basil sauce, again anaemic, and a gratin of artichokes. Nougat glacé and lemon tart were serviceable, not as good as the first course but, like the rest, 'good middling French cooking'. That meal has plenty of companions; others have found less favour, in detail mainly. In London terms, prices are on the low side. The very short wine list starts with house Partager at £6.25.

CHEF: Jacques Abdou   PROPRIETOR: Philippe Soulard
OPEN: Tue to Sat, exc Sat L
CLOSED: 2 weeks Sept
MEALS: 12 to 2, 7 to 10.30
PRICES: £14 (£20), Set L £12.95 (£18)
CARD: Access
SEATS: 28. 9 tables outside. Private parties: 15 private room. Children's helpings. No cigars in dining-room. Music

Sree Krishna   map 10

194 Tooting High Street, SW17 0SF	COOKING 1
081-672 4250	COST £12

A Buddha adorned with fairy lights occupies the back wall of this informal, dimly lit dining-room. Religious pictures line the walls, Indian music plays and the waiters bustle around efficiently. The restaurant is now under the same ownership as Ragam (see entry) and the menus are similar, with the emphasis on South Indian vegetarian dishes, especially from the Kerala coast. Spicing is often distinctive and meals are excellent value. Onion bhajias and masala dosai are above average, rice is well prepared and the cook knows how to make parathas and chapatis. The menu also includes less familiar specialities such as adai (a rice and lentil pancake) and avial (mixed vegetable curry flavoured with coconut, yoghurt and curry leaves). The meat dishes are not as successful. Drink lassi, Kingfisher beer or Indian Veena wine.

CHEF: Mullath Vijayan   PROPRIETORS: T. Haridas and family
OPEN: all week
MEALS: 12 to 2.45, 6 to 10.45 (11.45 Fri and Sat)
PRICES: £5 (£10). Minimum £2.50. Service 10%
CARDS: Access, Amex, Diners, Visa
SEATS: 120. Vegetarian meals. Children welcome. Wheelchair access (also WC). Music.
Air-conditioned

Several sharp operators have tried to extort money from restaurateurs on the promise of an entry in a guide book that has never appeared. The Good Food Guide *makes no charge for inclusion and does not offer certificates of any kind.*

Sri Siam

map 14

14 Old Compton Street, W1V 5PE
071-434 3544

COOKING 2
COST £14–£24

Restaurants come and go in Old Compton Street. Sri Siam moved in after the rise and fall of the new vegetarianism in the shape of Compton Green. That is the way of the world in Soho. Perhaps in deference to its predecessor, this Thai restaurant is the only one with a vegetarian menu approved by the Vegetarian Society. The restaurant is a long narrow room with speckled, sandy-coloured walls decorated with butterfly motifs plus prints of Thai monks, dangling puppets and dolls to add a touch of authenticity. Set lunches and dinners are excellent value and provide a trailer for the full menu, which deals in the mainstays of the Thai repertoire: soups, salads, stir-frys and curries of different colours (red, green or yellow, depending on spicing and intensity). Thai cooking relies on full-frontal immediacy, but it needs balance and subtlety as well. Sri Siam proves its merit with vivid fish soups, satays served with authentic peanut sauce, excellent fried beef with chillis, herbs and baby aubergines; and 'red curry' cooked with coconut milk and kaffir lime leaves. Vegetables and noodles are up to standard and the prawn crackers (krupuk) brought free before the meal really do taste of prawns. One lesser-known speciality is lamb from North Thailand – finely chopped meat cooked with ground toasted rice and served in a salad with a hot and sour dressing. Service is courteous and the restaurant is cool: efficient ceiling fans dissipate any chilli-induced sweat. Singha Thai beer is pricey but it suits the food well; otherwise drink tea or white wine which is moderately priced. House French: £6.95.

CHEF: Pong Chan PROPRIETOR: Hock Chua
OPEN: all week, exc Sun L
CLOSED: Christmas and New Year
MEALS: 12 to 3, 6 to 11.15 (10.30 Sun)
PRICES: £11 (£20), Set L £8.50 (£14), Set D £13.75 (£20). Service 12.5%
CARDS: Access, Amex, Diners, Visa
SEATS: 75. Private parties: 40 main room. Vegetarian meals. Children welcome. Wheelchair access. Music. Air-conditioned

Stephen Bull

map 13

5–7 Blandford Street, W1H 3AA
071-486 9696

COOKING 3
COST £37

Reactions exemplify the varying demands of the British public: some want velvet and carpets, others lean modernism laced with designer ideas. To each the other may be anathema, and colours the view of the food. Stephen Bull's intention was to produce good food cheaply but with class: the restaurant reflects this. Walls are bare plaster, hand-waxed, floors are noisy boards, variety comes from space and volume. Numbers and throughput determine economic viability, hence the occasional chaos and the usual streamlining of the service. Prices have risen this year, but they were set too low at the outset; the aim remains the same. The intentions are laudable, just as the ideas behind the cooking are creative and truthful to the materials. That they fall down in the execution, which they can do, revolves around organisation, transmission of instructions, and trying to please so wide a band of the public while producing a very particular recipe. Stephen Bull's food is invariably light and is usually refined. The flavours mobilised are intended to be exact and pointed, not bludgeoning. It is ideally suited to advertising executives, who seem to populate the place, and to those who *need* to eat out. This food won't kill. The danger is that it lacks the easy comfort of cream, may fall into heavy overstatement in coarser hands and, if it is done badly, will seem plastic, mute and anaemic. 'I would defy anyone to detect any flavour at all; the only flavour to a lobster bisque was orange; this was geriatric food attractively displayed,' was a comment from one meal. Yet the exact cooking and fine judgement of quantity and presentation is evidenced by numerous dishes reported through the year. A casserole of duck is served in a soup dish, the meat well rid of its fat, tender and cut into chunks laid in a light, sweet-edged gravy. On top of the whole is a small blanched cabbage leaf, emerald green, in the cup of which is piled shredded turnip quickly pickled to cut through any lingering richness in the main ingredient. A dish of salt cod, moist and flaky, is cooked with a herb crust and laid on to a bed of mashed potato moated by a light red wine sauce, mushrooms and French beans cut into micro-lengths. The kitchen salts the cod for four days, after which it is rinsed and soaked for a fifth – a mark of how much Stephen Bull works for his materials. These are great one-plate dishes and the catalogue of other recommendations goes on: soups, often spiced, such as broccoli and ginger or parsnips mostly with star anise; terrine of salmon and hake with a tomato vinaigrette; twice cooked goats' cheese soufflé (almost a fixture); crab and orange ravioli with basil cream; rabbit with mustard; a mixed plate of calf's, duck and chicken liver with onion marmalade and balsamic vinegar; smoked haddock with cardamom rice and crisp-fried onions; prune and armagnac tart and ice-cream; hazelnut and apple tart; flourless chocolate cake and many more. Bread is bought in and is acceptable, butter is good, cheese discs with drinks are excellent, coffee is decent espresso. There is a tendency to cut things into pieces or take them off the bone, which reinforces people's view of the food as being gutless. Compare ox-tail here to one at Alastair Little's: this one a small mound of shredded meat, no fat, no bone, perfectly tender and with a light gravy; the other a giant bowl of steaming chunks, not trimmed as well as it could be, a little firm to eat, but looking as if a Giono peasant had just come to table chilled to the bone by the Mistral. The wine list remains an intelligent selection, not too highly priced by London standards. It allows equal weight to regions old and new and offers a fair price range from named growers. Burgundies and Beaujolais seem the most interesting currently. Curiously, Italy is ignored. House French from £10.50.

CHEFS: Stephen Bull and Richard Corrigan   PROPRIETOR: Stephen Bull
OPEN: Mon to Sat, exc Sat L
CLOSED: 1 week at Christmas
MEALS: 12 to 2.30, 6 to 11.30
PRICES: £22 (£31)
CARDS: Access, Visa
SEATS: 60. Private parties: 50 main room. Children's helpings. Wheelchair access (1 step). Air-conditioned

Sud Ouest
map 12

27–31 Basil Street, SW3 1BB	COOKING 1
071-584 4484	COST £38

Being opposite Harrods, this brasserie and café in symbiotic linkage conjures up the fear of being punished by price. Rather, it attempts the new London formula of not charging the earth, just a continent. The room is bare enough, the walls plain white with an accented stairwell in dark blue leading down to further seats in the basement. Nigel Davis, the chef, is hardly a native of south-western France, the evident inspiration of name and cuisine, but he trained there. He was also influenced by Spanish Basque cookery, as may be seen in a paupiette of red pepper and salt cod; cod basquaise; or brill with parsley and garlic. The cooking has been considered mixed in standard, with more emphasis on looks than taste, but anyway overshadowed by the service that values casualness over promptitude and wields a massive pepper mill as readily as in any trattoria (unground sea salt is uselessly in bowls on the table). Dishes that have proved acceptable have included brill with watercress sauce; braised lamb's tongue with madeira sauce; gazpacho with crab, terrine of aubergine with a hint of coriander; duck with a black olive fumet and with braised cabbage; excellent *pain perdu*; and apple and armagnac pancake. If systems can come together, the place could work well. Next door in the small café, Toulouse sausage and lentils, Serrano ham, terrine and similar dishes are available the day long. It's noisy and uncomfortable, but again, the idea is a good one. The wine list is in two parts, one of which is south-western wines, all inexpensive, some very good such as Ch. Flotis, Ch. de Tiregand and the dry white Jurançon, Clos Guirouilh. There are no halves or wines by the glass in evidence, except sweet wines. House Côtes du Marmandais: £8.50.

CHEF: Nigel Davis   PROPRIETOR: Martin Davis
OPEN: Mon to Sat
MEALS: 12.30 to 3, 7.30 to 10.30
PRICES: £21 (£32)
CARDS: Access, Amex, Diners, Visa
SEATS: 90. Private parties: 60 main room, 50 private room. Children welcome. Wheelchair access (1 step). Music. Air-conditioned

Suntory
map 13

72 St James's Street, SW1A 1PH	COOKING 3
071-409 0201	COST £25–£67

Commercial practices change and Suntory, secure in its premises that were once Madame Prunier's, saw fit to abolish the cover charge and incorporate the service charge into its prices. Conservatism reigns in the food department, catering to the Japanese establishment who fill the tatami rooms (no chairs) downstairs. In the main restaurant, one-pot dishes such as shabu-shabu, sliced beef braised in broth at the table 'with the assistance of a waitress', or teppanyaki, prawns, lobster or meat cooked on a special griddle dropped into the table, are the centrepieces but sushi and sashimi are good in quality and stylishly prepared. There is even a cheaper set lunch consisting of sushi, dobin-mushi, a light fish and chicken soup; a plate of sashimi of tuna, salmon and one other; a green salad, prawns, mushrooms and fillet steak cooked on the teppan, sticky rice and fruit before coffee and Charbonnel and Walker mints, 'as imported into Japan by Suntory.' This is fair value, and service is punctilious. The wines number more than a hundred bins, 90 of them French: as thoroughbred as the food, but as dear as the *carte*, too. House claret and Muscadet are £10.

CHEF: M. Hayashi   PROPRIETORS: Suntory Ltd
OPEN: Mon to Sat
CLOSED: 25 Dec, 1 Jan, bank hols
MEALS: 12 to 1.30, 7 to 9.30
PRICES: £45 (£56), Set L £20 (£25) to £50 (£55), Set D £35 (£40) to £50 (£55). Service inc.
CARDS: Access, Amex, Diners, Visa
SEATS: 130. Private parties: 50 main room, 2, 6 and 12 private rooms. Children restricted.
Air-conditioned

Le Suquet   map 12

104 Draycott Avenue, SW3 3AE	COOKING 2
071-581 1785 and 225 0838	COST £41

The intensely French restaurant will try to make you as comfortable as the tight-packed, busy quarters allow – while you are eating, that is. Almost any restaurant in England that cooks only fish will have some misses as well as some hits. The hits at Le Suquet are memorable: 'superb' langoustines, scallops cooked in garlic, sea bream wrapped in foil and cooked rare, 'a testament to freshness'. Wines from Provence add individuality to the wine list. House wine: £8.50. Unfortunately it may be over all too quickly: 'customers are not encouraged to linger.' Having paid a cover charge as well as 15 per cent for service, they have every reason to expect to be allowed to linger without harassment.

CHEF: Jean Yves Darcel   PROPRIETOR: Pierre Martin
OPEN: all week
MEALS: 12.30 to 2.30, 7 to 11.30
PRICES: £22 (£34). Cover £1.50. Service 15%
CARDS: Access, Amex, Diners, Visa
SEATS: 50. 4 tables outside. Private parties: 16 private room. Children welcome. Smart dress preferred. Wheelchair access. Music. Air-conditioned

Surinder   map 11

109 Westbourne Park Road, W2 5QL	COOKING 1
071-229 8968	COST £22

Notting Hill might proclaim its good luck in this small restaurant that provides fair value without fuss. It is a pleasant room with bentwood cane chairs, a large windowed front screened from the street by potted pines, and a high counter defending the kitchen at the other end. The entrance is on Chepstow Road, even though the address says otherwise. The short menu is at a fair set price with small supplements for *bloc de foie gras*, fillet steak and half lobsters. The cooking is like the best bistros of the late 1960s: not always the recipe that you know from the classic books, but palatable none the less. Imam bayeldi is half a baked aubergine with cheese topping and a few spices; hors d'oeuvre varié is

143

a small plate of salad trimmings, a slice of pastrami, some mussels in cream dressing, a tomato salad and olives; entrecôte is generous, the meat fair, accurately cooked, with a pepper cream sauce; fish is fresh; vegetables are simple and often seem to include carrots in orange juice; chocolate pots are good and solid. Service is invariably charming. Lapses have been noted, but the intentions are honest and clear. Surinder himself takes breathers at a table by the entrance. The Italian and French wine list is not overpriced and more than adequate for the task. House Côtes du Rhône and Muscadet: £7.50.

CHEF/PROPRIETOR: Surinder Chandwan
OPEN: Tue to Sat, D only and Fri L
MEALS: 12 to 2.30, 7 to 11
PRICES: Set L and D £12.95 (£18). Service 10%
CARDS: Access, Amex, Visa
SEATS: 45. Private parties: 45 main room. Children welcome. Wheelchair access (2 steps)

Suruchi
map 11

18 Theberton Street, N1 OQX	COOKING 1
071-359 8033	COST £6–£10

A South Indian vegetarian café that is usually busy but, thanks to light, space and soft classical music, always pleasant. The short menu of multi-textured and exotically perfumed bhel pooris and light dosa pancakes is consistently praised for value, as is the Suruchi thali. Specials might be muttar paneer or vegetable biriani. One reader writes that crunchiness and spicing are a little feebler than a few years ago. A good choice of sweets includes kulfi every which way, and ras malai. Drink Kashmiri falooda (milk, China grass and ice-cream) or bring your own wine.

CHEF: Rafig Uddin   PROPRIETORS: Suruchi Partnership
OPEN: all week
MEALS: 12 to 2.30, 6 to 10.45
PRICES: £6 (£8), Set L and D £5.10 (£6)
CARDS: Amex, Visa
SEATS: 40. Vegetarian meals. Children welcome. Wheelchair access (1 step). Music

Surya
map 10

59–61 Fortune Green Road, NW6 1DR	COOKING 1
071-435 7486	COST £10–£19

'A pleasing addition to London's Indian vegetarian restaurants,' writes one knowledgeable reader. Surya is a tastefully decorated place, very much in the current style, with a white and green colour scheme, glass-topped tables and modern black chairs. Venetian blinds hang in the long windows. The menu is short but well thought out, with an enterprising additional list of daily specials. Classics such as samosas with coriander chutney; masala dosa with tamarind-flavoured sambhar and coconut chutney; and bhel puris have all been fresh, light and well spiced. Vegetables are distinctive: aubergine bharthe is baked and cooked in a tomato sauce. The list of specials ranges from spicy bread and potato rolls and kaddu (pumpkin) curry on Tuesday to stuffed green peppers and lotus stem curry on Saturday. Accompaniments are up-to the mark. To finish there are Indian sweets or Loseley ice-creams and sorbets. Drink lassi, Becks beer or masala tea. House wine: £5.95.

CHEF: H. Tiwari PROPRIETOR: R.C. Tiwari
OPEN: all week, D only and Sun L
CLOSED: 24 and 25 Dec
MEALS: 12 to 2, 6 to 11
PRICES: £8 (£13), Set Sun L £4.95 (£10), Set D £8 (£13) to £11 (£16). Minimum £6. Service 10%
CARDS: Access, Amex, Diners, Visa
SEATS: 34. Private parties: 20 private room. Vegetarian meals. Children's helpings (Sun L and early D, 6 to 7). Separate smoking area. Wheelchair access (1 step; also WC). Music

Sutherlands ▼

map 13

45 Lexington Street, W1R 3LG   COOKING 4
071-434 3401   COST £38−£49

The street frontage is so discreet that the unfamiliar may pass by several times before realisation dawns. Some have described the interior as a 'temple of gastronomy,' perhaps encouraged by the progression down a fairly narrow aisle to a top-lit 'shrine' at the end, complete with stained glass in the skylight. Chairs, too, tend to the ecclesiastical, in hardness if not appearance. Sutherlands has a tone all its own, from the modern hairstyles and demeanour of its staff to the distinctive menu and Garry Hollihead's cooking. This is enticing enough for people to wish to return for further tastes, inventive in the extreme, yet not so full of silly ideas as to be outrageous for its own sake. There is a certain seriousness about the staff that some people actually find disconcerting, but it rarely degenerates to superciliousness and is more often leavened by a light touch, typified by the eager proffering at most junctures in the meal of the signature rolls − often six flavours, the hazelnut getting the vote this year. Whereas the style of the carefully arranged plates has elicited the description 'jewel-like' too frequently, there has been detected a move towards larger portions and, some would say, fewer multi-layered flavours than hitherto. Even so, dishes are usually complicated. Hence an autumn meal began with a tartlet of spinach, leeks and quails' eggs with a butter sauce of rosemary and chives studded with horn of plenty mushrooms. The slight sweetness of the sauce gave depth to the quails' eggs, the mushrooms adding an extra dimension of flavour. 'I needed my bread to mop that one.' Following was a panaché of veal fillet and kidneys with morels. This was distinguished by both the quality and quantity of the mushrooms. The meat was on a bed of shredded mange-tout and baby vegetables, including superlative beetroot. 'I shall have to revisit for this,' wrote the reader. When he did, the beetroot was replaced by asparagus and the kidney by sweetbread, but the sauce was just as brilliant. These are genuine dishes from a menu of maybe eight choices per course. Recommendations have come for sea bass with fennel bound with mayonnaise; salad of quail with Chablis vinaigrette; courgette flowers stuffed with a chicken mousseline with a wild mushroom sauce; turbot with cucumber spaghetti; rack of lamb with sauté lamb's brain, a confit of potato and turnip in a tarragon sauce; grilled log of goats' cheese; hazelnut shortbread, apples and caramel sauce; a Christmas plate of plum pudding, mincemeat tart and nougatine glacé; lemon crème brûlée; a chocolate truffle torte with a marmalade mousse; and a lavender ice-cream. The last two have evinced particular rhapsodies. Not everyone finds all the flavours true, sometimes because of underseasoning (no pepper or salt on the tables) or because of mismatching. Thus a salad of scallops marinated in lime juice and served with citrus zests and green peppercorns somehow was buried beneath a sweet overlay reminiscent of fruit squash, and the elements of a finely cooked salmon with sorrel sauce and a ratatouille timbale did not cohere. Sometimes fine knifework seems to dissipate the flavours. There can also be problems of slowness, though the attempt is now being made to avoid logjams of orders by staggering bookings. The wine list grows slowly year by year. Because there is no great concentration on any country or region, it does seem as if each bottle is there because it is good; growers and properties are exemplary. Most people have confirmed this. Prices are not low, though some thought has been given to range among half-bottles as well as bottles. House wines start at £8.75.

CELLARMAN'S CHOICE: Châteauneuf-du-Pape, Clos des Papes 1985, Paul Avril, £28.50; Snoqualmie Fumé Blanc 1987, £14.75.

CHEF: Garry Hollihead PROPRIETORS: Siân Sutherland-Dodd, Garry Hollihead and Christian Arden
OPEN: Mon to Sat, exc Sat L
MEALS: 12.15 to 2.15, 6.15 to 11.15
PRICES: Set L £27 (£38), Set D £29.50 (£41). Service 12.5%
CARDS: Access, Carte Blanche, Visa
SEATS: 45. Private parties: 45 main room, 20 private room. Vegetarian meals. Children's helpings on request. No cigars/pipes in dining-room. Wheelchair access. Air-conditioned

Tante Claire ♥   map 12

68–69 Royal Hospital Road, SW3 4HP   COOKING 5
071-352 6045   COST £25–£71

The dining-room is likened to a Cunard liner, not for blandness but for a lightness that comes from pale colours and pale woods. That pallor does not carry over into the food, which has very firm characteristics and the stamp of a personality. Pierre Koffmann is another chef who has taken to literature in 1990, his book being strongest as an evocation of Gascony in the 1950s, as the old culture was about to be buried by the technocracy of the fourth and fifth republics. There is no strong sense of archaic regionalism in his menus today, though it may be reflected in the use of goose fat for his confit of salmon, duck stock as the poaching medium for lobster, or the overall richness of his cooking. That richness comes not from an excess use of butter or cream so much as from an interest in substantial dishes – stuffed pig's trotter is a case in point – and a wish to keep in touch with reality. Thus a piece of lamb is not trimmed of all its fat, so as to impart more flavour to the meat. This tendency is most apparent from the main *carte*. The short daily lunch menu – for many, still the best value in London – seems to be lighter in effect. Spices also figure largely in some of the cooking, for example, langoustines *à la nage exotique*, langoustines layered with filo with a sauce perfumed by fresh coriander, red mullet with cumin, or squab with nutmeg and cinnamon. Dishes that have been recommended this year have included a ragout of oysters and scallops – the first poached, the second seared a crisp brown – sitting on samphire and tomato; the yellow butter sauce had a salty edge to it but was lightened by fish stock. Another is the mille-feuille made up of layers of filo and just-cooked langoustine tails on a bed of salad with an aromatic sauce of which coriander is an important element. The first courses on offer seem sometimes limited by an affection for fish or foie gras, and there is certainly nothing 'plain'. But that foie gras might be with the *salade jardinière*, a piece of liver, 'warm, tender and quivering', on a crisp potato galette with a sweet white wine sauce stroked into acidity with lemon or orange. Acid balance is carefully considered at every turn, in consideration perhaps of the richness. Thus a perfectly hung piece of beef is served with crisp discs of aubergine as a top layer, the red wine sauce being thickened, one reader was prepared to suggest, with aubergine purée. At any rate, an edge was given to the whole. Similarly, lamb is wrapped in caul, stuffed with vegetable and white truffle, with sweetbreads and kidney and a stock sauce 'with a sharp tang' that lifted the dish. Vegetables may be built into many of the main courses, but often a side dish is produced which may not invariably be in tune with readers' expectations. A creamy gratin of potatoes was felt to be inapposite with both the stuffed trotters and halibut with wild mushrooms served to the same table. Plain boiled might have been better. Another night saw a dariole of sliced poached artichoke that might be fine with lamb, not so fine with fish. On a third occasion there was a confection of sliced potato, spinach, mushroom and cream – again, all right with some main courses, less so with others. Tastes do not let up with dessert. Pear poached in red wine, served on a honey ice-cream of great intensity; tarte Tatin 'worth its 15 minute delay'; croustade de pomme caramelisée, 'a delicate, plain yet seductively sweetened dish' of slices of apple with a heavily sugared flaky pastry topping, 'and I don't like sugar.' While the canapés and preliminaries merit comment, petits fours are usually dismissed relatively cursorily as not being any finer than usual for this standard of restaurant. By then, perhaps, it's too late to care. Service is well-oiled. Some find it admirable in every way; others fall victim to the double-booking of tables. Meals then become battles with time and waiters, no matter how smooth the production. It is not easy to get a table for dinner less than three weeks in advance. The pressure is therefore on the restaurant to accommodate as many people as possible, which can cause resentment. So, too, can the wine list, which seems expensive. Some of the mark-ups, however, are less than in places of a similar standing in the capital. It also shows some consideration for the less wealthy by its two pages of French country wines, starting at £11.30 for Ch. la Gordonne from Provence. It is a wholly French list with a good range of clarets and burgundies. The growers are not just the standard issue for grand restaurants.

CHEF: Pierre Koffmann   PROPRIETORS: Mr and Mrs Pierre Koffmann
OPEN: Mon to Fri
MEALS: 12.30 to 2, 7 to 11
PRICES: £50 (£59), Set L £21.50 (£25). Minimum £40 alc. Service inc
CARDS: Access, Amex, Diners, Visa
SEATS: 38. Children welcome. Smart dress preferred. Wheelchair access

Restaurateurs justifiably resent no-shows. If you quote a credit card number when booking, you may be liable for the restaurant's lost profit margin if you don't turn up. Always phone to cancel.

LONDON

Tatsuso map 11

32 Broadgate Circle, EC2M 2QS	COOKING 3
071-638 5863	COST £21–£90

If, as the blurb says, 'Broadgate is the new City of London', this elegant
Japanese newcomer is well located. The Broadgate Circle complex (marked
only in new A to Zs) with enormous greenhouse-like atria and acres of
concrete, is reminiscent of Tokyo. The restaurant, a long way into the complex,
is traditional rather than modern Japanese, spruce and clean-lined, with
exquisite porcelain on well-spaced tables, and immaculate service. At marbled
counters in the lower ground-floor teppanyaki bar, chefs chop and grill. The
carte is standard posh Japanese and there are formula set meals of varying
prices. Most interest is found amongst the 20 or so daily specials handwritten
on waitresses' notepads. It is worth getting a translation for such dishes as
scallops grilled with sea urchin on crunchy bamboo shoot, salt-grilled flounder
and some which are typical of home rather than restaurant cookery. The
scallops were 'wonderfully tender and tasty'. Eel, rare in Japanese restaurants
here, comes grilled in an omelette. Sushi was of fine quality and very fresh, and
wa-fu salad (vegetables and seaweed with tuna fish and sesame dressing) and
deep-fried tofu were as they should be. To finish there is assorted, beautifully
cut fruit on a purple and gold zebra-striped square plate. The mostly French
wine list, though mindful of expense accounts, has some good growers and
good years. House claret is £12.

CHEFS: Mr Maehara and Mr Hirai PROPRIETORS: Terrii-Broadgate Ltd
OPEN: Mon to Fri
CLOSED: bank hols
MEALS: 11.30 to 3, 6 to 9
PRICES: £23 (£37), Set L £13 (£21) to £60 (£74), Set D £14 (£23) to £65 (£80). Minimum £15
at L. Service 12.5%
CARDS: Access, Amex, Diners, Visa
SEATS: 130. Private parties: 30 main room, 6 and 8 private rooms. Vegetarian meals.
Children welcome. Wheelchair access. Music. Air-conditioned

Thailand map 10

15 Lewisham Way, SE14 6PP	COOKING 2
081-691 4040	COST £32

A tiny restaurant seating 25 in a square room that 'feels like someone's living
room', dominated by huge Thai paintings. The ceiling has a stained-glass map
of South-East Asia inset into the tiles. A prominent sign by the front door asks
customers to leave the table flowers intact. Victor Herman is Glaswegian; his
wife is an ethnic Lao, from the part of Thailand that was once Laos. She cooks
'the way she did in her own village', and the results have dazzled even those
who have eaten in Thailand itself. The menu of around 80 dishes is written in
Thai, with English descriptions but no anglicised names. It includes a number
of rare specialities from Laos. Highlights have included 'the best prawn yum
tum soup I have eaten outside Thailand, with the combination of chilli, lemon
grass and other spices judged to perfection.' Also mentioned are catfish in thick
chilli sauce, fried rice balls with minced pork, and various accompaniments

including prawn fried rice with fresh coriander, mixed Thai noodles, and vegetable curry in a coconut cream-based sauce. Fresh mango is the best way of finishing. The style is refreshingly unpretentious and service is charming. The restaurant also boasts a creditable wine list, of which some bottles are organic. Otherwise the range of drinks extends beyond Thai beer into organic apple juice and soya milk with honey and malt. House Sicilian: £6.50.

CHEF: Khamkong Kambungoet PROPRIETORS: Victor and Khamkong Herman
OPEN: Tue to Sun, D only
CLOSED: 25 and 26 Dec, 1 Jan
MEALS: 6 to 10.30
PRICES: £16 (£27)
CARDS: Access, Amex, Diners, Visa
SEATS: 25. Private parties: 25 main room. Vegetarian meals. Children restricted. Music

Tiramisu
map 11

327 West End Lane, NW6 1LN
071-433 1221

COOKING 1
COST £36

The London restaurant scene is seeing an Italian resurgence, and Tiramisu is part of the second wave. It is easy to spot the creamy white building with its black lettering, next door to the fire station. Inside feels Mediterranean. There are red tiles on the floor, prints of Italian scenes on the walls, and tiramisu itself holds pride of place on a square table in the middle of the slightly cramped dining-room. The menu is short and modern, dealing in colourful, vivid ideas. Many dishes are marked for vegetarians and for those who favour 'cucina naturale'. Ingredients – especially fish – are excellent, olive oil is everywhere, but dishes can lack flavour and noticeable seasoning. Even so, the kitchen can deliver some fine dishes: grilled oyster mushrooms piled on a rucola salad; medallions of monkfish on a bed of fresh spinach, surrounded by half a dozen mussels in their shells; risotto with scallops and lime. Fish dishes outshine meat and game, although Dutch calf's liver with spinach and cheese has been cooked perfectly pink. The quality of the pasta shows in cannelloni, perhaps done the old way with tomato and minced beef sauce, or the new way stuffed with aubergine and ricotta cheese. Vegetables are miniatures. Apart from the eponymous dessert, there's a small choice of creamy mille-feuille, fruit salad and strudel to finish. Service copes admirably, even under pressure. Italians rightly dominate the wine list; quality is there at a price but erratic annotations with growers not always listed do not encourage confidence. Any list which includes the Valpolicella 'La Grola' and the Rosso from Capezzano, however, shows intelligent and careful buying. House wine: £7.

CHEFS: Mrs Chiappa and Alberto Chiappa PROPRIETORS: Mrs Chiappa and Francesco Marzano
OPEN: all week, exc Sat L
CLOSED: 25 and 26 Dec
MEALS: 12 to 3, 6.30 to 11.30 (12 Sat)
PRICES: £20 (£30)
CARDS: Access, Visa
SEATS: 40. 5 tables outside. Private parties: 40 main room. Car-park, 4 places. Vegetarian meals. Children welcome. No cigars/pipes in dining-room. Wheelchair access. Music. Air-conditioned

Topkapi

map 11

25 Marylebone High Street, W1M 3PE
071-486 1872

COOKING 1
COST £17–£24

A reliable, if tight packed, goal for a lunchtime pilgrimage in Marylebone, where everything is cheerful. Meze, predictably, is the best bet. The menu is none too long: 15 meze dishes that keep to the orthodox. Also recommended are the mixed kebabs and the Adana kofte, served with a hot sauce. The rate of turnover is so fast that incidentals have no chance to hang about: the pitta, the big salads and the olives at the start. There are some Turkish wines at £8.50. Others are adequate, mostly French and not too expensive. House wine is from Alexis Lichine at £6.50 and £8.

CHEFS: R. Kalayci and Hasan Bafli   PROPRIETOR: U. Fahri
OPEN: all week
MEALS: noon to midnight
PRICES: £12 (£20), Set L and D £12.50 (£17). Service 10%
CARDS: Access, Amex, Diners, Visa
SEATS: 50. Private parties: 20 main room. Vegetarian meals. Children's helpings.
Wheelchair access (also WC). Music. Air-conditioned

Topsy-Tasty

map 10

5 Station Parade, Burlington Lane, W4 3HD
081-995 3407

COOKING 1
COST £24

Like its elder brother, the Bedlington Café (see entry), this place has inherited its name from a former life. It has decorated ceilings, a prettily tiled floor and soft wall lighting. The tables and chairs are embellished with stencilled patterns of little lemons. Prices are higher than at Fauconberg Road, but the menu is a similar vivid mix of Thai dishes backed up by a few specialities from Japan and Vietnam. An inspection meal featured fiery squid salad; chicken and coconut soup, fragrant with lemon grass and kaffir lime leaves; stir-fried Siamese pork with garlic; and Vietnamese king prawns with baby sweetcorn. 'We came away with lingering memories of fresh, herby flavours, and scents that could become very addictive.' The atmosphere is brisk and busy, and the restaurant does good business with takeaways. No credit cards and no licence, but you can bring your own – and coffee is a bottomless cup.

CHEF: Tsiva   PROPRIETOR: Mrs P. Priyanu
OPEN: Mon to Sat, D only
MEALS: 6.30 to 11
PRICES: £13 (£20)
SEATS: 45. Private parties: 40 main room. Vegetarian meals. Children welcome. Music

---

All details are as accurate as possible at the time of going to press, but chefs and owners often change, and it is wise to check by telephone before making a special journey. Many readers have been disappointed when set-price bargain meals are no longer available. Ask when booking.

▲ Truffles, Portman
Inter-Continental Hotel
map 11

22 Portman Square, W1H 9FL   COOKING 3
071-486 5844   COST £23–£35

It is never easy to create a restaurant within a large modern hotel. It has to play its part as a service to people staying the night but every chef would like to impose his own identity and have it a place to visit for its own sake. David Dorricott is a London chef who works within a classical framework – you need *Larousse Gastronomique* to translate the names of some of the dishes on the menu – and who deserves more notice. This dining-room has adopted the dark-wood-glazed-screen route to breaking up the large space needed to accommodate everybody, so that most tables are in their own booths. It works. The menu runs to maybe a dozen choices and is competitively priced for this level of London life. Even more competitive is the set-price lunch, no-choice but no stinting on materials. Classicism is evident in a dish such as 'royale de ceps aux têtes d'asperges' – a poached dariole of consommé, ceps, egg yolks and cream or bechamel, with a mushroom sauce that cleverly was made to taste quite distinct from the ceps. The overall effect was like eating solid mushroom soup. Modern cooking is also explored in a parsley soup that came with 'copeaux sarlaidaise', thin slices of potato and truffles. A liquor of flat parsley with cream, it was a perfect colour but almost too thick and certainly too salty. Similar contrasts between old and new wave may be made throughout the meal. A good standard fillet came with a confit of shallots on one side and goujons of grilled sea bass on a cool sauce of raw tomato, diced red pepper parsley and tarragon on the other. This latter combination was especially successful. Occasional moves towards gratuitous complexity are to be regretted and some of the ingredients, for example an artichoke mousse beneath langoustine tails, are so transmogrified in their rendering (classicism again) that they remain as textures, not flavours. The dessert trolley is acceptable; the bread basket is varied, some sorts better than others. The wine list, decently selected, deserves notice for efforts not to overcharge for everything, or at least to offer a range of prices with a fair number below £15, and two even below £10 along with a few half-bottles. House wine: £9.50 and £11.

CHEF: David Dorricott   PROPRIETORS: Inter-Continental Hotels Corporation
OPEN: all week, exc Sat L
CLOSED: 26 Dec
MEALS: 12.30 to 2.30 (3 Sun), 7 to 10.30
PRICES: Set L £18.50 (£23), Set D from £24.50 (£29). Service inc
CARDS: Access, Amex, Diners, Visa
SEATS: 75. Private parties: 400 ballroom, 20 to 160 private rooms. Vegetarian meals alc. Children's helpings. Wheelchair access (also WC). Music. Air-conditioned
ACCOMMODATION: 272 rooms, all with bath/shower. Rooms for disabled. Lift. B&B £152 to £162. Baby facilities. Guide dogs only. Afternoon teas. Tennis. Air-conditioning. TV. Phone. Confirm by 6

Tui

map 12

19 Exhibition Road, SW7 2HE
071-584 8359

COOKING 1
COST £31

'Authentic food, straight out of Phetburi Road, Bangkok', is one enthusiastic
view of the cooking in this modish restaurant overshadowed by the Victoria
and Albert Museum. It has shown up well on closer inspection, providing
better-than-average dishes at slightly higher-than-usual prices. The menu is
accessibly short, concentrating on soups, fish, curries and noodles. Prawn tom
yum, a classic soup, is vividly laced with chilli and lemon grass. Good
ingredients and well-judged spicing are the hallmarks of the kitchen. Other
recommendations have included fishcakes, spring rolls, catfish with chilli
sauce, and 'delicate' noodles with prawns and vegetables. Coconut ice-cream,
served inside a baby coconut shell, is better than most of the other sweets. The
decor is all black and white, with a black ceiling fan, long windows and dining
areas on various levels. Service is discreet: everything runs quietly and
efficiently in an atmosphere devoid of background music. An obligatory cover
charge on top of 12.5% service seems unjustifiable. The short wine list includes
house French at £7.25. Otherwise stay with Singha Thai beer.

CHEFS: Mr and Mrs Kongsrivilai PROPRIETOR: Ekachai Thapthimthong
OPEN: all week
CLOSED: bank hols and 25 Dec
MEALS: 12 to 2.30 (12.30 to 3 Sun), 6.30 to 11 (7 to 10.30 Sun)
PRICES: £15 (£26). Cover 75p. Service 12.5%
CARDS: Access, Amex, Diners, Visa
SEATS: 52. Private parties: 12 main room. Vegetarian meals. Children welcome. No cigars/
pipes in dining-room. Wheelchair access

Tuk Tuk

map 11

330 Upper Street, N1 2XQ
071-226 0837

COOKING 1
COST £17

A tuk tuk is a tricycle taxi that bombs around the streets of Bangkok. This café
restaurant opposite the Screen on the Green bears the same relationship to
London's Thai cookery as tuk tuks do to the more comfortable conventional
taxis: it buzzes with hurry and life, and you may have as much difficulty getting
service as you do getting a tuk tuk to carry you to an unusual destination. The
menu is not long and centres on one-plate dishes. The noodle dishes are best
liked, for instance pahd kai ohb. Tom yum kung hot soup with prawns and rice
is suitably fiery, though many of the dishes are less chilli-hot than their like in
the home country. Among the first courses the satay has been thought bland,
but tod man pla, fried fish patties, are often enjoyed. This is not a place for a
lingering meal, but it does offer fair value and usually a happy atmosphere.
There is a short list of basic wines, or Singha and Tiger beers.

*The text of entries is based on unsolicited reports sent in by readers, backed up by
inspections conducted anonymously. The factual details under the text are from
questionnaires the* Guide *sends to all restaurants that feature in the book.*

CHEF: Mr Phonphongsavat   PROPRIETOR: Stephen Binns
OPEN: Mon to Sat, exc Sat L
CLOSED: 25 and 26 Dec, 1 Jan, bank hols
MEALS: 12 to 3, 6 to 11
PRICES: £10 (£14). Service 10%
CARDS: Access, Amex, Visa
SEATS: 100. 2 tables outside. Private parties: 60 main room. Vegetarian meals. Children
welcome. Wheelchair access. Music

Turner's

87–89 Walton Street, SW3 2HP
071-584 6711

map 12

COOKING 3
COST £23–£41

The L-shaped room is light, not overburdened with decoration, comfortable
and more pleasant near the window than down the tongue by the kitchen. The
food, too, is light, technically expert, and pleasingly understated. This makes
Turner's a place to visit regularly, and at lunch it is more affordable. There have
been changes since the last *Guide* in kitchen and front of house, but Brian
Turner will often be seen at tables. He makes a good, not too pushy, host.
Service is 'among the best in London, an impeccable balance between
attentiveness and discretion.' The kitchen is able to cope with assertive,
reviving flavours as well as homogeneous balances. Red mullet grilled, then
laid on a braised fennel with an orange sauce 'really startled the palate into
life'; strips of young rabbit lightly cooked and marinated in virgin olive oil was
'a juxtaposition of simple forthright flavours'; while a brandade of sole and
garlic on a French bacon salad was a wonderfully rich taste cut through
piercingly by finely chopped green olives. Main courses that have been as
successful as these beginnings have included a whole sweetbread cooked in
caul, then served sliced lengthwise on a dark reduction tasting strongly of
truffles; fillet of veal wrapped in a cabbage leaf with a foie gras mousse on a
chive butter sauce that managed to be restrained enough for one who dislikes
too much foie gras; or monkfish on ratatouille with a tomato and saffron sauce
swirled with a little garlic mayonnaise. Vegetables come separately and are
usually praised, though the invariable gratin of potatoes is not always what is
needed. Pastry work is also efficient, witness a raspberry frangipane, an
individual apple and bilberry tart, and an apple strudel with great vanilla ice-
cream, though a shortbread with red fruits was not so well received. Just as the
cooking is well judged for balance, so its portions are none too gross, but 'my
18-year old nephew was contemplating a pizza for tea.' The music is on only at
the beginning and the end of the evening. The wine list is not too long but it is
well chosen. Search the bin-ends for possibilities. An award cannot be given as
a list was not sent to us. House wines: £11.50 and £12.50.

CHEF/PROPRIETOR: Brian J. Turner
OPEN: all week, exc Sat L
MEALS: 12.30 to 2.30, 7.30 to 11 (7 to 10 Sun)
PRICES: Set L £17 (£23) to £19 (£25), Set D £23.50 (£29) to £28.50 (£34). Service inc
CARDS: Access, Amex, Diners, Visa
SEATS: 52. Private parties: 22 main room. Vegetarian meals with prior notice. Children's
helpings. Smart dress preferred. Wheelchair access (2 steps). Music. Air-conditioned

Upper Street Fish Shop

map 11

324 Upper Street, N1 2XQ
071-359 1401

COOKING 1
COST £13

One of the best fish and chip restaurants in London: crowded, with a 'fun atmosphere'. The fun is in the hands of the ubiquitous Olga Conway. The fish is in the hands of husband Alan. He gets it fresh, then deep fries it to order. If it's sole or halibut it's shallow-fried in egg. Cod in traditional batter has a big following. Also to be had are Irish rock oysters and home-made fish soup that's more 'a chowder without shellfish'. Save room for English puddings with custard and for Bakewell tart. If you don't want to drink tea, bring your own bottles and glasses.

CHEF: Alan Conway PROPRIETORS: Olga and Alan Conway
OPEN: Mon to Sat, exc Mon L
CLOSED: bank hols
MEALS: 12 to 2 (3 Sat), 5.30 to 10
PRICES: £10 (£11). Unlicensed, but bring your own: no corkage
SEATS: 50. Children's helpings. Wheelchair access. Air-conditioned

Very Simply Nico SEE Chez Nico

Wakaba

map 11

122A Finchley Road, NW3 5LG
071-722 3854

COOKING 1
COST £13−£41

The dramatic interior of white panels, curving window, interesting shapes and pillars give pure form to the bare floor and tables. The sushi bar stretches across the back wall. The form is further reflected in the austere arrangement of the food. Sushi is the best item but salt-grilled fish, good soups and sukiyaki or shabu shabu prepared at the table are also satisfactory. Sapporo or Kirin beers or saké would be drinks in keeping with the food. There is also non-alcoholic calpis, an unusual milk-based drink.

CHEF/PROPRIETOR: Minoru Yoshihara
OPEN: Mon to Sat
CLOSED: 1 week Aug, 5 days at Christmas, 4 days at Easter
MEALS: 12 to 2.30, 6.30 to 11
PRICES: £23 (£27), Set L £9 (£13) to £12 (£17), Set D £21.50 (£25) to £30 (£34). Service inc
CARDS: Access, Amex, Diners, Visa
SEATS: 55. Private parties: 60 main room. Children's helpings on request. Wheelchair access (also WC). Air-conditioned

---

Consumers' Association is planning to publish Out to Eat, *a new guide to budget eating out in restaurants, pubs, cafés, brasseries and so on. Please send reports and recommendations to Out to Eat, FREEPOST, 2 Marylebone Road, London NW1 1YN.*

County Round-ups listing additional restaurants that may be worth a visit are at the back of the Guide, *after the Irish section. Reports on Round-up entries are welcome.*

Wiltons

map 13

55 Jermyn Street, SW1Y 6LX
071-629 9955

COOKING 2
COST £55

Wiltons is the paradigm of British restaurants in the capital. It is reasonably comfortable, though less spacious than some; the service is traditional and characterful; the cooking is simple and expensive. The fish and game is of high quality and it is cooked simply and well. The more complicated dishes, involving sauces, of which there are few, are not so well executed. Desserts and cheeses are equally traditional and plain. Prices are high, but the experience is more exclusive than in many such places. The wine list does not give much respite from expenditure, but house wine costs only £10.50.

CHEF: Ross Hayden PROPRIETORS: Wiltons (St James's) Ltd
OPEN: Mon to Sat, exc Sat L
CLOSED: 3 weeks Aug
MEALS: 12 to 2.30, 6 to 10.30
PRICES: £31 (£46). Minimum £12.50
CARDS: Access, Amex, Diners, Visa
SEATS: 90. Private parties: 20 main room, 16 private room. Vegetarian meals with prior notice. Children welcome. Smart dress preferred. No cigars in dining-room. Wheelchair access (1 step). Air-conditioned

Wódka

map 11

12 St Alban's Grove, W8 5PN
071-937 6513

COOKING 2
COST £30

This Polish restaurant occupies tiny premises in a corner of Kensington that might be a set for a lovable Ealing comedy about London eccentrics and backwaters. Decoration is grey and spare: tiles in the front room, stripped pine further back, not much downstairs, chairs that are comfortable for about an hour and a half, bare tables and music that goes on and on. The young staff are amiable and effective; the cooking is Polish with franco-brasserie overtones. The dominant flavouring is acid – pickles or dill or sour cream, for instance – mellowed especially by mushrooms, and the menu is fairly static. Dishes that may be recommended include the caviare and blinis; wild mushroom soup; pierogi filled with sauerkraut and mushrooms (these ravioli can be a mite tough, being finished in dry heat rather than boiled as is the style in other Polish restaurants); fishcakes with a dill sauce; zrazy, a beef olive wrapped round pickled cucumber and bacon; rhubarb kissel; and a slightly floury crème brûlée. Sauces are thinner than some Polish cooks produce, and the cooking is lighter – occasionally lighter on flavour, too. A pleasantly relaxed place to go, though it may get very busy. The food is easy to eat and delicious accompanied by Tetra beer or the range of good vodkas served at the right temperature, or with one of the thoroughly modern, intelligently chosen wines from the short list. House wine: £7.50.

All entries in the Guide *are rewritten every year, not least because restaurant standards fluctuate. Don't trust an out of date* Guide.

CHEF: Tony Rowe   PROPRIETOR: Jan Woroniecki
OPEN: all week, exc Sat L and Sun L
CLOSED: bank hols
MEALS: 12.15 to 2.30, 7 to 11
PRICES: £16 (£25)
CARDS: Access, Amex, Diners, Visa
SEATS: 60. Private parties: 10 main room, 30 private room. Vegetarian meals. Children welcome. 3 steps to rest. Music. Air-conditioned

Zamoyski's

map 11

85 Fleet Road, NW3 2QY
071-794 4792

COOKING 1
COST £16–£23

The advantage of many Polish and Eastern European restaurants in London is that they are cheap or good value. Their disadvantage is that the cooking could often be better. Zamoyski is a wine bar (downstairs) and restaurant (upstairs), and food may be had in each. The atmosphere is often jolly, with live music a couple of nights a week (violins, accordions and singers are mentioned) making it even jollier and softening the impact of hard benches and chairs. Polish food can be lighter and more delicate in taste than appears to the eye, and some dishes are well liked: potato and walnut latkes for a first course; pierogi (like a Polish ravioli) with three different fillings and a mushroom sauce; stuffed carp; zrazy (beef olives); and gotabki (stuffed cabbage). Main dishes come with potatoes and a hot vegetable and, disconcertingly, a cold cooked vegetable or salad. The microwave is in evidence in the wine bar and dishes in the restaurant can cool on a side-shelf if you have not yet finished your first course when they are ready. Desserts are not a strong point. Service is very willing and pleasing, but there is a lack of pacing in the accepted restaurant sense and 'one waitress between 38 customers' is not enough. The 'no-smoking area' is a somewhat indeterminate zone: there were ashtrays on every table on one night. There are vodkas, beer and a wine list with a fair spread and fairer prices. House wine: £6.75.

CHEF: Christopher Witkowski   PROPRIETORS: Kathy Witkowska and Christopher Witkowski
OPEN: Mon to Sat
MEALS: 12 to 2, 5.30 to 11
PRICES: £13 (£17), Set L £12 (£16), Set D £15 (£19). Service inc for parties of 5 or more
SEATS: 72. Private parties: 38 main room. Vegetarian meals. Children's helpings. Smart dress preferred. Music. Air-conditioned

Zen

map 12

Chelsea Cloisters,
Sloane Avenue, SW3 3DN
071-589 1781

COOKING 1
COST £19–£59

In its early years, this doyen of new-wave Chinese restaurants received high acclaim from the *Guide*. It seemed to redefine the notion of Chinese food in London with its overt emphasis on 'healthiness', stunning decor, and a deliberate fusion of East and West in the kitchen. Since then it has been bedevilled by inconsistency. One reader's experience was that: 'A meal for two dozen guests ranked as one of the finest Chinese meals I have ever enjoyed.' Yet a similar feast a few months later was 'not remotely comparable', with minimal quantities of 'almost cold' Peking duck, overcooked watery sea bass and, the final blow, the credit card slip left blank after £120 had been paid in service and cover charges for 19 people. However, the kitchen is capable of delivering the goods, and the menu does operate in areas that are not inhabited by most comparable Chinese restaurants: Szechuan-style spicy ducks' tongues; braised whole abalone with oyster sauce; barbecued eel fillet marinated in honey and shredded mooli with rice vermicelli and grated dried seafood show the possibilities. The dining-room was being revamped and extended with new 'party rooms' as we went to press; one hopes the kitchen will move up a gear in sympathy. A good wine list has a fair spread of price offering many below £14 and top-rank clarets at not impossible prices. Three well-chosen house wines: £9. CELLARMAN'S CHOICE: Meursault Chevalières, Dom. Prieur-Brunet 1987, £25.

CHEF: K.S. Leung PROPRIETOR: Lawrence Leung
OPEN: all week
CLOSED: 25 to 27 Dec
MEALS: 12 to 3, 6 to 11.30 (noon to midnight Sat and Sun)
PRICES: £19 (£39), Set L £11.50 (£19) to £13.50 (£22), Set D £28 (£39) to £38 (£49). Cover £1. Minimum £10 after 7pm. Service 15%
CARDS: Access, Amex, Diners, Visa
SEATS: 120. 35 tables outside. Private parties: 110 main room, 20 private room. Vegetarian meals. Children's helpings. Smart dress preferred. No cigars/pipes in dining-room. Wheelchair access. Music. Air-conditioned

Zen Central
map 13

20 Queen Street, W1X 7PJ   COOKING 1
071-629 8089   COST £40

The most recent of the Zen chain is a mirrored room with a cascade of plants at the back, 1930s style lighting and gushes of water that do not always run. The menu is confusing to follow, but looks more challenging than it really is. Zen's notion of 'nouvelle Chinese' seems to be confined to quantities; cooking styles and techniques don't offer much that is radically new. Many dishes seem timid and low on 'the scale of taste', but Zen's MSG-free policy is a scoring point. Readers have praised shark's fin and seafood soup; Peking ravioli (Zen-speak for 'wun-tun') with chilli sauce; tiny pieces of veal flash-fried with a fair coating of black pepper; and bean curd with Chinese mushrooms. Sea bass is cooked five ways: the steamed version with tangerine peel has been fresh, soft textured and fragrant. Service is very proficient: some dishes are given western-style 'silver service' treatment. The real sticking point is the pricing policy: dishes are not cheap, but accumulated extras of £14 for two (accounting for service and cover charges) are 'hideous by any standard'. The wine list mark-ups can also contribute sizeably to the bill, but it has been sensibly planned, with some good and appropriate bottles to match the food. House vin de pays £12.

CHEF: Michael Leung   PROPRIETORS: Blaidwood Ltd
OPEN: all week
MEALS: 12 to 2.30, 6.30 to 11.30 (6 to 11 Sun)
PRICES: £17 (£33). Cover £1. Service 15%
CARDS: Access, Amex, Carte Blanche, Diners, Visa
SEATS: 110. Private parties: 80 main room, 20 private room. Vegetarian meals. Children welcome. Smart dress preferred. Wheelchair access. Music. Air-conditioned

Zen W3   map 11

83 Hampstead High Street, NW3 1RE   COOKING 1
071-794 7863 and 7864   COST £15–£31

The Zen chain has always conjured up a designer version of Chinese cuisine, cleverly tailored to western tastes. For many, its authenticity and vividness are debatable. Zen W3 is the most extreme of the three related restaurants. Gone is the usual 'laundry list' menu: in its place is a small selection of 'healthy, evolved dishes, spicy salads, steamed fish, lightning-fried meat...' It is all very hyped, very modern. Dishes are given trendy cocktail bar names: 'Skinny Dips' are pieces of pork crackling and crispy chicken skin with a dipping sauce; 'Red Bird' is a variation of Yuk Shung – minced quail wrapped in raddichio rather than iceberg lettuce; the carnivorous-sounding 'Alligator Salad' is actually a vegetarian concoction of avocado and sesame oil. Opinion is so divided that it is difficult to see any kind of consensus. Some love the atmosphere, the elegance of the place and its 'pretty rooms', and praise the 'brilliant' crispy fried duck with pancakes and sea-spice aubergines. Others lament the minuscule portions, high prices, surly service and standards of cleanliness. Money may have been lavished on the dining-room, but one reader described toilets as 'squalid'. In keeping with the prevailing mood of westernised modernism, the wine list spans the globe for good vintages from good producers. House wine: £8.

CHEF: Michael K.S. Leung   PROPRIETORS: Blaidwood Ltd
OPEN: all week
CLOSED: 25 and 26 Dec
MEALS: noon to 11.30 (11 Sun)
PRICES: £13 (£26), Set L £9 (£15). Service 12.5%
CARDS: Access, Amex, Diners, Visa
SEATS: 135. Private parties: 100 main room, 24 private room. Vegetarian meals. Children welcome. Smart dress preferred. Wheelchair access (2 steps). Music. Air-conditioned

England

map 2

▲ Thame Lane House

1 Thame Lane, Abingdon OX14 3DS
ABINGDON (0235) 524177

COOKING 2
COST £16–£26

Look for the sign to the European School, pointing up a dead-end off the
Abingdon to Dorchester road. This guest-house stands at the corner of the lane.
It is itself European in that Marie-Claude Beech is French and cooks French
food. Non-residents must book for dinner or lunch in the small dining-room
with only a few tables. Pheasant à la parisienne, coarse pigeon terrine, and
petits pots au chocolat may imply this is just good home French cooking, but
mango and avocado salad with a lime dressing; salade tiède with chicken
livers; noisettes of lamb on a yellow pepper sauce; crème bavarois on a
strawberry sauce indicate that restaurant culture exists here too. There are two
or three choices in each course and the menu is composed each day according to
bookings. Residents get less choice but the cooking is as assured. There is a
short wine list, but longer and better than might be thought necessary for the
small operation. CELLARMAN'S CHOICE: Ch. de Fieuzal 1985, £20; Riesling
d'Alsace 1986, £9. More reports, please.

CHEF: Marie-Claude Beech   PROPRIETORS: Michael and Marie-Claude Beech
OPEN: all week
CLOSED: 2 weeks at Christmas
MEALS: 12.30 to 1, 7 to 8.30
PRICES: Set L and D £12 (£16) to £18 (£22). Service inc
SEATS: 16. Private parties: 16 main room. Car-park, 8 places. Children's helpings on
request. No children under 3. Smart dress preferred. No smoking in dining-room
ACCOMMODATION: 5 rooms, 1 with bath/shower. B&B £25 to £45. Deposit: £5. No children
under 3. Garden. TV. Doors close at 11.30. Confirm by 6.30

map 3

▲ Austins

243 The High Street, Aldeburgh IP15 5DN
ALDEBURGH (0728) 453932

COOKING 1
COST £16–£30

Some call it a plushly decorated guest-house, others a hotel, but all agree, it's
friendly, comfortable and an ideal touring base for this part of Suffolk.
Performers at the Festival may feel at home in the bar filled with theatrical

memorabilia. Julian Alexander-Worster's cooking has its supporters as well: well crafted and enjoyable with some emphasis on local fish in a short *carte* that may be supplemented by daily specials. 'After a concert, I had a very good supper of smoked salmon and scrambled egg Elizabeth David-style, goats' cheese and fruit followed by a smooth, rich, dark chocolate pot. The next day, asparagus soup with rings of asparagus and chicken brochette with satay sauce confirmed my favourable assessment.' The choice is meant to reassure, not amaze, with dishes such as a filo basket filled with steamed broccoli and a hollandaise; whitebait; plaice fillets round a duxelle of ham and mushroom with a white wine sauce; or pork on a pea purée with a tomato coulis. Service is extremely pleasant and very welcoming. There is a decent short wine list. House wine: from £6 and £6.40. CELLARMAN'S CHOICE: Mâcon-Clessé 1987, Signoret, £12.50; Beaumes-de-Venise rouge, Ch. Redortier 1985, £10.15.

CHEF: Julian Alexander-Worster   PROPRIETORS: Robert Selbie and
Julian Alexander-Worster
OPEN: Tue to Sat D, and Sun L (other days by arrangement for parties)
CLOSED: first two weeks Feb
MEALS: 12.30 to 2, 7.30 to 11
PRICES: £17 (£25), Set Sun L £11.50 (£16). Cover £1
CARDS: Access, Amex, Visa
SEATS: 30. Private parties: 30 main room. Children's helpings. No children under 12.
No cigars/pipes in dining-room
ACCOMMODATION: 7 rooms, all with bath/shower. B&B £35.75 to £61. Deposit: 10%. TV

Regatta

171–173 High Street, Aldeburgh IP15 5AN   COOKING 1
ALDEBURGH (0728) 452011   COST £13–£26

A wine bar and restaurant that may look nothing outside but is usually crammed with people, hung with good pictures, decorated with a dominant marine mural, and generally hums with fair satisfaction. Some readers prefer the informality, lower prices and simpler food of the wine bar side but all praise the enthusiasm of the service, forgiving occasional glitches. Chefs may come and go with discernible frequency but the essentially modern style of the cooking, leavened by fresh fish, continues. Recommendations, from both sides of the business, include smoked haddock and mushrooms dusted with Parmesan; steak and kidney pie; mushroom and courgette soup; terrine of trout fillets with sour cream and chives; Gressingham duck with sherry and soy sauce; grilled Dover or lemon sole; passion-fruit bavarois; and a chocolate and brandy mousse. The only down-note was a turkey lasagne three days after Christmas. Vegetarians report well on an onion and cream tart with a tomato coulis, and praise for soups is almost universal. The wine list is fuelled by Lay and Wheeler and fairly priced for a good range of bottles from more countries than France. The link with the firm Champagne de Villages, which meant some interesting Champagnes and other items, is no longer in evidence. House wine: £6.25. CELLARMAN'S CHOICE: Ch. Nicot 1988, £7.95; Riesling Henschke 1987, £9.95. There's a new sister branch, Bloxsome's Regatta, at 1 Church Street, Woodbridge (0394 380888).

CHEF: Mike Leeds   PROPRIETORS: Peter G.R. Hill and Sara E. Fox
OPEN: all week
MEALS: 12 to 2.30 (12.30 to 2 Sun), 7 to 10.15
PRICES: bar £9 (£13), restaurant £16 (£22)
CARDS: Access, Visa
SEATS: 90. 4 tables outside. Private parties: 25 main room. Children's helpings. Wheelchair access (2 steps)

ALFRISTON   East Sussex   map 3

Moonrakers ♟

High Street, Alfriston BN26 5TD   COOKING 1
ALFRISTON (0323) 870472   COST £28

Over the centuries, the level of the village High Street has gone up while that of Moonrakers, a handsome sixteenth-century house, has stayed the same. Hence the descent into the restaurant from the front door. The ground continues to fall away to the garden, where the diner may be constrained to wander in search of the outside lavatories. Elaine Wilkinson cooks a short set-price menu of six choices in each course. Her style pays little attention to culinary revolution but is well honed to what her customers like. Many of the dishes are fixtures and others are regular encores. Meals are sufficiently affordable to attract a strong following of regulars. It is they who 'insisted' that the hot Sussex smokie, flaked haddock in a bechamel browned under the grill, be retained from the menu of the Wilkinsons predecessors. Favourites include beef Wellington; duck, crisp and not fatty, with oranges or orange liqueur; and sole with a white wine sauce and prawns. The food is freshly cooked, but some find it a drawback that it is cooked according to old rules. Desserts have included excellent syllabub. The wine list has a good spread and some excellent growers from inside and outside France, at fair prices. Some of the 1984s may be taking a risk, but they have the justification of price in their favour. There is a nice set of Germans. House French is £6.50. CELLARMAN'S CHOICE: Ch. Thieuley 1987, £12.70; Ch. Tahbilk Shiraz 1985, £13.50.

CHEF: Elaine Wilkinson   PROPRIETORS: Elaine and Barry Wilkinson
OPEN: Tue to Sat, D only
MEALS: 7 to 9.15 (6.45 to 9.45 Sat)
PRICES: Set D £17.90 (£23)
SEATS: 32. 2 tables outside. Private parties: 32 main room. Children's helpings

---

ALNWICK   Northumberland   map 7

John Blackmore's

1 Dorothy Foster Court, Narrowgate,
Alnwick NE66 1NL   COOKING 3
ALNWICK (0665) 604465   COST £28

Dorothy Foster was a Jacobite of the eighteenth century, and certainly John Blackmore's restaurant, now equipped with a first-floor sitting-room for smoking and drinking, has signs of age from the flagstones to the big fires and

the relics of medieval Alnwick found while making improvements. Signs that
life is as commercially tough today as it was when the raiders crossed the
border are found in the decision to close for lunch. A pity for resident and
traveller both, but the Blackmores have found there's a limit to the day.
Evening prices have also increased on the *carte*, reinforcing the impression
gained from the furnishings that the aim is to go upmarket. The cooking is
dedicated to sauces. These may be too strong in some instances, although one
table was pleased by a dinner of roast partridge with a leek and asparagus
sauce (the asparagus definitely in the minor key); chicken with Emmenthal
cheese, wrapped in cured ham and served with a potato cake and a tarragon
sauce; and trout with a mousse of monkfish and prawns with a white wine,
smoked trout and dill sauce – even if the nearly raw vegetables, commented on
by others, were less impressive for anything but colour. Cooking is
professional and sometimes complicated, a small piece of salmon is, in this
instance, well balanced by a smoked salmon sauce, not too cream-laden to clog
up the fish and decorated with pastry squares and fresh tarragon. Dishes come
with built-in complements: a broccoli mousse with fillet steak, kidneys with
lamb noisettes, fish mousse with trout. Desserts can include hot dishes, such as
the apple and raspberry tart, or a correctly made crème brûlée. Truffles with the
coffee may be an incentive to stay on. The wine list grows, now having a fine
wine supplement at fairly stiff prices. The main list, however, is inexpensive
but there is little evidence of enthusiasm for the subject. House French: £5.90.

CHEF: John Blackmore   PROPRIETORS: John and Penny Blackmore
OPEN: Tue to Sat D
CLOSED: Jan
MEALS: 7 to 9.30
PRICES: £17 (£23)
CARDS: Access, Amex, Diners, Visa
SEATS: 25. Private parties: 30 main room. Vegetarian meals. Children's helpings. Smart
dress preferred. No smoking in dining-room. Wheelchair access (1 step). Music

---

AMBLESIDE   Cumbria   map 7

▲ Kirkstone Foot
Country House Hotel

| Kirkstone Pass Road, Ambleside LA22 9EH | COOKING 1 |
| AMBLESIDE (0966) 32232 | COST £25 |

The sweets trolley goes twice round the dining-room – and hardly a scrap
remains. Before that moment of sweet-tooth bliss, there is a choice of three in
two savoury courses separated by a soup. The Batemans have retired to the
south of France, sunny respite from Lakeland tempest, though they retain
ownership. Their daughter and son-in-law, whose presence had been noted in
the 1990 *Guide*, have taken over. It is only acknowledgement of the new,
perhaps, that caused one regular to say, 'I think it is better,' but certainly the
transition has been well handled. Jane Cross's cooking is 'of the type more
liked north of the Wash', substantial, generous and very fair value. The menu

will always carry a vegetarian main-course option – tortellini with cream cheese, for instance – as well as either meat or fish. Roasts often feature, but not invariably. First courses include a vegetable- or fruit-based composition and may be substantial, as in smoked Cumberland sausage with tomato, mushroom, onion and madeira sauce. After the trolley of sweets, of which the 'queen of puddings was superb,' comes cheese. The wine list is catholic with a strong Australasian selection and a full slate of Beaujolais crus from Duboeuf. There is generous provision of half-bottles; prices are reasonable. House Duboeuf: £6.

CHEFS: Jane Cross and Val Walker   PROPRIETORS: Jane and Simon Bateman
OPEN: all week, D only
CLOSED: Jan to early Feb
MEALS: 8
PRICES: Set D £16 (£21)
CARDS: Access, Visa
SEATS: 50. Private parties: 10 main room. Car-park, 30 places. Vegetarian meals. Children's helpings on request. No children under 7. Smart dress preferred. No smoking in dining-room. Wheelchair access (also WC). Music. One sitting
ACCOMMODATION: 16 rooms, all with bath/shower. D, B&B £39 to £84. Deposit: £20. Baby facilities. Pets welcome. Afternoon teas. Garden. Fishing. TV. Phone. Scenic

▲ *Rothay Manor* ▼

Rothay Bridge, Ambleside LA22 0EH   COOKING 2
AMBLESIDE (053 94) 33605   COST £9–£32

'It manages to get everything right' was one of many positive reports about the Nixons' country-house hotel a short sprint from Ambleside. The readers who found fault with the food acknowledged that the service was excellent and the welcome far warmer (for children, too) than they'd expected, given the polished antiques and formal flower sprays. Regency decor is most clear-cut in the brown and gold dining-room. Atmospheric overkill is restricted to the waitresses' long black gowns, white pinnies and mob caps. The set dinner menu lists recommended wines beside each dish. It is five courses but can be reduced to two with a price reduction. The cooking, essentially English, can be admirable. Favourable reports of decent vegetables, pea and ham soup, and pheasant with smoked bacon and fresh herbs balance those of undistinguished garlic mushrooms, overcooked duck, a lazy cheeseboard and lackadaisical seasoning. Liked were the kidneys in madeira and the white chocolate gateau. Weekday buffet lunches with good salads and, perhaps, rare roast beef, are inexpensive, as is the set Sunday lunch. One of the hotel lounges is now no-smoking as well as the dining-room. The long wine list has good years, a fine choice of clarets and burgundies, more than a token number of French country wines and bottles from Australia and the United States. Light or single imbibers can drink half a bottle of whatever and pay three-fifths the full price. Prices are generally fair, sometimes bargain. The layout looks demented, however. House Bulgarian is £6.50. CELLARMAN'S CHOICE: Hautes Côtes de Beaune, 1986, Robert Gibourg, £11.10: Orlando Cabernet Sauvignon, 1986,

£9.60; Gran Viña Sol, Torres, 1987, £12.30. The Nixons have a way of inspiring loyalty. Warmest praise comes from those who attend special weekends or festivals at the hotel. These constitute good value and the spirit of cheerfulness is infectious.

CHEFS: Jane Binns and Colette Nixon   PROPRIETORS: The Nixon families
OPEN: all week
CLOSED: last 3 weeks in Jan, first week Feb
MEALS: 12.30 to 2, (12.45 to 1.30 Sun), 8 to 9
PRICES: Set L £5 (£9) to £8 (£12), Sun L £11.50 (£16), Set D £16 (£21) to £21.50 (£27)
CARDS: Access, Amex, Diners, Visa
SEATS: 70. Private parties: 12 main room, 30 private room. Car-park, 30 places. Vegetarian meals. Children's helpings. Smart dress preferred. No smoking in dining-room. Wheelchair access (also unisex WC). Air-conditioned
ACCOMMODATION: 18 rooms, all with bath/shower. Rooms for disabled. B&B £60 to £94. Deposit: £50. Baby facilities. Afternoon teas. Garden. Fishing. TV. Phone. Scenic. Doors close at midnight. Confirm by noon [Which? Hotel Guide]

Sheila's Cottage

The Slack, Ambleside LA22 9DQ   COOKING 2
AMBLESIDE (053 94) 33079   COST £14–£32

What was once an exceptional tea-room in a slate-hung cottage off the busy marketplace has, by the conversion of a barn into the kitchen and adding dining space, graduated to a full-blown restaurant. Not that any of the team, still headed by the Greaves, has forgotten the origins. The teas continue in the upstairs café from 2.30 to 5, and so does the exemplary baking of breads and muffins. These, as well as sugar-baked ham, smoked salmon and potted shrimps, are offered alongside desserts from the restaurant menu to afternoon visitors. The principal menu of half a dozen items, buttressed by daily specials, concentrates on simplicity in modern dress: calf's liver on a rösti with Marsala sauce; chargrilled beef and brandy cream sauce; poached halibut and asparagus with a red pepper sauce. Reports agree that the team has responded well to the change of gear with but a few pockets of ignorance about the new-fangled cooking, and no more than occasional delays. Among the most favoured dishes have been: ham with rösti potatoes and fine relishes; wild venison with slightly bland Swiss noodles in a cheese sauce; grilled sea bream with a langoustine sauce; a seafood ragout; and puddings that strike an atavistic chord, such as syrup sponge, Swiss chocolate pudding or 'the best' sticky toffee pudding. Vegetables are served plain and copiously. There is a general desire to fuel the body substantially. Not that liquids are ignored: good tea, fresh orange juice, Swiss chocolate, home-made lemonade and country cordials feature, as well as an intelligent short wine list of sensible prices and range. House wine from Oisly and Thésée is £7.50. CELLARMAN'S CHOICE: Bernkasteler Lay Riesling Kabinett 1989, S.A. Prüm, £13; Antiguas Reservas Cabernet Sauvignon 1984, Cousiño-Macul, £9.25.

'In the New Forest apples and bananas appear to be exotic food.' On dining in Hampshire

CHEFS: Janice Greaves, Jane Sutherland, Peter Barnsley and Keith Anderson
PROPRIETOR: Stewart Greaves
OPEN: Mon to Sat
CLOSED: 2 weeks Jan
MEALS: 12 to 3.30, 6.30 to 9.30
PRICES: £17 (£23), Set L £8 (£14) to £12 (£18), Set D £16 (£23) to £20 (£27)
SEATS: 65. Private parties: 47 main room. Children's helpings (L only). No smoking.
Wheelchair access. Music

ASHBOURNE Derbyshire map 5

▲ *Callow Hall*

Mappleton Road, Ashbourne DE6 2AA COOKING 1
ASHBOURNE (0335) 43403 COST £16–£36

This large Victorian house, built by a corset manufacturer, started its new life as
a restaurant with rooms but has, by a process of restoration and improvement,
assumed more the character of an hotel. There are two dining-rooms: one
bright with views over the Dove valley, the other dark and enclosing. Match
the room to your mood. In either, the service will be formal, yet friendly and
attentive. David Spencer has translated his menu from French into English, a
triumph of common sense, and it reads appetisingly with a wide range of fish
available as either first or main course – remarkably wide given the Hall's
inland location. Readers have spoken well of first courses such as a warm salad
of pigeon with toasted almonds; good mussels; salmon fillet with a guacamole;
and light home-made rolls and brown bread. A main course of quails with
vermicelli was 'the best I've had for years' and others have remarked on well-
hung game and generous portions. Indeed, the cooking of the main course and
vegetables such as salsify, parsnips and broccoli, has been singled out as better
than the beginning of the meal – a rare attribute for chefs. Dessert may run to
the mousse/cream/ice end of the sweet spectrum, but most people stop at
pastries, puddings and tarts: Callow flan of almonds and raisins and light
bread-and-butter pudding set one man's evening alight. Coffee and petits fours
will finish the meal happily, away from the dining room if you are a smoker
where 'it is tolerated but not encouraged'. With two rooms, couldn't a more
definite policy be set? The wine list holds a number of bottles from the
merchants F. & E. May and does not overcharge for a range that shows most
interest in France. There are a few New Zealand bottles.

CHEF: David Spencer PROPRIETORS: David and Dorothy Spencer
OPEN: Mon to Sat D, and Sun L (other days by arrangement)
MEALS: 12.30 to 2.30, 7.30 to 9.30
PRICES: £22 (£30). Set Sun L £11 (£16), Set D £21.50 (£28)
CARDS: Access, Amex, Diners, Visa
SEATS: 80. Private parties: 50 main room, 50 private room. Car-park, 70 places. Children's
helpings (Sun L only)
ACCOMMODATION: 12 rooms, all with bath/shower. B&B £60 to £110. Deposit: £20. Baby
facilities. Garden. Fishing. TV. Phone. Scenic. Doors close at 11.30

Report forms are at the back of the book; write a letter if you prefer.

Buxford Mill

Bucksford Lane, Great Chart, TN23 2TZ   COOKING 2
ASHFORD (0233) 636247   COST £19–£41

The Mill at Buxford is lapped on either side by the tides of Ashford's new
housing, defended only by its waterworks and a new pond. It stands by its
heritage – a Kentish brick house with terrace entrance. Inside is arresting:
electric blue floral upholstery, pink cloths, pink lampshades and lavish table
settings within the context of English country architecture. Lunch and dinner
offer choices from a short *carte* and a no-choice set-price menu which Andrew
Leach cooks and presents in very much the English modern country mode. A
meal started with a moist and delicate gravlax; then a first course of a single
roast quail sitting on a potato galette, stuffed with pine kernels, with an
overstrong madeira glaze; loin of lamb with ceps and black-eye beans and a
thyme and red wine sauce; magret of goose with apples and oranges and a
jammy sauce sharpened with balsamic vinegar; moderately uninteresting
vegetables in the automatic modern fashion; and desserts of a fair bavarois and
a heavy shortbread cake of apricots. The kitchen is getting decent supplies and
the essentials of technique are there. Some of the peripherals, for example the
unthinking composition of apples and oranges with the magret of goose, suffer
from a 'modern British' love of messing things around or from a failure to
perceive faults even when they stare you in the face – such as the shortbread
cake. As with so many restaurants, future progress lies with the customers: if
elaboration is applauded, the cooking may get lost in a desire to impress; if
restraint and good flavour get the votes, ambition may be held in check so that
the basics are invariably correct. The wine list gives but a modicum of
information about growers and origins but includes a few decent options such
as wines from Durup, Guntrum and Leroy. House wines are £6.50. Running a
restaurant in Kent is not as easy as it should be. The customer base surely
appears rich, but there seems to be an unwillingness to go out to eat, unless it
be a splurge at weekends or power-eating for business. One consequence is
that prices are high. You cannot charge everyday prices if eating is only thought
of as a special event.

CHEF: Andrew Leach   PROPRIETORS: Anita and Barry Law
OPEN: Tue to Sun, exc Sun D
MEALS: 12 to 2.15, 7 to 9.45
PRICES: £26 (£34), Set L and D £12.95 (£19) to £15.95 (£23).
CARDS: Access, Amex, Diners, Visa
SEATS: 32. 3 tables outside. Private parties: 40 main room. Car-park. Vegetarian meals.
Children's helpings. Smart dress preferred. No smoking in dining-room. Wheelchair
access (2 steps)

---

*The 1992 Guide will be published before Christmas 1991. Reports on meals are most
welcome at any time of the year, but are extremely valuable in the spring. Send them to*
The Good Food Guide, *FREEPOST, 2 Marylebone Road, London NW1 1YN. No stamp
is needed if posted in the UK.*

ASTON CLINTON Buckinghamshire   map 3

▲ Bell ▮

Aston Clinton HP22 5HP   COOKING 3
AYLESBURY (0296) 630252   COST £22–£42

The Bell Inn is famous for its longevity – it was purchased by the late Gerard
Harris in 1940; for its wine list which is long, cheap, and mirrored by the stock
of the retail wine shop next door; and for its English character – although the
menu is in ornate French and the waiting staff is largely French. It has managed
to preserve some of the character of a country inn. People are even saying it
needs a face-lift, which is a sure sign of authenticity. Yet a further sign of
continuity is Jocelyn Rickards' murals of foodstuffs and bosky scenes in the
dining-room. They have a retro feel, harking back to the thirties, just as do the
dark polished tables and place mats. The menu, however, seems to have had bed
linen on the brain: fillet of red mullet on a 'duvet de nouailles', 'pillows of
mussel in a light saffron butter'. These are but prelude to 'a fine salad of
aphrodisiacs', and a dish that translates as 'treasure of the China seas drowned
in a fricassee of foie gras'; which must be the most horrible death sentence ever
passed on dish or diner. Such purple prose is restricted to the *carte*. This is quite
long and needs a buoyant trade to maintain the quality of supplies. The
cookery style is similar to the language: grandiose and ambitious, solecisms
not far round the corner. The daily lunch menu is cheaper by £2 than any main
course on the *carte*. It also includes a free kir at the bar. It can please immensely.
A warm salad of duck and quail with a raspberry vinaigrette; chilled
cauliflower soup with a trio of caviares; a mixture of seafood under a pastry
cover and genuinely perfumed with truffle; medallion of pork with a paprika
sauce in generous portions and accurately cooked. A handsome trio of sorbets
so enthused one reader that he substituted Champagne for the kir and did not
begrudge paying for it. There is also a set-price dinner menu which avoids the
extravagances, and the super-economic can have a 'one-plate lunch' as if in a
Chinese restaurant – for example, Irish stew with red cabbage. This attempt to
satisfy as wide a band of customers as possible is to be applauded. Some of the
more ambitious dishes on the *carte*, however, have been questioned: pig's
trotter stuffed with chicken was unevenly cooked, the sauce reduced to salt.
Other dishes did not seem to convey the luxury overtones implied in their
descriptions: truffles with lentil soup (a very modish mingling of the peasant
with the aristocrat); morels with salmon and asparagus. These luxuries crop up
everywhere, as in a risotto of langoustines and foie gras. While regulars are
convinced that standards this year have been higher than for some time past,
strangers have suggested that the cooking maintains a steady level just below
the prices charged for it. If the waiting staff fall down on their job – and
murmurs of 'aloof' and 'automata' have been heard – then conversion of
strangers into regulars will be the more difficult. The meal is accompanied by a
fine wine list of great length and modest cost. There is no nonsense about
wines being French only; the German, New World and Spanish choices are
worth pursuing. House wines are from £9. There is a full vegetarian menu.

CHEF: Kevin Cape   PROPRIETORS: The Harris family
OPEN: all week
MEALS: 12.30 to 2, 7.30 to 10
PRICES: £36 (£47), Set L £15.50 (£24), Set D £16.50 (£25) to £19.50 (£29)
CARDS: Access, Visa
SEATS: 100. Private parties: 20 and 200 private rooms. Car-park, 250 places. Children
welcome. No smoking in dining-room. Wheelchair access (also WC)
ACCOMMODATION: 21 rooms, all with bath/shower. Rooms for disabled. B&B £86 to £100.
Baby facilities. Pets welcome. Afternoon teas. Garden. TV. Phone [*Which? Hotel Guide*]

AYLESBURY   Buckinghamshire   map 2

▲ *Hartwell House*

Oxford Road, Aylesbury HP17 8NL
AYLESBURY (0296) 747444   COOKING 2
on A418, 3m S of Aylesbury   COST £22–£52

Few residents of the home counties can have been unaware of this grand new
country house which opened its doors to paying customers after a thorough
refurbishment that eradicated years of life as a billet and a female finishing
school. The effect is impressive and the commitment of management and staff
quite tangible. The beds are as large as any in England. Aidan McCormack
does the cooking. An autumn visitor found him fishing for pike in the lake –
some commitment here, too. Given that pike and trout do not last long in a
pond together, the question is whether diners would prefer to see truite au bleu
or quenelles de brochet on the short *carte* or one of the daily lunch and dinner
set-price menus. McCormack is a chef who came to notice in the first phase of
modern British cookery, so a number of mousses and mousselines remain, now
joined by more fashionable components like vegetable tagliatelle, a compote of
red onions, saffron potatoes, a fricassee of lentils or lemon grass sauce. The new
robustness, however, has not been pursued. If criticism needs be made it is that
of insipidity: a leek soup tasted of water; a ginger butter sauce was almost
unperfumed by the root; a basil mousse had to be hunted in a chicken breast.
On the other hand, a white and dark chocolate mousse cake was of a sickliness
more often found in chains other than Historic House Hotels. At the same time,
a reasonable level of consistent country-house cooking has been achieved with
home production of bread (though not the toast for breakfast), ices and petits
fours, some of which are satisfactory. Vegetables could be more imaginative:
roast potatoes don't go with fish and the spare arrangements of post-nouvelle
have had their day. In general, however, the first year has seen the hotel settle
its style and its staff into satisfactory routine and competence. There has been a
conscious attempt to balance the business and private element of the guest list.
The difficulty with these great piles is to make them feel lively without filling
them with jolly, and intrusive, partygoers. But even this can be preferable to
having only one other couple in the corner of a very large room. The wine list is
a fine one, still expensive, though. Is Sancerre ever going to be worth more than
£20 when as good a one can be found (with as good food) for £12? Make sure
the weather allows a walk in the park; it makes a special setting for a summer
Sunday lunch. House French: £10.50. CELLARMAN'S CHOICE: Brézème 1985,
J.H. Lombard, £21.50; Cabernet Sauvignon, Clare Valley 1986, J. Grosset, £28.

CHEF: Aidan McCormack   PROPRIETORS: Historic House Hotels Ltd
OPEN: all week
CLOSED: 24 to 26 Dec, exc to residents
MEALS: 12.30 to 2, 7.30 to 9.45
PRICES: £33 (£43), Set L £17 (£22) to £19.50 (£25), Set D £29.50 (£35). Service inc.
Minimum £29.50 at D
CARDS: Access, Amex, Diners, Visa
SEATS: 75. Private parties: 16 and 30 private rooms. Car-park, 70 places. Vegetarian meals.
No children under 8. Smart dress preferred at D. No cigars/pipes in dining-room.
Wheelchair access (also unisex WC)
ACCOMMODATION: 32 rooms, all with bath/shower. Rooms for disabled. Lift. B&B £92.50
to £294. No children under 8. Afternoon teas. Garden. Fishing. TV. Phone. Scenic
[*Which? Hotel Guide*]

Pebbles ▼

Pebble Lane, Aylesbury HP20 2JH
AYLESBURY (0296) 86622

COOKING 3
COST £26–£47

'Mr Blake O'Connor is a chef who can scale the culinary heights, and talk the
hind leg off a donkey.' Few visitors to this cottage in a footpath leading from
Kingsbury Square (which may leave you 'in fear of being mugged' on a
Saturday night) to the parish church can depart unaware of the forceful
personality of the chef-patron. He has had his ups and downs this year: the
abiding curse of no-shows (solved by asking for people's credit card number
when they book), and the unpredictability of staff have taken their toll. In
truth, the characterful low-ceilinged pair of dining-rooms to each side of the
front door (redecorated not before time in 1990) may be too serried a stage for
him to strut. Home Counties diners are very price-conscious, London's
propinquity notwithstanding, and he needs a slick delivery and
knowledgeable staff to put his talents in a more sympathetic context. There is a
cheaper lunch menu (this indeed is aggressively priced), a set-price *carte* of five
or six choices with daily specials at a supplement, and an eight-course gastro-
extravaganza. At various times, and on odd quiet nights, there are 'light' menus
and so on. All signal a great energy trying to drum up enthusiasm. A note of
reserve should be sounded on the daily specials: they are listed in summary
form – 'Foie Gras, Red Mullet,' etc – and customers have found details hard to
elicit in advance. There is also a vegetarian menu, for instance, gateau of
artichokes with asparagus and a chervil butter sauce, followed by a feuilleté of
wild mushrooms, then cheese and a sweet. There was a sense last year that
Jeremy Blake O'Connor was practising on many dishes that had been
elaborated in other fashionable kitchens. This is less in evidence on current
menus. The style is certainly up to date, but the absence of tagliatelle of this
and that is quite welcome. His dishes are still complex: a leg of chicken is
boned and braised, served with a port sauce and wild mushrooms with a
potato galette topped with foie gras, the plate well laden with choice little
trimmings. There is a willingness to avoid strong rich sauces, though they do
figure, so a steamed breast of chicken is served in a soup bowl with tiny
vegetables and a thin yet aromatic mustard sauce. Equally, a fricassee of game
– and Jeremy Blake O'Connor is talented with game – comes with all its
braising liquid and root vegetables. It goes without saying that the incidentals

to each meal are home made, from the selection of breads to the amuse-gueule and the petits fours with the coffee. The kitchen cares about the materials – gathered from a widespread network – and about balancing each dish on the plate, with a few outside props. Thus cassoulet of seafood in a Noilly Prat *nage* is served with a julienne of vegetables; lamb comes with a timbale of spinach, parisienne potatoes and cherry tomatoes (he's keen on these); and woodpigeon is made more interesting by ravioli of pheasant and wild mushrooms. The wine list has seen some movement in prices this year. The cheaper wines have gone up (but not unfairly) and the more expensive have been brought down. A magnum of La Tâche 1969 Dom. de la Romanée-Conti is £150 cheaper than it was in 1989. Though Italian wines seem to have been deleted, there is a stronger showing from North America, including Inniskillin vineyard in Canada. There are too many alternate vintages for comfort. House wines start at £9.75. CELLARMAN'S CHOICE: Réserve de la Comtesse 1984, £22.50; Condrieu 1986 from Cuilleron, £33.

CHEF/PROPRIETOR: Jeremy Blake O'Connor
OPEN: Tue to Sun, exc Sun D
MEALS: 12 to 2.15, 7.15 to 10.30
PRICES: Set L £16.50 (£26), Set D £28 (£39)
CARDS: Access, Visa
SEATS: 32. Private parties: 22 main room. Vegetarian meals. Children's helpings. Smart dress preferred. No cigars/pipes in dining-room. Wheelchair access. Music

---

BABBACOMBE Devon   map 1

Table

135 Babbacombe Road, Babbacombe TQ1 3SR   COOKING 3
TORQUAY (0803) 324292   COST £35

COUNTY OF THE YEAR RESTAURANT

It's easy to miss this small restaurant and difficult to park when you have found it. Even then, ring the bell at the side door or you won't get in. The young couple who run it have done it on a shoestring. All the money goes into the food and the decoration barely gets above the level of a front parlour, though everything is clean and tidy. The cooking is more ambitious than Torquay is used to, which may account for the paucity of customers. This is a pity for the restaurant deserves greater success. While there are times when Trevor Brooks overreaches himself, it is unfortunate that he cannot practise on a more attractive stage, which might be enjoyed for itself. A winter meal of confit of duck, pigeon with a deep redcurrant sauce, then a tarte Tatin was pronounced as good as anything Devon could produce. Others have eaten pig's trotter wrapped in caul, the meat shredded and lightly flavoured with herbs; a very smooth flavoured slice of foie gras poached in a stocking then served with a shallot and strawberry vinegar butter sauce that had no more than a finely judged touch of acidity; and a competent fish soup. A redundant and often not brilliant sorbet comes before main courses that may include skate with a veal stock and sherry vinegar sauce; salmon with black pepper and an asparagus vinaigrette luminously green against the china; loin of mutton with laver sauce

---

The Guide *always appreciates hearing about changes of chef or owner.*

where the meat is well hung, maroon and tender and the sauce made with shallots reduced with a mutton stock, port added and laver whisked in, 'a magical concoction'. Vegetables show more love in the preparation than invention in the cooking. Most people consider the savouries better than the sweets and certainly a tarte Tatin with an aberrant pastry, a caramelised pear tart of very slight flavour, and a 'very ordinary' chocolate mousse are not as good as the enjoyable petits fours, the cheese that is *not* stored in the refrigerator (even though there may only be one or two takers), the nice bread rolls or the well-judged tastes of many of the previously mentioned compositions. Although there are times when the intentions do not quite come off, the effort is rarely in vain and Trevor Brooks can turn from the stove to the sink to do the washing up with pride in his achievement. Jane Corrigan is an estimable ambassador for the kitchen, friendly and well informed. The long waits are inevitable when everything is cooked to order, even with only half a dozen customers. The wine list is just adequate but could branch out better to complement the food. Perhaps the start is to buy from a bigger range of merchants? House French: £9 and £9.50. CELLARMAN'S CHOICE: Beaune, premier cru 1979, Reine Pedauque, £18.50, Sancerre, Clos du Roy 1988, P. Millérioux, £12.50. Come on, Torquay.

CHEF: Trevor Brooks   PROPRIETORS: Trevor Brooks and Jane Corrigan
OPEN: Tue to Sun, D only
MEALS: 7.30 to 9.30
PRICES: Set D £23 (£29). Service inc
SEATS: 20. Private parties: 21 main room. No children under 10. Music

---

BAGSHOT Surrey   map 3

▲ *Latymer,*
Pennyhill Park Hotel

College Ride, Bagshot GU19 5ET   COOKING 3
BAGSHOT (0276) 71774   COST £20–£56

'Have you anything light for dessert?' asked a diner who was flagging after £27-worth of preliminary courses. 'How about caramelised banana on a coconut ice-cream topped with a fudge sauce?' suggested the very young waiter. This hotel, and country club with golf course, conference centre and Roman-style swimming-pool is described as a 'stately English Country Manor House' going back to 1849, when the architect wisely incorporated every style he could remember. The dining-room is Tudorbethan half-timber. This may occasion a wry smile until the bill comes. The chef, who is talented, is made to pay for a lot of gilding. The food reflects it as much as the prices: 'perhaps after an extended dose of *cuisine du terroir* we will hanker once more for such ornament.' David Richards' skill is not in question, only the way it is mobilised. Oven-baked scallops on a bed of winter leaves with écrevisses and a mango vinaigrette was unquestionably fresh, not overly sweet from the mango, a plate 'brimming with colour' from the leaves. Pan-fried smoked salmon on a ragout of crab with a toasted muffin and a quail's egg and mayonnaise sounds a dog's dinner. A square of smoked salmon sat on a bed of shredded crabmeat (a ragout!) supported by a muffin. The quail's egg was there, *à point*, and the mayonnaise but their function was hard to discern, though not unpleasant. 'Each of these would have been enough for one person's dinner but we soldiered on, into a canon of lamb.' This was made of three noisettes, vividly pink, encased in emerald spinach leaves, with a separating layer of white mousse and a rather plentiful sauce that needed reduction to concentrate flavours. The alternate main course was a tart of wild mushrooms surrounded by baby vegetables, glazed with a goats' cheese sabayon. The mushrooms were in a rich and eloquently fungal cream sauce, the sabayon giving a kick to the dish that reconciled a carnivore to vegetarian food. Vegetables were designed for each main dish, none of the 'chef's raw selection'. A dessert of citrus jelly and orange bavarois, lighter than the banana concoction, above, was 'so sharp and fresh-tasting, I scoffed the lot.' The chocolate selection has also been approved. Ignore the price if you can; ignore the apparent silliness; applaud the skill; applaud the buying policies – very good materials; praise the service – usually willing and keen as mustard. Trimmings are profuse and include a half-bottle of wine with the set lunch. The wine list is generously French with little else. House wine at £10.75 has been judged good. CELLARMAN'S CHOICE: Mâcon-Prissé 1988, Oudet, £18.50; Ch. Macquin-St-Georges 1986, £18.50.

CHEF: David Richards   PROPRIETORS: Pennyhill Park Ltd
OPEN: all week, exc Sun L
MEALS: 12.30 to 2.30, 7.30 to 10.30
PRICES: £34 (£47), Set L £18.50 (£20) to £22.50 (£25)
CARDS: Access, Amex, Diners, Visa
SEATS: 60. Private parties: 32 and 40 private rooms. Car-park, 150 places. Vegetarian meals. Children's helpings on request. Children restricted. Smart dress preferred at D. No cigars/pipes in dining-room
ACCOMMODATION: 54 rooms, all with bath/shower. B&B £116 to £152. Afternoon teas. Garden. Swimming-pool. Sauna. Tennis. Fishing. Golf. TV. Phone. Scenic

---

BAKEWELL Derbyshire   map 5

Green Apple

Diamond Court, Water Street,
Bakewell DE4 1EW   COOKING 1
BAKEWELL (0629) 814404   COST £13–£17

It is green in the modern or new sense of the word: leave smoking materials at the door and prepare for organic plate-loads. (Roger Green has assured the *Guide* that plates are washed with 'environment-friendly cleaning agents'.) In fact there are two doors; the front in an alley off the main town square, the back near the cattle-market. Although not exclusively vegetarian, the market is about as close as the cattle get to the kitchen. The menu, where the price of the main course includes a starter and dessert, is likely to feature courgette and cheese bake or hazelnuts and vegetable loaf with tomato sauce, but there may also be lamb in a lightly spiced casserole, chicken breast served with green chives and with bacon, and trout with gooseberry and elderflower sauce. One report notes a 'delicate flavoursome style of cooking'. For lunch there are self-service salads. Home-made desserts include banoffi and fresh fruit brûlée. Wines are now supplied mainly by Berry Bros, are sound and fairly priced and

include a good Almecenista sherry as well as some English wine. House French
is £8.75. CELLARMAN'S CHOICE: Berry Bros good ordinary claret, £9.80; Hill
Smith Cabernet Sauvignon 1988,£12.

CHEFS: Roger Green, Nick Andrews, Pam Wain and Alison Ray   PROPRIETORS: Roger and
Judith Green
OPEN: all week, exc D Mon, Tue and Sun (open Mon to Sat L, Thur to Sat D in winter)
MEALS: 12 to 2, 7 to 9.30
PRICES: L £7 (£13), Set D £12 (£19) to £17 (£24)
CARDS: Access, Diners, Visa
SEATS: 50. 8 tables outside. Private parties: 50 main room. Vegetarian meals. Children's
helpings. No smoking in dining-room. Wheelchair access. Music

---

BARNARD CASTLE   Co Durham   map 7

Market Place Teashop

29 The Market Place,
Barnard Castle DL12 8NE   COOKING 1
TEESDALE (0833) 690110   COST £12

'Recipe for success: find out where elderly ladies make for at lunchtime and
just follow.' This popular café-restaurant deals with all age groups and offers a
larger range than usual for a place open all day – soups that are enough on their
own for lunch, steak and kidney pie, pot-roast brisket and Yorkshire pudding,
Cumberland sausage, vegetarian samosas, enchiladas, and mushrooms stuffed
with spinach, served with a tomato sauce. This is cheerful and inexpensive
popular catering, crowned by home-made pies 'bursting with fruit and fresh
cream' and a variety of cakes from millionaire's shortbread to fruit and coconut
chocolate squares. Licensed, with a wide range of teas to boot.

CHEFS: James Moffat, Bob Hilton and Roy Varndell   PROPRIETOR: Bob Hilton
OPEN: all week, L only
CLOSED: 1 week at Christmas, Sun Dec to Mar
MEALS: 10am (3 Sun) to 5.30
PRICES: £6 (£10)
SEATS: 50. Private parties: 46 main room. Vegetarian meals. Children's helpings.
Wheelchair access

BARNET   Hertfordshire   map 3

Mims

63 East Barnet Road, Barnet EN4 8RN   COOKING 2
081-449 2974 and 447 1825   COST £20–£29

Between a row of shops and a garage, opposite a large Sainsbury, the restaurant
leaves readers deciding between 'conservatory' and 'bistro' in describing the
ambience created by blotchy green paint on the walls, garden furniture, and
steps between the different levels; watch your step on those to the lavatory
after drinking. What attracts the Saturday shoppers is a menu quite unlike the
East Barnet norm. Anyone who can offer calf's brains in July 1990 must have
some self-confidence. Ali Al-Sersy trained with the Roux brothers and his

cooking betrays European and north Mediterranean influences in dishes like soupe au pistou, scallop mousse, venison au poivre, calf's liver with beurre rouge, chocolate mousse on prunes with a cinnamon ice-cream. These are offered on a frequently changed set-price menu, still inexpensive for Greater London, and à la carte at lunchtimes. Techniques are also classical French, inventive as is much new-wave cooking, but not outrageous. Cod is marinated with cumin, garlic and tomato vinaigrette before baking; chicken is poached with leeks, gin, herbs and stock, the vegetables then liquidised, strained and reduced, the sauce mounted with butter. This assured technique has resulted in some satisfactory meals, though those reported have contained lapses. An outstanding onion tart with thin fresh pastry and accurately seasoned, light filling; a scallop mousse of good flavour and texture, trimmed with acceptable asparagus; soup of proper construction and taste; brill with asparagus and a chervil butter sauce impressed mightily. So nearly did the generously portioned breast of goose with a 'ciderish' apple sauce, but it was let down by the quality of the meat. There was an instance of very poor potato gratin and a bread-and-butter pudding of simple composition, which gained texture by a caramelised top, but fell short of full enjoyment through oiling from overheating. Bread is home made. It is clearly a restaurant of promise and an asset to the northern suburbs. A summer menu, with perhaps nine or ten choices in each course, presupposes a fair business to keep so many ingredients fresh, but is singular because there are very few makeweights on it; everything sounds simple yet appetising, not so easy a task as it might seem. The wine list is brief, not too dear and could be developed to match the enthusiasm of the food. House wine: £7.95.

CHEF: Ali Al-Sersy   PROPRIETORS: M. Abouzahrah and Ali Al-Sersy
OPEN: all week, exc Sat L
CLOSED: one week at Christmas
MEALS: 12 to 3, 6.30 to 11 (10.30 Sun)
PRICES: £14 (£20), Set D £16 (£22) to £18 (£24). Minimum £3 at L
CARDS: Access, Visa
SEATS: 50. Private parties: 50 main room. Car-park, 6 places, D only. Children welcome L. No cigars/pipes in dining-room. Wheelchair access (1 step). Music

---

Wings

6 Potters Road, New Barnet EN5 5HW	COOKING 1
081-449 9890	COST £21–31

There's not a Chinese lantern or dragon in sight at this elegant suburban restaurant. Some new dishes have been added to the menu, but the familiar Peking/Szechuan favourites are still well liked: recommended have been hot and sour soup 'just the right side of glutinous'; bang-bang chicken with smooth peanut sauce; crispy lamb wrapped DIY style in iceberg lettuce. Otherwise the choice ranges from sizzling steak with black-bean sauce and pork with mange-tout to steamed halibut. The service is attentive and unobtrusive. The constant supply of Chinese tea is at a price and better than the reported 'burnt-tasting coffee' to end. House wine: £6.45. Other wines are fairly priced but insufficiently annotated. Note that service is 15 per cent.

CHEF: Ho Yuen Wan   PROPRIETOR: Pak Wah Tse
OPEN: all week, exc Tue from Jan to Nov
MEALS: 12 to 2.30, 6 to 10.30
PRICES: £13 (£26), Set D £14 (£21) to £18 (£26). Cover 85p. Service 15%
CARDS: Access, Amex, Diners, Visa
SEATS: 80. Private parties: 40 main room. Vegetarian meals. Children welcome.
Wheelchair access

BARNSTAPLE Devon   map 1

▲ Lynwood House

Bishops Taunton Road,
Barnstaple EX32 9DZ
BARNSTAPLE (0271) 43695   COOKING 2
on A377, between Barnstaple and Exeter   COST £40

John and Ruth Roberts have celebrated 21 years in Lynwood House
overlooking the river Taw. When they started, he was teaching at the local
catering college and the business was a run down guest-house with 15 rooms.
Now it is a restaurant with rooms (only five and all en suite) and the second
generation, but babes in arms then, are joined with their parents in the
enterprise. The emphasis is on fish, as it should be – mostly local, though
salmon is Scottish for the most of the year and smoked salmon is from Loch
Fyne. A duck and a steak dish keep them company on a menu that evolves but
slowly over the years. The duck is called 'crispy', though one diner found it
anything but. There is, in addition, a slate of lighter dishes available every day
except Sunday for those who want to make a quicker visit. These can be good,
as in the fluffy prawn omelette served with a varied and sustaining salad. To
cap it all, 'they treated my two daughters like princesses.' John Roberts
remarks that 'manners matter more than age' when responding to our enquiries
about the acceptability of children. The fish has met approval for its quality –
'the best mussels I've eaten' – and the technique in such dishes as lobster with
garlic butter or Thermidor; a seafood platter; skate with capers and brown
butter, or pan-fried sea bass. One reader detected a lack of attack in the
Thermidor sauce, but this could be countered by another who found that a
langoustine sauce almost overpowered the fillet of brill it accompanied. Service
generally has a light touch and there is a good range of cream-laden sweets
from flummery through a double cream crème caramel in two sizes and extra
portions of farmhouse clotted cream. The wine list looks charmingly as if it
were the project of a GCSE candidate. It presents a decent range of French
wines at fair prices, and a handful from Germany, Spain, Greece, Italy and
Australia. House French is £6.50 and £7.50. Devonshire cider is available too –
mind the colic that plagued eighteenth-century drinkers of this.

'On finding a live worm in my fish the chef commented as follows on the back of the bill:
"As is commonly known, Nematodes are often found in perfectly healthy fish. One of the
nematodes had found its way into the heart of a small fillet of fish. There is nothing
unhealthy or unhygienic about this occurrence but it is regretted."' On eating at a top
West End restaurant

CHEFS: Ruth Roberts and Adam Roberts   PROPRIETORS: John and Ruth Roberts, Adam,
Matthew and Christian Roberts
OPEN: all week
MEALS: 12 to 2, 7 to 10
PRICES: £26 (£33)
CARDS: Access, Visa
SEATS: 70. Private parties: 70 main room, 24 and 70 private rooms. Car-park, 30 places.
Vegetarian meals. Children's helpings. No smoking in dining-room. Wheelchair access
(also WC)
ACCOMMODATION: 5 rooms, all with bath/shower. B&B £47.50 to £67.50. TV. Phone.
Scenic. Confirm by 6 [*Which? Hotel Guide*]

BARWICK   Somerset   map 2

▲ *Little Barwick House*

Barwick, Yeovil BA22 9TD   COOKING 2
YEOVIL (0935) 23902   COST £25−£32

The house stands tall above well-clipped lawns, borders and tall conifers. The
warm dining-room − deep rugs on board floors, cornice standing out white
against strong coloured walls − affords a haven for lovers of substantial
country cooking with an affection for pies and baking. Have drinks down in
the bar, which must once have been the kitchen, complete with stone flags and
range, and choose from a short menu supplemented by daily extras of 'really
large and filling stuff, and one can have seconds, too, if one can make room.'
Readers are warm in praise of the sense of hospitality, as well as the
complaisance of the young staff, and if the cooking approach is robust, it is
skilled and genuine, making much of roast meats − rack of lamb, duck, quail
with a walnut sauce − as well as enjoying a spot of curry in a chicken tikka and
avocado salad with a yoghurt and lime sauce or a little pot of curried kidneys.
In season, game is often a feature and those pies or tarts are a constant: duck
and fillet of beef with orange and port is an instance of the savoury, an apple
and almond tart of the sweet. Pancakes are also regulars. Fish dinners are
possible with supplies drawn from the Dorset coast. 'We started with gravlax
and smoked trout, then went on to lemon sole with cream and prawns or
meunière.' Vegetables are copious; puddings are always enjoyed. House
Duboeuf or Bulgarian is £8.50. CELLARMAN'S CHOICE: Mâcon blanc, Dom. de
Roally 1987, Goyard, £15; Gran Sangredetoro Reserva 1984, Torres, £12.

CHEF: Veronica Colley   PROPRIETORS: Mr and Mrs C. Colley
OPEN: Mon to Sat, D only
MEALS: 7 to 9
PRICES: Set D £18.90 (£25) to £20.90 (£27). Service inc
CARDS: Access, Amex, Diners, Visa
SEATS: 40. Private parties: 50 main room. Car-park. Children's helpings
ACCOMMODATION: 6 rooms, all with bath/shower. B&B £43 to £66. Deposit: £20. Pets
welcome. Garden. TV. Scenic. Doors close at 11 [*Which? Hotel Guide*]

---

*Restaurateurs justifiably resent no-shows. If you quote a credit card number when
booking, you may be liable for the restaurant's lost profit margin if you don't turn up.
Always phone to cancel.*

BASINGSTOKE Hampshire

map 2

Hee's

23 Westminster House, Town Centre,
Basingstoke RG21 1CS
BASINGSTOKE (0256) 464410 and 460297

COOKING 1
COST £17–£29

The word from regulars is that this is one of the better eating places in the
Basingstoke area. A few Cantonese specialities, such as barbecued pork and
baked crab with spring onion, appear on the menu, but the emphasis is on that
well-tried mix of Peking and Szechuan dishes that typifies so many county
Chinese restaurants nowadays. Bang-bang chicken, Peking dumplings deep-
fried shredded beef with chilli, and Kung Po prawns show the style. Reports
praise the high standard and consistency of the cooking, although there are
quibbles about the frenetic pressurised service. Saké and a dozen cocktails
provide more excitement than the run-of-the-mill wine list.

CHEF: Mr Leung   PROPRIETOR: Mr T. Lee
OPEN: all week, exc Sun L
CLOSED: 24 to 27 Dec, Sun of bank hol weekends
MEALS: 12 to 2, 6 to 11
PRICES: £15 (£24), Set L and D £11.50 (£17) to £17.50 (£24). Minimum £6. Service 12.5%
CARDS: Access, Amex, Diners, Visa
SEATS: 90. Private parties: 110 main room. Car-park, 50 places. Vegetarian meals.
No children under 4. No-smoking area. Music. Air-conditioned

BASLOW Derbyshire

map 5

▲ Fischer's at Baslow Hall ▼

Calver Road, Baslow DE4 1RR
BASLOW (0246) 583259

COOKING 3
COST £20–£42

The restaurant has been a long time coming, but here it is at last. Max and
Susan Fischer had a well regarded restaurant in Bakewell. When the Hall came
on to the market in 1988 they sought to convert it to a restaurant with rooms.
Not long before the scheduled opening they experienced a dreadful fire which
put back their plans by at least nine months. The house is twentieth century
though it looks seventeenth, standing at the top of a tree-lined drive just out of
the village. Three of the ground floor rooms are converted to dining,
paradoxically causing the entrance to shift from the grand front door to the back
of the building. Decoration has met with approval: vivid carpets and print
fabrics, wood panelling, a glorious stone fireplace in the reception area, and
well-spaced tables. Dinner offers two options, each at the same price. The first
is a no-choice menu of five courses and coffee, the second a four-course menu of
six to eight choices. Both have pasta at the course usually reserved for a soup in
the northern style. Dishes are succinctly expressed: 'home-made pasta', 'our
terrine', or 'rack of lamb with basil'. A visitor new to the Hall remarked that the
menu gave little hint of the splendour that arrived on the plate. Better that than
disappointment. Max Fischer is alive to the currents of modern cooking

without being their slave. He informs them with a strong classical bent. Dishes are not fussy, though care is taken with presentation and they are usually seasoned appositely to allow flavour some importance. In one meal, only one or two lapses into blandness were detected: a layer of *farce* in a fish terrine, and a raspberry mousse in a chocolate and raspberry slice. The repertoire is wide. A visitor on several occasions over the winter was able to praise orange and mint soup; seafood with noodles and orange sauce; ravioli with lobster sauce; good bread and butter rolls; steak and kidney pudding; plain roast pheasant; duck with honey and spice sauce; and good desserts that included strudel and Pavlova. Herbs seem well used, cropping up as a major ingredient in salmon with an olive oil and coriander vinaigrette, veal with watercress and sorrel sauce, and rack of lamb with basil. These sensible modern dishes remind one of the work of some current south-western cooks. Service appears already assured under the eye of Susan Fischer. Although we had heard that the hotel side of the business was taking a little time to settle down, this has not been said of the dining-room. It should be expected that the first year will see unevenness but Baslow Hall certainly has the potential for great success. At lunchtime in the week there is a short à la carte menu while on Sundays it is fixed price. The wine list is not long but is excellently chosen from the most modern growers. The range is fine, the prices very fair, the comments are pithy, the wines are generally on the young side. Look to Valentini, Jayer, Avril, Ch. Notton, Rolly Gassmann, Corsin, Guyot and Simi, among others. A pity there are not more halves. House wine is £7.99, a shop-like method of pricing that crops up elsewhere on the list.

CHEF: Max Fischer   PROPRIETORS: Max and Susan Fischer
OPEN: all week, exc Mon L and Sun D
MEALS: 12 to 1.30 (2 Sun), 7 to 9.30 (10 Sat)
PRICES: £18 (£26), Set Sun L £14.50 (£20), Set D £27.50 (£35)
CARDS: Access, Amex, Visa
SEATS: 35. Private parties: 35 main room, 10 and 25 private rooms. Car-park, 60 places. Vegetarian meals on request. Children's helpings (L only). No children under 10 at D. No smoking in dining-room. Wheelchair access (also WC). Music
ACCOMMODATION: 6 rooms, all with bath/shower. B&B £60 to £95. Garden. TV. Phone. Scenic [*Which? Hotel Guide*]

BATH Avon   map 2

Garlands

7 Edgar Buildings, George Street
Bath BA1 2EE   COOKING 1
BATH (0225) 442283   COST £13–£30

This was the lodging of Isabella Thorpe in Jane Austen's *Northanger Abbey*. The elevated Georgian terrace is a fine setting for a menu that has a light and modern feel: salmon, scallop and crab terrine in a tomato and basil vinaigrette, quenelles of sole and smoked prawns with noodles and tarragon sauce, and a vegetarian main course of stir-fried vegetables with soy sauce in puff pastry with a red peppercorn coulis. The emphasis, though, is on convention rather than invention, as in chicken breast with tarragon and watercress in a cream sauce or lamb with rosemary sauce. Nobody shouts 'place your bets, please' as you walk in the door yet the feeling of chance is unmistakable. 'Excellent, flavoursome,' says one reader of the salmon terrine; 'disappointing, coarse and flavourless,' says another. Likewise, a crème brûlée with apples is welcomed by some, despaired of by others. The wine list is short but decently chosen and prices are fair. There are a few interesting items, like a Ch. Beaucastel, tucked in. House French: £7.85.

CHEF: Tom Bridgeman   PROPRIETORS: William Baber and Tom Bridgeman
OPEN: Tue to Sun
CLOSED: 25 to 27 Dec
MEALS: 12.15 to 2.15, 7 to 10.30
PRICES: £17 (£25), Set L £7.50 (£13) to £11.95 (£18), Set Sun L £12.50 (£17)
CARDS: Access, Amex, Visa
SEATS: 30. Private parties: 14 main room. Vegetarian meals. Children welcome. Wheelchair access. Music

Moon and Sixpence

6A Broad Street, Bath BA1 5LJ
BATH (0225) 460962

COOKING 1
COST £14–£32

This bistro-style restaurant of old Bath stone is in a cobbled courtyard just off Broad Street. The menu for the most part sticks within the bounds of common sense. A galantine of wild rabbit and chicken with pistachios is well served by an apricot and ginger chutney, and marinated anchovies are nicely countered by pickled cucumber and tomato. But occasionally it topples over in its frenetic search for something new. How badly, for instance, do quenelles of crab need pink grapefruit, along with their mange-tout and lemon dressing? The kitchen, for the most part, delivers the goods: a main course of fish timbale with an avocado and cream cheese sauce and a dessert of passion fruit mousse have been well reported. An ill-prepared chicken liver met with less enthusiasm. Service on the whole has been friendly, even on that nadir of the eating week, Sunday night. At other times it has been poor. The Moon and Sixpence is good, but not consistently so. The wine list is rather more reliable and includes some vins de pays as well as New Zealand's finest Cabernet Sauvignon, Te Mata's Coleraine. House French: £6.75 and £7.25. CELLARMAN'S CHOICE: Castle Hill Sauvignon 1988, Te Mata, £15.50, Ch. Beaumont 1986, £15.95.

CHEF: Kevin King   PROPRIETOR: Keith Waving
OPEN: all week
MEALS: 12 to 2.30, 7 to 10.30
PRICES: £18 (£27), Set L £7.75 (£14) to £10.95 (£17). Service 10% for parties of 6 or more
CARDS: Access, Amex, Visa
SEATS: 70. 15 tables outside. Private parties: 30 main room, 25 private room. Vegetarian meals. Children's helpings on request. Music

Consumers' Association is planning to publish Out to Eat, *a new guide to budget eating out in restaurants, pubs, cafés, brasseries and so on. Please send reports and recommendations to Out to Eat, FREEPOST, 2 Marylebone Road, London NW1 1YN.*

Popjoy's

Beau Nash's House,
Sawclose, Bath BA1 1EU
BATH (0225) 460494

COOKING 2
COST £25–£43

'Popjoy's and its rather special style of cooking have become quite an institution in Bath,' wrote one reader, reflecting on John Headley's regime since the departure of Mark Anton Edwards. As they were colleagues, apostolic succession was assured with quite complicated food and a penchant for spices and fruit. Decoration sometimes seems irrelevant: 'two scoops, of beetroot and of carrot purée, adorned each main course regardless.' All this goes on in a great Georgian house next to the Theatre Royal. It has been redecorated: yellow walls, dark red carpet, grey ceiling and a new portrait of Beau Nash who lived in the house, 'looking rather ill or as if he'd had his face bashed in'. Trimmings to the meal are satisfactory until rather tedious petits fours; the bread is made to the restaurant's own recipe and enjoyed. The service, however, shows strain. 'Do you serve wine by the glass?' is a simple enough query. 'I don't know,' was the hopeless response. Reports detected a fluctuation in performance during the change-over period but suggest it is settling again. A summer meal of terrine of rabbit studded with figs and hazelnuts with home-made tomato chutney and toasted brioche; breast of duck flamed in cognac with a sauce of mangoes and raspberries; and gooseberry and apple tart with nutmeg, shared signs of overlarding the joint but still worked well. The terrine was stiff, yet made as much of light-flavoured rabbit as could ever be expected; the chutney was sweet, spicy and fresh; the brioche light, buttery, eggy but 'toasted with good reason'; accompanying salad leaves were dry, undressed and added nothing. Duck was properly cooked, of fair quality and benefited from its cognac. The stock-based sauce was not too sweet nor over-reduced and complemented the meat. Vegetables were plentiful and moderately successful. The tart was very fine: a gooseberry custard topped with sliced apple in a thin pastry case on cream crudely flavoured with calvados. These were good textures and flavours. Cheese is British and biscuits Bath Olivers (Reading, really). There is a fair wine list with a decent number of half bottles, though not of house wine, which comes dearly by the glass (the size of which seems to have shrunk over 12 months). House wine is £10.50.

CHEF: John Headley   PROPRIETORS: Avon Inns
OPEN: Tue to Sat, exc Sat L
MEALS: 12 to 2, 6 to 10.30
PRICES: L £16 (£25), Set D £20.50 (£31) to £25 (£36)
CARDS: Access, Amex, Visa
SEATS: 36. Private parties: 36 main room. Vegetarian meals. No children under 10 at D. Smart dress preferred. No smoking in dining-room. Wheelchair access (1 step; also WC). Music

---

Several sharp operators have tried to extort money from restaurateurs on the promise of an entry in a guide book that has never appeared. The Good Food Guide *makes no charge for inclusion and does not offer certificates of any kind.*

▲ *Priory Hotel*

Weston Road, Bath BA1 2XT	COOKING 3
BATH (0225) 331922	COST £26-£42

Management and staff have remained the same in this handsome suburban country-house hotel on the western edge of Bath that is a favourite resort for many a tourist. Its good taste has never been in question, even in the new bedroom wings, but reports since the last *Guide* have often found the output of the kitchen less enlivening than the price might imply. A dish of king prawns, home-made noodles and green peppercorns continues to receive praise for its materials and direct flavour, as have scallops on a tomato concasse; poached breast of pigeon with oyster mushrooms; and turbot with mussels and cream sauce. Vegetables are distinguished by their paucity. The *carte* is an exercise in modern classicism: a warm scallop mousseline wrapped in spinach with a beurre blanc; wild mushroom ravioli; sole and salmon with a crab sauce; veal and scallops with tarragon and white wine; quail with parsnips and chestnut purée; soft fruit Pavlova and a profusion of ice-creams. The food pleases its constituency and can be very exact in its flavouring and execution, but it may strike some as being no more than hotel fare at a price, served graciously in fine surroundings. The wines offer bargains among mature Rhônes and clarets in a serviceable general list most interesting in its red burgundies. House wine: £11. CELLARMAN'S CHOICE: Ch. Millet 1978, £21.50; Muscadet, Clos de Beauregard 1986, £11.75.

CHEF: Michael Collom PROPRIETORS: Select Country Hotels
OPEN: all week
MEALS: 12.30 to 2, 7 to 9.30
PRICES: £28 (£35), Set L £18 (£26) to £20 (£28), Set D £27.50 (£35). Service inc
CARDS: Access, Amex, Diners, Visa
SEATS: 64. Private parties: 40 main room, 22 and 40 private rooms. Car-park, 25 places. Vegetarian meals. Children welcome. Smart dress preferred. No smoking in dining-room. Wheelchair access
ACCOMMODATION: 21 rooms, all with bath/shower. Rooms for disabled. B&B £85 to £160. Deposit: one night (overseas clients). Afternoon teas. Garden. Swimming-pool. TV. Phone. Scenic. Doors close at 11.30 [*Which? Hotel Guide*]

Tarts ♥

8 Pierrepont Place, Bath BA1 1JX	COOKING 2
BATH (0225) 330280 and 330201	COST £20-£30

The interlinking rooms, including a small bar, have been refurbished, and candles in wine bottles and fun prints on the walls are the only vestiges of a bistro-like youth. The pastry with the same name as the restaurant usually lurks on the à la carte lunch and dinner menu. Classical French cooking, albeit spiced with more exotica than that implies, is the primary style. Meat dishes predominate, but good shellfish, especially a crab mousse first course, have garnered most praise, and vegetarians get a look-in. Readers approve, too, of

Report forms are at the back of the book; write a letter if you prefer.

the south-east Asian spicing that might be coconut milk, coriander, ginger and chilli with crab in filo pastry, or coconut, lime and ginger flavouring with roast guinea-fowl. Too much madeira and cream sauce on the calves' kidneys, moaned one reader, and chocolate and crème de menthe slice was more decadent than delicious. Interesting as well as competent vegetables are frequently noted. There is wide agreement that service is sensitive and expert. The wine list is worthy on all counts with stocks increasing but prices staying low. There are good bourgeois and classed growth Bordeaux plus a country French. Excellent growers abound and Spanish reds, particularly Gran Riserva Riojas, are gaining ground. Four house wines from £6.80 to £7.10. CELLARMAN'S CHOICE: CVNE Blanco Seco Riserva 1983, £13.40; Ch. Beaumont, Haut Médoc 1985, £15.80.

CHEF: Michel Lemoine   PROPRIETOR: John Edwards
OPEN: Mon to Sat
CLOSED: 3 days over Christmas
MEALS: 12 to 2.30, 6.45 to 10.45
PRICES: L £12(£20), D £16(£25). Service 10% for parties of 6 or more
CARDS: Access, Visa
SEATS: 50. Private parties: 22 main room, 8 and 12 private rooms. Vegetarian meals.
Children welcome. No cigars/pipes in dining-room. Music

BATTLE East Sussex   map 3

▲ *La Vieille Auberge*

27 High Street, Battle TN33 0EA   COOKING 2
BATTLE (042 46) 5171   COST £18–£36

'La Vieille Auberge, Bataille' might be the preferred address of this stone-built house in a town still dominated by its Norman inheritance, so keen are the owner and chef on French menus, wines and cooking. Yet they are English, as are the materials if not the characterful waiters. Decoration is also fairly British, the lounge being a paradigm of a certain taste. Paul Webbe's cooking (and Stephen Dickey's on Sunday and Monday) is direct and flavoursome, even though his style is one that descends to needless decoration and overworking in other hands. So dishes such as crab ravioli with lemon butter sauce; salad of confit of duck with orange; smoked salmon trout; a panaché of fish with a basil sauce and spinach; rack of lamb with sweet peppers or a rosemary sauce, have been enjoyed for good buying practices and taste even though presentation, for instance in meat butchery, may occasionally be robust. Puddings often include ice-cream; one combination of a raspberry mousse with white chocolate was emphatically regretted. Either end of the meal is well-laden with substantial nibbles (the sweet ones will be wrapped for you if they are too much at the time). The set menus are excellent value (particularly in calorific terms) and they do not ignore vegetarians. The wine list is steadfastly French (with a dozen exceptions) and is a bit light on halves. The growers, Gisselbrecht, Guigal, Colonge are some, and a scatter of top class growers and properties – les Forts de Latour 1979, Beychevelle and d'Issan 1982, de Suremain Monthélie 1985 and Bâtard-Montrachet 1985 from Gagnard – head a predominantly French and carefully chosen wine list, which is arranged by vintage. Prices start fair, house French is £7.25, but the percentage markup strains the pocket at the better end. CELLARMAN'S CHOICE: Ch. Potensac 1985; £16; Riesling 1986, Gisselbrecht £10.50.

CHEF: Paul Webbe   PROPRIETOR: Stephen P. Dickey
OPEN: all week, exc Mon L
MEALS: 12 to 2, 7 to 10
PRICES: £23 (£30), Set L £12.50 (£19) to £14.50 (£22), Set D Sun and Mon £16 (£23) to £22 (£30). Service inc
CARDS: Access, Amex, Visa
SEATS: 33. Private parties: 33 main room, 14 private room. Vegetarian meals. Children's helpings on request. No cigars/pipes in dining-room. Wheelchair access. Music
ACCOMMODATION: 7 rooms, 5 with bath/shower. B&B £29.50 to £55. Deposit: 50%. Afternoon teas. TV. Phone. Doors close at midnight. Confirm by 6

BEAMINSTER Dorset   map 2

▲ *Bridge House*

Prout Bridge, Beaminster DT8 3AY   COOKING 2
BRIDPORT (0308) 862200   COST £15–£30

The Bridge House is at root a thirteenth-century priest's house, but in a pretty garden behind there are newer buildings housing extra bedrooms, as well as a conservatory adding space to the public rooms. Bare stonework, heavy beams, large fireplaces and a candlelit dining-room dictate the atmosphere, which could never be called showy. The menu, too – set-price, changing weekly, five options at each course with cheese and coffee thrown in – gives every sign that Peter Pinkster wishes to work at the basics and leave the glory-bits to others (he is self taught, he says). A meal last summer included bortsch with a glass of iced vodka; an avocado mousse with bacon; mushroom pancakes; mixed fish in a chive cream sauce; good veal kidneys; monkfish in a Pernod sauce; a plate of various berries and home-made caramel ice-cream. Other visitors have reported decent wholemeal bread; pancakes filled with haddock, cheese, cream and bacon; gravlax, definitely not shop-bought; a ceviche marinated with lemon, lime, onion, coriander and oil; loin of lamb with a light lemon and mint sauce; casseroled hare with a crab apple jelly; and good beef. Buttered vegetables, accurately cooked, contribute to the fair weight of the food. Puddings are simple. Cheeses will be large, whole and cut at the table, perhaps a choice of Cheddar and French Brie, not Somerset. Coffee sometimes comes with truffles, but not invariably. Materials are first rate and mostly left uncomplicated. The wine list doesn't indulge in unnecessary flannel either: 15 wines with a top price of £13.80 and a supplementary sheet with another couple of dozen taking the price up to £26.80 for a Haut-Batailley 1978. House wine: £6.45.

'We were offered what must be one of the most dismal cheeseboards ever: rubbery Brie, tired Red Leicester, passé Stilton and boring Edam. Some of the biscuits were crisp. Some were not.' On eating in Wales

---

CHEF/PROPRIETOR: Peter Pinkster
OPEN: all week
CLOSED: 24 to 31 Dec
MEALS: 12 to 2, 7 to 9 (9.30 Sat)
PRICES: Conservatory L £10 (£15), restaurant Set D £18.75 (£25)
CARDS: Access, Visa
SEATS: 42. 3 tables outside. Private parties: 24 main room, 18 and 24 private rooms. Car-park, 22 places. Vegetarian meals with prior notice. Children's helpings with prior notice. No smoking in dining-room. Wheelchair access
ACCOMMODATION: 9 rooms, all with bath/shower. Rooms for disabled. B&B £35.50 to £55. Deposit: £10. Pets welcome, exc in public rooms. Afternoon teas. Garden. TV. Phone. Doors close at 11. Confirm by 6 [Which? Hotel Guide]

BECKINGHAM Lincolnshire　　　　　　　　　　　　　　　　　　　map 6

Black Swan

COUNTY OF THE YEAR RESTAURANT

Hillside, Beckingham LN5 ORF　　　　　　　　　　　　　COOKING 3
FENTON CLAYPOLE (0636) 626474　　　　　　　　　　　COST £16–£34

Inhabitants of the Lincolnshire-Nottingham borders must thank their lucky stars that the Black Swan swims on: good value, good food, pleasant welcome and now, open for lunch (though best to phone ahead). Anton Indans was London trained, and it shows, though he can still roast a fine sirloin, raise a red-hot Yorkshire pudding and blend a mean soup. Dinner menus are set-price and offer three choices at each course, with a few supplementary items. There is a sorbet before the main course. At lunch there is a *carte* as well as two set meals. Dinner kicks off well with a *surprise du chef* and has included such dishes as a pastry case of lambs' sweetbreads and spring onions in cream and raspberry vinegar sauce; smoked trout mousse with horseradish; marinated salmon on a yoghurt and cucumber sauce; monkfish with ratatouille and saffron noodles; magret of duck with rhubarb and a cinnamon and apple sauce. The desserts are good and show an aptitude for hot soufflés. Pastry and baking is well judged. The wine list has a couple of dozen reds and whites, all under £20 and most under £11. Then there is a range of burgundies and Champagnes with a bit more class, though fairly priced. House French: £6.20. CELLARMAN'S CHOICE: Ch. Lucas, Lussac 1985, £11.35; Rosemount Chardonnay 1988, £10.30. The Indans deserve to prosper.

CHEF: Anton Indans　　PROPRIETORS: Anton and Alison Indans
OPEN: Tue to Sat
MEALS: 12 to 2, 7 to 10
PRICES: £15 (£20), Set L £11.50 (£16) to £15.50 (£20), Set D £17.50 (£23) to £22 (£28)
CARDS: Access, Visa
SEATS: 30. Private parties: 24 main room, and 24 private rooms. Car-park, 9 places. Children's helpings (L only). No smoking in dining-room. Wheelchair access (also unisex WC). Music

---

Restaurateurs justifiably resent no-shows. If you quote a credit card number when booking, you may be liable for the restaurant's lost profit margin if you don't turn up. Always phone to cancel.

BERWICK-UPON-TWEED Northumberland

map 7

Funnywayt'mekalivin

COUNTY OF THE YEAR RESTAURANT

53 West Street,
Berwick-Upon-Tweed TD15 1AS
BERWICK-UPON-TWEED (0289) 308827 and 86437

COOKING 2
COST £15

The origins of this place are lost in a mist of craft shops, which is how Elizabeth Middlemiss came into business. This shows, perhaps, in the style of the interior as well as the direct, unforced and fresh approach she has to cooking. Dinners are at 8pm with no choice and set price. The plan as the *Guide* went to press was to add a Thursday night opening to the usual Fridays and Saturdays. The four-course meal will normally start with soup and often progress to a soufflé: a tomato and basil soup of 'rich and subtle flavour, just the right texture and amount of basil', then smoked salmon soufflé, 'just risen, light, again subtly balanced in flavour'. The meat at this meal was a stuffed shoulder of lamb, 'tender, full of herbs and onion', with a gratin dauphinois (properly creamy), followed by a blackberry and Cassis syllabub with home-made shortbread. On another night there could be carrot and apple soup, lemon sole stuffed with smoked salmon, roast lamb, Brie and oatcakes, and crème brûlée (magnificent!) or praline in an iced soufflé. There is an aperitif on the house before dinner, but otherwise a corkage is charged on bring-your-own bottles. No one minds. It does seem a happy place.

CHEF/PROPRIETOR: Elizabeth Middlemiss
OPEN: D Fri and Sat, also Thur in 1991 (L by arrangement for parties of 8)
MEALS: 8
PRICES: Set D £14.75. Service inc. Unlicensed, but bring your own: corkage £1.50
SEATS: 26. Private parties: 26 main room. Vegetarian meals. No children under 8.
No smoking during meal. Wheelchair access (1 step). Music. One sitting

BEXHILL-ON-SEA East Sussex

map 3

Lychgates

5A Church Street, Old Town,
Bexhill-on-Sea TN40 2HE
BEXHILL (0424) 212193

COOKING 2
COST £14–£30

There is not a lot left of old Bexhill and the longstanding buildings that remain, but Lychgates is part of it, a clapboarded wealden house close to the churchyard from which it takes its name. The Tysons run a small restaurant devoted to good value, which has helped them build up their business. At lunch there is a short choice of four items and at dinner the range and price increase to take in two different menus of three and five courses respectively. John Tyson is almost a Jekyll and Hyde among cooks. He may bake a breast of chicken with lemon and lemon balm or he may stuff a breast of guinea-fowl with cream cheese and pink peppercorns and serve it with strawberries and a butter sauce. He may cook a fair rabbit stew for lunch or produce a Blanc-like tartare of salmon. Witness is unanimous that simpler is better, but that tastes may be vitiated by faulty technique or poor materials. Thus a whiting and almond soup was curdled by overheating and a steak Esterhazy with a deep sauce had poor meat. Vegetables appear in unnecessary profusion, perhaps overstretching the kitchen. Service is invariably keen, by Sue Tyson on most days, but her husband will emerge from the kitchen to discuss the finer points of cooking. There is much eagerness here, and possibility, though the runny crèmes brûlées encountered by some readers is another instance of the need to tighten things up. The kitchen is close to the action, which is fine for delivering hot food but less fine for emitting odours of cooking fat. The wine list also shows enthusiasm in that the standard selection, and it is fairly standard, is beefed up with a short list of seven or more wines chosen to go with the menu offered that week. These are more interesting and have short notes by Adam Bancroft, MW. House wines from Mommessin are £7.75.

CHEF: John Tyson   PROPRIETORS: John and Sue Tyson
OPEN: Tue to Sat, exc Sat L
MEALS: 12.30 to 2, 7.15 to 10.30
PRICES: Set L £9.25 (£14), Set D £15.50 (£21) to £18.75 (£25)
CARDS: Access, Visa
SEATS: 26. Private parties: 18 main room. Children's helpings. No children under 8 at D. No cigars/pipes in dining room. Wheelchair access

---

BILLESLEY   Warwickshire   map 2

▲ *Billesley Manor*

Billesley B4G 6NF   COOKING 2
STRATFORD UPON AVON (0789) 400888   COST £22–£42

This large sixteenth-century mansion, wholly reconstructed now, is home to business and conference entertaining which may detract from its charms, increase some of its prices and ensure a certain basic set of equipment – from sauna to swimming-pool. Its attraction for meals is that Mark Naylor continues as chef even though the previous owners, Norfolk Capital, have been taken over by Queens Moat. If you cut through the undergrowth, his cooking is reliable and may be very good with simple dishes such as avocado with smoked salmon mousse; mange-tout soup; duck livers with bacon and saladings; fine salmon mayonnaise or with Champagne sauce; even a plain omelette. Prices make dinner dear but lunch is more feasible and it affords refuge from Stratford's crowds. Service has been slow on more than one occasion. Apart from house wines at £9.25, there is hardly anything below £13 on the carefully selected list. Mark-ups favour the top end, so brace yourself, and spend over £20 for good value, such as 1985 Guigal, Brune et Blonde at £24.

'I am writing to say that this place, which might be recommended to you for inclusion, should never be in the Guide. It represents all that is worst in English cuisine. After all we had spent (it being someone's birthday) the maitre d' arrived and announced ''I'm sorry, you're 55p light!'' This was on top of a notionally voluntary 12% service charge.' On eating in London

CHEF: Mark Naylor PROPRIETORS: Queens Moat Houses Plc
OPEN: all week
MEALS: 12.30 to 2, 7.30 to 9.30 (10 Fri and Sat)
PRICES: £25 (£35), Set L £15 (£22) to £17 (£24), Set D £23 (£30)
CARDS: Access, Amex, Diners, Visa
SEATS: 75. 6 tables outside. Private parties: 8 main room, 100 private room. Car-park, 150 places. Children's helpings. No children under 12. Smart dress preferred. No cigars in dining-room. Wheelchair access (also WC)
ACCOMMODATION: 41 rooms, all with bath/shower. Rooms for disabled. B&B £95 to £117. Baby facilities. Afternoon teas. Garden. Swimming-pool. Tennis. TV. Phone. Scenic. Doors close at 1am. Confirm by 6

BIRDLIP Gloucestershire map 2

▲ *Kingshead House* 🍷

Birdlip GL4 8JH — COOKING 2
GLOUCESTER (0452) 862299 — COST £17–£36

The Cotswold stone house probably dates from the sixteenth century, and is more noteworthy for informal comfort than country chic. Choose two or three courses from the set lunch menu and pay accordingly; for dinner, there's a fourth course and a heftier total. This year's reports have all been positive with minor reservations. Pretence is absent from Judy Knock's cooking, which none the less can hardly be called home cooking. Many ideas come from France, and she frequently harks back to pre-Victorian recipes. Organic produce and a fledgling herb garden have similar modern day/olden day affinities. Mushroom and almond tart; chicken with spinach, pine nuts and a little pasta; and hot strawberries on hazelnut meringue filled with raspberry sorbet are Knock favourites. A spring lovage and green pea soup was deemed satisfying. Filleted salmon with mushrooms and herbs in brioche pastry with hollandaise sauce, also known as koulibiac, was a success according to one winter visitor. Leg of lamb casseroled in mulled wine was well prepared but perhaps simpler than need be. A fragrant leg of lamb in devilled crust had more presence. Also complimented was the chocolate truffle encased in thin sponge. An intelligent list of nearly 70 carefully chosen wines is heavily weighted towards recent French bottles, with German and Italian contenders distant seconds. There's a good selection of half-bottles. House wine from southern France is £7.25. CELLARMAN'S CHOICE: Ch. La Garance, Graves, £13.50; Ch. de Mille, Côtes du Lubéron, £9.75. Musical evenings and regional menu events continue.

'Breakfast the following morning was even more like something out of Fawlty Towers. In addition to the aforesaid waitress, there were two men working; one was wearing a dinner jacket and bow tie whilst the other had an open-necked shirt with sleeves rolled up. He turned out to be the driver for a coach party staying at the hotel, who had decided to help out on account of not wanting to be delayed unduly. The final indignity came when the aforesaid waitress, after we had finished, removed our plates by putting a stack of other people's used plates on top, and then lifting ours at the bottom!' On staying in a Bournemouth hotel

---

CHEF: Judy Knock PROPRIETORS: Judy and Warren Knock
OPEN: Tue to Sun, exc Sat L and Sun D
CLOSED: 25 and 26 Dec, 1 Jan
MEALS: 12.30 to 2 (1.45 Sun), 7.15 to 10
PRICES: Set L £11.50 (£17) to £13 (£18), Sun L £12 (£17), Set D £20 (£27) to £22.50 (£30)
CARDS: Access, Amex, Diners, Visa
SEATS: 32. 2 tables outside. Private parties: 36 main room. Car-park, 12 places. Vegetarian meals. Children's helpings. No cigars/pipes in dining-room. Wheelchair access (1 step). Music
ACCOMMODATION: 1 room, with bath/shower. B&B £30 single, £46 double. Deposit: £10. Pets by arrangement. Garden. Scenic. Doors close at midnight. Confirm by 6

BIRKENHEAD Merseyside   map 5

Beadles

15 Rose Mount, Oxton,
Birkenhead L43 5SG   COOKING 1
051-653 9010   COST £25

'No change to the restaurant, but the kitchen has doubled in size resulting in miles more smiles from the chef,' writes Roy Gott of his restaurant in a gutted Victorian shop, now painted in dark colours brightened by pink tablecloths. The walls are site to a rotating show of his collection of prints: added incentive to regulars. It is these who do best, not from favouritism, but from knowing that they are in safe hands as he embarks on his orations about the food on offer. The menu gives a choice of about five dishes in each course of a conventional Anglo-French repertoire, with the occasional unusual touch, such as veal with a mango sauce or squash stuffed with red peppers, chestnuts and leeks. Hardy favourites are gravlax accorded a home vodka cure; grilled langoustines with aïoli; fennel à la grecque; beef with pickled walnuts; rack of lamb with provençal herbs; duck with apple and calvados or venison delivered by a friend of Roy Gott. Other game figures in season. Cooking is usually accurate, with not a lot of time spent on presentation, the occasional slip on duck (not crisp, not pink) or vegetables (soggy) being noted but not adjudged a capital offence. Desserts are rather more perfunctory. The wine list may occasion another five-minute discussion, but the result will be an apposite bottle from an interesting selection at a very fair price. House wine: £5.50.

CHEF: Bea Gott PROPRIETORS: Roy and Bea Gott
OPEN: Tue to Sat, D only
CLOSED: Aug
MEALS: 7.30 to 9
PRICES: £14 (£21)
SEATS: 34. Private parties: 30 main room. Children welcome. Wheelchair access. Music

---

The Guide *office can quickly spot when a restaurateur is encouraging customers to write recommending inclusion and sadly, several restaurants have been doing this in 1990. Such reports do not further a restaurant's cause. Please tell us if a restaurateur invites you to write to the* Guide.

Rondelle

11 Rose Mount, Oxton,
Birkenhead L43 5SG
051-652 8264

COOKING 2
COST £13–£32

When a front-parlour restaurant in Oxton says a signature dish is veal
sweetbreads roasted and layered with celery, with a garnish of scallops
chargrilled and trompettes de la mort, on a sauce of vermouth and carrot,
something worth investigating is going on. The Wirral is not exactly a
gourmet's paradise but this father and son team might still set it aflame. Not
that the setting helps them: it argues with the food and does not encourage
casual passers-by unless they read the menu, itself not a model of presentation.
The cooking shows care in buying materials and interesting methods of
cooking. Mark Wilkinson travels to London on his days off both to visit the
markets and to work a shift in famous kitchens. It shows. Early reports have
spoken of mussels with ginger and white wine; marinated scallops with fancy
leaves; venison and hare terrine with bramble dressing; poached lamb with
braised leeks; pigeon with fresh pasta and chocolate sauce; strips of beef in a
mustard sauce; salmon on a rhubarb sauce; rhubarb and ginger tart with
strawberry sauce; an orange mousse on a passion-fruit sauce with an almond
crunch or pear poached with caramel in a puff pastry box. Bread is in five
varieties, petits fours are legion, coffee excellent. The style, it is clear, is
London, which dazzles the unsuspecting visitor, for the restaurant is in a
constituency that 'seems to want only steak and chips'. The capacity to respond
to increased numbers is as yet unknown. The menu of half a dozen choices is
fixed price for the first two courses. The desserts cost extra but include a glass of
sweet wine. The wine list is from a good source but, like the menu, no model of
presentation. It was being revised as we went to press. Prices are very low but
you may have to see the bottle if you want full information. House wine is
£5.65. More reports, please.

CHEF: Mark Wilkinson   PROPRIETORS: Harry Wilkinson and Mark Wilkinson
OPEN: Mon to Sat, D only and Sun L (other days by arrangement)
MEALS: 12 to 2, 7 to 9.30 (10.15 Sat)
PRICES: Set Sun L £7 (£13), Set D £12 (£20) to £18.50 (£27). Service inc
CARDS: Access, Visa
SEATS: 30. Private parties: 36 main room. Vegetarian meals by arrangement. Children's
helpings. No children under 6. Smart dress preferred. No pipes in dining-room. Wheelchair
access (1 step). Music

BIRMINGHAM West Midlands   map 5

Adil

148–150 Stoney Lane,
Sparkbrook, B11 8AJ
021-449 0335

COOKING 1
COST £12

The Sparkbrook–Sparkhill area of Birmingham has the largest concentration of
Indian cafés and sweet centres in the city. Adil, opened in 1976, lays claim to

being the original, specialising in the balti style of Kashmir. Dishes are cooked and served in cast-iron pans rather like flattened woks. Unlike many of its neighbours, Adil has been 'discovered' and now draws in customers from way beyond its neighbourhood. Even so, the kitchen makes few compromises to Western tastes. A list of around 50 baltis moves beyond meat, mince and chicken into the exotic vegetables sold in the Ladypool Road shops: mustard leaf, tinda, lotus roots, and valor (Kashmiri beans). The proper accompaniment to these dishes is not rice but bread, and the Adil's output is outstanding. Be warned: tandoori 'chapatis' are actually huge, steaming hot roti the size of dinner plates, while a 'large nan' is sufficient bread for four people. There is a branch at 130 Stoney Lane.

CHEF: Mr Ashraf   PROPRIETOR: Mr Arif
OPEN: all week
MEALS: noon to midnight
PRICES: £7 (£10). Unlicensed, but bring your own: no corkage
CARDS: Access, Visa
SEATS: 70. Private parties: 50 private room. Vegetarian meals. Children welcome

Chung Ying

16–18 Wrottesley Street, B5 6RT   COOKING 2
021-622 5669 and 1793   COST £13

Birmingham's most reliable Cantonese restaurant survives stubbornly against the developers that are transforming the area around it. The Arcadia Shopping and Leisure complex looms large and the quasi-oriental architecture of China Court is nearby, but Chung Ying will not be moved. The kitchen has maintained its standards. The enormous 300-strong menu scores heavily with its range of dim-sum: around 40 choices, from steamed spare ribs and crabmeat and shark's fin dumplings to steamed ox-tripe with ginger and spring onion and Chinese sausage. Steamed green pepper stuffed with king prawns topped with an intense smear of garlicky black-bean and chilli sauce is excellent. There are also sizeable, freshly made, one-plate rice and noodle dishes which highlight the quality of the ingredients – particularly roast meats and seafood. Recommendations from other parts of the menu have included yuk shung; grilled prawns in satay sauce; and fried beef with ginger and spring onions. The kitchen avoids the westernised trimmings of other restaurants: chickens and ducks are authentically cleaved into pieces complete with bone and skin, and decorative garnishes are kept to a minimum. This is not a place to linger: the kitchen works fast and the service keeps pace. As the *Guide* went to press a complete refurbishment was planned.

CHEF/PROPRIETOR: Siu Chung Wong
OPEN: all week
MEALS: noon to midnight
PRICES: £9 (£13)
CARDS: Access, Amex, Diners, Visa
SEATS: 200. Private parties: 200 main room, 100 private room. Car-park, 10 places.
Vegetarian meals. Children welcome. Smart dress preferred. Music. Air-conditioned

Chung Ying Garden

17 Thorp Street, B5 4AT   COOKING 1
021-666 6622   COST £14−£25

This is a large restaurant with a long menu, a short wine list, and a lot of staff. Although Birmingham's Chinese quarter, to which there are now signposts, is also home to European restaurants, it is the Chung Ying and Chung Ying Garden that help make it worth the journey. The Garden is large, open-plan, slightly exotic, and disposed on different levels. Over 300 dishes include steamed ox tripe with ginger and spring onion; chicken feet in black-bean sauce; turnip paste; fish head and bean curd soup; roast piglet; and stewed eel with belly pork and garlic. Although the kitchen has had wobbly patches, the seriousness of intent is underscored by first-rate paper-wrapped prawns; deep-fried butterfly king prawns in a light batter − 10 in a first course portion and no excess oil in sight; crisply roasted salt-and-pepper spare ribs; fat free but tasty aromatic duck, served with pancakes and a grainy hoisin sauce with cucumber and onion. Sizzling dishes are less successful than stir-frys, and saucing can sometimes be bland, but ingredients are fresh and good. The overall impression is of lightness. Service is brisk and efficient. House French: £7.20 a litre.

CHEF/PROPRIETOR: Siu Chung Wong
OPEN: all week
MEALS: noon to midnight (11 Sun)
PRICES: £11 (£20), Set L and D £12 (£18) to £15 (£21). Service 10%
CARDS: Access, Amex, Diners, Visa
SEATS: 300. Private parties: 100 main room, 50 and 100 private rooms. Vegetarian meals. Children welcome. Wheelchair access (side entrance; also WC). Music. Air-conditioned

Days of the Raj

51 Dale End, B4 7LN   COOKING 2
021-236 0445   COST £10−£24

Sandwiched between a multi-storey car park and a night club, this north Indian restaurant is owned by lawyers and popular with them too, close as it is to Birmingham's courts. Westernised decoration, with lots of pinks, gives an impression of comfort to the first floor dining-room with a central fountain, lots of sepia photographs and a window on to the kitchen. Generally, the cooking has a subtlety of spicing that lifts it above the average − though the lack of saffron in the saffron rice seemed to overdo the subtlety. Meats and products of the tandoor are the most popular: tandoori cocktail, 'a small mountain of top quality lamb and chicken tikka with sheek kebab'; excellent rogan josh; and the tandoori special of five items from the tandoor with nan. Stuffed tomatoes and king prawn with ginger, garlic and 'mountain' herbs are two other well received dishes, though there have been regrets about the oversweet tomato sauce with butterfly prawns and the small range of sweets − in Birmingham of all places. Service has been generally praised though not by the party that waited two hours for one course of a meal. There is a good lunch buffet. House French: £5.95.

CHEF: Rashpal Sunner PROPRIETORS: Balbir Singh and P.S. Kulair
OPEN: all week, exc Sat and Sun L
MEALS: 12 to 2.30, 7 (6 Fri and Sat) to 11.30
PRICES: £12 (£19), Set L £5.95 (£10) to £8.50 (£13), Set D £11 (£15) to £16 (£20). Minimum
£7.50. Service inc
CARDS: Access, Amex, Diners, Visa
SEATS: 120. Private parties: 100 main room, 25 and 30 private rooms. Vegetarian meals.
Children's helpings (with prior notice). Smart dress preferred. Wheelchair access (also
WC). Music. Air-conditioned

Franzl's

151 Milcote Road, Bearwood, B67 5BN   COOKING 1
021-429 7920   COST £15–£26

The Geireggers do their best to impose a little bit of Austria on the West
Midlands. Cow-bells, decorative plates and stirring tourist-board music that
softens as the evening progresses all help the illusion. The converted corner
terrace house is less evocative. 'We must admit we still felt in the heart of
Birmingham.' The Austro-Hungarian tradition is represented by hearty *zigeuner
goulash*, consisting of chunks of pork, veal and beef impregnated with paprika
in a thick sauce based on tomatoes and onions; by venison cooked two ways;
by wiener schnitzel, of course; and by puddings that make much of chocolate,
cherries, cream and alcohol. Breadcrumbing and deep-frying, techniques
applied to pâté encased in bread, to mushrooms, and to a ham and cheese
pancake, meet with varying degrees of success. 'Tangy, juicy, succulent and
substantial' herring fillets marinated in sour cream and dill come highly
recommended. Vegetables include good rice, red cabbage, and spinach strudel;
or there are salads of haricot beans with a thyme vinaigrette, or shredded
cabbage with caraway. One thing is especially reminiscent of Austria: the
mountains of food. Iced coffee is a pudding in itself. Wines are commendably
under £10 for the most part, Austrian to a bottle, apart from Champagne, and
understandably dominated by whites. The wine is poured into a glass vessel, a
weinhaber, on the table, whence it is dispensed via a sort of optic into green-
stemmed glasses. House Austrian: £7.55.

CHEF: Adolf Geiregger PROPRIETORS: Adolf and Valerie Geiregger
OPEN: Tue to Sat, D only
CLOSED: first 3 weeks Aug, last week Dec
MEALS: 7 to 10.30
PRICES: Set D £9.55 (£15) to £15.95 (£22)
CARDS: Access, Visa
SEATS: 40. Private parties: 40 main room. Vegetarian meals. Children's helpings.
No children under 6. Music

*Several sharp operators have tried to extort money from restaurateurs on the promise of an
entry in a guide book that has never appeared. The Good Food Guide makes no charge
for inclusion and does not offer certificates of any kind.*

*See the inside of the front cover for an explanation of the 1 to 5 rating system recognising
cooking standards.*

Henry's

27 St Pauls Square, B3 1RB
021-200 1136

COOKING 1
COST £17–£24

Henry Wong's large Cantonese restaurant in Birmingham's newly polished jewellery quarter has chic decor and more square tables than round in a sunken dining area overlooked by the bar. The menu is a manageable length, leaning more to deep-fried than steamed items, and leaves vegetarians almost bereft. One reader liked the thick deep-fried scallops in a light batter, 'hot, crisp and fresh tasting'. King prawns with chilli and peppers was said to be a successful combination of light cooking and contrasting flavours of delicate and fiery. Special rice with prawns, peppers and pork is fluffy. Service has been criticised. It may be one of the smartest places in the area, but the cooking is not as sparkling as the paintwork. House French: £7.

CHEF: C.W. Choi   PROPRIETORS: Henry Wong and C.W. Choi
OPEN: Mon to Sat
CLOSED: one week Aug
MEALS: 12 to 2, 6 to 11 (11.30 Sat)
PRICES: £12 (£20), Set L and D £12 (£17) to £15 (£20). Service inc
CARDS: Access, Amex, Diners, Visa
SEATS: 100. Vegetarian meals. Children welcome. Music

Maharaja

23–25 Hurst Street, B5 4AS
021-622 2641

COOKING 1
COST £12–£23

Still one of the most popular Indian restaurants in the centre of the city, a few doors from the Hippodrome. The modest pink dining-room can seem cramped and smoky when it is busy, but the food is consistently a cut above the average. Indians eat here, which is an encouraging sign. The kitchen works to a short menu of north Indian and Punjabi dishes, with curries and vegetables outshining tandoori specialities. Chicken bhuna masala, rogan josh and lamb dhansak have been notable for the quality of the ingredients and the fresh, distinctive spicing. Sauces are intense, untainted by commercial pastes or mixes. Thick pulpy aloo palak pointed up with fresh coriander has also been positively reported. Rice is well handled, despite the use of colouring, and nan bread is more than acceptable. Service remains gracious and attentive, even under pressure. House wine: £6.10.

CHEF: Bhupinder Waraich   PROPRIETOR: N.S. Batt
OPEN: Mon to Sat
MEALS: 12 to 2.30, 6 to 11.30
PRICES: £9 (£18), Set L £6.50 (£12) to £10.50 (£16), Set D £8.50 (£14) to £13.50 (£19). Service 10%
CARDS: Access, Amex, Diners, Visa
SEATS: 65. 18 tables outside. Private parties: 30 main room. Vegetarian meals. Children welcome. Wheelchair access. Music. Air-conditioned

---

The Guide *always appreciates hearing about changes of chef or owner.*

▲ *Sir Edward Elgar*
Restaurant, Swallow Hotel

12 Hagley Road,	
Five Ways, B16 8SJ	COOKING 2
021-452 1144	COST £23–£48

By Five Ways, in a large 1930s modern office block, has come to roost a massive Swallow Hotel complete with an Ancient Egyptian leisure club, Langtry's terrace restaurant and this more formal one named after the composer. Idris Caldora, late of Bilbrough Manor, has taken up the challenge of cooking. The air is certainly one of luxury and the à la carte prices are not wholly justifiable, but the menu of the day, even when sampled by people less inclined to tug their forelock at all the flounce, has been thought fair value and good cooking. 'Food flowed from the initial greeting of olives, cheese straws and nuts, to hot canapés of scrambled egg in choux pastry, then followed by more at the table.' Exactly cooked was a meal of gazpacho; chicken livers on a bed of courgettes with a herb dressing and a tomato sauce; a chicken mousse, light flavoured and well textured, contained within the skin of a chicken leg served with a good walnut salad, the salad outshining the mousse; escalope of salmon with a white wine sauce, onions and carrots. Equally exact were nuggets of monkfish with lobster sauce, but a medley of seafood was drowned by too rich and copious a saffron sauce. Vegetables are fussy, inventive (a filo bag of wild mushrooms and onion) and enjoyable. A good summer pudding, robust and crunchy, and a cold peach mousse-soufflé, which had insufficient flavour to have any distinctiveness, brought up the rear. Idris Caldora has often been accused of gilding the lily, but he has skills which may or may not be allowed to blossom in the context of a large business-oriented hotel. The prices of the *carte* are extremely depressing as a harbinger of the hotel's priorities. Lily Langtry's has also been praised for fair cooking and the prices are less impossible. The wine list is instant prestige with big producers and négociants getting most attention. Prices are in line with the restaurant, though house wine is £9. More reports, please.

CHEF: Idris Caldora   PROPRIETORS: Swallow Hotels
OPEN: all week, exc Sat L
MEALS: 12.30 to 2.30, 7.30 to 10.30
PRICES: £33 (£40), Set L £16 (£23), Set D £27 (£34). Service inc
CARDS: Access, Amex, Diners, Visa
SEATS: 50. Private parties: 8 main room, 20 private room. Car-park, 90 places. Vegetarian meals. Children's helpings. Smart dress preferred. No-smoking area. Wheelchair access (also WC). Music (live). Air-conditioned
ACCOMMODATION: 98 rooms, all with bath/shower. Rooms for disabled. Lift. Rooms £97.50 to £120. Children welcome. Baby facilities. Pets welcome. Afternoon teas. Swimming-pool. Sauna. Air-conditioning. TV. Phone [*Which? Hotel Guide*]

▲ *This symbol means accommodation is available.*

Consumers' Association is planning to publish Out to Eat, *a new guide to budget eating out in restaurants, pubs, cafés, brasseries and so on. Please send reports and recommendations to Out to Eat, FREEPOST, 2 Marylebone Road, London NW1 1YN.*

Sloans

27–29 Chad Square, Hawthorne Road,
Edgbaston, B15 3TQ
021-455 6697

COOKING 3
COST £23–£41

Chad Square is a shopping precinct and an unlikely spot for a serious
restaurant equipped in accord with its self-image. Sloans has stayed the course
for a number of years and carries the torch for Anglo-French cooking in
Birmingham. Roger Narbett was chef of the year at Hotelympia 1990 with a
menu that was later served in the restaurant. It began with a salmon and
lobster sausage, flavoured with dill, in a lobster sauce; went on to rosette of
lamb with an onion and chive purée and a wild mushroom sauce (rather a lot of
buttons in evidence, according to one who sampled it); and finished with a
lemon cream custard ringed with fruit. This may be taken as a paradigm. Roger
Narbett's strength, however, seems to lie in fish cookery: steamed fillet of brill
with Champagne sauce; trout and monkfish with scampi and tomato; a
feuilleté of salmon with a hazelnut sauce; and sole wrapped around a salmon
and lobster mousse are dishes that have met approval for their freshness and
keen balance of flavours between sauce and main ingredient. There may be a
hot fruit soufflé or puddings involving fresh or soft fruit to finish the meal.
Raspberries and strawberries make many an unseasonal appearance – not
always to good effect. There is a shorter set menu at lunchtime but one visitor
observed that the many business people who predominate at midday seemed
happier with the *carte*. In the event, the set lunch proved uneven in execution.
CELLARMAN'S CHOICE: Jurançon, Dom. Cauhapé 1989, £11.75; Madiran, Dom.
Pichard 1983, £11.50. Good growers abound on the carefully chosen and
accessibly priced wine list. Burgundies excel and clarets are helpfully arranged
by commune. House French selection starts at £8.50.

CHEF: Roger Narbett   PROPRIETORS: W. J. Narbett and Roger Narbett
OPEN: Mon to Sat, exc Sat L
CLOSED: bank hols, first week Jan
MEALS: 12 to 2, 7 to 10
PRICES: £25 (£34), Set L £14.50 (£23)
CARDS: Access, Amex, Visa
SEATS: 60. Private parties: 30 main room. Car-park, 60 places. Children welcome. Smart
dress preferred. Wheelchair access (1 step; also WC). Music. Air-conditioned

---

BIRTLE Greater Manchester　　　　　　　　　　　　　　　　map 5

▲ Normandie ♥

Elbut Lane, Birtle BL9 6UT
061-764 3869 and 1170

COOKING 3
COST £24–£38

The site was once an inn, perhaps for drovers coming off the Pennines beyond.
Steady expansion since conversion to a hotel-restaurant has meant the addition
of a modern block to one side. This is where you eat. The Moussas have spent
time and money to bring the decoration up to scratch: you can drink amid
blues, greens and marble in the bar, then progress to a dining-room whose

main character is taken from brick-lined alcoves and flat modern arches that divide the space. Gillian Moussa and her son Max are responsible for the front of house and leave the kitchen to Pascal Pommier. Their intention is a serious French restaurant. Prices are indeed serious and may lead to comparison with other places of greater achievement but there is no denying the pleasure readers have had eating here, because of both the solicitous attention of the Moussas and the skill of the cookery. There is a seasonal menu of maybe six or seven items per course and a very much shorter daily set-price offering. The menu steers a sane course between interest, for example salmon with a light curry and saffron sauce, and the expectations of many of the customers, as in noisettes of lamb with a simple jus – made more fun with a small parsley flan. There are a couple of hot desserts of which the soufflés, much enjoyed, are 'fluffy yet melting'. The cooking is not heavy: a fricassee of scallops with noodles and a vegetable court bouillon should please the strongest health freak, just as did another scallop dish with an asparagus mousse and a parsley emulsion. The poultry and game has also been approved, from squab with baby vegetables to a breast of pheasant pot roasted with wine and served on a bed of savoy cabbage. The combination of lardons, wild mushrooms, a little citrus tang and reduction of the cooking liquid was excellent. The cheeseboard surprised one visitor from Belgium for its range and condition. Breakfast may include home-made croissants. The aura of peace among the hills is welcome respite from the bustle of Manchester, Britain's liveliest club scene. The wine list is almost too long a read. Ch. Angludet 1978 and Pommard Les Grands Epenots 1979 from Gaunoux show careful selection if over-pricing. But these are balanced by a decent range around £10. House French: £8. CELLARMAN'S CHOICE: Morgon le Clachet 1989, Brun, £14.60; Tokay Pinot Gris 1988, Cave Tradition, £11.65. Gillian Moussa notes that 'tipping is a totally archaic and unnecessary practice'.

CHEF: Pascal Pommier   PROPRIETORS: Gillian Moussa and Max Moussa
OPEN: Mon to Sat, exc Mon and Sat L
CLOSED: 26 Dec to first Sun in Jan, exc New Year's Eve, and 1 week at Easter
MEALS: 12 to 2, 7 to 9.30
PRICES: £26 (£32), Set D £18.50 (£24). No service charge, no tipping
CARDS: Access, Amex, Diners, Visa
SEATS: 60. Private parties: 70 main room. Car-park, 60 places. Vegetarian meals on request. Children's helpings. Smart dress preferred. No cigars/pipes in dining-room. Wheelchair access. Music
ACCOMMODATION: 24 rooms, all with bath/shower. Rooms for disabled. Lift. B&B £55 to £79. Baby facilities. TV. Phone. Confirm by noon

---

'The "aromatic duck" was so dried up and inedible that one would think twice before using it in a stock at home. I told the waitress that we were not prepared to eat it; the manageress came out and, after much arguing we put £12 on the table (very generous for what we had consumed) and said we were leaving. The manageress then locked us in and called the police. After ten minutes the policemen came in and with much good humour, took all our names and told the woman she could take us to court if she wanted to.'
On eating in Swindon

▲ *Mallory Court*

Harbury Lane,
Bishop's Tachbrook CV33 9QB
LEAMINGTON SPA (0926) 330214   COOKING 3
off A452, 2m S of Leamington Spa   COST £28−£54

The formal gardens and immaculate Edwardian house give way, once through
the doors, to a riot of upholstery and colour − though not in the more restrained
dining-room. Mallory Court is designed, some say over-designed, for comfort
and it shows, making it a sybaritic place to visit. The punctilious attention of a
myriad staff only confirms this: it is not a member of Relais & Châteaux for
nothing. The kitchen works in similar vein: luxurious, considered and
enjoyable with just a few signs of striving for effect, as in a main course of
chicken breast served with lentils, scallops and wild mushrooms on a curry
cream sauce. The menu is fixed price with various supplements if further
courses are required. The price has been set high enough to serve foie gras
without extra charge, though lobster still carries one of £2. Dishes that have
satisfied include a robust pheasant terrine accompanied by lightly pickled
vegetables; ravioli of langoustines; sea bass served with a mousseline of
scallops; a simple best end of lamb with a herb crust, decked out with a sorrel
and mint cream sauce and a little pile of ratatouille. A red mullet of impeccable
flavour serves to confirm that, though the restaurant is in the middle of
England, fish cookery is among its strong points. That luxury is never far away,
but usually discreetly handled, is seen from dishes such as asparagus with
broccoli mousse and morels in a feuilleté and a warm salad of quail, foie gras
and fried quails' eggs. That chef Allan Holland keeps his eye on the recipes and
methods of his confrères is evidenced by a tartare of salmon with cucumber,
sour cream and caviare as a first course and a roast saddle of rabbit with
mustard together with braised leg of rabbit in a tarragon gravy as a main dish.
Desserts are less obviously inviting than the first two courses although reports
still mention the chocolate trio of sorbet, white chocolate mousse with
redcurrant coulis to cut the richness, and a marquise, as well as the hot Grand
Marnier soufflé with an orange sorbet. Trimmings to the front and to the end of
the meal, as well as the baking in the middle, are well up to standard. 'Service
charge is neither made nor expected.' The wine list is conservatively French
and, within major sections such as claret, listed confusingly without date, place
or price. There are some good choices, though prices will keep them in stock for
a fair while; better value is to be had from the Rhône rather than the classic
regions. House wine: £7.95. CELLARMAN'S CHOICE: Cornas 1983, de Barjac,
£23.95; St Véran, Dom. des Vignemont 1987, £14.50.

The Guide *office can quickly spot when a restaurateur is encouraging customers to write
recommending inclusion and sadly, several restaurants have been doing this in 1990.
Such reports do not further a restaurant's cause. Please tell us if a restaurateur invites you
to write to the* Guide.

See the back of the Guide *for an index of restaurants listed.*

CHEF: A.J.G. Holland   PROPRIETORS: A.J.G. Holland and J.R. Mort
OPEN: all week
MEALS: 12.30 to 1.45, 7.30 to 9.30 (10 Sat)
PRICES: Set L £21 (£28), Set D £38.50 (£45). Service inc
CARD: Access, Visa
SEATS: 50. Private parties: 50 main room. Car-park, 50 places. No children under 12. Smart dress preferred. No cigars/pipes in dining room
ACCOMMODATION: 10 rooms, all with bath/shower. B&B £102 to £180. No children under 12. Afternoon teas. Garden. Swimming-pool. Tennis. TV. Phone. Scenic. Doors close at midnight

---

BLACKWATER   Cornwall   map 1

Long's

| Blackwater TR8 8HH | COOKING 3 |
| TRURO (0872) 561111 | COST £14–£32 |

Once the headquarters of a tin-mining company, the restaurant's conversion has been undertaken with some lavishness and thoroughness. Even the mineral water, Ramlösa in blue bottles, is in harmony with the colour scheme. Sunday lunch is a bargain set-price with only one choice, but the evening *carte* runs to four or five options, changing daily. The style of cooking is picture-book modern, with an apparent love of packaging: spiced rabbit fillets are served in a bread box; salmon is given a spinach coat; lamb and venison come with coverings or frames of pastry; duck gets a little wrapping of bacon; and prawns are folded into pancakes. That's on just one menu. The presentation may intrude, as in a box of fried bread that nearly sank a nicely cooked saddle of venison with a blueberry sauce. That sauce reflects another of Ann Long's preoccupations: fruit with meat or sweet with sour. Fillets of plaice in 'an open pie' have grapes; duck has blueberry; lamb, plum sauce; salmon, vanilla; venison, an 'onion jam'; and a first course of strips of goose and chicken is encased in an orange jelly. Combinations may be finely judged, as in the last instance, but can be gross when good judgement fails. Vegetables, arranged on a side plate, include purées and sauced items, and may emphasise the tendencies above. Delicacy also has a firm place within the repertoire: crabmeat with courgette chips and a basil mayonnaise; a rabbit terrine with a redcurrant sauce; well bought and accurately cooked meats. Desserts are not for the light-framed: rich chocolate bombe, oatmeal meringue with raspberries and cream or a large crème brûlée on an apple and blackberry base satisfy those who still have room, and tempt the surfeited as well. Ian Long is a forcible host and occasionally needs more help to zip round busy tables. He has constructed a short and fast-evolving wine list that includes Israeli wines as well as imports from François Paquet in Beaujolais. It is one of only a few lists that gives alcoholic strength for each entry. House wines from Paquet are £6.20. Tips are not encouraged.

The text of entries is based on unsolicited reports sent in by readers, backed up by inspections conducted anonymously. The factual details under the text are from questionnaires the Guide *sends to all restaurants that feature in the book.*

CHEF: Ann Long   PROPRIETORS: Ian and Ann Long
OPEN: Wed to Sat, D only, and Sun L
CLOSED: 4 weeks during winter
MEALS: 12.30 to 1.45, 7.30 to 10
PRICES: £18 (£27), Set L £9.95 (£14)
CARDS: Access, Amex, Visa
SEATS: 30. Private parties: 10 main room, 10 and 12 private rooms. Car-park, 20 places.
Children's helpings. No children under 12. Smart dress preferred. Wheelchair access
(also WC)

Pennypots

Blackwater TR4 8EY	COOKING 2
REDRUTH (0209) 820347	COST £29

The Viners' choice of name proves an accurate indicator of style: cottage-like
rooms, pictures on the walls entitled *In Disgrace* or *Silent Sympathy*, 'the best
appointed women's room outside a country-house hotel', soft toys here and
there in the bar. It has bags of charm and is suffused by Jane Viner's warm
enthusiasm for her customers and for her husband's much-laureated
professional cooking (certificates adorn many walls). Kevin Viner's skills shine
through: a fine and intense crab soup; excellent bread rolls (though slightly
sweet); pungent basil sauce with a squeakily fresh piece of turbot; desserts that
might enter a competition, so clever the spun-sugar cages; and petits fours that
might feed the whole of Truro. His prize-winning pastillage on show is a
further sign that sugar work is his first love. The materials, particularly fish, are
very good and solecisms are few, such as a sprinkling of not so good prawns on
a salad beneath a first-rate brochette of scallops. It is possible that greater
confidence will result in a shorter menu and fewer embellishments so that his
essential skill can shine still brighter. Bills paid by credit card are not left open.
The wine list is short and not too dear; it, too, may be improved as time passes.
House wine: £5.75.

CHEF: Kevin Viner   PROPRIETORS: Kevin and Jane Viner
OPEN: Tue to Sat, D only
MEALS: 7 to 10
PRICES: £19 (£24). Minimum £12
CARDS: Access, Amex, Diners, Visa
SEATS: 30. Private parties: 18 main room, 12 private room. Car-park, 10 places. Vegetarian
meals on 24 hours notice. Children's helpings on request. Wheelchair access (1 step). Music

BLANDFORD FORUM Dorset	map 2

▲ *La Belle Alliance*

Whitecliff Mill Street,	
Blandford Forum DT11 7BP	COOKING 1
BLANDFORD FORUM (0258) 452842	COST £14–£30

The profusion of window boxes, baskets and planters softens the outlines of
the house, proclaiming it different from the many nursing homes that line the
road. Within there are many signs of conversion and modernisation to a small

hotel. The birth of a baby to the Davisons may inevitably have caused some upset, for there has been greater unevenness in reports than hitherto. Both Davisons are now back on post. The set-price menu, offering maybe six choices in each course, promises well: strong on fish from the Dorset coast, no outlandish combinations, an adequate though not exciting range within a small compass. This is exemplified by dishes such as escalope of salmon poached in stock, with vegetables; warm salad of pigeon breast; salmon and monkfish on spinach with a saffron sauce; sole with a salmon mousse; sea bream with chives and cucumber; duck with sage and apple or with apricots; baked banana with a banana ice-cream; or bread-and-butter pudding unexpectedly topped with strawberries. Unfortunately the cooking has lacked accuracy, dried herbs seem to be in evidence in midsummer, vegetables have been ill chosen and poorly cooked. The reports have been up-and-down, coinciding perhaps with problems of new parenthood. Service from Lauren Davison is ever-willing, though her colleagues may need more training. The wine list is uneven; although it manages to choose some very good French growers, especially in Burgundy, it is much less exciting in other areas. It does not charge too much. This is estimable though it may now be thought profitable to shift the emphasis away from France in order to widen still further the appeal of a sensitive selection. House wines: £7.95. CELLARMAN'S CHOICE: Brouilly Ch. des Tours 1988, £10.95; Muscadet sur lie 1988, Bossard, £8.65.

CHEF: Philip Davison   PROPRIETORS: Lauren and Philip Davison
OPEN: Tue to Sat D; Sun L; bank hol Sun and Mon D
MEALS: 7 to 9.30 (10 Sat)
PRICES: Set Sun L £10.50 (£14), Set D from £19.50 (£23) to £21.50 (£25). Service inc
CARDS: Access, Amex, Visa
SEATS: 32. Private parties: 36 main room. Car-park, 14 places. Children under 7 by arrangement. No smoking in dining-room. Wheelchair access. Music
ACCOMMODATION: 5 rooms, all with bath/shower. B&B £45 to £58. Children under 7 by arrangement. Pets welcome. TV. Phone. Scenic. Doors close at midnight. Confirm by 6

BOLLINGTON Cheshire   map 5

Mauro's

88 Palmerston Street, Bollington SK10 5PW   COOKING 2
BOLLINGTON (0625) 573898   COST £25

An Italian trattoria in a village of stone terraces and old textile mills. The menu runs the gamut of old favourites – stracciatella, saltimbocca alla Romana – but the pasta is home made and readers are charmed by the ambience created by the Mauro family: Sra Mauro giving the welcome and Sr Mauro beavering away, on view through a glass screen, in the handsome kitchen before emerging at the end of service. People have spoken well of the noodle, bean and mussel soup, 'the best I've ever eaten' and linguini alle vongole as well as calf's liver and veal dishes. Most of the recommendations have come from the daily specials, the place to look for fish and fresh pasta with more interesting accompaniments. There is a big sweets trolley which may sometimes strike the eater as heavy (cakey) and a trifle dull. There have been moments when pressure of business has exceeded the capacity to serve. The wine list is exclusively Italian save for Champagnes and is worth a moment's pause for such good names as Ceretto and Lungarotti, though top-class wines with any age are disappointingly absent. House Italian: £7.65 litre. CELLARMAN'S CHOICE: Galestro, Antinori, £8.95; Rubesco 1985, Lungarotti, £10.45.

CHEF/PROPRIETOR: V. Mauro
OPEN: Tue to Sat
MEALS: 12 to 2, 7 to 10
PRICES: £14 (£21)
CARDS: Access, Amex, Visa
SEATS: 50. Vegetarian meals. Children's helpings. Wheelchair access (also unisex WC). Music

Randalls

22 High Street, Old Market Place,
Bollington SK10 5PH
BOLLINGTON (0625) 575058

COOKING 1
COST £13–£30

The rather precious phrasing of the menu does not inhibit this sparely furnished restaurant from being a popular local spot with a 'friendly welcome and strong desire to please'. All those bare boards do create a noise problem. The seasonal menu is long and much dearer than the mid-week 'market menu' that offers a very fair set price. Fruit and spices inform some of the recipes, such as sea bass baked with an oatmeal crust with a ginger and lime gravy, guinea-fowl with a grape and kümmel sauce, or rack of lamb with blackcurrant sauce, accompanied by a tamarillo fruit. Modernity is maintained by bresaola with a shallot and chive dressing or a vegetable terrine with virgin olive oil, but when the kitchen is faced with traditional Yorkshire pudding on a Sunday lunch, it appears that more practice is needed. Lemon tart, crème brûlée and bread-and-butter pudding are classic sweets; apple and armagnac strudel with a saffron ice-cream shows more invention. A short wine list is adequate to good, with Trimbach Alsaces and Faustino Rioja among the better bottles. Prices are fair. House wine from Cordier: £6.

CHEF: David Errington   PROPRIETORS: John and Jo Hough
OPEN: Tue to Sat D only, and Sun L
MEALS: 12 to 2.30, 7 to 10 (10.30 Fri and Sat)
PRICES: £17 (£25), Set Sun L £9.95 (£14), Set D, Tue to Fri, £9.95 (£14), Set Gourmet D, Wed to Fri, £22.50 (£28)
CARDS: Access, Amex, Diners, Visa
SEATS: 50. Private parties: 50 main room. Vegetarian meals. Children's helpings (Sun L only). Smart dress preferred. Wheelchair access (1 step). Music

'Salmon terrine with salad: rice salad and also ordinary salad shared a plate with the terrine. A bread roll (dry) with butter came as accompaniment. The terrine was (oddly, for salmon) white with an occasional dark speck, thus looking a little like a flat slab of blue cheese. It was extremely creamy, tasted only faintly of salmon, and contained chunks of jelly: overall, it was soft, gelatinous, melting, almost frothy. I have never tasted anything quite like it.' On dining in Derbyshire

BOTLEY Hampshire   map 2

Cobbett's

15 The Square, Botley SO3 2EA   COOKING 1
BOTLEY (0489) 782068   COST £17–£41

The half-timbered cottage with its dining-room on the ground floor sits snugly
in a British architectural mishmash of the classical and vernacular. The Square
was undergoing a facelift in spring, which may allow the Skipwiths to indulge
in pavement tables and other facets of the new Europeanism as well as develop
their Causerie vinothèque on the first floor. Charles Skipwith once worked in
the Bordeaux wine trade and his wife hails from St Emilion so the emphasis,
though she no longer does the day to day cooking, is emphatically French.
Feuilleté of asparagus is sauced with yoghurt, lemon, butter and almonds;
salmon marinated with lemon, coriander and olive oil; chicken and duck liver
gathered into a small boudin served with a port wine sauce for first courses of a
short *carte* of half-a-dozen choices at each stage - and there is also a prix fixe no-
choice. Main dishes are French provincial: duck with rosemary, garlic and
thyme; lamb with orange and Dubonnet; rib steak marchand de vin. Desserts
number at least seven and can be had as a 'symphony', which is a selection of
several delicacies and worth the extra cost according to one happy customer.
The short wine list has a pair from the antipodes but remains otherwise French.
Prices, like those for the food, are never giveaway. House Bordeaux is £4.95 for
a pichet, £9 for a bottle.

CHEFS: Lucie Skipwith and Peter Hayes PROPRIETORS: Charles and Lucie Skipwith
OPEN: Mon to Sat, exc Mon and Sat L
CLOSED: 2 weeks summer, 2 weeks winter
MEALS: 12 to 2, 7.30 (7 Sat) to 10
PRICES: £22 (£34), Set L from £8.50 (£17) to £14.50 (£23), Set D £16.50 (£25). Licensed, also
bring your own: £3.50
CARDS: Access, Amex, Visa
SEATS: 40. Private parties: 40 main room, 15 private room. Car-park, 15 places. No children
under 12. Smart dress preferred. No cigars/pipes in dining-room

BOUGHTON LEES Kent   map 3

▲ *Eastwell Manor*

COUNTY
OF THE
YEAR
RESTAURANT

Eastwell Park, Boughton Lees TN25 4HR   COOKING 3
ASHFORD (0233) 635751   COST £22–£48

There is often an element of uncertainty about country-house hotels of this
magnificence in the hands of a large company. Will the original intentions be
subverted in order to maximise profit? Will a talented chef be allowed to show
his potential? Eastwell is pretty magnificent: 3,000 acres of land; a house last
rebuilt in 1926 in massive baronial style, now carefully restored, with a
glorious dining-room of beams, grandeur and very big fireplaces. Mark
Clayton, who featured in the last *Guide* as the chef at Turner's in London (see
entry), is obviously skilled and is showing by his cooking and buying that he
intends well. Although the *carte* is as expensive as might be feared, the set
menus are not. Recent meals show as much care paid to the cheaper as the

dearer. Overall, there is a refreshing lack of preoccupation with luxuries without going overboard the other way with nostalgic 'granny cooking'. None the less his self-proclaimed signature dishes include braised knuckle of veal with a tagliatelle of leek and carrots and best end of veal on braised cabbage with a garlic sauce. The latter was judged 'an excellent modern sauce of stock, cream and garlic with flavoursome meat, cooked to retain its juices, on a bed of strips of carrot, leeks and white cabbage; an appetising combination of tastes.' A best end of lamb with herb and brioche crust comes with a sweet pepper and tarragon sauce. The meat was again of the finest quality, though overpowered by mustard in the crust. The sauce, caramelised too far, tasted recognisably of pimento. Vegetables, a modern jumble, have also shown good buying and timing. Desserts are adequate but not as brilliant as meat cookery. First courses are not the usual succession of foie gras and shellfish – indeed, on one night foie gras was only to be found on the set menu – but include fresh ravioli with spinach and goats' cheese in a fennel butter sauce or a gutsy red mullet soup. A warm salad of pigeon was well bought and handled to bring out robust flavours from the dressing. Trimmings – pastry, bread, coffee and petits fours – have ranged from poor to middling, though one reader's variation of salmon canapés was well conceived. Service is amiable though not wholly informed. The wine list is fairly spread over the world, which gives it fair price range from a base of about £13. With what must be a multiple mark-up, prices climb fast, but there are Chileans to fall back on. House wines: £12.75. CELLARMAN'S CHOICE: Mercurey 1988, Delorme, £22.50; Hunter Valley Chardonnay Show Reserve 1988, £21.

CHEF: Mark Clayton   PROPRIETORS: Queens Moat Houses plc
OPEN: all week
MEALS: 12.30 to 2, 7.30 to 9.30 (10 Sat)
PRICES: £31 (£40), Set L £12.75 to £15.50 (£22), Set D £22.50 (£29). Service inc
CARDS: Access, Amex, Diners, Visa
SEATS: 70. Private parties: 50 main room, 40 private room. Car-park, 100 places. Vegetarian meals. Children's helpings. No children under 7. Smart dress preferred. No cigars/pipes in dining-room. Wheelchair access (2 steps; also WC)
ACCOMMODATION: 23 rooms, all with bath/shower. Rooms for disabled. Lift. B&B £85 to £125. Deposit: 1 night. Baby facilities. Pets by arrangement. Afternoon teas. Garden. Tennis. Fishing. Snooker. TV. Phone. Scenic. Doors close at 11. Confirm by 6
[Which? Hotel Guide]

BOURNEMOUTH Dorset   map 2

Sophisticats

43 Charminster Road, Bournemouth BH8 8UE	COOKING 2
BOURNEMOUTH (0202) 291019	COST £28

Cats are the decorative theme, with a vengeance, but one newcomer remarked that it looks more like a smart pizzeria than anything. The style is not Italian. In truth, it offers sensible cooking at affordable prices that inspires local support and rescues not a few wet holidays. Steak and fish are the main business of an unchanging *carte*, with daily specials and a strong line in puddings to liven things up. Steak is cooked six ways including 'Javanese' style with soy sauce, wine and spices; veal is done three ways, one of them with apples, calvados and cream. Crispy duck with a sauce – cherry or ginger or green peppercorns – is well reported. John Knight informs us, in common with an increasing number of restaurants, that 'the fishmonger's account tends to get larger than the butcher's.' The catch determines the choice, but portions are generous and freshness is noticed. Take away the alcohol, cream and chocolate and there would not be much left of the puddings: pancakes are filled with cherries, chocolate and cream and flamed in kirsch, and meringue is served with a Tia Maria and hazelnut ice-cream, with hot chocolate sauce poured over. Hot soufflés are the thing at the end of the meal, or the iced lime version for something lighter. A standard list of 50 wines includes some inexpensive bottles. House French is £6.25.

CHEF: Bernard Calligan   PROPRIETORS: John Knight and Bernard Calligan
OPEN: Tue to Sat, D only
CLOSED: 2 weeks Jan, 1 week June, last 2 weeks Nov
MEALS: 7 to 10
PRICES: £15 (£23)
SEATS: 32. Private parties: 12 main room. Children welcome. Wheelchair access
(also male and female WC). Music

BOWNESS-ON-WINDERMERE   Cumbria   map 7

Porthole Eating House ▮

3 Ash Street,
Bowness-on-Windermere LA23 3EB   COOKING 2
WINDERMERE (096 62) 2793   COST £34

You can go a long way with charm, and perhaps even further with Italian charm. Gianni Berton has been here for 19 years. According to one reader, he 'must be the most accomplished front of house performer there is.' He and his wife Judy have created – or evolved – a Lake Windermere institution and a personal style of catering. He explains that the inspiration for many of the Italian dishes on the menu has come from his mother's old Venetian recipes and from his aunt Ancilla's Tuscan recipes. Chef Michael Metcalfe has put new zest in old favourites and has experimented with other influences. The results are often idiosyncratic, but happily, his efforts are usually confident; as they should be, after 15 years in the Porthole galley. Were he to flag, Gianni Berton is never far away: 'although I have left the kitchen, I continue to devise new dishes.' After a drink in the bustling upstairs bar, head for the 'Tonight's Specialities' part of the menu (in fact weekly specialities). Don't be surprised to find Scottish salmon sliced thinly and covered with a sauce of shallots, mushrooms, tomatoes, dry vermouth, cream, fresh basil and grilled for a few minutes, or mushrooms marinated in dry sherry, honey, soya sauce and ginger, deep fried and served with yoghurt and chive sauce. As might be expected there is bresaola: 'slightly spicy, tasty and moist', but also Dover sole with slices of Parma ham served with a white wine, chervil and cream sauce. Commented a reader, 'the pale, creamy sauce was so nice I could have eaten a sauceboat full.' At least half the dishes appear to be cooked with some sort of alcohol and there are two wine recommendations for each dish on the menu.

The ship's tiller and other nautical touches conspire to preserve a sort of Long John Silver feel. Says one reader, 'service was a bit hit and miss but got better as the bill got larger.' The buccaneering analogy would strike a chord with those who have suffered from lapses during the busiest season. 'The food is always consistently good but never exceptional. As a package, the evening out is superb but with less pressure in the kitchen it could be truly great.' The bar has more bottles than most duty-free shops. The wine list is a veritable monument to sustained, informed research and acquisition. Refreshingly, France has to wait its turn behind Italy, Spain, New Zealand and many others. These are fine wines at generous prices, the Italians especially allowing much happy exploration. The Rhône is nothing but classics, but Burgundy rather lacks the names of the smaller domaines expected on the best wine lists. There are many good half-bottles. With so many bottles on hand, it isn't surprising that there is almost always a happy buzz in the restaurant. House wine: £8 a litre. CELLARMAN'S CHOICE: Gewürztraminer Herrenweg, Zind-Humbrecht, 1987, £13; Tokay Vieilles Vignes, Zind-Humbrecht, 1988, £13.50.

CHEF: Michael Metcalfe   PROPRIETORS: Judy and Gianni Berton
OPEN: all week, D only exc Tue (L parties by arrangement)
CLOSED: mid-Dec to mid-Feb
MEALS: 6.30 to 11
PRICES: £18 (£28)
CARDS: Access, Amex, Diners, Visa
SEATS: 40. 6 tables outside. Private parties: 24 main room, 24 private room. Vegetarian meals. Children's helpings. Music

---

BOX Wiltshire   map 2

▲ Clos du Roy at Box House

Box SN14 9NR   COOKING 3
BATH (0225) 744447   COST £21–£53

Philippe Roy has served his first year in this fine eighteenth-century vicarage in sight of the great Box Tunnel constructed by Isambard Kingdom Brunel. The entrance hall is grand, allowing a left turn to a well-furnished lounge or a right to two or three small dining-rooms almost higher than they are broad. The place has the air of a museum, down to the large car park for visitors, but will flesh out as occupation lengthens. The cooking is anything but a museum piece. No one used to cook lamb chops with fillets of Dover sole. Nor has it much to do with our own practice in domestic kitchens up and down the land. If, therefore, you want a meal that is as unlike the product of a morning's labour at home as possible (an understandable demand of a restaurant), go to Clos du Roy. There is a short *carte* that may change slowly, a more rapidly evolving *menu gourmand* at fixed price, and regular daily specials. The cooking involves much craft as well as surprising combinations and gilding of the lily. This may be excellent, as in a boudin of duck liver with Roquefort sauce as a preliminary; a feuilleté of salmon with saffron sauce, though needlessly garnished with crayfish; a squab pigeon with well matched foie gras and wild mushrooms; or a casserole of John Dory and grayling with crayfish and chervil. It may also go badly wrong: food hot where it may taste better cold as in a terrine of salmon and broccoli; cold when more rapid transit through the kitchen would have ensured it arriving hot; or where all the work ends up failing the flavour test. One autumn meal was dismissed as entirely without flavour save in one salad dressing. As one letter arrives saying Philippe Roy has cracked it, so another comes reporting dissatisfaction. It is a vauntingly ambitious style and much application is necessary to bring it off. Wine is a strong point, its service enthusiastic and informed and very much tilted towards France. There are some excellent properties to contemplate such as Pouilly Fuissé from Forest, Gitten Sancerre and Dom. de Trévallon. But with Sancerre (albeit a good one) at £22.50, be warned that prices are high. The special selection of six good but modest bottles between £12.50 and £14.50 is the cheap end. Prices like this inhibit our giving an award.

CHEF: Philippe Roy   PROPRIETORS: Philippe and Emma Roy
OPEN: all week
MEALS: 12 to 2.30, 7 to 10
PRICES: £35 (£44), Set L £11.95 (£21) to £14.50 (£23), Set D £26.50 (£33). Service inc
CARDS: Access, Amex, Diners, Visa
SEATS: 55. Private parties: 28 main room, 15, 15 and 30 private rooms. Car-park, 50 places. Children's helpings. No-smoking area. Wheelchair access (1 step; also WC)
ACCOMMODATION: 9 rooms, all with bath/shower. B&B £70 to £95. Deposit: £20. Baby facilities. Pets welcome. Afternoon teas. Garden. Swimming-pool. Fishing. Golf. TV. Phone. Scenic. Doors close at 12.30. Confirm by noon

---

BRADFIELD COMBUST Suffolk   map 3

▲ *Bradfield House*

Bradfield Combust IP30 0LR   COOKING 1
SICKLESMERE (028 486) 301   COST £16–£28

A large half-timbered house is the scene for the Ghijbens' successful conversion. The menu happily includes Scotch broth side by side with crab mousse and an avocado vinaigrette. Cooking, then, is with a foot in domestic and restaurant camps, though with little obvious desire to stray into fields of wayward combination or modern fashion. Reported meals have included a sole mousseline with prawn sauce, garlic mushrooms with cream baked under a pastry lid; gravlax; sauté chicken livers; chicken with ham and mushroom sauce and madeira gravy; beef Stroganoff; poached monkfish provençale; good vegetables; a chocolate marquise with a marzipan shell filled with white chocolate and a brandy-snap basket filled with ginger ice-cream. Good coffee with truffles and fudge were the closing act. An inspection found tastes discreet to vanishing point but the cooking accurate in its techniques. Service is friendly and informed. The carefully chosen wine list affords ample range and fair prices. House wine from les Producteurs de Plaimont: £7.40. More reports, please.

The text of entries is based on unsolicited reports sent in by readers, backed up by inspections conducted anonymously. The factual details under the text are from questionnaires the Guide sends to all restaurants that feature in the book.

CHEFS/PROPRIETORS: Roy and Sally Ghijben
OPEN: Tue to Sat, D only, and Sun L
MEALS: 12 to 1.45, 7 to 9.45
PRICES: £18 (£23), Set Sun L £10.75 (£16), Set D £12.95 (£18). Service inc
CARDS: Access, Visa
SEATS: 36. 2 tables outside. Private parties: 24 main room, 16 private room. Car-park, 12 places. Children's helpings (Sun L only). No children under 8 at D. Smart dress preferred. No pipes in dining-room. Wheelchair access (1 step; also WC). Music
ACCOMMODATION: 4 rooms, all with bath/shower. B&B £35 to £50. Deposit: 10%. Garden. TV. Phone. Scenic. Doors close at midnight

---

BRADFORD West Yorkshire   map 5

Bharat

---

502 Great Horton Road, Bradford BD7 4EG   COOKING 1
BRADFORD (0274) 521200   COST £8–£22

The Mistrys say theirs is 'the only Gujerati Indian restaurant in Bradford'. It is also one of the best Indian restaurants in Bradford according to reports. Bharat is in a two-storey detached building on one of the main routes into town. Once settled inside, take advantage of the Indian version of healthy food: at least 10 vegetable dishes, high-quality meat trimmed of fat, and non-greasy sauces. Karahis and vegetarian thalis are specialities. Lamb karai has been reported as 'consistently good'. The nan and rice selections are also above average and the home-made kulfi is 'creamy with plenty of pistachio nuts'. One reader was asked, when ordering, if she wanted a break between first and main courses; she did and 'enjoyed it even more because we were allowed to digest properly.' Healthy eating with a vengeance. The wine list includes Paternina Gran Reserva Rioja and a Barolo, two wines built big enough for Indian food. A litre of house Italian is £5.10 but it might be best to stick to the Kingfisher Indian lager.

CHEFS: Mahendra H. and Pilip Parmar   PROPRIETORS: Mohan and Jantilal Mistry
OPEN: Tue to Sun
MEALS: 12 to 2, 6 to 12
PRICES: £10 (£18), Set L £4.95 (£8), Set D for 2 £19.95 (£23). Service inc
CARDS: Access, Amex, Diners, Visa
SEATS: 48. Private parties: 48 main room. Car-park, 8 places. Vegetarian meals. Children's helpings. No-smoking area. Wheelchair access. Music. Air-conditioned

---

▲ Restaurant 19,
Belvedere Hotel ♥

North Park Road, Bradford BD9 4NT   COOKING 4
BRADFORD (0274) 492559   COST £33–£44

The large Victorian villa sits on the edge of Lister Park in a suburb once of endless wealth, now at its mature best for the conjunction of trees and architecture. *Room at the Top* country. Restaurant 19 is in a hotel, but the casual visitor would not notice this fact save for the fine staircase going aloft.

The bedrooms continue to be upgraded. The two dining-rooms are an eye-opener: plasterwork as thick as a wedding cake, picked out in pink and white, hangs off (or supports) the ceiling; Russell Flint nude studies set the artistic tone; the tables are finely and elaborately set. The food is not what Bradford expects. A reader listened to an entire party, all under the age of forty, gradually denude the dishes they ordered of their accompaniments, sauces and flavourings: 'I'll have the sea bass without the lobster sauce and the noisettes of lamb without the kidney sauce.' Herbs and spices are indicated tentatively. None the less the four-course meals, in which soup or a salad comes second, do not avoid sophisticated and complex seasonings: roast leg of lamb with an orange, celery and cumin stuffing, or celeriac and spinach 'ravioli' with veal kidneys and shallot sauce are two instances. Nor are clever cooking methods and fashionable flavours shirked. Sea bass is served atop lobster pieces, set in turn on a potato galette, surrounded by a lobster sauce; accompanying it is a creamed parsley pudding/custard. Cod is placed on a bed of creamed leeks with a balsamic vinegar sauce. Trout is smoked over applewood, then served with cucumber 'spaghetti'. Bradford is privileged to have someone willing to experiment. The desire to attempt more than a single message on the plate is seen in a meal that began with a salad of salmon presented, cooked or cured in three ways with a cucumber relish and a herbed mayonnaise, and went on to another vertical arrangement on a potato galette base as the main dish. The first layer was smoked leg of lamb, the top was pan-fried loin. There was a pea and mint mousse or custard accompaniment. This dish was a triumph of complementary flavours, though the vegetables arranged round the giant meat plates were not so homogeneous, 'mange-tout and runner beans were more like ballet shoes and hobnail boots.' The end of the meal, a strawberry and redcurrant tart with a strawberry ice-cream, showed the value of reinforcement in a way that another dessert, a fine lemon tart and intense damson ice-cream, pointed to the dangers of two strong tastes clashing. Other meals have been recorded in flattering terms, one comment being that many of the tastes (though examples of underseasoning have been noted) are more intense than in the south-eastern restaurants of like quality. Good incidentals reinforce the judgement. Service is never less than affable; some have found it too informal; none has ever suggested it is unwilling. Indeed, Robert Barbour is a monument of tact. The wine list is not long but the bottles show class. The price range makes a few concessions to economical drinking and the margins are not excessive. Given the range of good wines from around the world that are available, this is a thoughtful attempt at constructing a generalist choice to give everyone something they might like or recognise without compromising good taste: no Mateus, Liebfraumilch or Niersteiner here. The house selection runs to a baker's dozen and starts at £8.95.

CHEF: Stephen Smith   PROPRIETORS: Stephen Smith and Robert Barbour
OPEN: Tue to Sat, D only
MEALS: 7 to 9.30 (10 Sat)
PRICES: Set D £24 (£33) to £27 (£37)
CARDS: Access, Amex, Visa
SEATS: 40. Private parties: 10 main room. Car-park, 16 places. Children welcome. Music
ACCOMMODATION: 4 rooms, all with bath/shower. B&B £60 to £70. TV. Phone. Doors close at midnight. Confirm 24 hours ahead

BRAITHWAITE Cumbria   map 7

▲ *Ivy House*

Braithwaite CA12 5SY   COOKING 1
BRAITHWAITE (0596) 82338   COST £20–£26

Tourism and the closing of railway lines are both big pursuits in the Lake District. The latter one doesn't really help the former. The Ivy House must be unusual in getting some advantage from leftover sleepers, sold when the local rails were pulled up: Nick and Wendy Shill have used cast-offs as decorative beams in their dining-room. As there are no trains, take the A66 to Keswick, turn off two miles north-west and slow down when you reach the tiny village of Braithwaite, then turn left after the Royal Oak Inn. The hotel, a seventeenth-century building, can be identified by its dark green facade. The atmosphere inside is cosy. Reports one reader, 'they treat you as though they have known you for years, although they are not overly familiar.' The dining-room, on the first floor, is spacious and green, candlelit in the evening. First course favourites here are Thai pork satay, mousseline of sole and paw-paw with prawns. To follow expect haunch of venison with redcurrant and port wine sauce, or fillet of beef en croûte with a mushroom sauce. The old-fashioned puddings are, perhaps, the best indication of overall cooking style. Save room for sticky toffee pudding, queen of puddings or fruit crumble; this is familiar, even 'comfort' food, prepared reliably. The five-course evening menu changes every day, though not much, and is good value. The wine list may be modest but there are many good bottles under £10. House French is £5.95.
CELLARMAN'S CHOICE: Brown Bros Cabernet Sauvignon/Shiraz 1985, £10.25; Chablis premier cru, Fourchaume, Dom. Toricon 1988, £15.95.

CHEF: Wendy Shill   PROPRIETORS: Nick and Wendy Shill
OPEN: all week, D only
MEALS: 6.30 to 7.30
PRICES: Set D £14.75 (£20) to £16.95 (£22)
CARDS: Access, Amex, Diners, Visa
SEATS: 36. Private parties: 10 main room. Car-park, 9 places. Vegetarian meals. Children's helpings. No smoking in dining-room. Music
ACCOMMODATION: 9 rooms, all with bath/shower. B&B £38 to £56. Deposit: £20. Pets welcome but not in public rooms. TV. Phone. Scenic. Doors close at 11.30. Confirm by 4.30
[*Which? Hotel Guide*]

BRAMLEY Surrey   map 3

Le Berger

4A The High Street, Bramley GU5 0HB   COOKING 3
GUILDFORD (0483) 894037   COST £17–£53

Here is more talent from the Roux stable: Peter Hirth. He and Mary Hirth opened in December 1988 behind a blue and white-painted shop front, with pink and green floral drapes, starched linen, silver cruets and smart china. He cooks, she steers diners unhurriedly through modern haute cuisine meals of three courses, in an informative and accomplished way. The style is as polished as the glasses. A speciality is 'three different eggs', each with its own garnish. A terrine combines baby leeks, foie gras and smoked bacon. Timing is assured, as with a cheese soufflé 'heralded by a glorious aroma and served in copper pans; rich in flavour, light and frothy in texture'; or with roast monkfish in a green grape sauce; fish seems to come off better than meat in this respect. Taste varies from negligible in a rib-eye of veal at inspection, to 'potent and gamey' in a firm pigeon mousse wrapped in thin slices of carrot and leek and served with beurre blanc. Luxuries are not in short supply. Significantly, textures are carefully considered. Duck, for instance, comes as a trio of foie gras, chunky confit and thinly sliced breast. A plate of chicken – breast, thigh, liver, foie gras and an egg – underscores the versatility of this humble bird. French apple tart shows off the pastry work at its crisp and succulent best; a plate of orange sweets is a welcome variation on the more usual plate of chocolate puddings, although there is that, too; sorbets are not up to much. The Roux-inspired cooking can produce bills of Roux magnitude. The fixed-price menu, which includes a half-bottle of wine per head, may halve expenditure. The 40 bottles and seven half-bottles on the wine list all hail from where we might expect and are decently chosen but perhaps with too many 1984 clarets to feel happy. 'Nowadays we do find that a totally French wine list lacks a little spice and interest,' comments one observer. It is an infant cellar, too, so vintages are recent. House burgundy is £15.50; house Muscadet, £10.

CHEF/PROPRIETOR: Peter Hirth
OPEN: Wed to Sun, exc Sat L and Sun D
CLOSED: 2 weeks Jan, bank hols
MEALS: 12.30 to 2, 7 to 9.30
PRICES: £33 (£44), Set L £15 (£17), Set D £25 (£28). Minimum £15 L, £25 D
CARDS: Access, Amex, Diners, Visa
SEATS: 24. Private parties: 10 main room. Children welcome. Jacket and tie. No-smoking in one dining-room

---

BRAMPTON Cumbria   map 7

▲ *Farlam Hall*

Brampton CA8 2NG
HALLBANKGATE (069 76) 234
on A689, 2m from Brampton (not at   COOKING 3
Farlam village)   COST £29–£36

The Quinion family make a positive contribution to their guests' enjoyment in a house that sits on a rising lawn, duck pond below. Dinner at a single sitting, served by well-drilled staff, the women in long floral skirts, engenders a certain community spirit. The menu is short, three choices to a course, with a sorbet halfway, cheese after the main course and sweets from a display on the sideboard. Cooking is varied without being flamboyant: a relatively modern choice of a salad of Conference pear with walnut and tarragon may be balanced by an old but good standard of seafood pancakes, or a hot terrine of seafood by a smoked chicken salad, while duck will come with kumquats, rather than oranges, and chicken breast will be stuffed with mushrooms. Vegetables are plentiful and manifold. Once past the mainly English cheeses, residents will be happy to relax with such substantial desserts as chocolate, almond and strawberry meringue or a nut fudge cake that recall the days prior to diet-consciousness. Although a member of Relais & Châteaux, Farlam Hall does not have the occasional solemnity or sense of consequence that may be felt in the walls of some of its colleagues. The plus of the wine list is the abundance of half-bottles. The selection lacks the ambition of the cooking but prices are fair. House wine: £6.75.

CHEF: Barry Quinion   PROPRIETORS: Quinion and Stevenson families
OPEN: all week, D only
CLOSED: Feb
MEALS: 8
PRICES: Set D £23 (£29) to £24 (£30)
CARD: Access, Visa
SEATS: 40. Private parties: 30 main room. Car-park, 30 places. No children under 5. Smart dress preferred. No cigars/pipes in dining-room. Wheelchair access. One sitting
ACCOMMODATION: 13 rooms, all with bath/shower. D, B&B £80 to £180. No children under 5. Pets by arrangement. Afternoon teas. Garden. TV. Phone. Scenic. Doors close at midnight. Confirm by 2 [Which? Hotel Guide]

BRAY Berkshire   map 2

Waterside Inn

Ferry Road, Bray SL6 2AT
MAIDENHEAD (0628) 20691

COUNTY OF THE YEAR RESTAURANT

COOKING 4
COST £30–£77

Take the signs off the main road to Bray village. That achieved, the restaurant is well indicated. It may look, from the lane, like a small weatherboard pub: be prepared for a surprise once through the doors. Michel Roux has been heard to observe (humorously, no doubt) that the British can cook very well but are not so good at running restaurants. Hence 60 per cent of his kitchen staff are English-speaking and 98 per cent of the waiters are French. There are many who would observe that the method of running restaurants which involves leaving the credit card slip untotalled when the menu states that service is included, is more Franglais than anything else. Ignore the grumbles, which come from encountering international financial standards along a country byway, and try to assess whether the restaurant deserves the praise that has been lavished on it. People jaded by the wearisome luxury of London and haute cuisine may be less impressed than one party who came to it from distant regions. For them, the discreet attention of the staff (one waiter 'doing nothing but topping up water glasses'), the lavish appointments, the gleaming efficiency of having one's car whisked away to an invisible car park – and returned undamaged at the end of the meal – and the happy affability of M. Roux's guided tour of his kitchen all contributed to a fairy-tale evening. The food was as good as the frame provided for it and the setting of great windows overlooking the Thames' sweet reaches brought to mind the lines, 'Forget six counties overhung with smoke,/Forget the snorting steam and piston stoke,/ ...And dream of London, small and white and clean,/The clear Thames bordered by its gardens green'. Whether William Morris would have approved of a bill of £143 for two people who drank modestly depends on your interpretation of his poetry and teaching. There is a long *carte*, entirely in French but clearly explained upon enquiry. There is also a *menu exceptionnel* to ease the problem of choice, and at lunchtime there is a much cheaper set-price menu. The lunches, within Waterside's terms of reference, constitute a bargain. The cooking can be quite conservative. People who had eaten at the Gavroche in the early 1970s would recognise some of the dishes and the style. There is quite a lot of cream and butter and an overall sense of richness. This fact alone could account for the dissimilarity of reaction observed above. However, M. Roux is married to an Australian and has obviously taken up some of the enthusiasm of that country for oriental flavours and light technique – a lobster dish with a sauce of soy, ginger and star anise (or so the eater thought) is an example. People have commented that this year the cooking has been very good indeed: 'We felt that it has improved tremendously since our last visit nine months ago'. A lunch began with paupiettes de saumon fumé Claudine (an old favourite): packets of smoked salmon glazed with a fish aspic are wrapped round a smoked trout and salmon mousse. A sliver of truffle crowns each parcel. The mildness of the salmon and the lightness of the mousse are exactly judged. Juicy shelled langoustines are arranged on an intense tomato coulis, itself encircled by a shellfish reduction finished with hazelnut oil. This more modern dish was the success of the meal. A saddle of veal is carved before the table, a gravy of stock and pan juices is flavoured with sage. Fillets of sole are rolled round a stuffing of sole, herbs and lobster and sliced like a swiss roll. They are laid on a Champagne sauce and accompanied by a julienne of carrot. Seasoning here is bold, nearly over-bold. Each dish has its own vegetables, including fresh white haricot beans. Dessert is a soup of red fruits with a lemon custard. The cheeses (all French) are, and always are, first rate. Another meal, dinner this time, began with an amuse-gueule of a pastry case filled with deep-fried soft roe and slices of potato and beetroot. A first course of prawns, lobster and langoustines tasted fresh and was cooked to perfect succulence – and this for someone used to Cornish fish. A main course of sea bream accompanied by a coronet of asparagus filled with a lobster mousse topped with caviare was providentially given a light wine sauce, but even so the effect was fairly heart-stopping. Almost more pleasure was had from a saddle of rabbit carved in strips criss-crossing a large circle of braised parsnips. The glossy armagnac sauce was 'so good, I had to slow up' to extract the maximum enjoyment. Dessert did not let this meal down: pastry is always good, so a mirabelle tart was well judged; the raspberry soufflé, urged to rise still higher as the sauce is poured into its centre, was as light and aromatic as could be hoped. Compliments abound this year. Reservations at the daunting scale of the operation are disarmed by the pleasant treatment meted out to visitors; but then, at that price, you would hope not to be ignored. The wine list does not include any non-French wine save port. It is extensive and expensive, with few (and those dear too) half-bottles. Everyone raves about the house cocktail of fortified Champagne and passion-fruit juices.

All details are as accurate as possible at the time of going to press, but chefs and owners often change, and it is wise to check by telephone before making a special journey. Many readers have been disappointed when set-price bargain meals are no longer available. Ask when booking.

CHEF/PROPRIETOR: Michel Roux
OPEN: Tue to Sun, exc Tue L, and Sun D Oct to Easter
CLOSED: 25 Dec to mid-Feb
MEALS: 12 to 2, 7 to 10
PRICES: £52 (£64), Set L £22.50 (£30) to £36.50 (£44) Set D £47.50 (£55). Minimum £30.
Service inc
CARD: Access, Carte Blanche, Diners, Visa
SEATS: 80. Private parties: 80 main room, 8 private room. Car-park, 30 places. Vegetarian
meals. Children restricted. Smart dress preferred. No cigars/pipes in dining-room.
Wheelchair access (2 steps; also WC). Air -conditioned

BRIGHTON East Sussex   map 3

Food for Friends

17A – 18 Prince Albert Street,
The Lanes, Brighton BN1 1HF   COOKING 1
BRIGHTON (0273) 202310   COST £11

A complete refurbishment, from the eating area right through to the kitchen,
has not altered the relaxed and friendly atmosphere. It is still a good meeting
place and very good value for money. There is counter service only and no
bookings are taken. The food is entirely vegetarian and organic produce is
increasingly used. There are vegan dishes, too, from cauliflower soup to stir-
fried vegetables with salted black beans and rice. The bakery supplies bread
and croissants for breakfast. Main dishes at lunch or dinner might include
Virginia spoonbread bake with aubergines, courgettes and sweet pepper in a
lightly spiced tomato sauce, or deep-fried pancakes filled with spinach, onions
and mushrooms in a white wine and nutmeg sauce. Pizza has been 'excellent,
the base crisp but not fragile and of just the right thickness'. Some of the
discomfort of queuing is 'made worthwhile by the quality of the food'.
Chocolate brownies and ginger slice feature among the desserts. There are
herbal and other teas, beer and house French wine at £4.15.

CHEFS: Karen Samuel and Phil Taylor   PROPRIETORS: Simon Hope and Jeremy Gray
OPEN: all week
MEALS: 9am (9.30 Sun) to 10pm
PRICES: £5 (£9)
CARD: Visa
SEATS: 50. Vegetarian meals. Children's helpings. Separate smoking area. Wheelchair
access. Music

Langan's Bistro

1 Paston Place, Brighton BN2 1HA   COOKING 2
BRIGHTON (0273) 606933   COST £31

The plain cream front hides a gallery of plates, prints and drawings –
hallmarks of Peter Langan's parentage – and stands next to the Hanbury Arms,
which sports a dome to rival the Pavilion, from its days as a mausoleum. The
Bistro concentrates on producing a short menu of food that is both comforting
and good; it may be short on adventure. Mushrooms stuffed with snails and

garlic, 'the tastiest I have had'; a salad of Stilton and bacon, 'delicious'; seafood terrine, 'very fresh taste', are comments about first courses. These may be echoed in reports about grilled salmon hollandaise; duck with honey and ginger; entrecôte bordelaise; a chocolate mille-feuille 'so delicate that a spoon cut through the layers', without that rubbery give so often met with; or an orange and Grand Marnier crème brûlée. Although waiters have been accused of hastening diners towards the exit, in general the service has been praised for its expertise: 'my father trained at Vevey and the Savoy and he found it a real pleasure to see things done properly.' And at so fair a price, might be added. The wine list is cursory, though the bottles offered are acceptable indeed.

CHEF: Mark Emmerson   PROPRIETORS: Coq d'Or Restaurants Ltd
OPEN: Tue to Sun, exc L Sat and Sun D
MEALS: 12.30 to 2.30, 7.30 to 10.30
PRICES: £20 (£26). Service 10%
CARDS: Access, Amex, Diners, Visa
SEATS: 48. Vegetarian meals. Children welcome. Music

▲ La Noblesse, Hospitality Inn

Kings Road, Brighton BN1 2GS
BRIGHTON (0273) 206700

COOKING 3
COST £25–£60

Given the constant groans about eating out in Brighton, from residents and visitors both, it might be expected that they would all be flocking here. Perhaps the price or the formality prevent. There is a full *carte* or a five-course set-price *menu gourmand*. Neither is cheap, but there is little stinting either and, as you sit at your sofa in borrowed jacket and tie, gazing at the petits fours arranged one to a branch of a tree-shaped stand, you may think it worth it. There is good judgement of flavours and skill in buying and cooking in dishes as simple as grilled goats' cheese on a multi-leaf salad; fresh scampi with avocado and a julienne of mango; cod with a watercress sauce; or salmon with white asparagus (though the thin escalope may have seen too much cooking). A breast of duck with sauce redolent of cloves and cinnamon, served with some creamed wild mushrooms and a mound of chopped spinach, showed accuracy, but also a certain tendency to put one thing next to another and hope for harmony. The French cheese, though generously supplied, may have too little custom to maintain condition, but form returned with desserts and petits fours. Iced lime soufflé with refreshingly zestful lime syrup shows the kitchen's abilities. For all the flash, the waiters are anxious to oblige, just as the wine list, apparently ostentatious (though in fact cannily chosen for a chain hotel operation), makes a concession to adventure and thrift by allowing more than half its bins to be tried by the glass. House French: £9.80 and £10.30.
CELLARMAN'S CHOICE: Muscat d'Alsace 1987, Dopff et Irion, £15.40; Chinon, Clos de l'Echo 1986, Dom. René Couly, £17.50.

See the inside of the front cover for an explanation of the 1 to 5 rating system recognising cooking standards.

CHEF: Richard Lythe   PROPRIETORS: Mount Charlotte Investments plc
OPEN: Mon to Sat, exc Sat L
MEALS: 12 to 2.30, 7 to 10.15 (10.30 Sat)
PRICES: £38 (£50), Set L £17.50 (£25) to £20 (£27), Set D £29 (£37) to £32 (£41)
CARDS: Access, Amex, Diners, Visa
SEATS: 45. Private parties: 45 main room. Car-park, 60 places. Vegetarian meals.
No children under 14. Smart dress preferred. No pipes in dining-room. Wheelchair access
(also WC). Air-conditioned
ACCOMMODATION: 204 rooms, all with bath/shower. Rooms for disabled. Lift. B&B
£107.50 to £135. Baby facilities. Pets welcome. Afternoon teas. Swimming-pool. Sauna.
Tennis. Air-conditioning. TV. Phone. Scenic. Doors close at 11. Confirm by 6

BRIMFIELD   Hereford & Worcester   map 2

Poppies, The Roebuck ♥

Brimfield SY8 4WE   COOKING 3
BRIMFIELD (058 472) 230   COST £41

The reader who wrote that the bar of the Roebuck, where they started their
meal, was 'pleasantly unaltered and unprepossessing' did not intend an insult.
She was doubtless influenced by the contrasting café-crème elegance of the
new dining-room with its light parquet floor, handsome fabrics and
outstandingly comfortable chairs. 'The quality of flavour was outstanding:
imaginative blends and very good ingredients' was her comment on her food,
prompted by the pigeons in red wine she had just eaten. After being shot in
Tewbury Wells they were delivered by the postman (in the last *Guide* he was
credited with bringing strawberries). The anecdote reflects several facts about
the energetic Evanses. The pub is a treasure, and John Evans an experienced
landlord (and gardener). The bar food is exemplary. Carole Evans has worked
for several years at building up the food side and her apotheosis into a full-
blown restaurateur is deserved. If sometimes the connections between
departments creak under pressure or through lack of staff assurance, the food
usually rises above this. The menu is long for a quiet country spot but the
resourcefulness with which it is supplied calms any fears of staleness. Even the
snails are local. There is a delight in fruit flavours with meats that is handled
better than most because of their astringency. The lamb has a mint and crab
apple sauce and the duck with white port and orange sauce has zest and tang
imparted by plentiful seasoning with home-made Seville orange marmalade.
Techniques are not amiss either: a spinach soufflé with an anchovy hollandaise
(more lemon than anchovy) did not fall during the time it took the waiter to
provide the necessary cutlery. Approvals of dishes are legion: artichoke with a
hollandaise; fresh pear with Stilton and walnut; pork stuffed with prunes,
wrapped with Parma ham which stiffened in the cooking yet kept the pork
nicely moist; and vegetables that are usually plainly cooked though the gratin
dauphinois is rich in nutmeg. Desserts such as a brandy-snap basket with ice-
cream and a caramel sauce, Eton mess, or poppyseed parfait are enjoyed, but
especial praise is reserved for the cheese board, usefully explained on a card.
The wine list is the evolving interest of John Evans. It has some good New
World bottles, including Californian Cabernet Sauvignons from the 1970s, all
at very fair prices. The French and European sections display more adventure

in their choice these days and offer excellent growers such as Durup, Isole e Olena and Robert Ampeau. For economy's sake, many will prefer exploring the less classic zones but price range has not been forgotten. Halves are not plentiful (except for Champagnes). House Rosemount: £9. Dunkerton's cider and organic beer are available.

CHEF: Carole Evans PROPRIETORS: John and Carole Evans
OPEN: Tue to Sat
CLOSED: 2 weeks Feb, 25 and 26 Dec, 1 week Oct
MEALS: 12 to 2, 7 to 10
PRICES: £24 (£34)
CARDS: Access, Visa
SEATS: 40. Private parties: 40 main room. Vegetarian meals. Children welcome. Separate smoking area. Wheelchair access
ACCOMMODATION: 3 rooms, all with bath/shower. B&B £35 to £65. No children under 10. TV. Phone. Scenic. Doors close at 12.30. Confirm by 6 [*Which? Hotel Guide*]

BRISTOL Avon   map 2

Bistro Twenty One

21 Cotham Road South, Kingsdown,
Bristol BS6 5TZ   COOKING 2
BRISTOL (0272) 421744   COST £32

Alain Dubois continues to run a bistro and a brasserie in Glamorgan though he spends more time here than there. 'A place to bring your friends rather than business clients,' is a comment that reflects the relatively spartan comfort of the busy rooms separated by just a counter from the flurries of the kitchen, but it also endorses the notable cheerfulness of the ambience and service. The menu is quite long for such a restaurant, taking in a dozen or more dishes at each course and including at least half a dozen sorts of fish. This length may explain the occasional delays that are reported. The style is 'modern' bistro in as much as it offers spinach and cream cheese pancakes, soups and simple mushroom dishes alongside more fashionable choices such as marinated scallops or salmon. Alain Dubois has been a chef in fancier kitchens, so is also able to turn his hand to good pastry and mousses when the spirit moves him. The consequence for many is a satisfactory combination of flavour, sophistication, simplicity and value. The wine list, too, shows experience and good sense in the buying, though prices are not give-away. House wine: £6.50.

CHEF/PROPRIETOR: Alain Dubois
OPEN: Mon to Sat, exc Sat L
CLOSED: 1 week Christmas
MEALS: 12 to 2.30, 6.30 to 11.30
PRICES: £20 (£27)
CARDS: Access, Visa
SEATS: 40. Private parties: 16 main room, 16 private room. Children's helpings. Wheelchair access. Music

---

County Round-ups listing additional restaurants that may be worth a visit are at the back of the Guide, after the Irish section. Reports on Round-up entries are welcome.

Edwards

24 Alma Vale Road, Clifton,
Bristol BS8 2HY
BRISTOL (0272) 741533

COOKING 1
COST £15–£25

John Selwyn Gilbert is a film-maker as well as restaurateur, so his notes from Clifton sound a mite glamorous: 'Just off to Samoa...' is a good beginning to any message. This is a prelude to hints of great menu changes when he's back. In the meantime, this oak-panelled, red plush restaurant continues along the same lines of good value and simple food in fair portions: scallops, salmon, scampi, steak, chicken, lamb and a pie are the main courses, preceded by pea soup, broad beans with ham and cheese, mushrooms, Parma ham, whitebait and scrambled eggs. Daily specials are written on the blackboard and may include pasta and smoked trout in a cream sauce, or venison and ginger pie. Sunday lunch is a set-price and not expensive for a compact choice, including roast pork, breast of chicken with garlic and spinach, spotted dick – the formula here does not change from year to year. Why should it? Cooking is very acceptable though some tastes and flavourings are less pronounced than they might be. Sixteen wines make up the list, with a handful of seasonal specials. House French: £5.95.

CHEF: Gerrard Perry   PROPRIETOR: John Selwyn Gilbert
OPEN: all week, exc Sat L and Sun D
MEALS: 12 to 2.30, 7 to 11
PRICES: £14 (£21), Set L £8.95 (£15)
CARDS: Access, Visa
SEATS: 44. Private parties: 40 main room, 12 private room. Vegetarian meals. Children's helpings on request. Smart dress preferred. No smoking tables on request. Wheelchair access (1 step)

Jameson's

30 Upper Maudlin Street,
Bristol BS2 8DJ
BRISTOL (0272) 276565

COOKING 1
COST £28

The menu is enormous: nine meats, four fish, two vegetarian dishes and eight variations on steaks. The only thing that changes is the price: salmon is still with hollandaise or a dill butter sauce; veal is still with mushrooms and madeira; Camembert continues to be wrapped in filo with basil and pine nuts. Duck has moved all the way from black cherries to blackcurrants. It may get boring for the kitchen but the product is consistent, as one reader commented after satisfactory stints during the Bristol boat show in two successive years. Good business leads to fluctuating service but the business stays because the cooking is of a standard. Desserts seem to rely on ice-cream or meringues of deathly hue. The short wine list does not charge too much for acceptable bottles, such as a good few Rioja and bourgeois clarets; other wines are rather sketchily described. House Avery Clochmerle: £7.95 a litre.

CHEFS: Ian Leitch, Jamie Smith and Carole Jameson
PROPRIETORS: Carole and John Holmes
OPEN: Mon to Sat, D only
MEALS: 7 to 10.30 (11 Fri and Sat)
PRICES: £16 (£23). Service 10% on parties of 6 or more
CARDS: Access, Visa
SEATS: 70. Private parties: 35 main room. Vegetarian meals. Children's helpings.
Wheelchair access (2 steps). Music

Lettonie ♥

9 Druid Hill, Stoke Bishop,
Bristol BS9 1EW
BRISTOL (0272) 686456

COUNTY OF THE YEAR RESTAURANT

COOKING 4
COST £20–£32

The comment of one reader, who couldn't remember the total of his bill when he reported, was, 'the best value for quality I could remember for some time.' These things stick in the brain. The image is not prepossessing: a row of shops in a northern inner suburb of Bristol on the far side of Clifton Down; a simple dining-room, too small for much ingenuity in table arrangement. Low-key is the word for it. Not so Martin Blunos's cooking, which manages to combine fair economy with apparent munificence: result, happy customers. Either end of the meal is marked by some complimentary culinary gesture: several petits fours with the coffee; some small dish, a cheese soufflé perhaps, or a bortsch, to start. In the middle, a simple description will yield a cornucopia of goodies. Smoked haddock and salmon ravioli served at lunch was a single plump ravioli on a bed of fresh green spinach, surrounded by small fish quenelles and mussels, with a tomato and white wine cream sauce. Vegetables were plentiful and good. It is not all complication. Noisettes of lamb are just roasted with rosemary, a straight *jus* to moisten, simple vegetables to support, all materials are of real quality. The cooking shows a fashionable approach to offal and luxuries. Pig's trotter stuffed with sweetbreads is a favourite, and the *carte* of six choices in each course may include lamb's tongue or ox-tail or a sauté of poultry livers. The short choice does lead to a certain imbalance, the position retrieved only by careful portioning to avoid excess. Thus the slate of main courses one night offered trotters stuffed with sweetbreads, braised ox-tail, or fried loin of pork with foie gras ravioli and braised lettuce, though the three other choices – a fish dish of sole with peppers, breast of guinea-fowl with a garlic cream sauce, and noisettes of lamb – were on the lighter side. Techniques are sufficiently mastered so that flavours come through strongly and ingredients are not skimped. When it says 'truffle-scented' sauce, the scent is there, as in the sauce for a boned and stuffed leg of guinea-fowl. Desserts continue the display of skill and talent for display, though they do not have the strong character of the savoury courses. They show cleverness in balancing flavour combinations that contributes refreshment as well as satisfaction: poached apples with an almond and rosemary cream; a Grand Marnier parfait with mango; rhubarb mousse with ginger; a chocolate marquise with caramel and pear sauce. Coffee is good. The wine list is very carefully chosen, not too long and nearly all French with some thoroughbred burgundies. The main run of prices is very fair. There are a few nice Loires and Rhônes that perhaps offer best value. House wines are from £8.25. Lettonie is the French for Latvia, Martin Blunos's birthplace; hence the bortsch mentioned above. Perhaps he danced in the streets of Stoke Bishop as 1990 was dawning.

CHEFS/PROPRIETORS: Martin and Siân Blunos
OPEN: Tue to Sat
CLOSED: 2 weeks Aug, 1 week Christmas, bank hols
MEALS: 12.30 to 2, 7 to 10
PRICES: Set L £12.50 (£20) to £18.95 (£27), Set D £18.95 (£27)
CARDS: Access, Amex, Visa
SEATS: 24. Private parties: 16 main room. Music

Markwicks 🍷

43 Corn Street, Bristol BS1 1HT — COOKING 3
BRISTOL (0272) 262658 — COST £18–£35

'As a frequent visitor to Bristol, this is just what has been needed for a long time – a charming, not over-fussy eating house. Once Stephen Markwick warms up, his dry sense of humour and general style are quite endearing.' The change in partnership arrangements since the last *Guide* means that Stephen Marwick is back full-time in the kitchen while Judy Markwick supervises the customers in this handsome basement in the middle of Bristol's 'Wall Street'. It was once a safety deposit and has that Victorian solidity needed to inspire confidence in depositors. The conversion to a restaurant has not been skimped, nor has the original impact of the vaults, grilles and hard surfaces been weakened. In the daytime, financial discussions may be animated, but the city folk have not taken over entirely. In the Bristol firmament, Markwicks occupies a different sector to Lettonie (see entry). Their aims are more robust, more demotic, though never descending to churning out bistro food. The menu reads simply with dishes like fish soup; egg Benedict; guinea-fowl with apples and calvados; monkfish dijonnaise. What marks this out from bistro is that the materials are first-rate and taste of something. Criticism revolves around occasionally meagre portions, but the general reaction is of relief that relatively simple yet assured handling can be so enjoyable. Particular mention has been made of lobster and spinach ravioli; artichoke bottoms with prawn; mussels marinière; the fish soup; calf's liver with mustard; fillet of veal with wild mushrooms; generally very good fish dishes; grape feuilleté; prune and armagnac tart ('they said 15 minutes for it to be cooked, I would have waited 15 hours'), coconut and banana ice-cream; ribbons of dark and white chocolate. Ancillaries such as bread are well made. Prices are inclusive and tipping is discouraged. The wine list, like the cutlery and glassware, is another mark that this is a serious restaurant. It does not go in for the very old or grand, though a seasoning of mature vintages is there for those who need it. The choice is catholic even if heavily weighted in favour of France; Australia produces the 'most-hyped' wines, they say. The growers are generally sound, the price range fair to all pockets and there are plenty of halves. House Muscadet and Beaujolais: £9. CELLARMAN'S CHOICE: is uncertain, in view of stocks. If they remain, look for Ch. Jaubertie; Jean Léon from Penedès; Ch. Peyros, Madiran; or Trimbach's Alsaces.

CHEF: Stephen Markwick   PROPRIETORS: Stephen and Judy Markwick
OPEN: Mon to Fri
MEALS: 12 to 2, 7 to 10.30
PRICES: £23 (£29), Set L £12.50 (£18) to £14.50 (£20). Service inc
CARDS: Access, Visa
SEATS: 50. Private parties: 8 and 14 private rooms. Children's helpings

Melbournes

74 Park Street, Bristol BS1 3AF	COOKING 1
BRISTOL (0272) 226996	COST £10–£22

Fair cooking at fair prices in a cheerful environment is the aim here, and the bring-your-own wine policy, Australian style, keeps prices down. The cooking is honest in intent and description and carefully presented. The range is both 'bistro' in the best sense of that misused word, and imaginative: as in a squid and horseradish mousse that formed part of a marinated fish platter; pork roasted and served with a mustard sauce; crème brûlée with a rhubarb sauce; or pear charlotte with a redcurrant sauce. The ample menu is a fixed price, supplemented by blackboard specials, especially of fish. A meal in the summer yielded satisfactory results, with faults stemming only from occasional mistiming and lack of courage in seasoning. The reception of outside bottles is invariably friendly and efficient, just like the rest of the service, though there is a wine list, more antipodean than French, if your cellar is bare. Lunch is even cheaper. A benefit to central Bristol and close to the University.

CHEFS: C. Cowpe and J. Thomas   PROPRIETORS: A. Wilshaw, N. Hennessy and C. Cowpe
OPEN: Tue to Sat, exc Sat L
CLOSED: week between Christmas and New Year
MEALS: 12 to 2, 7 to 10.30
PRICES: Set L £5.75 (£10) to £9 (£14), Set D £10.95 (£16) to £12.95 (£18). Service 10%.
Licensed, also bring your own: no corkage
CARDS: Access, Visa
SEATS: 70. Private parties: 40 main room. Vegetarian meals. Children's helpings.
No cigars/pipes in dining-room. Wheelchair access (1 step; also WC). Music

Muset

12 Clifton Road, Clifton, Bristol BS8 1AF	COOKING 1
BRISTOL (0272) 732920	COST £18–£25

The Australian concept of BYO (bring your own) wine keeps prices down and numbers up in this Clifton restaurant, already on three levels and with plans to extend as we went to press. Book early to get in at weekends. BYO is based on no corkage and is strictly for wine – no beer or spirits. There is none the less a wine list at very fair prices. The set-price menu does not change but a blackboard extends the choice with daily extras. The expectation may be bistro but the style of cooking is snappier than that, as in fresh scallops with a pimento and vermouth cream sauce; monkfish feuilleté with a sorrel and vermouth cream sauce; buckwheat pancake with mushrooms and blue cheese; pork with a piquant sauce; duck with a grapefruit glaze. The level of execution is very even. Desserts include crème brûlée and profiteroles. Garlic bread or French bread is charged for, so the bistro form is not yet dead. Bristol hopes it may survive a while yet.

CHEFS: D. Wheadon and M. Read   PROPRIETORS: A.J. Portlock and D. Wheadon
OPEN: Tue to Sat, D only
CLOSED: first 2 weeks Aug
MEALS: 7 to 10.30
PRICES: Set D £12.95 (£18) to £15.40 (£21). Licensed, also bring your own: no corkage
CARDS: Access, Visa
SEATS: 100. Private parties: 30 main room. Children's helpings. Children restricted. Music. Air-conditioned

Orient Rendezvous

95 Queens Road, Clifton,
Bristol BS8 1LW   COOKING 1
BRISTOL (0272) 745202 and 745231   COST £20–£25

Stylish and not cheap – added value, perhaps, from the dance floor – with a cabinet displaying Ch. Ducru Beaucaillou 1898 if you have the odd £399 to drink this with your lamb and yellow-bean sauce. Szechuan dishes get preeminent listing and sizzling scallops and oysters are also fancied. The Wong brothers offer a better wine list than usual, very inexpensively, which is doubtless another factor in the opinion that the restaurant is more serious than much local competition.

CHEF: David Wong   PROPRIETOR: Raymond Wong
OPEN: all week
CLOSED: 25 to 28 Dec
MEALS: 12 to 2.30, 6.30 to 11.30
PRICES: £11 (£21), Set D £15 (£20). Service 10%
CARDS: Access, Amex, Diners, Visa
SEATS: 150. Private parties: 150 main room, 10, 20 and 45 private rooms. Car-park, 25 places. Children welcome. Smart dress preferred. Music. Air-conditioned

Plum Duff

6 Chandos Road, Redland, Bristol BS6 6PE   COOKING 1
BRISTOL (0272) 238450   COST £19–£26

The shop conversion frontage is a plum colour, surprise, surprise. Inside, though, is heather and blue with a range of Victorian chairs that would do an auction room proud, and a generally neo-Victorian air. James West aims to cook simply and offers a fixed-price menu of mainstream moderns such as smoked chicken and mango salad; a warm salad of duck, pink grapefruit and avocado; a feuilleté of crab with mint and chive cream; pork with green peppers and mustard; monkfish with tomato and basil; and duck with apples and calvados. The short wine list includes decent choices such as La Vieille Ferme organic wines from the south of France, Hardy's from Australia and João Pires from Portugal. House wine: £6.50. CELLARMAN'S CHOICE: Savennières, Clos du Papillon 1988, £17.50; Montepulciano d'Abruzzo, Colle Secco 1985, £13.50.

CHEF/PROPRIETOR: James West
OPEN: Tue to Sat, D only and Sun L
CLOSED: 2 weeks from 26 Dec
MEALS: 12.30 to 2.30, 7 to 10 (11 Sat)
PRICES: Set L £12.95 (£19), Set D from £15.50 (£22). Service 10% for parties of 8 or more
CARDS: Access, Visa
SEATS: 40. 6 tables outside. Private parties: 24 main room. Vegetarian meals. Children
welcome. No cigars/pipes in dining-room. Wheelchair access (1 step) Music

---

BROADWAY   Hereford & Worcester   map 2

▲ Collin House

Collin Lane, Broadway WR12 7PB	
BROADWAY (0386) 858354	COOKING 2
on A44, 1m NW of Broadway	COST £12–£25

One reader in the course of the summer was concerned to find that Judith Mills
was on holiday from this small hotel and country restaurant in an old Cotswold
house. However, her alarm was quieted by a 'truly English meal': duck in fruit
sauce superbly crisp and flavoursome, with a steamed syrup sponge with
custard as a climax and finale. She appreciated, too, the simple surroundings,
though simple may mean 'homely', or even 'second hand' for some pieces of
furniture that others call 'antique'. The point is that Collin House establishes an
atmosphere of accessibility and direct amity that leads to appreciation of the
food offered on a short *carte* priced according to the main-course selection. The
repertoire remains stable from month to month though not entirely
unchanging. Hazelnut and cheese soufflé; Finnan haddock and smokies
poached in white wine; rabbit with ginger and pears; and a beef and ale
casserole have been enjoyed as preludes to possets, syllabubs, tarts and pies.
Lunch is entirely different. It is served in the bar and from an à la carte menu of
lasagne, ox-tail and the like. Those who have sampled both prefer dinner, but
the bar food is a good cut above a ploughman's. The wine list, with a section of
small and special purchases, shows John Mills' enjoyment of his cellar. The
choice takes in plenty of territory and good names, and though prices have
risen smartly, they are still acceptable. House wine: £8. CELLARMAN'S CHOICE:
Taltarni Cabernet Sauvignon 1983, £16.50; Marlborough Estate Chardonnay
1988, £17.85.

CHEFS: Judith Mills and Mark Brookes   PROPRIETORS: John and Judith Mills
OPEN: all week, exc Sun D
CLOSED: 5 days over Christmas
MEALS: 12 to 1.30, 7 to 9
PRICES: L £8 (£12), Set L and D £14.50 (£19) to £16.50 (£21)
CARDS: Access, Visa
SEATS: 24. 4 tables outside. Private parties: 32 main room. Car-park, 25 places. Children's
helpings (L only). No children under 6. No cigars/pipes in dining-room. Wheelchair access
(1 step; also WC)
ACCOMMODATION: 7 rooms, all with bath/shower. B&B £37.50 to £79. Deposit: £35
Children under 6 by prior arrangement. Garden. Swimming-pool. Scenic. Doors close at
11.30 [*Which? Hotel Guide*]

Hunters Lodge

High Street, Broadway WR12 7DT	COOKING 2
BROADWAY (0386) 853247	COST £17−£32

The Friedlis rule this place benevolently yet firmly. The tourist business of Broadway draws all manner of people, and they are welcoming to all. The William Morris look-a-like of a menu mixes conventional dishes with those having a mark of fashion: a stir-fry of chicken and prawn julienne with ginger and vegetables side by side with cod fillets and herb butter. Kurt Friedli has had long practice and makes sauces correctly. He is able to cook meats as instructed and attaches no odium to those who want them well done; vegetables may err on the overcooked side. Note has been made of a good vegetable julienne in filo with a yoghurt dressing; hake in mushroom crust; guinea-fowl with sage and onion stuffing; roast best end of lamb with a herbed crumb coating; and simpler set-price lunch dishes including pot-roast rabbit. Cooking is usually substantial and service traditional. People have felt let down by the array of desserts to one side of the dining-room: cheesecakes and Pavlovas of no allure. This is a fairly traditional restaurant, with heart, though it sometimes comes in conflict with views on smoking ('when you have the luxury of two dining-rooms and two bars, I cannot imagine why one is not made no-smoking'), but in general it has the qualities of experience and dependability. The wine list, in the same vein, makes no recourse to new-wave winemakers; it is very much tied to reliable négociants' wines. Clarets and half-bottles are provided generously and many bottles are under £15. House wine: £6.85.

CHEF: Kurt Friedli   PROPRIETORS: Kurt and Dottie Friedli
OPEN: Tue to Sun, exc Sun D
CLOSED: first 2 weeks Feb, first 2 weeks Aug
MEALS: 12.30 to 2, 7.30 to 9.45
PRICES: £17 (£26 L, £27D), Set L £12 (£17), Set D £18.50 (£24)
CARDS: Access, Amex, Diners, Visa
SEATS: 55. 6 tables outside. Private parties: 35 main room, 22 private room. Car-park, 20 places. Vegetarian meals. Children's helpings. No children under 8 (D). No cigars/pipes in dining-room. Wheelchair access (also WC)

▲ *Lygon Arms* ♥

Broadway WR12 7DU	COOKING 2
BROADWAY (0386) 852255	COST £24−£44

The courtyards stretch out behind this grand Cotswold building like those in a medieval manor house, save that today they are occupied by meeting rooms, bedroom wings, banqueting suites and, under construction as we write, a columned swimming-pool and country club. Eating goes on in the Great Hall on the street front of the original house, its blue and white barrel-vaulted roof, antlered stags and painted blazons exciting many visitors by its image of Heritage Britain. The press of business is heavy and Clive Howe has a hard task bringing the menu up to date and keeping output consistent. There is a seasonal *carte*, and a couple of set meals, one of them vegetarian. Dishes share the preoccupations of trendier places. Smoked food, either home-smoked monkfish or hickory-smoked beef, is enjoyed; sauces are light or do not exist save as the natural produce, or vehicle, of the cooking; vegetables figure in braised dishes and humble ingredients such as pearl barley or lentils get their outing. Meals reported have included melon and berry fruits with coriander and lime; a consommé with mushrooms and olive dumplings; guinea-fowl on a bed of salad with a nut dressing; a ballotine of smoked guinea-fowl with beetroot and oranges; medallions of salmon with mussels in a cider sauce; fillet of brill with a crab crust, ginger and spring onions; rabbit with mustard sauce; roast lamb with aubergine; and puddings such as 'Wait 'n' See' – a plate filled with a choux swan with cream, chocolate gateau, brandy-snap with ice-cream, and raspberry crème brûlée. Hot puddings are either steamed (a different one each day of the week) or fritters, maybe apricot with almond paste stuffing and an apricot purée. The cooking is not always perfect: there are comments about too many bad days, though this may be softened by the evident value of the lunch menu and the multiple trimmings at the beginning and end of the meal. Service may not always be the emollient needed to smooth over mistakes in the kitchen; again, there have been many slip-ups mentioned. The wine list gives good classic French coverage at acceptable prices for the style of restaurant; the provision of halves is generous and there is a good list of German bottles. Clarets are the strongest suit, including a couple of off-vintages of Latour and Lafite. House wines start at £7.50.

CHEF: Clive Howe   PROPRIETORS: The Savoy Group
OPEN: all week
MEALS: 12.30 to 2, 7.30 to 9.30
PRICES: £28 (£37), Set L £16.25 (£24), Set D £25 (£34)
CARDS: Access, Amex, Carte Blanche, Diners, Visa
SEATS: 90. Private parties: 90 main room, 20, 40 and 76 private rooms. Car-park, 150 places.
Vegetarian meals. Children's helpings. Smart dress preferred. No-smoking area.
Wheelchair access (also WC)
ACCOMMODATION: 66 rooms, all with bath/shower. Rooms for disabled. B&B £90 to £125.
Baby facilities. Pets welcome. Afternoon teas. Garden. Tennis. Snooker. TV. Phone. Scenic.
Confirm by 6

BROCKENHURST Hampshire   map 2

▲ *Poussin* 🍷

57–59 Brookley Road,
Brockenhurst SO42 7RB   COOKING 4
LYMINGTON (0590) 23063   COST £18–£44

Alexander Aitken is an expressive chef who enjoys a rapport with his customers, enabling him to explain, or perhaps to change, something that in their eyes has not worked. His commitment is the mark of an enthusiast, who has taken pains to be supported by a very professional French team at the front of house. The Gallic mood which they impart is echoed by the decoration. The lounge upstairs has 'meringue-plastered' walls; the dining-room below, with giant windows letting in invigorating light, was described by one more used to English reticence as 'unbelievable French two-star restaurant style with lamps with doves on their bases, wood and obscured glass'. In truth, the tables are well set and well spaced making it all the more surprising to find a lunch menu that would cost little more than an ordinary café. There's not a lot of reticence in the cooking: Alex Aitken still enjoys his 'festivals' and 'rendezvous'; petits fours come in two waves; and groups of three are almost a commonplace – three game meats; three butcher's meats; a trio of pear desserts; a trio of banana desserts. Some of the time this causes fuss on the plate to no other end than ornament, as in main courses with a scattering of micro-portions of vegetables. Most people enjoy the flavours that he extracts, for instance, from a breast of chicken stuffed with truffles on a powerful stock reduction, or a fricassee of pheasant on an almost fruity semi-glace, or a first course of lobster in a mille-feuille with aubergine, tomato and courgette. If game and wild mushrooms seem to be his signature – with truffles thrown in for good measure – they reflect the New Forest location, just as fish and shellfish – often accompanied by first-rate butter sauces – mark the proximity to the coast. Not only do the first courses invite choice of a generous cross-section of shellfish, but also main course fish dishes can be substituted as first courses at a cheaper price, an admirable practice that could stand to be more widely adopted. Many go to the Poussin for the *menu gastronomique* of four courses plus a sorbet and cheese, which comes with suggestions and servings of a different wine for each course. This menu, for two only, is well paced and well apportioned. In contrast, one meal from the à la carte was observed to have allocations of meat no larger than the set meal, notwithstanding the higher price. The approach shown in the repertoire is classical: although spices and single herb-scents have been observed, for example in a rendezvous of seafood in a turmeric sauce, the emphasis is on alcohol, butter and reduction sauces, and flavouring by mushrooms in all their guises. Some have said that the chief glory may lie in the desserts, though the cheese cannot be ignored. Hot banana soufflé with caramel sauce: 'light, delicate, even-textured, with slices of banana at the bottom, the fantastic sauce pure, thin and just sweet yet interesting'; 'poached pear with almonds, pear ice-cream and a pear sabayon looked too good to eat but was much too good simply to admire'; and terrine of white chocolate and praline on an orange sauce with a brunoise of exotic fruits are merely three from a wide-ranging repertoire. Coffee has not been invariably approved, nor the breads, but the petits fours are outstanding. There must soon come a time when we will turn against the front and back trimmings of a meal, when chefs find doing them a burden and diners reject eating them after all that has come before. Until that day, the truffles in three flavours and the other small pastries are quite excellent. Take note: smokers have their way only in the 'extremely comfortable' bar/lounge. The wine list has an impeccable collection of growers and properties. Its drawback is price range, which has little below £15. Rhône reds start at £17.50 and go on to £99. Some consolation may be found in the 'coup de coeur' selection that comes 'from the heart of our sommelier', from £10 to £20. The clarets are particularly well chosen.

The 1992 Guide will be published before Christmas 1991. Reports on meals are most welcome at any time of the year, but are extremely valuable in the spring. Send them to The Good Food Guide, *FREEPOST, 2 Marylebone Road, London NW1 1YN. No stamp is needed if posted in the UK.*

▲ *This symbol means accommodation is available.*

CHEF: Alexander Aitken   PROPRIETORS: Alexander and Caroline Aitken
OPEN: Tue to Sun, exc Sun D
MEALS: 12.30 to 2, 7 to 10
PRICES: £26 (£36), Set L £9.95 (£18) to £15 (£24), Set D £29.50 (£37)
CARDS: Access, Visa
SEATS: 35. Private parties: 35 main room. Vegetarian meals. No smoking in dining-room.
Wheelchair access (also WC)
ACCOMMODATION: 4 rooms, all with bath/shower. B&B £30 to £55. Deposit: £30. Baby
facilities. No smoking in bedrooms. Doors close at midnight. Confirm by 4

BRUTON   Somerset   map 2

▲ *Claire de Lune*

2–4 High Street, Bruton BA10 0EQ   COOKING 2
BRUTON (0749) 813395   COST £19–£28

A young couple run this small restaurant with rooms in an old storehouse at
the crest of the High Street. Nautical themes impose some unity on the busy
decoration and Kate Stewart provides 'a pleasant welcome' to those who try
her husband's cooking. This is offered on a fixed-price menu written in florid
French with English subtitles – 'Rêve d'Enfant' turns out to be fruit with
sorbet – reflecting classical Swiss training and work in fancy London places.
Parma ham, terrine of salmon and sole with a lemon and herb sauce, beef with
chanterelles, guinea-fowl with green peppercorns are par for the course; strips
of lamb and scampi with curry, pineapple and pimentos is more wayward.
Most plump for the saner side of the palette: pot-roast pheasant; prawns and
monkfish in white wine sauce; a warm salad of sweetbreads; duck roasted
English style with orange sauce or apple and calvados sauce; oeufs à la neige;
orange soufflé with a Cointreau sorbet; or crème brûlée. These are well
executed with some flair for presentation. Coffee is only moderate, chocolates
are undistinguished, and there are unannounced changes in wine vintage; but
the value is good and efforts are made. Away from the trend, cigars are
advertised on the menu itself. 'Organic produce' evenings are held
periodically, as well as nights with a classical guitarist. There is an adequate
short wine list though 20 alternate vintages are not necessary when it is set up
on a word processor. There is a tendency to lean towards wines from
négociants. The notes are helpful, the range acceptable, the prices fair. House
French: £7.95. CELLARMAN'S CHOICE: Firestone Chardonnay 1987, £12.50;
Senhorio de los Llanos Gran Reserva, Valdepeñas 1978, £12.50.

CHEF: Thomas Stewart   PROPRIETORS: Thomas and Kate Stewart
OPEN: Mon to Sat, D only (L by arrangement)
MEALS: 7 to 10 (10.30 Sat)
PRICES: Set D £14.75 (£19) to £19 (£23). Service inc
CARDS: Access, Visa
SEATS: 40. Private parties: 40 main room. Children's helpings. Smart dress preferred.
Wheelchair access (2 steps). Music
ACCOMMODATION: 3 rooms, 2 with bath/shower. B&B £20 to £35. TV. Scenic. Doors
close at 10

Truffles

95 High Street, Bruton BA10 0AR   COOKING 2
BRUTON (0749) 812255   COST £18−£29

This has the feel of a well-run family restaurant. The dining-room is tiny and neighbouring tables are close, but there is no music, and the no-smoking request is well observed. Denise Bottrill is a talented and gracious hostess, and Martin Bottrill a skilful cook. Colour photographs of his dishes presumably adorn the walls for a reason, although nobody yet claims to have divined what it is. The somewhat reverential approach to cooking – the menu is not just a menu but a 'gourmet menu' – fortunately does not mar enjoyment. The style owes something to classical French ideas and techniques. A globe artichoke base is filled with crab mousse and given a bisque sauce. Duck liver pâté is served with toasted brioche and a cassis dressing. While the approach is not always bound by tradition and sometimes teases with variety, it is tightly controlled and stops well short of the experimental free expression that some chefs confuse with real invention. Chicken and mushroom dumplings bob in the chicken consommé. Ravioli are filled with smoked haddock. Poussin, maize-fed of course, is boned, filled with a sweet pepper mousse, and served on wild rice. Fruit is kept in its proper place, on the dessert menu, where a kumquat sauce accompanies the tropical fruit créme brûlée, and rhubarb mousse is served with fruit salad. The abiding Truffles gateau combines chocolate sponge with chocolate mousse, lubricated with chocolate sauce. Lunch is good value, and the separate vegetarian menu shares the same outlook as the main one. 'Brie and avocado baked in strudel pastry with redcurrant sauce tastes better than it sounds,' comments one reader. Wines constitute a cautious but sound and reasonably priced selection, entirely in keeping with the house style, and there is a commendable list of decent half-bottles. House French: £6.95.

CHEF: Martin Bottrill   PROPRIETORS: Martin and Denise Bottrill
OPEN: Tue to Sat, D only and Sun L (weekday L and Sun and Mon D by arrangement)
MEALS: 12 to 2, 7 to 9.30
PRICES: Set L £11.50 (£18), Set D £17.25 (£24)
SEATS: 20. Private parties: 20 main room. Vegetarian meals. Children restricted. Smart dress preferred. Wheelchair access (1 step)

BUCKLAND Gloucestershire   map 2

▲ Buckland Manor

Buckland WR12 7LY
BROADWAY (0386) 852626   COOKING 2
off A46, 1m from Broadway   COST £22−£40

'Whenever one sees Buckland Manor, one is relieved that it hasn't been transported across the Atlantic stone by stone.' Not a comment from the county's most distinguished resident, Prince Charles, on hearing that an export licence had been refused, but recognition of its appeal from an overseas visitor. This is Cotswold country – Broadway is only a mile down the road – and the manor fulfils its brochure-potential with wings and gables in yellow Cotswold stone, mullioned windows, oak panelling, arched doorways, beamed ceilings and stone fireplaces. The menu is written unnecessarily in French with a long English explanation; thus *huitres tièdes au gratin de Xérès* becomes 'a half dozen Pembrokeshire Carew oysters in their shells beneath a Dry Sack sherry and cream glaze'. The nod to France is evident in more than just the wording. Mediterranean fish are set in a herb and saffron jelly; duck livers and hearts are served with home-cured duck ham; roast lamb comes with whole cloves of garlic and Provençal herbs. The ideas are sound, ingredients good, and a number of dishes are highly praised: asparagus in puff pastry; veal sweetbreads and prawns on a bed of spinach; and rare roast beef that could be carved with a spoon. 'Service is exceptional, and Mr and Mrs Berman are quite outstanding hosts.' The extensive and largely French wine list is so chatty it makes the menu seem tight-lipped. There are good value bottles under £15, and these are well chosen. Beyond that, the mark-up must limit choice from what is undoubtedly a good list. House wine: £7.75.

CHEF: Martyn Pearn   PROPRIETORS: Adrienne and Barry Berman
OPEN: all week
CLOSED: 3 weeks from mid-Jan
MEALS: 12.30 to 1.45, 7.30 to 8.45
PRICES: £21 (£33), Set Sun L £13.95 (£22)
CARDS: Access, Visa
SEATS: 34. 6 tables outside. Private parties: 10 main room. Car-park, 30 places.
No children under 8. Smart dress preferred. No cigars/pipes in dining-room.
Wheelchair access (also WC)
ACCOMMODATION: 11 rooms, all with bath/shower. Rooms for disabled. B&B £125 to £210.
No children under 12. Afternoon teas. Garden. Swimming-pool. Tennis. TV. Phone. Scenic
[*Which? Hotel Guide*]

BURNHAM MARKET Norfolk   map 6

Fishes'

Market Place, Burnham Market PE31 8HE   COOKING 1
FAKENHAM (0328) 738588   COST £12–£28

Fish and smoked goods can be bought as counter items in the restaurant on the green of this deservedly popular village on the North Norfolk coast, but the chief activity is serving fish lunches and dinners (with a little meat) in two rooms, the second being more of a sitting area unless business is pressing. Lunch is set price and decidedly cheaper than dinner's *carte*, which in itself is not excessive. Clearly the star turn is shellfish and fish fresh from Wells down the road: oysters, lobster, skate, Scottish salmon, Dover sole and crab are buttressed by taramasalata, gravlax, smoked salmon, cod's roe or eel. The main course comes with potatoes and salads, not vegetables; dessert will include ice-cream, syllabub, meringues or a cheesecake. Readers have enjoyed the fish pure and simple more than the sometimes bland concoctions, such as salmon fishcakes or gratin of scallops and prawns. The women who serve are helpful to those ignorant of fish. The menu hardly varies from year to year, but this at least means you know what you'll get. CELLARMAN'S CHOICE: from a short wine list is Sancerre, Crochet £14.50 and Mâcon-Villages, Jaboulet-Vercherre, £10.50. House French: £6.

CHEFS: Gillian Cape, Carole Bird and Paula Ayres   PROPRIETOR: Gillian Cape
OPEN: Tue to Sun, exc Sun D, and Mon bank hols
CLOSED: 25 and 26 Dec, 3 weeks Jan
MEALS: 12 to 2, 6.45 to 9
PRICES: £15 (£23), Set L £7.25 (£12) to £10.50 (£16)
CARDS: Access, Amex, Diners, Visa
SEATS: 48. Private parties: 30 main room. Children's helpings. Children under 5 before 8.30
at D. Wheelchair access (1 step)

BURY ST EDMUNDS   Suffolk   map 3

▲ Kingshott's

12 Angel Hill, Bury St Edmunds IP33 1UZ   COOKING 2
BURY ST EDMUNDS (0284) 704068   COST £35

This new hotel and restaurant in an old house on the square has an ambitious
carte: eight different meats or fish, foie gras and lobster, making for difficulties
if catering for less than full houses every night. However, first reports have
spoken well of pigeon in puff pastry with a red fruit sauce and goose with a
blackcurrant sauce. Sweetness and fruit is much on Gary Kingshott's mind:
apricots with pork, Sauternes with rabbit, mango and ginger with duck
mousse. Duck is grilled with molasses. Desserts, too, have been praised: a
passion-fruit mousse, crème brûlée, and a chocolate truffle cake. The wine list
is a very decent 'survey' list, taking in several territories though France
predominates, and using fair producers and négociants. Note Couly-Dutheil
from Chinon; Cattin's Gewürztraminer; Roux's Passetoutgrain and Ch. Rahoul
1982 from Graves. House wines: £6.85. CELLARMAN'S CHOICE: Pinot Blanc
1985, Hugel, £11.40; Ch. Léoville-Poyferré 1976, £33.50.

CHEF: Gary Kingshott   PROPRIETORS: Gary and Dianne Kingshott
OPEN: Tue to Sat, D only (L by arrangement)
MEALS: 7 to 9.30
PRICES: £21 (£29)
CARDS: Access, Visa
SEATS: 32. Private parties: 40 main room, 12 private room. Children welcome. Music
ACCOMMODATION: 6 rooms, all with bath/shower. B&B £50 to £65. Deposit: 20%. Pets by
arrangement. TV. Phone. Doors close at 11.30. Confirm by noon [*Which? Hotel Guide*]

Mortimer's

30 Churchgate Street,
Bury St Edmunds IP33 IRG   COOKING 1
BURY ST EDMUNDS (0284) 760623   COST £24

This is very clean, very light, and very white, with flashes of green from palms,
hanging plants, oilcloth table covers and serving staff's uniforms. Fish is the
only business; seascapes and ocean charts decorate the walls. There is a long
bar counter to perch at and six tables for non-smokers in a separate area.
Newspapers on sticks are all very well, but opening times are limited and
service pushes along at such a rate that there is precious little time to read them.
The menu differs in only the minutest detail from that of its sister restaurant in

Ipswich (see entry), but responds to the maritime seasons: local North Sea lobsters appear from April to September only, mussels take their turn from September to April. As many as 21 first courses are possible because, with taramosalata, marinated herring, Loch Fyne oysters, potted shrimps and a smoked fish platter, cooking is kept to a minimum. Main courses, which work round a core repertoire with small daily changes, are either plainly grilled or out of the traditional French provincial mould, with skate in black butter, rainbow trout with almonds, lemon sole Joinville. Simpler dishes, such as freshly dressed crab, work better than more complicated ones that are sauced and left too long under the grill for their own good. Puddings are good, from Greek yoghurt served with honey to light fresh lemon chiffon. The short wine list tells very little about origins but the Australian Chardonnay comes from Orlando and the Alsaces from Hugel. House French is £6.95.

CHEF: Kenneth Ambler   PROPRIETORS: Kenneth Ambler and Michael Gooding
OPEN: Mon to Sat, exc Sat L
CLOSED: bank hols, 23 Dec to 5 Jan, 2 weeks Aug
MEALS: 12 to 2, 7 to 9 (8.30 Mon)
PRICES: £14 (£20)
CARDS: Access, Amex, Diners, Visa
SEATS: 60. Private parties: 8 main room. Children's helpings on request.
No-smoking area/no pipes in dining-room. Wheelchair access (1 step)

CALSTOCK   Cornwall   map 1

▲ Danescombe Valley Hotel ♥

Lower Kelly, Calstock PL18 9RY   COOKING 3
TAVISTOCK (0822) 832414   COST £30

It is coincidence that the Schumacher Foundation ('small is beautiful') has its headquarters in the same region as Martin and Anna Smith's very personal hotel, which overlooks the Tamar from a Regency veranda nestling under the high ground downstream from Calstock. The Smiths are the very embodiment of Ernst Schumacher's economic philosophy: self-reliant, low key, unwilling to compromise with the usual ideas of growth. Thus the hotel will take outsiders only when there are rooms free, and it does not open for dinner on Wednesday or Thursday. Anna Smith cooks a no-choice meal of four courses, one of which is normally cheese. Much is made of local supplies: those cheeses; Martin Smith's allotment for vegetables (even Cape gooseberries in the last hot summer of 1989); kid from goatkeepers; salmon from the river at the front door, and much more. This may create the impression that you are dining on a grocery basket but Anna Smith often lifts it to a fine experience by slight and subtle means. The cooking is neither elaborate, showy nor complicated: parcel of salmon with vegetables; chicken with mushrooms and sherry or stuffed with pesto; kid baked in pastry with mushrooms. Puddings, too, are delicious but never simply restaurant stalwarts: apple and clove crumble cake, oatmeal meringue, almond tart, chocolate cake. Their appeal, other than the skill of execution, lies in freshness of taste and evident immediacy. There has been a slight Italian tilt this year, following a Tuscan holiday and capitalising on Anna

Smith's own heritage. This is seen from complete Italian evenings, more Italian wines, and dishes like risotto of artichokes, fried courgette flowers, veal with sage and lemon and the use of materials such as balsamic vinegar. At the end of a long season there may be moments when the exact judgement needed to bring this off memorably is lacking, and when tiredness levies its tribute. There is no staff, so the Smiths can only make adjustments to the workload in a way that shows up immediately; hence the disappearance of cooked breakfasts during 1989. The Smiths think of this as their home so they deal with their guests as they would with friends, first names and all. It may be worth staying the night both for the mechanical bath toys and the chance to try the wine list to its full potential. It is arranged by grape type and is very reasonably priced. It is not easy to look at but must be read like a book, so the instructive, but sometimes maybe superfluous, comments are inescapable. Italy does indeed feature more strongly, but the world is ransacked for excellent value and top quality. Tissot (Arbois), Chanzy (Mercurey), Avignonesi (Montepulciano), Chave (Hermitage), Tollana (South Australia), Sanford (California) are some of the growers and properties to mark. Half-bottles are notable for their absence.

CHEF: Anna Smith   PROPRIETORS: Martin and Anna Smith
OPEN: all week D, exc Wed and Thur
CLOSED: Nov to Easter
MEALS: 7.30 for 8
PRICES: Set D £22 (£25). Service inc
SEATS: 12. No children under 12. One sitting
ACCOMMODATION: 5 rooms, all with bath/shower. B&B £53 to £96. Deposit: £50. No children under 12. Garden. Golf. Scenic. Doors close at midnight. Confirm by 6

CAMBRIDGE Cambridgeshire   map 3

Midsummer House

Midsummer Common,
Cambridge CB4 1HA   COOKING 2
CAMBRIDGE (0223) 69299   COST £22—£47

There is some difference of opinion about where to sit in this many-chambered restaurant that needs careful navigation to find – the car park is distant, the house reached by towpath. Some favour the conservatory, equipped with the 'world's most comfortable restaurant seating' and looking onto the manicured garden, which has tables and umbrellas for really hot days. Others prefer the coolth of the downstairs dining-room, a cerulean blue with lavish curtaining. Still others enjoy the privacy of upstairs, though some feel ostracised, if not exiled, there. All this may indicate that going to Midsummer House is an event much discussed and enjoyed by the Cambridge community. It is aiming for metropolitan style and chic – even the staff are 'dressed for success' down to the waitresses' severe suiting. The menus are set-price and as modish as anyone's with such dishes as 'blackened salmon Cajun style with saffron risotto and ratatouille'. Lunch is slightly cheaper than dinner, but is for two courses only. When offered the dessert menu, the hungry luncher will find it unpriced. Perhaps the best course is to take coffee, which is served with excellent petits fours. Dinner prices depend on the number of courses and there are only a few supplements. For the style of the place, prices are generally reasonable. Although the descriptions of dishes appear modest and plain enough (though one person's juniper berries were in fact cranberries), they may mask a profusion of display on great big plates – in blue to match the walls. 'There is invariably fresh foie gras nestling in lollo rosso and lamb's lettuce on the plate to accompany the pigeon breasts. There will also be a flurry of asparagus and other vegetables,' wrote one reader. People have reported in equally extravagant terms their wild mushrooms in a 'basket' with basil sauce; carré of lamb persillade; a hot venison pie to begin a meal with 'gamey richness'; and a hot plum tart as dessert. There has also been noticed a gradual reduction in display, to the benefit of natural flavours, but the cooking has not yet settled to the even tenor that should be expected. Meals contain disappointments: chicken wrapped in filo pastry with a sauce incomplete in flavour and technique; a galantine of duck and foie gras with cider aspic not at its best condition; scallops and monkfish with saffron overcooked and tasting more of salt than saffron. The wine list offers a good spread across the world, with strength in clarets. Here, the zany prices of classed growths makes economy difficult and some of the *crus bourgeois* are not deeply explored. House wines, from Geoffrey Roberts, are £9.50. CELLARMAN'S CHOICE: Chardonnay, Cloudy Bay 1988, £21.50; Ch. Talbot 1983, £31.50.

CHEF: Hans Schweitzer   PROPRIETORS: Chris Kelly and Hans Schweitzer
OPEN: Mon to Sat, exc Sat L and Mon L
MEALS: 12 to 2, 6.30 to 9.30
PRICES: Set L £13.50 (£22) to £28.50 (£38), Set D £22.50 (£32) to £29.50 (£39)
CARDS: Access, Diners, Visa
SEATS: 35. 2 tables outside. Private parties: 35 main room, 12 private room. Children's helpings on request. Smart dress preferred. Wheelchair access

Twenty Two ♟

22 Chesterton Road, Cambridge CB4 3AX	COOKING 2
CAMBRIDGE (0223) 351880	COST £29

In the front and back rooms of a Victorian terraced house that manage to be 'clean, cramped and friendly,' it is a restaurant that 'I like because it's run by real people who cook real food. It's unpretentious; just good.' There is a short menu with a salad served automatically at course two. There are moments when the service is too amateur and when the food has fallen short of description or expectation but mentions have come of cold green melon and ginger soup; lamb and spinach pâté, sardines with yoghurt and horseradish; saddle of hare with red wine and port; pigeon breast with blackcurrant and orange sauce; lamb kebab with spiced rhubarb sauce; and first-rate vegetables. St Emilion au chocolat was rich enough; sorbets may still be traffic lights; brandy-snaps are snappy. There could be no greater contrast than the externals and style of this place and Midsummer House, and it must happen that fish from either pond feel out of water. People stress, however, that the welcome from the Sharpes and their helpers is exemplary. The wine list continues the theme established by the food of sensible and very fair prices for a good product. No-nonsense and brief, the selection is disarmingly intelligent; notice some canny choices from outside the classic areas, a 1961 Barolo for only £24 or the excellent Contino from Rioja – as well as top-quality Rhônes, burgundies and clarets. House wine: £6.50 and £7.50.

CHEF: Michael Sharpe   PROPRIETORS: Michael and Susan Sharpe
OPEN: Tue to Sat, D only (L by arrangement)
CLOSED: 24 Dec to 1 Jan
MEALS: 7.30 to 10
PRICES: Set D £17.50 (£24)
CARDS: Access, Visa
SEATS: 28. Private parties: 28 main room. Vegetarian meals. No children under 12. Music

Upstairs

71 Castle Street, Cambridge CB2 3AH   COOKING 1
CAMBRIDGE (0223) 312569   COST £20

'Mid-Eastern food and atmosphere' is the slogan on the menu, and this cramped restaurant above Waffles Café remains true to its intentions. In the context of the Cambridge eating scene, it is excellent value. Some readers reckon that the flavours are too delicate; others find it 'more strongly flavoured in actuality than memory'. The lanterns, Persian rugs and fretted window screens might have been lifted from the travel brochures, but the food has a gutsy, authentic edge. The static menu roams across the Middle East and North Africa for Moroccan beef soup with lentils and chickpeas; Armenian lamb with apricots, and Turkish kala gosh, a dish of clove-flavoured beef topped with yoghurt. Gagamp, beef rolled in cabbage leaves topped with tomato and raisin sauce, is reported to be a good starter, and fruit-flavoured crêpes are a good alternative to the authentic honey-dripping sweets. The well-chosen, fairly priced wine list looks to Europe for inspiration. House wine: £6.

CHEFS: Hywel Evans and Virginia La Charité   PROPRIETORS: Virginia and Pat La Charité
OPEN: all week, D only
CLOSED: Christmas to New Year, 2 weeks Sept
MEALS: 6.30 to 11.30 (11 Sun)
PRICES: £10 (£17). Service 10% for parties of 6 or more
CARDS: Access, Visa
SEATS: 36. Vegetarian meals. Children welcome. No smoking in dining-room. Music

CAMPSEA ASH Suffolk   map 3

▲ Old Rectory ♥

Campsea Ash IP13 0PU
WICKHAM MARKET (0728) 746524   COOKING 1
on B1078, 1m E of A12   COST £20–£26

'After a surfeit of international hotels, how refreshing to find a place where both the house and the menu reflect the taste of the owner.' That is one foreign visitor's opinion of Stewart Bassett's converted seventeenth-century rectory. Others have been less impressed, mentioning the subdued atmosphere and some inconsistent cooking. Clearly a place that goes its own way cannot hope to please everyone. There is no menu: meals are planned and arranged in advance, and the choice of wine may also be left to Stewart Bassett. When the kitchen is working well, it can produce some excellent dishes, such as spiced ragout of lamb cooked in a sealed pot and garnished with pickled quinces; fillet of monkfish with tomato and watercress sauce; and poussin in ginger and honey sauce. Most readers approve of the nicely cooked fresh vegetables. Crème brûlée, fruit tarts and poached pears stuffed with glacé fruits are well reported. Like the cooking, the service and organisation of the restaurant can be wayward: on some nights the whole operation can grind seemingly to a halt; at other times it can spark off good-humoured appreciation. 'We drank a toast to those who refuse to play by universal rules.' Any uncertainties should be forgotten, though, with the wine list; it is put together by an enthusiast who, with those generous prices, wants others to be enthused. Every section is a roll-call of fine, but not necessarily expensive, properties and growers.

CHEF/PROPRIETOR: Stewart Bassett
OPEN: Mon to Sat, D only
MEALS: 7.30 to 10
PRICES: Set D £16 (£20) to £17.50 (£22)
CARDS: Access, Amex, Diners, Visa
SEATS: 40. Private parties: 18 main room, 6 and 20 private rooms. Car-park, 20 places.
Children's helpings. No children under 10. Wheelchair access
ACCOMMODATION: 8 rooms, all with bath/shower. B&B £27 to £43. Deposit: £10. No
children under 8. Garden. Doors close at midnight. Confirm by noon [*Which? Hotel Guide*]

CARTMEL Cumbria   map 7

▲ *Aynsome Manor*

Cartmel LA11 6HH   COOKING 2
CARTMEL (053 95) 36653   COST £13–£26

A sheltered valley, some good eighteenth-century interiors, comfortable bedrooms and substantial cooking make this a good stop just beyond the main run of Lakeland resorts. The Varleys are a multi-generation team with son and daughter-in-law managing front-of-house. The small change in the kitchen has not altered the enthusiasm that seems to many an outstanding virtue. The menu is a five-course, set-price affair with a choice of three dishes either side of a second-course soup, then followed by a groaning sweets trolley and cheeses. Sunday lunch is along the same lines, but at nearly half the cost: fair value for roast sirloin as well as coffee on the house. Dishes such as choux pastry swans with prawns and mushrooms in a tarragon cream; home-made pâté with redcurrant and port wine sauce; salmon with cucumber and tomato hollandaise; veal with green peppercorn cream sauce; and pigeon in pastry with bacon and wild mushrooms on a madeira sauce mark the style. Vegetables are also plentiful, with two sorts of potatoes. This is substantial cooking to keep out the chill of cold days or to compensate for no lunch – and at a moderate cost. The wine list does not concentrate on France alone, familiar names – Duboeuf, Latour, Jadot, Brédif, Rosemount, Torres – abound in the 90-odd bins as do alternate vintages. House wine from Italy is £6.
CELLARMAN'S CHOICE: Tokay Pinot Gris 1987, Hugel, £15; Rosemount, Coonawarra Estate Cabernet Sauvignon 1987, £12.50.

CHEFS: Tony Varley, Ian Simpson and Sarah James
PROPRIETORS: Tony and Margaret Varley
OPEN: Mon to Sat, D only, and Sun L
CLOSED: 2 to 28 Jan
MEALS: 1, 7 to 8.15
PRICES: Set Sun L £8.50 (£13), Set D £16 (£22)
CARDS: Access, Amex, Visa
SEATS: 35. Private parties: 35 main room. Car-park, 20 places. Children's helpings.
No children under 5 at D. Smart dress preferred. No smoking. Wheelchair access.
One sitting Sun L
ACCOMMODATION: 13 rooms, 12 with bath/shower. B&B £26.50 to £56. Pets welcome.
Garden. Golf. TV. Phone. Scenic. Doors close at 11.30

▲ Uplands

Haggs Lane, Cartmel LA11 6HD   COOKING 3
CARTMEL (05395) 36248 and 36249   COST £18–£31

Turn opposite the Pig and Whistle in Cartmel village. At the top of the hill is
Uplands, looking out to Morecambe Bay with the Victorian resort of Grange-
over-Sands below. Di and Tom Peter used to work with John Tovey and
Uplands states it is 'in the Miller Howe manner' on its masthead. What this
means is a restaurant with rooms offering short daily menus at lunch and
dinner of two or three alternatives in each course with many dishes showing
the Tovey influence. There is a delight in fruit with meats and fish: lamb comes
with a mint sauce enhanced with diced apple; sole is stuffed with smoked
salmon and mango with a watercress sauce; breast of pigeon is served on a
pineapple salad; and loin of veal comes with fried pineapple and a mustard
and honey cream sauce (except on one person's plate, entirely innocent of the
proclaimed pineapple). Or dishes may show enjoyment of piquancy: lamb is
marinated in wine, soy, mustard, garlic and rosemary, then served with a
gherkin sauce. With all main courses comes a panoply of vegetables – Miller
Howe style – which normally please and impress, though one spirit observed
they were dauntingly heaped round the plate, and who would want red
cabbage with turbot and a mushroom and tarragon sauce? First courses such as
a hot sole and mushroom soufflé with a watercress sauce; scallops with
shallots, bacon and white wine; or a salmon mousse show particular ability
with fish cookery and the succeeding automatic soup course (at dinner) with its
accompaniment of a steaming hot loaf and fresh butter is always approved:
almond and fennel, tomato and basil, tomato, apple and celery, broccoli and
cheese are some of the flavours. Dessert will often include a pie or a pudding
(the sticky toffee is good, the banana, walnut and ginger pie 'irresistible'), a
mousse, something fruity or ice in a meringue or a brandy snap; but 'kiwi-fruit
and coffee meringue do not go together'. Cheese could be better when Grange-
over-Sands has Ainsworth's as excellent grocers. The very regular visitor may
find the repertoire repetitious; the lover of light food may find that cream and
sauces obscure some of the flavours; the proponent of simplicity may applaud
the bare pine tables but wish that the cook would leave well alone. These are
points of view. Others continue to aver that 'you leave for home feeling the
time was well spent among happy people who like making their guests happy'
and feeling well fed. The wine list is short and to the point with a few extras

235

(especially New World) named as 'wines of the month' on a separate card. Prices are reasonable but the choice is not so distinguished that one does not wish for a wider selection to accompany the good cooking. Prices in the restaurant are also reasonable; the value for money of lunch, for example, is enough to make a southerner weep. But people do question the 10 per cent surcharge added to every bill, especially those who stay the night and wonder why the fairly basic amenities and service should carry this levy. On the tariff card is the statement, 'A surcharge of 10 per cent added to bills in lieu of service charge.' How can it be 'in place' of service? Would it not be simpler to increase the price by 10 per cent and cancel service charges altogether?

CELLARMAN'S CHOICE: Plantagenet Shiraz, Mount Barker 1987, £12.95; Chardonnay 1989, Delegat, £12.50.

CHEF: Tom Peter PROPRIETORS: John J. Tovey and Tom and Diana Peter
OPEN: Tue to Sun and Mon bank hols
CLOSED: 1 Jan to 24 Feb
MEALS: 12.30 to 1, 7.30 to 8
PRICES: Set L £12.20 (£18), Set D £20 (£26). Service 10%
CARDS: Access, Amex, Visa
SEATS: 34. Private parties: 34 main room. Car-park, 18 places. No children under 8.
No smoking. Wheelchair access. Music
ACCOMMODATION: 5 rooms, all with bath/shower. B&B £40 to £80. No children under 8. Pets welcome. Garden. TV. Phone. Scenic. Doors close at 11. Confirm by 3
[*Which? Hotel Guide*]

CATTAWADE Suffolk   map 3

Bucks

The Street, Cattawade,
nr Manningtree, CO11 1RG   COOKING 1
COLCHESTER (0206) 392571   COST £29

In its transition from pub to restaurant, the Buck's Head has dropped the apostrophe and moved from images of hunting to the elegance of Regency dandies on the menu cover. Rude drinking has also been exorcised by the pastel shades of blue and pink in the dining-room. The team owe their training and inspiration to Robert Carrier's time at Hintlesham Hall and Anthony Peacock cooks dishes of an international nature much as his mentor used to write about: strips of lamb stir-fried with yoghurt, mint and ginger; chicken with pimento and okra; saddle of hare with a rhubarb and raspberry sauce are some of the main courses showing true old English eclecticism and experiment. Gravlax, generous, moist and sweet tasting, is served with a home-made lime jelly; yoghurt and mint get another outing in a tsatsiki salad of cucumber; and English tastes are gratified with ham, leek and Stilton turnovers with Stilton sauce among the first courses. Reports have spoken of the ginger sauce as nicely muted and almost smoky, of decent vegetables and of simple but generous cheeses, but also of desserts that missed their point through lack of flavour. Other meals – including perhaps potato gnocchi with a ratatouille, a filo nest of seafood with saffron, wine and cream, and a tart of Bramley apple purée and thin slices of dessert apple – have been praised for the accuracy of the cooking and the fact that the flavour of each component came through. There is a blackboard menu in the wine bar of simpler but not simple choices. The wine list, much from Lay and Wheeler, has a fair range from France and more distant countries, offered at very reasonable prices. House wine: £5.75. CELLARMAN'S CHOICE: Stoneleigh, Sauvignon Blanc 1988, £10.75; Fleurie 1987, Duboeuf, £10.95.

CHEF: Anthony Peacock   PROPRIETOR: Trevor Gilbert
OPEN: Tue to Sat
MEALS: 11.30 to 2.30, 6.30 to 10.30
PRICES: £18 (£24)
CARDS: Access, Amex, Visa
SEATS: 36 restaurant, 30 wine bar. 4 tables outside. Private parties: 36 main room. Car-park, 40 places. Children's helpings. Wheelchair access. Music

---

CHADDESLEY CORBETT   Hereford & Worcester   map 5

▲ Brockencote Hall

Chaddesley Corbett DY10 4PY   COOKING 2
CHADDESLEY CORBETT (0562) 777876   COST £21–£38

As the French chef has been replaced by an English one, so the menu has changed its language from one to the other. The style of cooking has been sufficiently international for the alteration in personnel to be smoothly effected. Canada geese settle on the lake in the surrounding parkland, the Malverns rise above the western horizon, the house is close to a picture-book English village: these are fine surroundings for a country-house hotel. The turn-of-the-century house incorporates earlier architectural fragments bought by its mercantile builders. Within, the feel has been likened to French château rather than squire's hall. The dinner menu comprises a choice of eight dishes at each course, but the price is set. The menu changes by the month rather than the day, but there are daily extras on another sheet, particularly of fish. Lunch is much cheaper, with a not much shorter menu. The Hall is near enough to Birmingham and its satellites to attract business as well as private custom. Sunday lunch is fair value and very popular with people seeking a day in the country. The cooking is often not too fussy: scrambled eggs with gravlax; veal escalope with oyster mushrooms; lemon tart with cream. This is accurately done. For the lover of fancy cooking there is no stinting on elaboration: a first course of quail is roasted, some livers fried beside it, with home-made noodles, red cabbage, a carrot galette, braised cloves of garlic and a game reduction sauce; a main course of guinea-fowl sees a generous portion of meat served on another stock reduction sauce, a sausage made of the meat of the drumsticks and some truffles, and a small filo purse of chopped vegetables accompanying it on the side; a dessert might be rum-soaked pineapple deep fried in a filo parcel and served on a caramel sauce. Many of these dishes have been appreciated, although it has also been observed that flavours can be muddied by complexity and techniques are occasionally lacking: in one dinner the terrine of duck and foie gras suffered from muted flavours and that of monkfish and lobster was too strident; both had poor texture. Cheeses, from Olivier are often good. The wine list, French with a small slate from down under, will offer the chance of drinking reasonably so long as Burgundy and Bordeaux are avoided. Shippers and growers are decent and some effort has been made with half-bottles but there is no question that this is a list for the well-heeled. House wine starts at £10.50 for a Tokay Pinot Gris from Turkheim. CELLARMAN'S CHOICE: Rully Clos St. Jacques 1986, Dom. de la Folie, £20.50; Chorey-Les-Beaune 1986, Tollot-Beaut £21.30. Children are welcome; teas are good; tips are not expected. As the *Guide* went to press, there were plans to open a new conservatory restaurant.

CHEF: David Ostle PROPRIETORS: Mr and Mrs J. Petitjean
OPEN: all week, exc Sat L and Sun D
MEALS: 12.30 to 2, 7.30 to 9.30
PRICES: Set L £15.50 (£21), Set D £26.50 (£32). Service inc
CARDS: Access, Amex, Diners, Visa
SEATS: 50. 2 tables outside. Private parties: 40 main room, 50 private room. Car-park, 45 places. Children welcome. Smart dress preferred. Wheelchair access (also WC). Music
ACCOMMODATION: 8 rooms, all with bath/shower. B&B £63 to £110. Afternoon teas. Garden. TV. Phone. Scenic. Doors close at midnight. Confirm by 6

CHADLINGTON Oxfordshire   map 2

▲ *Manor* ▌

Chadlington OX7 3LX   COOKING 2
CHADLINGTON (060 876) 711   COST £35

The large windows, high ceilings and bold colours of the Grants' early classical country house impart light and life, though new arrivals who found no greeting save their room keys on the hall table might wonder about that. The setting is quintessential England and Chris Grant's cooking is in an English vein as well. A short daily menu of soup, followed by a choice of three or four dishes as entrée and main course, then a longer slate of desserts, then cheese, is offered at a set price. The soups are the sort beloved of modern cooks: Stilton and celery or carrot, coriander and mint, for example. There is a fair quantity of fruit and strong flavourings to the savoury cooking: plum sauce with a duck terrine, redcurrant with venison, Stilton with chicken breast, orange, honey and ginger with duck, blackcurrants with calf's liver. Desserts often include steamed puddings such as sticky toffee, or hot ones such as baked bananas and rum and raisins. These have been enjoyed. The cooking is not elaborate, so the success rate should probably be higher. Service, too, has occasioned disenchantment. Never, however, has the wine list been other than praised. The clarets, particularly the long runs of first growths, are exceptional, mature and cheap, but bourgeois growths get a good showing – Ch. Citran 1982, at £16.50; Ch. Latour St Bonnet 1978, £19.50. Rhônes, white and red, are excellent. The other French wines are decent, usefully noted and not expensive. English and German wines are worth exploring, some being notable as well as cheap. Half-bottles abound, of mature years as well as current stuff. House Duboeuf is £7.50. No tips are expected; children are welcome.

Report forms are at the back of the book; write a letter if you prefer.

CHEF: Chris Grant PROPRIETORS: David and Chris Grant
OPEN: all week, D only
MEALS: 7 to 9
PRICES: Set D £23.50 (£29). Service inc
CARDS: Access, Visa
SEATS: 24. Private parties: 6 and 10 private rooms. Car-park, 16 places. Children welcome.
No smoking in dining-room
ACCOMMODATION: 7 rooms, all with bath/shower. B&B £65 to £110. TV. Phone. Scenic.
Doors close at 11

CHAGFORD Devon   map 1

▲ *Gidleigh Park* 🍾

Chagford TQ13 8HH
CHAGFORD (06473) 2367 and 2225
from Chagford square, turn R at Lloyd's,   COOKING 4
then R at first fork; continue 2m   COST £42–£66

Shaun Hill, the chef at this half-timbered piece of stockbroker Surrey
transplanted to the edge of Dartmoor, has joined the brigade of author-chefs,
publishing in the same month as his neighbour Joyce Molyneux of the Carved
Angel at Dartmouth. His book is usable, instructive and humorous. His
cooking has the same practicality and light touch. There are few more enjoyable
memories than a summer's day at Gidleigh Park. From the terrace, not far from
the Cruvinet machine that has 'on draught' Gaja, Petaluma or Maurizio Zanella
by the glass, the ground falls immaculately away to a tumbling river – a torrent
in winter – trees and rhododendron on its banks, massy lumps of granite in its
path. Beyond, the emerald turf of the new croquet lawn stretches round the
latest pair of bedrooms in the thatched cottage that would have been the
pavilion, roses entwining its veranda. Look further still: hills and woods meet
the sky. A spring menu – set-price, six choices in each course – reads
uncompromisingly, no padding to it: 'grilled red mullet with ginger, garlic and
tomato; fresh mint and pea soup with lobster; bresaola with poached leeks in
mustard dressing; steamed turbot with leeks and crab; grilled lamb fillet with
goat's cheese and tomato salad; sauté calf's sweetbreads with basil mashed
potato.' This has little to do with mousse-stuffed, butter-sauced, evenly
flavoured, classically inspired country-house cooking. If, in the event, it is less
extreme than it sounds, it has the merit of true flavours, shining through. Some
dishes that indicate the pleasures in store include scallops with a lentil and
coriander sauce. Shaun Hill describes how this, his own invention now
popular across Britain, began as lobster with a curried lentil purée, and
progressed through several stages before ending as a purée of lentils, tomato, a
stock of chicken and the scallop corals, ginger, cardamom, lemon and
coriander, mounted with butter and cream, then served under sliced scallops
seared in oil. It is a brilliant marriage of flavours. His understanding of fish is
seen, too, in poached fillets of Dover sole laid on a pesto made with flat-leaved
parsley with just a touch of basil. The granular texture of the pesto gives variety
to the firm but even fish, and its exquisite green sets off the milky white
ribbons. The afore mentioned mullet with ginger, garlic and tomato is as good

and as colourful as it sounds. Dover sole fillets may find themselves with a salad of three lettuces and a purée of lettuce, too. Scallops have also been served with caramelised chicory and lime zests: one reader found the sweet-sour balance maintained with difficulty; another liked the superb textures and the introduction of astringent lime. If a dab-hand with the fish, his meat cookery is also assured. Examples are pigeon on a bed of cabbage with foie gras surrounded by an array of vegetables that would put any Food Hall to shame; venison with red wine sauce, or with foie gras and madeira sauce; braised lamb in a light stock sauce with young vegetables and summer truffle; duck which is first steamed, then crisp-fried, with a salad with Cassis dressing. Even when foie gras is used as a component, the effect avoids heaviness. Cheese has always been a strong point at Gidleigh: French and British, unpasteurised, served with good breads and biscuits and by a staff sufficiently trained to describe them. Puddings may have got better over the years. They benefit from Shaun Hill's ability to make pastry: a feuilleté with white chocolate ice-cream, chocolate sauce and cherries was, in the words of one satiated consumer, 'a superior knickerbocker glory'. Another commented that vanilla ice-cream, strawberries and honeycomb 'was a bit OTT, so much delicious honeycomb'. Lemon tart is given a new angle by a crisp topping of caramelised banana. Ice-creams are excellent: cinnamon, vanilla, prune and praline. Baking is well attended to, whether in the pastry for the canapés, the breads or the biscuits, soda breads, brioches and croissants used for the hotel. What Shaun Hill is to the kitchen, Paul Henderson is to the hotel, though doubtless the two are symbiotic. Gidleigh was Paul and Kay Henderson's creation and their influence is never absent. When one reader visited for lunch, the staff were spending the morning at a tutored tasting of Italian wines. It was a display of very costly bottles and it was available to all the staff, not just a sommelier. The service has a pleasing quality of intelligence and proficiency. The wine list is fine, its strongest suits the upper-crust Italian reds, Californians and clarets. Burgundies, especially mature ones, are also excellent. A new pricing policy has been introduced this year, explained in a forward to the list. Given the cost of maintaining a really good cellar, Paul Henderson reckons it is in his interest to accelerate the sales of fine wines at the expense of the cheaper bottles. He has therefore costed the Sancerres, Mâcons and their equals at a very high rate of return, passing the benefit to the 1970 clarets, the first growths and the fine burgundies. A Sancerre will cost the same as in the most rapacious London hotel, but 1970 Mouton Rothschild is very fairly priced at £112. An abundance of white burgundies come in at under £40 and most of the magnificent red Italians are below £30. There are sufficient halves, but the Cruvinet machine may be more attractive as a way of varying the drinking through the meal. The bin ends at Gidleigh must be the most exciting set of any in Britain. Since the last *Guide* the hotel has begun to quote its prices inclusive of VAT. Tipping is 'discouraged'.

'For the first course I had spaghetti bolognaise which was very uninspiring. My wife, who was born in Kent but once visited Venice, makes one that would leave it for dead. My wife had melon and ham – not much you can do to that.' On eating in Cumbria

The Guide *is totally independent, accepts no free hospitality, and survives on the number of copies sold each year.*

CHEF: Shaun Hill   PROPRIETOR: Kay and Paul Henderson
OPEN: all week
MEALS: 12.30 to 2, 7 to 9
PRICES: Set L £33 (£42) to £43 (£52), Set D £43 (£52) to £50 (£58). Service inc. Licensed,
also bring your own: corkage varies
CARDS: Access, Visa
SEATS: 35. Private parties: 18 main room. Car-park, 25 places. Vegetarian meals. Children
welcome. Smart dress preferred. No cigars/pipes in dining-room. Wheelchair access
ACCOMMODATION: 14 rooms, all with bath/shower. B&B £140 to £290. Children are
restricted. Pets welcome. Afternoon teas. Garden. Tennis. Fishing. TV. Phone. Scenic.
Doors close at midnight [*Which? Hotel Guide*]

CHEAM Surrey   map 3

Al San Vincenzo

52 Upper Mulgrave Road, Cheam SM2 7AJ   COOKING 3
081-661 9763   COST £37

If Tony Hancock had taken Sid or Bill to a trattoria in that Cheam of blessed
memory, it would have had little resemblance to the Borgonzolos' place, save
perhaps in decoration. This avoids the excesses of chianti flasks and drooping
plants but does little to prepare anyone for the intense and purposive Italian
cooking that goes on. Trotters, eels, tongue, rabbit and excellent game are as
likely to be found as calf's liver or Italian predictables on the short menu of half
a dozen choices. Risotto with squid, mussels and smoked salmon is an object
lesson in cooking rice, just as cold tongue with *mostarda di Cremona* and beetroot
pickled in red wine vinegar is a sound introduction to the Italian liking for
sweet and sour. Family dishes such as leg of lamb stuffed with salami, hard-
boiled egg, parmesan, and parsley will be found side by side with 'instant'
cookery like calf's liver with wild nettles. Fish gets a showing, often with
saffron sauce, be it sole or red mullet. Italian cheeses come with Vincenzo
Borgonzolo's own bread – he's proud of its crust and 'realism'. Desserts may
include tiramisu with vin santo or a compote of dried and fresh fruits with
mascarpone. Al San Vincenzo does have its ups and downs (not helped by
ruining Mozart on the sound system). This cycle may occur because of the
strength of the owner's feelings about what he is doing. Occasional murmurs of
'not enough food' seem unjustified and the downs are often the result of too
few, not too many, customers. Elaine Borgonzolo serves discreetly and kindly.
Take note that only the set menu is served on Saturday. The wine list is wholly
Italian, short and carefully chosen. It changes frequently. Even in 1990, half of
it cost under £11. It shows enthusiasm, like the food. Try also the flavoured
grappas, the bitters and the less familiar Italian liqueurs.

CHEF: Vincenzo Borgonzolo   PROPRIETORS: Vincenzo and Elaine Borgonzolo
OPEN: Mon to Sat, exc Mon L
MEALS: 12 to 2.30, 7 to 10.30
PRICES: £22 (£31), Set L and D £24 (£31)
CARD: Access, Visa
SEATS: 34. Private parties: 12 main room. Children's helpings. No cigars/pipes in
dining-room

ENGLAND

CHEDINGTON   Dorset   map 2

▲ *Chedington Court* ▼

Chedington DT8 3HY
CORSCOMBE (093 589) 265   COOKING 2
off A356, 4m SE of Crewkerne   COST £34

The Victorian builder of Chedington Court knew where to place a house to its
best advantage and his successors have ensured that the immediate setting of
this jewel has equal sparkle. Some readers have observed that the jewel itself
may need a little polish, but the quintessential Englishness of the library and
drawing-room more than compensate for the austerity of the dining-room or
the bare essentials of the lavatories. The offering each evening is a choice of first
course, then a fish and a meat course without alternatives, then a sweet trolley
and a cheeseboard of about a dozen varieties. The style is quite restrained:
Hilary Chapman is not afraid to cook a lamb hot-pot as a centrepiece, nor
indeed a peppered steak, and is as likely to offer plaice as salmon (with carrot
and orange sauce). The cooking may be likened to the house and its decoration:
conservative with a small 'c'. First courses have included sweet cured herrings,
mushrooms and a chutney; a mixture of chopped egg, prawns and a cheese
sauce; or a five-leaf salad with croûtons and bacon. The mood continues
through roast pheasant or magret of duck to desserts that include crème brûlée,
floating island, syllabub or walnut tart. This was praised last year because the
kitchen appeared to have perfect pitch – there is nothing wrong with the
familiar if it is well done – but more recent reports have detected more false
notes: not everything has been well executed, from poor meat to simply tedious
flavours or tough pastry or ill-chosen cheese. The welcome and the service,
though on occasion complimented for seemly discretion, have also been
criticised for apparent unwillingness. If a place says it takes Visa, it never helps
for the owner then to state his clear preference for cash or cheque. The wine list,
when in full stock, has great merits. Prices generally are fair, with many good
bottles, an abundance of halves and some mature wines. It is an enthusiast's
list. House wine: £6.

CHEFS: Hilary Chapman and Nicholas Alcock   PROPRIETORS: Philip and Hilary Chapman
OPEN: all week, D only
MEALS: 7 to 9
PRICES: Set D £24.50 (£28). Service inc
CARDS: Access, Amex, Visa
SEATS: 30. 2 tables outside. Private parties: 32 main room, 32 private room. Car-park, 20
places. Vegetarian meals. Children's helpings. Smart dress preferred. No cigars/pipes in
dining-room. Wheelchair access (also WC). Music
ACCOMMODATION: 10 rooms, all with bath/shower. B&B £47 to £105. Deposit: £30. Baby
facilities. Garden. Snooker. TV. Phone. Scenic. Doors close at midnight. Confirm by 6
[*Which? Hotel Guide*]

---

*Several sharp operators have tried to extort money from restaurateurs on the promise of an
entry in a guide book that has never appeared.* The Good Food Guide *makes no charge
for inclusion and does not offer certificates of any kind.*

Le Champignon Sauvage ♥

24–26 Suffolk Road,
Cheltenham GL50 2AQ   COOKING 2
CHELTENHAM (0242) 573449   COST £20–£38

Look out for the Texaco garage on Suffolk Road and you are almost there. Once inside this small but smart restaurant the welcome is 'very friendly'. Helen Everitt-Matthias works hard to make sure. There is a set-price, two-course menu supplemented by a substantial cheese and pudding *carte*. Inspection of both creates an expectation of vigorous and confident cooking. One reader was far from disappointed: 'a tremendous improvement over the last two years; the complicated dishes now seem to be coming together.' There is a lot to come together. Among half a dozen first courses there may be a fresh tuna and mussel tart served with a ginger butter sauce or home-made wild boar sausage on a purée of rice and onions with a port sauce. From the same number of main courses expect poached or steamed fillets of brill or grey mullet with the inevitable wild mushrooms. Not that David Everitt-Matthias overdoes the fungi. His menus and dishes are varied and balanced, and he strives to use every ingredient to effect. Grilled sea bass with a scallop and lobster sauce for one diner was 'out of this world'. There are now up to 25 Olivier cheeses. A catholic range and carefully chosen properties make a good wine list; prices are fair and there is a scattering of useful half-bottles. House wines start at £6.75.

CHEF: David Everitt-Matthias   PROPRIETORS: David and Helen Everitt-Matthias
OPEN: Mon to Sat, exc Sat L
CLOSED: 2 weeks Jun, 1 week at Christmas, bank hols
MEALS: 12.30 to 1.30, 7.30 to 9.30
PRICES: Set L £9.50 (£20) to £13.95 (£24), Set D £16.95 (£27) to £24 (£32)
CARDS: Access, Amex, Visa
SEATS: 34. Private parties: 26 main room. Children welcome. Smart dress preferred. Wheelchair access (1 step). Music. Air-conditioned

Mayflower

32–34 Clarence Street,
Cheltenham GL50 3NX   COOKING 1
CHELTENHAM (0242) 522426 and 511580   COST £18–£29

A visiting Londoner was surprised: 'the first decent Chinese restaurant outside London and Manchester I have experienced. Pricey by Soho standards, but portions are generous. Recommended for cynics like myself who think Chinese food is only good in Chinatown.' Though the menu is not innovative, the kitchen does very well. Crispy aromatic duck with pancakes was moist, perfectly cooked, with a fine crisp texture. Pancakes were slightly dry, the sauce like a better bottled variety. The kung po king prawns were cooked correctly with enough chilli, not too oily, though a touch sweet. Sizzling lamb has also been recommended. Generally, the garlic and chilli are not held back. The restaurant has expanded this year but apparently quality has not suffered. The wine list is a cut above the norm, with acceptable notes and some well chosen bottles. Dom Perignon is still very cheap and Marc Brédif's Vouvray, Ch. Kirwan 1983 and Torres' Gran Coronas are signs of a fair list indeed. House Mommessin is £5.75.

CHEF: H.S. Truong   PROPRIETORS: The Kong family
OPEN: all week, exc Sun L
CLOSED: 25 to 28 Dec
MEALS: 12 to 1.45, 5.45 to 10.45 (11.15 Fri and Sat)
PRICES: £14 (£24), Set L and D £12.50 (£18) to £17.50 (£24)
CARDS: Amex, Diners
SEATS: 80. Private parties: 30 private room. Vegetarian meals. Children welcome.
Wheelchair access (1 step; also unisex WC). Music. Air-conditioned

---

CHESTER Cheshire   map 5

Abbey Green ♀

2 Abbey Green, Northgate Street,
Chester CH1 2JH   COOKING 2
CHESTER (0244) 313251   COST £14–£22

The cobbled alley is tricky to find, and this vegetarian restaurant is poorly signposted. Its studied and casual, even amateurish, image seems out of keeping with the civilised surroundings of soft Victorian furnishings and classical music. Lunchtimes sees it packed with Chester's office workers. The menu and expert cooking uphold previous assessments. Ingredients are mostly organic though, says Duncan Lochhead, 'we do not see ourselves as a "Health Food" restaurant – just finding the best-tasting ingredients.' Dishes are well described and are marked if they can be prepared without dairy products. The sampler Abbey Green platter, 'a journey through the menu', can be illuminating for the uninitiated. A Camembert roulade with piquant fruit sauce, and a balanced carrot and courgette soup were well received. Eastern flavours are frequently tapped with the likes of stir-fried vegetables with tofu and mushrooms in black-bean sauce, or spiced banana balls with Indian spiced vegetables. 'The thali section of the platter was comparable with the best South Indian food I have eaten.' Rum and raisin cheesecake and apricot syllabub rated well, cheeses are big on flavour, white and dark chocolate roundels served with coffee were well appreciated. 'Crunchy apple and hazelnut slice came with a very zingy plum sauce, huge baked potato and two salads, one mixed and the other grated carrot in a creamy dressing. Not as imaginative as it could have been but tasty. Friendly and attentive staff – even cynical omnivores would warm to the non-cranky atmosphere.' Nearly a third of the 65 wines are organic, including the French house white (but not the red) at £6.50. The chatty list ventures the globe but France is particularly well represented with several country examples as well. CELLARMAN'S CHOICE: St Joseph, Clos de l'Arbalestrier, 1984, £17.20 (red), and £15.90 (white). The glass award recognises sterling support of organic viticulture, fair pricing, and careful choice for a short list.

See the back of the Guide *for an index of restaurants listed.*

CHEFS: Michael Davies, Kevin Woods and Julia Dunning
PROPRIETORS: Julia Dunning and Duncan Lochhead
OPEN: Mon to Sat
MEALS: 12 to 2.30, 6.30 to 10.15
PRICES: L £9 (£14), D £12 (£18)
CARDS: Access, Visa
SEATS: 55. 24 seats outside. Private parties: 8 main room, 24 private room. Car-park, 20
places. Vegetarian meals. Children's helpings. No-smoking area. Wheelchair access. Music

▲ *Arkle,*
Chester Grosvenor Hotel ♟

Eastgate Street, Chester CH1 1LT
CHESTER (0244) 324024

COOKING 3
COST £20—£65

Dining takes place not in a loose box but amidst Hollywood classicism
complete with columns and atrium. The prices confirm the grandeur. Writing
them out in full, for example, 'Nineteen Pounds and Ninety-Five Pence' for
beef fillet Rossini, hardly minimises their impact and may abash more people
than £19.95 in small type. For all that, seats are comfortable, space is generous,
the bar is satisfactory – complete with a pianist – and the staff is accessible,
informed and effective. Paul Reed has developed the Arkle into a thoroughbred
restaurant. Some may prefer a humble cob as needing less luxurious feed from
the markets of Paris and London, happy to subsist on local pastures, delivering
steadier, more robust performance, but reports have stressed the visible
quality. It starts with a trolley (gone the workaday basket) of breads – onion,
walnut, Vienna, rolls, Granary-style and more – cut for you as you wish. It
continues with a manageable *carte*, shorter lunch menus and a menu gourmand
recited to you by the restaurant manager. A pasta and cucumber salad with
lobster and shellfish dressed with a light mayonnaise and vinaigrette of the
correct balance to bring the whole to life, and a wild mushroom consommé
with duck which made up for any lack of funghal intensity by a heavy aroma of
marjoram and other herbs, show that the kitchen values flavour as well as
setting store by a certain lightness of touch. Main courses have also succeeded
in balancing tastes. A guinea-fowl is arranged on sauerkraut that neither
overpowers the poultry nor clashes with the dark red wine sauce; a baked joint
of sea bass, acceptably enriched with scallops and roast button onions, was also
married to red wine though here the balance was more tenuous as the
reduction had gone too far. As in all modern restaurants, layers abound:
sweetbreads are sandwiched between potato galettes, on a truffle butter sauce
with a scattering of asparagus tips, girolles and truffle – a good dish even if it
reads like 'How to spend your first million in a few short weeks'; and
mandatory layering occurs at dessert with a marquise between wafers of fine
chocolate puff pastry, a variation that pleased immensely. Visitors wishing to
moderate the cost should go at lunchtime when a good short choice is on offer.
The Brasserie, too, offers less expensive, faster meals. Wines are intelligently
handled by a sommelier who knows his stock. That it is best on French classics
is only to be expected. Other territories are not ignored, however, even if the
choices are predictable; the dozen Spanish reds are the most varied of these
sub-groups. Claret is the strongest suit, Léoville-Barton the longest run of

vintages, back to 1945. Prices can be excessive – a Sancerre at a few pence below £20 – but not invariably. Some of the mature clarets are more fairly costed within terms of reference that put on a hefty surcharge for luxury; the difficulty is recognising the fact. Range, too, has been considered so that there is enough below £12 to give everyone the semblance of choice. Burgundies present a more difficult choice than clarets; the sources are quite mixed and the order in which they are listed means close reading to discover the full range. Half-bottles are not stinted.

CHEFS: Paul Reed and Simon Radley   PROPRIETOR: Duke of Westminster
OPEN: Mon to Sat, exc Mon L
CLOSED: bank hols, 25 Dec to 1 Jan
MEALS: 12 to 2.30, 7 to 10.30
PRICES: £38 (£54), Set L £13.50 (£20) to £17.50 (£24), Set D £35 (£43)
CARDS: Access, Amex, Diners, Visa
SEATS: 40. Private parties: 10 main room. Car-park. Vegetarian meals by arrangement. Children's helpings. Smart dress preferred. No cigars/pipes in dining-room and no smoking during meals. Wheelchair access (also WC). Music at D. Air-conditioned
ACCOMMODATION: 86 rooms, all with bath/shower. Rooms for disabled. Lift. B&B £105 to £175. Children welcome. Baby facilities. Afternoon teas. Sauna. Air-conditioning. TV. Phone. Confirm by noon day before

---

CHILGROVE West Sussex   map 3

White Horse Inn 🍾

Chilgrove PO18 9HX   COOKING 2
EAST MARDEN (024 359) 219   COST £22–£36

One reader put it that Barry Phillips is 'besotted with wine'. Then, realising the implications, suggested, 'really keen on wine'. Certainly the old bottles, the bin-ends on window sills, and the wine racks tucked hither and yon proclaim the enthusiasm for wine, but food is given its due. The White Horse Inn is in a great setting with great views. It keeps its external character by means of ramblers and wisteria while indoors it is an upper-crust pub with log fires, high polish to the tables and beamed ceilings. Menu prices are set: one for lunch, one for weekday evenings and one for Saturday night. There is no stinting on choice: there are at least seven dishes at each stage and plenty of verbal updates on fish and special extras. Desserts are also recited. At night there is a 'surprise' middle course built into the meal. This is more than an amuse gueule and more than a sorbet. A quail salad or a haddock and lobster terrine are two examples. Neil Rusbridger's cooking has its traditional side – caviare and steak au poivre vert are unchanging extras to the menu – and more adventurous angles, such as first courses of avocado and prawn bavarois or oyster mushroom salad with tomato parfait. One reader not immediately taken by 'modern' cooking wondered what on earth he should eat to follow a breast of pheasant with a whisky and ginger sauce: 'A sorbet? Stilton and port wine?' Despite his bemusement, he returned for more. Simple dishes have been favourably reported: breast of wood pigeon with crisp mustard coating sliced into a fan around a good celeriac purée with simple gravy; roast Gressingham duck with the legs coming to table after a longer cooking; enjoyable vegetables. Fish is worthy: scallops with spinach and a vermouth cream sauce; haddock with asparagus and white wine sauce; sea bass with ginger and spring onions; good crab from Selsey. Desserts are acceptable, from a fresh pineapple pancake to a chestnut mousse cake or a home-made Grand Marnier ice-cream. These made up for perfunctory coffee, in the eyes of one reader, who found that each extreme of the meal was not up to the standard of the middle. The wine list defies summary. It is resplendent with runs of clarets, burgundies, Californians, Italians, hocks and Mosels. Age is no bar: there are a dozen clarets from 1945, plenty of 1971 Germans, burgundies from the 1950s and Californians back to 1970. Price may be a hindrance, but not due to greed. The price range is very fair, with eight house recommendations between £7.95 and £10.95 and 13 wines by the glass. Large parties can hold back until the time for vintage port and madeira when choice is as beguiling as it is for the rest of the list. There must be some impishness that drives Barry Phillips to omit Sancerre from his remarkable selection; perhaps he wants us to think about what would really be best. Advice is freely given. There have been times when the wine proves difficult to find, or changes have occurred that escaped notation on the list.

CHEF: Neil Rusbridger   PROPRIETORS: Dorothea and Barry Phillips and Neil Rusbridger
OPEN: Tue to Sat
CLOSED: 3 weeks Feb, 1 week Oct
MEALS: 12 to 2, 7 to 9.30 (10.30 during Chichester theatre season)
PRICES: Set L £15 (£22), Set D £20 (£28) to £22.50 (£30). Service 10%
CARDS: Access, Carte Blanche, Diners, Visa
SEATS: 65. Private parties: 30 main room, 12 and 30 private rooms. Car-park, 200 places.
Vegetarian meals. No cigars/pipes until all diners are on coffee. Wheelchair access
(also male and female WC). Music. Air-conditioned

CHINNOR Oxfordshire   map 2

Sir Charles Napier Inn 🍾

Sprigg's Alley, nr Chinnor OX9 4BX   COOKING 1
RADNAGE (0494) 483011   COST £19–£37

For a party that arrived early to fit in a walk in the Chilterns before the sun went down, the food was too good to hurry over, yet the service was considerate and prompt so as to ensure departure before dusk. The Inn is well sited and busy, making for a happy atmosphere, though smoky. Eating outside is the rule on sunny days at lunchtimes, and a short walk is *de rigueur* in any case – to view the livestock, the progeny of which might be supper tomorrow. Oxfordshire sandy and black boars, American bronze turkeys and plenty of chickens are reared by the Griffiths family, who also grow herbs and smoke meats: it sounds the good life. Lunchtime menus are cheaper than the main *carte*, giving opportunity for pasta and casseroled dishes that are ignored come the evening. The preponderance of game makes for an interesting choice: wild duck, venison, 'wild' boar or pheasant were balanced by veal or beef on one evening. The meats are generally cooked with assertive flavours: duck with citrus fruits and madeira, venison with blackberries and port, boar with prunes, orange and rosemary. There is game in the first courses, too, but the emphasis is more on fish, the smoked fish with caper and anchovy mayonnaise

247

being especially recommended, but Baltimore soft shell crabs, mussels, smoked salmon and fish soup also figure on the list. Puddings continue the interest, though niggles about coffee resurface. The wine list is very interesting. It refuses to ignore the newer countries while giving ample space to the classic regions. It is by no means overpriced and it includes decent growers. Age is taken into account in the USA with Heitz's Martha's Vineyard 1973, in Australia with Rouge Homme Cabernet Sauvignon 1978, and in claret and burgundy. Spain is generally better treated than Italy. There is a very fine run of Vouvrays. House wine is £7.50 and is a selection from the main list.

CHEF: Batiste Tolu   PROPRIETORS: The Griffiths family
OPEN: Tue to Sun, exc Sun D
MEALS: 12 to 2 (3 Sun), 7.30 to 10 (10.30 Fri and Sat)
PRICES: £23 (£31), Set L £12 (£19) to £15 (£23). Service 12.5%
CARDS: Access, Amex, Visa
SEATS: 65. 10 tables outside. Private parties: 45 main room, 25 and 45 private rooms. Car-park, 60 places. Vegetarian meals. Children's helpings (L only). No children under 7 at D. No cigars/pipes in dining-room. Wheelchair access. Music. Air-conditioned

---

CIRENCESTER   Gloucestershire   map 2

Tatyans

27 Castle Street, Cirencester GL7 1QD   COOKING 2
CIRENCESTER (0285) 653529   COST £15–£30

It melds so well with the vaguely conservationist shop fronts of Cirencester, and likewise so conforms to their floral interiors that the casual wanderer would not presume it a Chinese restaurant. To boot, it is a cut above many found in small provincial towns. The menu is short, mainly Peking, with Szechuan and sizzling dishes given top billing. Spicing is subtle and accurate, cooking minimal. The freshness of the ingredients and the good timing have been singled out. The wine list is short but uncommonly well chosen. Maybe it helps having a good wine merchant in the town. House wine: £7.50.
CELLARMAN'S CHOICE: Mas de Cadenet rosé 1988, £8.50; Riesling 'Heimbourg' 1987, Turckheim, £12.50.

CHEFS: Y. Liang and T.S. Wong   PROPRIETORS: Lookhot Ltd
OPEN: Mon to Sat, exc Sat L
MEALS: 12 to 2, 6 to 10.30
PRICES: £14 (£24), Set L £8.50 (£15), Set D £12.50 (£19) to £18 (£25)
CARDS: Access, Amex, Diners, Visa
SEATS: 60. Private parties: 60 main room. Children welcome. Wheelchair access (1 step)

'To follow, a turban of Dover sole fillets wrapped around scallops on a saffron sauce – the fish tough (old, I suspect the previous week's), scallops not even warm, sauce heavy on the butter, light on the saffron. I sent it back since the fish wasn't even opaque – and waited 20 minutes for a replacement. I naively imagined that the delay at least meant that the dish was being prepared from scratch again but no, the original duly reappeared – reheated. I was surprised (to put it politely) that any cook would reheat shellfish. Meanwhile the waitress duly poured red wine into my white.' On dining in Wiltshire

CLEEVE HILL Gloucestershire   map 2

▲ *Redmond's* ⬤

Cleeve Hill, Cheltenham GL52 3PR   COOKING 4
CHELTENHAM (0242) 672017   COST £21–£42

Opinion is unanimous that the improvements to the ground floor have
transformed this place. Gone are the poky bars and lounges with woodchip
paper. Instead, a pair of rooms, one for sitting, one for dining, that combine
light, colour, nice pictures and comfort in understated good taste. All these
changes – to an Edwardian house sitting high on the ridge above Cheltenham
with incomparable views to the Malvern hills – have done Redmond and
Pippa Hayward much good as well: the staff has increased in number and the
bedrooms provide some steady income. The menu offers four dishes per course
with an option of cheese, and coffee is included in the set price. The cooking is
of a high order, subtle yet simple. Almost every dish on a summer menu
contained an arresting flavour: horseradish 'rouille' with a smoked fish soup; a
rosemary sabayon with mushroom mousse; a shellfish and coriander sauce
with tortellini of crab; lemon grass and ginger with skate and scallops; red
cabbage spiked with cinnamon with marinated pigeon breasts. In another
season, it contained three spiced ice-creams: cardamom, cinnamon and cloves
united by a Marsala sabayon. These experiments with flavours are greeted with
praise. Indeed, the regret voiced is that the spicing is undetectable at times. A
potted oxtail set in its own jelly had a horseradish butter which needed more
fire to point up the gentle flavour of the meat. One reported dinner exposes the
strengths of the cooking. Tiny pizza and onion tarts began the episode. Then a
boned duck stuffed with a mousse of chicken and pigeon with chives and sage
was served with mixed salad leaves and the odd 'spaghetti' of carrot for colour
and texture; with it came a burgundy-coloured plum chutney. Next was a pink
fillet of lamb sliced into six medals in the centre of the plate. To one side was a
garlic and potato purée, to the other a thin parsley sauce. Both set the lamb off
exactly. The vegetables, a celeriac purée with grated carrots, new potatoes and
broccoli were well chosen and cooked to time. The dessert was a hot banana
soufflé, hot soufflés being a frequent if not inevitable item on the menu. It rose
two inches above the lip of the dish, crisp on top and soft within. With this was
served coconut ice-cream. Coffee with baby meringues, tuiles and truffles in
white chocolate baskets made a fitting end. Execution is rarely faulted and
timings are correct, if too short for some tastes on occasion. Difference of
opinion comes from the flavourings: too strong, not apt, too weak. The
argument is subjective and a matter of small degree. The achievement is that
Redmond Hayward's cooking makes people think about taste. The wine list is
a model. In the first place, halves are in a separate part and real effort has gone
into them. Second, the illustrations are either amusing or interesting. Third, the
notes really help without being prolix. Fourth, the prices are not greedy. Fifth,
the wines and the range are chosen with an eye to price, taste and quality,
without geographical prejudice. House wine: £9. CELLARMAN'S CHOICE:
Stewart Chardonnay 1987, £15.50; Ch. Tertre Rôteboeuf 1987, £18.75.

CHEF: John Redmond Hayward   PROPRIETORS: John Redmond and Pippa Hayward
OPEN: Mon to Sat D only, and Sun L (other days by arrangement)
CLOSED: first week Jan
MEALS: 12.30 to 2, 7.15 to 10
PRICES: Set Sun L £16 (£21), Set D £27 (£31) to £30 (£35). Service inc
CARDS: Access, Visa
SEATS: 36. Private parties: 24 main room, 12 private room. Car-park, 16 places. Children's
helpings on request. No children under 5. No smoking in dining-room
ACCOMMODATION: 5 rooms, all with bath/shower. B&B £40 to £60. Garden. TV. Phone.
Scenic. Doors close at midnight. Confirm by 6

CLITHEROE Lancashire   map 5

Auctioneer

New Market Street, Clitheroe BB7 2JW   COOKING 3
CLITHEROE (0200) 27153   COST £16–£31

It could be said that at Foxfields restaurant in its heyday, luxury took
precedence over quality. Now that its former chef, Henk Van Heumen, is his
own boss at this newly opened quasi-bistro overlooking the cattle market, the
emphasis has shifted. Simple furniture and almost austere surroundings are the
setting for the stylish à la carte lunches and set four-course dinners, the latter
with half a dozen choices in all but the second course. Few dishes show
abandon, however, as ingredients are simply handled. 'Very tasty' nibbles of
Dutch minced veal meat balls moistened with bechamel sauce set one reader
'in a good frame of mind for what was to follow.' He was not disappointed.
Texture as well as taste gets due consideration in a moist terrine of chicken
liver parfait studded with chicken and pistachio nuts. Another well-executed
combination that pleased was ceviche of fresh salmon on an orange and frisée
salad. Sorbet to clear the palate comes next, or else a soup which might be a
plain but clearly stated cream of watercress. An inspector was won over by the
maize-fed chicken with button mushrooms; it tasted of chicken, and Riesling
and lemon made an excellent sauce. Dutch apple pie, flaky and apple-
crammed, came freshly baked from the oven, and the chef's ice-cream parfait
was good ice-cream made interesting with nuts and fresh seasonal fruit. Bread,
vegetables and coffee and chocolates draw good reports, as does the
knowledgeable service from Frances Van Heumen. It's fine value, especially if
you steer clear of the several supplements. The wine list of 35 hardly
adventurous labels is at least modestly priced, with only two Champagnes
topping £20. House burgundy is £7.50. CELLARMAN'S CHOICE: Mâcon-
Peronne, Dom. du Bicheron, 1988, £11.25; St Véran, Dom. du Valanges, £11.75.
Theme evenings celebrate French regional food and wine or holidays such as
Good Friday with its 'feast of fish dinner'. Note: There is no connection
between this and the Auctioneer in Preston.

The Guide *relies on feedback from its readers. Especially welcome are reports on new
restaurants appearing in the book for the first time.*

▲ *This symbol means accommodation is available.*

CHEF: Henk Van Heumen PROPRIETORS: Henk and Frances Van Heumen
OPEN: Tue to Sun
MEALS: 12 to 1.30, 7 to 9.30
PRICES: £10 (£16), Set D £14.95 (£21) to £20 (£26)
CARDS: Access, Visa
SEATS: 44. Private parties: 10 main room, 22 and 24 private rooms. Children's helpings
(L only). Music

CLUN Shropshire   map 4

▲ *Old Post Office* ♥

9 The Square, Clun SY7 8JA   COOKING 2
CLUN (058 84) 687   COST £17–£34

Offa's Dyke was the Mercian king's rampart against the Cambrian hordes, and
modern walkers of the Dyke can find restoration and fuel at this last
gastronomic outpost of England before entering Powys. The situation is
desirable, the outlook from the terrace of this converted shop on the small
square is 'a jewel to set any English heart singing, a clutter of rooftops giving
way to the squat, square-set church and patchwork of fields and hills beyond'.
The Arbuthnots offer two simple rooms and substantial breakfasts, full of
energetic home baking to keep those walkers on the trail the day long. In the
restaurant, obviously once a shop towards the front but stretching quite deep
towards a small extension beyond a central drinking and sitting area, there is a
carte of half a dozen choices in each course at dinner and some 20 to 25 dishes of
first-course size for lighter, cheaper meals at lunch. Richard Arbuthnot's
approach is quietly inventive, though execution may not match the
expectations aroused by the description. It may read like the same old modern
English repertoire but touches give it distinction. Examples are asparagus tart
with spring onion sauce; lambs' sweetbreads or calf's liver with a whisky and
rosemary sauce: salmon with lentils, lardons and horseradish; venison with
damson and wine sauce; or a small appetiser of anchovy ice-cream. Nor is the
supporting cast of a meal ignored: the selection of breads (soda bread as well as
yeast doughs) and excellent butter; good salads, for example of lamb's leaves
alone, with nut oil dressings; a wide choice of British cheeses, 15 or more, all
properly identified and explained; and interesting desserts such as caraway
ice-cream; hazelnut and honey mousse with strawberry sauce; or lemon and
basil sorbet. Teas from Whittards are given equal billing with the cafetière
coffee from Suchard. The cooking pleases many, as does Anne Arbuthnot's
effective service, though the shortage of labour may mean a long meal on busy
nights. The wine list is consumer-friendly. It is none too long but choices have
been carefully made, especially in the lower price band. Only a dozen out of
more than 70 (disregarding Champagnes) cost more than £15: a sign of low
mark-ups and an effort to discover good cheaper wines. Raise the sights a little
and there are still bargains: Côte Rôtie 1980, Guigal at £18.90 or Ch. Fuissé
from Vincent 1986 at £18. The bulk are French, but the Australasians, from
Hugo, Mountadam and Rongopai, are worth noting. House wines: £6.95.
CELLARMAN'S CHOICE: Ch. Rouet, Fronsac 1983, £10.45; Côtes du Rhône,
Séguret Blanc 1988, Meffre, £10.

ENGLAND

CHEF: Richard Arbuthnot PROPRIETORS: Anne and Richard Arbuthnot
OPEN: Wed to Sun, exc Wed L
CLOSED: 1 week after Aug bank hol, 24 Dec to 3 Jan, 22 Jan to 14 Mar
MEALS: 12.30 to 1.30, 7.15 to 9.30
PRICES: L £10 (£17), D£19 (£28)
CARDS: Access, Visa
SEATS: 30. 2 tables outside. Private parties: 25 main room. Vegetarian meals. Children
welcome. No cigars/pipes in dining-room. Music
ACCOMMODATION: 2 rooms. B&B £38 (double only). Scenic. Doors close at midnight.
Confirm by 6 [Which? Hotel Guide]

COCKERMOUTH Cumbria   map 7

Quince and Medlar

13 Castlegate, Cockermouth CA13 9EU   COOKING 2
COCKERMOUTH (0900) 823579   COST £20

'Perhaps the best way to summarise it is not to say that it is good vegetarian
cooking; it is good cooking which happens to be vegetarian,' concludes one
report. Greater awareness about the arterial implications of animal fats, plus
the odd scare about beef, persuades more people that vegetarian food has a
place in an omnivore's diet. The numerically insubstantial ranks of doctrinaire
vegetarians have been swelled by large numbers of eaters concerned about a
balanced intake of food and the general state of their body. Quince and Medlar
displays the skills Colin Le Voi brought with him from Sharrow Bay (see entry,
Ullswater). The dining-room is slightly cramped and rather chintzy, but quite
comfortable. Some of the dishes would not look out of place in a cosmopolitan
brasserie: Stilton soufflé; terrine of young vegetables layered with chives,
cream and spinach with a red pepper sauce, or roasted aubergine soup; a
pancake made with soya flour and incorporating poppyseeds, spinach,
mushrooms and toasted cashew-nuts, served with a tomato and basil sauce.
There is also an imaginative mushroom and watercress roulade served with
asparagus sauce, or pecan and apricot ice-cream. Cooking is accurate, plates are
crowded, and side salads are piled high. 'I was favourably impressed, and shall
do what I can to see that it survives during the winter in a tourist town
surrounded by sheep farms.' Wines are rudimentary but include Hugh Rock's
elderflower and sparkling gooseberry, a brace of Greek bottles basking in the
Vegetarian Society's approval, and a dry organic German wine. House
wine: £5.50.

CHEF: Colin Le Voi PROPRIETORS: Colin and Louisa Le Voi
OPEN: Tue to Sun, D only
CLOSED: 2 to 3 weeks Jan to Feb
MEALS: 7 to 9.30
PRICES: £12 (£17). Minimum £8.50
CARDS: Access, Visa
SEATS: 26. Private parties: 14 main room. Vegetarian meals. Children restricted. Smart
dress preferred. No smoking in dining-room. Music

The Guide always appreciates hearing about changes of chef or owner.

252

Baumann's Brasserie

4–6 Stoneham Street, Coggeshall CO6 1TT   COOKING 1
COGGESHALL (0376) 561453   COST £15–£31

The livery is green and white, outside and in. The bar is centrally placed with
tables arranged all round it in a space once occupied by smaller rooms, their
partitions now a puff of dust. The overall effect is calming and pleasant, with
variety offered by pictures. More a restaurant than a brasserie, this was
founded by the late Peter Langan, and Mark Baumann was chef. He has
continued the business, leaving the look much as it was – lived in and not too
manicured – though the menu shows new tendencies towards florid language
and olde English script. Soup is 'summery', sauces are 'subtle', puff pastry is
'spilling' with haddock. The *carte* operates at lunch and dinner but the earlier
meal also offers a fairly priced, set menu chalked illegibly on a board. This is
recommended. Examples of cooking under the new regime have displayed
unevenness and a desire for complexity not always justified by results. Thus a
plate of grilled salmon and turbot with celeriac in a sorrel and green
peppercorn sauce sounds nearly good but in the event looked untidy and was
dominated by the celeriac flavour. Underneath it all, the fish was good. A
version of beef Wellington was overcooked with very tame 'wild' mushrooms.
First courses have shown similarly mixed results. The haddock spilling out of a
pastry case was enjoyable, if salty, but slices of Brie pan-fried then strewn with
toasted almonds and apple pieces was not so successful. Goats' cheese works,
Brie doesn't. Vegetables by contrast are handled very well indeed. Desserts
may include a chocolate truffle cake or strawberries with a glazed Champagne
sabayon. Bread or garlic bread comes at a price. The simplicity of the original
concept seems in danger of being submerged by over-elaboration, and less
variation in handling of flavours and more accuracy would help achievement of
self-set goals. The short wine list covers a fair range though perhaps with more
over £12 than is acceptable for a brasserie. An 'older vintages' sheet at the end
may reveal bargains. House French is £7.50. CELLARMAN'S CHOICE: Mâcon-
Burgy 1988, Goyard, £12; Châteauneuf-du-Pape, Dom. du Vieux Télégraphe
1985, £17.

CHEFS: Mark Baumann and Doug Wright   PROPRIETORS: Baumann's Brasserie Ltd
OPEN: Tue to Sun, exc Sat L and Sun D
MEALS: 12.30 to 2 (2.30 Sun), 7.30 to 10
PRICES: £18 (£26), Set L £9.85 (£15)
CARDS: Access, Amex, Diners, Visa
SEATS: 75. Private parties: 75 main room. Children's helpings. Music

---

'There are two dining-rooms: red for smokers, but no pipes or cigars please, and blue for
non-smokers. Only the blue was open, however, much to the chagrin of my companion
who muttered darkly. She also muttered darkly about other rules written in the folder, eg.
"Casual wear, such as jeans, corduroy, tee shirts and sweatshirts are not acceptable
evening wear" but "trouser suits for ladies may be worn and on hot nights men need not
wear a jacket"!' On dining in Scotland

COLCHESTER Essex   map 3

Warehouse Brasserie

12 Chapel Street North,
Colchester CO2 7AT   COOKING 1
COLCHESTER (0206) 765656   COST £19

'I went on what must have been the hottest day of the year and they had a party
of 45 shoe salesmen. No matter, the air-conditioning dealt with the heat and the
efficient staff coped with the boisterous foot men. Here they have Champagne
by the glass and the best lamb I have tasted in a restaurant. It is well above
average and wonderful for Colchester.' The formula, it seems, still works a
treat. It is an eclectic choice of dishes: deep-fried Camembert with a peach
chutney; chicken satay with cucumber; scallop and ham croustade; chargrilled
guinea-fowl with mushroom and green peppercorn sauce; lots of fish, often in a
Mediterranean style; even moussaka. To end, an old fashioned rice pudding,
tarte Tatin, banoffi pie or a steamed pudding. Occasionally popularity works
against it, and hurry causes bumps outside and hiccups inside the kitchen.
Daily changes to wines by the glass are on the blackboards, and orange juice is
fresh. The wine list offers two and a half dozen good bottles, not dear: Cloudy
Bay Sauvignon Blanc is £14.50. House wine: £5.95. CELLARMAN'S
CHOICE: Ch. de Monge 1985, £6.75.

CHEFS: Gerry Ford, Anthony Brooks, Karen Bussell and Stuart Mott
PROPRIETORS: Gerry and Jane Ford
OPEN: Mon to Sat
MEALS: 12 to 2, 7 to 10
PRICES: £11 (£16)
CARDS: Access, Visa
SEATS: 75. Private parties: 20 main room. Vegetarian meals. Children's helpings.
Wheelchair access (1 step). Air-conditioned

COLERNE Wiltshire   map 2

▲ *Lucknam Park*

COUNTY
OF THE
YEAR
RESTAURANT

Colerne SN14 8AZ   COOKING 3
CORSHAM (0225) 742777   COST £24–£80

This glorious house, approached by a fine avenue of trees, gap-toothed by
recent storms, got off to a bad start. During 1990 its kitchens have been taken
over by Michael Womersley and, although some experiences have been ill-
fated, others have been very fine indeed. The frame is sumptuous, though
careful to give that extra frisson of personality that induces total relaxation in so
grand a setting. The dining-room, complete with painted ceiling of gold-tinged
clouds, has floor-to-cornice windows flooding it with light. On offer is a set-
price menu of substantial cost and fair length. Nothing is cheap at Lucknam.
However, some would say it can be fair value. A warm salad of chargrilled,
steamed, and pan-fried Cornish fish with a red pepper sorbet, has grilled grey
mullet, fried red mullet, steamed sole and John Dory ranged round half a large
plate. In the centre, a scoop of sorbet – smooth and intense – with a caramel
touch from the initial grilling of the peppers, melts into a pepper and virgin oil

emulsion. The rest of the plate has a fan of frisée spiked with chives. The aroma, the contrasts in fish cooking and flavour, the condition of the raw materials, all make for a fine beginning that had already been presaged by excellent canapés. A main course of Gressingham duck with Sauternes sauce, peaches and figs was again faultless save that the sauce was nearly over-sweet given the composition of the whole. Vegetables arrive on the plate and vary according to the dish. A dessert of hot caramel soufflé with caramel ice-cream under a net of spun sugar, resting on a puddle of set caramel and a few crumbs of shortcrust, was both a well-executed soufflé and an interesting variation on the theme of caramel. Coffee was moderate, bread light but good, petits fours excellent. Had this meal been repeated every time, a high cooking mark would be imperative. Recent developments have led to a strengthening of the kitchen team which may bring about more consistent performance, for experiences in the spring were by no means always satisfactory. Service is hot on silver domes and generally willing, even pushy, when it comes to wine. The list is a document whose prices should be set in amber so high are they. The range is not a bad one and growers are often exemplary, but 300 per cent gross profit is not an encouragement to fine drinking, and too many of the wines carry that sort of mark-up. Too often we see places like this, where charges effectively exclude the general run of the population, lose their way and become submerged by the wrong priorities. Lucknam has already been through sticky times, if our reports are anything to go by. May Michael Womersley be allowed to do what he can do best.

CHEF: Michael Womersley   PROPRIETOR: Christopher Cole
OPEN: all week
MEALS: 12.30 to 2, 7.30 to 9.30
PRICES: Set L £16.50 (£24) to £21 (£28), Set D £31.50 (£39) to £60 (£67). Service inc
CARDS: Access, Visa
SEATS: 75. Private parties: 75 main room, 8 to 25 private rooms. Car-park, 70 places. Children's helpings. Smart dress preferred at D. No cigars in dining-room. Wheelchair access (also WC). Music
ACCOMMODATION: 39 rooms, all with bath/shower. Rooms for disabled. B&B £105 to £120. Baby facilities. Afternoon teas. Garden. Swimming-pool. Sauna. Tennis. Fishing. Snooker. TV. Phone. Scenic [*Which? Hotel Guide*]

CORSE LAWN   Gloucestershire   map 2

▲ Corse Lawn House Hotel ▮

Corse Lawn GL19 4LZ
TIRLEY (045 278) 479   COOKING 3
on B4211, 5m SW of Tewkesbury   COST £19–£42

The lawn is neither the house nor its garden, but the long common fringed by dwellings and trees that surrounds this tall red-brick Queen Anne building now balanced either side by new, highly conservationist, bedroom wings. From a restaurant with rooms to a full-scale hotel was the 10-year programme set by the Hines, achieved with but a two year overrun. All that remains is to knock off the rough edges, perhaps landscape the new land bought to protect

the peace and quiet, and run the show like they have always done. That means Denis Hine in the bar and restaurant, his ebullience spilling over, and Baba Hine working away in the kitchen. Their influence may be modulated by a larger and more reserved staff than before, and by Tim Earley's considerable help in the kitchen, necessary if they are to run all week. Corse Lawn has always felt more purpose-built than many of its country-house competitors, if only because the dining-room is indeed just that, but the core of the old house is still an enjoyable interior. Food is on offer in all departments: the bar is almost more popular at lunchtime, and meals are also served round the pond (once a coach-wash) at the front of the house on fine days. In the restaurant itself are two long menus, one fixed-price and one *carte*, composed for each meal, plus a separate one for vegetarians. The cooking is direct, with few excesses in view, and the simple descriptions mask both craft and subtlety. A meal at the beginning of the year began with mussels marinière well laced with cream, and a bavarois of smoked trout wrapped with home-smoked salmon. The delicacy of the salmon was almost toppled by the strength of the trout, though a squirt of lemon redressed the balance to advantage. The main courses were medallions of veal with foie gras and calf's kidney in a rich butter sauce of particular quality, acidulated to balance the richness of the butter. The vegetables with these – broccoli, a fennel tartlet, spinach and very good dauphinois potatoes – are a sign of the care usually taken with this stage, assuring a mixture of the plain and the artful. Desserts were a composite dish of strawberry ice-cream, sorbet and shortbread and a hot brochette of tropical fruit with brandy butter. This latter recalls other successes, such as a hot butterscotch sponge with its accompanying sauce or the prune and armagnac tart with meringue that had one reader promising himself a return visit. Cheese, a dozen English and a like number of French from Olivier, is more than enough for a savoury finish. Reservations have been heard mainly in relation to very busy nights which place the kitchen under strain, but none at all for the breakfasts, 'the perfectly ripe mango, with lime coulis, sure beats muesli or bran, and a fine kipper was followed by home-made brioche, blackcurrant juice and runny marmalade.' The wine list strikes a balance between France and the rest of the world and affords fair choice in clarets particularly. The burgundies show an affection for the big names of Latour, Sauzet, Leflaive, Ampeau and Faiveley. Prices are generally upbeat but several lower-priced wines, available by the glass, can ease the finances. House Bordeaux: £7.50.
CELLARMAN'S CHOICE: Ch. Beaumont, Haut Médoc 1983, £18.80; Sauvignon de Touraine, Dom. des Maisons Brûlées 1987, £13.50.

CHEFS: Baba Hine and Tim Earley   PROPRIETORS: Baba and Denis Hine
OPEN: all week
MEALS: 12.30 to 2, 7 to 10
PRICES: £27 (£35), Set L £15.50 (£19), Set D £22.50 (£26). Service inc
CARDS: Access, Amex, Diners, Visa
SEATS: 45. 8 tables outside. Private parties: 55 main room, 24 and 35 private rooms. Carpark, 50 places. Vegetarian meals. Children's helpings. Wheelchair access (also WC)
ACCOMMODATION: 19 rooms, all with bath/shower. Rooms for disabled. B&B £60 to £85. Baby facilities. Pets welcome. Afternoon teas. Garden. Swimming-pool. Tennis. TV. Phone. Scenic. Doors close at midnight. Confirm by 6 [*Which? Hotel Guide*]

COSHAM Hampshire   map 2

Barnards

109 High Street, Cosham PO6 3BB   COOKING 2
COSHAM (0705) 370226   COST £14–£29

Cosham High Street is not the most prepossessing of spots and the stranger's
heart may sink when negotiating the traffic towards this small front-room
restaurant which even shares the owners' bathroom upstairs. David Frank
Barnard cooks his heart out and deserves every success. The setting is not grand
but the tables are neat, the flower arrangements pretty, Mrs Barnard solicitous
and the sounds of much hand-whisking in the background encouraging. There
is a short *carte* at dinner and lunch is set price (and very reasonable) with a
choice of three dishes at each stage. The menus are in French with English
subtitles – play at spotting the inevitable mistake or filling in the accents – and
there is a complementary sorbet of Earl Grey or lemon (not brilliant) after the
first course. These are two signs of cooking of the last decade but there are
others which show more current awareness: light sauces with flavours distinct
yet not bludgeoning, good vegetable cookery, a new ice-cream machine. The
range of ingredients chimes with Cosham's tastes, not London's, but diners are
impressed by the skill and effort shown in salmon with a dill cream sauce;
ravioli of crab and tomato with a tomato sauce; fillet steak with a chicken
mousse that sounds weird (a combination of dietary horror stories) but worked
out well because of the brave seasoning and flavour of the chicken mousse –
even if the madeira sauce was over strong; a good strawberry mousse complete
with biscuit basket and spun sugar dome. Amuse-gueule and petits fours, if
not the bread, show that commitment to handicraft allied to good taste runs
through all departments of the venture. The wine list remains short, French
(with some bottles from Yapp and Jadot burgundies) and inexpensive. House
French: £6.75. CELLARMAN'S CHOICE: Sancerre 1988, Vatan, £12.25; Ch.
Lamothe 1985, £10.95. Service is included in the price and that's it.

CHEF: David Frank Barnard   PROPRIETORS: Mr and Mrs D.F. Barnard
OPEN: Tue to Sat, exc Sat L
MEALS: 12 to 2, 7.30 to 10
PRICES: £19 (£24), Set L £10.95 (£14). Service inc
CARDS: Access, Visa
SEATS: 20. Private parties: 20 main room. Children's helpings. Wheelchair access. Music.
Air-conditioned

COUNTESTHORPE Leicestershire   map 5

Old Bakery

Main Street, Countesthorpe LE8 3QX   COOKING 1
LEICESTER (0533) 778777   COST £13–£25

What was once a bakery is now a restaurant recommended for its steady
performance and value, especially at lunch. The execution is traditional
English in dishes such as grapefruit segments with blackcurrant sorbet;
mushrooms in garlic butter; veal Marengo; home-made game pie (but in the

summer?); and traditional puddings with custard. The wine list, prepared by G.E. Bromley of Leicester, is estimable for choice of decent bottles, mostly priced at below £10. House French: £6.25. CELLARMAN'S CHOICE: Ch. Ferrasses 1983, £9.75; Ch. la Courançonne, Côtes du Rhône Blanc 1988, £9.50.

CHEF: R. Gilbertson   PROPRIETORS: R. Gilbertson, P. Chivers and G. Turner
OPEN: Tue to Sun, exc Sat L and Sun D
MEALS: 12.15 to 1.45 (2.15 Sun), 7 to 9 (9.45 Fri and Sat)
PRICES: Set L £8.95 (£13), Set Sun L £9.95 (£14), Set D £15.50 (£21)
CARDS: Access, Visa
SEATS: 50. Private parties: 50 main room. Car-park, 20 places. Vegetarian meals. Children welcome. Smart dress preferred. Wheelchair access (also WC). Music

---

CRANLEIGH Surrey   map 3

Restaurant Bonnet

| High Street, Cranleigh GU6 8AE | COOKING 2 |
| CRANLEIGH (0483) 273889 | COST £17–£32 |

The restaurant, once a wine bar, is hardly the place that would be expected to serve French food, even Surrey French, for it looks more like Surrey Olde Englishe. But Jean Pierre Bonnet, who cooks in the refitted gleaming kitchen, and his wife Ann, produce a long menu at a set price, higher in the evenings than at lunch. Some question whether the change in hours entirely justifies the change in cost even though an aperitif and a half-bottle of house wine are included in the dinner price. There has been guarded approval for the cooking, though occasional reflection that the tastes are muted. Salmon and leek terrine with truffle sauce is one style, while potted pork and lentils represent an earthier aspect of French tradition. Fillet of pork on a bed of onions; monkfish with a delicate red pimento sauce; pan-fried chicken breast with smoked bacon are some main dishes that have been noticed, and a good mille-feuille and an imaginative chocolate terrine with fruit among the desserts. Meringue in an *île flottante* and a tarte Tatin where the most interesting thing was the garnish, have not been so successful. More worrying have been comments about abruptness on the part of the staff and management, of an unwillingness to serve children's portions, and difficulties with wine stocks. A good start last year seems to have developed into a slightly irritated inconsistency. House French: £7.50.

CHEF: Jean Pierre Bonnet   PROPRIETORS: Jean Pierre and Ann Bonnet
OPEN: Tue to Sun, exc Sat L and Sun D
MEALS: 12 to 2, 7 to 10
PRICES: Set L £12.50 (£17) to £14 (£19), Set D £22.50 to £26.50
CARDS: Access, Amex, Visa
SEATS: 50. Private parties: 35 main room. Smart dress preferred. No pipes in dining-room. Wheelchair access (1 step). Music

---

denotes an outstanding wine cellar; *denotes a good wine list, worth travelling for. See the Introduction for a fuller explanation.*

All letters to the Guide *are acknowledged with an update on latest sales, closures, chef changes and so on.*

CROYDE Devon   map 1

▲ *Whiteleaf* ♥

Croyde EX33 1PN   COOKING 2
CROYDE (0271) 890266   COST £28

Only residents and their guests may eat at David and Flo Wallington's guest-house, which often surprises by the scale and ambition of the cooking. A captive audience helps David Wallington plan his work, but he is singular among guest-house proprietors in that he maintains a much wider choice, divided between a standing menu and a daily list of specials. He is also something of a magpie of recipes and dishes: he had cooked at least three dozen soups during a six-month period. There are perhaps two emphases in his cooking: English and Italian. Englishness is apparent in the generous treatment of vegetables as well as in first courses such as Herefordshire brawn with pickled vegetables; relishes like Grandmother Drew's Dittisham plum; or main courses of rabbit pie or stewed rabbit with parsley dumplings. Italian propensities, evident immediately in the wine list, emerge in pasta e fagioli, zuppa al pavese, turkey Bolognese or chicken wrapped with Parma and stuffed with mozzarella and Parmesan. Would that all guest-houses went in for home-made bread, fresh orange juice and such meals. The fairly priced wine list matches the food for enthusiasm. A page of clarets and a run round the main French regions is offered before a refreshingly serious two dozen Italians, including a 1961 Barolo from Borgogno and a 1962 Chianti from Badia. House Duboeuf: £6.85. CELLARMAN'S CHOICE: St. Joseph, Clos de l'Arbalestrier 1983 (red) and 1985 (white) E. Florentin, £11.30.

CHEF: David Wallington PROPRIETORS: David and Florence Wallington
OPEN: all week, D only (residents and their guests only)
MEALS: 7.30 to 8.30
PRICES: Set D £20 (£23). Service inc
CARDS: Access, Visa
SEATS: 16. Car-park, 10 places. Children's helpings. Smart dress preferred
ACCOMMODATION: 5 rooms, all with bath/shower. B&B £29 to £48; D,B&B £40. Deposit: £25. Baby facilities. Pets welcome. Garden. TV. Phone. Scenic. Doors close at midnight. Confirm by 7 [*Which? Hotel Guide*]

CROYDON Surrey   map 3

Hockneys

98 High Street, Croydon CR0 1ND   COOKING 1
081-688 2899   COST £8–£16

Part of the Croydon Buddhist Centre, together with Hockneys Wholefood, the restaurant is vegetarian and has for some years been one of the more adventurous exponents of the form. Lunch is cheaper than dinner, when waiter service operates. The daily menu, changed at every meal, offers perhaps four main courses with numerous supporting items. These include dishes such as Kythera, a soya, mushroom and tomato loaf with a tomato sauce, served with an apricot pilau, fennel and orange salad and a mint raita; or Wu Tai, tofu fritters, a casserole of Chinese mushrooms and ginger, with noodles and pickled vegetables. Sweets are mainly based on home-made ice-creams. Although much of the cooking is influenced by the Far East, there is also a Mediterranean strain in lasagnes, moussakas and risottos, as well as a dash of the modern in the broccoli custard pie with deep-fried Camembert and a blackcurrant sauce. There is live music occasionally, including a South American harpist. Wine drinkers can bring their own; beer drinkers can bring three cans.

CHEF: Simon Beckett   PROPRIETORS: Rainbow (Croydon) Ltd
OPEN: Tue to Sat
CLOSED: 1 week Christmas, Good Fri, Easter Mon
MEALS: noon to 5.30, 5.30 to 10
PRICES: L £6 (£8), D £10 (£13). Unlicensed, but bring your own: corkage £1.50 per bottle
CARDS: Access, Amex, Diners, Visa
SEATS: 80. Private parties: 80 main room. Vegetarian meals. Children's helpings. No smoking in dining-room. Music

34 Surrey Street

| 34 Surrey Street, Croydon CR0 1RJ | COOKING 1 |
| 081-681 3316 and 686 0585 | COST £31 |

Set in the Surrey Street Market, its conservatory bar complete with pianist or trio and soft-covered sofas, this is a theme restaurant with confidence and some style. A laid-back yet well informed and motivated staff, a hotch-potch of tables and chairs, and eclectic objets trouvés on the walls contribute to a good atmosphere, even if service is slow on really busy nights. The main feature is fresh exotic fish, of which there are between 10 and 20 varieties available, flown in chilled but not frozen. Florida Bay bass, red snapper, mahi-mahi and barracuda were taken by one party in the winter; on another night, half the specials were warm-water, the rest were monkfish, halibut, sole, prawns and lobster. The fish are usually marinated, for instance in oil, herbs, garlic and red wine for monkfish, then char-grilled. These simple things are worth trying; some of the sauced items may suffer from lack of finesse though, with the fish, the ingredients are sound. Salads, vegetables and desserts are par for the course. Pecan pie has been found good. The wine list, with much imported direct from California, offers a fair fistful of France as well, at acceptable prices. Mirassou Vineyards are a major Californian item, but there are also bottles from Leeward and Dry Creek. Of French bottles, look for Chablis from Collett and Beaujolais from Trichard. House French and Californian: £6.95 and £7.95. More reports, please.

CHEFS: Scott Archibald, Neil Tyson, Steve Hughes and Wayne Seaton
PROPRIETOR: Harry Coelho
OPEN: all week, exc Sat L
CLOSED: most bank hols, 25 Dec
MEALS: 12 to 2.45, 7 to 10.45
PRICES: £18 (£26). Service 12% for parties of 5 or more
CARDS: Access, Amex, Diners, Visa
SEATS: 80. Private parties: 100 main room; 60 and 100 private rooms. Vegetarian meals. Children's helpings. Wheelchair access (also WC). Music

CRUDWELL Wiltshire   map 2

▲ Crudwell Court

Crudwell SN16 9EP   COOKING 1
CRUDWELL (066 67) 355 or 7194   COST £23–£32

This small hotel in a former rectory house has merits and demerits. High among the first are: the building itself, of wonderful stone and slate; its site, with walled gardens overlooking the church; its plain and refreshing redecoration; the happy reception by owner Brian Howe; and the relative cheapness of its food served in a double, half-wainscoted dining-room with comfortable wicker chairs. Demerits may run to adequate but not outstanding service; a propensity to decorate plates of food with meaningless trimming; and a failure to think equally about all the parts of the meal so that ancillaries are not as good as the core. None the less, enthusiastic reports have been received for a menu that has worryingly lengthened in recent months. It has some simple dishes: soft roes poached in wine with cream and tarragon, or saddle of lamb on a tomato and garlic cream sauce. It has the more complex, too: sole fillet with a salmon soufflé on a ginger sauce or chicken with a prawn mousse on a brandy and crayfish sauce. Usually the frills come in trimmings of courgette balls or strips, or even carrot strips. A 'turbot mousseline on a dill cream sauce' had fine texture (and mystifyingly included pieces of salmon) and a good deep sauce (of fennel, not dill). Breast of pigeon was well handled, with a simple blackcurrant sauce. Desserts have had less satisfactory comment but are often good substantial English puddings. The wine list is compiled with help from Remington Norman, MW. It has a fair spread and is not excessively priced, though never cheap. The price range means that there is plenty at single figures though halves are rather sparse. House wine: £7.50. CELLARMAN'S CHOICE: Savennières, Clos St Yves 1987, Baumard, £11.50; Côtes du Rhône 1988, La Vieille Ferme, £9.

CHEF: Paul Lawrence   PROPRIETORS: Brian and Susan Howe
OPEN: all week, exc Sat L
MEALS: 12.30 to 1.45, 7.30 to 9.30
PRICES: Set L and D £15.50 (£23) to £18.95 (£27)
CARDS: Access, Amex, Diners, Visa
SEATS: 50. 6 tables outside. Private parties: 50 main room, 20 private room. Car-park, 40 places. Children's helpings on request. Wheelchair access (also WC)
ACCOMMODATION: 15 rooms, all with bath/shower. B&B £47 to £70. Deposit: £50. Baby facilities. Pets welcome, exc in public rooms. Afternoon teas. Garden. Swimming-pool. TV. Phone. Scenic. Doors close at midnight [Which? Hotel Guide]

Prices quoted in the Guide are based on information supplied by restaurateurs. The figure in brackets below an entry is the average for a three-course meal with service, coffee and half a bottle of house wine, as calculated by computer. The prices quoted at the top of an entry represent a range, from the lowest average meal price to the highest; the latter is inflated by 20 per cent to take account of the fact that very few people eat an average meal, and also that prices are likely to rise during the year of the Guide.

CUCKFIELD   West Sussex   map 3

▲ Jeremy's at the King's Head

South Street, Cuckfield RH17 5VY   COOKING 3
HAYWARDS HEATH (0444) 440386   COST £25–£34

In one section of the pub, on the corner of the lane leading down to the church, Jeremy Ashpool has an independent franchise on two dining-rooms and a kitchen. Accommodation, bars and bar food are the preserve of the landlord. Surroundings are spartan but there is symbiosis between the bare boards and the rudimentary gloss given to presentation of fairly priced food that is high on taste and freshness, though variable at times. Two thick tender pieces of pigeon that sat on a hillock of saffron rice and mushrooms were given a striking balsamic vinegar and walnut sauce; haddock mousseline was lifted by a lime and ginger dressing; three pieces of rabbit were served with noodles and an excellent sauce of fried aubergine, cider and mustard; vegetables are simple – grated carrot with orange juice, plain potatoes and crisp green beans. The menu is invariably short, set-price at dinner but individually priced at lunch. In contrast the list of sweets is long, from sticky toffee pudding to gutsy prune and armagnac ice-cream. Materials are very carefully bought and fish is excellent. Flavours are assertive, nearly strident. Enthusiasm may occasionally lead to over-enthusiastic technique, but the value and invention are considerable. The short wine list is good value: all French with some Spanish, Australian and Lebanese reds, but customers seeking adventure will go unrewarded. The base price is £9, but most bottles are under £15.

CHEF: Jeremy Ashpool   PROPRIETOR: Peter Tolhurst
OPEN: Tue to Fri
CLOSED: bank hols
MEALS: 12.30 to 2, 7.30 to 10
PRICES: £17 (£25), Set D £19.50 (£28). Service 10% for parties of 6 or more
CARDS: Access, Amex, Visa
SEATS: 33. Private parties: 20 main room. Children welcome. Wheelchair access
ACCOMMODATION: 9 rooms, 8 with bath/shower. B&B £37 to £49. Baby facilities. Pets welcome. Garden. TV. Confirm by 6 [Which? Hotel Guide]

▲ Ockenden Manor

Ockenden Lane, Cuckfield RH17 5LD   COOKING 1
HAYWARDS HEATH (0444) 416111   COST £22–£43

A Tudor and seventeenth-century original, the house is run as a small hotel within sight of Cuckfield church. The dining-room has aspects of the posh, as in the silver-plate domes that come atop the main courses, but a lot of the cooking has an earthier approach, rather like adventurous home cooking. This means that suave finish may not be there, but flavours can be enjoyable. Service, too, may have pretension but the staff do not know what's on the cheese trolley, and one reader described some members as apparently 'male au pairs'. The menu offers five or six items per course, at a set price that changes according to the number of courses consumed. It has a nouvelle British tinge, in the combination of flavours, as in chicken on a ginger and mint sauce; lamb with a raspberry confit; salmon with orange and pink peppercorns; fillet of lemon sole grilled with walnuts on a mulberry vinegar sauce, or red snapper with a lavender sauce. Fruit is never far distant: calf's liver with spring onion and port confit gets extras of a mint leaf and some blackcurrants. That said, the flavours are not left to be mimsy and the result can be palatable even though excessively sweet-and-sour. Desserts are really cheerful: a banana cheesecake with a banana sauce was almost health food, and a stiff marquise came with a coarse orange sauce that brought it to life. Good growers, properties and vintages abound on the wine list; but with Sancerre at £19, drinking of any quality does not come cheap. There is virtually nothing below £13, apart from Duboeuf house wines at £8.50. CELLARMAN'S CHOICE: Chablis, Dom. des Valery 1988, Durup, £19.95.

CHEF: Philip Guest   PROPRIETORS: Mr and Mrs H.N.A. Goodman
OPEN: all week
MEALS: 12.30 to 2, 7.30 to 9.15 (9.30 Sat if busy)
PRICES: Set L £15.50 (£22) to £16.50 (£23), Set D £21.95 (£29) to £28 (£36)
CARDS: Access, Amex, Diners, Visa
SEATS: 50. Private parties: 30 main room, 70 private room. Car-park, 40 places. Vegetarian meals. Children's helpings. Smart dress preferred. No smoking in dining-room. Wheelchair access (also unisex WC)
ACCOMMODATION: 22 rooms, all with bath/shower. B&B £65 to £135. Deposit: £25 per person for weekend breaks. Afternoon teas. Garden. TV. Phone. Scenic. Doors close at 11.30. Confirm by 6 [Which? Hotel Guide]

DALLINGTON East Sussex   map 3

▲ *Little Byres*

COUNTY OF THE YEAR RESTAURANT

Christmas Farm, Battle Road,
Dallington TN21 9LE   COOKING 3
BRIGHTLING (042 482) 230   COST £17–£34

Ignore the sign saying 'Motel' noticed by visitors last year. It's more than that. Chris and Evelyn Davis accepted the offer of a job in France, didn't like it, married and returned to buy the place they had run for the last two or three years. Little Byres is so called because it is a converted barn and cow shed (the bedrooms are in the byres). Agricultural hangovers survive: overnight guests emerge to be greeted by geese and ducks. The barn makes a good dining space, winter and summer. In the cold, the wood stove crackles; in the heat, the giant double doors encourage a draught. Beams, rafters and brick in the great space are softened by fabrics and put in human context by the skills of hospitality and ingenuous charm of Evelyn Davis – and sometimes by her husband, who may come out from the kitchen if advice on wine is needed. Menus are a set price and offer five dishes in each course, with cheese before dessert. The price includes coffee. Chris Davis takes a deal of care with his supplies: cheese, fish, vegetables and speciality meats are as good as any in England. His style of cooking, reflecting perhaps a Sussex strain exemplified by John Kenward (whose restaurant, Kenwards, has closed) and Jeremy Ashpool (still going strong, see Cuckfield), relies on fine materials setting each other off on the plate, or speaking for themselves without too much underpinning from heavy

ENGLAND

sauing. Thus poached turbot was balanced by fat mussels and Florence fennel and no more than the poaching liquid. This may be a risky procedure since the dish may need drawing together to avoid dullness, but it shows courage. At the same meal, a roast partridge with a red wine sauce, chestnuts and caramelised red cabbage succeeded entirely, the cabbage being exactly the correct vehicle and accent. Vegetables show artistry: at one meal a butternut squash and a Jerusalem artichoke were both hollowed out and filled with their own purée, and the cooking gave the correct balance of resilience and tenderness. The flavours of these vegetables showed, too, the skill of buying. First courses may have some emphasis on fish. Certainly salmon marinated with basil, lime and olive oil was eloquently fresh yet given sufficient life by the seasoning, and a parsley soup with a fricassee of shellfish had fine herb flavour, if slightly imbalanced by too much seafood. Other dishes that have been extolled include a salad of wild mushrooms and foie gras with a nut dressing; a light tart of Roquefort and leeks with a pea and walnut salad; saddle of venison with mushroom ravioli, crisp parsnips and a wine sauce; sea bass with a mussel sauce; squab with a roulade of cabbage and pulses; good French cheeses including a Brie soaked in calvados and several goats' cheeses; a Fontainebleau with raspberries; and a 'chocolate collection' that almost defeated a most serious eater of chocolate who found but one, a chocolate mint sorbet, with which he disagreed. Baking is well executed. Pastry is best seen in a warm apricot tart, intended to be served with a mango purée but in fact given an over-strong raspberry coulis. Chris Davis achieves almost singlehandedly all the expected ancillaries, such as crudités and petits fours, with panache. The wine list is not long, is carefully chosen, but contains no halves save the house wine, a Champagne and some pudding wines. It is French, with half a dozen Australian, very fairly priced, and some good bottles of high renown, many from Corney & Barrow. House wine is £6.95. CELLARMAN'S CHOICE: Cloudy Bay, Sauvignon Blanc 1989, £16.50; Bourgogne Blanc, Les Sétilles 1987, Olivier Leflaive, £12.60.

CHEFS/PROPRIETORS: Chris and Evelyn Davis
OPEN: Mon to Sat D
MEALS: 7 to 9.30
PRICES: Set D £16.50 (£21) to £22.50 (£28)
CARDS: Access, Diners, Visa
SEATS: 35. Private parties: 40 main room, 20 private room. Car-park, 18 places. Children's helpings. Wheelchair access (also WC). Music
ACCOMMODATION: 5 rooms, all with shower. Rooms for disabled. B&B £25 to £40 Deposit: £25. Pets welcome. TV. Scenic. Confirm at least 24 hours ahead

DARLINGTON Co Durham   map 7

Victor's

84 Victoria Road, Darlington DL1 5JW   COOKING 1
DARLINGTON (0325) 480818   COST £11–£25

The Robinsons have figured in the last five *Guides* and continue to offer inexpensive lunches and more elaborate dinners on a fixed price menu. The four-course dinners include a soup or sorbet after the first course and coffee comes at no extra charge. The restaurant itself, a former shop premises, is low key, not to say basic, in greys and pinks. The kitchen makes a creditable stab at self-sufficiency with home-made rolls, biscuits for cheese, petits fours and so on, some of which are pleasant indeed although one reader did question whether careful shopping may not sometimes produce better results on the biscuits – but where do you do the careful shopping? The cooking explores some familiar but enjoyable avenues such as a tomato and black olive tart; a marinated trout with fresh ginger; braised beef with hazelnut stuffing; lambs' sweetbreads with bacon and mushrooms and cream; lemon sole fillets stuffed with crab and served with a cheese sauce. Execution, however, may lack a certain finesse and the flavours may not be sufficiently thought through. Coffee is percolated; tea is a bag; cheese is often good and local but not invariably up to the mark. All in all it offers value for money, sensationally so at lunchtime. One reader who had had to get the lights switched on and the doors unlocked when they turned up at a 7.20 for a 7.30 booking, observed that Peter Robinson's sense of humour is 'unique'. A short unambitious wine list is at least cheap.

CHEFS: Peter and Jayne Robinson and Trudie Doig
PROPRIETORS: Peter and Jayne Robinson
OPEN: Tue to Sat
MEALS: 12 to 2.30, 7 to 10.30
PRICES: Set L £6.50 (£11), Set D £16 (£21)
CARDS: Access, Amex, Diners, Visa
SEATS: 26. Private parties: 26 main room. Vegetarian meals. Children's helpings. Wheelchair access (2 steps). Music

---

DARTMOUTH Devon   map 1

▲ *Billy Budd's*

7 Foss Street, Dartmouth TQ6 9DW   COOKING 1
DARTMOUTH (0803) 834842   COST £11–£29

'Genial conviviality ... the atmosphere of a really good bistro ... great fun.' That is the feel that Gilly White engineers without appearing to try. She is helped by some standard accoutrements – rough white walls, wine racks, big baskets of French bread and a blackboard for aperitifs and desserts – but in the end it comes down to the personal style. Cheery advice and good humour fly about like feathers at a pillow fight. Keith Belt's cooking suits the mood: simple, familiar and as ambitious as it needs to be. Camembert fritters, onion soup and salade niçoise may have been done to death, but he does these simple dishes well. A hot twice-baked soufflé – cooked, up-ended, refrigerated, and brought back to life with Gruyère, Parmesan and cream – is full of flavour. Lamb sweetbreads are full of garlic. Brill, John Dory, English fish chowder with aïoli and garlic croûtons, and a turban of sole wrapped around a cranium of scallops, make the most of the location. Desserts can be as solid as sticky toffee pudding or as light and springy as a strawberry-filled chocolate sponge. Minor niggles get swallowed up in the general camaraderie. Wines are of a piece with the food and ambience: fair prices and decent.

CHEF: Keith Belt   PROPRIETORS: Gilly White and Keith Belt
OPEN: Tue to Sat
CLOSED: Feb
MEALS: 12 to 1.30, 7.30 to 10
PRICES: £6 (£11), Set D £15.50 (£22) to £17.50 (£24)
CARDS: Access, Visa
SEATS: 35. Private parties: 20 main room. Vegetarian meals on prior notice. Children's helpings. No children under 9 at D. Wheelchair access (1 step). Music
ACCOMMODATION: 2 rooms. B&B £14.50. TV

Carved Angel 🍾

2 South Embankment, Dartmouth TQ6 9BH	COOKING 4
DARTMOUTH (0803) 832465	COST £28−£47

'If I fall off my perch tomorrow I shall die a happy man,' wrote one who had finally eaten at the Carved Angel and met Joyce Molyneux, describing her cooking as 'having the stamp of individuality and understated simplicity combined with weight of experience and empathy with ingredients. My impression is that risks are taken not by piling one taste on another but by pulling back as far as possible yet still making the dish sing.' Two fellow restaurateurs from distant parts of the country add their tributes: 'what a restaurant should be − brilliant, calm, unstuffy' and 'so right, stylish but unpretentious, no nostalgia.' The Angel's uncurtained windows gaze impassively across the Dart to Kingswear; inside, St Michael − carved in wood − surveys the relaxed simplicity of the restaurant and its open-plan kitchen, 'surprisingly well ordered and, despite the feverish activity, the sounds are comforting rather than distracting.' The lack of division between restaurant and kitchen applies also to the staff, so that waiters and waitresses, familiar with the food and its preparation, are generally knowledgeable as well as friendly, and only occasionally slow and lacking finesse. There is no bar (the upstairs room is used for parties) and aperitifs are sipped at table, along with fine olives and nibbles − and, too often reported this year, other diners' cigarette smoke. New British cooking can probably be best translated as eclectic, and Joyce Molyneux is that; but above all she is original and innovative in her own right, in her adaptations of traditional recipes and in her unique combinations of flavours. She inspires willing suspension of distrust in even chary eaters-out: here, if anywhere, is the place to risk lobster jelly with sour cream; roast lamb with laver sauce and turnips; salmon with rhubarb and Champagne; John Dory with a sorrel mousseline and saffron sauce; hot nectarine brioche with basil ice-cream; or crème brûlée with prunes and armagnac. Disciples who have followed her from Bath's Hole in the Wall will find old favourites − salmon in pastry with ginger and currants, for example, served with a herb cream sauce, or St-Emilion au chocolat, which often appears on 'a plate of chocolate puddings', alongside orange charlotte, coffee truffle and a chocolate ice. The unstuffiness of her approach shows in the menu, where dishes are named and simply described in English: Dittisham asparagus with melted butter; a plate of home-made charcuterie with spiced fruit; guinea-fowl marinated with orange and thyme, chargrilled and served with Sauternes sauce and carrot tart; oatmeal-snap basket with tropical fruit. As well as the obvious inspiration of the Mediterranean, seen in the love of garlic, chillies, saffron, oil and southern vegetables, there is an overlay of British affection for spices, pickles and strong fruity flavours, with a bold approach to saucing and seasoning. Alongside these vibrant flavours is the understatement shown in, for example, the treatment of many fish and vegetables, where the materials are allowed to speak for themselves. Diners not necessarily on the same wavelength may find their expectations confounded: a fish soup too thin and not fishy enough, vegetables lacking zest. But few fail to appreciate the quality of the raw materials, the c..re with which they are treated, and the generosity with which they are served: a plate of small and succulent Dartmouth prawns, with a mound of buttery potted lobster and a salad of avocado and tomato; a plate of lamb's offal including kidneys with mustard butter, liver with onions, sweetbreads with Marsala and a pungent tomato sauce; quail with a plum and beetroot sauce; summer pudding with the right sort of bread and 'not too sweet'. The Carved Angel is compared in the past year's reports with Lucas Carton in Paris and Tante Claire in London, but it keeps its own country style in, for example, the mixture of hand-thrown pottery and smooth factory china; in the shelves of splendid pickles (for sale if you want a souvenir – the pineapple and the Chinese are special favourites); and in the generous sharing of a recipe of quince cheese or whatever. Prices are closer to Paris and London than regulars would like, both for set price meals (seven choices per course at dinner, two at lunch) and for the *carte*, but prices are totally inclusive and tips are neither expected or encouraged. The disaffected may niggle at less than professional service and a lack of ornate flourishes with truffles or foie gras; devotees pay willingly for inspired simplicity. The wine list is long and mainly French with small outside reinforcements of impeccable pedigree. Prices, though fair at the bottom, soar to great heights as the flat percentage mark-up bites. The many fine dessert wines include three Australian liqueur Muscats by the glass – a match for that plate of chocolate puddings; the Nelson Late-Harvest Rhine Riesling from New Zealand should be listed with the other sweet wines, many of them in useful halves. Some of the other halves are by now too elderly. Don't miss the fine range of marcs, armagnacs and calvados (Groult is the name to note here). The six house wines cost £10.

CHEFS: Joyce Molyneux and Nick Coiley   PROPRIETORS: Joyce Molyneux and Meriel Boydon
OPEN: Tue to Sun, exc Sun D
MEALS: 12.30 to 1.45, 7.30 to 9.30
PRICES: £32 (£39), Set L and D £22.50 (£28) to £30 (£35). Service inc
SEATS: 30. Private parties: 30 main room, 15 private room. Children's helpings. Wheelchair access

Mansion House

Mansion House Street,
Dartmouth TQ6 9AG
DARTMOUTH (0803) 835474

COOKING 3
COST £24–£42

The Mansion House is grand, imposing and quiet. In the dining-room a marble fireplace, moulded plaster ceiling and blue and coral drapes combine with comfortable padded chairs, fine glass and china to create an air of hushed sophistication. The menu is short, a sensible precaution in view of the gothic complexity of some of the dishes. In one May meal there was warm boudin of sole and sorrel on a prawn and leek vinaigrette, and red mullet grilled with strips of anchovy served with caviare niçoise to start; then to follow, chicken baked in salt crust with turnips and parsley-scented veal stock, or ragout of pork with rosemary, Roquefort, and parsnip chips. The effect can be stunning. Sea bass keeps moist and full of flavour inside a crust made from breadcrumbs, pine-kernels, mustard, basil and cheese, its tomato and basil sauce having 'the taste of early summer', its noodles tossed in good olive oil. The timing and skill with fish shows in firm, sweet, fresh, moist scallops wrapped in a filo-pastry moneybag. There are times, though, when the richness becomes excessive. Fatty chicken needs a juicy sauce rather than oily mayonnaise to balance it. Quail salad doesn't really need a burger-like quenelle of smoked chicken. But when one diner baulked at a surfeit of glazed duck breast and its wrappings, the not inconsiderable remains were, quite spontaneously, wrapped in greaseproof paper and presented for use in sandwiches the following day. Less richness, less food, and less money, might be a formula that would fill more tables. Certainly there is no argument about the sound foundations on which the cooking is built. Crème brûlée is exemplary with a crisp, light, thin layer of sugar that splinters with a tap; vanilla and rhubarb ice-creams are exceptional. The wines are chosen carefully and safely; pricing favours the bottom end but imposes large premiums at the other. House French: £7.50. CELLARMAN'S CHOICE: Pouilly-Fumé, les Bascoins 1988, Masson-Blondelet, £14.50; Ch. Siran 1979, £36.50.

CHEF: Richard Cranfield   PROPRIETORS: Richard and Helen Cranfield
OPEN: Tue to Sat, exc Tue, and Sat L
MEALS: 12.30 to 1.30, 7.30 to 10
PRICES: Set L £18 (£24), Set D £22 (£28) to £26.50 (£35)
SEATS: 44. Private parties: 30 main room, 14 private room. Vegetarian meals by arrangement. Children welcome. No-smoking area. Wheelchair access (also WC)

DEDHAM Essex   map 3

▲ Le Talbooth 🍾

Gun Hill, Dedham CO7 6HP   COOKING 3
COLCHESTER (0206) 323150   COST £26–£48

'Half-timbering by the riverside' may summon up the image of this restaurant's teashop origins. In the 38 years of development in the hands of Gerald Milsom, it has progressed to a sprawling property offering food of luxury status and price. Steven Blake has established continuity and peace in a kitchen that had lost its way for a year or two, and it has settled to ultra-modern, professional cooking matched by a large service brigade. The repertoire takes in a return to peasant origins: braised ox-tail wrapped with cabbage; salmon baked on lyonnaise potatoes; and turbot on a bed of lentils with a beer butter sauce were three winter dishes. Come the summer, there's less of the peasant and more of the light Mediterranean feel to dishes such as rabbit with endives, tomato, olives and rosemary; braised kidneys scented with tarragon; salmon on a pimento and tomato dressing; lamb with ratatouille; or carpaccio with fresh noodles. Few of the sauces have a cream, or even a butter, base and flavours remain in the neo-classical mainstream with the exception of two firm favourites: Thai-spiced Gamba prawns and spiced chicken winglets with livers and a sherry sauce. Execution is as professional as the knifework producing the minutely chopped vegetables and the vertical piles that mark the style of arrangement on the plate. Desserts have been designed with chocaholics in mind as at least half of them fall into the section labelled 'chocolate fantasies'. The wine list is as long as may be expected in a restaurant like this. Apart from the six house wines priced from £8.50, there is little else below £15. Middle band wines – Sancerre, Gigondas or New Zealand Sauvignon – are pushed well towards extreme London prices, but the top band enjoys almost modest mark-ups. This is a pity when the selection is as careful and wide-ranging as this one. Confident customers should take a breath and order the 1982 Hermitage from Guigal at the surprisingly low £24.75. Adnams beers are available. CELLARMAN'S CHOICE: Riesling, Princess Abbes 1986, Schlumberger, £15.50; Ch. Nicot, Bordeaux Blanc 1988, £10.50.

CHEF: Steven Blake   PROPRIETOR: Gerald M.W. Milsom
OPEN: all week
MEALS: 12.30 to 2, 7 to 9 (9.30 Sat)
PRICES: £31 (£40), Set L £17 (£26). Service 10%
CARD: Access, Visa
SEATS: 70. Private parties: 70 main room, 24 private room. Car-park, 70 places. Children welcome. Smart dress preferred. No cigars/pipes in dining-room. Wheelchair access
ACCOMMODATION: 10 rooms, all with bath/shower. Rooms for disabled. B&B £80 to 135. Garden. TV. Phone. Scenic. Doors close at 10.30 [*Which? Hotel Guide*]

DENT Cumbria   map 7

▲ *Stone Close*

Main Street, Dent LA10 5KL   COOKING 2
DENT (058 75) 231   COST £10–£14

This report came from one who went to Dent by train: 'Horton-in-Ribblesdale (the nearest station) is the highest station in England, efflorescent with primroses in May – and five miles and 500 feet above Dent. Use it and help save the Settle-Carlisle line. I stayed here two nights and fed exactly as I would have wished, were I cooking for myself and old friends. If such places were cloned 200 times in summer-visited villages, civilisation would be almost round the corner. The food at the day-long café – fish pâté with oatcakes, cheese and onion pie, Yorkshire curd tart – was as authentic as the set-price, all-but-choiceless evening meal (choice of puddings at least, plus an optional extra real cheese at a supplement). Mushroom tartlets, braised beef, good soups, crumbed chicken with a juice, inventive vegetables (especially the baked parsnip mélange), and a treacly sponge are the sort of thing to expect.' A tiny wine list, or some damson gin, may help you enjoy the meal, or there's strong farmhouse cider. Stone Close is a seventeenth-century farmhouse in a cobbled village that feels of much the same era. Would that there were more such places that refused to compromise with packages or convenience, yet did it with the natural reticence and good taste of Graham Hudson and his colleagues in the kitchen. House wine: £6.30 per litre.

CHEFS: Patricia Barber and Hazel Haygarth   PROPRIETORS: Graham Hudson and
Patricia Barber
OPEN: all week
CLOSED: Jan and first 2 weeks Feb. Tea shop closed mid-week Nov to mid-Mar
MEALS: 10.30 to 5.15, 7.30
PRICES: £6 (£10), Set D £8.50 (£12)
SEATS: 40. Private parties: 25 main room, 20 private room. Vegetarian meals. Children's
helpings. No smoking during meals. Wheelchair access. Music. One sitting at D
ACCOMMODATION: 3 rooms. B&B £13 to £22. Deposit: £10. Baby facilities. Pets welcome.
Afternoon teas. No smoking in bedrooms. Scenic [*Which? Hotel Guide*]

DERBY Derbyshire   map 5

524

524 Burton Road, Little Over,	
Derby DE3 6FN	COOKING 1
DERBY (0332) 294524	COST £15–£25

The erstwhile brasserie has turned into a restaurant, though with not a lot of
outward change beyond a new porch. Reports state that the new owner has put
new beams in the ceiling but has wisely retained the services of Steve Chell in
the kitchen. While he is working there, execution is satisfactory in such
offerings as apricots stuffed with cream cheese and deep fried in a filo
wrapping; ramekins of mushrooms and shrimps with garlic and butter; a
mixture of fish in a tarragon sauce; duck with orange and calvados; a list of
vegetarian dishes; steaks and a dozen other choices. The wine list is short, basic
and reasonably priced. House wine: £5.95.

CHEF: Steve Chell   PROPRIETORS: K.K.W. Enterprises Ltd
OPEN: Tue to Sun, exc Sat L and Sun D
MEALS: 12 to 2, 7 to 10
PRICES: £15 (£21), Set L and Set D £10.95 (£15)
CARDS: Access, Diners, Visa
SEATS: 36. Private parties: 45 private room. Car-park, 16 places. Vegetarian meals.
Children's helpings. Smart dress preferred. Music

DISS Norfolk   map 6

▲ *Salisbury House*

84 Victoria Road, Diss IP22 3JG	COOKING 1
DISS (0379) 644738	COST £16–£31

The house is early Victorian with an older core once serving as a storehouse to a
nearby windmill. Now the gardens, cushioning guests against noise, store
aviary, pond, summerhouse and croquet lawn. A series of rooms, including a
conservatory for drinks or breakfast, are devoted to the restaurant: gentle
lighting, small-print wallpapers, antique cutlery, elegant crockery tend
towards an image of polished, yet homely, sophistication. Barry Davies cooks a
carte of six or seven choices in classic modern British style: ballotine of duck

with spiced fruits; scallops in a pastry case with cream and basil sauce; breast of chicken stuffed with a leek mousse. Messages are conflicting. A mousseline of salmon was nicely set off by a stem ginger butter sauce; sauté quail was bland, on a salad with walnut oil dressing; hare was tender and gamey but its sauce acidic; magret of duck was accurately cooked with a powerful ceps sauce; vegetables may be very inconsistent; desserts may on one hand yield an 'explosion of flavour' from a satsuma sorbet or an intense bitter chocolate ice-cream 'like frozen truffle' on mint custard, or on the other a characterless rhubarb and cinnamon flan. There are times when ambition outstrips performance, but people do enjoy staying here, for the Davieses are energetic and welcoming. The wine list is long, almost entirely French and none too informatively laid out or accurately typed. This gives it a miscellaneous air, partly borne out by closer inspection. It has many mature clarets, though the 1972s and 1973s may be over the hill by now. The claret prices are fair but the generally rather disorganised character of the list extends to curiously random pricing. House wines are £7. CELLARMAN'S CHOICE: Montagny premier cru 1987, Bertrand, £15.80; Bourgogne Passetoutgrain 1985, Lamarche, £11.50 for 50 cl.

CHEF: Barry Davies   PROPRIETORS: Barry and Sue Davies
OPEN: Tue to Sat, exc Sat L
CLOSED: 1 week at Christmas, 2 weeks July
MEALS: 12.15 to 1.45, 7.30 to 9.15
PRICES: £18 (£26), Set L £11 (£16)
CARDS: Access, Visa
SEATS: 38. 3 tables outside. Private parties: 20 main room, 14 private room. Car-park, 10 places. Children's helpings. No smoking. Wheelchair access (1 step). Music
ACCOMMODATION: 3 rooms, all with bath/shower. Rooms for disabled. B&B £35 to £52. Baby facilities. Garden. TV. Doors close at 11.30 [*Which? Hotel Guide*]

DORCHESTER-ON-THAMES Oxfordshire   map 2

▲ *George Hotel* ♟

High Street,
Dorchester-on-Thames OX10 7HH   COOKING 1
OXFORD (0865) 340404   COST £18–£41

The attractive coaching-inn near the bridge and abbey offers more than meat and two vegetables in its timbered dining-rooms. The *carte* of half a dozen choices in each course might be characterised as 'modern hotel' rather than 'old roadhouse' and, though some may prefer sea fish to carp with beansprouts and soy, or guinea-fowl with onions and red wine to one served with a timbale of its leg meat on a passion-fruit reduction, these are by most accounts competently cooked. Not everything is calculated to irritate conservatives: home-made noodles; a coarse game terrine; a quail soup; spatchcocked partridge; a trio of fillets with cheese glazes; bramley and calvados ice-cream; a small but substantial choice of cheese; banana baked in flaky pastry have all pleased. Roasts come up at Sunday lunch. The wine list is more than adequate for its task, with some support from countries other than France for a noteworthy small group of mature clarets more affordably priced than elsewhere. Some wines have an asterisk indicating good value for price and quality. This is helpful, provided it's accurate. House wine: £7.50.

CELLARMAN'S CHOICE: Chablis premier cru Beauroy 1988, Dom. Fromont-Moindrot, £17.95.

CHEF: Neil Cordner   PROPRIETORS: Neville and Griffin Ltd
OPEN: all week
MEALS: 12.30 to 2, 7 to 9.45 (9 Sun)
PRICES: £25 (£34), Set L £12.50 (£18) to £14 (£20), Set D £17 (£23) to £25 (£32)
CARDS: Access, Amex, Diners, Visa
SEATS: 40. Private parties: 30 main room, 20 private room. Car-park, 50 places. Vegetarian meals. Children's helpings. Smart dress preferred
ACCOMMODATION: 18 rooms, all with bath/shower. Rooms for disabled. B&B £54 to £72. Baby facilities. Pets welcome. Garden. TV. Scenic. Confirm by 4 [*Which? Hotel Guide*]

DORRINGTON Shropshire   map 4

▲ *Country Friends*

Dorrington SY5 7JD
DORRINGTON (074 373) 707   COOKING 3
5m S of Shrewsbury on A49   COST £20–£29

The restaurant can't be missed on its bank above the main road, nor should it be. Charles and Pauline Whittaker have developed a very personal style of cooking and of hospitality in their years here, and at Northleach before that. Indeed, it was an old acquaintance from Gloucestershire days who remarked how refreshing was their exuberant informality. The restaurant has both a *carte* and a set-price, no-choice menu, which reflects the Whittaker's firm commitment to quietly innovative cookery. They do not surprise by shocking combinations, nor do they bore with the wholly predictable: fillet of beef with home-made pasta and a sour cream and dill sauce; lamb, still done with a crab mousse and curry sabayon in the style of Raymond Blanc, but also with a parsley mousse and two pimento sauces; a trio of salmon – marinated, smoked and roast; or chicken quenelles with a coriander and pink peppercorn sauce. Even sorbets have a nice touch, as in celery, thyme and lemon. Main courses come with an English plethora of vegetables: new potatoes, lyonnaise potatoes, red cabbage, green cabbage, mange-tout on one day. They may not go with everything, but they are well handled. Good handling seems the case with much of the food, especially baking skills of all sorts, and fair and accurate seasoning. The set menu in the summer was 'pig with everything', starting with mushrooms and bacon, garlic cream and cheese, then going on to loin of pork with apple and cider sauce. The bedrooms are much valued, as are the breakfasts, though not the possible noise from the road. Much turning of pages, with only two or three wines on each, reveals an adequate list with some highlights especially among the clarets – Ch. la Croix de Gay 1979 at £25 – and generally fair prices. House wine starts at £6.80.

The text of entries is based on unsolicited reports sent in by readers, backed up by inspections conducted anonymously. The factual details under the text are from questionnaires the Guide *sends to all restaurants that feature in the book.*

CHEFS: Charles Whittaker and Tim Greaves   PROPRIETORS: Charles and Pauline Whittaker
OPEN: Tue to Sat
MEALS: 12 to 2, 7 to 9 (9.30 Sat)
PRICES: £18 (£24), Set L and D £14.50 (£20)
CARDS: Access, Visa
SEATS: 40. Private parties: 45 main room. Car-park, 40 places. Children welcome.
Wheelchair access
ACCOMMODATION: 4 rooms, 1 with bath/shower. B&B £26 to £38. Garden
[*Which? Hotel Guide*]

DREWSTEIGNTON Devon   map 1

▲ *Hunts Tor House*

Drewsteignton EX6 6QW   COOKING 2
DREWSTEIGNTON (0647) 21228   COST £20

The Harrisons run the sort of place that most people hope to find when
travelling. It is peaceful, homely in the nicest way, and costs the same for three
nights as for one in a posh hotel. There is no choice on the menu – in fact there
is no menu, so Sue Harrison likes to know about people's allergies or aversions
in advance. Note that she cooks for residents only. The repertoire revolves
around dishes such as smoked lamb with onion marmalade, a feather-light
salmon mousse, goose with sage and apple jelly, or pork fillet with prunes in a
redcurrant and elderberry wine sauce, for which they use home-made
elderberry wine. One might call it 'English Provincial' if that term did not
sound patronising or perjorative. Cooking is accurate, which makes crème
brûlée a particular delight. Breakfast is good. The 20-bottle wine list, compiled
with equal care, is very fairly priced. House Duboeuf: £6. CELLARMAN'S
CHOICE: Alsace Sylvaner, Louis Gisselbrecht 1986, £8.

CHEF: Sue Harrison   PROPRIETORS: Sue and Chris Harrison
OPEN: all week, D only (residents only)
MEALS: 7.30
PRICES: Set D £14 (£17). Service inc
SEATS: 8. Private parties: 12 main room, 8 private room. Vegetarian meals. No children
under 14. One sitting
ACCOMMODATION: 4 rooms, all with bath/shower. B&B £23 to £36. Deposit: £20.
No children under 14. Pets welcome. Doors close at midnight. Confirm by 4

▲ *Old Inn*

The Square, Drewsteignton EX6 6QR   COOKING 1
DREWSTEIGNTON (0647) 21276   COST £21–£26

Two London visitors arrived on a cold spring night, ravenous. They left unable
to eat another thing. Although the set price of the meal is not low, even by
London standards and especially when the absence of fore and aft trimmings is
taken into account, the food is honest, fresh and substantial. The Old Inn has
left the pursuit of beer and skittles to the Drewe Arms and Mrs Mudge, the
oldest licensee in the county, but still has the air of an old village tavern. Rose
Chapman cooks a short menu that may include smoked fish pancakes (good

thin pancakes, fresh, moist fish); mushroom gougère (a homely supper dish that had no faults); venison in red wine and port; or breast of pigeon in filo pastry (more like a pie, really). The meat and game has left something to be desired: pigeons can be dramatically tough. Puddings are substantial with pear and almond tart a teenager's delight after an active day out, and treacle tart continuing to please. A cursory wine list with house French at £5.95.

CELLARMAN'S CHOICE: Rosemount Estate, Chardonnay 1989, £11.80; Brouilly, Dom. Martin 1988, P. Thevenin, £11.95.

CHEF: Rose Chapman   PROPRIETORS: V.L. Chapman and Rose Chapman
OPEN: Tue to Sat, D only
CLOSED: Weekdays in Feb
MEALS: 7.30 to 8.45
PRICES: Set D £18 (£21) to £19 (£22). Service inc
SEATS: 20. Private parties: 20 main room. Vegetarian meals. Children restricted. No smoking
ACCOMMODATION: 3 rooms. B&B £14 to £28. No children under 12. Pets welcome. Scenic. Doors close at 11.30. Confirm by 5 [*Which? Hotel Guide*]

DULVERTON Somerset   map 1

▲ *Ashwick House*

Dulverton TA22 9QD
DULVERTON (0398) 23868   COOKING 1
Signposted from B3223 N of Dulverton   COST £19–£32

The house, red brick with steep roofs and dormer windows, sits above a lake wild with growth in summer. Beyond, Exmoor beckons. Richard Sherwood cooks for those who stay at the house and for a few outside customers. He likes prior warning of a day or two. Menus are handwritten and given scrolled and tied to each party. Dinners of four courses offer choice only for the first and last, when a pair of dishes appear. However, likes and dislikes may be expressed when the booking is made. Cooking is as it might be for a careful dinner party: without serious elaboration, but carefully purchased and properly made. The reported components of a meal are soup, or perhaps stuffed mushrooms; a mousse of Roquefort or quenelles of trout with ginger sauce; a roast, possibly pork with a herb and sausage stuffing, or a piece of salmon; a couple of good desserts or some cheese. A short wine list from Avery's spans a price range from £5.95 for one house wine to a Corton Clos du Roi 1982 at £37.75, but most are well under £15.

CHEF/PROPRIETOR: Richard Sherwood
OPEN: Tue to Sat, D only and Sun L
MEALS: 12.15 to 1.15, 7.15 to 8.30
PRICES: Set Sun L £12.75 (£19), Set D £19.75 (£27)
SEATS: 30. 3 tables outside. Private parties: 30 main room. Car-park, 30 places. No children under 8. Smart dress preferred.
ACCOMMODATION: 6 rooms, all with bath/shower. D,B&B £46 to £78. Deposit: £25. No children under 8. Afternoon teas. Garden. TV. Phone. Scenic. Doors close at 11.30. Confirm by 6

EAST BERGHOLT Essex   map 3

Fountain House 🍾

The Street, East Bergholt CO7 6TB   COOKING 1
COLCHESTER (0206) 298232   COST £18–£24

The impression is of well-used domesticity. Heavy beams, a flagstone floor, saggy chairs and sofas with tapestry upholstery are countered by 'the best ever' women's room. The food and cooking are of the same order as the ambience: pursuing well-travelled paths, sometimes with success because ingredients are well bought, sometimes falling down because of execution and heavy presentation. The menu is short but very fairly priced. Choice often includes avocado; a combination with smoked mackerel mousse is only outdone by pairing it with Stilton and baking it with puff pastry. It also crops up with prawns. Main dishes will perhaps include beef as a Wellington or as a steak, simple fish, and quite heavy treatments of pork or chicken. The wine list is very modern and adventurous, in its way a contrast to the style of cooking. The world is put into proper perspective, with due prominence given to Australia (Yarra Yering, Penfold), New Zealand (Cloudy Bay), the United States (Mondavi, Duckhorn), Italy (Tedeschi's Soave, Giacosa's Barbaresco, Altesino's Brunello, and a page of mature Italians), and Spain (Torres, Marqués de Murrieta). Within France, Alsace gets its own page of mature vintages and the best growers, and there is good support from the Rhône and Loire. Prices are reasonable and there are 75 half-bottles. CELLARMAN'S CHOICE: Montlouis demi-sec 1985, Dominique Moyer, £10; Crozes-Hermitage 1985, Michel Ferraton, £13.

CHEF: Wendy Anne Sarton   PROPRIETOR: James F. Sarton
OPEN: Tue to Sun, exc Sun D
CLOSED: 2 weeks end Feb
MEALS: 12.30 to 2, 7.30 to 10
PRICES: Set L £12.50 (£18), Set D £14.50 (£20)
CARDS: Access, Visa
SEATS: 32. 3 tables outside. Private parties: 16 main room. Car-park, 12 places. Children's helpings. No cigars/pipes in dining-room. Wheelchair access. Music

---

EASTBOURNE East Sussex   map 3

Byrons

6 Crown Street, Old Town,
Eastbourne BN21 1NX   COOKING 2
EASTBOURNE (0323) 20171   COST £26

Once a bistro, now a restaurant in two tiny rooms set well back from the seaside zone, and still run with relaxed aplomb by the Scruttons, as for many years. Simon Scrutton has never ignored culinary developments around him, so he may serve hot lobster sausage with a spring onion sauce or warm salad of scallops with walnut oil. But his feet are also on long-trodden ground in main courses like stuffed chicken Périgord using chicken livers, mushrooms and herbs, with a madeira sauce; or pork wrapped in bacon and filo with a mustard sauce. Care is taken over materials: free-range poultry, organic vegetables, local fish. It is a pleasant place for a quiet dinner in intelligent and capable hands. There is a five per cent discount for cash payment. The wine list is short but decent and not too expensive. House Côtes du Ventoux or de Duras are £7.40. CELLARMAN'S CHOICE: Ch. la Touche (organic Muscadet) 1988, £9.80; Côtes du Rhône 1985, Pascal, £9.95.

CHEF: Simon Scrutton PROPRIETORS: Simon and Marian Scrutton
OPEN: Mon to Sat, D only (L by arrangement)
CLOSED: 1 week at Christmas
MEALS: 7.30 to 10.30
PRICES: £15 (£22). Service inc
CARDS: Amex, Diners, Visa
SEATS: 22. Private parties: 10 main room, 10 private room. Children welcome. No smoking during meals. Music

---

EAST BUCKLAND Devon
map 1

▲ Lower Pitt

East Buckland, EX32 0TD
FILLEIGH (059 86) 243
off A361 at Stag's Head, 3m NW of
South Molton

COOKING 2
COST £26

Self-catering holidays need places of resort in the evening, lest the domestic round of cooking and washing takes over completely. Touring holidays need both beds and meals. This long farmhouse between Westward Ho! and Exmoor can satisfy each demand as well as pleasing local custom. 'The atmosphere is just right: half-way between home and efficient small hotel.' There is an extra conservatory dining-room coming on stream in 1990. The number of small growers and food-related businesses in north Devon is not quite so high as in the south of the county but can nonetheless add lustre to menus of cooks like Suzanne Lyons who delights in showing off the possibilities in dishes such as loin of Devonshire pork with apples, shallots, Hancock's cider and cream. The cooking acknowledges current tastes in a brandade of salmon; lamb with aubergines, tomatoes, apricots and coriander; and a chicken stir-fry with sesame oil. Devon cream is implicit in the home-made ice creams; Pavlova; hazelnut maringue gateau with raspberry cream; and chocolate roulade filled with chocolate and cream. English cheeses are on offer and there is an adequate slate of half-bottles on the wine list for small parties or those who want to order both red and white. Prices for wine, as well as food, are not grasping. The Sancerre, a useful marker, is very reasonable. Jerome Lyons knows his wines, mainly bought from Christopher Piper, and steadies the service by cheerful local women. House wine is £6.90 a litre and there is that Hancock's cider. No tips are expected.

All details are as accurate as possible at the time of going to press, but chefs and owners often change, and it is wise to check by telephone before making a special journey. Many readers have been disappointed when set-price bargain meals are no longer available. Ask when booking.

CHEF: Suzanne Lyons PROPRIETORS: Jerome and Suzanne Lyons
OPEN: Tue to Sat, D only
MEALS: 7 to 9
PRICES: £15 (£22)
CARDS: Access, Visa
SEATS: 28. Private parties: 14 main room. Car-park, 25 places. Children's helpings. Music
ACCOMMODATION: 3 rooms, all with bath/shower. B&B £25 to £40. Deposit: £10.
No children under 10. Garden. Scenic. Doors close at 11. Confirm by 6 [*Which? Hotel Guide*]

EAST GRINSTEAD West Sussex   map 3

▲ *Gravetye Manor* 🍾

Vowels Lane, East Grinstead RH19 4LJ   COOKING 3
SHARPTHORNE (0342) 810567   COST £33–£53

It is not certain what is more remarkable about this manor house set in the
Wealden forest south of East Grinstead: the panelled interior, faceted wood
catching glints of sunbeams through motes of dust kept largely at bay by
endless polishing, or the flower gardens, woodland and lake, brought to a pitch
of English arcadia by the gardener William Robinson and now maintained and
improved by Peter Herbert after more than 30 years of keeping a hotel and
country club. These surroundings make it a favoured goal of weekend
expeditions, even if not staying overnight, for what better than a walk to create
appetite or accelerate digestion? Dining takes in drinks before and coffee after
in the comfortable English sitting-rooms with the meal in one of two panelled
dining-rooms in between. Pressure of numbers is sometimes so great as to
make these moves timed with too great precision. Service is formal, quite
young, and this year has been felt lacking the ease of confidence. A long *carte* of
maybe a dozen dishes in each course is supplemented by set-price menus at
lunch and dinner. Mark Raffan achieves a good balance between plain British
cooking and recipes with a more modern tilt. Typical of the first are the set
menu offering of grilled Dover sole or the steak, kidney and oyster pie on the
carte. The second tendency is seen in collops of brill cooked under a bell jar
with onion marmalade and slivers of foie gras, or roulade of salmon and savoy
cabbage with a lobster and ginger sauce. Desserts may include an English
pudding as well as ideas like a lemon grass sabayon with poached pear or a
rich apricot and curd tartlet. Materials are well bought or produced on the
premises. The smoke-house yields excellent salmon and the gardens fine
vegetables – even if the choice of red cabbage served with fish, for example, is
not so well judged. Many items have been recommended but there have also
been comments on a lack of finish or technique, small details in the main but
detracting from the success of the whole. Thus foie gras served with salad
leaves and lentils was accompanied by beetroot that contributed little to the
balance of flavour and was in poor condition; ravioli of crayfish was thick pasta
and thin filling; a tart of chicken and vegetables had no unifying taste or sauce
to lift it to more than chicken and vegetables. The cheeseboard looked like last
week's when one reader was finishing an otherwise excellent meal that had
started with a warm salad of scallops and langoustines with an orange and
chervil sauce, 'the herb shining through triumphantly', and had included the

worrying combination of foie gras and brill which, however, was brought off with skill and success in his opinion. The wine list at Gravetye is never cheap, but it is long and impressive and the price range means there is a fair choice below £15. Its length gives it depth in several sections: magnums of all sorts; a decent set of halves; old clarets; an exemplary choice of New World growers; very fine Germans and Alsaces. The choice of growers in Burgundy is conservative but is also thoroughbred. House Louis Latour: £14 and £15. CELLARMAN'S CHOICE: Maximin Grünhaus Abtsberg Riesling 1983, half-bottles £15.30; Chassagne-Montrachet 1985, Ramonet-Prudhon, £43. Prices are still exclusive of VAT though inclusive of service. This really does not help calculations in the dining-room, though only the host is given a menu with prices: Gravetye is one of the very few places left in Britain to pursue this strange and embarrassing policy.

CHEF: Mark Raffan   PROPRIETORS: Peter Herbert and Leigh Stone-Herbert
OPEN: all week
CLOSED: 25 Dec D to non-residents
MEALS: 12.30 to 1.45, 7.30 to 9.45 (10 Sat)
PRICES: £28 (£44), Set L £19 (£33), Set D £22 (£36). Service inc
SEATS: 50. Private parties: 10 main room, 20 private room. Car-park, 30 places. No children under 7. Smart dress preferred. No smoking in dining-room
ACCOMMODATION: 14 rooms, all with bath/shower. B&B £98 to £190. No children under 7. Garden. Fishing. TV. Phone. Scenic. Doors close at midnight [*Which? Hotel Guide*]

EDENBRIDGE Kent   map 3

Honours Mill

87 High Street, Edenbridge TN8 5AU   COOKING 3
EDENBRIDGE (0732) 866757   COST £21–£41

'Five slices of scallops around a bird's nest of home-made fettuccine, flecked with rough-chopped fresh basil and accompanied by skinned tomatoes were laid on a sauce of butter, fish stock and white wine.' The basil afforded peppery highlights, the tomatoes sweet depth, the sauce a rich (perhaps too rich) platform. The dish was a resounding success; the scallops were of palpable freshness. So began one report, echoed by many others, of a meal in this restored corn mill with rushing water audible in the bar downstairs, a terrace for summer drinks where moorhens may be observed, and a dining-room that is 'an absolute celebration of timber', where the tall may, after a glass or two of Chablis, crack their skulls. This weatherboarded house, on a main road but somehow proof against traffic noise, is presided over by Giles Goodhew. His brother Neville, helped by Martin Radmall, cooks a seasonal menu of six or seven choices at each course with perhaps half a dozen daily specials. The flavours are not etiolated by fancy presentation or technique. Excellence has been detected in a dish such as slices of beef with a sauce of white port, parsley and garlic – 'I had expected no more than a competent, modern version of a more or less obligatory restaurant dish, yet this was really exciting.' Other things that have been noticed are a salmon mousse with spinach and a lobster mousse with asparagus; red mullet with a red wine and shallot sauce; snail and pistachio terrine; Dover sole with butter and ginger sauce; and first rate vegetables – perfectly timed and including one spring evening a potato 'terrine' of new potatoes chopped into a binding of egg, parsley and ham. Desserts often revolve around soft fruit and ice-cream. A biscuit glacé of boldly chopped pralined peanuts with a powerful blackcurrant sauce convinced at least one that it was worth persevering to the end of the meal. Reservations about the cooking concentrate on the sauces: they may be too rich or too powerful for the main ingredient. All comers are impressed by the quality of the raw materials; charmed by the service and welcome; and find no fault with the incidentals, especially the petits fours. While there may be no objections to an all-French wine list, the offerings here do not reflect the enthusiasm of the kitchen. Prices are high and choice conservative. House wine: £8.50.

CHEFS: Neville Goodhew and Martin Radmall PROPRIETORS: Sarah Manser, Neville, Duncan and Giles Goodhew
OPEN: Tue to Sun, exc Sat L and Sun D
CLOSED: 1 week after Christmas, 1 week Mar, 2 weeks early June
MEALS: 12.15 to 2, 7.15 to 10
PRICES: Set L £16.95 (£21) to £28.95 (£34), Set D £28.95 (£34). Service inc
CARDS: Access, Visa
SEATS: 38. Private parties: 20 main room. Children's helpings. Children under 12 Sun L only

---

EDGWARE Greater London   map 3

Wing Ki

29 Burnt Oak Broadway, HA8 5LD   COOKING 1
081-205 0904   COST £11–£29

Changing tastes in Chinese food may be traced from menus of succeeding years at places like Wing Ki. Wing Ki Yeung and his Irish wife Hannah have been responsive to customer demand: changes in the most recent menu, therefore, include a long list of 26 vegetarian dishes – vegetables served with pancakes, Singapore noodles vegetarian style, spring rolls with hot sweet vegetables are three – and several new items mostly stressing chilli and garlic such as chicken with mange-tout garlic sauce, spicy prawns in paper or chilli prawns and garlic. This only confirms the shift towards hot food and adoption of garlic as a national flavour: witness the universal serving of new season's garlic in the summer of 1990. Appreciation of local tastes may also explain why pork comes as sweet-and-sour but forms the component of few other dishes on the menu out of respect for kosher preferences, and why Wing Ki tends towards the sweet side of the palate range. People enjoy the cleanliness, the magic service of Hannah Yeung, and emphasis on Szechuan cooking.

The Guide relies on feedback from its readers. Especially welcome are reports on new restaurants appearing in the book for the first time.

All letters to the Guide are acknowledged with an update on latest sales, closures, chef changes and so on.

CHEF: Wing Ki Yeung PROPRIETORS: Wing Ki and Hannah Yeung
OPEN: Tue to Sun and bank hol Mons
MEALS: 12 to 2.30, 6 to 11.30
PRICES: £15 (£24), Set L £6.50 (£11) to £7.50 (£12), Set D £15 (£20) to £16.50 (£21).
Minimum £8 at D. Service inc
CARD: Access, Visa
SEATS: 56. Private parties: 60 main room. Vegetarian meals. Children's helpings. Children
restricted. Smart dress preferred. Wheelchair access. Music. Air-conditioned

---

ELY Cambridgeshire   map 6

Old Fire Engine House ♥

25 St Mary's Street, Ely CB7 4ER   COOKING 2
ELY (0353) 662582   COST £26

The place is something of an institution now. It has been cooking food from the
Fens for over 20 years and is as popular as ever. 'Everyone is very welcoming
and the prices are so reasonable as to make you ask how on earth they do it'.
More the wonder when second helpings of the main course are regularly
offered. It has a comforting homely air about it, an unmistakable stamp of the
family-run restaurant. The style is English, even down to the perceived
amateur approach. Perhaps it does not move with the times, perhaps it does
have a mission to bring the occasional zander, pike, bunch of samphire, pint of
Brancaster mussels and smoked fish from Welney to set before the
unconverted. And perhaps it does this with more zeal than fine timing, balance
or accuracy. But this ingenuousness and lack of guile reflect no more than an
absence of streetwise city cynicism, which would be as much out of character as
it would be unwelcome. It is a stone's throw from the cathedral and, like any
place that doubles as an informal gallery for the work of local artists, has a
slightly studied and determined air of casualness. Soups (lovage, ham and pea,
Scotch broth) are hearty. There is an unbroken tradition of serving the kind of
satisfying dishes that are coming back into fashion elsewhere as 'cuisine
grandmère' or some such: casserole of rabbit with mustard and parsley, pork
chops in Suffolk cider, jugged hare, and pies from beef and mushroom to eel or
pigeon. 'Menus change with every meal, but are built around a core of 20 to 30
dishes which recur with some regularity.' English puddings abound,
reminding some of school and childhood: bread-and-butter, apple Betty,
treacle, sherry trifle, rhubarb crumble, whim whams. The wine list shows that
as much time and affection is lavished on it as concern for customers' pockets.
New wine regions have been taken in to preserve the price/value ratio but
France is obviously Michael Jarman's first love. The choice is not over-long but
the growers are model and the prices generous: Guigal, Durup, Latour-Giraud
are some to watch or the Bulgarian or Chilean Cabernets if economy is the
thing. The real savings, however, are on the bin-end list, try the Mouton
Rothschild 1970 at £60, it won't be cheaper for miles. House French wines
start at £6.40.

---

*County Round-ups listing additional restaurants that may be worth a visit are at the back
of the Guide, after the Irish section. Reports on Round-up entries are welcome.*

CHEFS: Ann Ford, Michael Jarman and Terri Kindred   PROPRIETORS: Ann Ford and
Michael Jarman
OPEN: all week, exc Sun D
CLOSED: 2 weeks from 24 Dec and bank hols
MEALS: 12.30 to 2, 7.30 to 9
PRICES: £16 (£22)
SEATS: 36. 8 tables outside. Private parties: 36 main room, 22 private room. Car-park, 8
places. Vegetarian meals. Children's helpings. No smoking in main dining-room

---

EMSWORTH Hampshire   map 2

36 on the Quay

47 South Street, Emsworth PO10 7EG   COOKING 2
EMSWORTH (0243) 375592   COST £19–£41

The Quay itself is quite small and 36 on the Quay is actually on the corner of
South Street. There is a new owner and a new chef, winner of the Young Chef
of the Year competition in 1989. The cooking has taken a more fashionable,
metropolitan air – dishes such as lobster ravioli and stuffed pig's trotter run the
modernist flag high up the mast. It's early days yet, but reports have confirmed
skill within the context of a set-price menu of maybe five options at each stage.
The lobster ravioli was served in a consommé with strips of vegetables with a
rouille to give it bite; a foie gras mousse, very small and delicate, was
overpowered by a sweet apple sauce, almost a toffee apple sauce; the trotter
was stuffed with sage and bacon but the 'piquant' sauce was sweeter than it
should have been; a confit of duck glazed in honey, on a bed of red cabbage
(vertical arrangements are the thing here) was very satisfactory, as have been
strawberries on a warm brioche with a sabayon, and a hot Grand Marnier
soufflé with a chocolate sauce. The wine list is almost wholly French. Bottles
below £12 are a rarity and although many are good, the mark-up raises the
odds unreasonably. House wine: £9.50. CELLARMAN'S CHOICE: Ch. Millet
blanc, Graves 1989, £16.95; Hermitage, Cuvée Marquise de la Tourette 1982,
£26.95. More reports, please.

CHEF: Richard Wicks   PROPRIETOR: Raymond Shortland
OPEN: Mon to Sat D, Tue to Fri L
MEALS: 12 to 2, 7 to 11
PRICES: Set L £12.50 (£19), Set D £25.95 (£34)
CARDS: Access, Amex, Diners, Visa
SEATS: 42. Private parties: 22 main room, 10 and 10 private rooms. Car-park, 8 places.
Vegetarian meals. Children's helpings. No children under 5. Smart dress preferred.
No cigars/pipes in dining-room. Music

---

*'The proprietor has an unfortunate habit of listening to his guests' conversations and
joining in with anecdotes which he anticipates will be of interest. This is not always the
case. Perhaps this might be excusable if the quality of the food and wine made up for it. It
does not.'* On eating in the Midlands

*The Guide is totally independent, accepts no free hospitality, and survives on the number
of copies sold each year.*

EPWORTH Humberside

Epworth Tap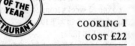

map 5

9–11 Market Place, Epworth DN9 1EU
EPWORTH (0427) 873333

COOKING 1
COST £22

John Wynne calls his wine bar 'off the beaten track' but there must be a million people within driving distance, even if the Isle of Axholme has never entered the list of international gourmandism. The trouble of a journey is amply repaid by robust cookery and a catholic and thoroughbred wine list. The menu is à la carte on week nights but at a set price on Saturdays. It is never long, everything is cooked on the premises, and dishes do not have a fashionable air to them, though they are presented with as much care and forethought as any magazine stylist's: marinated herring; spare ribs; a chicken and vegetable terrine; braised beef in red wine; lasagne; venison casserole; sticky toffee pudding; lemon chiffon. Indeed, the repertoire develops slowly. Within that frame, however, techniques do change: 'We refuse to do any deep frying; meat sauces, with very few exceptions, contain no fresh cream; we cook with olive oil and use extra virgin cold-pressed for our dressings; we trim our meats rigorously.' John Wynne, who admits to going all out on the puddings, has himself been through heart trouble and, fortunately, recovered. It puts a slightly different perspective on restaurant cooking, yet, to counter all those advocates of the 'eat well and die' school, it need not taste worse. How different would be the methods of cooking the dishes mentioned earlier in the 1960s! But who is to say they tasted better? The wine list is served without pretension and without high pressure. If you want guidance, ask because the list has no notes. The prices are exemplary and there are few attempts to stock very old, very expensive bottles. Clarets stop short of first growths, but the 'super-seconds' are plentiful and cheap by anyone's measure. Red burgundies may be the most interesting: good growers, runs of communes for comparison and contrast, fair prices. The Italian selection will set the taste buds tingling and New World Chardonnays might have been chosen for students whose project is 'Discuss the use of oak in wine making'. House Montepulciano d'Abruzzo, £7.50 or white Duboeuf, £6.50.
CELLARMAN'S CHOICE: Pinot Blanc 1988, Rolly Gassmann, £12.50; Gigondas 1973, Jaboulet £13.50.

CHEFS: Helen Wynne and Noreen Smith   PROPRIETORS: Helen and John Wynne
OPEN: Tue to Sat, D only
MEALS: 7.30 to 10 (10.30 Sat)
PRICES: £12 (£18), Set D £12.75 (£18). Minimum £12.75, exc Sat
CARDS: Access, Visa
SEATS: 74. Private parties: 50 main room, 24 private room. Vegetarian meals. Children welcome. Separate smoking area. Wheelchair access (3 steps). Music

---

Cellarman's Choice: A wine recommended by the restaurateur, normally more expensive than house wine.

Restaurateurs justifiably resent no-shows. If you quote a credit card number when booking, you may be liable for the restaurant's lost profit margin if you don't turn up. Always phone to cancel.

ERPINGHAM Norfolk   map 6

Ark

The Street, Erpingham NR11 7QB	COOKING 2
CROMER (0263) 761535	COST £13–£26

The Kidd family tend every stage of the production of food – garden, stove, waiter's tray – in this brick and pantiled cottage characterised by one reader as 'love in turnip-land'. Flowers accompany the visitor at each turn: garden; on pastries; little hedgerow bouquets on the table. Cooking is resolutely non-trendy and generous, though it has absorbed modern lessons in dishes such as a trio of aubergine hors d'oeuvre; gravlax; blinis and sour cream; or a strong suit in vegetarian recipes. Vegetables figure prominently anyway: the accompaniment to a spiced beef and chestnut pie was parsnips, cauliflower, excellent red cabbage with cider, honey and vinegar, and potatoes in several ways, more fitting for Norfolk in January than baby corn, mange-tout and gratin dauphinois might be. Sheila Kidd is not frightened to construct a menu that revolves around long-cooked, family recipes as much as short-order 'restaurant' cooking: Sussex spiced braised steak or pasta with rabbit sauce sit happily with venison noisettes and fillets of lemon sole baked with a prawn, cheese and herb crust, hare agrodolce and 'weeping lamb' with a potato and mushroom gratin with tournedos with caramelised shallots and quail roasted with apples. In the wake of BSE, the beef dishes may come with the note, 'Soil Association organic beef'. Desserts usually comprise substantial fruity tarts and chocolate confections as well as ice-creams and simple mousses. Cheeses are mostly British and well chosen. Chocolates that are served with coffee are homemade. 'How can one promote midweek business?' asks Mike Kidd. His plea, while viewing a packed Saturday night and a blank diary for the rest of the week, will be echoed throughout the land. The short wine list gives more than adequate support. House French: £6 and £6.50. CELLARMAN'S CHOICE: Mâcon-Lugny Les Charmes 1988, £9; Châteauneuf-du-Pape, Ch. Beaucastel 1982, £16.50.

CHEF: Sheila Kidd PROPRIETORS: Mike and Sheila Kidd
OPEN: Tue to Sat, D only and Sun L
MEALS: 12.30 to 2, 7 to 9.30 (10.30 Sat)
PRICES: £16 (£22), Set L £9 (£13) to £11 (£15)
SEATS: 32. Private parties: 38 main room. Car-park, 15 places. Vegetarian meals. Children welcome. No smoking in dining-room. Wheelchair access (1 step; also WC)

ESHER Surrey   map 3

Les Alouettes

7 High Street, Claygate, Esher KT10 0JW	COOKING 3
ESHER (0372) 64882	COST £33–£47

The menu still shows no lack of variety: if you don't like shellfish, the choice of first courses might be salmon, asparagus, Bayonne ham and foie gras – a predictable list for a place that pursues quasi-classic French cooking. Main courses, too, run a routine line through butcher and fishmonger: meat or fish, sauce and trimmings. This apparent conservatism may account for a failure to prepare for a vegetarian who had forewarned of her needs. In the event, it was the customer who told the kitchen what to cook. Charges, too, are predictably high. That vegetarian's meal for two, consisting of four courses and including one and a half portions of a warm truffle salad, cost £88 before service and wine. The restaurant occupies a Victorian half-timbered villa on an exposed corner; park in the British Legion nearby and run if it's raining. The dining-room has many curtains, long tablecloths, mirrors, Russell Flints and a mezzanine balcony on the way to the kitchen (which may in its turn be viewed on the way to the lavatories). Tables are well spaced, the variety of level is pleasing, service (though not invariably with a command of English) more than competent. Michel Perraud's technical standards are high as shown by the square salmon mousse wrapped in a pancake with a bull's-eye of barely cooked sole mousse running through it, ringed by spinach, on a rich beurre blanc; a warm salad of truffles (generous these) with potatoes, beans and an oversharp vinaigrette; a giant but well-chosen tournedos of beef with shallots; or, more recently, calf's liver with a cinnamon sauce and gaufrettes potatoes. Cheeses come in many French varieties, from Olivier. Desserts do not hold any surprises: generally mousses, unctuous and comforting but not arresting. The chocolate mousse parfait that was layered with a thin flaky biscuit had great richness and flavour even if the thin coffee sauce was insufficiently bitter to counter it. The wine list gives good coverage to French classics though skirting round many of the most favoured properties and growers of today. There is a collection of fine clarets at fine prices, including some unfamiliar years. There are plenty of halves on the list, though they did not seem to be profusely available at one winter meal. Menu prices are for two courses and coffee with dessert extra. House wines, a Côtes de Duras and a Côteaux de Languedoc, are £8.75. CELLARMAN'S CHOICE: Ch. Gromel Bel Air 1982, £17; Chablis, premier cru Montée de Tonnerre 1987, Simonet, £27.

CHEF: Michel Perraud   PROPRIETOR: Steve Christou
OPEN: Mon to Sat, exc Sat L
CLOSED: 1 to 12 Jan, 12 Aug to 28 Aug, bank hols
MEALS: 12.15 to 2, 7 to 9.30 (10 Fri and Sat)
PRICES: Set L £19 (£33), Set D from £24 (£39). Service 12.5%
CARDS: Access, Amex, Diners, Visa
SEATS: 75. Private parties: 85 main room. Vegetarian meals. Children's helpings. Smart dress preferred. Wheelchair access (3 steps). Music. Air-conditioned

Le Petit Pierrot

| 4 The Parade, Claygate, Esher KT10 0NU | COOKING 2 |
| ESHER (0372) 65105 | COST £19–£35 |

The Brichots used to have the Pierrot in Esher and then took over these premises, formerly Read's. Hence the *Petit* to the name. Long residence in England has occasioned a particular menu Franglais, as in 'Fricassée de coquilles St Jacques aux mange-tout and pine kernels.' The Brichots have not changed the tented ceiling, but the menu has taken on a French slant, though marinated salmon with quails' eggs, bresaola, calf's liver with sage and lime, and exotic fruit salad with sorbets are standard English restaurant fare. The food is improved by its sauces: a rich Emmenthal sauce with a mousseline of guinea-fowl layered with spinach was well reduced and had taste enough to deserve mopping up with an extra roll; the beurre blanc scattered with pine kernels was great for the mange-tout, even if the scallops were of lower standard. The tarragon and madeira sauce with four plump lamb chops with a herb crust had good texture and taste, but the tarragon was evanescent. Desserts are enjoyable, from Christmas pudding ice-cream to a rich, calvados-soaked terrine of chocolate or a charlotte of apples that was in fact sliced poached apple wrapped in a filo bundle. A pleasant neighbourhood restaurant in which Annie Brichot makes you welcome and Jean-Pierre may tour the tables. There is a short, unambitious wine list, mainly French, of course. House wine: £6.75.

CHEF: Jean-Pierre Brichot   PROPRIETORS: Jean-Pierre and Annie Brichot
OPEN: Mon to Sat, exc Sat L
MEALS: 12.15 to 2, 7.15 to 10
PRICES: Set L £13.75 (£19) to £16.50 (£22), Set D £18.50 (£26) to £21 (£29)
CARDS: Access, Amex, Diners, Visa
SEATS: 28. Smart dress preferred. Wheelchair access. Music. Air-conditioned

EVERSHOT Dorset   map 2

▲ *Summer Lodge* ♟

Evershot DT2 0JR   COOKING 1
EVERSHOT (0935) 83424   COST £19–£32

The Corbetts have a new chef in Roger Jones, formerly at the Rising Sun, St Mawes, and reports speak of his changing the style of the kitchen at this country-house hotel, always appreciated for the warmth of its welcome and sure anticipation of guests' wants. However, to date the verdict is unclear and the jury must remain out. One comment was that there was too much 'using up', that the laudable French ideal of economy in the kitchen was taken too far. Some successes have been recorded: a loin of lamb with rosemary mousse and plain lamb gravy; a piece of brill with langoustines; pork fillet with tomatoes. Baking has also been appreciated, from hot-cross buns to pastry. The format of the menu is a set price for a choice of three first courses, a soup in the middle, again three choices of main course, then cheeses and various puddings and sweets. The main courses will be one vegetarian, one fish and one meat, so choice for conservative eaters is more restricted than it seems. The improvement in the wine list is more certain. Prices are not high at all and there is a long list of clarets and burgundies with strong support from Italy and useful Spanish and New World sections, plus many half-bottles. House wine: £7.95. CELLARMAN'S CHOICE: Ch. du Marbuzet 1981, £14.65; Pinot Grigio del Piave 1988, Stepski-Doliva, £10.60.

Consumers' Association is planning to publish Out to Eat, *a new guide to budget eating out in restaurants, pubs, cafés, brasseries and so on. Please send reports and recommendations to Out to Eat, FREEPOST, 2 Marylebone Road, London NW1 1YN.*

CHEF: Roger Jones PROPRIETORS: Nigel and Margaret Corbett
OPEN: all week
CLOSED: 2 to 23 Jan
MEALS: 12.30 to 1.30, 7.30 to 8.30
PRICES: Set L £13.75 (£19), Set D £22.50 (£27). Service inc
CARDS: Access, Visa
SEATS: 48. 28 tables outside. Private parties: 28 main room. Car-park, 30 places. Vegetarian
meals. No children under 8. Wheelchair access (also WC)
ACCOMMODATION: 17 rooms, all with bath/shower. Rooms for disabled. B&B £60 to £100.
No children under 8. Pets welcome. Afternoon teas. Garden. Swimming-pool. Tennis.
Fishing. Golf. Phone. Scenic. Doors close at midnight. Confirm by 6. [*Which? Hotel Guide*]

EVERSLEY Hampshire   map 2

New Mill

New Mill Road, Eversley RG27 0RA
EVERSLEY (0734) 732277   COOKING 2
off A327, ½m N of Eversley   COST £21–£41

A mill conversion where outside dining is possible with views of ducks on the
pond and the haze of midsummer inducing contentment. New chef Robert
Allen is cooking an ambitious menu, as might be expected from his experience
at the Dorchester in London and Hintlesham Hall. People have reported
favourably on terrines with home-made chutneys; whitebait; three vegetable
mousses with watercress sauce; salmon with tarragon sauce; roast pork with
prunes; banana cheesecake; summer pudding; and decent cheeses. The *carte*
comes dear, especially with a stiff surcharge for vegetables, but the set-price
menus seem fair value. Service is described as invariably willing though
sometimes either slow or amateur. The wine list is a good one, obviously cared
about. The notes are long. The selection is a mixture of big names and smaller
but thoroughbred growers. Prices are not low, with little below £12 and
climbing steeply thereafter. House wine: £9. CELLARMAN'S CHOICE: Ch. Haut-
Brisson, St Emilion 1985, £21.50; Bourgogne Blanc, les Clous 1987, A. de
Villaine, £17.50.

CHEF: Robert Allen PROPRIETORS: New Mill Restaurants Ltd
OPEN: all week, exc Sat L
MEALS: 12 to 2, 7 to 10 (9 Sun)
PRICES: £25 (£34), Set L £16.50 (£21) to £17.50 (£22), Set D £19.50 (£24) to £24.50 (£29).
Service inc
CARDS: Access, Amex, Diners, Visa
SEATS: 75. 6 tables outside. Private parties: 100 to 250 main room, 10 and 30 private rooms.
Car-park, 50 places. Vegetarian meals. Children's helpings on request. No-smoking area on
request. Wheelchair access (2 steps; also unisex WC). Music

---

*The 1992 Guide will be published before Christmas 1991. Reports on meals are most
welcome at any time of the year, but are extremely valuable in the spring. Send them to
The Good Food Guide, FREEPOST, 2 Marylebone Road, London NW1 1YN. No stamp
is needed if posted in the UK.*

The Guide always appreciates hearing about changes of chef or owner.

▲ Cedar Restaurant, Evesham Hotel ♥

Cooper's Lane, Evesham WR11 6DA   COOKING 1
EVESHAM (0386) 765566   COST £12–£25

John Jenkinson's sense of humour rolls on and on in this comfortable house with a cedar of Lebanon on the lawn and a new wing that has avoided obtrusiveness. 'I know some people find it (that sense of humour) over the top, but I always have a wonderful time. He obviously loves his work.' His work means pleasing everybody, including the children, who will find toys in the lavatories as well as their own menu, complete with jokes, at the table. The cooking, too, is rumbustious, occasionally misfiring on all cylinders, but pleasing many with meals such as baked gratin of mushrooms; spinach and prawn roulade with tomato coulis; breast of pheasant with a whisky sauce; lamb's liver with Cassis; a light meringue cake with chocolate mousse; or a redoubtable banoffi flan with good pastry. There is a bargain lunchtime buffet, but starters, desserts and coffee are extra. The man's humour is catching, and the staff treat you amiably as well as effectively. Wines and spirits are a strong point with lists that go beyond France – indeed stray into it only for Marquis de Sade and a few other Champagnes. If you need a range of Tunisian, Peruvian or Mexican bottles, refer to the Cedar. The wild collector's instinct has netted some excellent New World makers such as Wynn, Knapstein, Blass, Montana and Cloudy Bay from Australasia, or Heitz, Iron Horse, Ridge and Acacia from California, as well as names from every other North American wine-producing state. House wines: £6.40. CELLARMAN'S CHOICE: Cousiño Macul Antiguas Reservas 1983, £10.40, from Chile; Fall Creek Sauvignon Blanc 1988, £14.50, from Texas. Prices are very fair. Tips are not expected.

CHEF: Ian Mann   PROPRIETORS: The Jenkinson family
OPEN: all week
CLOSED: 25 and 26 Dec
MEALS: 12.30 to 2, 7 to 9.30
PRICES: £17 (£21), L buffet £5.80 (£12) to £12 (£18). Service inc
CARDS: Access, Amex, Diners, Visa
SEATS: 55. Private parties: 12 main room, 15 private room. Car-park, 50 places. Vegetarian meals. Children's helpings. Wheelchair access (also WC)
ACCOMMODATION: 40 rooms, all with bath/shower. B&B £54 to £70. Baby facilities. Pets welcome outside public rooms. Afternoon teas. Garden. Swimming-pool. TV. Phone. Scenic. Doors close at midnight. Confirm by 6 [Which? Hotel Guide]

'I have never had much difficulty squaring my conscience regarding the amount I am prepared to spend on excellent eating out, but I have to say that spending around £45 on a meal centred on plaice and chips seems to me to represent an act of gross vulgarity when people are living in cardboard boxes not far away.' On dining in Chelsea

See the inside of the front cover for an explanation of the 1 to 5 rating system recognising cooking standards.

EXETER Devon	map 1

▲ *Tudor House*

Tudor Street, Exeter EX4 3BR	COOKING 2
EXETER (0392) 73764	COST £15–£30

Exeter survived the last war in small patches. Tudor House is a leftover of a town changed beyond recognition. In the last year Jean Cooke has added guest bedrooms, 'comfortable but not luxurious', a service welcomed by at least two who stayed a month, eating often, while on business in the city. There are times when the half-timbered, heavily beamed house with leaded windows gets as much comment as the food, but there has been plenty of enjoyment of the set-price lunch and dinner menus and a *carte* of more than half a dozen dishes at each course. This last works to a formula little changed from year to year: lamb, steak, fish, scaloppines of veal and Ken Lo's duck in yellow-bean sauce. The variations are built on this scaffolding. Thus the veal may be done with redcurrant and leeks where before it came with mushrooms and wild rice. This certainly keeps the butcher sane. Fish cookery is enjoyed, both what the market may bring and regularly featured salmon. Game or near-game, too, will be offered on the set-price menu or as an extra: a pie of pigeon, rabbit and guinea-fowl cooked with Guinness under an excellent crust has been appreciated. The desserts also see old favourites such as syllabub or squidgy rhubarb cake with clotted cream and toffee sauce. Cheese, with many Devon examples, is well presented. Service is always amiable, sometimes characterful and often knowledgeable about the wines offered on a list that arranges them by colour and weight. The cellar has grown in the last year, taking in some more from Italy and the New World. Christopher Piper continues to be an important supplier; note particularly his excellent Brouilly, Ch. des Tours. The range is adequate, but the mark-up system strongly favours the lower end. House Duboeuf is £6.45. There is three per cent surcharge on payment by credit card, noted on the bill but not the menu.

CHEF/PROPRIETOR: Jean Cooke
OPEN: Tue to Sat
MEALS: 12.15 to 1.45, 7.15 to 9.45
PRICES: £16 (£25), Set L £9.95 (£15) to £12.95 (£18), Set D £14.90 (£21)
CARDS: Access, Amex, Diners, Visa
SEATS: 44. Private parties: 65 main room. Vegetarian meals. Children's helpings. Wheelchair access (2 steps; also WC). Air-conditioned
ACCOMMODATION: 4 rooms, all with bath/shower. B&B £23 to £46. Children welcome. Phone

FARNHAM Surrey	map 3

Krug's

84 West Street, Farnham GU9 7EN	COOKING 2
FARNHAM (0252) 723277	COST £30

There's *The Sound of Music* in the Surrey hills and Gerhard Krug cooks a menu as thoroughly Austrian as the table settings and ornaments found in the raftered dining-room of this deceptively large restaurant. The menu changes not at all:

three soups; rye bread; marinated herrings; fondues; veal, pork, and even plaice, *schnitzeln*; four sorts of steak. What lifts this above caricature is professionalism and fair ingredients. The breadcrumbs for the wiener schnitzel are home-made, the meats lightly fried, vegetables cleanly cooked – including red cabbage with crisp apple and sultanas 'wonderfully pungent with cloves.' Although the frying pan is in constant use, also the fondue pot, there is also a braised dish of sauerkraut with bratwurst and dumpling. Puddings of nockerln, sachertorte and strudels show the natural Austrian flair for sweet baking. 'The sachertorte was a very light chocolate sponge with a soft slightly bitter chocolate icing over the apricot glaze. Although rich, the lightness of the cake reconciled us to it entirely.' The short wine list includes a handful of Austrian bottles. There are no halves but there is a one-eighth litre of Glühwein. House Australian: £7.80 a litre. There is plenty of ice-cold schnapps.

CHEF: Gerhard Krug   PROPRIETORS: Gerhard and Karin Krug
OPEN: Tue to Sat, D only
MEALS: 7 to 10.30 (11.30 Sat)
PRICES: £16 (£25)
CARDS: Access, Visa
SEATS: 90. Private parties: 50 main room, 50 private room. Children welcome. Wheelchair access. Music

---

FAVERSHAM Kent   map 3

Read's ♟

Painter's Forstal, Faversham ME13 0EE   COOKING 3
FAVERSHAM (0795) 535344   COST £19–40

'Apparently an old supermarket and still looks like it from the outside,' was the comment of one who braved the plate-glass windows and sat down to an excellent and fair-priced lunch. This offers a reasonable choice of dishes that would cost almost double on the *carte*. It is often appreciated. The food is modern and professional. Some might say that it is also slick, which may be from surprise that a full-dress restaurant should survive in such an unpropitious spot. The best dishes can have pronounced flavours and creative composition: a hot mousse of smoked haddock had decent texture, a good butter sauce with diced tomato and chives and a matchlessly *mollet* quail's egg perched on top of the mousse; a beef tournedos was sauced with a very modern oily warm vinaigrette and wreathed by a selection of Provençal vegetables – onions done in oil, olives, tomatoes, artichoke buttons, courgettes, mushrooms and slivers of anchovy. The sauce was excellent, the beef of decent quality. Other ideas have been well received, for example a breast of duck with blackcurrant sauce impressed a reader by the flavour of the duck itself, and amused by the pile of shredded duck skin cooked until the fat ran, but was disappointing for the crudeness of the caramelised sauce. The arrangement on the plate often involves wreaths – circlets of vegetables, a ring of crème caramel – and there is sometimes an overemphasis on decoration – every vegetable must be turned. That detracts from taste. This may be especially apparent in the desserts. David Pitchford likes to engage the customer in some give-and-take, so invites comments on juxtaposed ingredients: two types of

289

asparagus, three sorts of smoked fish mousses (salmon, trout and mackerel). He also has eminently sensible and constructive views on feeding children, even if he does allow pipe smokers to puff away and charges extra for vegetables, and has recruited a well-motivated and helpful staff. The wine list is a surprising collection of 'odds' and mainstream bottles; the quality and prices of the bin-end wines indicate that they might move fast. Generally prices are fair and vintages, especially for clarets, top-rate. There is something for every pocket, from the 1978 Côte-Rôtie from Jamet at £42 to a very fair selection under £12; order with confidence. House French: £9.50. CELLARMAN'S CHOICE: St-Véran 1988, Latour, £11; Ch. Langoa-Barton 1978, £29.

CHEF: David Pitchford   PROPRIETORS: David and Rona Pitchford
OPEN: Tue to Sat
MEALS: 12 to 2, 7 to 10
PRICES: £22 (£31), Set L £12.50 (£19), Set D £26 (£33). Service inc
CARDS: Access, Amex, Diners, Visa
SEATS: 60. 3 tables outside. Private parties: 60 main room, 12 private room. Car-park, 30 places. Children's helpings. Wheelchair access (1 step; also WC). Music

---

FELSTED   Essex   map 3

Rumbles Cottage

Braintree Road, Felsted CM6 3DJ   COOKING 2
GREAT DUNMOW (0371) 820996   COST £15–£28

'Cottage' is the right description for the whitewashed building with almost a 'tea shoppe' interior, in the centre of the village. There is no Miss Marples dwelling therein, but a cook with an eye for adventure: Joy Hadley likes to experiment with herbs (some of which she grows herself), spices and combinations. She offers 'guinea-pig' menus Tuesday to Thursday at dinner to confirm her findings and cooks an eclectically British repertoire: cream and cottage cheese gateau with a watercress sauce; tomatoes filled with basil mousse; tarragon chicken with raisins; calf's sweetbreads with Meaux mustard; red pepper and Gruyère roulade; enterprising vegetables; banana, rum and coffee ramekin; marmalade ice-cream. When it fails, it does so resoundingly, but reports are warmly in favour of her enthusiasm and that of all the staff (who are expected to work both in front of and behind the kitchen door). Prices, for a place so near London, are quite pre-inflationary. House wines: £6.50. The modest wine list is appropriately priced and contains a few good wines – especially Italian – but there are too many from the big houses to promote full confidence. CELLARMAN'S CHOICE: Chardonnay 1988, Montana, £9.45; Ch. Pindefleurs 1985, £14.50.

CHEF: E. Joy Hadley   PROPRIETORS: E. Joy Hadley and M. Donovan
OPEN: Tue to Sat, D only and Sun L
CLOSED: 3 weeks Feb
MEALS: 12 to 2, 7 to 9
PRICES: £16 (£23), Set L £11.50 (£16), Set D mid-week £10.50 (£15)
CARDS: Access, Visa
SEATS: 46. Private parties: 24 main room, 8 and 10 private rooms. Vegetarian meals. Children's helpings. No smoking arranged on booking. Wheelchair access

FLETCHING East Sussex   map 3

▲ *Griffin*

Fletching TN22 3NS   COOKING 1
NEWICK (0825) 722890   COST £25

Like all good English villages, Fletching has a Norman church and an only
slightly less ancient pub. They are about 50 yards apart along a street littered
with ye olde half-timbered houses. The Griffin has two bars; in winter there
will be a roaring fire in one. From the restaurant there are views of a garden. In
the summer it appears extensive; in any season it leads to Sheffield Park, a
National Trust property, and to the South Downs. Any pub with ambitions to
serve good food inevitably finds itself in an unforgiving territory between the
twin peaks of pubs and restaurants. Readers have reported that they are
grateful that the Griffin has made a foray into potentially hostile culinary
country. Natives and visitors alike have begun to appreciate Nigel and Bridget
Pullan's efforts, won over by meals that have included boned quail with an
apple and calvados mousseline; fillet of red mullet with a rosemary butter
sauce, brill with paprika mousse, and warm salad of pigeon breasts and pine
nuts. A few dishes, like watercress pancake filled with a fricassee of monkfish,
are either over-ambitious in concept or too demanding to be executed
satisfactorily. Meat tends to be overcooked, so stipulate your requirements.
Desserts are basic and coffee can be weak. The wine list is fairly adventurous,
carefully constructed and generously priced. Although there are no halves, a
laudable number of wines are available by the glass. House French is £6.80.
The alternative is real ale from Harveys. If it becomes prudent not to drive
home, there are comfortable bedrooms, some with four-poster beds.
CELLARMAN'S CHOICE: Breaky Bottom, Seyval Blanc 1989, £10.50; Ch. Bonnet,
André Hunton 1987, £10.90.

CHEF: Ann Read   PROPRIETORS: Nigel and Bridget Pullan
OPEN: all week, exc Sun D
CLOSED: 24 Dec D, 25 Dec
MEALS: 12 to 2, 7 to 10 (10.30 Sat)
PRICES: £15 (£21). Service 10%
CARDS: Access, Amex, Visa
SEATS: 110. 6 tables outside. Private parties: 50 main room, 30 private room. Car-park, 25
places. Vegetarian meals. Children's helpings. Wheelchair access (1 step)
ACCOMMODATION: 4 rooms, all with bath/shower. B&B £25 to £50. Baby facilities. Garden.
Snooker. TV. Scenic. Doors close at 11.30. Confirm by 6

FOWEY Cornwall   map 1

Food for Thought

Town Quay, Fowey PL23 1AT   COOKING 3
FOWEY (072 683) 2221   COST £23–£41

The Billingsleys' quayside restaurant continues to deliver not only fine fish
dishes but self-assured cooking right across the board. Some items are
deceptively simple, allowing the ingredients and natural flavours to assert

themselves: grilled lemon sole, rack of lamb roasted with rosemary sauce, breast of French duck cooked exactly as ordered and fanned out on a burgundy sauce. But there are more elaborate ideas too. Mille-feuille of Scotch salmon is topped with asparagus and served with a white wine and chive sauce enriched with hollandaise. The quality of the raw materials and execution shows in the 'memorable' rendezvous of mixed fish (John Dory, brill and salmon, with scallops, mussels and squid) with cream and wine sauce. Meat dishes like kidneys on brioche with port wine sauce or a salad of pigeon breasts show the same willingness to cook fairly straight dishes with aplomb and good taste. Sticky toffee pudding has sometimes lacked that essential stickiness, but caramelised lemon tart and poached William pear with spun sugar and vanilla and raspberry sauce have been excellent. Presentation is pretty, but portions are anything but nouvelle. Even petits fours come in abundance. Although clarets are well chosen, the wine list generally lacks the ambition of the cooking; prices are fair. House Muscadet: £6.95. CELLARMAN'S CHOICE: Cabernet Sauvignon Shiraz, Brown Bros 1985, £10.75.

CHEF: Martin Billingsley   PROPRIETORS: Martin and Caroline Billingsley
OPEN: Mon to Sat, D only
CLOSED: Jan/early Feb
MEALS: 7 to 9.30
PRICES: £23 (£34), Set D £16.50 (£23)
CARDS: Access, Visa
SEATS: 38. Private parties: 20 main room. No children under 5. Wheelchair access

---

FRAMPTON-ON-SEVERN Gloucestershire   map 2

Saverys

The Green, Frampton-on-Severn GL2 7EA   COOKING 2
GLOUCESTER (0452) 740077   COST £31

The front door, off the largest green in England, leads into the restaurant in an old brick house. Once inside the small room – where pink seems a favourite colour and the *Four Seasons* may be the forty by the end of the night – the visitor will not find many tables, will see a set-price menu of perhaps four alternatives chalked on a blackboard, and will be served satisfying food. John Savery cooks quite simply: mushrooms in a cream curry sauce; beef consommé; grilled Dover sole; kidneys with a mustard sauce; beef with madeira; lots of vegetables; apple pie; sticky toffee pudding; white chocolate mousse. The sauces are direct, the meats are often of good quality. A visitor, initially unimpressed by the menu, went away happy that the duck he had been served was the paradigm of British restaurant duck. In short a country place delivering sound food. Patricia Carpenter's friendly approach creates the feel of a family-run enterprise, but avoids intruding on those who wish solitude. The wine list is short and sweet. House wine from Boisset is £7.45.

Restaurateurs justifiably resent no-shows. If you quote a credit card number when booking, you may be liable for the restaurant's lost profit margin if you don't turn up. Always phone to cancel.

CHEFS/PROPRIETORS: John Savery and Patricia Carpenter
OPEN: Tue to Sat, D only (lunch by arrangement)
MEALS: 7 to 9.15
PRICES: Set D £18.95 (£26)
CARD: Access, Visa
SEATS: 26. Private parties: 26 main room. No children under 12. No pipes in dining-room.
Wheelchair access. Music

FRESSINGFIELD Suffolk   map 6

Fox and Goose ▼

Fressingfield IP21 5PB   COOKING 2
FRESSINGFIELD (037 986) 247   COST £24 −£41

The Clarke family pioneered a system whereby you booked a table, received a
menu by post and chose your meal in advance. Turning up at the half-timbered
former inn next to the churchyard, built in the eighteenth century, you had only
to select a wine and get down to the food. Nearly 25 years on, Adrian Clarke
has maintained the arrangement, though he has added a range of shorter menus
for casual visitors without the time or foresight to phone ahead. Even on these,
the feeling that everything is cooked just for you is preserved. On Sundays
there are two menus: the 'family' lunch centres on a roast chicken, cooked and
carved for each table of at least two people. The 'seasonal' lunch might be a
gigot of spring lamb en croûte, again cooked for each table. The advantages to
the Clarkes are easier planning and the opportunity to offer a greater range of
produce without resorting to constant freezing. Cooking has not moved into the
olive oil, chilli, lentil and lollo rosso phase. Sweetbreads 'Adrian' are served
with a white wine, cream and mushroom sauce in a puff pastry case; a summer
salad is of quails' eggs, langoustines and king prawns with mayonnaise and
horseradish; a range of steaks come with good substantial sauces; duck −
perhaps the speciality − is crisp of skin and takes half a bottle of port in the
orange sauce, or is cooked with an apple, prune, calvados and cream sauce.
Desserts usually include a hot soufflé: pear with an apricot sauce or raspberry
with a raspberry coulis. There are other fairly substantial items, not least the
ice-creams, or a 'Fox and Goose Special' of fruit sponge soaked in alcohols and
served in a chocolate case. There are some who think the set-price meals are
better value than the *cartes*. This is in part due to the latter dealing
predominantly in prime ingredients. The wine list includes some enterprising
bottles though its principal strength lies in claret. It has an impressive range of
vintages and properties, but a shortage of half-bottles. Burgundy is strong,
with growers of the class of Sauzet and Dujac prominent. Lower priced wines
are carefully chosen as well. French house wine: £10. CELLARMAN'S CHOICE:
Châteauneuf-du-Pape, Dom. du Vieux Télégraphe 1985, £19.

The Guide *office can quickly spot when a restaurateur is encouraging customers to write
recommending inclusion and sadly, several restaurants have been doing this in 1990. Such
reports do not further a restaurant's cause. Please tell us if a restaurateur invites you to
write to the* Guide.

CHEF: Adrian Clarke   PROPRIETORS: Adrian and Rachel Clarke
OPEN: all week, exc Tue L and D and Sun D
CLOSED: 2 weeks Jan to Feb, 2 weeks mid-Sept
MEALS: 12 to 1.30, 7 to 9
PRICES: £24 (£34), Set L and D £16.50 (£24). Licensed, also bring your own: corkage £3.
CARDS: Access, Amex, Diners, Visa
SEATS: 26. Private parties: 32 main room. Car-park, 30 places. No children under 10.
No smoking except between courses at bar

FROGHALL   Staffordshire   map 5

Wharf

Foxt Road, Froghall ST10 2HJ
IPSTONES (0538) 266486   COOKING 1
just off A52   COST £14–£25

The restored Caldon Canal is home to this warehouse, base for canal trips in a
narrow boat and site of inventive cookery by Mrs Young, a vegetarian who is
willing to knock up a demi-glace for those of different persuasion. The
approach is creative modern, imbued with that catholicism of ingredients
promoted by eschewing meat. Fruits get frequent outing with meat,
particularly in first courses, and sauces may be based on vegetable purées as
much as stock or alcohol reductions. Sunday lunch, not expensive, is popular,
especially as full advantage can be taken of the setting. Service may be tenuous
when busy. Three dozen wines include the Vegetarian Society's approved
Greek organics, Disos, and some decent inexpensive bottles. Details are fairly
sparse in some instances. House wine: £7.30.

CHEF: J.M. Young   PROPRIETORS: R. and J. Young and M.L. St Claire
OPEN: Tue to Sat, D only and Sun L
MEALS: 12 to 1.30, 7.30 to 9.15
PRICES: £16 (£21), Set L £10.25 (£14). Service inc
CARDS: Access, Visa
SEATS: 32. Private parties: 32 main room. Car-park, 50 places. Vegetarian meals. Children's
helpings. Wheelchair access (1 step). Air-conditioned

GILLINGHAM   Dorset   map 2

▲ Stock Hill House

Wyke, Gillingham SP8 5NR   COOKING 3
GILLINGHAM (0747) 823626   COST £24–£37

This Victorian manor house, built around 1830, stretches the 'Lloyd George's
secretary slept here' school of publicity almost to the limit. It was 'once the
home of Osbert Lancaster's grandfather'. Refurbishment has brought
'solecisms and gaudy colours, but the overall impression is homely and
welcoming.' This is helped by the scale of the house – more intimate than
grand – as well as by Nita Hauser's natural talent as hostess. The strong
temptation to spot the influence of the proprietors' Austrian background in
everything is probably best curtailed: the food owes more to good supplies and

intelligent treatment than to the sometimes restricting demands of a national cuisine. What stands out is the classic simplicity of dishes, at least until we reach the puddings. Braised ox tongue is served with madeira sauce, medallions of pork with a light mustard sauce. Look in vain for risky undertakings; praise instead the attention to detail. Vegetable soups such as carrot and celeriac, are 'rich, flavoursome, outstanding', and constitute the second of four courses. Seafood and game are a delight, from Dorset hare to red sea bream to crab and leek terrine served with tomato mayonnaise. Unabashed plainness, as in fillet steak with green peppercorn sauce, works because of the high quality of ingredients. Linzer cake with cream works because it is rich and complicated. Brûlées, tarts, Malakofftorte, and pineapple meringue Suchard are among the other sweet distractions. Wines are fairly priced and include good value among petit château clarets, along the Loire, and in Provence. The amount of good drinking for under £15 a bottle is commendable. CELLARMAN'S CHOICE: Gigondas, Dom. St Gayan 1985, £14.80; Cassis, Clos Ste Magdelaine 1988, £12.40.

CHEF: Peter Hauser PROPRIETORS: Peter and Nita Hauser
OPEN: Tue to Sat, D only (lunch by arrangement weekdays)
MEALS: 12.30 to 1.45, 7.30 to 8.45
PRICES: Set L £18 (£24), Set D £25 (£31)
CARDS: Access, Visa
SEATS: 26. Private parties: 12 main room, 12 private room. Car-park, 25 places. Children's helpings (L only). No children under 7. Smart dress preferred. No smoking in dining-room
ACCOMMODATION: 8 rooms, all with bath/shower. B&B £60 to £130. Deposit: £40. No children under 7. Garden. Swimming-pool. TV. Phone. Scenic. Doors close at midnight. Confirm by 8 [Which? Hotel Guide]

GLASTONBURY Somerset   map 2

▲ *Number 3*

Magdalene Street, Glastonbury BA6 9EW   COOKING 1
GLASTONBURY (0458) 32129   COST £33–£48

Number 3 is a handsome Georgian house surrounded by a lush small garden. First-time visitors may be in for a shock when the door is opened: this house is *decorated*. Strong colours or wallpapers give it a doll's-house air, in the dining-room especially, where deep crimson carpet and walls are separated only by a white dado. It is memorable. Anne Tynan's repertoire remains very stable over the years – desserts are almost identical to those of 1988 –although a vegetarian dish has been added to the main courses and there is a welcome emphasis on lightness – for example, using fromage frais and yoghurt in sauces rather than cream. Fruit is a favourite highlight to savoury dishes: a smoked chicken salad is garnished with a strawberry as well as avocado and two sauces: mango and raspberry; calf's liver is cut thick, too thick for some, and finished with kumquats and a madeira sauce. Generally the small menu revolves round good materials fairly cooked; lobsters are thus kept live in the tank that has long been a feature. They are cooked to order and the shells resurface in the stock for the shellfish sauce used with a fish – perhaps sea bass or salmon – wrapped in filo. Desserts are good on ice-cream: the vanilla served with the strawberry vacherin was excellent. Cream or yoghurt is offered with the brandy-snaps filled with fresh fruit. Chocolate addicts are still served by the chocolate truffle soaked in cognac with nuts and cherries, now accompanied by a white chocolate and Malibu sauce – enough to undo any lightness that may have come before. There is a century of wines. House wine: £8.50.

CHEF: Ann Tynan   PROPRIETORS: John and Ann Tynan
OPEN: Tue to Sat, D only
CLOSED: Jan
MEALS: 7 to 9.15
PRICES: Set D £24 (£33) to £30 (£40)
CARDS: Amex, Visa
SEATS: 28. 2 tables outside. Private parties: 12 main room. Car-park, 8 places. Children's helpings on request. No children under 5. Smart dress preferred. No smoking in dining-room
ACCOMMODATION: 6 rooms, all with bath/shower. B&B £40 to £60. No children under 2. Garden. TV. Phone. Scenic. Doors close at 11.30. Confirm by 6

GLEMSFORD Suffolk   map 3

Barretts ♥

31 Egremont Street, Glemsford CO10 7SA   COOKING 3
GLEMSFORD (0787) 281573   COST £17–£37

The style is becoming more assured as the restaurant evolves and matures. Diane Barrett supervises the service with courtesy and charm, in a room whose decor is considered unworthy of her and her husband's talents. If there is to be an imbalance, that way is preferable. Nicholas Barrett's cooking fires readers with enthusiasm. Lightness of texture and deftness in saucing are among his trademarks, and the fluency of ideas shows to best advantage in first courses: tomato and red pepper sauce beside oyster mushrooms in paper-thin pastry; a herby dressing with fillets of red mullet. There is a freshness about the ideas and a simplicity of design that appeal. Breast of quail is served on a galette of potato with a rosemary sauce; smoked haddock hot-pot comes with leeks and a soy sauce, tuned to the right degree of piquancy. The pace slows for main courses, but ingredients and technique do not waver. Venison casserole with sweet onions and a red wine sauce, and breast of pheasant in a port sauce, were two successes in winter. 'Nicholas Barrett is keen on lobsters, which he keeps alive until ready for cooking; this shows in the quality of the flesh when it is served.' Puddings – especially those made from chocolate – benefit from his lightness of touch, and there is a dream of a soufflé into which a ball of ice-cream is dropped at the moment of serving. Presentation is attractive. Cheeses are British. The New World receives the attention it deserves on the wine list, which means that we get plenty of taste for our money. Among the pleasures are Rothbury Estate's Brokenback Chardonnay 1988 from the Hunter Valley and New Zealand's best Cabernet Sauvignon, Te Mata's Coleraine 1986. Italy and Spain have barely a mention. There is a good spread of prices, from three figures on the short fine wine selection to house Duboeuf at £7.75.

CHEF: Nicholas Barrett   PROPRIETORS: Nicholas and Diane Barrett
OPEN: Tue to Sat, D only and Sun L
MEALS: 12 to 2, 7 to 9.30
PRICES: £25 (£31), Set L £12.95 (£17). Service inc
CARDS: Access, Visa
SEATS: 18. Private parties: 12 main room. Car-park, 10 places. Children's helpings (Sun L only). Wheelchair access

---

GLEWSTONE   Hereford & Worcester   map 4

▲ *Glewstone Court*

Glewstone, Ross-on-Wye HR9 6AW   COOKING 1
LLANGARRON (098 984) 367   COST £15–£26

Orchards and a cedar of Lebanon act as a frame to this eighteenth-century house with Victorian additions. The Reeve-Tuckers make a point of relaxed hospitality, yet seem to get things done at the same time. One person remarked it was like 'wandering into the house of an eccentric couple' where meals are served. Four children, cats and dogs tend to keep one's grip on reality quite firm, 'eccentric' or not. The house in winter is filled with bowls of potpourri and great vases of everlasting flowers; the walls are ragged, stencilled, stippled and variously painted. As for the food, combinations of flavours on the short daily menu do not invariably work: baked mushrooms with cream cheese and avocado is never going to be strongly flavoured, nor is a three-nut pâté with a sour cream and chive sauce. What stand out are the satisfying partnerships of good raw materials and decent sauces, as in Wye salmon with a lemon sauce; grilled breast of duck with an apricot sauce or fresh pasta with a bacon and basil sauce. Vegetables have been enjoyed – often organic, often home-grown. Desserts may be British (Sussex pond pudding); modern British (banoffi tart); or fruity (fresh pineapple with mango sorbet). The wine list is short in quantity and detail, and cheap. House wine: £6. More reports, please.

CHEF: Christine Reeve-Tucker   PROPRIETORS: Christine and William Reeve-Tucker
OPEN: Tue to Sat, D only, and Sun L (other days by arrangement)
CLOSED: 25 and 26 Dec
MEALS: 12.15 to 2, 7 to 9.30
PRICES: Set Sun L £10.95 (£15), Set D £16.95 (£22)
CARDS: Access, Amex, Visa
SEATS: 36. 3 tables outside. Private parties: 24 main room, 26 and 34 private rooms. Car-park, 24 places. Vegetarian meals. Children's helpings. Wheelchair access (also unisex WC). Music
ACCOMMODATION: 7 rooms, all with bath/shower. B&B £39 to £58. Deposit: £10. Baby facilities. Pets welcome but not in dining-room. Garden. TV. Phone. Scenic. Doors close at midnight. Confirm by noon

---

Consumers' Association is planning to publish Out to Eat, *a new guide to budget eating out in restaurants, pubs, cafés, brasseries and so on. Please send reports and recommendations to Out to Eat, FREEPOST, 2 Marylebone Road, London NW1 1YN.*

Report forms are at the back of the book; write a letter if you prefer.

GLOUCESTER Gloucestershire   map 2

College Green

9 College Street, Gloucester GL1 2NE   COOKING 1
GLOUCESTER (0452) 20739   COST £13–£23

College Street connects Westgate with the Cathedral Green, and this restaurant
on the sloping first floor of a half-timbered house is a useful local resource. It is
much valued by business people and habitués of nearby courts. 'I never
thought there would be a place like this in Gloucester,' remarked one visitor to
the Three Choirs Festival who found the early evening opening useful before
going to a concert. Soups, perhaps leek and potato, spiced tomato or onion; a
sparky kedgeree; asparagus mousse with chervil and leek sauce; lamb with
madeira sauce; pork stuffed with herbs; pheasant in a cider sauce; and plentiful
vegetables are some of the dishes enjoyed. These steer a course between
adventurous and steady. Casseroles of lamb or beef are not ignored and Severn
salmon is offered during most of the season. Desserts have included good
lemon tart. The wine list shows the same good sense as the cooking. Bottles are
far from run of the mill, yet there are not too many of them and prices are sane.
House wine: £7. CELLARMAN'S CHOICE: Gigondas, Dom. St Gayan 1985, £12;
Côtes du Rhône Blanc 1987, Puyméras, £8.50. Service is invariably
characterised as friendly, obliging and assiduous, if on occasion gently paced.

CHEF: David Spencer   PROPRIETORS: David and Frances Spencer
OPEN: Mon to Sat, exc Mon and Tue D
CLOSED: bank hols
MEALS: 12 to 2, 6.30 to 9.30
PRICES: £14 (£19), Set L £9.50 (£13) to £14.50 (£18). Service inc. Licensed, also bring your
own: corkage £3 per bottle
CARDS: Access, Amex, Visa
SEATS: 30. Private parties: 44 main room, 30 private room. Children's helpings

GOLCAR West Yorkshire   map 5

Weavers Shed

Knowl Road, Golcar HD7 4AN   COOKING 1
HUDDERSFIELD (0484) 654284   COST £14–£29

This converted eighteenth-century stone cloth mill attracts mixed reports. It is
valued for a 'traditionally English feel in dishes and presentation' which will
be apparent from beef and venison with a green peppercorn sauce; lamb cutlets
with a rosemary jelly; or black pudding with hot apple and mustard sauce. Less
traditional, but still very English, is pineapple filled with prawn and avocado
or a filo parcel of goats' cheese with fresh coriander. Materials are often good
though technique a little heavy, the sauces not always shining as they should.
Fish can be excellent, for example a sea trout with a dill hollandaise. Desserts,
which will include hot puddings such as sticky toffee or bread-and-butter are
not elaborate. There is a new development of an inexpensive set-price lunch
with good hearty casseroles. The restaurant can be cold. The wine list is a
careful selection, including plenty from around the world and not charging the
earth for them. Some properties and growers are good to note, including Ch.

Lyonnat from St Emilion, Roux's Gigondas, Phelps' Syrah, CVNE's Rioja, and Gigou's Jasnières. House wine: £6.95. CELLARMAN'S CHOICE: Brown Bros Dry Muscat 1988, £10.95; Moulin-à-Vent 1986, Bocuse, £13.95.

CHEFS: Peter McGunnigle and Ian McGunnigle PROPRIETORS: Peter and Kate McGunnigle
OPEN: Tue to Sat, exc Sat L
CLOSED: first 2 weeks Jan, last 2 weeks July
MEALS: 12 to 2, 7 to 9 (9.15 Sat)
PRICES: L £10 (£18), D £17 (£24), Set L £8.95 (£14)
CARDS: Amex, Access, Visa
SEATS: 70. Private parties: 40 main room, 30 private room. Car-park, 40 places. Children welcome. Smart dress preferred

---

GOOSNARGH Lancashire   map 5

Solo

Goosnargh Lane, Goosnargh PR3 2BD   COOKING 1
BROUGHTON (0772) 865206   COST £15–£28

'As the bill is printed just like the menu, one assumes that frequent or sweeping changes to the cuisine are not anticipated.' But that doesn't bother customers. Solo - brightly lit outside, subdued blue inside – offers a simple choice and full value for money. Once past such awkward menuspeak as 'mushrooms aux Stilton' there are good ingredients. Steak and veal dominate main courses, beef is properly hung, and cooking is well timed. The Euroflag is hoisted for carpaccio, pasta, veal kidneys Cambozola, and scallops cooked in armagnac (with, it must also be said, mango and garlic). The food works, despite combinations such as steak and Stilton with port sauce. Puddings are standard, as are some of the wines; details of vintage and producer would be helpful. House Italian: £7.50.

CHEFS: Rafaele Arrellaro and Simon Easthan PROPRIETORS: Vincent and Susan Villa
OPEN: all week, D only and Sun L
MEALS: 12 to 2, 7 to 10
PRICES: £16 (£23), Set Sun L £8.20 (£15)
CARDS: Access, Carte Blanche, Visa
SEATS: 48. Private parties: 50 main room. Car-park, 50 places. Children welcome. No cigars in dining-room. Wheelchair access (also WC). Music

---

GOUDHURST Kent   map 3

Hughenden

The Plain, Goudhurst TN17 1AB   COOKING 1
GOUDHURST (0580) 212065   COST £29

The setting is a converted Grade II listed building beside the village pond. It used to be a tearoom. Local farmer Michel Levett has transformed it into a chintzy country restaurant with a sofa by the fire in the bar and a beamed dining-room full of wheelback chairs. Sarah Levett cooks a short fixed-price menu making use of local produce; her style is straightforward but based on good ingredients, skilful timing and nicely judged sauces. An inspection meal began with prettily arranged fresh pasta with scallops, mussels and shrimps before sauté calf's liver with mustard seed and celery. The burnt orange cream to finish was well received. Rack of lamb is roast with honey cider and rosemary; breast of chicken is cooked with vermouth, cream and chives, and there is fish from the market. An attentive team of waitresses keep the service flowing at a sensible pace. 'It inspires a feeling of comfort and well-being.' An eminently sensible wine list, with a good geographical spread provided within a modest number of bins, will not alarm the economically minded nor disappoint the more extravagant. Much reliable drinking under £10 is balanced by good value such as Ch. Grand-Puy-Ducasse 1979 at £23. House French: £6.25.

CHEF: Sarah Levett PROPRIETORS: Sarah and Michel Levett
OPEN: Tue to Sat, D only
MEALS: 7.15 to 9.30 (9.45 Sat)
PRICES: Set D £18.25 (£24). Service 10% for parties of more than 8
CARDS: Access, Visa
SEATS: 35. Private parties: 40 main room. Children welcome. Smart dress preferred. No pipes in dining-room. Wheelchair access (also female WC). Music

---

GRAMPOUND Cornwall

map 1

Eastern Promise

1 Moor View, Grampound TR2 4RT   COOKING 1
ST AUSTELL (0726) 883033   COST £20–£24

'Is there anything that stands out as unusual?' is a question asked of readers who report to the *Guide*. 'Yes,' came the answer about this Chinese restaurant. 'It was busy on a Monday night and, if you knew Grampound, you would understand that no evening there is busy.' The Tses used to have a Chinese store in Truro and their move to Grampound made them more accessible to towns lying on the main road. The premises are tight packed, though a room has been added, and many come for the sizzling dishes, likened by one to the flambé dishes of the old days – we all love a show. The cooking is more than acceptable across a fairly predictable provincial Chinese repertoire, but it may be that the spicing of the many Szechuan dishes has been moderated to suit Cornish palates. The set dinner does not include dessert. House wine, including Great Harmony, is £5.50.

CHEF: Liza Tse PROPRIETOR: Philip Tse
OPEN: all week, exc Wed, D only
MEALS: 6 to 11
PRICES: £12 (£21), Set D £14.50 (£20)
CARDS: Access, Amex, Diners, Visa
SEATS: 64. Private parties: 40 main room, 24 private room. Car-park, 18 places. Vegetarian meals. No children under 3. Music. Air-conditioned

---

The Guide *relies on feedback from its readers. Especially welcome are reports on new restaurants appearing in the book for the first time.*

▲ *Lancrigg*

Easedale, LA22 9QN	COOKING 1
GRASMERE (096 65) 317	COST £22

One visitor sums up the style and setting of the Whittingtons' enterprising
country hotel: 'Arrive early, walk up to Easedale Tarn (1 hour), return (½ hour)
and enjoy what is nearly home cooking'. Not only is this a vegetarian restaurant
and hotel, but the owners are fully committed to organic produce. Breads and
wholemeal croissants come from the Village Bakery at Melmerby (see entry),
using flour from the watermill at Little Salkeld; vegetables are from local
growers and eggs are free-range. This translates into a fixed-price menu with
no choice until the sweets, special diets catered for. A typical meal might begin
with marinated vegetables topped with feta cheese, followed by lovage soup,
then courgette and tarragon casserole with cheese dumplings. Desserts might
range from queen of puddings to banana and ginger flan. Children will be
given earlier meals, between 5 and 6, if desired. The organic philosophy
extends to the wine list, which is fairly priced, and supplied by the excellent
Haughton Fine Wines. Wine enthusiasts can be relieved that not just good but
top class wines such as Ch. Beaucastel Châteauneuf-du-Pape (the 1981 offered
for £16.95 and the 1986 at £15.50), creep in under the organic banner. There are
also organic cognacs, meads, Pinkus organic beers from Germany, Aspall apple
juice from Suffolk and non-organic coffee, regular and decaffeinated, from
Taylors of Harrogate. House wine: £6.50. The Whittingtons are adding more
bedrooms to the hotel, installing whirlpool baths and planning to open a
'hikers' tea barn' for snacks.

CHEF: Robert Whittington   PROPRIETORS: Robert and Janet Whittington
OPEN: all week, D only (L by arrangement)
MEALS: 7
PRICES: Set D £13.50 (£18). Minimum £13.50
CARDS: Access, Visa
SEATS: 25. Private parties: 30 main room. Car-park, 60 places. Vegetarian meals. Children's
helpings. No smoking in dining room. Wheelchair access (also WC). Music. One sitting
ACCOMMODATION: 15 rooms, 12 with bath/shower. Lift. D,B&B £35 to £92. Deposit: £25.
Baby facilities. Afternoon teas. Garden. TV. Scenic *[Which? Hotel Guide]*

▲ *Michael's Nook* ♟

Grasmere LA22 9RP	COOKING 3
GRASMERE (096 65) 496	COST £27–£46

The poetic connotations of the name may summon up images of a pastoral idyll,
but in fact the house is large and set in fine gardens on the side of a hill just
north of Grasmere. The nearest one reader got to shepherding flocks was being
greeted by the resident Great Dane. The style is that of a relaxed country house
and the cooking fits this bill. It is modern British on a set-price menu of four
courses at lunch and five at dinner, with choices at each stage.
Recommendations have included warm salad of duck breast on a complex
mixture of saladings and vegetables; scallops marinated in a mint vinaigrette;

excellent soups, such as fennel and orange, lobster bisque, or mushroom and thyme, coming within the set-price structure as second course; main courses such as steamed sole with cucumber spaghetti and orange and grapefruit; timbale of braised leg of lamb with an outer layer of aubergines; or salmon served on a bed of spinach; and toothsome sweets such as crème brûlée, sticky toffee pudding, passion-fruit soufflé or a filo basket filled with a compote of spiced apples with a calvados caramel sauce. The wine list is long, strongest in clarets and burgundies, but not lacking in good Rhône and Alsace offerings. Price and taste range is helped by a decent sprinkling of French regional wines and Italian and New World offerings. Some of the prices are very reasonable indeed.

CHEF: Heinz Nagler   PROPRIETOR: Reg Gifford
OPEN: all week
MEALS: 12.30 to 1, 7.30 to 8 (7 to 9.15 Sat)
PRICES: Set L £21 (£27), Set D £31.50 (£38)
CARDS: Amex, Diners
SEATS: 45. Private parties: 35 main room. Car-park, 20 places. Children's helpings by arrangement. No children under 12. Smart dress preferred. No smoking in dining-room
ACCOMMODATION: 11 rooms, all with bath/shower. D, B&B £105 to £224. Garden. Fishing. Golf. TV. Phone. Scenic. Doors close at 11.30

▲ White Moss House 🍷

| Rydal Water, Grasmere LA22 9SE | COOKING 4 |
| GRASMERE (096 65) 295 | COST £31 |

Peter Dixon cooks refined food set firmly within the English tradition, now hallowed by the cooks of a hundred Lakeland hotels. His execution is among the most sensitive. Soup is followed by a fish dish, most often a soufflé, but sometimes unadorned fish or perhaps a terrine. Then comes a roast meat, three vegetables and a potato. The sweet course is the first occasion for a choice: an ice-cream, something cold and often creamy, a pie or cake and the crowning glory, a hot English steamed pudding. Thereafter comes a slate of English cheeses with oat biscuits and coffee. The repertoire is not large but benefits from careful practice. Reports speak of accurate seasoning and beautifully modulated flavours. Typical soups are: broccoli and basil; carrot, coriander, lentil and orange; cold cucumber, yoghurt, mint and rose petal where the tastes blend, yet each is singly discernible – the addition of rose petal in that last is a sign of the refinement of palate. Soufflés of smoked haddock and sea bass with basil; sea bass, sea trout and straw asparagus; or wild salmon, smoked salmon and straw asparagus are delivered simultaneously to each diner in perfect condition (up to 18 at a time); yet for one party they were topped by a four-fish terrine with a sorrel and samphire sauce. Veal is served with a pistachio and prune stuffing and duck with sage and onion. Venison may have a red wine sauce and a side dish of pickled damsons while the same fruit will be deployed in a wine sauce for mallard duck. Veal will get a classically inspired wild mushroom and madeira sauce on one night, mushroom, Marsala and marjoram another. Mrs Beeton's chocolate pudding, cabinet pudding – 'a match for Mosimann's bread-and-butter pudding' – Guardsman's pudding and plum duff are among the most loved steamed puddings. A great advantage in sitting down at the same time as everyone else is that each dish should be freshly cooked and delivered piping hot. A disadvantage is that a slight hiccup is magnified into a failure. The cooking is not without its critics. On some nights, presentation has been leaden and evanescent flavours have meant blandness. White Moss is a pleasant stone-built house plumb in the middle of walking country. The breakfasts will set you up and the dinners pack you soundly to bed. The arrangement of eating times means that conversation between different parties is almost inevitable. People like this. Susan Dixon is an accomplished hostess. Peter Dixon will advise the wavering on the wines. The list is particularly strong in claret, remarkably few of them from the 1980s but a fine set from 1978 and many from 1966 and 1961, not to mention earlier vintages. The price of these is very reasonable. Burgundies also offer maturity and a mixture of growers and négociants. The half dozen from 1969 would make inspiring comparisons. A short list of 'recent additions' shows some determination to extend the boundaries more enthusiastically, though clarets remain the centre of interest. Choice would be simpler with a clearer, more differentiated listing. The Germans, from Deinhard and Bürklin-Wolf, for instance, are also worth a nod. House wine: £7.

CHEF: Peter Dixon   PROPRIETORS: Susan and Peter Dixon
OPEN: Mon to Sat, D only
CLOSED: mid-Nov to mid-Mar
MEALS: 8
PRICES: Set D £22 (£26). Service inc
SEATS: 18. 18 tables outside. Private parties: 18 main room. Car-park, 10 places. Children welcome. No smoking in dining-room. Wheelchair access. Music. One sitting
ACCOMMODATION: 7 rooms, all with bath/shower. D,B&B £55 to £75. Garden. Fishing. TV. Phone. Scenic. Doors close at 11. Confirm by 4 [Which? Hotel Guide]

GRAYSHOTT Hampshire   map 2

Woods

| Headley Road, Grayshott GU26 6LB | COOKING 2 |
| HINDHEAD (0428) 605555 | COST £42 |

The ceiling rails once used for hanging meat are now festooned with plants in this converted butcher's shop. Well-worn white tiles on the walls, stripped wood and a dresser full of china reinforce the rustic image, and there are some homely touches in the crocheted curtains and table decorations. Eric Norrgren's short menu is modern with a few traditional European overtones such as gravlax; fillet of beef marinated in madeira with a horseradish and mustard dip; and blinis with smoked salmon and Danish caviare. Salad of scallops and king prawns with fresh tomato sauce is rather like an old-fashioned version of a 'salade tiède'; slices of new season's lamb are arranged in a wreath with a creamy sauce of garlic and puréed onions; and calf's liver is served with a Dubonnet and orange sauce. Vegetables are excellent, although quantities may be minuscule and they are charged as extras. Strawberry sablés with home-made shortbread biscuits and a fresh strawberry sauce works well because the fruit is nicely ripe. Service is slow, there is a great deal of chatting with customers, and the Norrgrens' young children are usually to be seen as well as heard. The wine list is short, more reasonably priced than the food and contains some good drinking. House French: £6.90. CELLARMAN'S CHOICE: Givry Rouge, Dom. Baron Thénard 1987, £15.

CHEF: Eric Norrgren PROPRIETORS: Eric and Dana Norrgren
OPEN: Tue to Sat, D only
MEALS: 7 to 10.30
PRICES: £25 (£35)
CARDS: Access, Amex, Diners, Visa
SEATS: 35. Private parties: 12 main room. Children's helpings. Wheelchair access (also WC)

GREAT DUNMOW Essex   map 3

▲ Starr ♟

Market Place, Great Dunmow CM6 1AX   COOKING 1
GREAT DUNMOW (0371) 874321   COST £23–£46

The inn juts into the road and its walls conceal an older structure of beams and panelling that becomes clear enough on entering the restaurant. In the yard behind, the weatherboarded stables now contain bedrooms: the Starr rises. Cooking keeps to the same recipe: a daily menu written on blackboards, paraded and explained to each party. Fish is a strong point and may be the vehicle of the most interesting dishes, such as quenelles of pike with sea vegetables, red mullet with rosemary and leeks, or fresh crab and pink grapefruit. For the rest, the kitchen cooks to please a loyal regional audience: duck with orange and raisins, medallions of beef and venison with a piquant sauce or spatchcocked poussin with a mustard sauce. On Sundays there is a roast joint, though one reader's lamb came innocent of its apricot stuffing and from a poor butcher. The standard of cooking may not always be the same level as the prices. However, the atmosphere is relaxed, 'last orders were 1.30, but we were able to stay chatting until 5,' and the service is attentive. The wine list is not as dear as the food and is a good selection of French wines, including a section devoted to second labels of fancy châteaux, bolstered by some excellent New World material such as De Bortoli's botrytis-affected Semillon from Australia. House Muscadet and Beaujolais are £9.50 and £10.50. CELLARMAN'S CHOICE: Sancerre 1988, Dezat, £12.25; Côtes du Rhône 1985, Guigal, £9.95.

CHEF: Mark Fisher PROPRIETOR: Mr and Mrs B. Jones
OPEN: all week, exc Sat L and Sun D
CLOSED: 1 week from 1 Jan
MEALS: 12 to 1.30, 7 to 10
PRICES: Set L £16.50 (£23) to £18 (£25), Set D £16.50 (£23) to £30 (£38). Service 10% on parties of 6 or more. Licensed, also bring your own: corkage £4
CARDS: Access, Amex, Visa
SEATS: 60. Private parties: 8 main room, 12 and 30 private rooms. Car-park, 15 places. Children's helpings. Wheelchair access (also WC). Music
ACCOMMODATION: 8 rooms, all with bath/shower. Rooms for disabled. B&B £55 to £110. Baby facilities. TV. Phone. Doors close at midnight. Confirm by noon

---

All entries in the Guide *are rewritten every year, not least because restaurant standards fluctuate. Don't trust an out of date* Guide.

GREAT GONERBY Lincolnshire   map 6

Harry's Place

---

17 High Street, Great Gonerby NG31 8JS   COOKING 3
GRANTHAM (0476) 61780   COST £35–£48

It still only seats 10, but Harry and Caroline Hallam's place, in a Georgian
house just off the main shopping street, now has comfortable new chairs,
mirrors and paintings. The *carte* of half a dozen choices at each course smacks a
mite of complacency, with oft-repeated items, such as melon and grapes
marinated in lemon and mint, and chicken livers sauté with herbs and cognac.
None the less, the cooking – rated A+ on one report – still vibrates. First
courses favour fish and shellfish, for example, poached Loch Fyne queen
scallops and mussels with leeks and carrots or soupe de poissons. Soufflés are
an innovation – a fine tomato and basil as a first course, or Grand Marnier as a
dessert. Alcohol in all guises is variously employed to lift sauces as in the
guinea-fowl roasted with tarragon, white wine and Pernod, or loin of lamb
roasted with vintage cider and rosemary. Baked apple and almond galette, and
strawberry pancake with ice-cream were positively reported. Service is
'pleasant and unrushed'. It is feared that some prices have taken a larger leap
than the upgraded surroundings warrant. Last year the cheese selection cost £5.
Now, even at lunchtimes when main course prices are considerably cheaper,
it's £7.50. The all-European wine list is short but offers decent bottles at fair
prices. CELLARMAN'S CHOICE: Sancerre rosé 1988, Clos de la Louisonne,
Christian Salmon, £13.50; Cabernet, Mas Chichet 1985 Jacques Chichet, £9.70.

CHEF: Harry Hallam   PROPRIETORS: Harry and Caroline Hallam
OPEN: Tue to Sat, Sun and Mon by arrangement
CLOSED: 25 Dec, bank hols
MEALS: 12.30 to 2, 7 to 9.30
PRICES: L £26 (£35), D £31 (£40)
CARDS: Access, Visa
SEATS: 10. Private parties: 10 main room, 4 private room. Car-park, 4 places. Children's
helpings on request. No smoking

GREAT MILTON Oxfordshire   map 2

▲ *Le Manoir aux Quat' Saisons* ♥

Church Road, Great Milton OX9 7PD   COOKING 5
GREAT MILTON (0844) 278881   COST £39–£92

The check list might read: new conservatory dining-room, rebuilt and enlarged
kitchens, bigger wine cellar, landscaped and improved gardens, extra
bedrooms, new and better pictures on the walls. Raymond Blanc has
transformed this Jacobean manor into a luxury country hotel with a restaurant
to match. Save for the final bill, few could deny it is better all round. The
conservatory, violently green, is a dazzling place to eat. After a wander round
the gardens, half a day may happily be spent over lunch. The food is finely
judged; the tastes are not intense but they are true. You need to concentrate

while eating because everything is there for pleasure, but can easily be missed if the attention wavers. One reason for eating here is the technical expertise: how a particular effect is achieved was the main topic of conversation at a summer meal. A sauce with duck, though dark and lustrous, had the heady taste and perfume of jasmine tea, yet with no hint of tannin or bitterness. A sabayon yielded an underlying flavour of truffle to buoy up the distinct taste of wild mushrooms in a mousse that filled courgette flowers. A double consommé of tomato was clear to the eye, yet tasted of a whole box of tomatoes. A hot raspberry soufflé rose effortlessly from its pie crust with no hint of skin or leather to sides or top. In each instance the effect could rarely be matched by other kitchens. 'How did he do it?' had to be the question of the day. The bill is a fee for this cleverness, rather like paying more for a car that is safer, cleaner, faster or quieter. You pay for the performance, not mere luxury. The question, for the private customer, is whether you want to spend your money that way. The menus give a lot of options. There is a seasonal *carte*, a daily list of a quartet of extras, a dinner *menu gourmand* and a short fixed-price *menu du jour*. This lunch menu costs more on Saturday and yet more on Sunday when there are eight courses. Fish is not given as much pre-eminence as elsewhere, though what there is can be among the best in quality anywhere: mark especially the scallops. There may also be a slight over-emphasis on the sabayon or emulsion sauces, which may mask some of the purer tastes. One meal seemed to involve them at every course. The restaurant is mercifully free of faddish tricks of mixing fish and offal or harsh effects of balancing strong flavours with equally strident, and often jammy, accompaniments. The garden informs the cooking, as in those courgettes whose flowers were filled with wild mushroom mousse, or in the plate of seven vegetables – beetroot, spring onion, turnip, mange-tout, broccoli, Swiss chard stalks, and skinned broad beans on one day – that comes, at extra cost, with the main course. The quality of thought behind the recipes comes out in their harmony: tastes build up and complement rather than counteract. Sometimes this can lead to a sense that impact is lacking.

Except for set pieces like the café crème or raspberry soufflé, design on the plate is less obtrusive than it might be. Sauces in dishes having two of them, leach into each other, which some find detracts from their impact but which at least makes presentation less self-conscious. A 'try this' list of Raymond Blanc's specialities stretches down the back of his menus. Among readers' recommendations has been a dish of three pasta with three sauces: a 'spartaco' of tagliatelle scented with white truffle; ravioli filled with duck on a bed of celeriac; and two lasagne with black truffle sitting on Swiss chard – the sauce with the ravioli outstanding. Also commended are a jellied terrine of Provençal fish and shellfish with a saffron vinaigrette – 'the herbs, vegetables, spices and vinaigrette were like imbibing a mouthful of Provence'; a crab soufflé baked in a 'dish' of crab at the bottom with a sole fillet curled around to form the walls, the thin sauce flavoured with ginger; noisettes of hare wrapped in puff pastry with a blackish sauce of chocolate and game stock, all sprinkled with new season's walnuts; and scallops and monkfish roasted together on a bed of seaweed with an oyster sabayon and a light meat sauce scented with lemon thyme; and finally a mousseline of scallops wrapped with courgettes, topped with slices of whole scallop and served with seaweed – 'unbelievably fresh scallops, the slightly crunchy courgette, the smoothness of the mousseline and the seaweed's own texture made this memorable for more than just taste.'

Desserts can be gentler tasting, if only because red fruits are not the main ingredient: caramel, almonds, pears, vanilla feature more significantly. Chocolate is not wheeled out for every choice so that the simple interplay of acid and richness it affords is left aside for more subtle effect − or, in some people's eyes, more boring. If the kitchen's enlargement has meant greater range and a greater number of meals, so the new wine cellar has caused a longer list. No-one can fail to pause at the prices, though they are no higher than in the West End. It is, of course, largely French with some Italians and Californians − but even most of these cost over £30. It is a patchy selection, very strong in claret and long in burgundy, lacking a great range of growers, of whom a lot are rather conservative. The lesser regions are not given so much attention but there is a useful set of Provençal, south-western and Jura bottles. Halves exist, but there could be more. Despite the high prices − house Champagne is £32 − there is sufficient under £20 for the less rich. House wine: £20.60. The Manoir is a monument to the enthusiasm of one man, Raymond Blanc. His presence informs the whole service: 'when we arrived, he was talking to late lunchers; pre-dinner he was around chatting and afterwards he was talking to every table. Early next morning, there he was taking on the builders. Then, at breakfast, he bursts in, "Good morning to you both, it's going to be a lovely day!" Such was his charm, we bought his book.' So recorded one who stayed the night. The rest of the staff need to run hard to keep up. Many of them succeed, but there is occasionally an air of disarray about some of the fluttering at table or wine bottle. And then, what happens when Raymond Blanc is not there to oversee?

CHEF: Raymond Blanc   PROPRIETORS: Blanc Restaurants Ltd
OPEN: all week
CLOSED: 4 weeks from 22 Dec
MEALS: 12.15 to 2.30, 7.15 to 10.30
PRICES: £59 (£77), Set L Mon to Fri £24.50 (£39), Sat £28.50 (£43), Sun £56 (£70), Set D £54 (£68). Service inc
CARDS: Access, Amex, Diners, Visa
SEATS: 95. 4 tables outside. Private parties: 45 private room. Car-park, 45 places. Vegetarian meals. Children's helpings. Smart dress preferred. No smoking in dining-room. Wheelchair access (also WC). Air-conditioned
ACCOMMODATION: 19 rooms, all with bath/shower. Rooms for disabled. B&B from £159 for 2. Deposit: £100. Baby facilities. Pets welcome grounds only. Garden. Swimming-pool. Tennis. TV. Phone. Scenic [*Which? Hotel Guide*]

GREAT MISSENDEN Buckinghamshire   map 3

La Petite Auberge

---

107 High Street, Great Missenden HP16 0BB   COOKING 1
GREAT MISSENDEN (024 06) 5370   COST £40

In a tiny cottage at the end of the High Street, the restaurant occupies the two downstairs rooms, the second a few steps higher than the first. Decoration is muted. The intentions for the food are signposted by a menu that includes caviare, wild mushrooms and foie gras de canard as well as the odd truffle. Snails with mushrooms and garlic; vegetable terrine with a herb vinaigrette; feuilleté of asparagus; chicken sauté with oyster mushrooms and vin jaune;

turbot steamed with courgettes; or duck with raisins and honey are some of the choices from a long-standing *carte* of six or more choices in each course. Cooking is not adventurous, nor does it return to the inspiration of the domestic hearth. Rather is it solidly professional but with insufficient attention to tastes that should cause the diner to pause and savour. Sauces tend to the universal. Desserts are current standards: a nougat glacé, a gratin of fruits, a lemon tart. A chocolate and walnut parfait was adjudged good. There is a short wine list offering decent value, with room for only three half-bottles among the two dozen choices. More reports, please.

CHEF: H. Martel   PROPRIETORS: Mr and Mrs H. Martel
OPEN: Mon to Sat, D only
CLOSED: 25 Dec, Easter, bank hols
MEALS: 7.30 to 10.30
PRICES: £24 (£33)
CARDS: Access, Visa
SEATS: 30. Private parties: 35 main room. Children welcome. Smart dress preferred.
No-smoking area. Wheelchair access. Music

GREAT YARMOUTH Norfolk   map 6

Seafood Restaurant

85 North Quay, Great Yarmouth NR30 1JF   COOKING 2
GREAT YARMOUTH (0493) 856009   COST £40

The restaurant was originally a pub but shows few signs of this apart from the curved Victorian front and high windows. The dining-room can glimpse the spruce open-plan kitchen from the comfort of deep banquettes while deciding on lobster or seafish from the vivier and cold cabinet that displays the day's delivery. If meat is the wish, it will be steak, or surf and turf. This year sees shark added to the shortlist of local catches, a sign of taste changes as sure as was the elevation of monkfish to gourmet status during the 1970s. Fish may be had grilled, poached or fried in batter, with or without a sauce. There is another list of dishes already sauced. The owners' Cypriot origins are seen from first courses such as taramosalata and kalamari, but there is also a full range of crab claws, smoked salmon, scampi and the like. Enormous salads cost extra but are worth it; sweets come on a trolley and are not as remarkable as the fish. Coffee is Greek and plentiful. The wine list, with a reasonable emphasis on whites, has some good bottles, particularly burgundies. House wine: £8.50 a litre.
CELLARMAN'S CHOICE: Bourgogne Aligoté 1988, Sorin, £10.70; Rully 1986, Dom. Protheau, £15.60.

CHEFS: Mark Chrisostomou and Gary Crompton   PROPRIETORS: Christopher and
Miriam Kikis
OPEN: Mon to Sat, exc Sat L
MEALS: 12 to 2, 7 to 10.45
PRICES: £22 (£33)
CARDS: Access, Amex, Diners, Visa
SEATS: 40. Private parties: 40 main room. Children's helpings. Smart dress preferred. Music

GRIMSTON Norfolk   map 6

▲ *Congham Hall*

Lynn Road, Grimston PE32 1AH   COOKING 3
HILLINGTON (0485) 600250   COST £21−£48

Behind a screen of trees on the King's Lynn Road out of Grimston, the Hall sits
on the flattest of lawns with views of grazing sheep in the park from the deep
windows of the house or the glazed orangery that forms an extension to the
dining-room. The rooms have excellent proportions, their decoration is bold
and unfussy, furnishings are comfortable without falling into the trap of
furbelowed opulence. The same might be said of the style of hotelkeeping: the
staff have a natural enthusiasm that is the product of good motivation, not
excess training in sycophancy. Cooking is as satisfactory. There have been
rumours about over-rich sauces, but no fault has been found with a chilled
seafood terrine, an almond and broccoli soup, or a navarin of lamb with parsley
and mushrooms. Fruit and sour-sweet combinations occur in dishes like
guinea-fowl with Grand Marnier or the same bird with a block-busting
blackcurrant sauce, but accuracy of balance was praised. This was also true of a
first course of marinated salmon, prawn and monkfish with a citrus salad, and a
sensational garden dessert of raspberries, two sorts of strawberries, black and
redcurrants and blackberries. Soda bread is repeatedly welcomed as a contrast
to 'chef's rolls'. Vegetable cooking is a strong point, with endive, celeriac and
marrow giving some variations to the constant baby sweetcorn (what more
tedious a vegetable), broccoli and beans found in modern kitchens. The higher
priced set dinner has eight courses. The wine list runs through a fair range of
bottles, adequate protection from an East Anglian gale. There are good
properties but also discomforting ranges from the same négociant. Mark-ups
are predictable. House French: £8.50. CELLARMAN'S CHOICE: Woodstock
Chardonnay 1987, £16.50; Ch. Fourcas Hosten 1983, £22.

CHEF: Clive Jackson   PROPRIETORS: Trevor and Christine Forecast
OPEN: all week, exc Sat L
MEALS: 12.30 to 2, 7.30 to 9.30
PRICES: Set L £14.50 (£21), Set D £27.50 (£35) to £32 (£40)
CARDS: Access, Amex, Diners, Visa
SEATS: 50. Private parties: 8 main room, 12 private room. Car-park, 50 places. No children
under 12. Smart dress preferred. No smoking in dining-room. Wheelchair access (also WC)
ACCOMMODATION: 14 rooms, all with bath/shower. B&B £70 to £95. No children under 12.
Garden. Swimming-pool. Tennis. TV. Phone. Scenic. Doors close at 11. Confirm 24 hours
ahead [*Which? Hotel Guide*]

GUILDFORD Surrey   map 3

Rumwong

16−18 London Road, Guildford GU1 2AF   COOKING 2
GUILDFORD (0483) 36092   COST £24

The dining area has been enlarged and some improvements in decoration made
in this popular Thai restaurant. The royal family of Thailand now gaze down on
the contented diner. The food makes more impact than the interior and the

menu offers a range of one-plate meals of noodles or rice. Other dishes draw on the Bangkok tradition rather than on the long-cooked cuisine of Chiang Mai and the north. Fish, therefore, is well liked, as in golden thread fried and served with ginger, mushrooms, beans, pork, pimentos and oyster sauce; the poh-taek, a large soup of mixed seafood served in a large pot for two or more people; or gung tod, prawns marinated with garlic and pepper, then deep fried. Meats are not ignored: duck with a rich coconut milk and pineapple or beef with mushrooms and spring onions. Desserts get little endorsement. Service is cheerful, whether in the main restaurant or the smaller Khan Tok room where dining is at knee height in the old Thai style. The wines are not expensive and there is Singha beer. House wine: £6.50

CHEF: Keow Sae Lao   PROPRIETORS: Wanjai and Lumyai Poonum
OPEN: Tue to Sun
CLOSED: 2 to 15 Aug
MEALS: 12 to 2.30, 6 to 10.45 (10.30 Sun)
PRICES: £10 (£20), Set L and D £14 (£20). Service 10% alc, 12% set
CARDS: Access, Visa
SEATS: 160. Private parties: 120 main room, 40 private room. Vegetarian meals. Children's helpings. Smart dress preferred. Wheelchair access. Music. Air-conditioned

---

HAMBLETON   Leicestershire   map 6

▲ *Hambleton Hall* ♟

Hambleton LE15 8TH
OAKHAM (0572) 756991   COOKING 3
off A606, 3m SE of Oakham   COST £30–£58

This monument to the art of conservation – for the conversion of the Victorian mansion is seamless in its restraint – stands next to that other landmark, Rutland Water, tribute to the interaction of modern technology and the natural world. Tim and Stefa Hart's hotel is luxurious without fussiness and the wheels run smoothly, though sometimes not in the dining-room. The routine is as well practised as the gardens, stepping down towards the lakeside, are manicured. Where most such places go for excess, this achieves its ends through understatement. Meals begin in the bar: the house cocktail is good, but Lillet or Suze are not available. Over canapés there is time to run through the 31 pages of the wine list and a menu with five or six choices in four courses, as well as a set-price menu which, in this context, is fair value. This is good, conventional country-house cooking of a high level of achievement though not treading many new bounds. Certain tendencies, however, are constant: an affection for Mediterranean vegetables that comes out in halibut with courgettes and red peppers, a pizza of red mullet with an avocado and parsley sauce, or a fillet of red mullet sitting on a terrine of aubergine with a brunoise of red peppers; a fashionable pleasure in cabbage, either red or green under a pot-roasted squab with roast cloves of garlic, or as spring greens under a loin of veal with a wild mushroom sauce. There is serious intent to use vegetables as more than minor trimming: a sorrel and watercress soup; a smooth mousse of peas flavoured with mint, accompanied by crisp vegetables in a basil vinaigrette; braised fennel with turbot; salmon with spinach and deep-fried artichokes. The menu sometimes strikes an unexpected balance: one April night there were six fish dishes and four meats offered; in the winter, it was felt that game and shellfish received undue weight. Fish has normally been well selected, although at least one party wished the hotel were nearer the sea. Soups can be good, as in a vegetable broth with noodles, fresh basil and garlic or a clear lobster consommé with lobster and halibut ravioli, 'an excellent version of wun tun soup,' given a generous sprinkling of fresh coriander. Other dishes that have been endorsed are a fish hot-pot; a timbale of chicken livers with a salad of rocket; loin of lamb (the lamb is often remarked upon) with a simple garlic and tomato sauce, though one reader would have liked potatoes as well as vegetables; that pot-roasted squab on a bed of cabbage with lardons of Rutland bacon; a wide choice of cheese, French and English; desserts that go from the grand 'symphony' (for two) composed of a chocolate cheesecake, a tuile basket with four sorbets, a praline parfait, a compote of rhubarb and blood oranges, and fresh strawberries to the relative simplicity of crème caramel with wild strawberries. Coffee and petits fours are up to scratch, though truffles are better than pastry work. Eating here is sometimes slow because it is so intended, but on bad days because systems have been known to break down. The expectation is of perfection but the tone of reports is that too often small errors detract from that. Prices are inclusive and 'no further payment is expected.' The wine list gives good support to the food. Over the years, the range of old bottles has contracted but maturity is still not ignored. Prices are in keeping with the surroundings and the first two pages of bottles under £16 may be welcome relief from the rest. Growers are carefully chosen: Parent, Roumier, Juillot and Gaunox from Burgundy; Edna Valley, Heitz and Acacia from California; Petaluma and Cape Mentelle from the short Australian section that is a new addition this year. The spread of clarets looks in need of thought, as it is very uneven. House wine: £12 and £13.

CHEF: Brian Baker   PROPRIETORS: Tim and Stefa Hart
OPEN: all week
MEALS: 12 to 1.45, 7 to 9.30
PRICES: £35 (£48), Set L £24 (£30) to £26 (£32), Set D £29.50 (£36) to £35 (£41). Service inc
CARD: Access, Visa
SEATS: 60. Private parties: 45 main room, 20 private room. Car-park, 40 places. Children's helpings. Smart dress preferred. No cigars/pipes in dining-room. Wheelchair access
ACCOMMODATION: 15 rooms, all with bath/shower. Rooms for disabled. Lift. B&B £85 to £200. No children under 9. Baby facilities. Pets welcome. Garden. Tennis. Fishing. Golf. TV. Phone. Scenic. Doors close at midnight [Which? Hotel Guide]

HARROGATE North Yorkshire   map 5

Drum and Monkey

5 Montpellier Gardens, Harrogate HG1 2TF   COOKING 2
HARROGATE (0423) 502650   COST £19–£24

Downstairs feels like an oyster bar, upstairs is a bustling, tight-set restaurant with simple slate tables and red plush chairs. Stuffed fish (not for eating) displayed on both floors and on the stairs set the theme: meat is not on the menu. So many pack the place that the produce cannot fail to be fresh: huge steaming bowls of mussels; kebabs of monkfish with bacon and mustard;

Pacific oysters at very fair prices; and plain grilled soles are among more than two dozen choices. There is a fair balance between sauced and plain food, and it may be for the latter that people most enjoy visiting a good fish restaurant. The lunch menu is shorter than dinner, a little cheaper, and popular: people were 'waiting in the hallway with a bottle of Mâcon.' It benefits from a staff and proprietor who enjoy working there. The short wine list is all white bar two and has some useful growers: Duboeuf from the Mâconnais, Bougrier from the Loire, Firestone from California. Prices are low. House wine: £5.35.

CHEF: Patrick Laverack PROPRIETOR: William Fuller
OPEN: Mon to Sat
CLOSED: Christmas to New Year
MEALS: 12 to 2.30, 7 to 10.15
PRICES: L £13 (£19), D £14 (£20)
CARDS: Access, Visa
SEATS: 48. Private parties: 8 main room. Children's helpings

Millers

1 Montpellier Mews, Harrogate HG1 2TG   COOKING 3
HARROGATE (0423) 530708   COST £18–£40

Simon Gueller's little restaurant is in a pedestrian court that tries hard to create an impression of quaint good taste, complete with an old-fashioned telephone kiosk painted black. Inside there are 'shout-aloud' still lifes of vegetables, and patriotic red, white, and blue curtains. Against this, the fixed-price menu of half a dozen options at each course shows more restraint. It is a balanced selection of succinctly described modern dishes with French overtones. Gueller is no slouch. Marco Pierre White of Harveys in London and Messrs Reid and Long from the Box Tree at Ilkley are ex-colleagues or mentors and he has worked in some prestigious kitchens. It shows in his thoroughness and delicate touch. Readers have commented on the fish soup, the deft use of threads of fresh ginger in ravioli with scallop mousse, and the vividness of the fresh thyme *jus* accompanying surprisingly 'juicy' guinea-fowl. Other typical dishes might be fillet of red mullet sauté with truffle oil or pig's trotter stuffed with crab and ginger. Impeccable crème caramel and délice of passion-fruit custard on a sponge cake base have impressed as desserts. Service is distinguished by 'scrupulous courtesy' – but does this compensate for outdoor lavatories? Details show the need for thoroughness to get to the next level of achievement: poor bread, austere to undercooked vegetables, moderate coffee, terrible salt and pepper pots were reported on one visit alone. The short wine list seems besotted with highly priced items so that a slip of the tongue may get a London-sized bill. House Côteaux de Tricastin or Saumur: £7.90.

CHEF: Simon Gueller PROPRIETORS: Simon Gueller and Rena Polushko
OPEN: Mon to Sat, exc Mon D
CLOSED: 10 days at Christmas, 1 to 15 August
MEALS: 12 to 2, 7 to 10
PRICES: L £12 (£18), Set D £19.50 (£24) to £25 (£33)
CARDS: Access, Visa
SEATS: 24. 4 tables outside. Private parties: 24 main room. Children's helpings.
No cigars/pipes in dining-room. Wheelchair access (also WC). Music

HARROW   Greater London   map 3

Country Club

160 College Road,
Harrow-on-the-Hill HA1 1BH   COOKING 1
081-427 0729   COST £15–£34

The restaurant poses a problem for enthusiasts of Chinese cooking. On the
surface it is like other Chinese restaurants: sizzling dishes, Peking duck, a fair
amount of seafood. This is cooked well according to some, and not
outstandingly according to others, but served politely and pleasantly by Mrs
Chu and her staff. The problem is how to get the best out of it. Mr Chu is one of
the few Shanghai chefs in the country who trained in a Shanghai-Peking
restaurant in Taiwan. There are Shanghai dishes on the menu: dumplings,
spring rolls, sandpot soups, red-cooked Chinese cabbage or mushrooms and
bean sprouts. The solution to the problem is to telephone and discuss a meal a
day or two in advance. Then, crab with yellow bean sauce, sea cucumber with
onion, shredded pork with salted vegetables, and stir-fried prawns are among
dishes that open up as part of the repertoire. This is the case of a gem whose
real identity has been hidden by a desire to please the suburban community.

CHEF/PROPRIETOR: T.A. Chu
OPEN: all week, D only
MEALS: 6 to 11
PRICES: £16 (£25), Set D £11 (£15) to £24 (£28). Minimum £7. Service inc set only
CARDS: Access, Visa
SEATS: 55. Private parties: 50 main room, 14 private room. Car-park, 50 places. Children
welcome. Music

HARWICH   Essex   map 3

▲ The Pier at Harwich ♥

The Quay, Harwich CO12 3HH   COOKING 2
HARWICH (0255) 241212   COST £15–£40

Every port, every seaside town, should have a restaurant like this. But they
don't, which is why the Pier is cherished. Right on the quay, it narrows the gap
between sea and customer to something approaching the minimum. Lobster is
served either cold with mayonnaise or Thermidor; sea bass is steamed with
vegetables and a Chablis sauce. Potato-capped fish pie combines cod, scallops,
salmon, scampi and prawns in a saffron sauce. Smoked fish – from salmon to
trout to haddock – rings the changes, and there is plain fish and chips for
children. Downstairs is less formal. Wines are little short of exemplary: from
vin de pays through the Loire, Alsace and Burgundy to Germany, Italy,
Australia and California; anyone who wants change from £10 can get it.
Anyone who enjoys good burgundy won't. House French from £7.50 to £11.50.

The Guide *is totally independent, accepts no free hospitality, and survives on the number
of copies sold each year.*

CHEF: C.E. Oakley   PROPRIETOR: G.M.W. Milsom
OPEN: all week
MEALS: 12 to 2, 6 to 9.30
PRICES: £22 (£33), Set L £8.50 (£16), Set Sun L £13.50 (£22). Service 10%
CARDS: Access, Visa
SEATS: 80. Private parties: 85 main room, 50 private room. Car-park, 10 places. Children's
helpings. Wheelchair access (2 steps). Music
ACCOMMODATION: 6 rooms, all with bath/shower. B&B £40 to £65. TV. Phone. Scenic
[Which? Hotel Guide]

HASLEMERE Surrey   map 3

Morels ♟

25–27 Lower Street, Haslemere GU27 2NY   COOKING 4
HASLEMERE (0428) 51462   COST £25–£50

The succession of cottages sits on a high pavement, making approach tricky,
especially by car. Inside, cool blues, white, and varying levels give the
impression of light and space. A pleasing spot to visit, made the more
enjoyable by assiduous and keen service. Most are agreed that the set-price
menus are outstanding value, though no one calls any of it outrageous. The
repertoire has some constants: blinis with smoked salmon and 'Danish
caviare', and little tartlets of marinaded salmon with cucumber and sour cream
are two instances. It is a discreet, but not boring, approach to modern French
cooking, including conventional dishes such as asparagus with an orange
hollandaise, but also refreshing combinations such as a Roquefort soufflé with
creamed and shredded chicory. Jean-Yves Morel is not anxious to deploy too
many luxuries, though truffles occur, for example in loin of pork served with a
truffle-scented mousseline and sauce – a sort of 'hunters and the hunted' dish.
He is also willing to deal with humble commodities in a successful springtime
dish of mackerel, first marinated, then served warm with a cold jellied confit of
garlic. The popular desserts may be more than enough for one person, but most
reports mention the excellence of the crème brûlée with four fruit sorbets. An
accumulation of lemon – a tart, a soufflé and curd – is a sign of the times we
live in. Cheese appetisers and an amuse-gueule of beef on a tiny skewer come
with even the cheapest lunch confirming the sense of value. This may help
reconcile diners to paying for coffee, even if with a good range of petits fours.
Apart from a single Cava, the wine list is entirely French and concentrates on
the classic regions; it has a fair range of claret, including some older vintages, as
well as burgundy – note Jayer, Lequin-Roussot, Rousseau, Defaix and
Gagnard among the growers. Lesser regions are adequate but not exciting.
Mark-ups are not impossible. Krug is even cheap! House wine: £9 and £10.
CELLARMAN'S CHOICE: Ch. Villegeorge 1979, £18.50; Pouilly-Fuissé, Ch.
Fuissé 1986, Vincent, £29.

---

*Several sharp operators have tried to extort money from restaurateurs on the promise of an
entry in a guide book that has never appeared. The Good Food Guide makes no charge
for inclusion and does not offer certificates of any kind.*

CHEF: Jean-Yves Morel PROPRIETORS: Jean-Yves and Mary Anne Morel
OPEN: Tue to Sat, exc Sat L
CLOSED: 25 Dec, bank hols (exc Good Fri), 2 weeks end Feb, 2 weeks Sept/Oct
MEALS: 12.30 to 1.45, 7 to 10
PRICES: £31 (£42), Set L £16 (£25), Set D £19 (£29)
CARDS: Access, Amex, Diners, Visa
SEATS: 45. Private parties: 12 main room. Children's helpings. No cigars/pipes in dining-room. Wheelchair access (1 step)

HASTINGLEIGH Kent   map 3

▲ *Woodmans Arms Auberge*

Hassell Street, Hastingleigh TN25 5JE   COOKING 3
ELMSTED (023 375) 250   COST £23-£40

Ask for directions; the Auberge (which was once a tavern) is not exactly en route for anywhere, and Hassell Street is a hamlet, not a road. After many years and many places, this may be the Campions' paradigm of catering and hostelry. The recipe – a tiny house, a dining-room that can barely admit non-residents, gentle, cajoling and cosseting attention – is appreciated by as many as can be fitted in. Some find the little exhortations tiring (no smoking, sit down to eat at 7.30, keep the drains free, for example), but the majority sit back and enjoy it. 'It is like nothing so much as spending a weekend with friends one does not know too well.' There is no choice for the four-course dinner, served in spotless surroundings by Gerald Campion as he is 'harangued' through the hatch by his wife. The word, used by one reader, does not catch the affectionate tone of the conversation and banter that makes this place so special. Susan Campion's cooking is applauded ('the best lamb I've ever eaten' regularly crops up in accounts). It is far above domestic but stops short of professional. Chilled pea soup; artichoke soup; pancakes with a ricotta, tarragon and tomato stuffing; roast leg of Romney Marsh lamb with raisins and peanuts; roast wild duck; entrecôte béarnaise; gratin of wild salmon trout; bread and butter pudding; meringues with fresh fruits; and peach and brandy roulade have all been praised, along with first-class olives, especially good vegetables and freshly ground decaffeinated coffee (which is another mark of serious intent even in so lilliputian a venture). Fault, if fault were found, might be the occasional over-heaviness of three savoury courses in succession, each involving cream or mayonnaise. The wines, Gerald Campion's concern, are worth a long look (the list is left in each bedroom). If, as perchance befell one party, your bottle is below par and you don't mention it at the time, Gerald Campion's 'wonderful attitude' comes into play. One party got a letter of apology with a £5 cheque after he had tasted what they left and agreed that it wasn't very good.

'The music played ranged from full-blooded Mozart to a sing-something medley that included 'If you were the only girl in the world', through the 2nd movement of Dvorak 9 on to the Grieg Piano Concerto with five minutes' silence between movements one and two.'
On eating in Lancashire

CHEF: Susan Campion   PROPRIETORS: Susan and Gerald Campion
OPEN: all week, D only
CLOSED: 1 week Apr and 3 weeks from 1 Sept
MEALS: 7.30
PRICES: Set D £17.50 (£23) residents, £27.50 (£33) non-residents. Service inc
SEATS: 8. 3 tables outside. Private parties: 8 main room. Car-park, 6 places. No children
under 16. No smoking. One sitting
ACCOMMODATION: 3 rooms, all with bath. B&B £63.50 to £80.50. Deposit: 25%.
No children under 16. Garden. TV. Scenic. Doors close at 11 [*Which? Hotel Guide*]

HAWKSHEAD Cumbria   map 7

▲ *Field Head House* ▼

Outgate, Hawkshead LA22 0PY   COOKING 2
HAWKSHEAD (096 66) 240   COST £25

The great square-paned Georgian windows are sheltered from the sun by a
veranda, and visitors protected from the hurly-burly of lakeland roads by the
gardens that ensure peace and quiet. The mildly stark, almost Scandinavian
dining-room seats fewer than the house accommodates, so in high season
outside bookings may be tricky. Residents pay less for their dinner. Both
residents and casual callers need to alert the Van Guliks about their intentions
as the house is run very much like a private home and quantities are finely
judged to ensure freshness each day. Dinner is a set piece of five courses with a
choice only at dessert: always one pudding and perhaps syllabub or mousse.
The scale of the business gives the cooking immediacy. Bob Van Gulik
comments that the trout for fillet of trout with a caper and herb beurre blanc is
caught on the afternoon that he prepares it. Vegetables, in season, come largely
from the garden and meat, from Richard Woodall, is free of hormones and hung
for enough time to develop flavour. The balance of the meals induces well-
being among the guests and dissolves any deprivation at being denied choice.
A March evening saw a ramekin of smoked haddock and cheese, succeeded by
celery soup as prelude to a Dutch recipe for lightly spiced braised beef served
with red cabbage, carrots and mushrooms, fennel with madeira, mange-tout,
and creamed potato disposed around the plate Tovey style. Cheeses were
Stilton and goats' from Bexton, then a choice of rich lemon ice-cream or sticky
toffee pudding, which more resembles a butterscotch bread-and-butter
pudding than the steamed pudding with dates or fruit that is met so often.
Wine suggestions are made at the bottom of each menu but there is a very long
list which also shows enthusiasm and affection. The notes may need more
minutes to absorb than afforded by an aperitif. Prices are reasonable indeed.
The Guliks are not too dignified to ignore the shelves of the local Tesco and not
too secretive to tell you which wines came from there. The list is not heavy in
old glories but shows curiosity in seeking out good value and good drinking
from all major wine zones. House wine: £5 and £5.50. CELLARMAN'S
CHOICE: Pacherenc de Vic-Bilh 1988, Dom. Bouschasse, £8.70; Ch. Musar,
Lebanon 1982, £11.80.

The Guide *always appreciates hearing about changes of chef or owner.*

CHEF: Bob Van Gulik   PROPRIETORS: Bob and Eeke Van Gulik
OPEN: all week, D only, exc Tue
CLOSED: last 2 weeks Jan, week before Christmas
MEALS: 7.30 for 8
PRICES: Set D £18 (£21). Service inc
SEATS: 12. Private parties: 18 main room. Car-park, 10 places. Children welcome.
No smoking in dining-room. Wheelchair access (3 steps;also WC). One sitting
ACCOMMODATION: 7 rooms, all with bath/shower. B&B £34 to £68. Deposit: £30. Baby
facilities. Pets welcome. Garden. Fishing. Golf. TV. Scenic. Doors close at midnight.
Confirm by noon [*Which? Hotel Guide*]

HAWORTH West Yorkshire	map 5

▲ *Weavers*

15 West Lane, Haworth BD22 8DU	COOKING 2
HAWORTH (0535) 43822	COST £29

While in the village of the Brontë museum, do not omit to call at this
neighbouring group of converted cottages. Its three interconnected dining-
rooms and bar are generously festooned with objects old, new, English and
French that make it stylish and cosy at the same time. Like these items of
decoration, the menu is also nostalgic, ('Yorkshire pud'wi'gravy') modern
('fresh fruit and bacon salad with mint julep dressing') English ('sticky toffee
pudding') and a little French ('fillet of beef with a béarnaise sauce'). Like the
rooms, the food has style sufficient for its message and is simple enough to
remind diners of all that is best about home cooking. Quantities are generous,
meats are well chosen, vegetables are fresh (sometimes cooked less well than
others). Signature dishes might be cow pie; Gressingham duck with a rhubarb
sauce; pork fillet on apple and potato cake with sage sauce; a parcel of
Wensleydale and spinach with an apple and peach chutney. Vegetarian dishes
are always offered though one party's cashew and parsnip roast with onion
sauce and stuffed cabbage with tomato sauce, were blandly flavoured, while
applauded for enterprise. The star attraction seems to be the sweet course:
sticky toffee pudding, light-as-air spotted dick, trifle and crème brûlée are all
approved. The wine list takes from all over the world and does not charge
highly for the privilege. House wines: £7.50. CELLARMAN'S CHOICE: Crozes-
Hermitage Blanc 1988, Jaboulet, £10.50; Bandol, Dom. de Cagueloup 1986,
£10. There is an 'early doors' menu at a bargain price for those who turn up at
7pm. One fervent supporter of Jane Rushworth's cooking and Colin
Rushworth's gently humorous hospitality commented: 'If there were more
like this, eating out would not be such a nerve-wracking experience in Britain,
and maybe it would help to put many of the so-called fine restaurants into
proper perspective.'

---

*Several sharp operators have tried to extort money from restaurateurs on the promise of an
entry in a guide book that has never appeared.* The Good Food Guide *makes no charge
for inclusion and does not offer certificates of any kind.*

Report forms are at the back of the book; write a letter if you prefer.

CHEFS/PROPRIETORS: Colin and Jane Rushworth
OPEN: Tue to Sat, D only and Sun L (Oct to Easter)
CLOSED: 2 weeks June to July, 2 weeks at Christmas
MEALS: 12 to 1.30, 7 to 9
PRICES: £16 (£24)
CARDS: Access, Amex, Diners, Visa
SEATS: 45. Private parties: 14 main room, 14 private room. Vegetarian meals. Children's helpings. Music. Air-conditioned
ACCOMMODATION: 4 rooms, all with bath/shower. B&B £45 to £55. Deposit: by arrangement. Children welcome. TV. Phone. Scenic. Doors close at midnight. Confirm 24 hours ahead.

HAYDON BRIDGE Northumberland   map 7

General Havelock Inn

Radcliffe Road, Haydon Bridge NE47 6ER   COOKING 1
HAYDON BRIDGE (043 484) 376   COST £13–£25

Ian Clyde may watch the cricket while serving in the bar, but one couple who ran across the pub with a restaurant a few years ago were moved to comment that the Clydes give 'more than a service, it's a ministry.' There are rumours of sale in the air, but such things move slowly nowadays. The dining-room has a fine view, the food is substantial, the welcome is generous. Mussels marinière, with garlic, ginger and cider; hot 'Shields' smokie, smoked cod, cheese sauce and white wine; breast of chicken not just with tarragon but also cheese and ginger in the sauce; cod with prawns, mushroom, fennel and Parmesan – these are indicators of Angela Clyde's style, shown on a set-price four-course menu. At Sunday lunch there are roast joints and several vegetables. Banoffi pie and Danish chocolate bar, a confection of melted Bourneville, nuts, raisins, biscuits, rum and cream that might be the Tyneside version of a Yorkie, keep the desserts up to scratch for substance and honesty. Bar meals are also approved. There is an adequate wine list made more interesting by 10 extras chosen not for their expense but for the opposite reason – they are inexpensive, decent examples of their type. House wine is £6.10.

CHEF: Angela Clyde   PROPRIETORS: Ian and Angela Clyde
OPEN: Wed to Sun, exc Sun D
CLOSED: first two weeks Jan
MEALS: 12 to 1.30, 7.30 to 9
PRICES: Set L £8 (£13) to £11 (£16), Set D £15 (£20) to £18 (£21)
SEATS: 28. 4 tables outside. Private parties: 30 main room. Car-park, 12 places. Vegetarian meals. Children's helpings. 1 step to rest. Wheelchair access (1 step; also WC)

All details are as accurate as possible at the time of going to press, but chefs and owners often change, and it is wise to check by telephone before making a special journey. Many readers have been disappointed when set-price bargain meals are no longer available. Ask when booking.

See the back of the Guide *for an index of restaurants listed.*

HELFORD   Cornwall   map 1

▲ *Riverside* ♥

Helford TR12 6JU	COOKING 3
MANACCAN (032 623) 443	COST £24–£35

Helford village sits either side of the creek that tips quickly into the wide stretches of Helford river. It is picture-book Cornwall, reached by a long trip along high-sided lanes ending in the car park. Riverside, the width of the lane and a few walls away from the water itself, is a covey of cottages and small outbuildings now converted to accommodation. The drift of the set-price menu is firmly set towards the water: all bar two of the six or eight main courses are fish and the ratio is repeated in the first courses. Fish is of top quality – Riverside must get deliveries a day earlier than all those places up-country that proudly proclaim their reliance on Helford supplies – and is cooked with sensitivity by David Rayner. There is some invention, too, for menus succeed in ringing the changes in recipes and methods: baked hake with a crab crust; new potatoes filled with salmon and new season's broad beans; monkfish and asparagus on a lime butter sauce; John Dory with langoustines, thyme and pearl onions; or monkfish salad with blood oranges. Not surprisingly it is the weekenders, either staying at the restaurant itself or just visiting the area, who are warmest in their praise 'even if travelling in these creek-restricted regions demands patience.' They will not be as surprised as the locals by the firm prices. The wine list is most remarkable for a run of mature clarets, some decently affordable; but it is also a well-balanced collection giving value at lower price levels and not ignoring newer regions of production. Excellent makers abound and it is in many respects a model for this standard of restaurant. House wines are £8.50. CELLARMAN'S CHOICE: Savennières, Clos du Papillon 1988, £9.50; Gewürztraminer 1985, Hugel, £10.60.

CHEFS: David Rayner and Susie Darrell   PROPRIETOR: Susie Darrell
OPEN: all week, D only; Sat and Sun L
CLOSED: early Nov to mid-Feb
MEALS: 12.30 to 2, 7.30 to 9.30
PRICES: L £18 (£24), Set D £24 (£29). Service inc
SEATS: 35. 4 tables outside. Private parties: 30 main room. Car-park, 12 places. No children under 12. No pipes in dining-room. Wheelchair access (2 steps)
ACCOMMODATION: 6 rooms, all with bath/shower. B&B £50 to £82. Deposit: £100. Baby facilities. Garden. TV. Scenic. Confirm by 6 [*Which? Hotel Guide*]

▲ Mount Somerset

Lower Henlade, Taunton TA3 5NB
TAUNTON (0823) 442500

*Since going to press this
establishment has closed.*

Fat Tulip

The Old Wye Bridge,
2 St Martin's Street, Hereford HR2 7RE   COOKING 1
HEREFORD (0432) 275808   COST £31

A report in the summer commented, 'needs encouraging.' Whether this was a
reflection of attitudes or business was not revealed but this brasserie is a light
in a dark forest. Some dishes – crab pancakes and quails stuffed with calf's
liver, to name two – are relative fixtures on a *carte* of half a dozen choices at
each course and that, too, works along the same lines as at the first blooming of
the Tulip. This is simple and short enough to be executed by a small team in the
kitchen yet is more than the brasserie food usually found in such surroundings.
Venison with elderberry and ginger sauce shows modern English tendencies
and a pleasure in careful presentation, while those seeking more fiery tastes
may be satisfied by king prawns with chilli. It must sometimes be hard for
Hereford to adjust to the possibility of lunching on a salad of goats' cheese and
tapenade – a snack that might be envisaged in Grasse or Nice – rather than
brawn and brown pickle. No wonder the restaurant needs encouragement.
Desserts are simple and are supplemented by a fair cheeseboard and an
espresso machine. The wine list is also a cut above brasserie levels in range,
price and presentation. Note Mâcons from Dom. de la Bon Gran; Brédif's
Vouvray; Pacherenc de Vic-Bilh; and Stoneleigh wines from New Zealand.
Half-bottles remain thin on the list. House wine:£7.55.

CHEF: Kevin Powles PROPRIETORS: Kevin and Susan Powles
OPEN: Mon to Sat, exc Sat L
MEALS: 12 to 1.45, 7 to 9.30
PRICES: £21 (£26). Service inc
CARDS: Access, Amex, Visa
SEATS: 35. Private parties: 20 main room. Children welcome. Wheelchair access
(1 step). Music

The Guide *office can quickly spot when a restaurateur is encouraging customers to write
recommending inclusion and sadly, several restaurants have been doing this in 1990.
Such reports do not further a restaurant's cause. Please tell us if a restaurateur invites you
to write to the* Guide.

HERSHAM Surrey   map 3

La Malmaison

17 Queens Road, Hersham KT12 5ND   COOKING 3
WALTON-ON-THAMES (0932) 227412   COST £18–£37

Jacques Troquet was once chef to the French Ambassador and has continued to
cook pre-eminently French food. The aspect that gains most comment is his
sauces. La Malmaison is a pleasant house with quiet dining-rooms, supervised
by Lisa Troquet at all times. Her presence makes this a very personal restaurant,
only reinforced by her husband's occasional outings from the kitchen to discuss
the niceties of what has gone before, after the cooking is done. Fish is a strong
suit on the *carte* of maybe eight choices in each course. It often comes from a
Norbiton fishmonger used by Japanese expatriates, so its condition is not in
question. Some that have been mentioned are sea bass on fennel with a
béarnaise; fish soup; scallop mousse encased in carrots and courgettes on a sea
urchin sauce; thin slices of salmon lightly grilled on a bed of salad leaves with
a walnut oil dressing and a beurre blanc; turbot roasted with shallots with a
strong mushroom sauce. Firm fleshy fish may get substantial sauces, a madeira
and shallot sauce or the mushroom sauce already mentioned, for instance. Light
meats like veal may get a fishy sauce of sea urchin. Meats are by no means
ignored: beef in three peppercorns sauce; casserole of rabbit with young
vegetables; sweetbreads with nettles are examples of the range of cooking
styles. A decent range of cheese arranged on the plate may finish the meal but
many opt for what one called 'glutton-friendly' desserts: two chocolate
mousses on a thin sponge with two chocolate ice-creams and a vanilla sauce or
a nougat glacé with passion-fruit sauce. The many details in the meal are
carefully considered. One has the impression that the Troquets do little they
have not thought about and discussed for many hours. There is a shorter,
cheaper lunch menu. Occasional 'evenings', of jazz and Provençal cooking so
far, are intended to give zest to quiet weekdays. Four dozen French wines avoid
excessive price and give decent support to the cooking. House vins de pays:
£7.80. CELLARMAN'S CHOICE: Mâcon Vergisson 1988, £12.60; Palette, Ch.
Simone 1985, £17.60.

CHEF: Jacques Troquet   PROPRIETORS: Jacques and Lisa Troquet
OPEN: Mon to Sat, exc Sat L
MEALS: 12 to 2.30, 7 to 10
PRICES: £22 (£31), Set L £12.50 (£18) to £14.50 (£20). Service 10%
CARDS: Access, Diners, Visa
SEATS: 40. 4 tables outside. Private parties: 55 main room, 12 private room. Children's
helpings. Smart dress preferred. No smoking in one dining-room. No smoking in main
dining-room during meals. Vegetarian meals by arrangement. Wheelchair access. Music

---

*The text of entries is based on unsolicited reports sent in by readers, backed up by
inspections conducted anonymously. The factual details under the text are from
questionnaires the Guide sends to all restaurants that feature in the book.*

*The Guide is totally independent, accepts no free hospitality, and survives on the number
of copies sold each year.*

HETTON

HERSTMONCEUX East Sussex   map 3

Sundial

Gardner Street, Herstmonceux BN27 4LA   COOKING 2
HERSTMONCEUX (0323) 832217   COST £23–£44

The tile-hung cottages, with al fresco dining in the summer, still offer 'a very special liver pâté with truffles' for two people only and the menu, though ostensibly changing every fortnight, shows there is mileage in the adage '*plus ça change, plus c'est la même chose.*' The formula and style of Giuseppe Bertoli's cooking seem unaffected by changes in taste that have gone on around him though he does now offer a very full vegetarian menu. This adherence to the tried and true might be seen as estimable consistency, if it does not slip into mechanical repetition. There is, on top of the *carte* and vegetarian menu, a set-price menu of 10 options per course and a further half-dozen dishes of the day. This means a kitchen cooking for 70 covers is offering about 30 choices in each of the first two courses. An inspection meal this year yielded mussels cooked with Pastis that indeed tasted of the announced ingredients, though the mussels were neither as plump nor smooth-textured as they might have been; then followed a plate of noisettes of lamb and breast of pigeon with a single strong stock sauce which should have tasted of garlic but did not; dessert was an iced Grand Marnier soufflé of good texture. Decoration and trimmings are decidedly old-fashioned, as can be the cooking of vegetables. In the centre of the room is a tiered table of cream and cake-like desserts that may stay there for much of the dining period. Service is amiable and efficient although the move from table to bar (for coffee) may be encouraged to release space for latecomers. With so many wines over £50, including half a dozen Dom. de la Romanée Conti between £145 and £275, should the customer be entitled to expect something better than Pinot below £15? Italy tucked in at the end is probably the safest bet. The house wines at £8.25 and £9.25 may be much enjoyed.

CHEF: Giuseppe Bertoli PROPRIETORS: Laurette and Giuseppe Bertoli
OPEN: Tue to Sun, exc Sun D
CLOSED: mid-Aug to Sept, 25 Dec to 20 Jan
MEALS: 12.30 to 2 (2.30 Sun), 7.30 to 9.30 (10 Sat)
PRICES: £28 (£37), Set L £14.50 (£23), Set Sun L £16.50 (£25), Set D £22.50 (£31). Service 10%
CARDS: Access, Amex, Diners, Visa
SEATS: 70. 8 tables outside. Private parties: 50 main room, 22 private room. Car-park, 25 places. Vegetarian meals. Children's helpings. No smoking in dining-room. Wheelchair access (also WC). Music

HETTON North Yorkshire   map 5

Angel Inn ♥

Hetton BD23 6LT   COOKING 3
CRACOE (075 673) 263   COST £16–£26

Praise has showered upon this pub's food in bar and restaurant and has contributed to the genuine press of custom. There are two sittings in the restaurant so promptness is advised. Otherwise, like a party arriving at 7.45, you might 'be told that your table is needed by 9.' The hustle and bustle is promoted by the willing young waiters, needlessly added to by the dreadful light music, and skilfully co-ordinated by the deft control of the restaurant manager. The cooking, offered on a good-value, set-price menu of eight or nine choices per course, swelled further by daily specials, and a bar menu of even greater value for money, is most praised for its fish, occasionally criticised for things like a summer pudding in March, and generally appreciated for skill, speed and quality. The chefs are capable of finesse, as in a salmon tartare with dill; of skill, as in the lobster sauce with the deservedly popular moneybags of fish in a filo purse; and of generosity, as in the lashings of vegetables with every main course, which a few find too dressed with butter or sauce for their own good. Meat never gains the plaudits of fish dishes such as a monkfish and crab mousseline wrapped with a lettuce leaf; moules marinière; salmon with white wine sauce; or queenies baked with garlic. None the less, lamb fillet on a good stock and pan-juice sauce, duck with a curaçao sauce and pigeon with a wild mushroom sauce have also been enthusiastically mentioned, and there has been general approval of the raw materials. As one reader put it, 'after the expectations raised by the fish' it was difficult to be as taken by the meats. Desserts can also be popular: a strong mocha sauce was a good foil to the chocolate marquise; the toffee sponge was fresh and honest as well as large (diners work up large appetites by the time they get to the Angel), but over-sweetness can be a problem. An enthusiast's wine list; by summer 1991 the Cissac 1979 at £16 will probably have gone. Do not despair; the strong section of Italian reds, from Brunello 1979 from Caparzo at £15.95 to a Chianti Riserva at only £9.85, and the very good Rhônes, will all please. Prices are all very fair, and names and vintages generally chosen meticulously. Bin-ends are shown on a blackboard. House French: £6.75, CELLARMAN'S CHOICE: Pinot Noir, Caves de Buxy £10.70; Sauvignon de Touraine, £9.54.

CHEFS: Denis Watkins and John Topham   PROPRIETORS: Denis and Juliet Watkins and John Topham
OPEN: Mon to Sat D and Sun L
CLOSED: 26 Dec and 1 Jan
MEALS: 12.15 to 2, 7 to 9.30
PRICES: bar £10.50 (£16), restaurant Set Sun L £11.50 (£16), Set D £16.95 (£22). Minimum £16.95 at D
CARDS: Access, Visa
SEATS: 36. 15 tables outside. Private parties: 40 main room. Car-park, 17 places. Children's helpings (Sun L only). Smart dress preferred. No pipes in dining-room. Wheelchair access (also WC). Music

HIGH ONGAR Essex	map 10

Shoes

The Street, High Ongar CM5 9ND	COOKING 2
BRENTWOOD (0277) 363 350	COST £34

Diners out in this part of south Essex have waited a while for a serious restaurant. Shoes fulfils their hopes. The sixteenth-century coaching-inn still has original beams and impressive rafters, and the walls are decorated with paintings from a local gallery. Lyndon Wootton runs the place with panache.

Chef Paul Spry has had stints at Inigo Jones, Café Rouge and Harveys, among others, and his regularly changing menu still shows the marks of his mentors. He can cook, although early reports suggest that he is stronger on raw materials and timing than on sauces and pastry. Fashion looms large. The vogue for strange ways with sausages shows in venison sausage served with chocolate noodles and Grand Marnier sauce, or a 'gutsy' rabbit version paired with lobster sauce. Extra fish dishes precede the main course: perhaps trout in puff pastry with a herby tomato and lemon beurre blanc. Fine main courses have included perfectly timed calf's liver with juniper and gin sauce based on veal stock. Otherwise the menu might feature fricassee of chicken and artichokes with fresh coriander, or medallions of pork with sherry sauce, buttered apples and brazil nuts. Fish specials are dictated by the market. Vegetables are 'crunchy enough for the locality' and salads have 'glorious' dressings. Crème brûlée is given an extra flourish with a layer of strawberries, and the prune and almond tart has been excellent. Service is very English, occasionally nervous, but happy to chat and invariably efficient. The wine list, which has a sensible range of prices with much around £10 and a few grander offerings clustering around a firm middle ground, shows Lyndon Wootton's background at Corney & Barrow. There is a well-spread selection from Europe and the New World. House French: £7.25. CELLARMAN'S CHOICE: Montes Cabernet Sauvignon, Curico Valley 1987 £12.50; Ch.Musar 1982, £13.95.

CHEF: Paul Spry   PROPRIETORS: Lyndon Wootton, P.J. Gowan and D.C. Gowan
OPEN: all week, exc Sun D
CLOSED: 1 week after Christmas
MEALS: 12 to 2.30, 7.30 to 9.30
PRICES: £18 (£28)
CARDS: Access, Visa
SEATS: 60. Private parties: 40 main room, 20 and 40 private rooms. Children's helpings on request. Smart dress preferred. Wheelchair access (1 step). Music

---

HOCKLEY HEATH   West Midlands   map 5

▲ *Nuthurst Grange*

Nuthurst Grange Lane,
Hockley Heath B94 5NL   COOKING 3
LAPWORTH (0564) 783972   COST £26–£50

The M40 extension is now open and sweeps close to this comfortable and welcoming hotel on the outer limits of Birmingham. There are two set-price menus on offer for dinner, accumulating into a very adequate range of choice, even though prices are not low. Presentation is a strong point, although flavour may be variable and obscured by a plethora of ingredients. Dishes that have been recommended include pasta with curried crab, chicken and smoked bacon; avocado with pine nuts, bean sprouts and toasted goats' cheese; tomato and basil soup; brill cooked with lentils or, on another occasion, with beetroot and garlic sauce; veal escalope with lemon sauce; and braised ox-tail with sage. One visitor was pleased to be offered a good little turkey brioche as a complementary dish at the beginning. Desserts seem a resounding success, from orange soufflé, bread-and-butter pudding, apricot sorbet under a spun sugar cage with a mango coulis, to crème brûlée. Service is invariably cheerful and willing. The wine list affords fair range, with Californians from Mondavi, Australians from Brown Bros, Alsaces from Kuentz-Bas and burgundies including Parent, Damoy and Delorme. Clarets include a couple of 1967s which, even for first growths, must be speculative. House wines start at £7.80.

CHEFS: D.L. Randolph and S. Wilkes   PROPRIETORS: D.L. and D.A. Randolph
OPEN: all week, exc Sat L
MEALS: 12.30 to 2, 7 to 9.30
PRICES: Set L £17.50 (£26), Set D £27.50 (£37) to £32.50 (£42)
CARDS: Access, Amex, Diners, Visa
SEATS: 50. 5 tables outside. Private parties: 30 main room, 20 private room. Car-park, 40 places. Vegetarian meals. Children's helpings. Wheelchair access (1 step)
ACCOMMODATION: 8 rooms, all with bath/shower. B&B £85 to £125. Baby facilities. Garden. TV. Phone. Scenic. Doors close at midnight

---

HOLDENBY   Northamptonshire   map 3

▲ Lynton House

Holdenby NN6 8DJ   COOKING 2
HOLDENBY (0604) 770777   COST £18–£29

The house, formerly a rectory, is between the A50 and the A428 on the road from Church Brampton to East Haddon. Since the Bertozzis moved into this larger 'country restaurant' from their small canalside place at Stoke Bruerne three or four years back, the style has become more anglicised. Even lasagne is now served with vegetables. The food continues to please, none the less: crisp, tasty duck breast; ricotta and spinach pancake flavoured with nutmeg; wonderful mussels; good vegetables. The four-course menu is long, but first courses do not involve the kitchen in much last-minute preparation. Apart from the more predictable Parma ham or pasta salad are potato and Gorgonzola soup, and scallops in filo pastry. Main courses can be as simple as charcoal grilled escalope of veal with rosemary and lemon, or as hearty as venison in berry and Barolo sauce. Desserts include zabaglione and zuppa inglese. Coffee has not improved. Wines include Champagne, burgundy, some 1982 claret, and a tantalising glimpse of Italy. For the most part, sadly, wines are bereft of vintage or producer; in that respect at least Lynton House remains resolutely Italian. House Soave and Valpolicella: £8.50.

CHEF: Carol Bertozzi   PROPRIETORS: Carlo and Carol Bertozzi
OPEN: all week, exc Mon L, Sat L and Sun D
CLOSED: 2 weeks in summer, Christmas
MEALS: 12.15 to 1.45, 7.15 to 9.45
PRICES: Set L £11.75 (£18) to £14 (£20), Set D £18.75 (£24). Service inc
CARDS: Access, Visa
SEATS: 45. Private parties: 55 main room, 20 private room. Car-park, 30 places. Vegetarian meals. Children's helpings (Sun L only). No children under 6. Smart dress preferred. No cigars/pipes in dining-room. Wheelchair access
ACCOMMODATION: 5 rooms, all with bath/shower. B&B £52 to £65. No children under 6. Garden. Golf. TV. Phone. Scenic. Doors close at 12.30. Confirm by 9 [Which? Hotel Guide]

HOLMFIELD   West Yorkshire   map 5

▲ *Holdsworth House* ♀

Holdsworth, Halifax HX2 9TG
HALIFAX (0422) 240024   COOKING 2
On A629, 2m N of Halifax   COST £31

You won't get in by the front door but need to go right round to find the
entrance. Within there is plenty of local colour, heavy beams, panelling and
polished tables, though the bar is in a new extension and the garden has been
invaded by conference facilities. The hotel is deceptively large and perhaps
determines the tilt of the restaurant, which surprisingly makes no lunchtime
concession of a set meal or more competitive pricing. The menu reads
ambitiously with possibilities such as avocado with warm scallops in wine
butter and salad greens or duck with oregano, kumquats and foie gras with a
confit of the leg. Execution may fall short on detail and intensity of flavour,
however. Thus a hake and shellfish terrine was characterless, saved only by a
pink peppercorn sauce, while sweetbreads with a shiitake mushroom sauce
suffered from the reverse problem. Soups are often satisfactory and correctly
made and may encompass nice ideas, such as nettle and spinach or wild
mushroom consommé with smoked bacon. Pink breast of goose, sliced à la
nouvelle, had crisp skin and combined well with its marjoram and pear sauce,
and sliced fillet of fallow deer with mustard and tarragon sauce, arranged
around a cranberry filled tartlet, was pink and tender. Chocolate délice with
good apricot coulis, ginger caramel creams, or even bread-and-butter pudding,
might follow. Service can be brisk to the point of overzealous, and bread or
rolls in addition to melba toast would be welcome. The wine list stretches to
over a hundred and fifty bottles; including a fair small New World section,
excellent Italians and some mature classics. Its drawback is a generally high
starting price. There is not much below £14, even from America and Australia.
In compensation, there are 12 house wines starting at £7.95. CELLARMAN'S
CHOICE: Sancerre, Clos du Roy, 1988, Paul Millérioux £17; Fleurie 1988, Dom.
des Rageats, £17.60.

CHEF: Eric Claveau   PROPRIETORS: Kim Pearson and Gail Moss
OPEN: all week, exc Sat L and Sun L
MEALS: 12 to 1.45, 7 to 9.30 (9 Sun)
PRICES: £20 (£26). Service inc
CARDS: Access, Amex, Diners, Visa
SEATS: 65. Private parties: 8 main room, 14 and 100 private rooms. Car-park, 40 places.
Vegetarian meals. Children's helpings. Smart dress preferred. Wheelchair access (also
unisex WC)
ACCOMMODATION: 40 rooms, all with bath/shower. Rooms for disabled. B&B £65 to £80.
Baby facilities. Pets welcome but not in public rooms. Afternoon teas. Garden. Snooker.
TV. Phone. Scenic. Confirm by 6 [*Which? Hotel Guide*]

*The text of entries is based on unsolicited reports sent in by readers, backed up by
inspections conducted anonymously. The factual details under the text are from
questionnaires the* Guide *sends to all restaurants that feature in the book.*

HOLT Norfolk

map 6

Yetman's

37 Norwich Road, Holt NR25 6SA
HOLT (0263) 713320

COOKING 1
COST £20–£28

The yellow card of the menu echoes both the colour wash of the small house
and the T-shirt sometimes worn by Peter Yetman, a point of sartorial discussion
among those who think waiters should make more effort in their dress. Alison
Yetman's garb causes no such dissension and her food provokes approval. It is
offered on a daily *carte*, three or four dishes at each stage, and may include ham
and beetroot; skate and black butter; chicken with a mint and curry sauce;
cassoulet or pork with home-made pickles. Lunch dishes may be more homely
than dinner but, then, the approach is that of the good home cook. Local
luxuries – artichoke, asparagus, lobster, crab – are presented simply. There is
always a vegetarian dish in each course, even on so small a menu. Puddings
tend to the substantial. Lack of finish sometimes means that intensity of flavour
is ignored, even in soups, and that sauces are not proper reductions, strong yet
delicate, capable of enhancing the main ingredient. Many value this place for
its frank and open approach – a relief from stuffiness – and efforts not to
charge too much. This extends to the wine list from Lay and Wheeler. Provision
of wines by the glass is good and generous and half-bottles are on the increase.
New World wines get their fair share of attention in a straightforward
mainstream list. House wines: £6.65 and £7.50. CELLARMAN'S CHOICE:
Montagny 1988, Leflaive, £15; Aloxe-Corton 1986, Leflaive, £18.50.

CHEF: Alison Yetman PROPRIETORS: Alison and Peter Yetman
OPEN: Wed to Sun
MEALS: 12.30 to 2, 7.30 to 9
PRICES: L £14 (£20), D £17 (£23)
SEATS: 32. Private parties: 20 main room. Vegetarian meals. Children's helpings. No
smoking in dining-room. Wheelchair access (1 step)

HOPTON CASTLE Shropshire

map 4

▲ Park Cottage

Hopton Castle SY7 0QF
BUCKNELL (05474) 351
off B4367, 11m W of Ludlow

COOKING 2
COST £23

In a flower-bedecked garden, against a backdrop of Marcher hills with mist
rolling down their slope, Park Cottage sits in some of England's most unspoilt
countryside. Ask for directions when booking. This is good walking country
and some seize the opportunity by staying in one of John and Josephine
Gardner's two guest bedrooms. Most come to eat in an intimate, oak-panelled
dining-room seating no more than a dozen. It's a comfortable place decorated
with personal mementos, porcelain and books. 'We try to serve food which
reflects the local environment'. This seems to please local regulars, of which
there appear to be many – one reason for some lack of variety but also the basis
for what has been called 'honest cooking'. Fish cannot figure too prominently

on menus which have but a choice of three main courses, but salmon from the Wye is often served simply with a 'sauce made from the stock and the garnishes'. Simple is the byword. Steak, duck and venison tend to be grilled, roasted or casseroled; vegetables come from the garden and may be well cooked. Meringues – with raspberry or apricot – are a longstanding favourite. Prices are even better value than before. The wine list relies on Tanners of Shrewsbury. House wine: £6 and £6.50. CELLARMAN'S CHOICE: Châteauneuf-du-Pape, Dom. du Vieux Télégraphe 1986, £14.50; Pouilly Fumé, Les Loges 1988, £14.30.

CHEF: John Gardner   PROPRIETORS: Josephine and John Gardner
OPEN: all week (advance booking out of season)
MEALS: 12 to 1.30, 7.30 to 8.30
PRICES: £13 (£19)
SEATS: 12. 2 tables outside. Private parties: 10 main room, 8 private room. Car-park, 8 places. Children's helpings. No children under 7
ACCOMMODATION: 2 rooms, both with bath/shower. B&B £20 to £36. Deposit: £10. No children under 7. Afternoon teas. Garden. TV. Scenic. Doors close at 10. Confirm by noon

---

HORTON Northamptonshire   map 3

French Partridge ▮

Horton NN7 2AP   COOKING 3
NORTHAMPTON (0604) 870033   COST £22–£28

The restaurant has served Northamptonshire well for more than a quarter of the century, cooking honest food and charging consistently fair prices. Even the tip is included in the price. But it is not some archaeological relic of a country 'bistro français'. It changes over the years: chicken pâté of the 1960s has become chicken liver parfait with a muscat jelly and brioche toast, and Alain Senderens has been cited as the source of a dish of skate baked in pastry. What has not altered is putting taste before fanciful presentation and offering a measured version of current French cooking to the English. The milieu is English enough: two green rooms in a long farmhouse conversion with service supervised by Mary Partridge and a four-course set-price menu arranged to a fairly constant formula. Ennui may be provoked among regulars by the pattern of melon, pâté, a cold fish and soup as first courses; a hot fish and often a quiche or perhaps a mushroom dish in second place; then a lamb and two poultry dishes for the main course, joined by a fourth, perhaps offal, veal, or rabbit. Steak does not figure, but braised or long-cooked recipes will be given their due: a sausage of sweetbreads, chicken and ham, or pig's trotter stuffed with a mousse of sweetbreads are two examples. It may sound trammelling, but room is left for manoeuvre: soups that reveal good stocks such as a lettuce and green pea or pumpkin and tomato; Arbroath smokie pâté with avocado salad; salmon in flaky pastry with a dill sauce; venison with glazed chestnuts and baby onions; home-cured loin of pork with gnocchi and tomato sauce; and generous vegetables brought in dishes to the table are some of the credit points made in the course of the year. The meal ends with a choice of six desserts, a savoury or cheese. These usually get a good press, whether for mushrooms on toast; the ice-creams; iced pear soufflé with chocolate sauce; black cherries topped with yoghurt and cream, then sprinkled with brown sugar; or prunes soaked in armagnac with a prune and armagnac ice-cream. Consistency is the watchword and is generally achieved. The wine list has always been one to revel in, though a few of the entries need more detail to help make a choice. Mary Partridge will know the answer. The range for France and Germany is very fine (despite an inadvertently implied criticism in last year's *Guide* entry) and the price range is almost charity itself. There are a few Antipodean selections and the classic French regions are bolstered by seven good south-western wines from Madiran, Cahors and Bergerac. Growers and properties are good ones; there are sufficient halves and the prices put many to shame. House wines start at £6. Note the restaurant doesn't take credit cards.

CHEFS: David Partridge and Justin Partridge   PROPRIETORS: David and Mary Partridge
OPEN: Tue to Sat, D only
CLOSED: 2 weeks at Christmas and Easter, 3 weeks July to Aug
MEALS: 7.30 to 9
PRICES: Set D £19 (£22) to £20 (£23). Service inc
SEATS: 50. Private parties: 10 main room. Car-park, 50 places. Children welcome. Wheelchair access

---

HOXNE Suffolk	map 3

Swan

Low Street, Hoxne IP21 5AS	COOKING 1
HOXNE (037 975) 275	COST £22

Edmund, the martyred king of East Anglia, was captured by the Danes at Hoxne not long before his execution. Today the strongest whiff of the Middle Ages may come from the Hoxne Hundred, a Morris dancing troupe, but the Swan manages satisfactory cooking for modern frames in both the bar and the restaurant beyond. The menu is short, but there is care in the presentation and the cooking of dishes such as eggs with a watercress mousseline – the eggs soft as they should be; pork fillet with prunes; and duck with a parsnip and wine sauce. A lunch of spinach pancakes and a gazpacho, washed down by a bottle of Sancerre, shows that the enthusiasm has spread to the bar. The building is satisfyingly timbered and ancient. Adnams beers on draught. House wine from £5. CELLARMAN'S CHOICE: Ch. Notton 1973, £15.80; Leroy d'Auvenay 1983, £11.50.

CHEFS: Frances Thornton-Jones and Chris Beecham   PROPRIETORS: Tony and Frances Thornton-Jones
OPEN: Wed to Sat, D, and Sun L
CLOSED: 25 Dec
MEALS: 12 to 2, 7 to 9
PRICES: £13 (£18)
SEATS: 36. 8 tables outside. Private parties: 36 main room. Car-park, 45 places. Vegetarian meals with prior notice. Children welcome. No smoking in dining-room

---

All letters to the Guide *are acknowledged with an update on latest sales, closures, chef changes and so on.*

HUDDERSFIELD West Yorkshire   map 5

▲ *Lodge Hotel*

48 Birkby Lodge Road, Birkby,
Huddersfield HD2 2BG   COOKING 1
HUDDERSFIELD (0484) 431001   COST £14–£29

Ample grounds insulate this small hotel from Huddersfield suburban life,
worth seeking out if only for the exceptional art nouveau interiors by
Mancunian architect Edgar Wood. The restaurant, which is obviously aiming
for a life independent of the dozen bedrooms that have been converted, is not
so much art nouveau as colour-co-ordinated: the pink tablecloths are set off by
crimson overcloths and paper napkins and match the chairs to a T. Early reports
of the cooking show that care is being taken not merely for pretence's sake.
Scallops with prawns and an anisette sauce; pigeon with wild mushrooms;
kidneys in a filo purse on a *sauce choron* are substantial first courses which are
followed by a soup (often good) or a salad in the four-course set-price menu –
half the price at lunch for somewhat simpler food. The main courses reported
have continued the vein of substance, with sauces that mince nothing in terms
of taste – a chicken liver and madeira sauce for fillet of beef and a grape and
brandy sauce for hare are two that have been cited. These may contain
trimmings that add little to flavour and much to muddle, for example, a celery
and mushroom pâté with a steak. Some of the desserts have been a similar
mixture of good and not so good. The service learns its way and vegetarians
have their way with a separate menu. The wine list makes a fair
accompaniment to the food, with a small connoisseur's section, and is not
overpriced. House wines: £5.95.

CHEFS: Richard Hanson and Simon Copley   PROPRIETORS: David and Kevin Birley
OPEN: all week, exc Sat L and Sun D
MEALS: 12 to 2, 7.30 to 9.45
PRICES: Set L £8.95 (£14), Set D £17.95 (£24)
CARDS: Access, Amex, Visa
SEATS: 60. 4 tables outside. Private parties: 24 main room, 20 and 24 private rooms. Car-
park, 40 places. Children's helpings. Smart dress preferred. No smoking in half of dining-
room. Wheelchair access (1 step; also WC). Music
ACCOMMODATION: 11 rooms, all with bath/shower. Rooms for disabled. B&B £45 to 50.
Baby facilities. Afternoon teas. Garden. Snooker. TV. Phone. Scenic. Doors close at 12.30.
Confirm 24 hours ahead

Pisces

84 Fitzwilliam Street,
Huddersfield HD1 5BD   COOKING 1
HUDDERSFIELD (0484) 516773   COST £18–£32

New chef Michael Rowley, learning his lesson from assisting the previous chef,
has pleased customers after initial misgivings. A *carte* and cheaper set menu co-
exist on weekday evenings, offering perhaps eight sorts of fish and three or four
meats. The approach remains simple, though not plain: warm salad of
monkfish; salmon with sorrel sauce; sole on a bed of leeks with a shellfish

sauce; scallops in filo with a red pepper sauce; or red mullet with fennel have proved satisfactory. Puddings are simple, too: sorbets or banana with ice-cream and hot toffee sauce are two recent instances from reports. A basic wine list lacks growers' names but is not unreasonably priced. House French is £6.45.

CHEF: Michael Rowley   PROPRIETORS: T.Y. and S.J. Wormald
OPEN: Mon to Sat
MEALS: 12 to 2, 7 to 9.30
PRICES: £19 (£27), Set D £13.50 (£18)
CARD: Access, Visa
SEATS: 50. Private parties: 50 main room. Car-park, 22 places. Children welcome. Smart dress preferred. Wheelchair access. Music. Air-conditioned

---

HURSTBOURNE TARRANT Hampshire   map 2

▲ *Esseborne Manor* ♥

Hurstbourne Tarrant SP11 0ER
HURSTBOURNE TARRANT (026 476) 444
on the A343 1m N of   COOKING 2
Hurstbourne Tarrant   COST £14–£42

The name comes from Domesday, the house is late Victorian, the decorative treatment late twentieth century: warm, all-over colours, plump upholstery, comfort, and human scale mark it out. The cooking by Mark Greenfield continues in a resolutely modern vein. A daily five-course dinner menu gives choice in the first and last courses and none for the fish and meat in the middle. These are, however, fleshed out by a seasonal flight of six extra dishes printed on the menu cover. At lunch a shorter meal is on offer: a 'quickie' of two or more normally three courses at an extremely fair price. Nor is there a service charge or anything else expected. Presentation is an art form, as it might be for an alumnus of the Savoy and the Lancaster, Paris. Tastes, too, have been reported positively, in dishes such as salmon marinated in lime juice and sesame oil; quails' eggs and smoked salmon in aspic with a tapénade; turbot with a shallot and saffron dressing; sweetbreads with sorrel and lemon; and fruit-laden desserts such as apple tart with cinnamon sorbet or strawberries with Melba sauce and cherries cooked in red wine. The wine list is a very sound general selection, well balanced for the most part and not overpriced. Rollin, Ampeau, Brocard in Burgundy; Ch. Potensac, de Pez and Figeac in Bordeaux; and Rothbury in Australia are among the properties and growers to watch. House wines are from Murray Tyrrell at £10.60.

CHEF: Mark Greenfield   PROPRIETORS: Michael and Frieda Yeo and family
OPEN: all week
MEALS: 12.30 to 2, 7.30 to 9.30
PRICES: Set L from £9 (£14), Set D £26.50 (£32) to £29.25 (£35). Service inc
CARDS: Access, Amex, Diners, Visa
SEATS: 36. Private parties: 28 main room, 10 private room. Car-park, 20 places. No children under 12. Smart dress preferred. No cigars/pipes in dining-room. Wheelchair access
ACCOMMODATION: 12 rooms, all with bath/shower. B&B £75 to £100. No children under 12. Afternoon teas. Garden. Tennis. TV. Phone. Scenic [*Which? Hotel Guide*]

ILFRACOMBE Devon   map 1

Whites

12 Beach Road, Hele Bay,
Ilfracombe EX34 9OZ   COOKING 1
ILFRACOMBE (0271) 862821   COST £16–£24

If you are on your way to anywhere when passing Whites, you are going
swimming. This tea-shop lookalike is home to enterprising cooking, for North
Devon particularly. Everything is home made, from Mary Blanche's four sorts
of bread roll (from local flour) to the ice-creams that get an extended outing at
pudding time. What marks out this kitchen is not the menu, a trifle long and
not very exciting at first sight, but the consistency of the cooking and Robin
Blanche's real desire to do things himself – orange juice is fresh, a rare
experience. Many of the principal dishes have alcohol in the sauces, as do the
desserts, 'I am surprised anyone can drive home afterwards.' A meal in the
summer produced tomato soup that preserved the sweetness of fruit at a pitch
of ripeness, and scallops that were correctly timed, fresh, and came with a
blockbuster mushroom sauce. Pastry work with the scallops was light-handed.
Prawn cocktail is offered, the Blanches not having seen fit to offend local
preference, and steak and pigeon pie. The bird turns up again inside a home-
made ravioli with a game stock sauce finished with cream. Vegetables are
plentiful, never ending, and imaginative – the peperonata has been singled out
for praise. Desserts are a parade of ice-creams with funny names and parasols.
'Number One Kingswood Villas' is named after the house of the Blanches'
carpenter, whom they wished to recognise. The wine list is short and very
cheap. Twenty-nine bins take in eight countries of origin, which may be a
record. Vegetarians are honestly treated. 'I make soups with vegetable stocks so
that I can serve them to vegetarians;' says Robin Blanche. How many can say
this, hand on heart? House wines are £5.25. CELLARMAN'S CHOICE: Sauvignon
de St Bris 1986, £8.50; Marquès de Murrieta Reserva 1984, £11.50.

CHEF: Robin Blanche   PROPRIETOR: Robin and Mary Blanche
OPEN: Wed to Sat, D only
CLOSED: Christmas and first 2 weeks Jan
MEALS: 7 to 9.30
PRICES: £14 (£20), Set D £12.25 (£16)
CARDS: Access, Amex, Visa
SEATS: 20. Private parties: 15 main room. Vegetarian meals. Children's helpings. Smart
dress preferred. Wheelchair access (1 step). Music.

ILKLEY West Yorkshire   map 5

Box Tree

29 Church Street, Ilkley LS29 9DR   COOKING 4
ILKLEY (0943) 608484   COST £25–£38

From year to year Edward Denny and the Box Tree manage to retain curiosity
and interest in cooking. Although favourites are on the menu to satisfy
recidivists – the tuile of strawberries with a rose sorbet has figured since time
began, and partridge with a peach gravy might occur from one season to

another – there is a sense of innovation that enlivens potential boredom even if, here and there, the new combination is judged less than worth the effort. The cottage has lost none of its ability to charm, 'like a little museum, it has an intimate and cosy atmosphere.' The slightly kitsch juxtaposition of curios, pictures, music and very sophisticated food can be traced back to its origins in the 1960s and the personalities of its founders. They were succeeded in 1987 by the Texan Eric Kyte, who has managed to motivate the staff even if his presence is only periodic. The mix of menus – a short daily choice, a longer gourmet meal or a *carte* of several options but one price – gives sound value at the bottom end for very careful cooking, although prices are high. From the short daily choice has been recommended an outstanding terrine of fish wrapped in a pancake where the *farce* had no excess baggage of blandness and the fish flavour was exactly pointed by lemon seasoning, the whole lightened by a balsamic vinegar dressing. This was followed by two breasts of wood pigeon on a bed of shredded cabbage with a good port and stock reduction sauce. Vegetables were no more than dull but the finishing note of crème brûlée, though familiar, was resoundingly successful. The trimmings of butter, canapés, petits fours and excellent coffee are usually of the standard demanded. A more expensive choice might take in a mushroom consommé poured over a mushroom ravioli; a range of seafood with ginger and cream sauce; home-made noodles with seafood, a terrine of red mullet spiked with leaf coriander; or poached pears with honey ice-cream and pine kernels. English cheeses are good, but the staff don't always know them. Edward Denny is prepared to mix with the moderns, as in a first course of skate with a langoustine coulis that captured luxury with an everyday material of exemplary condition and flavour. Where he scores over many regional competitors is in the sophistication of conception. The wine list does not allow much economy and and the careful diner, happily content with the cheaper menu, may come seriously unstuck. Half-bottles are provided generously but only a few reasonable bottles sneak in under £12. Growers and vintages are faultless.

CHEF: Edward Denny   PROPRIETOR: Eric Kyte
OPEN: Tue to Sat, D only and Sun L
CLOSED: 25 and 26 Dec, 1 Jan
MEALS: 12.30 to 2, 7.30 to 9.45
PRICES: Set L £14.95 (£25), Set D £21.50 (£32)
CARDS: Access, Amex, Diners, Visa
SEATS: 50. Private parties: 30 main room, 16 private room. Children welcome. Smart dress preferred. No cigars/pipes in dining-room. Wheelchair access

INKPEN Berkshire   map 2

Swan Inn

Lower Inkpen, Newbury, RG15 0DX   COOKING 1
INKPEN (048 84) 326   COST £26

The energetic who are ready for food at the Swan may have completed, or be anticipating, a circular walk from Combe church over Inkpen Beacon (see *Holiday Which? Good Walks Guide*, walk 69). The Swan is not far from the start of this. Esther Scothorne provides good pub fare at lunchtime but branches out into south-east Asian cookery in the evening. It's just the thing along with beers that are real and not greedily priced – if the wind on the downs was too bracing. Though Singapore is the foundation, the cooking is as receptive to outside influence as it is on the island itself. So there may be Szechuan, Cantonese, Indonesian or Indian dishes to be found on the short word-processed menu. Satay has been praised, its sauce appreciated for its 'delayed kick', as has Szechuan chicken, the strong chillies cutting through the slightly sweet sauce. Rendang, the long-cooked Indonesian beef and coconut speciality, was less dry than some interpretations and redolent of generous coriander, lemon grass and coconut. There is dill-flavoured or plain boiled Thai rice and one-plate dishes such as nasi goreng ('very garlicky'), and fried cabbage with prawns and egg. Desserts turn to the American way of life: 'Death by Chocolate' or apple flan and ice-cream. Persistence may bring a grilled steak to those whose preference goes that way. There are a dozen wines. House wine: £7.

CHEF: Esther Scothorne   PROPRIETORS: Mr and Mrs J. Scothorne
OPEN: Tue to Sat, D only and Sun L
MEALS: 12 to 1.45, 7 to 9.30
PRICES: £12 (£22)
CARDS: Access, Visa
SEATS: 38. 6 tables outside. Private parties: 38 main room. Car-park, 50 places. Children welcome. Smart dress preferred. Music

---

IPSWICH Suffolk   map 3

Kwok's Rendezvous

23 St Nicholas Street, Ipswich IP1 1TW   COOKING 1
IPSWICH (0473) 256833   COST £17–£22

One of the better outposts of Chinese cooking in East Anglia. Chef/proprietor Thomas Kwok maintains standards and the service is first-rate. The menu is a varied and concise selection of around 50 dishes, mostly Pekinese and Szechuan favourites including bang-bang chicken, hot and sour soup, twice-cooked pork, aromatic crispy duck and drunken fish in Chinese wine sauce. More remarkable is the wine list, which is a serious collection of vintage Champagnes, petit château clarets and burgundies with good Loire and Alsace wines to match the food. The usual staples of Liebfraumilch and Niersteiner cower on a back page. The notes are good, the prices not excessive. House wine £6.50. CELLARMAN'S CHOICE: Chablis, Jean Pierre Grossot 1986, £16.50.

CHEF: Thomas Kwok   PROPRIETORS: Lucia and Thomas Kwok
OPEN: Mon to Sat
MEALS: 12 to 2, 7 to 10.30
PRICES: £11 (£18). Set L and D £12.50 (£17) to £14.50 (£18). Minimum £12.50. Service inc
CARDS: Amex, Diners
SEATS: 50. Private parties: 30 main room. Car-park, 50 places. Vegetarian meals. Children welcome. Smart dress preferred. Wheelchair access (also WC). Music

---

The Guide *always appreciates hearing about changes of chef or owner.*

Mortimer's on the Quay

Wherry Quay, Ipswich IP4 1AS   COOKING 2
IPSWICH (0473) 230225   COST £26

This is the sister restaurant to Mortimer's at Bury St Edmunds (see entry) and, like that, specialises in fish. The quay in question is on the river Orwell, in the midst of Ipswich docks and among working wharves. The building was once a warehouse and has been done out plainly but comfortably. Constants exist on the menu: first courses roll on from year to year; Loch Fyne oysters and smoked fish are always offered; the varieties of North Sea fish remain the same, even if their treatment differs in detail. The fish, of good quality, may sometimes be swamped by the sauces. However, portions are generous, prices are fair and the fish is not badly handled. Comment has been made that vegetables may be sparse and desserts basic. This is not a place for modern fish cookery but 'it is better value than some famous restaurants and busier too'. House wine is £6.95, but the purse won't be stretched if something more adventurous is taken from the list. This gives little enough detail, except sweetness grading and has only half a dozen reds. As there is no meat on the menu, this should suffice.

CHEF: Kenneth Ambler   PROPRIETORS: Kenneth Ambler and Michael Gooding
OPEN: Mon to Sat, exc Sat L
CLOSED: bank hols and day after, 24 Dec to 5 Jan, 2 weeks Aug
MEALS: 12 to 2, 7 to 9 (8.30 Mon)
PRICES: £15 (£22)
CARDS: Access, Amex, Diners, Visa
SEATS: 60. Private parties: 8 main room. Children's helpings on request. Smart dress preferred. No-smoking area. Wheelchair access (1 step)

Orwell House Restaurants

4 Orwell Place, Ipswich IP4 1BB   COOKING 1
IPSWICH (0473) 230254   COST £11–£32

John Gear continues as chef at this twin restaurant and bistro arranged split-level in a Georgian shell, and under new ownership since the last *Guide*. The downstairs bistro, changes its menu monthly and is substantially cheaper than the main restaurant. The cooking is serviceable and prices, especially in the bistro, are realistic. Less so is offering pheasant in summer, and pricing lobster at an unvarying level while encouragingly listing Dover sole at a daily 'market price'. Dishes that set the character of the restaurant include a salad of smoked chicken; smoked halibut filled with a prawn mousse; loin of pork with pistachio and apple in filo pastry; chicken stuffed with a spinach mousse. Lamb cutlets *réforme*; beef bourguignonne; smoked salmon and peppercorn pâté; and guacamole are what you might be offered in the bistro. The wine list, rather erratically annotated, takes in a little from beyond France. House wines: £7.

Restaurateurs justifiably resent no-shows. If you quote a credit card number when booking, you may be liable for the restaurant's lost profit margin if you don't turn up. Always phone to cancel.

CHEF: John Gear   PROPRIETOR: Jonathan King
OPEN: Tue to Sat
MEALS: 12 to 2, 7 to 9.30 (10 Sat)
PRICES: bistro £10 (£15), restaurant £20 (£27), Set L £7 (£11), Set D £8 (£13) to £12 (£17).
Service inc
CARDS: Access, Amex, Diners, Visa
SEATS: 80. 4 tables outside. Private parties: 40 main room, 20 and 40 private rooms. Car-
park, 12 places. Vegetarian meals. Children's helpings. Smart dress preferred. No smoking.
Wheelchair access (also WC) in bistro. Music

Singing Chef

200 St Helen's Street, Ipswich IP4 2RH   COOKING 1
IPSWICH (0473) 255236   COST £17–£28

The French bistro formula of dripping candles, wonky wooden tables, paper
tablecloths, and bread without plate or butter hasn't changed much, nor has the
regional France bent. As always, *le patron chante ici* when encouraged, and
occasional jazz evenings are held, when the menu is creole in style. There is
now more vegetarian fare on a separate *carte*, but the cooking has been off key
of late, hence the demoted score. On inspection, rough pâté de campagne with
modern lettuce salad had a full fresh flavour, as did simple peasant-style ham
in white wine with mushrooms. The sauce of a coq au vin Mâconnais was thin
and contained celery, but the dish worked none the less. Less acceptable were
sloppy potatoes in a vague gratin, overcooked vegetables, and unrecognisable
lemon sorbet. Service, alas not included, has been called slow and slipshod.
The wine list of 80 French bottles specialises in single vineyard Champagnes;
the enthusiasm for vineyard names and growers is not matched in other
sections, which are short on detail. Prices are modest. House Burgundy is
£7.25. CELLARMAN'S CHOICE: Cahors, Pelvillain et Fils 1986, £10.

CHEFS: Kenneth Toyé and Jeannine Toyé   PROPRIETORS: Cynthia and Kenneth Toyé
OPEN: Tue to Sat, D only (L by arrangement)
MEALS: 7 to 11
PRICES: £17 (£24), Set L £12 (£17) to £18 (£24), Set D £15 (£20)
CARDS: Access, Visa
SEATS: 35. 4 tables outside. Private parties: 20 private annexe. Children's helpings.
Wheelchair access (also WC). Music

IXWORTH Suffolk   map 6

Theobalds

68 High Street, Ixworth IP31 2HJ   COOKING 2
PAKENHAM (0359) 31707   COST £19–£38

Inglenook fireplace, timbered ceiling, fine china and good furniture are found
behind a plain frontage in the centre of the village. The restaurant attracts a
loyal following: 'I have been going two or three times a year these last six
years;' 'we have Sunday lunch at least 45 times a year.' The adage that the best
restaurant is the one you know and are known in is a good one, but even
occasional visitors find the going good: artichoke soup with hazelnuts; double-

baked cheese soufflé; moules marinière; mushrooms with onion and ham; skate with tarragon butter; lamb with basil and tomato; blackberry bavarois; a good small cheeseboard; and exact crème brûlée. These are competently cooked with attention to details such as vegetables and niceties of service. Regulars, in truth, might detect a recurrent pattern to the menus, a love of alcohol in many of the sauces and an affection for old favourites. The wine list is especially generous in provision of halves, but the wholes also give a good spread of French produce with some New World support. Marquis de Laguiche, Henri Clerc, Couly-Dutheil, Ch. Nairac, Durup and Cattin are some names worth noticing. CELLARMAN'S CHOICE: Beaujolais Blanc 1987, Thibert, £13.55; Chinon, Barronie Madeleine 1983, Couly-Dutheil, £17.25.

CHEF: Simon Theobald   PROPRIETORS: Simon and Geraldine Theobald
OPEN: all week, exc Mon L, Sat L, Sun D
MEALS: 12.15 to 2, 7 to 10
PRICES: Set L £12.50 (£19), Set Sun L £12.95 (£19), Set D £19.50 (£27) to £24.50 (£32)
CARDS: Access, Visa
SEATS: 36. Private parties: 36 main room. Children's helpings. No children under 8. No-smoking area on request

---

JEVINGTON East Sussex   map 3

Hungry Monk

Jevington BM26 5QF
POLEGATE (032 12) 2178   COOKING 2
on B2105, between Polegate and Friston   COST £29

'We ate here about 14 years ago,' begins one report, 'and were glad to find it hadn't changed much.' That testament to the Monk's continuity, quite apart from the reader's memory, is impressive in a world where some restaurants change from week to week. The good value of the fixed-price menu also impresses: three courses with generous choice plus coffee and a glass of tawny port. 'How do they do it?' wonders one diner. Partly by adding supplements of £1.50 to £2.50 for some dishes, which is less popular with customers than the proprietors might imagine. But the package still pleases. The restaurant is a maze of small rooms full of furniture, some containing objets d'art, some just objects, but all adding up to an enfolding warmth that is invariably described as 'cosy'. Dishes, chalked on the blackboard, are pulled from a timeless repertoire that includes pork and pigeon terrine with Cumberland sauce; fillet of Dover sole stuffed with salmon mousseline; or rack of lamb with garlic and redcurrant sauce. Occasionally there are flashes of something that may not have been on the menu 14 years ago, such as goats' cheese in sesame seeds with crisp bacon, or the incorporation of passion-fruit into the Marsala sauce that accompanies roast duck. Cooking is robust rather than exact, which catches the mood of diners, although vegetables – too many and too careless – continue to annoy mildly. Desserts constitute a roll call of all that is most indulgent, from banoffi pie to hot madeira cake with ice-cream and fudge sauce; from summer pudding to treacle pudding; from tarte Tatin to chocolate marquise. The cream bill must be enormous. Classic French bottles, which make up the wine list's backbone, are fleshed out with a selection from around the globe at prices which make a reasonable start from the middle band but get pushed inexorably to rather unreasonable heights. Jevington's location in the heart of viticultural England is reflected in a clutch of wines that includes Breaky Bottom Müller-Thurgau 1989; its location down the coast from Hastings may be reflected in the price of £10.66. House wine: £7.30 and £7.60.

CHEFS: Claire Burgess and Thai La Roche   PROPRIETORS: Nigel and Susan Mackenzie
OPEN: all week, D only and Sun L (other days by arrangement for large parties)
MEALS: 12.15 to 2.30, 7.15 to 10.30
PRICES: Set Sun L and D £16.95 (£24). Service 10% for parties of 8 or more
SEATS: 36. Private parties: 36 main room, 10 and 16 private rooms. Car-park, 17 places.
Vegetarian meals. Children's helpings. No children under 3. Smart dress preferred.
No smoking in dining-room

KENDAL Cumbria   map 7

Moon

129 Highgate, Kendal LA9 4EN   COOKING 1
KENDAL (0539) 729254   COST £19

'Everyone's going to the Moon' is the house slogan – and the place is filled to the rafters. Supporters are enthusiastic enough to partake in the Moon ten-mile road race and two-mile fun run (perhaps for those who have just eaten), an event that shows a Lakeland love for athletic endeavour, like the Porthole's cycling time-trial (see Bowness-on-Windermere). 'Cheap and cheerful' might have been invented for the Moon, comments one visitor, who recommends the salads as best showing off the kitchen's talents, detecting a blandness in some of the more adventurous sounding vegetarian main dishes and beginnings. The repertoire displayed on a blackboard is certainly wide, encompassing a strong vegetarian tendency that is cooked by owner Val Macconnell. Dishes such as pineapple with date, orange and cream cheese filling; spinach and feta strudel; curried mushrooms; or mushrooms, broccoli and mozzarella filling for a brioche are balanced by chicken with Moroccan prune and cinnamon sauce; rump steak (organically reared beef from Devon was being used as the *Guide* went to press) in a sweet-and-sour plum sauce; or prawn, courgette and dill with tagliatelle. Spicy meat dishes are warmly applauded. Desserts continue the inventiveness, as in greengage and ginger ice-cream or raspberry and elderflower cheesecake. A dozen wines, chosen carefully, include CVNE Rioja and Hill-Smith Riesling. House French: £6.45 a litre.

CHEFS: Sharon Moreton and Val Macconnell   PROPRIETOR: Val Macconnell
OPEN: all week, D only (L for parties by arrangement)
MEALS: 6 to 10 (10.30 Fri and Sat)
PRICES: £10 (£16)
CARDS: Access, Visa
SEATS: 40. Private parties: 24 private room. Vegetarian meals. Children's helpings.
Wheelchair access. Music

The Guide *relies on feedback from its readers. Especially welcome are reports on new restaurants appearing in the book for the first time.*

KENILWORTH Warwickshire

map 5

Restaurant Bosquet ♥

97A Warwick Road, Kenilworth CV8 1HP
KENILWORTH (0926) 52463

COOKING 3
COST £27–£40

Bernard Lignier produces food with great sensitivity in surroundings which those in favour call 'without pretence' and others think could do with some improvement. He is French and he cooks classically in a repertoire including dishes such as artichoke heart filled with foie gras and sweet onion with a Jurançon sauce; ravioli of guinea-fowl and truffle with a leek and cream sauce; veal with a sweetcorn and lime sauce; or noisettes of lamb coated with crumbs and truffles served with a port and cream sauce. The style of the food is not showy, which sometimes leads people to undervalue its fine consistency. This extends to the repertoire, which is a slow developer, although it could be said that dishes have been less artfully complicated this year. There has been no capitulation to the advocates of lentils, olive oil and peasant cookery, although most menus contain at least one long-cooked dish such as guinea-fowl *en cocotte* or ox-tail taken off the bone and enveloped in a cabbage leaf. Pastry work is good, fully evidenced by desserts and petits fours; the *assiette de chocolat* has been as highly approved as the raspberry feuilleté and the lemon tart 'as good as anyone's, including the late Alain Chapel's.' The wine list is a model for a French-only selection: sufficient length without overload; some interesting country wines; a fair price spread, though prices are not bargain-basement; some good properties including Guigal and Avril from the Rhône; Janodet from Beaujolais; some interesting petits châteaux; Roty and Mongeard-Mugneret from Burgundy. CELLARMAN'S CHOICE: Madiran, Ch. Martus 1985, £14; Jurançon, Dom. Cauhapé 1988, £13.

CHEF: Bernard Lignier PROPRIETORS: Bernard and Jane Lignier
OPEN: Tue to Sat D; Tue to Fri L by arrangement
CLOSED: last 3 weeks July
MEALS: 7 to 10
PRICES: £23 (£33), Set L and D £17.50 (£27)
CARDS: Access, Amex, Visa
SEATS: 28. Private parties: 30 main room. Children welcome.

KESWICK Cumbria

map 7

▲ *Brundholme Country
House Hotel*

Brundholme Road, Keswick CA12 4NL
KESWICK (07687) 74495
From A66 roundabout take Keswick road,
then first left after garage

COOKING 2
COST £11–£28

The house is predominantly early nineteenth-century, the work of George Basevi. It is elegant 'but slightly run to seed' and set among typically spectacular Lakeland scenery above the River Greta. In winter it may seem bleak. The views cannot have changed much since Wordsworth and Coleridge were here, nor has it become easier to find; ask for directions or a map. Although not one of Lakeland's high flyers, Brundholme provides a good meal at a reasonable price in comfortable surroundings. Meals are now served in the conservatory as well. Many ingredients are local. Borrowdale trout is filled with a mousseline of seafood; loin of Lakeland lamb is given a crust of rosemary and brioche crumbs and served with a red wine sauce; paper-thin slices of smoked venison are served with a leafy salad. The kitchen can impress with a lightness of touch, as in lobster mousse on a julienne of raw vegetables, or two baby cheese soufflés with a white wine and tomato sauce. Unfortunately there is heavy handedness too. Seasonings can go astray, and some dishes are very run-of-the-mill. Nevertheless, the balance is favourable, especially as vegetables and cheeses are praised. There are some good bottles on a generally less than inspired, but modestly priced, wine list. House Duboeuf: £6.50.

CHEFS: Ian Charlton and Bruce Jackson   PROPRIETORS: Ian and Lynn Charlton
OPEN: all week
CLOSED: 23 Dec to 1 Feb
MEALS: 12.15 to 1.30, 7.30 to 8.45
PRICES: Set L £6 (£11), to £10 (£15), Set D £17.50 (£23)
CARDS: Access, Visa
SEATS: 50. Private parties: 55 main room, 55 private room. Car-park, 25 places. Vegetarian meals. Children's helpings with prior notice. No children under 12. Smart dress preferred. No smoking in dining-room. Wheelchair access (also WC)
ACCOMMODATION: 11 rooms, all with bath/shower. B&B £37 to £74. Deposit: £20. No children under 10. Fishing. Golf. TV. Phone. Scenic. Doors close at 11.30. Confirm by 6 [*Which? Hotel Guide*]

La Primavera

Greta Bridge, High Hill,
Keswick CA12 5NX
KESWICK (076 87) 72537 and 74621

COOKING 2
COST £27

The bar meals are nearly as useful as the full restaurant to summer visitors who may wish to pause by the river on the outskirts of Keswick. The front of the property was once an industrial school of art – the industry is lead pencils – but most of the action takes place in a large extension towards the back. The menu ranges over familiar Britalian territory, takes advantage of daily fish deliveries and is recommended for serving good meat, a fair list of pasta, and composed Italian dishes such as melanzana parmigiano off the list of daily specials. The setting is luxurious and the service keen and tactful. The wine list is largely Italian with a fair sprinkling from all the main regions. House Italian is £7.80. Perhaps as recognition of their previous incarnation as publicans in Bassenthwaite, the Guarracinos stock Jennings ale.

CHEF: Giuseppe Guarracino   PROPRIETORS: Giuseppe and Pamela Guarracino
OPEN: Tue to Sun
CLOSED: mid-Jan to mid-Feb
MEALS: 12 to 2, 7 to 10
PRICES: £16 (£23)
CARDS: Access, Visa
SEATS: 90. 20 tables outside. Private parties: 80 main room. Car-park, 20 places. Vegetarian meals. Children's helpings. Wheelchair access (also WC). Music. Air-conditioned

KEYSTON   Cambridgeshire   map 6

Pheasant Inn ♟

| Keyston P18 0RE | COOKING 1 |
| BYTHORN (080 14) 241 | COST £26 |

'Be prepared for controversy on this one,' remarked one reader at the end of her report. This thatched cottage of a pub evolving into a restaurant is in an area hard-pressed for places to eat. Confusion reigned on one occasion when none of the four servers knew what the last had done. Bill Bennett creates a menu and bar snacks from a wide repertoire: game, pub fare like steaks and chicken breasts, Thai satays, and a bit of fancy French cooking go into the long seasonal menu. Dishes such as scallops with noodles in a gratin; brandade of smoked salmon; sweetbreads with a madeira sauce; salmon with pink peppercorns; pigeon with garlic and mustard; petit pot au chocolat; rhubarb and ginger sorbet; or coffee parfait with walnut sauce indicate the range. Execution can be rough and ready, the sauces overly pungent from technical error rather than design, while meats, the game especially, are well cooked and flavourful and the vegetables excellent. Bar food is also extremely popular and robust. Interestingly, all the dishes in each course cost the same. The wine list, as in all Poste Hotels, is a great document: not too long, though never short, with even-handed attention to all regions, useful notes and an arrangement sympathetic to the occasional drinker. The price range is carefully tailored to the milieu and, though mark-ups are not conspicuously low, there is plenty of real interest for those with less money. Half-bottles are not forgotten. House wine: £6.95. CELLARMAN'S CHOICE: Côteaux du Giennois 1989, Balland-Chapuis, £10.80, a little-known Loire Sauvignon; and Gaillac rouge 1987, Cros, £9.35.

CHEF: Bill Bennett   PROPRIETORS: Poste Hotels Ltd
OPEN: all week
MEALS: 12 to 2, 7 to 10
PRICES: £18 (£22). Service inc
CARDS: Access, Amex, Diners, Visa
SEATS: 100. 7 tables outside. Private parties: 40 main room, 40 private room. Car-park, 50 places. Children's helpings. Air-conditioned

KILN PIT HILL   Northumberland   map 7

Manor House Inn

Carterway Heads DH8 9LX	
EDMUNDBYERS (0207) 55268	COOKING 1
on A68 2m S of Kiln Pit Hill	COST £26

This old stone coaching-inn stands just off the A68 about five miles north of Castleside, with fine views over the Derwent Valley and reservoir. New arrangements mean that the restaurant is open in the evenings only but lunches can be arranged for parties. The short menu is more ambitious than 'meat and sauce', taking inspiration from several quarters: the East with kebabs and yoghurt; Italy with cannelloni with spinach and ricotta; and France with pork with prunes and brandy. Although some reports have been encouraging, others have implied that staff difficulties have interfered with the Pellys' progress in converting the restaurant into a useful stopping place. A sensibly short wine list is fairly priced. Vaux and Wards beers are on tap. House wine: £5.95. CELLARMAN'S CHOICE: Pacherenc de Vic-Bilh 1988, Capmartin, £9.55; Tempranillo 1987, £11.30.

CHEFS: Jane and Elizabeth Pelly   PROPRIETORS: Anthony, Jane and Elizabeth Pelly
OPEN: Tue to Sat, D only; L by arrangement for parties; Sun and Mon D by arrangement
CLOSED: Tue and Wed 7 Jan to 31 Mar
MEALS: 7.30 to 10
PRICES: £16 (£22). Service inc
SEATS: 40. Private parties: 40 main room. Car-park, 30 places. Vegetarian meals.
No children under 12. Wheelchair access (1 step; also WC)

KING'S LYNN Norfolk   map 6

Riverside

27 King Street, King's Lynn PE30 1HA	COOKING 1
KING'S LYNN (0553) 773134	COST £18–£29

The restaurant is in a converted fourteenth-century warehouse which also boasts a theatre and coffee shop, owned by the National Trust. Beams and bare brick set the style. On good days, meals can be eaten on the patio overlooking the River Ouse. The quick lunch menu earns its share of praise with Arbroath smokies cooked with cream and cheese; bacon and mushroom omelette; chicken curry; and spinach and mushroom pancakes. More ambitious evening meals move from carrot and herb tart to beef Wellington and grilled steaks, taking in poached skate with tarragon and caper sauce or guinea-fowl with prune and apricot sauce along the way. Many of the vegetables are home grown, while ice-creams and sorbets are provided by the firm of Prospero, along the coast in Wiveton. Reports always mention the pleasant, relaxed atmosphere and service. The short wine list is fairly priced but erratically annotated. It has been upgraded and there are usually some bin-ends as well. House Bulgarian: £7.50. CELLARMAN'S CHOICE: Ch. Le Boscq, St Estèphe 1982, £12.60.

CHEF: Dennis Taylor   PROPRIETORS: Michael and Sylvia Savage
OPEN: Mon to Sat
MEALS: 12 to 2, 7 to 10
PRICES: L £13 (£18), D £17 (£24)
CARDS: Access, Visa
SEATS: 65. 24 tables outside. Private parties: 75 main room. Car-park, 10 places. Vegetarian meals. Children's helpings. Music

---

'We decided against leaving anything for service (the service charge was optional). Our whole evening was completely ruined when a member of the management challenged us in front of all the other diners in this small restaurant as to why we had not left a service charge and told us because of this we would not be welcome at the restaurant in future.'
On eating in W1

▲ Buckland-Tout-Saints Hotel ▼

Kingsbridge TQ7 2DS
KINGSBRIDGE (0548) 853055
2m N of Kingsbridge

COOKING 2
COST £20–£43

Down many high-banked Devon lanes lurk substantial country houses, though few so handsome as this: a Queen Anne building set upon green lawns. The Shephards, two generations present at all times, run an efficient hotel. They have done well to retain Alastair Carter as their chef. He has a sense of the value of local foodstuffs – there is almost a South Devon school of chefs supporting a number of small producers – and it shows both in the prime materials and in secondary items such as the cheeseboard. Recommendations have come for a salad of smoked guinea-fowl and chicken livers with a balsamic vinaigrette; tagliatelle with fresh crab and lemon sole; and tortellini of smoked chicken and pistachio for first courses. Fish gets a good outing in steamed turbot with a hazelnut mousseline and chive butter sauce, or steamed red mullet with an orange and basil sauce that was discreet enough to allow full enjoyment of the texture and taste of the fish. Spotted dick or baked apple may appear on the more conventional Sunday lunch menu but during the week the desserts tend towards the modern. The hotel is currently on the market, this may account for less satisfactory reports in recent months. The fixed-price menu, giving four choices at each course, changes daily. Coffee and petits fours, like the rest of the ancillaries, are done in-house. They may be taken in whichever of three rooms takes your fancy. The wine list has shed its wordy commentary and contents itself with useful short notes. The range is excellent in price and quality, with plenty of halves. The fingers may tire in turning its 40-odd pages but wines are helpfully marked with a triple asterisk if they are outstanding. Six carefully selected house wines start at £8.

CHEF: Alastair Carter   PROPRIETORS: The Shephard Family
OPEN: all week
CLOSED: 2 or 3 weeks from 2 Jan
MEALS: 12.15 to 1.45, 7.30 to 9 (10 Sat and Sun)
PRICES: Set L £14 (£20) to £23 (£29), Set D £25 (£31) to £30 (£36). Service inc
CARDS: Access, Amex, Diners, Visa
SEATS: 30. Private parties: 10 main room, 20 private room. Car-park, 14 places. No children under 8. Smart dress preferred. No smoking in dining-room
ACOMMODATION: 12 rooms, all with bath/shower. B&B £75 to £145. Deposit: £100. No children under 8. Afternoon teas. Garden. TV. Phone. Scenic. Doors close at midnight. Confirm by 4 [Which? Hotel Guide]

Consumers' Association is planning to publish Out to Eat, *a new guide to budget eating out in restaurants, pubs, cafés, brasseries and so on. Please send reports and recommendations to Out to Eat, FREEPOST, 2 Marylebone Road, London NW1 1YN.*

The Guide *relies on feedback from its readers. Especially welcome are reports on new restaurants appearing in the book for the first time.*

KINGSTON UPON THAMES Surrey

map 3

Ayudhya ♟

14 Kingston Hill,
Kingston upon Thames KT2 7NH
081-549 5984

COOKING 2
COST £18–£28

Regular visits to Thailand mean that Somjai Feehan is able to bring back carved
teak chairs to reinforce decoratively the message already carried by the long
menu. This restaurant has always moved with the times, witness the vegetarian
section grafted onto the body of the menu, but continues to mobilise the full
range of Thai flavours to maintain standards – lemon grass, kaffir lime leaves,
pea aubergines, Thai green beans, dried seafood. An addition this year has
been a range of set meals, Chinese banquet fashion. Salads of green papaya,
Thai roasted aubergine, or a stir-fry of morning glory greens show off Thai
ingredients, just as chicken wings stuffed with pork and shrimp display that
balance of sweet and hot that the Thais strive for. Coffee is a 'bottomless cup'.
Prices include service and tipping is 'not encouraged'. The wine list is worth
noting for its modest prices, especially for Greater London, and the fact that
each bottle seems to have been chosen, not merely stocked from the nearest
shelf in the Cash and Carry. It is arranged by grape type, and takes from all over
the world. Most bottles are under £10.

CHEF/PROPRIETOR: Somjai Feehan
OPEN: all week, exc Sat L
CLOSED: Suns before bank hols, 25 Dec, 1 Jan, Easter Sun
MEALS: 12 to 2.30 (3 Sun), 6.30 to 11 (11.30 Fri and Sat)
PRICES: £13 (£20), Set L and D £15 (£18) to £20 (£23. Service inc
CARDS: Access, Amex, Diners, Visa
SEATS: 84. Private parties: 30 main room, 20 and 28 private rooms. Children welcome.
Wheelchair access. Music

KINGTON Hereford & Worcester

map 4

Penrhos Court ♟

Kingston HR5 3LH
KINGTON (0544) 230720

COOKING 2
COST £15–£29

If the sound of hammers drowns out the knife on the chopping board it is only
that Martin Griffiths and Daphne Lambert are intent on opening a 19-bedroom
hotel in the farmhouse and related buildings that make up this remarkable
group by 1991. The atmosphere in the barn, which serves as a restaurant, may
sometimes be amateur, and is not helped by repeated Mozart through the
evening. Daphne Lambert needs help in the kitchen to lift good conceptions
into finished compositions, but the will is there and the produce is fresh. There
are periodic medieval banquets, researched by Daphne Lambert herself, that
have included sweet-and-sour salmon, gilded chicken and fantastic saffron
bread, but the day to day affair is a short *carte* of simple dishes such as crudités
with anchoïade; queen scallops with garlic butter; chicken with morels and a
cream sauce; rabbit with mustard; blackcurrant parfait; or white and dark
chocolate cake with black cherries – but 'you have to be really peckish for that,

dear, a reader was told. Pastry and bread are first-rate and mushrooms may come from the woods around. Construction may cause variations in opening times, so it is best to ring first, also to get directions. The wine list is a very intelligent short choice of good bottles, worthy of an award for fair pricing and providing a range of quality to suit anyone. House wine is £6.50.

CHEF: Daphne Lambert   PROPRIETORS: Daphne Lambert and Martin Griffiths
OPEN: Wed to Sat, D only and Sun L
CLOSED: 25 and 26 Dec
MEALS: 12.30 to 2, 7.30 to 10
PRICES: £18 (£24), Set L £10 (£15)
SEATS: 20. 10 tables outside. Private parties: 50 main room. Car-park, 100 places.
Children's helpings. Wheelchair access (1 step; also WC)

KINTBURY Berkshire   map 2

▲ *Dundas Arms* ▌

Station Road, Kintbury RG15 0UT   COOKING 2
KINTBURY (0488) 58263   COST £23–£38

Many have been the voices in defence of the reputation of this pub restaurant by the side of canal and river, with its calm green dining-room looking over garden and water beyond. The set-price menus at dinner and lunch differ in price but the style remains the same: vibrant but simple cooking. Good gravlax with dill and mustard sauce, or a salade composée of foie gras, or smoked duck quickly shown the pan, accompanied by a home-made sweet pepper conserve, are beginnings that have met approval, while meats may be a simple rack of lamb with a garlic and rosemary sauce or something more eclectic like beef fillet sauced with soy, star anise and fresh coriander. The modish *cuisine grandmère* appears in pheasant served with lentils, while fish is not ignored, with sorrel beurre blanc accompanying salmon, a beginning of fresh anchovies, or a nicely spiced tomato sauce with red mullet. Service is relaxed, with occasional peppery moments. The wine list is excellent: good years on the whole, very competitive prices, remarkable length in claret and burgundy with properties such as Ch. Siran, Haut Bailly, D'Issan and Chauvin, and growers Gaunoux, Jayer, Grivot, Ampeau and Durup showing canny selection. The regions of France and the New World are not so numerous but they are, again, well chosen. House wines start at £7.50.

CHEF/PROPRIETOR: David A. Dalzell-Piper
OPEN: Tue to Sat
CLOSED: Christmas to New Year
MEALS: 12.30 to 1.30, 7.30 to 9.30
PRICES: Set L £15 (£23), Set D £23 (£32)
CARDS: Access, Amex, Visa
SEATS: 36. 10 tables outside. Private parties: 22 main room. Car-park, 40 places. Children's helpings. Smart dress preferred. No cigars/pipes in dining-room. Wheelchair access (2 steps; also WC)
ACCOMMODATION: 5 rooms, all with bath/shower. Rooms for disabled. B&B £50 to £60. TV. Phone. Scenic. Doors close at 11.30. Confirm by 6 [*Which? Hotel Guide*]

KIRKBY LONSDALE Cumbria   map 7

▲ *Lupton Tower*

Lupton, Kirkby Lonsdale LA6 2PR
CROOKLANDS (044 87) 400   COOKING 3
off A65, NW of Kirkby Lonsdale   COST £22

This is a vegetarian hotel and restaurant in a Nash-looking picturesque country
house – there is indeed a tower at one end, and residents commend the room
there for two-way views. Dorothy Smith's cooking is designed to please all
palates as well as vegetarians, and consultation with guests takes place in
advance. Hence, 'not a lot of pulse dishes are included as I have found them
heavy if you are not used to eating them.' The consequence is a set dinner menu
of some refinement, with a choice only of sweets. The first course may be a
vegetable terrine made with sour cream wrapped in a pancake, accompanied
by a simple tomato salad. Then follows a soup with hazelnut or walnut bread,
though one diner detected no hint of nuts. The soup, too, may have nuts, as in
cauliflower with almonds or Jerusalem artichoke with pine kernels, and will
certainly be two-flavoured, for example cauliflower and red pepper or
courgette and rosemary. The main course seems to favour wrapped things:
pancakes filled with cheese and mushrooms; light cheese quenelles wrapped
in spinach and lettuce; lettuce moulds filled in turn with carrot and apricot
purée, cream cheese, and mushroom and hazelnut pâté. These have forethought
and subtlety; hence the cheese quenelles numbered three envelopes, two with
spinach, one with lettuce, and each was made with a different cheese. They
were set off, visually and for taste, by a bright yellow saffron sauce. Vegetables
steer a line between simplicity and discord with the main component:
asparagus, stir-fried courgettes, leeks with spring onions, broccoli with a
lemon sauce. Sauces are properly made: beurres blancs, for example, not floury
white ones. Desserts continue the willingness to ignore the stodgy-lump
school of cookery, or even that of wholesome plenty. Crème brûlée; tarte Tatin
of apples or pears; apple and blackcurrant mousse; apple ice-cream with a
blackberry sauce are examples, even if tiramisu or apple and cranberry crumble
yield more in terms of quantity. The value, of the rooms as well as the food, is
remarkable. Take note that there is no smoking indoors. The wine list is not
elaborate with some very decent bottles at reasonable prices. House wine:
£6.50 a litre.

CHEF: Dorothy Smith   PROPRIETORS: Mr and Mrs G.J. Smith
OPEN: all week, D only
CLOSED: Mon and Tue in winter if no room bookings
MEALS: 7.30 to 8
PRICES: Set D £13.50 (£18)
SEATS: 32. 3 tables outside. Private parties: 28 main room, 12 private room. Car-park, 16
places. Vegetarian meals only. Children's helpings. No smoking in dining-room.
Wheelchair access (2 steps; also unisex WC). Music
ACCOMMODATION: 6 rooms, 4 with bath/shower. B&B £18.50 to £37. Deposit: £10.
No smoking in bedrooms. Baby facilities. Pets by arrangement. Garden. Scenic. Doors
close at 1am. Confirm by 4

KIRKHAM Lancashire   map 5

Cromwellian

16 Poulton Street, Kirkham PR4 2AB   COOKING 2
KIRKHAM (0772) 685680   COST £16–£30

The Fawcetts are now well established and settled into the routine of a new
three-course menu monthly. Of five main dishes, two are invariably steaks and
one is a vegetarian dish of the day. The others might be seafood pancake or
roast guinea-fowl stuffed with brown rice; sole filled with prawn mousse or
pork with sage and apple purée and Pinot Noir sauce. The *Guide's* comments
last year resulted in a chorus of 'hands off our vegetables' from supporters: 'I
particularly liked the individual dishes of some six or seven vegetables for each
diner,' says one of the milder ones. Changes – a little anisette glaze for the
carrots, parsnip purée, herb and oil dressings to reduce cholesterol – were not
welcome. 'We are now back to our original, simply prepared vegetables with a
choice of around half a dozen different types lightly coated with butter,'
confirm the Fawcetts. Whatever else, it shows that customers can persuade
restaurants to serve the kind of food they like if only they shout loud enough.
Soups, pâté, fruit with a sharp or spicy dressing, and something in filo pastry
with a sauce (chicken and boursin, smoked trout with horseradish and dill)
make up the pattern for first courses. There is cheese or ice-cream for anyone
who flinches from treacle tart, apple and almond crumble, pineapple oatmeal
meringue with hot chocolate sauce, or rhubarb brown betty. The atmosphere is
warm, relaxed and friendly, and the 50-strong wine list helpfully reduces
'blind stab' uncertainty by incorporating a sweetness scale for whites and a
body scale for reds. France dominates as, sadly, do wines from négociants. A
scheme for matching wines to the menu is in prospect. House French: £7.50.

CHEF: Josie Fawcett PROPRIETORS: Peter and Josie Fawcett
OPEN: Tue to Sat D, Sun L
MEALS: 12.30 to 3, 7 to 9.30
PRICES: Set L £10.50 (£16), Set D £16.95 (£22) to £19.95 (£25). Service inc
CARDS: Access, Amex, Visa
SEATS: 30. Private parties: 17 main room, 12 private room. Vegetarian meals. Children's
helpings (with prior notice). Wheelchair access. Music

KNUTSFORD Cheshire   map 5

▲ *Belle Epoque*

60 King Street, Knutsford WA16 6DT   COOKING 2
KNUTSFORD (0565) 3060   COST £37

If you had possession of Knutsford's former council offices, designed in quite
remarkable art nouveau style, you too would turn the inside into a celebration
of the turn of the century. 'Back home it would be a museum', remarks one
Canadian. It must also afford some respite from Elizabeth Gaskell's *Cranford*,
for which Knutsford was the model. Cooking is by no means Edwardian or
Victorian, however, even if the azure fabrics and marble columns still draw the
eye. Veal terrine with a curried apple relish; crab ravioli; guinea-fowl with a

redcurrant and wine sauce; lamb stuffed with a chicken and garlic mousseline; or rabbit with a liver and herb mousse, then wrapped in bacon, are some of the dishes that have been noticed, along with varied British and Irish cheeses. There can be rough edges to the meal, a certain heaviness of flavouring (for example, over-enthusiastic seasoning or herbing) that may make the food less exciting than the setting and the menu leads you to expect, but the number of satisfied customers is large. The place has always been high on self-advertisement – used as a set for Granada's *Brideshead Revisited* and so on – but readers have sensed a welcome matter-of-factness at recent visits: 'the ambience is better now they have got over their fame as a film set.' Keith Mooney runs a tight ship at the front of house: 'service from young staff is efficient and helpful.' A page of French wines counterbalances the carefully selected main list, which is peppered with Californians and Australasians. The mark-up pushes inexorably on the better wines but there is excellent drinking below £15. You must dine here if you wish to stay in the well-decorated rooms above; roof-top weddings are possible for all.

CHEFS: David Williams, Graham Codd, Anne Mitchell and Mary Horne
PROPRIETORS: Keith and Nerys Mooney
OPEN: Mon to Sat, D only
CLOSED: first week Jan
MEALS: 7.30 to 10
PRICES: £20 (£31). Service 10%
CARDS: Access, Amex, Diners, Visa
SEATS: 70. Private parties: 60 main room, 20,60 and 80 private rooms. No children under 10. No pipes in dining-room. Music
ACCOMMODATION: 5 rooms, all with bath. B&B £30 to £45. No children under 10. Garden. TV. Scenic. Doors close at midnight. Confirm by 2 [*Which? Hotel Guide*]

LACOCK Wiltshire   map 2

▲ *At the Sign of the Angel*

Church Street, Lacock SN15 2LA   COOKING 1
LACOCK (024 973) 230   COST £21–£37

The Angel has long batted for Englishness, its cocooning warmth encouraging something of the drawbridge mentality. 'There is a roaring fire in winter and virtually total privacy', says one report of a Sunday evening in December. 'One eats in comfort and quiet like a medieval baron who has banished the court'. The inn has taken the baronial idea to the point of kitting out one of the rebuilt bedrooms with a four-poster. A curious law is observed to operate in the minds of some customers: the quality of the food varies in inverse relation to the number of dishes available. Thus with only a single main course of roast beef, pork, or turkey: 'The roast pork was very ordinary', says one; 'if that is all there is then it should be the best.' 'The main course should have been of better quality,' says another. Anyway, the angel's halo has slipped occasionally, and been noticed. To go back to the law of inverse relation, first courses and puddings offer several choices and those of ham, haddock and prawn bake, soup, or lamb kidneys in madeira sauce, plus hot and cold puddings, have knocked it back into place. The wines have been assembled by somebody who loves them and can be said to be an evangelist, offering very fair prices as he

does. Ch. Coutet 1979, Ch. Fombrauge 1982 and a run of fine ports show the
possibilities. House French: £6.40. CELLARMAN'S CHOICE: Ch. les Forts de
Latour 1979, £28.50; St Aubin, premier cru, les Chamois 1987, £19.

CHEF: L.M. Levis PROPRIETOR: J.S Levis
OPEN: all week, exc Sat L and Sun D
CLOSED: 22 Dec to 4 Jan
MEALS: 1 to 1.30, 7.30 to 8.30
PRICES: Set L £16 (£21) to £20 (£26), Set D £20 (£26) to £25 (£31)
CARDS: Access, Amex, Visa
SEATS: 40. Private parties: 20 main room, 20 private room. No children under 8. Smart
dress preferred
ACCOMMODATION: 8 rooms, all with bath/shower. B&B £65 to £90. No children under 8.
Pets welcome. Garden. TV. Phone. Scenic. Doors close at midnight. Confirm by 5.30
[Which? Hotel Guide]

LANGHO Lancashire   map 5

▲ Northcote Manor

Northcote Road, Langho BB6 9BB
BLACKBURN (0254) 240555   COOKING 2
on A59, 9m E of M6 exit 31   COST £16–£41

This Victorian mill-owner's rather solid house, 50 yards down a lane north of
the A59 at the Langho roundabout, was built with brass made from cotton.
Close as it is to Blackburn and Preston, it turns its face towards the Ribble
valley and the comfortable life. Some visitors may find it spartan in the
wuthering depths of winter, but the chill is taken off with a friendly welcome
and courteous polite service that relaxes. A few whispers remind you that
industrial Lancashire is no' but a cock stride away – a nibble of pickled tripe
with pre-dinner drinks perhaps, or Thornley's black puddings for breakfast –
but these always remain sotto voce. The main business of the house is a *carte*
that plays with fine ingredients – fish may be halibut, Dover sole or lobster, for
instance – and mostly handles them well. Simple preparation such as oysters
on crushed ice or grilled sole contrast with dishes that take time to construct. A
Lunesdale duckling is served with blinis of 'meadow mushrooms' on a
trompette mushroom sauce; and fillets of Suffolk lamb are wrapped around a
mousseline of chicken and basil in a puff pastry crust and served with madeira
sauce. Puddings mine the same elaborate vein; one consists of caramelised
wafers of puff pastry layered with strawberries and mango on a lime-flavoured
yogurt with a citrus jelly. Quibbles have centred on tactical gaffes and minor
misjudgements in execution rather than large-scale strategic errors. Some local
produce is used, bread is home made, and the kitchen responds to the seasons.
Lunch is a bargain, even at the higher cost on Sunday. Expansion of the wine
list, selected by a slightly unsure hand, has defused some of the complaints
about high prices; these have not been lowered, but wines are now available
from around the world that make it possible to get change from £15. A half-
bottle of Champagne is listed on the breakfast menu. At other times, house
French is £7.90.

CHEF: Nigel Haworth   PROPRIETORS: Craig J. Bancroft and Nigel Haworth
OPEN: all week
MEALS: 12 to 1.30, 7 to 9 (10 Sat)
PRICES: £25 (£34), Set L £10.50 (£16) to £12.50 (£18)
CARDS: Access, Visa
SEATS: 70. Private parties: 60 main room, 20 private room. Car-park, 50 places. Children's helpings. Smart dress preferred. Music
ACCOMMODATION: 6 rooms, all with bath/shower. B&B £60 to £70. Afternoon teas. Garden. TV. Phone. Scenic. Confirm by 6 [*Which? Hotel Guide*]

LANGLEY MARSH Somerset   map 2

▲ *Langley House Hotel*

Langley Marsh TA4 2UF   COOKING 2
WIVELISCOMBE (0984) 23318   COST £26–£34

A Tourist Authority award for interior design and another for the garden might be hints enough that this small Georgian house is a riot of colour inside and out. A daily four- or five-course menu is offered, the only choice being when desserts hover. On Friday and Saturday, dinner starts at the same time for everyone, doubtless so that the Wilsons can cope virtually unaided. A common pattern is a cold dish to begin, then soup, fish, meat, and dessert. It is not complex food, nor surprising nor novel; it is more mainstream English country-house cooking without the overtones of luxury often encountered. The repertoire also moves slowly. Thus avocado and orange salad with a walnut dressing; carrot, orange and coriander soup; poached Dover sole with sherry and wine; fillet of lamb roast with herbs. Dessert is often traditional: burnt cream, bread-and-butter pudding and flummeries figure a lot. This is a kitchen that knows its limitations and cooks carefully, often to good effect. The wine list is well resourced from the region's best merchants. Like the cooking, it makes few concessions to adventure, but uses impeccable makers and properties such as Ampeau, Guigal, Leflaive, Jaboulet and Goulet. House wine: £7.25. CELLARMAN'S CHOICE: Nelson Vale Redwood Sauvignon 1987, £17.50; Châteauneuf-du-Pape, les Cèdres 1983, Jaboulet, £19.50.

CHEF: Peter Wilson   PROPRIETORS: Peter and Anne Wilson
OPEN: all week, D only
MEALS: 8 to 9, 8.30 Fri and Sat
PRICES: Set D £19.75 (£26) to £23.50 (£28). Service inc
SEATS: 18. Private parties: 35 main room, 18 private room. Car-park, 10 places. Vegetarian meals. Children's helpings. No children under 7. No smoking in dining-room. Wheelchair access (also WC). One sitting Fri and Sat
ACCOMMODATION: 9 rooms, all with bath/shower. B&B £57.50 to £82.50. Deposit: £10. Children by arrangement. Baby facilities. Pets welcome but not in public rooms. Afternoon teas. Garden. Fishing. TV. Phone. Scenic. Doors close at midnight. Confirm by 6 [*Which? Hotel Guide*]

The Guide *office can quickly spot when a restaurateur is encouraging customers to write recommending inclusion and sadly, several restaurants have been doing this in 1990. Such reports do not further a restaurant's cause. Please tell us if a restaurateur invites you to write to the* Guide.

351

LAVENHAM Suffolk

map 3

▲ *Great House*

Market Place, Lavenham CO10 9QZ
LAVENHAM (0787) 247431

COOKING 2
COST £16–£41

The market square is a feast of grey and white half-timberings. Next door to the sunny yellow plasterwork of the medieval Little Hall, the fifteenth-century Great House had a white Georgian face-lift, yet remains beamed and oak-panelled within. The architecture may be quintessentially English, but the service is doggedly French. Menus echo the mix – with inept English spelling – and include bar snacks as well as a *carte* and three-course set menu. Traditional dishes such as gazpacho or Bayonne ham with melon sit alongside more modern ones: a salade tiède of crisp duck breast or tomatoes filled with marinated salmon. Flavours are forthright rather than subtle: medallions of roasted monkfish are given a butter sauce densely populated with strong green peppercorns. The food can be better than it sounds, as in an unevenly cooked fillet of lamb wrapped in spinach leaves and pastry which was brought to life by the shock of orange zest. Puddings include chocolate mousse and crème brûlée. Bread is so good that it could have been flown in from Paris. The wine list is a scrapbook of labels, maps, newspaper clippings and 116 handwritten names, largely French, and the selection is as erratic as the presentation. There are good names and properties, especially in Burgundy, but alas, the mark-up pushes prices to giddy heights, and too many wines are listed without the name of the grower. House wine: £12.

CHEF: Regis Crepy PROPRIETOR: John Spice
OPEN: Tue to Sun, exc Sun D
CLOSED: Jan
MEALS: 12 to 2.30, 7 to 10.30
PRICES: £23 (£34), Set L £7.90 (£16) to £11.90 (£21), Set D £13.95 (£23). Service 10%
CARDS: Access, Carte Blanche, Visa
SEATS: 65. 7 tables outside. Private parties: 50 main room, 30 and 50 private rooms. Vegetarian meals. Children's helpings. No cigars/pipes in dining-room. Music
ACCOMMODATION: 4 rooms, all with bath/shower. B&B £55 to £70. Deposit: £20. Baby facilities. Pets welcome. Garden. TV. Phone. Scenic. Doors close at 1 am [*Which? Hotel Guide*]

LECK Lancashire

map 7

▲ *Cobwebs* 🍷

COUNTY OF THE YEAR RESTAURANT

Cowan Bridge LA6 2HZ
KIRKBY LONSDALE (052 42) 72141

COOKING 3
COST £23

'Perhaps Cobwebs is a little gem to be discovered by the wider world.' That reader couldn't have known about the several reports received by the *Guide* that may signify discovery already. Paul Kelly who serves and Yvonne Thompson, who cooks, are enthusiastic. This is apparent from the zealous showing of the rooms upstairs, the wine list, the gimmicks like the split soups at every meal, and the keen but not obtrusive service. The two seem to do it all themselves, from three slightly solid breads to refreshing sorbets after the first courses and the tray of petits fours handed round with coffee. The form is a no-choice menu, the content of which is given over the phone when booking. It is taken all together in a small dining-room seating but half a dozen more than the rooms can accommodate. The owners call the house a 'Country Guest House'. It is of remarkable comfort, set in decent grounds with views to the Lune Valley and the Pennines. Yvonne Thompson does like duality. The split soups, two halves of a soup plate with a swirl of cream, may even be one hot, one cold – Stilton (cold) and tomato and thyme (hot), for example – and will usually be complementary and enjoyable: carrot and orange/celery and fennel (a sort of double dualism); carrot/onion and sage; or courgette and rosemary/curried parsnip. The theme comes up again in a succeeding sorbet, almost never a single flavour but the likes of lime and basil, grapefruit and basil, or lime and thyme. The use of a herb keeps it in the savoury line. More duality occurs in main courses: chicken stuffed with asparagus with a diced leg of meat sauté to one side and a tomato and mint sauce and watercress sauce spiked with mustard is one; poultry rolled with spinach on leek and shellfish sauces is another. Cheese is the exception – not two but 18 were counted by one reader, all local save a Stilton; they are served with soda bread. Dessert continues to be no-choice and may be a blackcurrant and chocolate ice-cream in a brandy-snap basket with now mandatory fruits as trimming, or lemon and lime mousse with praline and more fruits. This account lets the enthusiasm speak for itself and it is infectious. Most tastes are detectable, though some miscalculation is inevitable from a repertoire that seems unwilling to settle down at all. Enthusiasm is endorsed when the price is seen and after the wine list is presented. This at present is untidy, containing rarities with prices only on application, but also listing a collection of New World and classics at prices keener than almost any other. As one diner said regretfully, 'Veuve Clicquot 1982 at £22 can't last.' Nor will Krug at £45. The appearance is miscellaneous but it reflects fervour particularly for Australasia, Alsace, Champagnes, Rhônes, Ribera del Duero, and Ch. Palmer. A short list of seasonal selections, with good notes, is a preface. There are plenty of halves. The restaurant holds gourmet evenings, with wines, once a month. House wine: £7.25 and £8.50.

CELLARMAN'S CHOICE: Cloudy Bay Sauvignon Blanc 1988, £13; Nuits St Georges, Clos des Porets 1985, H. Gouges, £24.

CHEF: Yvonne Thompson   PROPRIETORS: Paul Kelly and Yvonne Thompson
OPEN: Mon to Sat, D only
CLOSED: end Dec to mid-Mar
MEALS: 7.30 for 8
PRICES: Set D £15.50 (£19). Service inc
CARDS: Access, Visa
SEATS: 16. Private parties: 16 main room. Car-park, 15 places. No children under 12. Smart dress preferred. No smoking in dining-room. Music. One sitting
ACCOMMODATION: 5 rooms, all with bath/shower. B&B £25 to £40. Deposit: £10. Children welcome. Garden. Fishing. TV. Phone. Scenic. Doors close at 1am. Confirm by 6
[Which? Hotel Guide]

The text of entries is based on unsolicited reports sent in by readers, backed up by inspections conducted anonymously. The factual details under the text are from questionnaires the Guide sends to all restaurants that feature in the book.

LEDBURY   Hereford & Worcester   map 2

▲ *Hope End* ▮

Hope End, Ledbury HR8 1JQ
LEDBURY (0531) 3613
⅔m N of Ledbury, just beyond   COOKING 3
Wellington Heath   COST £34

St Catherine of Ledbury, said Wordsworth, was persuaded by divine
intervention to settle in the town, 'Till she exchanged for heaven that happy
ground.' The creation of a little piece of heaven seems the object of the
Hegartys, who have surrounded their low house – relict of a large, grander
affair as witness the minaret that survives – with a gardener's paradise of
orchard and plantation. The house sets itself against the maelstrom of the
outside world: organic husbandry, the encouragement of moribund fruit
varieties, intensive cultivation of walled gardens all fuel a kitchen that
reinterprets British cooking in the light of new techniques and new
perspectives on diet and health. The food tastes so good that people wish to
sample it again and again. The emphasis of the dinners, with little choice at all
stages and none for the main course, is understandably on the garden:
vegetable soups (consistently praised); outstandingly fresh vegetables; a salad
before three British cheeses (one hard, one blue, one soft) with some of the
Hegartys' own apples. There is a choice of three sweets, often a meringue, often
ice-creams, perhaps a heavier chocolate item. Patricia Hegarty's style is clear
and light, sometimes austere. Although hollandaises and even cream are used,
the prime ingredients stand out more than in other places: ice-creams (using
yoghurt) have pieces of fruit in them, vegetables usually stand alone, their
freshness their all. Among dishes that have been complimented, soups and
puddings come first: cardoon and lobster hot-pot; spinach and coconut,
pumpkin, or celery, lentil and chive soups; consistently successful meringues,
perhaps with soft fruit sauces or with the fruits themselves in season; chocolate
marble tart, a marvellously gooey substance on crisp pastry; baked custards,
perhaps with caramel and praline, or with orange and an orange compote. This
is very British food. The cooking has sufficient accuracy to cope well with fish:
scallops served with a delicate saffron sauce, their corals set off by tomato; even
humble whiting in fillets with a cider and lovage sauce, a scallop for company;
halibut with a rich but not cloying hollandaise. The setting for this is a house
that has been refitted with little obeisance to former glories: some good
paintings and a lot of pine panelling are leitmotifs. For some, the dining-room
has too much pine and 'the atmosphere of a railway carriage'. John Hegarty's
attentions are infused by a quiet humour and none of the fuss of country-house
formality. He will always know the variety of potato served, the origins of the
red chard cooked as a vegetable that night, and the history of the apples that
come with the cheese. He will also know about the wine, from a list that is
generous in its provision of half-bottles and very fairly priced. There is decent
age to the clarets and some of the Rhônes as well. Guigal's Côte Rôtie and
Chave's Hermitage of 1978 are notable. There is not much from beyond France.
House wines are £6. CELLARMAN'S CHOICE: Mâcon-Viré 1987, Bonhomme,
£12; Ch. Chicane, Graves 1982, £12. Dunkerton's cider and perry are
also available.

CHEF: Patricia Hegarty   PROPRIETORS: John and Patricia Hegarty
OPEN: Wed to Sun, D only
CLOSED: Dec to Mar
MEALS: 7.30 to 8.30
PRICES: Set D £25 (£28). Service inc
CARDS: Access, Visa
SEATS: 24. Private parties: 6 main room. Car-park, 10 places. No children under 14. Smart
dress preferred. No smoking. Wheelchair access (2 steps)
ACCOMMODATION: 9 rooms, all with bath/shower. B&B £70 to £120. Deposit: £60.
No children under 14. Garden. Phone. Scenic. Doors close at 11. Confirm by arrangement
[*Which? Hotel Guide*]

LEEDS   West Yorkshire   map 5

Bryans

9 Weetwood Lane, Headingley,
Leeds LS16 5LT   COOKING 1
LEEDS (0532) 785679   COST £12

A refurbishment has not brought this fish restaurant to luxury status but the
fish and chips, served by a team of informed waitresses, please the public.
Portions are generous, fish fresh, batter crisp, chips fried in lard. Halibut, hake,
haddock and plaice are the main varieties, though salmon, trout and scampi are
available. If there is no 'jumbo' haddock (and it is jumbo), baby haddock,
consisting of two or three smaller pieces, is recommended. Drink strong tea.
The set lunch at under £4 is laid on for senior citizens only from 2.30 to 4.30pm.

CHEF: Alan Germaine   PROPRIETOR: Jan Fletcher
OPEN: Mon to Sat
MEALS: 11.30am to 11.30pm
PRICES: £8 (£10)
SEATS: 140. Private parties: 100 main room. Car-park, 50 places. Children's helpings.
Wheelchair access. Music. Air-conditioned

Grillade

Wellington Street, Leeds LS1 4HJ   COOKING 1
LEEDS (0532) 459707 and 459952   COST £14–£25

'I have eaten here many times and the food has been consistently well cooked.
It is a good example of plain French cooking – fresh and uncluttered. The
atmosphere is particularly welcoming and relaxing; dinner jacket or jeans are
equally at home.' This is no-nonsense French cooking in a lively whitewashed
basement. Grills are the main business, from steak and frites to chateaubriand,
but the blackboard also advertises fish soup, boudin noir, beef bourguignonne
and the like. Sweets are chiefly ices and sorbets, backed up by chocolate
mousse and apple tart. This is one of the city's favourite venues and the
atmosphere sizzles. House French: £6.20.

CHEF: Orenzo Padolino   PROPRIETORS: Meritlight Ltd
OPEN: Mon to Sat, exc Sat L
CLOSED: bank hols and Christmas week
MEALS: 12 to 2.30, 7.30 to 11
PRICES: £17 (£21), Set L and D £10.80 (£14). Service inc
CARDS: Access, Visa
SEATS: 62. Children welcome. No cigars/pipes in dining room. Air-conditioned

Jumbo Chinese

120 Vicar Lane, Leeds LS2 7NL
LEEDS (0532) 458324

COOKING 1
COST £16–£25

The basement restaurant was once a Greek taverna and the archaeologically
inclined may still be able to detect this fact. However, expansion on to the
ground floor is scheduled for the end of 1990. The Jumbo may have more
competition in Leeds now but it still has strong support, certain inconsistencies
notwithstanding. Generally the service is welcoming and helpful. The menu
does not surprise for range or depth but recommended dishes include salt and
pepper spare ribs; Peking capital pork; fillet steak with OK sauce; satay
chicken or beef; and rice with char siu pork and prawns. House wine: £5.90.

CHEFS: Yat Sun Lo and Lin Dai Lai   PROPRIETORS: Lin Dai Lai, Tony Kwan and Yat Sun Lo
OPEN: all week
CLOSED: 25 to 27 Dec
MEALS: noon to midnight
PRICES: £8 (£16), Set D £12 (£17) to £16 (£21)
CARDS: Access, Amex
SEATS: 150. Private parties: 150 main room. Children welcome. Music. Air-conditioned

Paris

36A Town Street, Horsforth,
Leeds LS18 4RJ
LEEDS (0532) 581885 and 588200

COUNTY OF THE YEAR RESTAURANT

COOKING 2
COST £12–£24

This upstairs restaurant with bentwood chairs and tight-packed tables has
elected the route to success that goes via low prices and lots of customers. The
menu doesn't stray into double figures (until the total) and is especially low for
the 'early-bird' set-price menu served between 6 and 7.30: a sort of happy hour
for gourmets (and a half-bottle of wine is included). The menu is enormous –
there are 15 daily blackboard specials in addition to the two dozen dishes on
offer on the *carte* – but the kitchen has not sought refuge in boil-in-the-bag or
industrial supplies. There is a strand of brasserie cooking – cassoulet,
choucroûte garnie, beef bourguignonne – running alongside restaurant dishes
wrapped in pastry or steamed in a cabbage leaf. There is also a strong emphasis
on fresh fish, mostly listed on the blackboard. Dishes reported have included a
very 'restaurant' avocado pear with an elderflower sorbet and blackberry sauce;
stuffed pig's trotter with strong madeira sauce; queen scallops in a pastry case
with a Gruyère cheese sauce; a fish soup with aïoli and croûtons; scallops,
mussels, salmon and lemon sole cooked en

papillote with tarragon; breast of chicken stuffed with cream cheese, spinach and chives, served on a tomato sauce; lamb with apricot purée; and calf's liver with spring onions, mushrooms, bacon and sage. The cooking, even on so large a scale, has been accurate and genuine; the staff is both eager and well informed. One reader commented: 'The fish is spankingly fresh, the fish stocks light yet deeply flavoured, the meat stock sauces muscular.' There is plenty of choice, too, for sweet tooths: crème brûlée; summer pudding with crème fraîche; steamed ginger pudding; or a white chocolate cup filled with an orange iced soufflé on a raspberry and vanilla sauce. The wine list is on two sides of a large sheet of paper parchment. These pack in a range large enough for anyone, including a good Australian choice and excellent French properties (not always detailed) at acceptable prices. Champagne is Bruno Paillard. House Duboeuf is £6.50. CELLARMAN'S CHOICE: Ch. Musar 1981, £12.50; Renmano Trophy Chardonnay 1988,£20.95. More reports, please.

CHEF: Steven Kendell PROPRIETORS: Martin Spalding and Steven Kendell
OPEN: all week, D only
MEALS: 6 to 10.30 (11 Fri and Sat)
PRICES: £12 (£20), Set D £9.95 (£12)
CARDS: Access, Amex, Visa
SEATS: 86. Private parties: 16 main room. Vegetarian meals. Children welcome. Music

---

LEICESTER Leicestershire   map 5

Rise of the Raj

6 Evington Road, Leicester LE2 1HF   COOKING 1
LEICESTER (0533) 553885   COST £20

This pink and maroon restaurant out towards the prosperous suburb of Evington has more in common with London new-wave than old-style curry houses. The style is mainly North Indian with the tandoor at centre stage. Regulars enjoy it for consistency, for being open every day of the year, and for the long hours. The karahi or skillet is in evidence in karahi chicken and the 'Raj karahi mixed,' a new dish. People speak well of the onion bhaji; chicken jalfrezi; chicken dhansak; and the vegetable dishes. A list of lurid cocktails starts with 'Tiger's tail' ('this will blow your stripes off') and ends with a non-alcoholic, pink, 'Dhaka Duck'; otherwise, drink lager or lassi.

CHEFS: Abdul Bashir and Rouf Ullha PROPRIETOR: Abdul Bashir
OPEN: all week
MEALS: 12 to 2, 6 to 11.45
PRICES: £10 (£17). Minimum £6.95 D. Service 10%
CARDS: Access, Amex, Diners, Visa
SEATS: 70. Private parties: 40 main room, 45 private room. Vegetarian meals. Children's helpings. No children under 5. Smart dress preferred. Wheelchair access (2 steps). Music

---

Restaurateurs justifiably resent no-shows. If you quote a credit card number when booking, you may be liable for the restaurant's lost profit margin if you don't turn up. Always phone to cancel.

Water Margin

76–78 High Street, Leicester LE1 5YP	COOKING 1
LEICESTER (0533) 516422 and 24937	COST £9–£30

Ask for the dim-sum and noodle menu. The waiters won't bring it otherwise and it is for the dim-sum and one-plate dishes that this friendly, informal place stands out in Leicester. There are some who would place the cooking of the fairly standard main menu (more variety in seafood when it is available) among the town's second division. But it is cheerful, even chaotic, and brighter with its new murals. House French: £6.

CHEF: K.F.Lam   PROPRIETOR: Y.W.Lam
OPEN: all week
MEALS: noon to 11.30
PRICES: £16 (£25), Set L £4.50 (£9), Set D £4.50 (£9) to £8.50 (£14). Service 10%
CARDS: Access, Amex, Diners, Visa
SEATS: 170. Private parties: 100 main room, 100 private room. Set vegetarian meals for 2 or more. Children welcome. Wheelchair access. Music

---

LEIGHTON BUZZARD Bedfordshire   map 3

▲ Swan Hotel

High Street, Leighton Buzzard LU7 7EA	COOKING 1
LEIGHTON BUZZARD (0525) 372148	COST £17–£35

The refurbishment is appreciated, as is the lack of pretension. There is generous choice from a *carte* that changes seasonally and fixed-price menus that move more quickly. Ideas are commendably simple without being naive. Stilton and celery fritters on salad leaves might come with port wine sauce; scallops and spinach cooked in walnut oil are served on pastry with a lime butter sauce; braised kidneys, with shallots and mushrooms, are flavoured with juniper and claret. Crisp duck and pink calf's liver are praised, as are wild mushrooms lightly sauté with shredded lean bacon, and both the onion gravy and cinnamon-spiced apple sauce that are served with black puddings. Vegetables and service attract differing degrees of support. Puddings can be rich; coffee could be improved. 'A Busy Body's' lunch at £5.95 recognises that one course and coffee may be enough for some. The 85-strong wine list takes a predominantly European stance but there is something for all pockets. House red is from Corbières at £7.50; house white is from Duboeuf at £7.75.

Prices quoted in the Guide *are based on information supplied by restaurateurs. The figure in brackets below an entry is the average for a three-course meal with service, coffee and half a bottle of house wine, as calculated by computer. The prices quoted at the top of an entry represent a range, from the lowest average meal price to the highest; the latter is inflated by 20 per cent to take account of the fact that very few people eat an average meal, and also that prices are likely to rise during the year of the* Guide.

CHEF: Stephen McNally   PROPRIETORS: Eric and Felicity Stephens
OPEN: all week
MEALS: 12 to 2, 7 (7.30 Fri and Sat) to 9.30 (10 Fri and Sat, 9 Sun)
PRICES: £21 (£29), Set L £12 (£17) to £14.50 (£20), Set D £17.50 (£23) to £18.50 (£25)
CARDS: Access, Amex, Diners, Visa
SEATS: 80. 3 tables outside. Private parties: 80 main room, 40 and 40 private rooms.
Car-park, 10 places. Vegetarian meals. Children's helpings. No-smoking area. Wheelchair
access. Air-conditioned
ACCOMMODATION: 38 rooms, all with bath/shower. B&B £65 to £85. Baby facilities.
Air-conditioning. TV. Phone. Doors close at 11.30. Confirm by 1 [*Which? Hotel Guide*]

LEWDOWN Devon   map 1

▲ *Lewtrenchard Manor*

Lewdown EX20 4PN
LEWDOWN (056 683) 256
from A30 Okehampton to Launceston, turn L   COOKING 3
at Lewdown for ¾ mile   COST £21–£46

Sabine Baring-Gould once lived here, and was responsible for bringing
together the house, and particularly the interior, as it now stands. Elizabethan
on the outside, the rooms, decorative plasterwork and heavy panelling inside
are, an idiosyncratic Victorian re-interpretation of Jacobethan. This gives the
place character. Cooking here is anything but Victorian. David Shepherd
produces a *carte* and *menu gourmand* that fit into the mainstream of modern
country-house cookery: very keen on mousses and mousselines, as adjuncts as
well as dishes in their own right; fond, too, of wild mushrooms; keen on
decoration and multiplication of frills, though by no means at the expense of
the central ingredients or dishes. Feuilleté of seafood with tomato and basil;
fillet of beef with Camembert and girolles; coconut and passion-fruit ice-cream
bombe were components of a meal that enjoyed good sauces (butter, alcohol
and stock) founded on correct kitchen procedures. He even managed to cope
with the intervention of Camembert into an otherwise classic dish, though the
end result was still 'decadent'. House wine: £7.50.

CHEF: David Shepherd   PROPRIETORS: James and Sue Murray
OPEN: all week D only (L by arrangement)
MEALS: 12 to 2.30, 7.15 to 9.30
PRICES: £31 (£38), Set L £15 (£21), Set D £26.50 (£33.50)
CARDS: Access, Amex, Diners, Visa
SEATS: 40. Private parties: 8 main room; 16 and 50 private rooms. Car-park, 50 places. No
children under 8. Smart dress preferred. No smoking in dining-room. Wheelchair access
ACCOMMODATION: 8 rooms, all with bath/shower. B&B £55 to £110. No children under 8.
Pets welcome. Afternoon teas. Garden. Fishing. TV. Phone. Scenic. Doors close at 12.
Confirm by 6 [*Which? Hotel Guide*]

The Guide *office can quickly spot when a restaurateur is encouraging customers to write
recommending inclusion and sadly, several restaurants have been doing this in 1990.
Such reports do not further a restaurant's cause. Please tell us if a restaurateur invites you
to write to the* Guide.

LIFTON Devon   map 1

▲ *Arundell Arms*

Lifton PL16 0AA
LIFTON (0566) 84666   COOKING 2
on A30, 3m E of Launceston   COST £18–£38

'A stone-built accumulation of a building' says one visitor about Anne Voss-
Bark's creeper-clad coaching-inn. For years it has been the haunt of fishing and
shooting types and ornithologists. A sporting retreat if ever there was one,
although food is never neglected. Philip Burgess heads a young kitchen team
with high aspirations: his sous-chef, Martin Hadden, won the Diners Club/
Roux Brothers Scholarship in 1989. Bread, ice-creams and sorbets are now
made on the premises, and the kitchen delivers sound cooking of good
ingredients. A duo of pâtés is served generously with Cumberland sauce;
mixed smoked fish salad comes with baby artichokes, and there is good South
Devon roast beef. Fish is cooked with flair and a feel for the locality: Tamar
salmon might be marinated with lemon and fennel or served with marsh
samphire; fillets of red bream are steamed with leeks; Tavy trout is pan-fried
with strips of smoked salmon and capers. Cheeses continue the West Country
theme. Around 80 carefully selected wines are backed up by some classy
vintage ports. House wines start at £7.75. CELLARMAN'S CHOICE: Ch. Lanessan
1981, £18.

CHEF: Philip Burgess   PROPRIETOR: Anne Voss-Bark
OPEN: all week
CLOSED: 4 days at Christmas
MEALS: 12.30 to 2, 7.30 to 9
PRICES: £24 (£32), Set L £12 (£18), Set D £19.75 (£28)
CARDS: Access, Amex, Diners, Visa
SEATS: 70. Private parties: 80 main room, 30 private room. Car-park, 80 places. Vegetarian
meals. Children's helpings. No smoking in dining-room. Smart dress preferred. Wheelchair
access (2 steps)
ACCOMMODATION: 29 rooms, all with bath/shower. B&B £46 to £75. Baby facilities. Pets
welcome. Afternoon teas. Garden. Fishing. Golf. TV. Phone. Scenic. Doors close at 11.30

LINCOLN Lincolnshire   map 6

Harvey's Cathedral Restaurant ▮

1 Exchequergate, Castle Square,
Lincoln LN2 1PZ   COOKING 1
LINCOLN (0522) 510333   COST £10–£31

Bob Harvey is energetic and it shows in his menus, wine list and business.
Since the last *Guide* he has taken on the catering at Doddington Hall, a local
stately home. His wife has also rejoined him in the kitchen at Exchequergate
after a spell commuting to a job in London, but he has been seen more at the
stove than on the floor of the dining-room. Wanting to be accessible to as many
customers as possible has kept him exploring popular catering and suitable

technology to keep standards high. He has learnt their limitations, particularly in Troffs, the bistro above the restaurant, where standards have fluctuated. Harvey's stands in the shadow of the cathedral gate, its two dining-rooms preceded by a reception area hung with mirrors and Victorian photographs. (Among these are hidden some of Bob Harvey himself.) The evening menu, six or seven choices at a set price, has some connection with the 'Businessman's Menu' offered at lunchtime. These keep company with two cheaper menus called 'Visitor's' and 'Choice'. Lunch does constitute good value. One reader commented that her crab bisque had pieces of white crabmeat in it, 'a change from the slimy pieces of red meat encountered in another place'; a smoked salmon mousse with dill sauce was a mite solid but had a fair flavour; beef steak pie with Guinness was made with decent beef and tasted of something. Pies and braised dishes are Harvey's strong points – some 1960s casseroles like coq au Riesling or beef bourguignonne, other 'Old English' like steak and kidney, turkey, sausage and bacon, or Somerset pork with apple. Some would say that culinary finesse is not a strong point but all may change with the extra hand on the tiller. The generous 'Pay as you drink' scheme means that the customer pays only for actual consumption, though most customers are unlikely to leave too much in these splendid bottles. The list is mostly French as Bob Harvey likes some New World wines but not Australian or Californian; it is fairly priced. Such excellent growers as Natter in Sancerre, Blain-Gagnard in Burgundy and Huet in Vouvray, together with good half-bottles, make it a friendly collection, though choice is small at the very top of the range. House wine: £6.95. CELLARMAN'S CHOICE: Crozes Hermitage red 1985 and white 1987, Desmeures, £10.50 and £11.95, obviously from his favourite region: 'Nobody buys my 1978 Hermitage and Côte Rôtie; if only they knew what they were missing. The 1983s are waiting in the cellar. I shall probably have to swap them for Châteauneuf and Sancerre.'

CHEFS: Bob Harvey, Adrianne Harvey and Andy Gibson PROPRIETORS: Adrianne and Bob Harvey
OPEN: all week
CLOSED: 26 Dec
MEALS: 12 to 2, 7 to 9.30
PRICES: Set L £5.50 (£10) to £9.50 (£15), Set D £17.50 (£23) to £19.50 (£26)
CARDS: Access, Visa
SEATS: 50. Private parties: 60 main room, 32 private room. Vegetarian meals. Children's helpings. Music

Wig & Mitre

29 Steep Hill, Lincoln LN2 1LU	COOKING 2
LINCOLN (0522) 535190 and 523705	COST £29

You go upstairs or downstairs to parts of this pub/restaurant, depending on which level you enter from. The car park is 'upstairs' on Drury Lane, the bar is 'downstairs' on Steep Hill. The building is old, very old, although the new decoration downstairs tends to mask the antiquity to a degree. The aim of the place is encouraging: to serve as wide a range of food in a variety of contexts all day and everyday. So meals can be cheap or dear, formal or informal, even if the press of business makes some of the 'formal' become 'bustling' for latecomers.

The team cooks gammon and eggs or braised tongue with red wine and oyster mushrooms. British cheeses are served: Milleen, Yarg, Bonchester. A meal of seafood and asparagus mousse followed by chicken with Parma ham in pastry and a decent range of vegetables nearly reconciled one reader to the 350 per cent profit on mineral water. The range of cooking is bold for Lincoln, particularly because it responds day by day to what is available and is not afraid to run out. The approach is modern: quail salad is dressed with walnut oil, a salmon mousse enfolding generous chunks of shellfish is presented with a vermouth butter sauce. On many days the execution is exact, though sheer numbers may provoke mistakes. The intentions, along with the Sam Smith's, are wholly admirable and the staff seems well motivated to put them into action. Tips are 'not encouraged'; though the menu doesn't have a note to that effect. The wine list is a classic of obscure computer layout and hides a short range not as adventurous as the ideas behind the food. There is the occasional gem, though, for the knowledgeable. House wine: £7.95. CELLARMAN'S CHOICE: Muscadet, Ch. du Cléray 1988, Sauvion £11.95; Côtes du Rhône 1985, Guigal, £14.80.

CHEFS: Paul Vidic, Lino Poli, Peter Dodd and Simon Shaw   PROPRIETORS: Valerie and Michael Hope
OPEN: all week
CLOSED: 25 Dec
MEALS: 8am to 11pm
PRICES: £16 (£24)
CARDS: Access, Amex, Diners, Visa
SEATS: 100. 6 tables outside. Private parties: 38 main room. Vegetarian meals. Children's helpings. Children restricted. Wheelchair access (1 step)

LITTLE WALSINGHAM Norfolk   map 6

▲ Old Bakehouse

33 High Street,
Little Walsingham NR22 6BZ   COOKING 2
WALSINGHAM (0328) 820454   COST £15–£26

'What a selection of vegetables! Spiced red cabbage, not stewed but served plain with orange, clove and nutmeg; carrots with sultanas, enough to give them sweetness; sliced leek sparingly cooked with a few pine kernels; potato soufflé with a sprinkling of mushroom.' Those who like their vegetables plain, be warned. Puddings are praised too: 'over the top for some, with lots of cream, it may be wise to ask for small portions,' but banoffi pie, Danish whisky cake or toffee and butterscotch pudding constitute paradise for many. The Padleys run a small restaurant with rooms where prices are reasonable and surroundings are handsome without overkill. Savoury dishes do not ignore cream either, and the cooking so far has not moved into the vinaigrettes, lentils and light bouillons of more fashionable places. Magret of Barbary duck with orange is a popular constant on the menu and other dishes that have been approved include a ramekin of mushrooms in brandy and cream; seafood pancake; veal escalope with saffron and cream; venison with blackcurrants. The *carte* numbers half a dozen alternatives at each course and there is a set meal for residents only which is as attractive as the room charges. Decent cafetière coffee is served and jugs of iced water are dispensed automatically, a practice welcome to those who don't mind nitrates and object to paying for bottled water. The wine list offers a sound range from France to Chile and closes with a fine wine section. The choices here are more expensive than they need be, but there are many halves. House French: £6.95.

CHEFS/PROPRIETORS: Christopher and Helen Padley
OPEN: Tue to Sat, D only, Apr to Dec; Fri and Sat, D only, Jan and Feb; Thur to Sat, D only, Mar
CLOSED: 3 weeks Jan to Feb, 2 weeks Oct to Nov, 1 week June
MEALS: 7 to 9.30
PRICES: £15 (£22), Set D £10 (£15)
CARDS: Access, Visa
SEATS: 36. Private parties: 40 main room. Vegetarian meals. No children under 12. Smart dress preferred.
ACCOMMODATION: 3 rooms, 2 with bath/shower. B&B £18 to £36. Deposit: £5. No children under 12. Pets welcome. Scenic. Confirm by 6

LIVERPOOL Merseyside   map 5

Armadillo

20–22 Matthew Street, L2 6RE   COOKING 2
051-236 4123   COST £16–£29

The great thing about the Armadillo is that it is inventive, with a certain informality that makes it accessible to all. The price of the lunchtime and early supper menu, which is the same, is 'great for impoverished gourmets', though by the end of the day some items may be missing. It is served non-stop till 5 on Saturday, but with a mid-afternoon break on other days. When the dinner menu comes into operation, prices rise a bit, but they remain fair. The place is so well used that the slightly rickety decoration may show wear but many don't mind when they can enjoy dishes like a guinea-fowl and spinach terrine with an aubergine relish; farmhouse Cheddar and leeks in puff pastry; mushroom dumplings; rendezvous of fish and mussels in a herb and white wine sauce; a vegetarian prasopita, pine kernels, leeks and olives in filo pastry; lamb with Gruyère, wrapped in vine leaves; monkfish on a skewer with limes and coconut; plenty of vegetables; and decent sweets, either big and good puddings or less substantial mousses and ice-creams. Occasionally, everything is too laid back and cooking goes wrong or delays get too long. The wine list is judged to be good, the only place in Liverpool to stock Cloudy Bay, and the range is wide and intelligently chosen with many top-class growers at very fair prices.

CHEFS: John Scotland and Martin Cooper   PROPRIETORS: Martin and Angela Cooper
OPEN: Tue to Sat
CLOSED: bank hols
MEALS: 12 to 3, 5 to 6.45 (daytime menu), 7.30 to 10.30 (12 to 5, 7.30 to 10.30 Sat)
PRICES: Daytime £11 (£16), D £18 (£24)
CARD: Access
SEATS: 65. Private parties: 75 main room. Vegetarian meals. Children's helpings on request. Music. Air-conditioned

La Grande Bouffe

48A Castle Street, L2 7LQ   COOKING 1
051-236 3375   COST £15–£26

Liverpool's well-known basement bistro continues to please a mainly business
clientele with reasonably priced food and decent service from waiters in ankle-
length white aprons. Eclectic, with French overtones and distinct vegetarian
leanings, sums up the full evening menu. It roams cuisines for trout pâté
parcels, authentic cassoulet, ragout of salmon and monkfish with saffron sauce,
and vegetable satay with peanut and chilli sauce. Sweets such as lemon galette
with raspberry sauce are mostly Gallic, as are the cheeses served with oatcakes
or wheat wafers. A jazz guitarist plays on Tuesday and Saturday evenings. At
lunchtime the place functions as a self-service brasserie and the crowds appear.
A short wine list includes house Bordeaux at £5.95.

CHEF: Jean Kassim   PROPRIETOR: Frank Nyland
OPEN: Mon to Sat, exc Sat L
MEALS: 12 to 2, 6 to 10.30
PRICES: £16 (£22), Set L £8.95 (£15). Service 10%
CARDS: Access, Amex, Visa
SEATS: 80. Private parties: 60 main room, 20 private room. Vegetarian meals. Children's
helpings on request. Music. Air-conditioned

Jenny's

Old Ropery, Fenwick Street, 2LZ 7NT   COOKING 2
051-236 0332   COST £14–£25

The name and the address might imply some jolly salt's landing place with
matelot waiters and fishnet on the ceiling. In fact, it is a business people's
restaurant in downtown Liverpool, waiters in dinner jackets, a strong line in
Muzak, and the only signs of the sea restricted to wall plaques and shell vases.
The long printed menu makes some concession to daily marketing but the
kitchen evidently feels confident of perpetual supplies of halibut, grouper,
scampi, scallops, monkfish and sole. The cooking of fresh fish has given
satisfaction to some readers, though the recipes are more likely to be found in
Escoffier or Madame Prunier than Richard Stein or some other current fish
cook's compendium. First courses, including five soups, and a sweets trolley,
with few concessions to lightness, are in the same vein. A straightforward wine
list, adequate in half-bottles. House French: £6.95.

CHEF: Tom Parry   PROPRIETOR: Judy Hinds
OPEN: Mon to Sat, exc Mon D and Sat L
CLOSED: 24 Dec to 1 Jan, last week Aug, first week Sept
MEALS: 12 to 2.15, 7 to 10
PRICES: £15 (£21), Set L and D £9.95 (£14) Service 10%
CARDS: Access, Amex, Visa
SEATS: 45. Private parties: 50 main room. Vegetarian meals on request. Children's helpings
on request. Smart dress preferred. No pipes in dining-room. Music. Air-conditioned

The Guide *always appreciates hearing about changes of chef or owner.*

LIVERSEDGE   West Yorkshire   map 5

▲ *Lillibet's*

64 Leeds Road, Liversedge WF15 6HX	COOKING 1
HECKMONDWIKE (0924) 404911	COST £15–£22

The square-built stone house has a buffer of a garden protecting it from the din
of a large road in front. Once through the door and, like a library or a chapel,
the outside world seems to fall away, 'perhaps that's why everybody seemed to
whisper.' The hush is not improved by hearing the instrumental version of *I just
called to say I love you* three times during the evening. Elizabeth Roberts cooks in
robust modern bistro manner to deliver a fair-value four-course menu priced
according to the choice of main dish. Second course is a sorbet or a soup in
northern style. Dishes such as chicken strips with mushrooms; chicken with a
garlic and cheese crumble; even sirloin steak (which turned out to be rump)
cooked well-done as ordered, are properly executed; there are serve-yourself
vegetables. It is not old-fashioned inasmuch as there are plenty of mousses and
stuffings, and flavourings may include ginger, Pernod and lime, but nor does it
embrace any of the insubstantiality of pretentious cooking. Desserts are often
enjoyed: meringues seem a favourite, whether fruit filled or with citrus cream
or in the form of a cake layered with praline and chocolate ice-cream. The half-
century of wines are not expensive. House French: £7.95. CELLARMAN'S
CHOICE: Stoneleigh Sauvignon Blanc, £12.95; Givry 1983, Montessay, £11.75.

CHEF: Elizabeth J. Roberts   PROPRIETORS: Martin Roberts and Elizabeth J. Roberts
OPEN: Mon to Sat, D only (L by arrangement for a minimum of 10)
CLOSED: 1 week between Christmas and New Year, 2 weeks end Aug
MEALS: 7 to 9.30
PRICES: Set L £10 (£15) to £15 (£21), Set D £16 (£22) to £18.50 (£25)
CARDS: Access, Amex, Visa
SEATS: 50. Private parties: 70 main room. Car-park, 23 places. Children's helpings. Music
ACCOMMODATION: 12 rooms, all with bath/shower. B&B £40 to £60. Garden. TV. Phone.
Doors close at midnight [*Which? Hotel Guide*]

LOUGHBOROUGH   Leicestershire   map 5

Restaurant Roger Burdell

11–12 Sparrow Hill, LE11 1BT	COOKING 2
LOUGHBOROUGH (0509) 231813	COST £24–£34

Currents of national economy and changing tastes in eating out have caused the
restaurant to retreat to the first floor leaving the ground floor as a bistro at lower
prices. This development occurred too late in the *Guide* year for a full report, but
Roger Burdell continues to cook in very much the same vein as before, one
hopes on a sounder footing. His style is classical and so is the execution. There
are many emulsion sauces: sorrel butter sauce with salmon; béarnaise with
haddock or with beef. Recipes might also gladden the heart of traditionalists:
chicken with burgundy and shallots or guinea-fowl with redcurrant, lime and
madeira. A party whose guests were drawn from all points of the compass, and
who thus selected Loughborough as the geographical modal point, were not
disappointed in their meal. Dishes that fitted the bill well were warm salad of

seafish with mushrooms, lemon and garlic; terrine of salmon, sole and spinach with ginger butter sauce; and wild mushroom soup; main courses of lamb with tomato and basil, and plait of salmon and sole; and desserts that came fully elaborated on a plate, such as chocolate and banana tart with coconut ice-cream and toffee sauce, or poached pear with kiwi fruit, lemon ice-cream and a tuile. There is a short fairly standard wine list. House wine: £9.25 and £9.50.

CHEF/PROPRIETOR: Roger Burdell
OPEN: Mon to Sat, exc Mon L
MEALS: 12.30 to 2, 7.15 to 9.15
PRICES: Set L and D £17.50 (£24) to £21.10 (£28)
CARDS: Access, Visa
SEATS: 45. Private parties: 24 main room. Children welcome. No cigars/pipes in dining-room

---

LOUTH Lincolnshire

map 6

Alfred's

Upgate, Louth LN11 9EY
LOUTH (0507) 607431

COOKING 1
COST £29

The Dickers, who have moved here from the Angel at Wainfleet, have concentrated less on decoration and more on cooking, with some success. The dining-room and kitchen are in full view of each other. The triptych menu opens to reveal a short set-price menu with four or five choices at each course, and changing monthly. Dishes steer a course between adventure and sound convention: sole soufflé with lemon and ginger sauce; moules marinière; cod baked in the oven, stuffed with smoked salmon, with a tomato sauce; or medallions of veal with pink grapefruit sauce. There is sensible use of herbs, as in chicken livers fried with marjoram or lamb cutlets with mint and sorrel, and only occasional fashionable nonsense like the supreme of chicken with scallops and mushrooms with a mild curry sauce. A spring meal yielded evidence of underseasoning in scallops sauté with chervil, chives and thyme in a light cream sauce but more accurate tasting in a piece of braised beef on a bed of spinach with another cream sauce, this time with tarragon. A companion dish of guinea-fowl with lentils and red wine would have benefited from a more robust approach, treating lentils as a valid component rather than garnish. Details may still need development, in the service and knowledge of what's in the cooking as much as at the stove itself: almond essence may not help towards almond flavour in an apricot frangipan tart. The wine list, of 50 odd bottles is arranged clearly by style rather than geography. Selection is sound, with excellent growers scattered about – Hollick from Australia, Zind-Humbrecht in Alsace – and prices are fair. House wines cost 'around £7.50' but change frequently.

The text of entries is based on unsolicited reports sent in by readers, backed up by inspections conducted anonymously. The factual details under the text are from questionnaires the Guide *sends to all restaurants that feature in the book.*

CHEF: Rosemarie Dicker   PROPRIETORS: Paul and Rosemarie Dicker
OPEN: Tue to Sat D (L by arrangement Tue to Fri)
CLOSED: bank hols, 25 and 26 Dec
MEALS: 7 to 9.30
PRICES: Set D £19.95 (£26)
CARDS: Access, Visa
SEATS: 50. Private parties: 45 main room. Children's helpings. Wheelchair
access (3 steps). Music

LOWER BEEDING   West Sussex   map 3

▲ *South Lodge*

Brighton Road, Lower Beeding RH13 6PS   COOKING 1
LOWER BEEDING (0403) 891711   COST £25–£50

A Victorian plant collector's domain whose Chinese journeys left their mark on
house and garden alike; even a piece of the Great Wall can be found. From the
handsome public rooms – well restored rather than well conceived by the
original architect – 'vistas, not views' give on to gardens and downland. Tim
Franklin's cookery has had mixed notices owing to inconsistent technique,
lack of flavour and needless elaboration: there were four different sorts of
vegetables, all more or less transmogrified, to accompany a plate of venison
already trimmed with two sauces, apple spätzli and rösti. Others have
approved well-timed soufflés, well-hung meat, good British cheeses, and more
complex dishes such as provençal vegetables in a red pepper mousse. Cooking
still harks to the days of nouvelle cuisine, so choice should be made with an
eye to simplicity and flavour. Dining is on the dear side but lunches are very
much cheaper. There have been rumblings about staff who know very little
about what they serve. 'I had the feeling I was there as a training ground.'
Some good New World and Italian wines extend a mainly French selection that
does not stint on halves. House French: £10.25.

CHEF: Tim Franklin   PROPRIETORS: Laura Hotels Ltd
OPEN: all week
MEALS: 12.30 to 2.30, 7.30 to 10 (10.30 Fri and Sat)
PRICES: £30 (£42), Set L £15 (£25), Set D £23 (£31) to £30 (£38)
CARDS: Access, Amex, Diners, Visa
SEATS: 40. Private parties: 8 main room, 14, 45 and 80 private rooms. Car-park, 80 places.
Children's helpings. Smart dress preferred at D. No cigars/pipes in dining-room.
Wheelchair access
ACCOMMODATION: 39 rooms, all with bath/shower. Rooms for disabled. B&B £80 to £210.
Afternoon teas. Garden. Tennis. Golf. TV. Phone. Scenic

The Guide *office can quickly spot when a restaurateur is encouraging customers to write
recommending inclusion - and sadly, several restaurants have been doing this in 1990.
Such reports do not further a restaurant's cause. Please tell us if a restaurateur invites you
to write to the* Guide.

*See the inside of the front cover for an explanation of the 1 to 5 rating system recognising
cooking standards.*

LOWER BRAILES Warwickshire   map 5

▲ *Feldon House*

Lower Brailes OX15 5HW   COOKING 2
BRAILES (060 885) 580   COST £21–£30

This mellowed Victorian house with a spacious and well-kept garden is in a
quiet village next to the church. It feels like the private house that it is, with
welcoming, friendly and unfussy service. There are three things to note. First,
you cannot turn up unannounced; without a booking there will be no food.
Second, the phone call serves to register strong likes or aversions, since the
menu on the day will consist of four courses without any choice. 'The danger is
that a no-choice menu involves a risk of disappointment or even
embarrassment. We suffered neither.' Third, the apparent simplicity of the
menu disguises some impressive cooking. It might read artichoke soup, crab
salad, breast of chicken stuffed with almonds, prune tart, coffee, but the
sophistication and finesse of the presentation came as a pleasant surprise. 'Mr
Witherick is clearly an imaginative cook and the combination of tastes is as
pleasing as the visual effect.' Chicken liver pâté comes dressed with half a
quail's egg and a fan of gherkins, served with half a tomato in a honey and
mustard sauce, and a barrel of cucumber filled with finely chopped onion, toast
and several kinds of good bread. There may be a slight blandness of taste in an
effort not to offend, but this is not invariably so: monkfish is spiked with the
right amount of Pernod, and roast guinea-fowl is rescued from its natural
dullness by a perfectly blended sauce of onion and brandy. The 22-bottle wine
list, unevenly annotated, incorporates a variety of styles. Among several gems
are Frescobaldi's Pomino Il Benefizio (Chardonnay) and Te Mata's Coleraine
(Cabernet Sauvignon and Merlot) from New Zealand. CELLARMAN'S
CHOICE: Gigondas, Dom. du Gour de Chaule 1983, £17.50.

CHEF: Allan Witherick   PROPRIETORS: Allan and Maggie Witherick
OPEN: all week, exc Sun D
MEALS: 12.30 to 2, 7.30 to 8.30
PRICES: Set L £16.75 (£21), Set D £21.50 (£25). Service inc
CARDS: Access, Visa
SEATS: 14. Private parties: 10 main room, 4 private room. Car-park, 9 places. Vegetarian
meals by arrangement. Children's helpings by arrangement
ACCOMMODATION: 4 rooms, all with bath/shower. B&B £30 to £40. No children. Garden.
Phone. Scenic. Doors close at 11. Confirm by 4

LUDLOW Shropshire   map 4

▲ *Dinham Hall*

Ludlow SY8 1EJ   COOKING 2
LUDLOW (0584) 876464 and 873669   COST £20–£38

The Johnsons' tall, Adam-style, merchant's house near the castle has been
handsomely converted to a small hotel and restaurant offering an urban
variation on the country-house theme. There has been some adjustment, both
of staff and presentation, during the first full year of business. This may be the
mark of settling down, though even more furious nest-building is anticipated

by some readers who still find the public rooms slightly lacking in 'atmosphere'. This is amply compensated for by the staff, who may occasionally be fledgling (the sous chef once seconded as the wine waiter), but are at least happily willing. Chris Galvin cooks in quite an advanced manner, certainly for Ludlow, though blasé hoppers from one country restaurant to another might recognise the style in dishes like supreme of salmon with wild mushrooms; medallions of venison with home-made noodles or mousseline of sole and lobster with a fresh tomato sauce. The approach gives rise to crunchy vegetables and messed about bread-and-butter pudding: 'a slice of something cold served with a pleasant sauce doesn't work; it's not a pudding, it's a sweet'. Successes in people's eyes have been ravioli of crab and spinach; soups, for instance carrot or cold mushroom; scrambled egg on brioche excellently spiked with chives; first-rate apple tarts and chocolate mousse. Failures, when they occur, make the place the more lacklustre because – all power to it – it has ambition. The cheeses are from Rance of Streatley and have been noted as less than perfect at quiet times of the year. Sunday lunch remains a palpable bargain. The wine list is long on words but short on precision – few growers are named. Its strongest section is Australasia.

CHEF: Chris Galvin   PROPRIETORS: Paul and Marian Johnson
OPEN: Thur to Sun L; all week D, exc Sun
MEALS: 12.30 to 2, 7.30 to 9.30
PRICES: Set L £14.95 (£24), Set Sun L £11.95 (£20), Set D £22.50 (£32)
CARDS: Access, Diners, Visa
SEATS: 35. Private parties: 40 main room, 24 private room. Car-park, 17 places. Vegetarian meals. Children's helpings. Smart dress preferred. Wheelchair access (2 steps). Music
ACCOMMODATION: 14 rooms, all with bath/shower. B&B £55 to £115. No children under 6. Garden. Sauna. Fishing. Golf. TV. Phone. Scenic. Doors close at 1am. Confirm by 8

LYMPSTONE Devon   map 1

▲ *River House*

The Strand, Lympstone EX8 5EY   COOKING 2
EXMOUTH (0395) 265147   COST £43

In the summer there are peaceful and impressive estuary views; when the winds howl, as they do along the River Exe, do your viewing in warmth and comfort beside the fire. A sea breeze blows through the menu to some extent. As you would expect, there is fish (though storms interrupt supply) and Shirley Wilkes tries to conjure variations in the ways it is cooked and sauced. You may find prawn and mussel soup inspired by a peppery recipe from France's Basque country; whole lemon sole on the bone is stuffed with herbs from the garden as well as mushrooms and orange and baked in wine; brill fillets are steamed in more wine and cooked with more herbs; fresh salmon is poached in Noilly Prat and served on a bed of leeks, courgette, thyme and sorrel. Menu arrangements, within set-prices, are bewildering in their potential mixing and matching from one course and one menu to another. None of this is cheap and may even be overpriced, though a light lunch *carte* offers a way of eating for less. The cooking is quite cream-laden and substantial and may include unseasonal meats such as pheasant in May. Cheese is a favourite flavour enhancer, or flavour on its own: soufflé suissesse, chicken with a cheese crust, fish grilled with cheese. Vegetables, at least six, are copious. Simplification to a degree, or reduction in range and number, would be no bad thing. The wine list is also mix-and-match: five house wines (£5.90 to £8.90 per bottle) are also available by the glass, the half litre and the litre. The list, much of it from Corney & Barrow and Christopher Piper, is adequate and fairly priced. Booking is essential: prospective lunch customers have been turned away in mid-summer when the Wilkes have decided to close the restaurant if no one has reserved. CELLARMAN'S CHOICE: Côtes du Rhône, Ch. de Saint Georges, 1986, £7.60, California Dry Creek Fumé Blanc 1988, £14.25.

CHEF: Shirley Wilkes   PROPRIETORS: Mr and Mrs J.F.M. Wilkes
OPEN: Tue to Sun, exc Sun L
MEALS: 12 to 1.45, 7 to 9.30 (10.30 Sat)
PRICES: L £15 (£21), Set L £29.50 (£36), Set D £25.50 (£31) to £29.50 (£36). Minimum £8.25 at L
CARDS: Access, Amex, Visa
SEATS: 35. Private parties: 25 main room, 14 private room. Vegetarian meals. Children's helpings. No children under 6. Smart dress preferred. No cigars/pipes in dining-room
ACCOMMODATION: 2 rooms, both with bath/shower. B&B £48 to £62. Deposit: £10. No children under 6. TV. Scenic

---

MACCLESFIELD Cheshire   map 5

Topo's

15 Church Street, Macclesfield SK11 6LB   COOKING 2
MACCLESFIELD (0625) 22231   COST £13–£29

The cobbles and red brick terraces of Church Street still have the feel of a country town; elsewhere the centre of Macclesfield has been blighted by development. Topo's is a converted shop with a tiny cramped dining-room; there are quarry tiles on the floor and Italian plates on the white plastered walls. 'Smartly rustic' sums it up. Philip Wright learned his trade at the Midland Hotel in Manchester and he knows about cooking. His menu may read like an unpromising mix of well-worn French and Italian classics, but it is redeemed by a proper respect for ingredients. Shellfish is from Loch Fyne, salmon is the wild kind and chicken is grain-fed. Above all, the kitchen avoids conjuring tricks, concentrating its efforts on producing honest food that tastes of itself. Fish may well be served complete with skin and bones, but the quality and timing are spot on. Salmon with hollandaise and poached turbot have both drawn good reports, and the fish soup has had all the unrefined authenticity of northern France. Others have mentioned the salad of warm chicken with avocado and Cumberland dressing; steak *au poivre*, and noisettes of lamb. Vegetables are interesting and abundant. Home-made ice-creams are the pick of the sweets. Both lunch and dinner menus offer plenty of options – single courses, pasta dishes and set meals as well as a full *carte*. The wine list is a mixed bag from Italy, Franch and Germany. House wine £6.95.

See the back of the Guide *for an index of restaurants listed.*

CHEF/PROPRIETOR: Philip Wright
OPEN: Tue to Sat
CLOSED: 25 and 26 Dec
MEALS: 12 to 2, 7.30 to 10
PRICES: £16 (£24), Set L £9.75 (£13), Set D £10.75 (£14) to £11.75 (£15). Service 10%
CARDS: Access, Amex, Visa
SEATS: 60. Private parties: 35 main room. Vegetarian meals. No children under 10. Smart
dress preferred. Wheelchair access (1 step; also WC). Music

MAIDEN NEWTON Dorset   map 2

Le Petit Canard

Dorchester Road, Maiden Newton DT2 0BE   COOKING 2
MAIDEN NEWTON (0300) 20536   COST £23–£29

Dorset may be full of villages with such names as Toller Porcorum (whence Le
Petit Canard draws its mineral water), but it also has fish and chip shops
aplenty. This restaurant used to be one, and after that a café, before the
Chapmans began their brave enterprise offering food that has a rather
unexpected feel to it of American West Coast Pacific Rim. They are Canadian
themselves and worked in Vancouver; hence the style. The cottage has some
remnants of café: spindleback chairs, beamed ceilings and stone walls; these
have been overlaid by decent table linen, a plethora of pottery ducks and a set-
price menu that offers dishes like scallops and baby corn stir-fried with oyster
sauce and spring onion on pasta; pork rolled with Japanese ginger and spring
onions on a honey and five-spice sauce; char-grilled breast of duck on
beansprouts and a pink peppercorn sauce. The menu changes every three
weeks and offers about seven dishes at each course, including a vegetarian one.
Menu descriptions undersell the reality. Thus quail 'garnished' with a breast of
duck turns out to be a single quail, boned, roasted and stuffed with pimento
and bacon with a whole duck breast (actually tasting more exciting than the
quail) on an excellent calvados fumet, rich and full of apple flavour. Quite a lot
of stuffing goes on: for example, a chicken is bolstered by a bacon and green
peppercorn mousse – too solid – and a first course filo parcel reveals its
contents as asparagus tips, bacon, and feta cheese. Ravioli, not surprisingly, are
also popular, filled in one instance with salmon on a dill sauce, or with goats'
cheese and herbs, with a fresh tomato salsa. Attention is paid to presentation:
vegetables come in bundles tied with leeks, the same ones for almost
everything – even, superfluously, with a dish of stir-fried vegetables. The
intentions are bold and meet with much local approval. Some of the
combinations serve only the cause of elaboration, and the technique, though
assured in its creamless sauces and nice use of juices and stock, can be heavy or
forgetful. Thus dishes with a specific herb flavour announced on the menu do
not in fact taste as expected. The transatlantic theme crops up again in desserts
like the New York strawberry cheesecake, a dark brown cooked cheesecake
with pronounced fruit flavour. Two puddings enthusiastically reported have
been a white chocolate mousse in a hazelnut cookie tulip or a cleverly
ornamented mille-feuille of dark and white chocolate mousses on a pool of
raspberry. Cheese restricts itself to two or three British varieties, often local.

The wine list, organised by Lin Chapman, is commendably short. Her service, often single-handed, is always applauded. Drawing largely from Eldridge Pope in Dorchester, she offers a couple of dozen bottles and half a dozen halves. With no prejudices regarding the origins, the choice is interesting enough to reconcile many to its lack of range. Nor are prices too high. House wine varies frequently. CELLARMAN'S CHOICE: Rhinefarm Valley Zinfandel 1987, £13.95, Rully premier cru Margoté 1986, Dury, £15.95.

CHEF: Geoff Chapman   PROPRIETORS: Geoff and Lin Chapman
OPEN: Tue to Sat, D only
CLOSED: 3 weeks early Nov
MEALS: 7 to 9.30
PRICES: Set D £15.95 (£23) to £16.95 (£24)
CARDS: Access, Visa
SEATS: 28. Private parties: 28 main room. Vegetarian meals. No children under 8. Smart dress preferred. No cigars/pipes in dining-room. Music

---

MAIDSTONE Kent   map 3

Suefflé

The Green, Bearsted, Maidstone ME14 4DN   COOKING 2
MAIDSTONE (0622) 37065   COST £25–£44

The restaurant squeezes a quart into a pint pot of two terraced cottages beside the large and handsome village green. The front garden/terrace/patio suitable for open air dining is a signal example of miniaturisation. A menu is written (in French) on a blackboard and you are guided through it by patronne or waitress. At weekends, the price climbs steeply and the options narrow. Cooking is described as 'new classic' although dishes like moules marinière or profiteroles may remind one of yesteryear's bistros – in concept if not execution. Andy Blyth manages to impart some style to a feuilleté of pigeon and pheasant; a game pie of pigeon, chicken, foie gras and pheasant; rack of lamb with madeira sauce; excellent vegetables; or a strawberry timbale – again, timbale more in thought than deed though it is a 'gorgeous version of a modern dish.' Performance has been less assured with soufflé suissesse that gained a cheese taste only from slices of Cheddar melted on top, game that has been flavourless and a disappointing selection of cheese. Service may be keen and kindly but production can slow to snails' pace on busy nights. The fairly priced French Regional Selection followed by a few petits châteaux from decent vintages seem the best choice from a rather uneven wine list. Prices are ungenerous, although there are good names, especially on the bin-end and older vintages pages. Many blank pages make it difficult. The name is not misspelled. It derives from a culinary improvisation on the owner's first name.

Several sharp operators have tried to extort money from restaurateurs on the promise of an entry in a guide book that has never appeared. The Good Food Guide *makes no charge for inclusion and does not offer certificates of any kind.*

CHEF: Andy Blyth PROPRIETOR: Sue Dunderdale
OPEN: Tue to Sat, exc Sat L
CLOSED: 25 Dec to 2 Jan
MEALS: 12 to 2, 7 to 10
PRICES: Set L and D £17.50 (£25) (exc Fri and Sat D), to £28.50 (£37)
CARDS: Access, Amex, Carte Blanche, Diners, Visa
SEATS: 44. 6 tables outside. Private parties: 44 main room. Car-park, 14 places. Vegetarian
meals. Children's helpings. Wheelchair access (3 steps). Music. Air-conditioned

---

MALVERN WELLS Hereford & Worcester   map 2

Croque-en-Bouche

221 Wells Road, Malvern Wells WR14 4HF   COOKING 4
MALVERN (0684) 565612   COST £40

So many of the best and most memorable British restaurants are small. They do
not mount the treadmill of success and growth, and are loath to sacrifice
immediacy. It shows in their cooking. The Jones have such a place. It is known
nationally, but they still run it alone, cooking, serving, doing the books,
weeding the garden, answering the phone. One might object that the British
public would never support a Croque-en-Bouche three times as large – it is too
mean and uninterested in food. Equally one might argue that the very character
of such places would not admit aggrandisement. British cookery is not 'grand'
cookery in that way but it can be very good and the Croque-en-Bouche is a fine
example. The nightly production is a short menu at a fixed price for soup, fish,
meat, salad, cheese and dessert. There are three choices of fish and meat and
five of dessert. The menu changes weekly but it is a well-loved repertoire.
Reasonably enough, dishes that gain acceptance are not lightly abandoned, but
they do change and there is no way they could be called old-fashioned. A menu
from the summer shows much interest in oriental ingredients in such dishes as
monkfish with mizuna greens and hijiki seaweed with a soy, sherry vinegar
and chervil sauce; the matchless salad has coriander leaves in it; a Turkish
borek has spinach and shiitake mushrooms, albeit with a madeira sauce.
Dishes also reflect the single-mindedness of the enterprise: the lamb is home-
smoked with applewood and rosemary; the garden contributes to dish after
dish – Bath asparagus, saladings, herbs. Only the bread, surprisingly, is not all
baked on the premises; the walnut loaf is, however, and it is first-rate. A
summer meal that shows the possibilities consisted of vegetable broth, full of
pesto, vaporous with the smells of garlic and pecorino; a globe artichoke and
crab mousse with a 'créosa' sauce made with diced peppers, capers, mustard
and vinaigrette; Gressingham duck, brushed with honey and roasted, served
with brown lentils, 'perfect meat in perfect condition', with exactly timed
lentils in a duck stock with shallots and Cabernet Sauvignon, 'thin but with
lots of flavour'; good classical dauphinois potatoes; salad 'so good I asked to eat
the remaining half after the cheese'; a dozen British cheeses in prime condition;
and a composite dessert of Charentais melon and Champagne sorbets, banana
ice-cream, and alpine strawberries from the garden with a Galia melon sauce
('how to make something extraordinary out of something fairly ordinary'), all
in perfect condition, subtle yet intense flavours, not the usual trio of claggy

ENGLAND

chocolate sweets; then at last, good coffee and fine yet not showy petits fours. Serious stuff, with a lot of flavour, not moderated by one egg-based sauce (a trait mentioned in last year's *Guide*). The service is a balancing act which some find worrying, though it is Robin Jones who needs to worry, as he does it all. Main courses are delivered to the table on serving platters, soup comes in a tureen, the rest is plated. People have nothing but praise for his approach: 'He takes people for a quick run through the menu on arrival, his knowledge of what goes on in the kitchen is unsurpassed, he memorises the evening's customers so as to greet them by name when they come to the door'. He even helps travellers in distress. Fame and long-service, perhaps, are mellowing. He also runs the wine list: now in one volume for red and another for white. A reader suggested comparison with the encyclopaedias of the grand establishments – the Manoirs and the Inter-continentals. At Croque-en-Bouche the range is larger, the list tells about the wines, and the price is probably halved. He is also more willing to buy cheaper wines – even Chinese. The range is startling – there has been a great expansion of the Australian section, and the rest of the world now takes up nearly as much space as France. The strong points occur all the way through, especially as a property may figure in four or more vintages, thereby increasing the interest immeasurably. There are plenty of halves, two dozen house wines from £5.90, and suggestions for appropriate accompanying wines on each menu. Unless you are super-keen, these are a sound bet as they always include the curious and good. Order with total confidence not just in the quality of the wine, but also knowing that the price charged has a real relationship with that quality. Wine service is straightfoward: Robin Jones draws the cork, you pour. Decanting is rare and red wines are served on the cool side. Can nights occur when all is not good? Yes, but they are rarely reported and even then, shafts of brilliance puncture the clouds.

CHEF: Marion Jones PROPRIETORS: Robin and Marion Jones
OPEN: Wed to Sun, D only
CLOSED: Sun before Christmas to Wed after New Year
MEALS: 7.30 to 9.15
PRICES: Set D £28 (£33). Service inc
CARDS: Access, Visa
SEATS: 24. Private parties: 8 private room. Children welcome. No smoking in dining-room. Wheelchair access

---

MANCHESTER Greater Manchester   map 5

▲ Armenian, Granada Hotel

404 Wilmslow Road, Withington, M20 9BM   COOKING 2
061-434 3480   COST £20

The restaurant in the basement of the Granada Hotel has been a fixture of Manchester's eating scene for many years. A recent facelift and a change of ownership have given it a new lease of life. Hanni Al-Taraboulsy, who made

County Round-ups listing additional restaurants that may be worth a visit are at the back of the Guide, after the Irish section. Reports on Round-up entries are welcome.

his name at Hanni's in Altrincham, brought most of his team with him when he took over, and the style is recognisably similar. The red and brown dining-room is less bleak than it used to be and the kitchen can deliver some of the most authentic Middle Eastern food in the city. Meze is an impressive selection, including hummus, ful medames, tabouleh, pickles, stuffed vine leaves, grilled aubergines and spicy Armenian sausages. Main courses are dominated by the chargrill, but move beyond the Middle East to the North African coast of Morocco. An immense couscous piled with lamb and vegetables served with a bowl of fiery harrisa sauce was mightily impressive, 'a well-executed, satisfying dish' despite rather than because of its proportions. There is also grilled or fried halibut, steaks and assorted salads. A whole roast lamb stuffed with rice and nuts is popular with parties (minimum of 12 and ordered in advance). Cardamom-flavoured Turkish coffee goes well with the sticky sweets made by a local woman who knows her trade. Service is kindly and concerned. Ch. Musar at £12.50 is the pick from a rudimentary wine list. House French: £6.50 a litre.

CHEFS: Mrs Minto and Mr Hovnanian   PROPRIETORS: Hanni Al-Taraboulsy and Mr Jajoo
OPEN: all week, D only
MEALS: 6 to 10.30 (11 Fri and Sat)
PRICES: £11 (£17)
CARDS: Access, Amex, Diners, Visa
SEATS: 50. Private parties: 65 main room. Children's helpings. Music
ACCOMMODATION: 11 rooms, all with bath/shower. B&B £35 to £45. Baby facilities. TV.
Phone. Confirm by 5

Blinkers French

16 Princess Street, M1 4NB	COOKING 1
061-228 2503	COST £15–£34

This comfortable basement is a bastion of European cooking on the verges of Chinatown. Its long menu – a fixed *carte* and a daily changing list of fish from the market – is supplemented by short, simpler and much cheaper fixed-price meals. The cooking has taken a turn to complexity in the first courses, mixing flavours in an apparent medley, for example smoked salmon garnished with wild rice, smoked halibut, Stilton and pimentos. Classicism is evident in the fish cookery and extravagance in the 'lobster week', when half a dozen marriages of lobster with fish or beef were on offer at lobsterish prices. The business lunchers appreciate the comfort, good yet quiet service, and careful cooking of such choices as stuffed mushrooms; ratatouille; breast of chicken with herbs; or grilled salmon trout at a very fair cost. The wine list has a page of fine wines for the lobster eaters, and is otherwise an adequate range, with some more than acceptable makers. House wine: £7.50. CELLARMAN'S CHOICE: Côtes du Rhône Séguret, Réserve du Goudray 1983, £14.50.

'Our ordering a bottle of wine as an aperitif shook the place to its foundations. We were (honestly) brought the same bottle of wine for inspection by four different youngsters.'
On eating in Wales

CHEF: Steve Heginbotham   PROPRIETORS: Lewis and Christine Gerezdi
OPEN: Mon to Sat, exc Sat L
MEALS: 12 to 2.30, 7.15 to 10.30
PRICES: £19 (£28) Set L £9.95 (£15), Set D £16.95 (£24). Service 10%
CARDS: Access, Amex, Diners, Visa
SEATS: 45. Private parties: 70 main room. Vegetarian meals. Children's helpings. Children restricted. Smart dress preferred. Music

Café Istanbul

79 Bridge Street, M3 2RH	COOKING 1
061-833 9942	COST £8–£18

As in so many middle-eastern restaurants, portions are generous and value for money is fair though consistency may occasionally be in question. Cooking is in full view of the tables and the menu is a familiar litany of Turkish specialities of which the following have been recommended: spinach tarator; lentil soup; fasulya beans, onion and tomato salad; doner kebab and mixed meats (which may be mostly doner). There is a bargain set lunch and some of the pastries have been enjoyed. House French is £5.50. CELLARMAN'S CHOICE: Buzbag, a Turkish full-bodied red.

CHEF: Hasan Bicer   PROPRIETOR: Sacit Onur
OPEN: Mon to Sat
CLOSED: 25 and 26 Dec
MEALS: 12 to 3, 6 to 11.30
PRICES: £10 (£15), Set L £4.20 (£8)
CARDS: Access, Visa
SEATS: 40. Private parties: 45 main room. Vegetarian meals. Children's helpings. Smart dress preferred. Wheelchair access (also WC). Music

Koreana

Kings House, 40 King Street West, M3 2WY	COOKING 2
061-832 4330	COST £9–£26

Increasing numbers of Korean artefacts on the walls and charming waitresses in national costume reinforce the authentic atmosphere of this basement dining-room. It is still something of an undiscovered oriental gem amid the tourist buzz of Chinatown, with a confident kitchen that can deliver classic bulgogi – sweet marinated beef cooked at the table on a metal shield – and other genuine dishes. These include mando (steamed dumplings served in a soup), bindac tok (a shallow-fried soy-bean pancake) and sliced fried fish with courgettes, all distinctly flavoured yet subtle. Korean rice cake cooked in soy sauce makes a good finish. Special banquets, including a five-course feast for vegetarians, are excellent value. Drink Korean saké or ginseng or green tea. The house wine at £6.80 is quite up to its task.

Restaurateurs justifiably resent no-shows. If you quote a credit card number when booking, you may be liable for the restaurant's lost profit margin if you don't turn up. Always phone to cancel.

CHEFS: Hyun K. Kim and H.S. Shin PROPRIETORS: Koreana Restaurant Ltd
OPEN: Mon to Sat, exc Sat L
MEALS: 12 to 2.30, 6.30 to 11 (11.30 Sat)
PRICES: £12 (£19), Set L £4.30 (£9) to £6.95 (£11), Set D £11.50 (£16) to £19.50 (£22).
Service inc
CARDS: Access, Amex, Diners, Visa
SEATS: 56. Private parties: 60 main room. Vegetarian meals. Children welcome. Smart dress preferred. Music

Kosmos Taverna

248 Wilmslow Road, M14 6LD	COOKING 1
061-225 9106	COST £18

'Kosmos delivered as always', is one regular's comment on this reliable taverna. It's the kind of place where you can relax at the bar with a bottle of retsina before sitting down to hummus, which seems to have the virtue of not being bought in, feta cheese parcels, dolmades with hot tomato sauce, and chargrilled kebabs. All the Greek favourites are here, plus specialities such as rabbit stefado, pigeon, octopus cooked in wine. House wine is £6.10 a carafe. The list has a dozen Greek wines, including a few 'new' selections, though it hardly exposes the real novelty of serious Greek wine production now in train.

CHEF: Loulla Astin PROPRIETORS: Stewart and Loulla Astin
OPEN: all week, D, and Sun L
CLOSED: 25 and 26 Dec
MEALS: 6.30 to 11.30 (1 to 11.30 Sun)
PRICES: £10 (£15)
CARDS: Access, Visa
SEATS: 80. Private parties: 40 main room. Vegetarian meals. Children's helpings.
Wheelchair access (also WC). Music. Air-conditioned

Lime Tree

8 Lapwing Lane, West Didsbury, M20 8WS	
061-445 1217	COOKING 1
2m from M56 exit 10	COST £15–£28

If Manchester's Chinese restaurants show the world how to produce good food at moderate cost, the Lime Tree at least matches them. The surroundings are no more elaborate than they need be, though a conservatory extension has given more space and atmosphere. Service is informal, willing and cheerful for the most part, but may not be able to help on fine details without calling for help themselves. Nights get so busy that this may take time. The cooking is not just 'any old bistro' but makes an effort to provide upwardly mobile ingredients – asparagus or smoked salmon – at fair cost as well as a seam of modern recipes: avocado and crab in layers of toasted brioche; calf's liver with onion and clove cream sauce; loin of lamb with marjoram and garlic on a tomato *jus* with wild rice; or halibut with spring onions, ginger and soy. Puddings may include a hoary favourite like steamed chocolate pudding with butterscotch sauce, or a brandy-snap with ice-cream or raspberry and guava parfait, though cakes and profiteroles of poor consistency have also been reported. The extension of opening times may have caused periodic strain in the kitchen; certainly moments of less than perfection can occur at busy times. A short wine list is further enforced by a second list of bin-ends, halves and fine wines. The main selection is adequate and cheap. Music is loud.

CHEFS: Patrick Hannity, Alison Eason and Simon Haywood   PROPRIETORS: Patrick Hannity and Robert Williams
OPEN: all week, D only and Sun L
MEALS: 12 to 2, 6.30 to 10.30
PRICES: £16 (£23), Set L £8.95 (£15)
CARDS: Access, Visa
SEATS: 80. Private parties: 50 main room. Vegetarian meals. Children's helpings (Sun L only). Wheelchair access. Music

---

Little Yang Sing

17 George Street, M1 4HG   COOKING 1
061-228 7722   COST £17–£26

There is a lot of competition in Manchester's Chinatown. Prices here may be slightly higher but the repertoire is big and the preparation confident, on the whole. Cantonese is the single cuisine pursued. Dim-sum is 'excellent – crisp, ungreasy spring rolls with a meat filling; steamed dumpling of fine dough surrounding a spicy meat, peanut and coriander filling.' Fried sliced duck with pineapple and ginger had 'crisp skin – the rich meat offset by the sharpness of pineapple'. Fish is a strength. There are some one-pot dishes, for instance, brisket and sliced duck with Chinese greens, and the menu does not stray far into the realms of innards, extremities and fish lips. The staff hustle and cajole, and refurbishment is threatened. As the *Guide* went to press, plans were underway to start serving lunch. There is Chinese beer. House French: £6.50.

CHEF/PROPRIETOR: Warren Yeung
OPEN: all week, D only
MEALS: 5.30 to 11.30 (11.45 Fri, 12 Sat)
PRICES: £12 (£22), Set D £11.50 (£17). Service 10%
CARDS: Access, Amex, Visa
SEATS: 80. Private parties: 80 main room. Vegetarian meals. Children welcome. Music. Air-conditioned

---

Market Restaurant

104 High Street, M4 1HQ   COOKING 2
061-834 3743   COST £23

'You half expect to see Noel Coward or Jack Buchanan' in these pea-green premises opposite the Smithfield markets. Anne O'Grady, according to one report, dresses in keeping with the style and maintains a tremendously friendly atmosphere. The menu reflects a catholic approach: quails' eggs with tapénade, tiropitakia, tabouleh with red peppers, or watercress and cucumber soup for first courses; chicken with juniper, salmon with a courgette crust or lamb with asparagus for a more northern European tilt to the main courses.

Mary-Rose Edgecombe, who began the restaurant in 1980, has returned to the stove after Lin Scrannage's departure. Reports indicate that the place has gone from strength to strength. Upstairs in the Elizabeth Raffald Room (named after Manchester's great contributor to British cookery) is held the Pudding Club, where a menu of five British sweet delights is fronted by a single main dish. The formula has been so popular that the restaurant has now begun a mirror-image Starters Club for savoury lovers. The wine list is sensible, not highly priced, and has a 'miscellany' of extras from around the world. There is an exceptional range of bottle-conditioned Belgian beers. 'We have always offered real beer to accompany the real food,' observes Peter O'Grady.

CHEFS: Mary-Rose Edgecombe, Paul Mertz, Dawn Wellens and Lisa King
PROPRIETORS: Peter O'Grady and Anne O'Grady
OPEN: Tue to Sat, D only
CLOSED: 1 week in spring, 1 week at Christmas, Aug
MEALS: 5.30 (7 Sat) to 9.30
PRICES: £15 (£19)
CARDS: Access, Amex, Diners, Visa
SEATS: 40. Private parties: 40 main room, 25 private room. Vegetarian meals. Children welcome. Music

Mr Kuks

55A Mosley Street, M2 3HY   COOKING 1
061-236 0659   COST £14–£34

The atmosphere in the basement dining-room is civilised, the service good, and special set menus are the main attractions for large gatherings. Individual items such as barbecued spare ribs, sesame prawn toasts with seaweed, aromatic crispy duck and sizzling fillet steak have all been praised. The full menu of 160 dishes is tilted towards meat, with some unusual offerings such as sweet-and-sour chicken liver and double-cooked belly pork. Fish is dominated by king prawns and cod. There's a decent showing of dim-sum and one-plate rice and noodle dishes. The chopsticks are wooden, the tea comes in western cups. House French wine: £5.50.

CHEF: Mr Lau   PROPRIETORS: Stephen Kuks and Geoffrey Cohen
OPEN: Tue to Sat and Sun D, bank hol Mons
MEALS: 12 to 2.30,6 to 11.15
PRICES: £19 (£28), Set L and D £9.50 (£14). Service 10%
CARDS: Access, Amex, Diners, Visa
SEATS: 95. Private parties: 95 main room. Children's helpings. Music. Air-conditioned

Consumers' Association is planning to publish Out to Eat, *a new guide to budget eating out in restaurants, pubs, cafés, brasseries and so on. Please send reports and recommendations to Out to Eat, FREEPOST, 2 Marylebone Road, London NW1 1YN.*

Several sharp operators have tried to extort money from restaurateurs on the promise of an entry in a guide book that has never appeared. The Good Food Guide *makes no charge for inclusion and does not offer certificates of any kind.*

▲ Moss Nook

Ringway Road, M22 5NA
061-437 4778
on B5166, 1m from Manchester   COOKING 3
Airport, M56 exit 5   COST £28–£42

Pauline and Derek Harrison's brick house is more pleasantly suburban than ring road, and the otherwise bland exterior is lent cheer by hanging boxes and white shutters. It was once a vegetarian restaurant; now weighty Victoriana sets the scene for more meaty fare. One regular wrote: 'Still Manchester's best Anglo-French restaurant, but it seems locked in a time warp of materials and techniques. Sauces are reductions with butter and often fruit or peppercorns, everything is boned and pan-fried. Fish is either salmon, sole or lobster; meats, fillet of beef, lamb or veal. A good daube or stew, perhaps some offal, maybe some more pasta would be welcome. Everything is geared towards a 'business' definition of luxury. There is a lack of spontaneity – no game in November – in a kitchen which is yet so capable and skilled.' All-inclusive prices have hardly budged since last year, and readers have few complaints about ingredients or competence of cooking. Presentation, service and comfort are as good as always. The menu is à la carte save for the seven-course *menu surprise*. One reader thought marinated halibut with capers, pine nuts and tomato 'quite exquisite', another enjoyed tomato and basil soup; and many people mention the walnut and raisin bread. Terrine of lobster enclosed by sole fillets in a light herby sauce featured on an autumn surprise menu and was proclaimed excellent. The elaborate dessert at the same meal, pastry tarts of chocolate, ice-cream, spun sugar and fruit, did not impress to the same extent, but good generous coffee and petits fours made a pleasing finale. The wine list begins with a page of Champagnes, but carries on with a largely French selection with but a nod to the New World. The growers and properties are unusual and deserve experiment. House Bergerac: £8.75 and £9.75. CELLARMAN'S CHOICE: Graves, Dom. de Grandmaison 1986, £15.50; Crémant de Bourgogne Blanc de Blancs, £18. Tips are not encouraged. There is now a cottage adjacent to the restaurant for overnight stays, with double bedroom, lounge, kitchen and two bathrooms.

CHEFS: Robert Thornton and Kevin Lofthouse   PROPRIETORS: Pauline and Derek Harrison
OPEN: Tue to Sat, exc Sat L
CLOSED: 24 Dec for 2 weeks
MEALS: 12 to 2, 7 to 9.30 (10 Sat)
PRICES: £29 (£35), Set L and D £24 (£28). Service inc
CARDS: Access, Amex, Diners, Visa
SEATS: 50. 8 tables outside. Private parties: 10 main room. Car-park, 50 places. No children under 12. Smart dress preferred. No cigars/pipes in dining-room. Air-conditioned
ACCOMMODATION: Cottage, 2 baths/showers. D, B&B £130. TV. Phone

---

'We tried the restaurant a month ago. You are right about the quality of the food but our table was cramped – the chef-proprietor agreed when told. The price was £200 for two, with two half-bottles of medium-priced wine. Stiff I think. He charged for a copy of the menu as well!' On dining in Oxfordshire

Pearl City

33 George Street, M1 4HQ
061-236 2574

COOKING 1
COST £9–£40

Another Chinatown giant, with dim sum and one-plate meals the most recommended items of a menu that gives fair value, though not especially large portions. These include crabmeat balls; sui mai; har gow; beef dumplings with ginger and spring onion; crispy belly pork with good rind and creamy fat; and duck webs or braised chicken feet. The duck with prawn meat stuffing; steamed bass with ginger; and plate meals like pork chop with special sauce or three roast meats have their supporters for freshness and flavour, though garnishings may detract a little.

CHEF: Mr Lee PROPRIETORS: Paul Cheung and Lin Hung Kan
OPEN: all week
MEALS: noon to 4am, noon to midnight Sun
PRICES: £16 (£29), Set L £3.30 (£9) to £10 (£16), Set D £12 (£19) to £25 (£33). Minimum £5. Service 10%
CARDS: Access, Amex, Diners, Visa
SEATS: 300. 40 tables outside. Private parties: 300 main room, 200 private room. Children's helpings. Music. Air-conditioned

Quan Ju De

44 Princess Street, M1 6DE
061-236 5236

COOKING 1
COST £15–£29

The original Quan Ju De restaurant in Beijing was founded by a successful poultry merchant in the 1860s and has since acquired an international reputation, playing host to heads of state from many countries. The new Manchester venue is a gastronomic ambassador, ranking alongside Mr Kuk's (see entry) as the main representative of Pekinese cuisine in the city. Princess Street is the heartland of Manchester's Chinatown with scores of restaurants and cafés, mostly specialising in Cantonese cooking. As if to emphasise its distinctiveness, Quan Ju De has been elegantly designed with cool modern touches everywhere: a flight of polished wooden stairs go past a sculpture of a heron – up to the spacious, light dining-room with its wooden floors, glass screens and carved black dining chairs. The walls are hung with abstract paintings, and the corners are filled with plinths bearing porcelain vases. Even the crockery is classy: white and octagonal. The menu has many challenging dishes, highlighting the eclectic regional influences of Peking cuisine. An extensive choice of hot and cold first courses includes 'an incredibly generous pile' of marinated duck breast with bean paste; grilled dumplings with a sharp vinegar dip; crispy fried smoked chicken and superb sweet-and-sour pickled cucumbers. Marinated 'sea crunchy' (actually sea anemone) is a refreshingly satisfying oddity. Main dishes have also drawn good reports. An inspector's meal featured excellent shredded fried beef with chilli, and deep-fried Peking chicken and aubergines with green pepper and bean curd. Some dishes have been bland, however, and the apparent preference for frozen rather than fresh fish is disappointing, but in all this is an exciting addition to the Manchester scene. Vegetarians even get a separate set menu at £12.50. Service is careful and well-informed. Tea is unlimited. House French: £6.50.

CHEF: F.L. Shu   PROPRIETOR: Hoo Man Lau
OPEN: all week
CLOSED: bank hols
MEALS: 12 to 2.30, 6 to 11
PRICES: £11 (£20), Set L and D £9.50 (£15) to £17.50 (£24). Service 10%
CARDS: Amex, Visa
SEATS: 120. Private parties: 90 main room, 30 private room. Vegetarian meals. Children welcome. Smart dress preferred. Music. Air-conditioned

Sanam

145–151 Wilmslow Road,	
Rusholme, M14 5AW	COOKING 1
061-224 1008	COST £11

Rusholme is Manchester's 'little India', full of sweet centres, cafés and restaurants. This Sanam outlet – there are others nearby – has been trading under the same ownership since 1976 and keeps its edge for authentic cooking and value for money. The decor may be bright and the marble-topped tables closely packed, but the kitchen delivers potent tandooris, kebabs and karahi dishes as well as the standard crop of kormas, dhansak and Madras curries. Also look for specialities: lightly spiced lamb's brains, quail, and deep-fried aloo tikka spiked with green chillies. On Sunday there's a special moghlai biriani plus rare katlamma and puri chana with semolina halva. Takeaways from the counter include a full range of Indian sweets. Unlicensed, but there are jugs of lassi and mango milk shakes to drink. At the time of going to press, an extension increasing the seating capacity to 350 was underway.

CHEF: Munir Chaudry   PROPRIETORS: Abdul Ghafoor Akhtar and Sons
OPEN: all week
MEALS: noon to midnight (1am Fri and Sat)
PRICES: £7 (£9). Service inc
CARDS: Access, Visa
SEATS: 150. Private parties: 100 main room, 60 private room. Vegetarian meals. Children's helpings. Wheelchair access (also WC). Music. Air-conditioned

Siam Orchid

54 Portland Street, M14 QU	COOKING 1
061-236 1388	COST £8–£25

The decoration develops a certain Thai atmosphere, the more readily to be distinguished from the strong Chinese presence in Manchester. That indeed is one of its hidden advantages: the freshness and heat of the cooking makes a welcome change, further reinforced this year by a planned extension to the menu to bring it up to the length of its sister restaurant, Royal Orchid, round the corner in Charlotte Street. People speak well of the soups, the curries and the noodle dishes. This is almost wholly a stir-fry restaurant with none of the long-cooked, up-country dishes. Drink beer.

CHEFS: C. Sirisompan and Doy Parry   PROPRIETORS: C. Sirisompan and K. Sirisambhand
OPEN: all week, exc Sat and Sun L
MEALS: 11.30 to 2.30, 6.30 to 11.30 (6 to 11.30 Fri and Sat, 5 to 11 Sun)
PRICES: £13 (£21), Set L £4 (£8), Set D £7 (£12). Service 10%, exc inc Set L. Licensed, also
bring your own: corkage £3
CARD: Access, Visa
SEATS: 55. Private parties: 55 main room. Children welcome. Music. Air-conditioned

That Café

1031 Stockport Road,	
South Levenshulme, M19 2TB	COOKING 1
061-432 4672	COST £16–£25

The homely informality of Joe Quinn's converted terraced house is like a
breath of fresh air in this run-down part of the city. Inside it is full of greenery,
old-fashioned fireside chairs and a jumble of bric-à-brac. Even the bar feels
more like a cosy parlour than a 'fidgety ante-room'. Joe Quinn's short menu
gives vegetarian and meat dishes equal billing: deep-fried Brie, and mushroom
and broccoli crêpes sit side by side with pork and orange liqueur sauce, and
noisettes of honey-roast lamb with an 'excellent' redcurrant and citrus sauce.
Fresh fish is advertised on the dining-room mirrors. Unlimited cups of proper
ground coffee are welcome. The short, reasonably priced wine list is well
chosen. House French: £6.50. CELLARMAN'S CHOICE: Hugh Rock's Sparkling
Gooseberry wine, £8.95.

CHEF/PROPRIETOR: Joe Quinn
OPEN: Tue to Sat D and Sun L
MEALS: 12 to 2.30, 7 to 10.30
PRICES: £14 (£21), Set D Tue to Thur only £9.95 (£16)
CARDS: Access, Amex, Visa
SEATS: 75. Private parties: 50 main room, 25 private room. Vegetarian meals. Children's
helpings. Music

Tung Fong

2 Worsley Road, M28 4NL	COOKING 1
061-794 5331	COST £10–£29

Tony Wu has moved from Hopewell City in Chinatown to this half-timbered
house in the suburbs (near junction 12 of the M62). It is an unlikely setting for
a Chinese restaurant that has impressed early visitors with the freshness of
materials and its ability to cook them. There is a range of Cantonese, Shanghai,
Hunanese and Szechuan dishes on offer. The dim-sum has been thought nearly
up to Chinatown standards and other recommended dishes have been salt and
pepper ribs; Szechuan prawns; Hunanese lamb with ginger and spring onion;
and char siu. The quality of the prawns by contrast with the meats would imply
that the chefs' hearts are in Canton rather than the inland provinces.

The Guide *relies on feedback from its readers. Especially welcome are reports on new
restaurants appearing in the book for the first time.*

CHEFS: K. Lee and Tony Wu PROPRIETOR: Tony Wu
OPEN: Mon to Fri
CLOSED: 25 Dec
MEALS: 12 to 2, 5.30 to 11.30
PRICES: £11 (£22), Set L £4.30 (£10), Set D £13 (£19) to £17.50 (£24). Service 10%
CARDS: Access, Amex, Visa
SEATS: 100. Private parties: 25 each in four private rooms. Car-park, 6 places. Children
welcome. Music

Woodlands

33 Shepley Road, Audenshaw, M34 5DJ COOKING 2
061-336 4241 COST £19–£34

The suburban restaurant in a brick detached Victorian house does not attract a
flood of nominations, but it does satisfy the regulars. Mushroom soup with
fresh rolls and lemon sole with smoked salmon mousse are among the dishes
that satisfy. Fish is the main draw: warm lobster mousse is served with goujons
of sole; green lip mussels come with a cheese and herb sauce; steamed fillets of
sea bass are given a lemon butter sauce spiked with ginger. There is a lot of
cream and butter in the saucing, quite a bit of alcohol, and much mixing of fish:
Noilly Prat with brill and salmon; Riesling with scallops and scampi;
Champagne with sole and crab. Seven vegetables are served in small
quantities, an echo of Miller Howe. In general terms, Mark Jackson has
adapted a Savoy training to northern appetites. The 45-bottle wine list is
reasonably priced and very French. House wine: £6.95.

CHEF: William Mark Jackson PROPRIETORS: Mr and Mrs D. Crank
OPEN: Tue to Sat, exc Sat L
CLOSED: first week Jan, 1 week after Easter, 2 weeks Aug
MEALS: 12 to 2, 7 to 9.30 (10 Sat)
PRICES: £20 (£28), Set L £11.95 (£19), Set D £13.95 (£21)
CARDS: Access, Visa
SEATS: 36. Private parties: 22 main room, 14 private room. Car-park, 12 places. Children's
helpings. Smart dress preferred. No cigars/pipes in dining-room. Wheelchair access
(3 steps). Music. Air-conditioned

Yang Sing

34 Princess Street, M1 4JY COOKING 2
061-236 2200 COST £17–£21

The food gets almost universal raves, but a long-time patron feels Manchester's
foremost Cantonese restaurant somehow lost its way in its move to these low-
ceilinged basement premises. Once the menu oozed creative genius and
evolved with the seasons; now it seems stuck in a groove. Often the most
authentic dishes are not available. If you can fend off relentless pressure to go
for the run-of-the-mill banquets, there is still well-timed cooking and well-
judged seasoning producing fresh, distinct flavours in, for instance, sizzling
fillet steak with spring onion, lotus root and bamboo shoots, and meaty
gingered spare ribs. Also fine was the moist steamed duck with Chinese
vegetables, and lobster with ginger and spring onions. Dry-fried rice sticks

with beef had a good barbecue taste and texture. Special fried rice with prawns and pork is consistently impressive. Creditable dim-sum might include good beef dumplings with ginger and spring onion, and clearly flavoured Chinese mushrooms stuffed with prawn and pork. In early spring, fresh fruits in a melon was a tasty assembly of Asian and Western varieties. A visitor over many years reflected after a Sunday dim-sum lunch that many of the items were of exemplary standard: excellent texture of the pastry with the beef dumplings and a good taste to the Chinese fishcakes, if poor pastry with spicy nut dumplings. Yet the report confirmed other people's uneasiness at the whole experience. It seems that only careful planning or very careful ordering can bring out the best the restaurant remains capable of providing. Service can be off-hand – often rushed when it's full and slow when it's not – and staff can't help much with the finer points of the cooking. Drink lager or Chinese tea.

CHEF: Harry Yeung   PROPRIETORS: Yang Sing Restaurant Ltd
OPEN: all week
CLOSED: 25 Dec
MEALS: noon to 11
PRICES: £12 (£18), Set L and D £11.50 (£17). Service 10%
CARDS: Access, Amex, Visa
SEATS: 140. Private parties: 220 main room, 30 and 70 private rooms. Children welcome. Wheelchair access. Music. Air-conditioned

---

MASHAM North Yorkshire   map 7

Floodlite

7 Silver Street, Masham HG4 4DX   COOKING 2
RIPON (0765) 89000   COST £11–£23

A roast loin of lamb with rosemary and garlic and a roast saddle of hare with wild mushrooms helped Charles and Christine Flood's dimly lit restaurant take last year's county restaurant of the year award. Reports this year confirm masterful treatment of both dishes. Several offerings – including hare and pistachio pâté, and prawns and squid with ginger, garlic and soy sauce – are still extant, too; others are slight variations on a previous theme. The fillet steak with mushroom purée and hollandaise sauce, another long leaseholder, misfired for one visitor in spring. But on the mid-length *carte* have been well-received oysters in a pastry case with hollandaise sauce, and good half a melon filled with lemon sorbet. Clementine pancakes with a Cointreau sauce also impressed. The three-course Sunday lunch has variety. Italy, South Africa and Lebanon now join the mainly French, 50-bottle strong wine list. House French is £5.95. CELLARMAN'S CHOICE: Vina Real Reserva, Rioja 1981, £13.50; Pouilly Fumé 1988, Cailbourdin £12.95.

CHEF: Charles Flood   PROPRIETORS: Charles and Christine Flood
OPEN: Tue to Sun, D; Fri to Sun, L (other days by arrangement)
MEALS: 12 to 2, 7 to 9.30
PRICES: £13 (£19), Set L £7.25 (£11)
CARDS: Access, Visa
SEATS: 36. Private parties: 28 main room. Vegetarian meals. Children's helpings on request. No-smoking area. Music

MATLOCK Derbyshire

map 5

▲ *Riber Hall*

Matlock DE4 5JU
MATLOCK (0629) 582795 COOKING 1
1m off A615 at Tansley COST £21–£38

The fine Elizabethan house is set at the end of a very steep lane that climbs from the village of Tansley up to the top of the scarp above Matlock. Outside is all paving, walls, gate piers and enclosure, enhanced by a wealth of plant life on walls, in troughs and in small corners; inside is a plethora of four-posters and beams, with a good overmantle in the lounge and polished tables in the dining-room. Evening prices for a *carte*, almost too long for the size of the dining-room, are not low, but the shorter set-price lunch menu is fair value and appreciated by visitors. Dishes such as a chicken terrine studded with green beans, mange-tout and mushrooms, given seasoning by a sharpened tomato concasse, or a hot Stilton soufflé with horseradish sauce, have pleased as first courses, while lamb cutlets on a bed of shallots with a red wine and tarragon reduction accompanied by a side plate of crisp vegetables, or fillet of pork with mushrooms and madeira have been acceptable main courses. Duke of Cambridge tart, crystallised fruits in a rich syrup, or a gratin of strawberries with kirsch may close the meal. Menus don't change frequently and presentation may be fussy. The wine list is a very good set of French classics, starting with the excellent Canard Duchêne Champagne, moving through several excellent burgundies, mature clarets, with some good support from other countries. Marking up is erratic; although generally highly priced, bargains can be spotted. House wine: £8.95.

CHEF: Jeremy Brazelle PROPRIETOR: Alex Biggin
OPEN: all week
MEALS: 12 to 1.30, 7 to 9.30
PRICES: £23 (£32), Set L £12.50 (£21)
CARDS: Access, Amex, Diners, Visa
SEATS: 42. Private parties: 34 main room, 14 private room. Car-park, 50 places. Vegetarian meals. Children's helpings. No children under 12. Smart dress preferred
ACCOMMODATION: 11 rooms, all with bath/shower. B&B £63 to £88. Deposit: £35. No children under 12. Afternoon teas. Garden. Tennis. TV. Phone. Scenic [*Which? Hotel Guide*]

MELMERBY Cumbria

map 7

Village Bakery

Melmerby CA10 1HE COOKING 2
LANGWATHBY (076 881) 515 COST £14

On the green of this small Cumbrian village stands a converted barn and house that operates as a bakery first and foremost (with a wood-fired Scotch oven), a daytime café and restaurant and a small craft gallery. Lis and Andrew Whitley run it on organic lines: a few acres at the back produce eggs and chickens, as well as vegetables and fruit for the restaurant; the flour and other imported materials are from organic sources. The restaurant starts with breakfast – their own granola, fresh bread and croissants, Cumberland sausages – before lunch and hot snacks, served all day. The Bakery is by no means vegetarian, so meat dishes such as local lamb baked in the oven are on offer, as well as poached Lakeland char, served with salad. Cumberland rum Nicky, a tart of dates ginger and rum butter, is a long-standing sweet speciality. Cooking is robust and substantial and draws its benefit from good materials; breads and pastry are often lighter than found in such places. The Bakery does not pretend to sophisticated presentation, but food is seemly and the flavours and textures are often true. There are a couple of wines: an organic Zweigelt from Hungary and Gros Plant from Guy Bossard at £5.95, as well as organic Pinkus lager and Aspall and Avalon ciders.

CHEF: Diane Richter   PROPRIETORS: Andrew and Lis Whitley
OPEN: all week, day time only
CLOSED: Sun, Jan and Feb
MEALS: 8.30am to 5pm (L 12 to 2)
PRICES: £8 (£12)
CARDS: Access, Visa
SEATS: 40. Private parties: 25 main room. Car-park, 8 places. Vegetarian meals. Children's helpings. No smoking. Wheelchair access (1 step)

MIDDLE WALLOP Hampshire   map 2

▲ Fifehead Manor

Middle Wallop SO20 8EG   COOKING 3
ANDOVER (0264) 781565   COST £21–£40

Fifehead has been feeding and watering the Wallops for some years and the arrival of chef Hans de Gier from the Netherlands is to be welcomed. The Dutch flag flutters in the forecourt in homage to him and to the owner Margaret van Veelen, a Dutchwoman long resident in Britain. The repertoire is marked by quiet modernism within a classical palette of flavours; it contains no surprises but is executed with consistent accuracy. Accent is given to sauces by capers with turbot, vermouth with scallops, orange with veal, and red wine with venison. Enough variety is given to tried ideas to enliven the appetite, however. A first course, called a trio of salmon, consists of a slab of smoked salmon, a scoop of smoked salmon mousse and a salmon terrine encased in a further thin slice of smoked salmon. 'What was so good about the idea was that it was three variations on one theme; the flavours neither fought with each other nor tried the palate with mere complexity. The flavour of the mousse was pointed and light and the thickness of the cut of plain smoked salmon made it all the easier to appreciate its flavour and the texture contrasts. Unfortunately, the terrine was too close textured and its flavour too bland.' The skill of Hans de Gier may lie in his sauces. Reports have stressed the intensity, for instance, of a wild mushroom sauce with pigeon breasts, 'luscious, yet neither cream-laden nor rich, the flavour and fragrance pure wild mushrooms.' The pigeon, well hung, sat on a pile of spinach. Skill is confirmed by the standard of supporting elements of the meal, vegetables, canapés and petits fours, though coffee on occasion has been lacklustre. A *carte* is flanked by two short set-price menus, that for lunch being appreciably cheaper than dinner. Reports are united in praising the service in all departments – 'how rare it is to meet a waiter (not owner) who is actually pleased to have a customer show an intelligent interest in the food.' The chief merit of the short wine list, which has a few well-chosen clarets, is that it does not pile on the profit. House wine: £8.50.

CHEF: Hans de Gier PROPRIETOR: Margaret van Veelen
OPEN: all week
CLOSED: one week at Christmas
MEALS: 12 to 2.30, 7.30 to 9.30
PRICES: £24 (£33), Set L £15 (£21), Set D £21 (£28)
CARDS: Access, Amex, Diners, Visa
SEATS: 40. Private parties: 16 main room, 14 private room. Car-park, 50 places. Vegetarian meals on request. Children's helpings. Wheelchair access (also WC)
ACCOMMODATION: 16 rooms, all with bath/shower. Rooms for disabled. B&B £45 to £90. Baby facilities. Pets welcome. Afternoon teas. Garden. TV. Phone. Scenic. Doors close at midnight. Confirm by 6

MIDHURST West Sussex   map 3

Hindle Wakes

1 Church Hill, Midhurst GU29 9NY   COOKING 2
MIDHURST (0730) 813371   COST £29

Midhurst inhabitants must eat out a lot: at least five restaurants make a living from this corner of West Sussex. Hindle Wakes is one of the newer ones. Its young owners continue to cook and serve a modern interpretation of 'English' cooking with enthusiasm and fair aplomb. This may encompass hot Sussex goats' cheese with a salad, in the manner of the Roux brothers' twice-baked soufflé (those well-known English cooks) or mutton with red cabbage, haddock mousseline with a horseradish cream, excellent brown-bread ice-cream and burnt creams from Trinity (that is, crème brûlée). Lisa Francis-Lang was once a doctor but gave up the forceps for the pot-hook. Christopher Ross looks after the wines and serves the food. Together, they have created a peach-pretty dining-room, with sponged paintwork and fabrics in close harmony. The pantiled house is at the top of Church Hill – it is best to park near the church itself at the bottom. The menu is never long, about six choices in each course and shorter still at lunchtime. The range of dishes on the regular menus has satisfied readers, and adjustments for individual taste have satisfied further. The cooking, by all accounts, has been steadier this year. The menu clearly states: 'We do not impose a service charge' and the owner says tips are not expected or encouraged. To complement the menu is a well-chosen wine list; its length belies its range which, instead of offering quantity, is more concerned to give real choice. It is an intelligent and sensibly priced list with many winners. House French: £7.50. CELLARMAN'S CHOICE: Savennières, Clos du Papillon 1988, Baumard, £12.25.

'The cooking is so amateurish that one wonders what sort of meals the customers have at home, if they're prepared to leave their firesides and pay good money to eat here.'
On eating in Essex

CHEFS: Lisa Francis-Lang and James O'Meara   PROPRIETORS: Christopher Ross and
Lisa Francis-Lang
OPEN: Tue to Sat, exc Tue L
MEALS: 12.30 to 1.45, 7 to 9.30
PRICES: £17 (£24)
CARDS: Access, Visa
SEATS: 20. Private parties: 16 main room. Children welcome. No cigars/pipes in dining-room. Wheelchair access. Music

Maxine's

| Red Lion Street, Midhurst GU29 9PB | COOKING 2 |
| MIDHURST (073 081) 6271 | COST £14−£26 |

The de Jagers occupy a perfect Midhurst house: half timbered, steep steps to the entrance (and further up to the cloakrooms), an atmospheric and intimate setting right next to the Swan Inn. The short *carte* of half a dozen choices does not change a great deal over the year. Variation is introduced by means of daily specials, including fish. A cheaper option is a set-price menu of simple construction. Although there may be an unchanging litany of salmon, prawns, beef, lamb, duck and pork, in fact there are more exciting things such as wild boar, brains and fresh pasta waiting in the wings, lunchtime and dinner. Robert de Jager can cook skilfully and consistently. Marti de Jager is a natural hostess, one who also single handedly keeps the place running smoothly. They deserve their following. The short wine list, which shows encouraging signs, has some French vins de pays among its more predictable offerings. House wine: Cuvée Georges Blanc at £6.95.

CHEF: Robert de Jager   PROPRIETORS: Robert and Marti de Jager
OPEN: all week, exc Mon and Tue L, Tue D
MEALS: 12 to 2, 7 to 10
PRICES: £17 (£22), Set L and D £9.95 (£14) Service inc
CARDS: Access, Amex, Diners, Visa
SEATS: 27. Private parties: 30 main room. Children's helpings

---

MILFORD ON SEA Hampshire   map 2

Rocher's

69−71 High Street	
Milford on Sea SO41 0QG	COOKING 3
LYMINGTON (0590) 642340	COST £15−£29

This small restaurant by the seaside in a pretty pink building (with a pink inside too) has had emphatic support for quality, value and welcome. It is in some sense a spin-off from Chewton Glen Hotel (see entry, New Milton) in that both Rochers once worked there – and Alain Rocher continues to cook classically inspired and classically correct food. Milford-on-Sea is on most people's road to nowhere, which is part of its charm. A visit to Rocher's thus comes as a discovery, and surprise (or relief) is an important element in people's response to it. There is a *carte* of six choices at each course in the evenings and a slightly shorter menu at a bargain set price on Sundays. The cooking is assured in a repertoire that has been worked on for two or three years now: chilled watercress soup; warm leek mousse; salad of prawns, chicken, pineapple and mayonnaise; feuilleté of spinach tossed with shallots, with a cream sauce; duck with green peppercorns; pheasant with orange and white wine sauce; guinea fowl with raspberry vinegar; crème caramel; coffee crème brûlée; white chocolate mousse with a coffee sauce are all reported with enthusiasm. There is not too much complexity. Materials are good, tastes are direct and generous sauces are properly made. Vegetables are simple so as not to muddy the sauce, but exactly trimmed. The service is enjoyed – 'no dour solemnity, with elderly regulars being particularly made to feel at home.' The wine list's strength is the Loire, with some interesting items at no great cost. Some good claret and burgundies too but prices are higher. There are only half a dozen half-bottles. House French: £6.75. CELLARMAN'S CHOICE: Chinon, Ch. de Ligré 1985, £9.95; Châteauneuf-du-Pape Blanc, Dom. du Terre Ferme 1987, £14.35.

CHEF: Alain Rocher PROPRIETORS: Alain and Rebecca Rocher
OPEN: all week D, exc Tue, and Sun L
CLOSED: 14 Jan to 14 Feb
MEALS: 12.30 to 2, 7 to 10
PRICES: £17 (£24), Set L £10.50 (£15)
CARDS: Access, Visa
SEATS: 30. Private parties: 30 main room. No children under 16. Smart dress preferred. No cigars/pipes in dining-room. Wheelchair access. Music

---

MOLLINGTON Cheshire   map 5

▲ *Crabwall Manor*

Parkgate Road, Mollington CH1 6NE   COOKING 3
GREAT MOLLINGTON (0244) 851666   COST £19–£47

The red brick Tudorbethan house stands a few miles north-west of Chester on the A540 to Parkgate. It is a natural resort for anyone visiting the city, if only for the 'best-value Sunday lunch' in the district. Michael Truelove's cooking has received much praise, although a certain increase in portion size and a slightly heavier saucing have also been observed. Portion size has indeed been a bugbear – people worry as much about being outfaced as starved. A delicate line needs be trod; a delicate line, too, between a full and over-full dining-room. Though reports of service have been more optimistic, there have still been some notable failures, due mainly to press of business. The piano player (of an evening) may do doughty service in calming anticipation but there are limits. Some viewed the prospect of an enlarged dining-room with alarm as the hammering and building work were much in evidence during the spring. None the less, Crabwall does offer comfort in the country-house manner and grace to the act of dining. The food, too, is often assured: some inspectors think it a good candidate for a higher rating. The chef's free offering at the start may be a tiny smoked salmon quiche or a roll-mop and potato salad (superior, of course). First courses take in such dishes as pancakes chock-full with salmon on a chive and white wine sauce; fillets of red mullet on a bed of shredded cabbage with an orange sauce; or a slightly undercooked salad of sweetbreads with mange-tout and an excellent extra-virgin oil and lime juice dressing. Main courses show that added weight already mentioned: lamb with haricot beans and garlic and a demi-glace flavoured with basil; calf's liver cooked with Chinese spices and again a substantial demi-glace; or braised ham on a bed of cabbage and a madeira sauce 'that tasted of madeira'. Desserts have also had much praise: a lemon tart of the lightest pastry with a creamy but not too rich filling, and a terrine of summer fruits with a red berry sorbet running through the the centre and a lemon ice-cream ring surrounding it, all on a sea of red fruit juice and garnished with bilberries, blackcurrants and blackberries. This was 'exhilarating' even if it was October and the berries came from far away: at least they weren't strawberries. Another high point of a meal was a poached pear with cinnamon ice-cream in a red wine sauce with almond toast. Coffee and petits fours are good, too. As one reader put it, 'lunch is very reasonable when it includes splendid duck livers with crisp bacon, a tartlet of quails' eggs, good roast pork, excellent chocolate Genoese sponge and delectable bread-and-butter pudding with apple, as well as the coffee and sweetmeats and delicious canapés with drinks.' The wine list may prove a stumbling point for those on a budget, although the wine waiter, 'with a French accent, though hailing from Cardiff' according to one comment, plays fair by recommending reasonable options rather than 'a nice young Lafite, sir'.

CHEF: Michael Truelove   PROPRIETOR: Carl Lewis
OPEN: all week
MEALS: 12 to 2, 7 to 9.30
PRICES: £26 (£39), Set L £12.95 (£19), Set Sun L £13.90 (£21), Set D £22 (£29),
Set Sat D £25 (£33)
CARDS: Access, Amex, Diners, Visa
SEATS: 120. Private parties: 85 main room, 45 and 100 private rooms. Car-park, 120 places.
Vegetarian meals. Children's helpings. Smart dress preferred. No cigars/pipes in dining-room. Wheelchair access (2 steps; also unisex WC), ramps available. Music. Air-conditioned
ACCOMMODATION: 48 rooms, all with bath/shower. Rooms for disabled. B&B £77.50 to £105. Children welcome. Baby facilities. Afternoon teas. Garden. Snooker. TV. Phone.
Scenic [Which? Hotel Guide]

MONTACUTE Somerset   map 2

▲ Milk House

17 The Borough, Montacute TA15 6XB   COOKING 1
MARTOCK (0935) 823823   COST £13–£25

'Mr Dufton's welcome is unforced and friendly and I feel unhurried as in few other restaurants; the beauty of the old building and enormous fires merely added to the occasion.' Restoration of the handsome stone house was prelude to setting up a very personal restaurant where concern for a proper diet marches in step with a desire to make it taste pleasant. In Elizabeth Dufton's own words: 'That catering goo called "death by chocolate" reflects a general belief that food cannot be really delicious unless it is packed with calories and cholesterol. A customer, who had just told me how hugely he had enjoyed his meal, said, "I do advise you to avoid that dreadful word organic on your menu. It sounds so horribly intestinal, and really, people would never guess if you didn't mention it." So the Duftons gently go on their way, using organic foods where they can, cooking with properly made vegetable oils, serving butter and cream at table but offering smetana (only 10 per cent butter fat) and soya ice-cream to those who want it, and generally considering people's diets 'without belabouring it'. So they cook a simple repertoire: mushrooms à la grecque; soups; smoked mackerel hot-pots; spinach pancakes filled with mushrooms; salmon with sorrel and butter; Barbary duck with an orange zest sauce; ham with a saupiquet; brown sugar meringues with fruit and smetana or cream; banoffi crumble; layered plum purée; smetana and kiwi-fruit are some of the regulars. The last items on that list are proof that the Duftons don't shirk sugar even if they suspect cream. The cooking and presentation are innocent of artfulness to allow flavours to show. Sorbets are good, coffee is not, petits fours or 'bons bons' are interesting combinations of nut pastes, fruit and chocolate. Tipping is 'discouraged'. The carefully selected wine list has some good organic wines, including Rhônes from La Vieille Ferme and red Solopaca, which comes from north of Naples and is made by the Ocone family. Prices for everything are very fair. House wines start at £8.20, though Duboeuf vin de table is the cheapest thing on the list at £5.95. CELLARMAN'S CHOICE: Châteauneuf-du-Pape 1985, Pierre André (organic), £14.90. There is a comfortable smoking room for those who indulge.

CHEF: Elizabeth Dufton   PROPRIETORS: Elizabeth and William Dufton
OPEN: Wed to Sat, D only and Sun L
MEALS: 12.30 to 2, 7.30 to 9
PRICES: Set L £9.50 (£13) to £12 (£15), Set D £14 (£17) to £17.95 (£21). Service inc
CARDS: Access, Visa
SEATS: 24. 3 tables outside. Private parties: 24 main room, 24 private room. Vegetarian meals. Children welcome. Smart dress preferred. No smoking in dining-room. Wheelchair access
ACCOMMODATION: 2 rooms, both with bath/shower. B&B £58 (double room). Deposit: £10. No children under 12. No smoking in bedrooms. Pets welcome. Doors close at 11.30. Confirm by 4

MORPETH Northumberland   map 7

La Brasserie

59 Bridge Street, Morpeth NE61 1PQ   COOKING 1
MORPETH (0670) 516200   COST £12–£34

Upstairs in the plain dining-room, made pretty by curtains and pictures, there is a bewildering range of menus and prices to suit every pocket. The best bet is the Italian side, as one of the original proprietors was Italian and the kitchen still cooks substantial pasta dishes. Alongside these are 'fish 'n' feathers', chicken with prawns, 'surf 'n' turf,' sirloin with deep-fried prawns, or chicken with crab. There is a vegetarian menu as well and a strong oriental influence that comes out in tempura sardines or chicken or pork satay. People find the welcome cheerful. The Italian connection resurfaces on the wine list, where it is the strongest suit and not too highly priced. House Italian: £7.50.
CELLARMAN'S CHOICE: Menetou-Salon, Pelle, £11.50; Ch. Musar 1982, £11.25.

CHEF/PROPRIETOR: R.H. Wilkinson
OPEN: Tue to Sun, exc Sun D
MEALS: 11.30 to 2, 6.30 to 11
PRICES: £20 (£28), Set L £7 (£12) to £12 (£17), Set D £11 (£16) to £16 (£22)
CARDS: Access, Amex, Diners, Visa
SEATS: 50. Private parties: 30 main room, 50 private room. Car-park, 6 places. Vegetarian meals. Children's helpings

---

MOULSFORD Oxfordshire   map 2

▲ Beetle & Wedge

Moulsford OX10 9JF   COOKING 1
CHOLSEY (0491) 651381   COST £21–£44

One reader rates this 'among the best riverside sites in England.' Even those who stop short of eulogy are variously impressed, seduced or simply gratified. The main dining-room is in the converted Victorian hotel, but there is also a boathouse bar with beamed ceilings and grill, and a conservatory. Since eating outside is half the fun of being by the river, the garden is now set up with a barbecue and buffet. Perhaps the boathouse works best, combining informality with sound but simple cooking, a style that Richard and Kate Smith have successfully developed. The food is hardly 'bar snacks' though, since the menu runs to asparagus with hollandaise sauce, crispy duck, grilled lamb kidneys, stuffed aubergine with noodles and chive sauce, cheese and a good selection of sweets. Chargrilling is a favoured technique throughout. Perhaps because it aims higher, the restaurant attracts more critical appraisal. There is enthusiasm for a salad of crab and warm scallops, gazpacho with garlic croûtons, venison with wild mushrooms, and grilled salmon. Roast veal was a nice try in winter, although the result was indifferent. Vegetables are a strong point, often steamed, with plenty of bite. Fish might include oysters and locally smoked salmon, while apple and raspberry crumble or blackcurrant and sloe gin pancake bring up the rear. Service is extremely good, 'friendly without being pushy.' Adnams and Wadworths ales complement a wine list that has been carefully chosen. To make up for the lack of half-bottles, a full bottle will be opened for a premium of 75p – a nice touch. Vintages are good and growers reliable. House French: £7.50. CELLARMAN'S CHOICE: Tokay 1985, Trimbach, £11.50; Châteauneuf-du-Pape, Dom. du Vieux Télégraphe 1985, £22.50.

CHEF: Richard Smith   PROPRIETORS: Richard and Kate Smith
OPEN: restaurant all week, exc Sun D; boathouse all week
MEALS: 12.30 to 2, 7.30 to 10
PRICES: restaurant £28 (£37), Set L and D £19.50 (£26); boathouse £16 (£21)
CARDS: Access, Amex, Diners, Visa
SEATS: 60. 16 tables outside. Private parties: 60 main room, 50 private room. Car-park, 35 places. Vegetarian meals in bar. Children's helpings. Smart dress preferred. No cigars/pipes in dining-room. Wheelchair access (also WC)
ACCOMMODATION: 13 rooms, all with bath/shower. B&B £60 to £70. Children welcome. Baby facilities. Pets welcome. Afternoon teas. Garden. Fishing. TV. Phone. Scenic. Doors close at 12.30. Confirm by 6 [*Which? Hotel Guide*]

MOULTON North Yorkshire	map 7

Black Bull

Moulton DL10 6QJ	
DARLINGTON (0325) 377289	COOKING 3
1m SE of Scotch Corner, 1m from A1	COST £15–£37

'Civilised, renowned for miles around, always busy and well run,' pronounced a reader after a recent visit. Reports continue to indicate high quality and good value. This consistent success appears to have been achieved in the Bull's three principal dining areas: the Victorian-style seafood bar; 'Hazel', the newly renovated Pullman carriage from the Brighton Belle side-tracked in the garden; and the comfortable conservatory. Adulation for the fish and seafood dishes is undiluted. Poached turbot is 'first-rate': a huge portion served with buttered and parsleyed baby new potatoes and fresh calabrese. Ten large Dublin Bay prawns arrive split and grilled with garlic butter. A 'delightful' dressed salad comprised chopped green and spiced red cabbage, diced spring onions and green and red peppers. The few non-fish dishes that are served, like rack of lamb, also earn praise. The same attention is paid to soups and puddings: look out for cream of asparagus to start and crêpes Suzette to finish. Service is relaxed and good humoured. The owners lead double-lives – they are also wine merchants. Thus, choices are at least sound if unexciting, while prices are very fair. House Duboeuf is £6.75. CELLARMAN'S CHOICE: Sancerre, Clos du Chêne Marchand 1988, £14.25; Pouilly Fumé, Ch. de Tracy, 1989, £14.95.

CHEF: Stuart Birkett PROPRIETORS: G. H. Pagendam and Mrs A Pagendam
OPEN: Mon to Sat
CLOSED: 23 to 31 Dec
MEALS: 12 to 2, 6.45 to 10.15
PRICES: £23 (£31), Set L £9.75 (£15)
CARDS: Access, Amex, Visa
SEATS: 100. 4 tables outside. Private parties: 30 main room, 10 and 30 private rooms. Car-park, 80 places. No children under 7. Wheelchair access (also WC)

NAILSWORTH Gloucestershire	map 2

Flynns

3 Fountain Street, Nailsworth GL6 0BL	COOKING 3
NAILSWORTH (045 383) 5567	COST £19–£36

The stylish small menu indicates a 'designer' approach not usually expected in Nailsworth. It extends to decoration and furnishings in the modern building, to the cooking by Garry Flynn, and to the hospitality from Deborah Reid. There are two short set-price menus at dinner with half a dozen options at each course, and a cheaper lunch. It is, however, possible to mix dishes from the two menus, or to order a single course. There is no mistaking the kitchen's modern affiliations with dishes such as chilled slices of roast duck filled with a forcemeat and served with a cherry chutney; breast of guinea-fowl with wholewheat noodles, the leg filled with a mousse of guinea-fowl, on a thyme sauce; salmon ravioli with a basil sauce; a salad of asparagus, bacon and pine nuts; or a teriyaki of squid with ginger, served in a crisp potato basket. Many of these are first courses, but invention does not cease with principal dishes ranging from simple ones like lemon sole with a beurre blanc to John Dory with a smoked salmon sauce and tagliatelle, or desserts such as figs poached with Amaretto with caramel ice-cream and a pear and pomegranate compote, or a dark and white chocolate terrine (a lot of white chocolate). Fish is frequently mentioned, both for its treatment and its quality. The wine list of 40 may be short, but it is very much to the point. It steers an intelligent and middle way and gives good geographical spread: Australasia and the United States get a good show and the major regions of France are chosen impeccably. With the addition of a few meticulously chosen Italians and more halves, this would be a model list. House wine: £6.95. Also available is Cotswold cider by Dr Kit Morris. CELLARMAN'S CHOICE: Pinot Blanc d'Alsace 1987, M. Deiss, £11.45.

CHEFS: Garry Flynn and Robert Drew PROPRIETOR: Garry Flynn
OPEN: Mon to Sat, exc Mon L
MEALS: 12.30 to 2, 7 to 9.30
PRICES: £20 (£27), Set L £13.50 (£19), Set D £18.45 (£24) to £23.95 (£30)
CARDS: Access, Visa
SEATS: 40. Vegetarian meals. Children's helpings. No pipes in dining-room

Markey's Stone Cottage

Old Market, Nailsworth GL6 0BX   COOKING 2
NAILSWORTH (045 383) 2808   COST £30

The Markeys have settled well into this old cottage with beamed ceilings, pink napery, fresh flowers and two small dining-rooms. Ian Markey, who did much of the conversion, is in the kitchen and Anne, who prepares pastry and sweets, looks after front of house with a friendliness that disarms all criticism. One reader protested strongly at our calling it 'bistro cooking' in the last *Guide* and indeed it's more than that. The set menu is priced at under £20, yet the style of the dishes – and there are seven or eight to choose from in each course – belies their relative cheapness. A shortcrust pastry skillet filled with a ragout of lamb's kidney and mushrooms in a madeira sauce; prawn and egg mousse with a fanned avocado and salad leaves in a mustard dressing; breast of pheasant sauté in butter served with red cabbage shallots, and salpicon of the leg in red wine and port sauce; five nuggets of best-end of lamb with rosemary sauce and a tomato filled with an intense mushroom purée; a choice of eight decent cheeses, plus celery; great chocolate pudding – these are some things that have pleased mightily. The sauces are true and forceful, the materials good, the vegetables fresh and carefully prepared. Coffee has not been so good. The wine list has extended by at least 30 bins and is now a proper choice for the food. Mainly French, and reliable, including names like Mardon (Touraine), Passot (Chiroubles), Ch. Patache d'Aux (Médoc) and Gitton (Sancerre), it has a few from Down Under, including Nobilo's Chardonnay. House French is £7.

All details are as accurate as possible at the time of going to press, but chefs and owners often change, and it is wise to check by telephone before making a special journey. Many readers have been disappointed when set-price bargain meals are no longer available. Ask when booking.

CHEF: Ian Markey PROPRIETORS: Ian and Anne Markey
OPEN: Tue to Sat, D only
MEALS: 7.30 to 10
PRICES: Set D £18.95 (£25)
CARDS: Access, Diners, Visa
SEATS: 32. Private parties: 22 main room, 10 and 22 private rooms. No children under 12. Wheelchair access (also WC). Music

---

NAYLAND Suffolk   map 3

Martha's Vineyard

18 High Street, Nayland CO6 4JF   COOKING 3
COLCHESTER (0206) 262888   COST £20

COUNTY OF THE YEAR RESTAURANT

The Warrens met at Gidleigh Park (see entry, Chagford) and worked at the Warehouse Brasserie in Colchester (see entry). Thus do two streams of cooking join into a dish of lemon pasta tossed with smoked chicken and asparagus tips: 'one of the most wonderful dishes I have ever eaten', starts a sentence that goes on too long for this space. This magic confluence occurs in a yellow-washed, brick-paved room with small booths, folksy curtains, paper napkins and crowds that know good value – and smoke like chimneys. 'Nouvelle-Dixie' is what the menu is called by Larkin Warren, who cooks and is American. So you can order 'bread of the day' – (potato and caraway perhaps) – Chesapeake crabcakes with roasted red pepper sauce, chicken shrimp gumbo, and Georgia peach pie for the Dixie element; and pigeon breast on a salad, black pepper pasta in cream with peas, steamed salmon and grey mullet in Pernod sauce, and summer pudding 'Lyn Hall' for the nouvelle. That is just one day's possibles. One meal threw up some faults, caused by too many people, and some dishes that were less than adventurous. The vegetable cookery is inventive and the classical skills very assured, as in a Champagne sabayon for strawberry shortcake. Service is kindly but often hurried. This is a chance for Suffolk. The pleasure of being surprised has made this report warm; we hope the Warrens keep up the standards. The concise wine list is a boon for the bibulous: not much over £10, all good, from all over the world, and enough halves. House wines: £5.50; CELLARMAN'S CHOICE: Muscadet sur lie, Ch. du Plessis 1988, £7.35; Côtes du Rhône, Ch. St Estève d'Uchaux 1988, £8.85.

CHEF: Larkin Warren PROPRIETORS: Christopher and Larkin Warren
OPEN: Tue to Sat, D only
CLOSED: 2 weeks summer, 2 weeks at Christmas, 2 days at Easter
MEALS: 6.45 to 9 (9.30 Fri and Sat)
PRICES: £12 (£17)
CARDS: Access, Visa
SEATS: 45. Private parties: 8 main room. Vegetarian meals. Children's helpings on request. Wheelchair access. Air-conditioned

---

Consumers' Association is planning to publish Out to Eat, *a new guide to budget eating out in restaurants, pubs, cafés, brasseries and so on. Please send reports and recommendations to Out to Eat, FREEPOST, 2 Marylebone Road, London NW1 1YN.*

NEWBRIDGE   Cornwall   map 1

Enzo's

Newbridge TR20 8QH   COOKING 2
PENZANCE (0736) 63777   COST £16–£23

An unlikely assemblage: an Italian restaurant in an old Cornish stone house a few miles from Penzance owned and run by a Scottish family. Tiled floor notwithstanding, the large plant-filled conservatory hardly looks Italian, but it makes a pleasant space for dining. When the Blows arrived in 1986, they reckoned the locals might balk at total change. So antipasto, charged by the portion, and pasta as well as the Italian language still pertain, but the emphasis has shifted from tomato to cream and wine sauces, whipped up by Anne Blows in full view of conservatory diners. (Son Hamish cooks behind stage.) A frequent visitor vouches for continued high standards. Fans of garlic should be well pleased, and local shellfish is incorporated with good results, often in a cream sauce with flat fish as a daily blackboard special. The international dessert trolley also favours cream: there might be tiramisu, Scottish crowdie, oranges in brandy, rum and raisin cheese cake and apple strudel. Italy dominates the wine list with many good growers represented; other countries are treated with respect and prices throughout are fair. House Italian is £6.80.
CELLARMAN'S CHOICE: Santa Cristina, 1988 Antinori, £8.65.

CHEFS: Anne Blows and Hamish Blows   PROPRIETORS: Anne and Bill Blows
OPEN: all week, D only
CLOSED: 2 weeks Feb, 2 weeks Nov
MEALS: 7 to 9.30 (9 Sun)
PRICES: £11 (£19), Set D £11.50 (£16)
CARDS: Access, Amex, Diners, Visa
SEATS: 70. Private parties: 50 main room, 40 private room. Car-park, 25 places. Vegetarian meals. Children's helpings. No-smoking area. Wheelchair access (1 step). Music

NEWCASTLE UPON TYNE   Tyne & Wear   map 7

Dragon House

30–32 Stowell Street, NE1 4XQ   COOKING 2
091-232 0868   COST £9–£34

Stowell Street in Newcastle is the heart of Britain's most northerly Chinatown. New restaurants open regularly and they are proving more successful than other ethnic rivals. Dragon House manages to steer a course between luxury and good value. The decor is certainly aimed at an upmarket clientele, although the Muzak probably isn't. Much of its success is due to the fact that it is a 'hands on' operation run by a young husband and wife team, Barry and Beverley Yu. The main menu makes familiar but promising reading, with its prawn toasts, chicken with ginger and spring onion, deep-fried oysters and sizzling dishes, backed up by a few Szechuan and Shanghai specialities. More enterprising and challenging is the list of chef's recommendations, such as monkfish and roast pork hot-pot with sweetcorn sauce. The restaurant also pays more than lip service to vegetarian cooking, with an extensive menu of non-meat or fish dishes. These have drawn good reports: hot-and-sour soup, home-made spring rolls; stir-fried vegetables in an edible bird's nest; and aubergines with spicy yellow-bean sauce have all been liked. Weekday business lunches are good value, and booking is essential for the Sung Dynasty menu served on Sundays between noon and 3. There is a decent wine list. House French: £6.

CHEF: Colin Ly   PROPRIETOR: Barry Yu
OPEN: all week
CLOSED: 25 Dec
MEALS: 12 to 2, 6 to 11 (noon to midnight Sun)
PRICES: £22 (£28), Set L £4.50 (£9) to £6.25 (£10), Set D £12.50 (£17) to £16.50 (£22)
CARDS: Access, Amex, Diners, Visa
SEATS: 150. Private parties: 70 main room. Vegetarian meals. Children welcome.
Wheelchair access. Music. Air-conditioned

Fisherman's Lodge

Jesmond Dene, NE7 7BQ   COOKING 3
091-281 3281   COST £18−£46

Jesmond Dene is the Hampstead of Newcastle: green trees and space, smart. The Lodge is an echo of *Hansel and Gretel* in Lord Armstrong's town park: pointy Victorian gables and long thin windows; but the car park is full of swish motors. It maintains its position as a good place for a blow-out, with fish the prime attraction. The decoration has lightened in tones but deepened in luxury over a decade and more of life. Reds and greens have changed to sky blue, but the chairs are now upholstered. Comfort rules. Some would say it is overbearing. The Cetolonis are improving the bar area and hope this will enable them to declare the dining-room a smoke-free zone. This description may seem to indicate a preoccupation with interior decorating, but it is done to draw a parallel with the changes in the cooking. The Lodge's long menu, nearly half of which changes daily according to the market, has never been thought lean and spare in execution. Just like the meal as a whole, there are plenty of frills fleshing out the experience: preliminary complimentary confections, rich chocolate petits fours, many assiduous waiters. The food itself has parcels, furbelows and a fair quantity of cream. But just as the paintwork has responded to taste, so the food has lightened, with components broken into sections rather than smothered by a single blanket. Lobster was once either grilled, boiled or Thermidor. The Thermidor is no longer and the extra lobster dish has ginger and spring onions. There is not much truck with new-wave Italian methods: not a lot of saffron, olive oil or fragrant stews. Fish is prime turbot, sole or halibut, not the oily ones, but then the fishing grounds are northern waters, home of the best, meaty, slow-growing flesh. Favourite accompaniments are asparagus and wild mushrooms, the latter also popular with meat dishes like guinea-fowl and duck breast with artichokes and mushrooms or fillet of beef wrapped in Parma ham with a fricassee of mushrooms. There have been moments when execution has not matched the brilliance of the raw material, when the existence of surf'n' turf − fillet steak with a half lobster and garlic − seems to indicate excess. Generally, however, the cooking remains true to its previous form: substantial and enjoying display, but working with, not against, the sea's bounty. The wine list is long enough and has as many

German bottles as white burgundies. None the less it is predominantly French, though there are eight nicely chosen Italian reds and a paltry set from the New World for reinforcement. Few bottles cost more than £20, many less than £15. Halves are scant. House wine is £8.40 a litre. CELLARMAN'S CHOICE: Chardonnay, Mitchelton 1988, £13; Faustino, Gran Reserva 1982, £14.50.

CHEF: Steven Jobson   PROPRIETORS: Franco and Pamela Cetoloni
OPEN: Mon to Sat, exc Sat L
CLOSED: 25 to 28 Dec
MEALS: 12 to 2, 7 to 11
PRICES: £28 (£38), Set L £12.50 (£18) to £14.50 (£20)
CARDS: Access, Amex, Diners, Visa
SEATS: 70. 3 tables outside. Private parties: 14 main room, 14 and 40 private rooms.
Car-park, 45 places. Children's helpings. No children under 6. Smart dress preferred.
No smoking in dining-room. Wheelchair access

Rupali

6 Bigg Market, NE1 1UW	COOKING 1
091-232 8629	COST £23

The emphasis is on food rather than decor. Flock wallpaper and close-packed tables with paper cloths are the price paid for the wide range of dishes from all over the Indian sub-continent. The menu is longer than many a Cantonese one and takes the trouble to explain briefly the difference between, for example, dhansak dishes from the west coast, cooked with lentils, spices and pineapple, and those from Kashmir in the north, made with butter, cream, almonds, cashew-nuts and spices. A baker's dozen of vegetarian dishes include a biriani and a Gujerati thali, and a special mint sauce and pickles are complimentary. The whole enterprise relies heavily upon Abdul Latif's ability to be everywhere at once; when he is not cooking he is supervising service and advising on the choice of meals. Some have felt there is a certain underlying uniformity to the flavours despite the apparent variety promised by the menu. Thursday is Happy Night: a basic three-course meal with a glass of wine and liqueur coffee costs £6.95. Lunch specials and an early eater's menu on some evenings can also keep the bill even lower. House French: £6.25.

CHEF/PROPRIETOR: Abdul Latif
OPEN: all week, exc Sun L
MEALS: 12 to 2.30, 6 to 11.30
PRICES: £10 (£19)
CARDS: Access, Amex, Diners, Visa
SEATS: 54. Private parties: 50 main room. Vegetarian meals. Children's helpings. Music

21 Queen Street

21 Queen Street, Princes Wharf, NE1 3UG	COOKING 3
091-222 0755	COST £18–£43

The initial impact has been sustained, indeed has grown. One reader claimed his meal 'the best in 18 years in the city,' a nice affirmation for modern elegance in the redeveloped quayside area. There is a short *carte*, daily specials from the market – fish mostly – and an affordable fixed-price lunch menu. Although Terence Laybourne was chef at Fisherman's Lodge (see entry) for a number of years, his own restaurant does not place the same emphasis on seafood. Not that it is absent, as one day's offering of Dublin Bay prawns, skate, turbot, salmon, lobster and halibut indicates. A London visitor over three nights, while noticing that service was sometimes less assured than the food deserved, was happy with a terrine of red mullet, 'firm and with defined flavours' on a nicely sharp sauce, ringed by grilled peppers; grilled halibut of stark simplicity and superlative quality accompanied by new potatoes, leeks and green beans 'in architectural arrangements' on a separate plate; and a panaché of lamb which consisted of roast lamb and its offal where 'each offering on the plate had sharply distinct flavours.' Details before and after are exemplary – 'had I known about the petits fours, I would have skipped the sweet course'. The style of the cooking is modern indeed: scallops with a Thai dressing; wild mushroom soup with truffle and foie gras ravioli; veal cutlet with pistachio stuffing and chicory; venison with a sweet-sour sauce and fresh pasta; *terrine* of fresh fruits; or hot rhubarb strudel. The outlandish combos of more avant-garde British chefs, however, do not get an outing here. Monkfish with potatoes and artichokes and a Beaujolais sauce or roasted peppers with anchovies and virgin olive oil show that Newcastle is at one with London in developing earthy flavours and using Italian recipes as a vehicle. House wine from south-western France: £8 and £8.20. A decent, mostly French, wine list is in the making but enthusiasm may be curtailed by the mark-up which pushes better bottles to unreasonable levels. Little to choose from below £12 while excellence in half bottles is virtually absent. Food of this quality deserves more imagination and concern for the wine than is evident here. CELLARMAN'S CHOICE: Auxey-Duresses 1987, J.-P. Diconne, £22; Côtes du Rhône 1986, Guigal, £12.30.

CHEF: Terence Laybourne   PROPRIETORS: Susan and Terence Laybourne
OPEN: Mon to Sat, exc Sat L
CLOSED: 25 and 26 Dec, 1 Jan, bank hols
MEALS: 12 to 2, 7 to 11
PRICES: £27 (£36), Set L £12 (£18)
CARDS: Access, Amex, Diners, Visa
SEATS: 50. Private parties: 50 main room. Children's helpings. Smart dress preferred. No pipes in dining-room

---

NEW MILTON Hampshire   map 2

▲ *Marryat Room,*
Chewton Glen Hotel ♥

Christchurch Road, New Milton BH25 6QS   COOKING 4
HIGHCLIFFE (0425) 275341   COST £26–£56

Chewton Glen is glossy, but the shine comes from many coats of minute attention; it is not spray-on. This is the reason for people's high esteem and acceptance of the superhuman sparkle. The luxury does all work, and there is more taste than in *Dynasty*, so the pictures and the rugs are good ones, the colour schemes have panache, and eating in the latest conservatory extension to the dining area is a treat. Pierre Chevillard offers a stiff set-price dinner with ample choices at each course. At lunch there is a shorter menu costing little more than half. His cooking was described by one reader as 'masculine but not macho'. Although he has espoused the cause of thinner stock sauces and more robust ingredients over bland luxuries, he has not gone so far as the devotees of 'chargrilled red peppers and everything doused in virgin olive oil'. There are, however, bits of truffle in almost all the dishes and the unprepared can still come out feeling surfeited on cream and butter. Lunch may see a more earthy approach than dinner: one day's offering was a shin of beef with horseradish butter, a cassoulet of haricot beans (not flageolet as stated on the menu) and paupiettes of lemon sole. The dinner meats, by contrast, are more 'international' in appeal. Sauces have used specific fish stocks to great success: toothsome Dublin Bay prawns with ceps and a langoustine and cognac sauce, or fillet of salmon with fried onions and rings of squid with a reduction of brown salmon stock, are two instances. Dishes have also balanced richness with clean flavours to great effect, as in scallops marinated in coconut milk and lime served with shavings of lime rind and a salad of mango, or in 'one fat wobbling slab of foie gras, the consistency of bone marrow, straddling a croûte surrounded by half-moons of kohlrabi in a dark translucent duck consomme'. Traditional tastes are catered for, as must be expected in a hotel of this character and clientele: a pastry cornet filled with asparagus, like arrows in a quiver, with a fine hollandaise; or roast beef 'as good as I have ever tasted' with Yorkshire pudding cooked with the immediacy that only happens in the best regulated homes, though with roast potatoes of less than domestic quality and vegetables in puny quantity – save, for one party at least, cherry tomatoes which managed to ornament every plate served them throughout the meal. Buying for Chewton Glen is extravagant and enthusiastic: markets are ransacked, local growers are encouraged and Pierre Chevillard organises mushroom hunts. It shows in the quality of the cheese trolley – English and French, including on one day five different crottins. It shows, too, in the range of fruits served at dessert, as in terrine of exotic fruits, gratin of berry fruits or a feuilleté of warmed strawberries and raspberries – though traditional pastry work, tarte Tatin or a tart with caramelised apple served with a caramel sauce, is of equally high standard. The staff is enthusiastic and have been well trained in the simple skill of assured welcome. The wine list is long and impressive with several strengths, not least a run of Latour and Les Forts de Latour. Price range has some sensitivity to the less than wealthy, though mark-ups are never charitable. Growers are sometimes predictable, for example, Louis Jadot in Burgundy and Jaboulet in the Rhône, but the cellar is large enough to have breadth of choice and older vintages as well as striplings. The sommeliers are well informed and half-bottles have not been ignored. House wine: £8 and £9.10. CELLARMAN'S CHOICE: Borro della Sala 1988, Antinori, £15.75; Rioja Gran Reserva 1980, Paternina, £15.50.

'One sweet on X's pudding list was ''sweets from past and present menus''. One presumes this was a way of describing a a large plateful of titbits, however, it sounded more like a clearing of the third shelf of the fridge.' On dining in Wiltshire

The Guide is totally independent, accepts no free hospitality, and survives on the number of copies sold each year.

CHEF: Pierre Chevillard PROPRIETOR: Martin Skan
OPEN: all week
MEALS: 12.30 to 2, 7.30 to 9.30
PRICES: Set L £22 (£26), Set D £40 (£47). Service inc
CARDS: Access, Amex, Diners, Visa
SEATS: 120. 6 tables outside. Private parties: 20 main room, 6 and 80 private rooms.
Car-park, 100 places. Children's helpings. No children under 7. Smart dress preferred.
No cigars/pipes in dining room
ACCOMMODATION: 58 rooms, all with bath/shower. Rooms for disabled. B&B £155 to £400.
Deposit: one night. No children under 7. Afternoon teas. Garden. Swimming-pool. Tennis.
Golf. Snooker. TV. Phone. Scenic. Doors close at midnight [*Which? Hotel Guide*]

NORTH HUISH Devon

map 1

▲ *Brookdale House* ▮

North Huish TQ10 9NR
GARA BRIDGE (0548 82) 402 and 415

COOKING 3
COST £38

Charles Trevor-Roper prefaces his menu with a note on suppliers. The list is
impressive, and they all come from a radius of 20 miles. It shows what England
can do: quail, barbary ducks, chicken, pork and pork products, herbs, specialist
vegetables and soft fruit, reared or grown by individuals along organic lines;
beef and lamb from an 'organic' butcher; sea fish fresh off the Brixham boats;
dairy goods from local makers or brought to South Devon by a shop
specialising in unpasteurised and soundly produced cheeses. It is possible to
eat sanely yet normally, particularly in restaurants that care. The pity of it is
that for a private individual to replicate this network, more time and driving is
needed than most of us can manage, and very few retailers outside the big cities
offer us the chance of one-stop shopping for this class of material. Brookdale is
a small, slightly gloomy late Victorian house at the bottom of a Devon valley.
Trees, steep slopes, rushing streams press in. It has been done out with a sure
touch, ensuring immediate obliteration of any sense of looming enclosure. The
quality of welcome is palpable: 'Nothing too much trouble; this place offers the
best, from bathrobes to salted almonds.' Terry Rich cooks a daily set-price
menu of half a dozen choices, with salad and cheese an automatic prelude to the
dessert. The cooking is modern but not outré. Sauces run the gamut of cream,
butter, stock reductions and coulis as well as the up-to-date vinaigrettes and
olive oil emulsions. Materials, always praised, combine the expected with the
unfamiliar: one night's main courses were venison, squab, tuna, pork fillet and
lambs' tongues. A spring dinner began encouragingly with appetisers of tiny
lamb kebabs and sweet onion in filo shells, though this party's salted almonds
were not so fine as noticed above. The meal took in a substantial mussel soup
and a boned quail stuffed with an eggy rather than mushroom-laden mousse,
supported by a strong reduction sauce that was thought excellently presented
and well balanced in flavours. Monkfish on a saffron sauce was thought better
than strips of beef with pasta and a green peppercorn sauce that appeared to be
the victim of delay. Three cheeses – Dunsyre Blue, Lancashire and Duet – were
in good condition, balancing strong by mild, with walnut bread and biscuits.
The salad (dressings are always enjoyed) was an interesting selection of leaves.
Puddings included a sticky toffee that needed its sharp orange sauce and a

vanilla bavarois that needed more vanilla. Although the cooking sounds rich, the portions are well judged and sauces are restrained. Some alleviation of the cream-laden English sweet course is found in dishes like a tuile filled with a honey oatmeal and yoghurt ice-cream served with a raspberry coulis, or orange yoghurt mousse with a compote of rhubarb. Charles Trevor-Roper's particular concern is the wine – and the overall well-being of his guests. The list is wholly admirable; not old, but excellently chosen with a catholic view of the world's production. Wines are described accurately and the entire list is presented clearly with a refreshing lack of fuss. The only fault is a disproportionately small choice of half-bottles. Prices of the whole bottles are very competitive and there is no needless weighting of the list towards the rich and famous. The makers, from all countries, are enviable: Marqués de Murrieta white Rioja, Sancerre from Natter, Schlumberger Alsace, a brilliantly starry set of white burgundies including Sauzet and Michelot; every wine a winner. Anyone wishing to see what to drink instead of Chablis, claret and Beaujolais should go for a weekend to try things out; they will be educated as well as entertained.

CHEF: Terry Rich   PROPRIETORS: Charles and Carol Trevor-Roper
OPEN: all week, D only
MEALS: 7.30 to 9
PRICES: Set D £25 (£32)
CARDS: Access, Visa
SEATS: 24. Private parties: 16 main room. Car-park, 15 places. No children under 10. No smoking in dining-room. Wheelchair access
ACCOMMODATION: 8 rooms, all with bath/shower. B&B £68 to £95. No children under 10. Garden. TV. Phone. Scenic. Doors close at midnight. Confirm by 6 [*Which? Hotel Guide*]

NORTHLEACH Gloucestershire   map 2

Old Woolhouse

The Square, Northleach GL54 3EE   COOKING 3
COTSWOLD (0451) 60366   COST £44

'The most French – la vieille France – restaurant in England. Why can no one else be like this?' The Astics run a very small restaurant, just four tables, with a short menu that works to familiar dishes from a slowly evolving repertoire: the format is usually a choice of two first courses, three main dishes and four desserts. Fish is normally the first course, meats the main dishes. Signature productions are of the likes of a fish, maybe brill or sea bass, with a boozy, buttery lobster sauce; rib of beef with mustard sauce; or noisettes of lamb with red wine sauce. Gratin dauphinois is an invariable accompaniment and St Marcellin cheese follows a green salad; desserts major on prune and armagnac tart but there are others. It's 'old France' because it sticks to its last, because Jacques Astic's accent is so noticeable, and because it is in a mind-set that no one, not least the regular customers, seems to wish to change. If you are not regular, you may find it an interesting experience. Some find it daunting; others find it 'a great treat to be spoiled by the Astics.' In other words, it's personal. So, too, is the wine list, mostly over £25 and no house wine to soften the blow. There is usually a bottle available for consumption by the glass.

ENGLAND

CHEF: Jacques Astic PROPRIETORS: Jacques and Jenny Astic
OPEN: Tue to Sat, D only (L by arrangement)
CLOSED: Christmas
MEALS: from 8.15
PRICES: Set D £25 (£37). Service inc
SEATS: 18. Children welcome

Wickens

Market Place, Northleach GL54 3EJ   COOKING 3
COTSWOLD (0451) 60421   COST £30

The setting is a typical Cotswold stone house in one corner of the market place.
It couldn't be more English, and the cooking takes its cue from the
surroundings. Like Hope End (see entry, Ledbury) the theme is renewal, with
the emphasis on local producers and a loyalty to the traditions of British
cookery. The directness, clarity of flavours and good sense of the food continues
to impress visitors. The fixed-price menu runs for four courses and there are
different dishes every week, with a blackboard of additional specials. This
year's recommendations include a salad of warm black pudding with apples
and bacon; veal and ham terrine; Cotswold lamb casseroled with perry and
chargrilled with white onion caper sauce; ox-tail cooked with beer and whole
grain mustard; roast partridge accompanied by onion and parsnip purée; and
fillet of hake coated in oatmeal with a fish and tomato sauce. There is always
something promising for vegetarians, such as lentil and wild rice rissoles or a
pastry case filled with mange-tout and celery served with gado-gado sauce.
Following the main course is a small and wisely chosen selection of British
farmhouse cheeses, perhaps Shropshire Blue, Wackley Farm ewe's cheese and
Sharpham from Totnes. These are kept in perfect condition, presented and cut
from large wedges and, thankfully, explained with proper knowledge. Joanna
Wickens's home-made puddings provide the final flourish: sticky toffee
pudding, superbly light apple dumplings and a prettily done, very simple fresh
apricot and cream cheese tartlet. She also keeps an eye on the dining-room,
playing the unobtrusive hostess and ensuring that service is helpful and
unhurried. Comments on wine are constrained by the owners' firm intention to
list only wines 'from where English is the main language', although a few
French classics are admitted. Eccentric, even a pity, to exclude good matured
Italian and robust Spanish bottles, which continue to provide good value and
quality. Current listings are carefully chosen and offered at fair prices.

CHEFS/PROPRIETORS: Christopher and Joanna Wickens
OPEN: Tue to Sat, D only
MEALS: 7.15 to 9.15
PRICES: Set D £19.75 (£25)
CARDS: Access, Visa
SEATS: 36. Private parties: 22 main room. Vegetarian meals. Children welcome.
No smoking in dining-room. Music

*The text of entries is based on unsolicited reports sent in by readers, backed up by
inspections conducted anonymously. The factual details under the text are from
questionnaires the Guide sends to all restaurants that feature in the book.*

NORWICH Norfolk   map 6

Adlard's ♟

79 Upper St Giles, Norwich NR2 1AB	COOKING 4
NORWICH (0603) 633522	COST £21–£41

Upper St Giles once carried through traffic. Now it has been bisected and truncated by a ring road, making a micro-climate sympathetic to rearing restaurants and small shops unhindered by the ebb and flow of journeys. The deep greens of Adlard's, inside and out, may echo this new peace. The restaurant, apparently once a shop, has more variety of level and angle than that use might imply. This gives privacy without loneliness, noise without intrusion. David Adlard, ruling the kitchen while Mary Adlard rules the tables, has again been in the wars. This year it was a ruptured Achilles tendon that caused him aching confinement to a chair or stool until it mended. This induced him to bring extra staff into the kitchen to make Adlard's a little more like a 'professional restaurant'. The reports sent to the *Guide* show no adverse effects from this change. One reader wrote in October 1989 that 'this was the best meal of the decade.' Adlard's offers a small menu of perhaps four items at each stage which, little by little, change over the days and weeks. The price, which regulars notice rises slightly faster than inflation but not so fast as to make it anything but good value, depends on whether you have three or four courses. The cooking has not changed, though new dishes do give variation. It continues to be classic stuff, with first-rate sauces, convincing by its calm assurance, not by fireworks of display or liberal dowsing in cream or alcohol. David Adlard also has an understanding of texture: 'the chartreuse of duck had layers of lightly braised carrot and savoy cabbage sandwiching shredded duck. With each bite, the caraway or dill seed followed the cinnamon flavour in the sauce in rapid but distinct succession.' Similarly, a fish mousse with a mosaic of mussels was given textural contrast by some parsnips. He is not afraid to work without the prop of fancy ingredients: mussels rather than oysters are the norm and there is little lobster or foie gras, though decently smoked salmon and wild mushrooms do appear. 'My excellent venison, just pink in the middle, had plenty of pleurottes (and some tagliatelle on a separate plate). The sauce was peppery pungent, it left a tingle on the lips, but was not needlessly reduced. It seemed criminal to waste it.' Fish figures strongly, as in brill and scallops with two sauces; scallops with a ginger butter sauce and oyster mushrooms and courgette; turbot with a slightly sweet curry sauce; or sea bass duglthe (with tomatoes, parsley and onions). Vegetables usually include a dauphinois: always properly creamy but often underseasoned. Bread is hot out of the oven, with an estimable crust. Desserts always have an ice-cream or sorbet among them; lemon and lime tarts are always satisfactory, as is most of the pastry work. The trimmings before and after meals are perfunctory to some people, but others find the cheese straws and, perhaps, a crust with smoked cod's roe well made and a pleasant rest from the full production now favoured by chefs more anxious to justify very high prices. Mary Adlard's attentions are never less than assured and informed; her staff are equally hospitable. This is a restaurant that gives abiding pleasure. The wines are a useful selection of good vintages, good growers and very fair prices. From the rich Gran Collegiata Toro 1985 at £8, through a range of very reasonably priced Rhônes, to Italy, briefly but strongly represented by wines with some age such as 1982 Rubesco from Lungarotti, the choice in reds alone is catholic, robust and not trying to impress with blockbuster prices. Sensible but far from boring, anything from this list would please, even if a few of the half-bottles are tiring. House French: £7.

CHEF: David Adlard PROPRIETORS: David and Mary Adlard
OPEN: Tue to Sat, exc Sat L
MEALS: 12.30 to 1.45, 7.30 to 9
PRICES: Set L £13 (£21) to £15 (£23), Set D £23.50 (£32) to £25 (£34)
CARDS: Access, Visa
SEATS: 35. Private parties: 35 main room. Children's helpings on request. Wheelchair access (also WC)

Brasted's

8–10 St Andrews Hill, Norwich NR2 1AD   COOKING 1
NORWICH (0603) 625949   COST £37

The dining-room is tented and 'each table has its own sense of space': an important consideration in the morphology of restaurants. Add to that the sofas and reading matter in the small bar and an evening may go smoothly by. Sensible emphasis is laid on fish: the potted crab, for instance, 'clearly tasting fresh, a good balance of brown and white meat, correctly seasoned with mace,' or fish soup, 'not that monotonous taste of old bones and skins boiled to glue.' Another aspect of the cooking mentioned by one reader was the accuracy of the sauces. A Stilton and port sauce with chicken was neither too strong nor too sweet; a tarragon and Vouvray sauce with lamb chops Villandry was clear flavoured on a good stock reduction base, tasting of the herb stated. Therefore, the ability to cook is not in doubt though there have been evenings when it does not work so well. The *carte* is not too long and seems to have less emphasis on the 'old English' side noticed in previous years. There are moments of preoccupation with numbers at the expense of clarity: a salad had nuts, raisins, apple and spring onions as well as leaves, and an acceptable vanilla ice-cream was interfered with by an endless succession of rather bland fruits. Service is often very good. The wine list is short but supplemented by nearly as many again of 'fine and unusual' wines, including Pétrus 1970 and 1952, a 1964 Gigondas from Jaboulet, and some other odd bottles. It makes for adventure.

CHEF: Paul Chipperfield PROPRIETOR: John Brasted
OPEN: Mon to Sat, exc Sat L
MEALS: 12 to 2, 7 to 10
PRICES: £21 (£31)
CARDS: Access, Amex, Diners, Visa
SEATS: 22. Private parties: 14 main room. Children welcome

'The French head waiter said Hermitage was a Bourgogne, and knocked over my glass of water. I was rushed a little, then ignored a little. They consistently forgot to replenish water and wine, yet had placed both out of my reach.' On inspecting in Sussex

See the inside of the front cover for an explanation of the 1 to 5 rating system recognising cooking standards.

La Folie

20 St John's Maddermarket,
Norwich NR1 1DN
NORWICH (0603) 622777

COOKING 2
COST £34

The name seems to be a reference to the dancing clown on the masthead: Will Kemp, the clown in Shakespeare's company, who danced from London to Norwich for a wager. It is also a punning reference to Maddermarket, where this Georgian house is found close by the theatre. Though it has a French name, French food, French wine list and French menu (which translates *ris de veau* as lamb's sweetbreads and serves the lamb ones, too), it is run by an English couple, of whom the chef, Stefan Dumas, trained in France. So it all hangs together, and even if it is 'not as good as they think it is', it makes a welcome addition to the Norwich scene. There are moments when chaos reigns – 'we were pleased the guitarist played so well as we waited 45 minutes for our order to be taken' – but most have enjoyed the fresh enthusiasm of the young team when the cogs mesh more smoothly. The short *carte* is quintessential Anglo-French: salade lyonnaise, feuilleté of fish, beef in pastry, saddle of lamb with ratatouille, gratin of fruits, iced chocolate soufflé with orange sauce. It can often be accurately cooked and robustly sauced: good venison with pine kernels and raisins; lemon sole nicely poached with a deep shrimp sauce; leek and mushroom tart of great flavour; a roast pheasant rather too liberally sauced with a brandy bottle but partnered by a well seasoned cabbage and bacon chartreuse. The last stage of the meal has not yet received so many plaudits and coffee may be poured in the kitchen, not at table. The wine list remains French, French, French, and seems to offer two half-bottles (of white wines) among its four dozen bottles. House wine: £7.45. There is one dining-room for non-smokers and two for the rest. The proprietors will often cater for theatregoers if prearranged.

CHEFS: Stefan Dumas and Ian Carter   PROPRIETORS: Stefan and Polly Dumas
OPEN: Mon to Sat, exc Sat L
CLOSED: 1 to 15 Jan
MEALS: 12 to 2.30, 7 to 10
PRICES: £18 (£28)
CARDS: Access, Amex, Visa
SEATS: 46. Private parties: 22 main room, 12,14 and 20 private rooms. Vegetarian meals. Children's helpings. No-smoking in one dining-room. Wheelchair access (2 steps). Music. Air-conditioned

Marco's

17 Pottergate, Norwich NR2 1DS
NORWICH (0603) 624044

COOKING 1
COST £23–£35

Marco Vessalio's new livery is black and gold, 'the dining-room is even slightly plush,' and the old second dining-room has been converted to the Marco Polo bar/lounge in a major refurbishment of this long-established Norwich institution. The menu has shortened, but still includes old favourites such as cannelloni, a fish stew 'genovese', or salmon baked en papillote with vegetables and a herb butter. There are many regulars who swear by his cheery welcome and his wife's capable management of the front of house. The price of the set lunch has increased sharply. All wines are Italian with a few interesting other bottles, but there is a dearth of the new names that have emerged in recent years. House Italian: £7.

CHEF/PROPRIETOR: Marco Vessalio
OPEN: Tue to Sat
CLOSED: 20 Aug to 20 Sept
MEALS: 12.30 to 2, 7.30 to 10
PRICES: £20 (£29), Set L £16 (£23)
CARDS: Access, Amex, Carte Blanche, Diners, Visa
SEATS: 20. Private parties: 12 main room, 16 private room. Vegetarian meals. Children's helpings. Wheelchair access. Music

---

NOTTINGHAM Nottinghamshire map 5

Les Artistes Gourmands/ *Café des Artistes* ♀

61 Wollaton Road, Beeston,
Nottingham NG9 2NG
NOTTINGHAM (0602) 228288 and 430341

COOKING 2
COST £20–£35

Eddy Keon has been a central figure on the Nottingham restaurant scene for a number of years, and his well-established venue a couple of miles out of the city continues to evolve. Most of the inconsistencies reported in the last *Guide* have been ironed out, now that Mark Ashmore has been promoted to head chef and Sylvie Navoret is restaurant manager. Eddy Keon puts his faith in local suppliers and producers: most of the meat, poultry and fish is from outlets in Nottingham; game from the Victoria market has recently been supplemented by geese from a farm near Grantham; the restaurant's vegetable and herb garden is moving over to organic production. From further afield there is wild boar from Sussex and French cheese produced by Rouzaire Dairy. This translates into a regular changing menu of classic and modern French dishes. Terrine of pigeon breast with prunes; quenelles of smoked salmon served on chicory leaves with watercress sauce; and duck breast with blackcurrant sauce show the style. A French pâtissier produces 'hand-crafted desserts' such as hazelnut choux with chilled dark chocolate sauce. A feature of the menu is the expanding list of high-fibre, low-fat dishes, ranging from poached chicken breast with ratatouille to timbale of plaice with crab mousse and cucumber sauce. Café des Artistes is run in tandem with the restaurant, but the emphasis is on cheaper, bistro-style dishes and an informal atmosphere. Children are encouraged. Pasta is supplemented by smoked salmon crêpes, sauté lamb with fresh mint and sirloin steak with port sauce. The menu clearly states that there is no service charge. The concise and intelligent restaurant wine list has good French growers and properties that just merits a glass award. Half-bottles are few and the hints of wine-making beyond the French border could be expanded. The café has a short but good list. House French: £9.40.
CELLARMAN'S CHOICE: Burgundy Dom. Roche, 1988 £13.90; Gigondas 1983, Jaboulet, £13.80.

CHEF: Mark Ashmore   PROPRIETOR: Eddy Keon
OPEN: Mon to Sat, exc Mon L and Sat L
CLOSED: 1 week Jan, 1 week Aug
MEALS: 12 to 2, 7 to 10
PRICES: Restaurant £22 (£29), Set L £15.90 (£21), Set D £19.90 (£25) to £22.90 (£28). Café
£15 (£20). Service inc
CARDS: Access, Amex, Diners, Visa
SEATS: 60. Private parties: 35 main room. Vegetarian meals. Children's helpings.
No smoking. Wheelchair access. Music

Loch Fyne Oyster Bar

17 King Street, Nottingham NG1 2AY	COOKING 1
NOTTINGHAM (0602) 508481	COST £17

'Returning the oyster to its nineteenth-century popularity and affordability
should be one of the great gastronomic crusades,' writes one enthusiast. Quite
right too. Every major city should support a place like this. What is surprising
is that the Oyster Bar and Seafood Shop is right in the heart of the landlocked
Midlands, a couple of minutes' walk from the monumental stonework of
Nottingham's town hall. This is a modest branch of the enterprising parent
company in Cairndow in Scotland (see entry) and most of the ingredients are
air-freighted from there overnight. Outside is maritime blue paintwork; inside
are hefty pine tables and chairs, and oyster plates on the walls. Seafood is the
main business – excellent-value oysters, langoustines, clams, crab and plump
mussels tossed with white wine, cream and onions, excellent gravlax and
smoked fish. There isn't much real cooking apart from grilling kippers,
preparing soup and making dishes such as salmon with cucumber sauce. The
style is flexible: call in for a full meal, open sandwich or even a cup of tea and a
cake. Service is casual and relaxed. A short well-chosen wine list offers plenty
of appropriate and affordable drinking. House French: £5.95. More reports,
please.

CHEFS: Mark and Jeanne Hatton   PROPRIETOR: Andrew Lane
OPEN: Mon to Sat
CLOSED: bank hol Mons, 25 Dec
MEALS: 9am to 8.30pm
PRICES: £10 (£14)
CARDS: Access, Visa
SEATS: 35. Private parties: 40 main room. Children's helpings. Wheelchair access. Music.
Air-conditioned

Ocean City

100–104 Derby Road,	
Nottingham NG1 5FB	COOKING 2
NOTTINGHAM (0602) 475095	COST £10–£37

Nottingham's minor Chinese revolution continues, and Ocean City is still the
front-runner of the new wave. It set the style in 1986 and its menu has
spawned more than a handful of imitators. The cavernous, labyrinth of a
dining-room has its front entrance in Derby Road and a back door in Woolaton

Street. It offers all kinds of options, although the waiters can make assumptions about the eating habits of Western customers and direct them towards 'accessible set meals' rather than the authentic output of the kitchen. The full English menu of around 150 dishes has a big showing of sizzling specialities (including Ocean City's signature dish: monkfish with chilli and black-bean sauce), plus edible bird's nests, seafood, and stuffed duck. Beyond that, it is worth investigating the enterprising list of esoteric Cantonese specialities such as braised whelks with ginger and spring onion, stewed belly pork with yams, crabmeat braised in milk, and grilled chilli and green pepper stuffed with minced pork and prawns. Musical vegetarians might consider trying 'Chinese guitar tofu with seasonal vegetables'. There's also a separate menu, written in Chinese characters, containing some excellent one-plate rice and noodle dishes. And there's more. At lunchtime a dim-sum menu, controlled by a dim-sum chef from Hong Kong, brings in lecturers from the nearby university, as well as Chinese students with some spare cash to spend on a few baskets of ginger beef ball dumplings, stuffed bean curd roll and char-siu buns.

CHEF: Mr Ly   PROPRIETORS: Dragon Wonder Ltd
OPEN: all week
CLOSED: 25 Dec
MEALS: 12 to 3, 6 to 11.30 (noon to midnight Sat, noon to 10.30 Sun)
PRICES: £23 (£31), Set L £4.50 (£10), Set D £9.50 (£16) to £18 (£25). Minimum £8.50 after 6pm
CARDS: Access, Amex, Diners, Visa
SEATS: 250. Private parties: 200 main room, 80 and 120 private rooms. Vegetarian meals. Children welcome. Wheelchair access (also WC). Music. Air-conditioned

Saagar

473 Mansfield Road, Sherwood,
Nottingham NG5 2DR
NOTTINGHAM (0602) 622014

COOKING 1
COST £9–£24

Saagar (an adjustment of spelling from the last *Guide*), continues its popular way in quite elegant surroundings with the prospect of a second dining-room round the corner. The list of specialities changes against a steady backdrop of predominantly north Indian cookery. Readers especially praised a tandoori meal of boti lamb kebab followed by Makhani chicken tikka, chicken tikka masala, aloo gobi, aloo paneer, nan, puri and rice. Good accounts have also been recorded of korma chicken nicely sharpened with mint. The baking and the generosity of the servings are mentioned too.

CHEF: Amjaid Habib   PROPRIETOR: Mohammed Khizer
OPEN: all week
CLOSED: 25 Dec
MEALS: 12 to 2.30, 5.30 to 12.30am
PRICES: £11 (£20), Set L £4.15 (£9), Set D £12 (£18)
CARDS: Access, Amex, Visa
SEATS: 45. Private parties: 45 main room. Car-park, 6 places. Vegetarian meals. Children's helpings. No pipes in dining-room. Music. Air-conditioned

OAKHAM Leicestershire

map 5

▲ *Whipper-in*

Market Place, Oakham LE15 7DT
OAKHAM (0572) 756971

COOKING 2
COST £17–£35

The image of a country-town hotel is quite well preserved: solid furniture, old prints and dark carpets. The menu, which may include veal stuffed with crab, could thus be thought surprising, though such dishes are balanced with a range of plain grilled meats. The pattern has not changed: a short set-price daily menu, an eight-choice *carte* and that selection of grilled dishes. Cooking is quite complex: noisettes of lamb in pastry with ham and spinach on a garlic sauce; asparagus tips with a chervil and lemon butter, with a pastry case and woodland (more like farmland) mushrooms; or salmon with Greenland mussels, a lattice work of pastry and a saffron sauce. Menu descriptions tend to be florid, as do some of the compositions on the plate. None the less, the cooking can work very well, even if herbs proclaimed on the menu are often fugitive in the eating. Sauces may be correctly made, sometimes evoking the shores of the Mediterranean more than nearby Rutland Water, as in collops (small, too) of monkfish with a tomato and basil sauce and home-made noodles. A meal in the summer revealed that some of the complexities interfered with potential success though vegetables that included a 'terrine' of carrot and swede with a core of baby sweetcorn was witness to the fact that effort and forethought can also pay dividends. A bi-coloured chocolate mousse virtually solid with gelatine was not so successful. Service is usually adequate, but has broken down under pressure. The wine list is not too long nor too dear; the price range is carefully thought out and some decent growers and properties figure, such as the generic Bordeaux from Ch. Lynch Bages, Cuvée Michel Lynch; Duboeuf Beaujolais; Ch. Rahoul and Australians from Delatite. House Duboeuf is £7.50.

CHEFS: Paul Cherrington and David Toffiluck PROPRIETORS: FSI Plc
OPEN: all week
MEALS: 12.30 to 2, 7.30 to 9.30
PRICES: £21 (£29), Set L £11.95 (£17), Set D £18.95 (£25)
CARDS: Access, Amex, Diners, Visa
SEATS: 45. 3 tables outside. Private parties: 16 main room, 14 and 40 private rooms. Vegetarian meals. Children's helpings. Smart dress preferred. Wheelchair access. Music ACCOMMODATION: 24 rooms, all with bath/shower. Rooms for disabled. B&B £68 to £90. Baby facilities. Pets welcome. Afternoon teas. TV. Phone [*Which? Hotel Guide*]

OLD BURGHCLERE Hampshire

map 3

Dew Pond

Old Burghclere, RG15 9LH
NEWBURY (0635) 27408
off A34, 3m W of Kingsclere

COOKING 3
COST £22–£35

The restaurant has a marvellous setting, for which you are not prepared by the approach down a narrow lane. Once through the cramped bar into the pair of dining-rooms, one an extension to the house, the rolling countryside sweeps across in vivid yellows and viridian. On the left, Watership Down; on the right, Beacon Hill; in the centre, many sheep. The Marshalls run this as a family enterprise: Keith and Julie are in the kitchen, father is in the dining-room, brother in the bar. The set-price menu is kept short and the food reflects the merits of concentration and freshness. The style is neo-classical and gimmicks are few, though there are touches of the modern love of sweetness and extreme flavours to point up a dish. These are kept in check and seem well handled. There is a consistent emphasis on game and on plain roast meats with sauces. A meal in the summer afforded nothing more gamey than rabbit or roe deer. The rabbit was in a light terrine, pungently accompanied by a plum jam as astringent as cranberry sauce. The roe deer was a quickly roasted saddle with caramelised apples and a calvados sauce mounted with butter. Other components of the meal included a filo sandwich of oyster mushrooms with a breadcrumb and Stilton crust, sitting on a chive beurre blanc. Star of the show was best end of lamb with a high-flavoured ratatouille in a tart case, showing that Keith Marshall can slice a dice as small as anyone but can still keep some taste in. The sauce, a light gravy made luxurious with mint and honey, is finely crafted. British cheeses and a Brie can be eaten with decent home-made bread, and desserts will entice the appetite to return. This is a serious kitchen, doing it all itself despite its isolation. The wine list is kept short, mainly French, but with some New World support. Burgundies are best, but prices are not low. House wine: £8 and £10.

CHEF: Keith Marshall   PROPRIETORS: Keith and Julie Marshall
OPEN: Tue to Sat, exc Sat L
CLOSED: 2 weeks mid-Aug, first 2 weeks Jan
MEALS: 12 to 2, 7 to 10
PRICES: Set L £14.50 (£22), Set D £21.50 (£29)
CARDS: Access, Visa
SEATS: 40. Private parties: 50 main room, 25 private room. Car-park, 25 places. Vegetarian meals. No children under 12. Smart dress preferred. Wheelchair access (also WC)

OLDBURY   West Midlands   map 5

▲ Jonathans

16 Wolverhampton Road,
Oldbury, B68 OLH   COOKING 2
021-429 3757   COST £25–£46

The theme restaurant with a vengeance, this is Heritage Britain in action. Note there are now bedrooms. The menus are priced in old money, save that three shillings and five pence actually means £3.50. The menus also celebrate Victorian cooking, save that nearly every dish accords with popular modern prejudices of acceptable combinations: steak stuffed with a Cheddar and Stilton mousse or duck with a highly fruited sauce. Descriptions would make Dickens blench: Trout Bowes-Lyon is 'designed to meet with the approval of Her Majesty the Queen Mother, being the freshest of freshwater trout completely boned and bi-stuffed with two delicate mousses.' If you can bear all this, the staff are anxious to please and the dining-room is a masterpiece of pastiche. Materials are good and the food is competently cooked, though the flavours often seem to revolve around cheese, fruit and pickles, and some combinations – asparagus wrapped in smoked salmon served with prawns – have little justification save status. A cheese and hazelnut cake made with oatmeal and butter; a gratin of mackerel and apple; chicken and duck salad with pickled raspberries; fillet steak set in a Yorkshire batter pudding with 'carrack' sauce – 'the essence of Mrs Beeton'; pan haggerty; a good spotted dick; chocolate pot with cinnamon cream have received honourable mention. Reference has also been made to the herb bread, the need for the appetite of a Titan, often good pastry, not so nice petits fours and the multitude of deals open for one sort of customer or another: businessmen's club, gourmet club, weekenders, and so on. In the context of the West Midlands, this is a useful resource and, while the concept is rather flim-flam, the food is enthusiastic and fair. The wine list takes in the world, even if the emphasis is on France. Prices are not too high, though best buys come from outside the clarets. Some good properties include Javillier, Juillot and Guigal; the Luncheon Club list fleshes out the cheaper sections. House Duboeuf is £6.50.

CHEFS: Jonathan Bedford and Graham Bradley   PROPRIETORS: Jonathan Bedford and Jonathan Baker
OPEN: all week
MEALS: 12 to 2 (4 Sun), 7 to 10.30
PRICES: £30 (£38), Set L and D £19.50 (£25)
CARDS: Access, Amex, Diners, Visa
SEATS: 160. 10 tables outside. Private parties: 60 main room, 6, 10, 18 and 30 private rooms. Car-park, 10 places. Vegetarian meals. Children's helpings (Sun L). Children restricted. No smoking till adjacent tables finish meal. Wheelchair access (also WC). Music
ACCOMMODATION: 10 rooms, all with bath/shower. Rooms for disabled. B&B £65 to £85. Afternoon teas. Snooker. TV. Phone. Confirm by 4

ORFORD Suffolk   map 3

Butley-Orford Oysterage

Market Hill, Orford IP12 2PQ   COOKING 1
ORFORD (0394) 450 277   COST £20

Near the church in the middle of the square, the Oysterage is a café-cum-restaurant on two floors, with a shop next door for home supplies. It continues in the good-natured hands of the Pinneys, mother and son, who themselves ensure that the oysters, smoked eel and salmon, lobster and fish are tip-top quality and laudably fair in price. Surroundings are bare – in truth, rudimentary – which makes the supreme freshness, plumpness, succulence and quivering readiness of the product the more enticing to consume. 'We shared the lobster, caught that morning, slightly warm still from the cooking'. Others, however, sound warning notes about the standard of sauce making, the poor quality of the bread and the unimaginative nature of the salads. 'While they serve wonderful fish, they cannot actually cook', is the way one reader put it. So, go there for the oysters, etc, etc. The wine list is short but well judged with plenty of halves and not exorbitant.

Report forms are at the back of the book; write a letter if you prefer.

CHEF: Mathilde Pinney   PROPRIETORS: Mathilde Pinney and William Pinney
OPEN: all week May to Oct; L all week and Sat D Nov to Apr
MEALS: 12 to 2.15, 6 to 8.30
PRICES: £11 (£17). Licensed, also bring your own: corkage £2.50
SEATS: 75. Private parties: 25 main room. Car-park, 20 places. Children welcome.
Wheelchair access (also WC)

OXFORD Oxfordshire   map 2

Al-Shami

25 Walton Crescent, Oxford OX1 2JG	COOKING 1
OXFORD (0865) 310 066	COST £23

The residential street looks unlikely; persevere and you'll find the popular Al-Shami, the dozen or so linen covered tables tightly packed into the corner-site dining-room with brick walls. The bowl of uncut salad vegetables, delivered after you order, is copious, as are the platefuls of the ensuing Lebanese specialties. A baked aubergine, chickpea and tomato dish was enjoyable, smoky and moist; fried lambs' sweetbreads, and minced lamb kebabs with cracked wheat and pine kernels were also good. Boned, marinated and chargrilled chicken, deemed succulent, is a lighter option. Scented pastry sweets from the trolley get snapped up early. One reader, who may have hit a bad night, was disappointed by the sullen welcome, 'tough, grey and tasteless' lamb, and the vegetarian options. The mainly Lebanese wine list contains several vintages of Ch. Musar, and a smattering of European wines. House wine starts at £5.50. CELLARMAN'S CHOICE: Ch. Musar, 1982, £12.

CHEF/PROPRIETOR: Mimo Mahfouz
OPEN: all week
MEALS: noon to midnight
PRICES: £11 (£19). Cover £1
SEATS: 40. Private parties: 60 main room. Vegetarian meals. Children welcome. Wheelchair access (also WC). Music

---

▲ Bath Place Hotel

4–5 Bath Place, Holywell Street,	
Oxford OX1 3SU	COOKING 3
OXFORD (0865) 791812	COST £19–£37

It might be a doll's house, made up as it is of three or four small interlinked seventeenth-century cottages that stand at the bottom of a court off Holywell Street. The major crowds peel off halfway down this alley to the Turf Tavern. The hotel stays demurely behind a low fence and wicket gate. Because of its origins, no room is large and all are low. Doors and passages lead to unexpected quarters; a man is seen on the right-hand side and next pops up on the left. A short menu has three to five choices in each course; at lunchtimes the choice is shorter. The kitchen's approach is redolent of nouvelle cuisine in as much as portions are spare indeed. It has also taken modern manners to such a point that carbohydrate levels are extremely low. It is thus possible to leave feeling hungry, yet unable to eat more protein. Sauces are light and occasionally light in flavour, but cooking is generally accurate and perhaps needs the touch of popularity to bring it alive. A small breast of flavourful chicken is roasted and placed atop a pile of tagliatelle with a few girolle mushrooms; the flavours, from cooking and a very light sauce, are exact. Similarly, a tiny piece of salmon sits on virgin olive oil scented with basil and is made eloquent by simple ingredients and good cooking. Soup, chilled leek and potato, is unsuccessful by contrast. Main dishes include monkfish with a mustard and tarragon sauce, restrained enough to allow the fish full value, but almost too bashful through light seasoning. Rack of lamb with a rosemary and madeira sauce is accompanied by fine potatoes (but only two minuscule torpedoes) roasted with garlic, and these are remembered longer than the main component of the dish. Raspberries layered with shortbread is good; purée of bitter chocolate is not bitter at all; lemon tart is a mite solid. When this place was first reported for the 1990 *Guide*, it was riding high on a French chef and publicity. It has since drawn in its horns and moderated some of its prices, but remains committed to fair cooking. We remarked then that Oxford has a way of stifling restaurants as well as nurturing them. In a sense, this one is still struggling for breath. The wine list remains largely French. House wine: £7.50.

CHEF: Graham Corbett   PROPRIETORS: The Fawsitt family
OPEN: Tue to Sun, exc Sun D
CLOSED: late Jan to early Feb, 2 weeks Aug
MEALS: 12 to 2.15, 7 to 9.30 (9.45 Fri and Sat)
PRICES: Set L £12.95 (£19), Set D £24.50 (31). Service inc
CARDS: Access, Amex, Carte Blance, Diners, Visa
SEATS: 34. 4 tables outside. Private parties: 10 main room, 10 private room. Car-park, 4 places. No children under 10. No cigars/pipes in dining-room. Music. Air-conditioned
ACCOMMODATION: 8 rooms, all with bath/shower. B&B £65 to £95. No children under 10. TV. Phone. Doors close at 10. Confirm by 10:30am [*Which? Hotel Guide*]

Cherwell Boathouse ♥

Bardwell Road, Oxford OX2 6SR	COOKING 1
OXFORD (0865) 52746	COST £17–£22

Fairly basic surroundings in fine circumstances: watching the punts on the river. Set-price menus at lunch and dinner are short, not expensive, and if not geared to students, then certainly to lovers of the simple. Tomato salad with a herb dressing; Greek salad with feta cheese; soups; salmon mayonnaise; pork with wild mushroom sauce; always a vegetarian dish; gooseberry crumble and raspberries and cream are typical of summer fare. Many would agree that the simpler the better, for these can be accurately executed. To accompany the food is a wine list equally fairly priced. Although not long, it has rarities among old clarets and very aptly chosen wines from the merchants Morris and Verdin. Burgundies from Rion, Leflaive and Comte Lefon; Alsaces from Ostertag; Californians from Au Bon Climat are just a few of a glittering throng. They would make a punter's heart beat faster. The range of prices is remarkable with much below £10, which may be some compensation for a paucity of half-bottles. At lunch, snacks such as steak sandwiches are available, which then

makes it the best wine bar in town. House French: £5. CELLARMAN'S
CHOICE: Pinot Gris 1986, Ostertag, £11.50; Meursault, Goutte d'Or 1987,
Comte Lafon, £28.

CHEF: Gerard Crowley   PROPRIETOR: Anthony Verdin
OPEN: Tue to Sun, exc Sun D
CLOSED: 4 days at Christmas, L Oct to May
MEALS: 12 to 2, 7 to 10
PRICES: Set L £12.50 (£17), Set D £13.50 (£18). Service 10% for parties of 6 or more
CARDS: Access, Amex, Diners, Visa
SEATS: 50. 5 tables outside. Private parties: 50 main room. Car-park, 12 places. Vegetarian
meals. Children's helpings. Wheelchair access (1 step; also WC)

15 North Parade

15 North Parade, Oxford OX2 6LX	COOKING 1
OXFORD (0865) 513773	COST £17–£34

There has been a change, including a change of chef. The ambience has become
more relaxed and less formal, and a firm break has been made from nouvelle
cuisine. The approach of the new chef, Stanley Matthews, is perfectly modern
though: swordfish chargrilled with beans, red onions and virgin olive oil
might come from a Californian beach restaurant, just as loin of veal with lentils
and tarragon might be on a London brasserie menu. A fixed-price option has
also been introduced in the evenings, a gesture for customers who have less
money to spend on eating out than formerly. Fifty wines have been chosen
carefully and intelligently from across the world. Such a list makes the
suggested invitation 'to bring your own fine wine and we will charge our
house wine price' perhaps unnecessary, especially as prices are fair. House
wine: £7.

CHEF: Stanley Matthews   PROPRIETOR: Georgina Wood
OPEN: all week, exc Sun D
MEALS: 12 to 2, 7 to 10
PRICES: £21 (£28), Set L £10.75 (£17), Set D £15.75 (£22). Licensed, also bring your own:
corkage £7.
CARD: Access, Visa
SEATS: 55. Private parties: 55 main room. Vegetarian meals. Children's helpings.
Wheelchair access (also WC). Air-conditioned

Liaison

29 Castle Street, Oxford OX1 1LJ	COOKING 1
OXFORD (0865) 242944	COST £20–£35

At last, a decent Chinese restaurant in Oxford. The setting is a sparsely
decorated black-and-white Jacobean building that once housed a French
restaurant. The menu casts its net wide for Cantonese, Pekinese and Szechuan
dishes, and first reports suggest that the cooking is fresh and creditable.
Steamed scallops are either 'garlic-juicy' or cooked with black-bean sauce;
deep-fried duck comes with a contrasting crust of minced prawns; and fish
slices are braised with oyster sauce. Otherwise the menu takes in stir-frys and
sizzlers, grilled bean curd and aromatic Mongolian lamb. Despite some

TRY WHICH?
MAGAZINES FREE!

As well as books and Action Packs, Consumers' Association also publishes magazines: Which?, Gardening from Which?, Which? way to Health and Which? Wine Monthly.

If you'd like a free trial of any of these magazines, simply complete and return this card to us, post free, and we'll send you details.

☐ Which?

☐ Gardening from Which?

☐ Which? way to Health

☐ Which? Wine Monthly

(tick those that interest you)

Name (Mr/Mrs/Miss/Ms)_____

Address_____

_____

_____

_____Postcode_____

BFL1

Consumers' Association
FREEPOST
Hertford X
SG14 1YB

language problem, service is extremely polite. Wines are a decent selection, fairly priced. House wine £6.50.

CHEF: Kok Leung Lam   PROPRIETOR: Timmy Tsang
OPEN: all week
CLOSED: 3 days at Christmas
MEALS: 12 to 3 (4 Sun), 6.30 to 11.30 (12 Fri and Sat)
PRICES: £14 (£20), Set D £13.75 (£22) to £20 (£29). Service 10% for parties of more than 5
CARDS: Access, Amex, Visa
SEATS: 90. Private parties: 60 main room, 18 private room. Vegetarian meals. Children's helpings. Wheelchair access (2 steps). Music

Munchy Munchy

6 Park End Street, Oxford OX1 1HH   COOKING 2
OXFORD (0865) 245710   COST £15

A refurbished, larger Munchy Munchy gives up the queues and blackboard of previous years for table service and a menu – still short and fast changing. The place remains very popular indeed. There has been no decline in Ethel Ow's cooking of Indonesian and Malaysian food: six or seven dishes, perhaps a chicken, beef and lamb, a vegetable stir-fry, a fish and a couple of prawn items, all accompanied by plain rice to mop up the fragrant juices at once rich, sharp and sweet from the liberal use of coconut, tamarind, lime leaves and lemon grass. This cuisine, for example a recipe of squid, papaya, apple, mint, lime and chilli, achieves the combination of fruit and fish or meat very eloquently, to the benefit of all ingredients. Ices and fruits are the only desserts. Aspects of the service are nearly peremptory, perhaps from years of dealing with students. Ten per cent service is added to people's bills if they have booked. This discrimination, practised in a few restaurants, is incomprehensible. If you want wine, bring the bottle with you for the menu says 'We cannot allow you to occupy tables whilst going out to get drinks.' There is separation of smokers and non-smokers.

CHEF: Ethel Ow   PROPRIETORS: Tony and Ethel Ow
OPEN: Tue to Sat
CLOSED: 3 weeks Aug, 3 weeks Dec
MEALS: 12 to 2, 5.30 to 10
PRICES: £8 (£12). Minimum £5. Service 10% on bookings and parties of 5 or more.
Unlicensed, but bring your own: corkage 50p per person
SEATS: 60. Private parties: 10 main room. No children under 6 Fri and Sat D. No-smoking area. Wheelchair access

PADSTOW   Cornwall   map 1

▲ Seafood Restaurant ▮

Riverside, Padstow PL28 8BY   COOKING 4
PADSTOW (0841) 532485   ·   COST £29–£54

There are not many fish restaurants approaching this calibre in the British Isles. To ensure survival, however, Rick Stein has turned himself into a veritable enterprise, with a prize-winning cookery book (and another in preparation), uncluttered but comfortable bedrooms above the restaurant with views over town and harbour, a delicatessen selling cheese, pastries, fish soup and other specialities from the restaurant, and now a bakery, using flour from Crowdy Mill in South Devon, baking for the restaurant and shop and making pasties to bolster out-of-season turnover – a giant step up from the refrigerated lorries that seem the only other source of Cornish pasties in the south-west. The restaurant is still the hub of all this whirling activity. Clear, white, hard-surfaced with lots of green plants and bright posters of every art exhibition possible, the place has an unlikely city atmosphere for a small Cornish town that is half fishing port, half holiday resort. And the customers: 'where do all these smart people come from?' asked one reader, who also said how surprisingly elegant the dining-room is. It takes some people by surprise, as if they expect only a small bistro with nets and glass balls hanging off the ceiling. Some of the splendour is to do with the cost, of course. 'I had probably the most expensive meal I have ever had – but the four of us were unanimous in our praise,' even if they did find the lighting too harsh. The money is not ill-spent, for materials are generously dispensed and strenuously worked for. The menu is either set price with a choice from three dishes at each course or a *carte* of another dozen items. The prix fixe is not expensive at all, in line with any number of country places, but escalation may occur with supplementary specials that include turbot, crayfish, lobster and salmon. The menu is not the old-fashioned sort that offers plain grilled slabs of fillet, oysters and lobster mayonnaise. Each dish is considered, the sauce and main ingredient connected by reasoned sensibility if not the actual process of cooking. When grilling is undertaken, it is over charcoal, and when something truly simple is produced, such as fruits de mer, it is with such abandon that all comment is quelled until it is consumed. A meal that met with approval started with mussels grilled with coriander and hazel-nut butter, and fresh whitebait, deep-fried, with persillade; next came escalope of salmon with Champagne and chive sauce, moist thin fish appealingly presented, and monkfish baked in the oven with garlic and fennel; a selection of vegetables on a side plate, cooked *à point*, confirmed the quality of the incidentals, as did the bread and butter. This was not let down by the chocolate marquise with coffee sauce and correctly textured meringue with blackberries and cream. Coffee was up to par, with little meringues as a monotone sweetmeat. British cheeses are served, with home-baked walnut bread. While willing to let his ingredients speak for themselves, Rick Stein is clever with flavours. One reader annotated a menu for a wine-tasting: sliced cured duck with melon and pickled ginger, 'vinegary, lemon-grassy, an unusual vibrant taste'; steamed sea bass with small beach clams and queens, 'three large fillets, with clams and queens in the shell, a delicate sauce of fish stock and shellfish enhanced by chopped shallots, parsley and chives.' A classic dish indeed. What problems there are revolve around the sheer number of customers, fraying the service, shortening the limits of politeness and sometimes causing the cookery to drop a notch. Tempers may be soothed by the accomplished jazz piano playing of Jill Stein's father at the weekend, or perhaps resort to the winning wine list which does not ignore red wines even if the main tilt is towards white. It is mainly French, but there are some good Australasians and a note that the Californian section is 'due for serious overhaul.' Prices are very fair indeed and properties are first-rate, whether Ampeau or Latour-Giraud in Burgundy, Jaboulet or Vernay in the Rhône, Ch. Caronne-Ste-Gemme in Bordeaux or Avignonesi in Italy. The notes are just enough to give the searcher confidence to strike a bargain and they reflect personal experience. White house wine is £8.25, red £12.50. CELLARMAN'S CHOICE: de Villaine's Aligoté de Bouzeron 1987, £12.50; Ch. Constantin 1986, £20. If you are looking for the delicatessen, be warned: 'Padstow has a lot of winding streets, mostly called Market Street.' Middle Street, the site of the shop, is not far from the restaurant.

CHEF: Richard Stein   PROPRIETORS: Richard and Jill Stein
OPEN: Mon to Sat, D only
MEALS: 7.30 to 9.30 (10 Sat)
PRICES: £35 (£45), Set D £21.95 (£29)
CARDS: Access, Visa
SEATS: 75. Private parties: 24 main room. Children's helpings. Air-conditioned
ACCOMMODATION: 10 rooms, 8 with bath/shower. B&B £27 to £80. Baby facilities. Pets welcome. Fishing. TV. Phone. Scenic. Confirm one week ahead [*Which? Hotel Guide*]

PAULERSPURY Northamptonshire   map 3

▲ *Vine House*

100 High Street, Paulerspury NN12 7NA
PAULERSPURY (032 733) 267   COOKING 3
off the A5, 2m s of Towcester   COST £23–£49

The piped music may get some people down, but otherwise the ambience of the spacious dining-room set within a long Northamptonshire farmhouse is enjoyed, and reckoned satisfactory for the serious cooking of Jonathan Stanbury. This does get unanimous praise – 'Milton Keynes needs him' – although the prices come in for local questioning. In fact, the availability of set menus starting at £14.95 should reconcile almost anyone who eats out to the not outrageous cost (given the ingredients) of the rest of the options. Jonathan Stanbury worked at the Connaught Hotel and was there at the same time as Kevin Cape, now chef at the Bell, Aston Clinton (see entry). He has not cast his haute cuisine aside, nor his appreciation of current fashion, so a dish off the *carte* of about seven choices in each course might be a warm salad of red mullet and artichoke with a goats' cheese mousse and a lemon vinaigrette; fried goose liver with a gratin of potato and apple; ravioli of crab and lobster with Thai spices; duck with ginger and soy and a filo parcel of onion and coriander; or a civet of lobster, onions, mushrooms and bacon. These are sane compositions, carefully executed and enthusiastically discussed: 'We talked until the early hours and I returned home with a recipe for chicken and my foie gras from the Touraine that took him only minutes to imagine.' An autumn meal (set price) began with the creamy soft curds of scrambled eggs sandwiched between two leaves of puff pastry, scattered with ceps and morels; then a breast of wild duck, 'almost quacking as it came to table' but 'jolly hot' and no complaints, on rösti potatoes with fanned apple at each end. Vegetables were good but 'did nothing' to complement the meat. This is becoming a common complaint of people who are served standard vegetables, usually undercooked and often offered separately. Some readers will remember when this was the height of modernity – about 1974 – and our criticism of it is a measure of fashion as well as of absolutes. The cheese course was toasted goats' cheese on a salad dressed with rosemary vinegar, 'the sort of detail that makes a visit worth it.' Dessert was blackberry and apple crumble, a reminder of Northamptonshire, and crème fraîche, a totem of another culture. There is always at least one hot dessert, but 'rhubarb charlotte was complete with spun sugar, light sponge and stunning visuals; the assiette of chocolate is also remarkable.' Cheese comes from Britain and France; coffee has been condemned as weak. Details are often good: the amuse-gueule of prawns grilled with a sesame coating, regular theme evenings such as the good-value Beaujolais Nouveau night happened on by chance visitors; though others have commented on too great a uniformity between sauces at different stages of a meal, bottled orange juice, and service that sometimes does not match the prices. The wine list has expanded, particularly at the top end, giving better depth to match the food. It has not ignored either price range or half-bottles, but it is not a cheap collection. Kuentz-Bas from Alsace; Andrew Hendry from Coopers Creek, New Zealand; and la Rioja Alta's Viña Araña Reserva 1982 are some growers and bottles to note. House wine: £7.50. CELLARMAN'S CHOICE: Châteauneuf-du-Pape 1986, Salavert, £14.50; Pernand-Vergelesses Blanc 1987, Chanson, £16.50.

CHEF: Jonathan Stanbury   PROPRIETORS: Karen and Christine Snowdon
OPEN: all week, exc Mon L, Sat L and Sun D
CLOSED: 25 Dec, 1 Jan, 2 weeks end of Mar
MEALS: 12 to 2, 7 to 9.30
PRICES: £29 (£38), Set L and D £14.95 (£23) to £32 (£41)
CARDS: Access, Visa
SEATS: 43. Private parties: 30 main room, 12 private room. Car-park, 15 places. Vegetarian meals. Children's helpings. Wheelchair access. Music
ACCOMMODATION: 6 rooms, all with bath/shower. B&B £53 to £65. Pets welcome. Garden. TV. Phone. Scenic. Doors close at 11. Confirm by 4 [*Which? Hotel Guide*]

PETWORTH   West Sussex   map 3

Soanes

Grove Lane, Petworth GU28 0HY
PETWORTH (0798) 43659
SE of Petworth. Take A285 S, signed
Chichester; after 1m L to Pulborough   COOKING 2
road, then first L   COST £21–£41

Petworth's traffic system is a nightmare, so ensure you leave it by the Chichester road. Carol Godsmark cooks in an old farmhouse looking out on to the South Downs and wrapped by a modern conservatory, which makes a nice spot for drinks (or a convenient exile for cigar smokers). The dining-room, divided by skeletal partitions, offers a variety of menus through the week. Thursday is fish night (though some meat is available). On other nights there is a set-price, two-course *carte* of half a dozen choices and on Sundays a more traditional, three-course roast lunch of lamb, beef, pork, or less traditional salmon. The pricing on Sunday has to be applauded: children pay £1 per year of age and 'those slightly older' get a benefit of £1 (up to £5) per year over the age of 75. This, and the statement that the staff are paid well enough to be 'independent of gratuities and tipping', show real desire to please the customer, just as does the quiet concern of Derek Godsmark and his young staff. And readers have been pleased: marinated salmon with tarragon; a scallop soup; asparagus wrapped in filo, with hollandaise or a wild mushroom and madeira sauce; fillet of beef with Roquefort sauce; poached peach in Champagne with redcurrant sauce; raspberry tart lined with whipped cream. Occasionally there have been faults of description – quenelles of smoked trout turned out to be fillets laid beside a quenelle-shaped avocado purée – and a feeling that flavours announced on the menu have not been determinedly followed through on the plate, making for a less exciting dish than expected. The menu has been translated into English, hurrah! The wine is as sensibly priced as the food and the short list has a mixed choice of French standards with a few fine burgundies from the likes of Puligny, Sauzet, Bonneau du Martray and Chandon de Briailles. There are also some good clarets at fair prices. House French: £9.

CHEF: Carol Godsmark   PROPRIETORS: Carol and Derek Godsmark
OPEN: Wed to Sat D and Sun L (Wed to Fri L by arrangement)
MEALS: 12.30 to 2, 7.30 to 11
PRICES: Set Sun L £15 (£21), Set D (2 courses) £16.50 (£28) to £22 (£34). Service inc. Licensed, also bring your own: corkage £9
CARDS: Access, Visa
SEATS: 24. Private parties: 30 main room. Car-park, 16 places. Children's helpings (Sun L only). No pipes in dining-room. Wheelchair access (2 steps). Music

---

PINNER   Greater London   map 3

La Giralda

66 Pinner Green, Pinner HA5 2AB   COOKING 1
081-868 3429   COST £10–£22

La Giralda may give the impression of a Spanish restaurant, it may have friendly Spanish waiters and a wine list of Spanish provenance, but it does not serve Spanish food. What it does, however, is produce good value food that includes some excellent materials (mainly fish) as well as less desirable elements: packet butter and poor desserts, according to one visitor. The value is achieved through popularity and concentration on the essentials. Paella and gazpacho are on offer, but the tapas revolution has passed it by. Choose instead smoked halibut with a dill sauce; salmon with lobster sauce; pastry filled with monkfish and sole; swordfish with garlic; or skate with black butter. The waiters may not be able to fill in the details missing from the wine list. There is a matchless collection of old Spanish wines that should be pursued by enthusiasts.

CHEFS: David Brown and Derek Knight   PROPRIETOR: David Brown
OPEN: Tue to Sat
MEALS: 12 to 2.30, 6.30 to 10.30
PRICES: Set L £5.50 (£10) to £9 (£14), Set D £9 (£14) to £13 (£18)
CARDS: Access, Amex, Diners, Visa
SEATS: 120. Private parties: 50 main room, 16 and 35 private rooms. Vegetarian meals. Children's helpings. Wheelchair access. Air-conditioned

Perkins Bar Bistro

Old Railway Station, Plumtree NG12 5NA   COOKING 2
PLUMTREE (060 77) 3695   COST £23

The point about Tony Perkins' bistro in a converted railway station is that you pay precisely for what you order: everything from the bread rolls to the vegetables is clearly priced on the menu boards. Tony feels strongly about this: 'Vegetables and potato dishes do merit singular attention.' It should also be noticed that value is very good indeed. The regularly changing menus and lunchtime snacks have a strong French accent: brochette of chicken livers with bacon and grapes; poached salmon with hollandaise sauce; noisettes of lamb with herbs and rosemary sauce. Readers have also liked the grilled sardines and pork wiener schnitzel, as well as the whisky and orange cheesecake. 'Charm' sums up the service in the words of one visitor. This may be because Tony Perkins is a good motivator and people like working here as much as the customers enjoy eating. A new conservatory faces the sun, and lucky visitors may even see an engine running on the tracks. A short, adequate list includes plenty of half-bottles. Four house wines by the glass or bottle, red and white from Georges Duboeuf: £6.15. CELLARMAN'S CHOICE: Cabernet Sauvignon, Wolf Blass 1985, £9.75.

CHEF: Tony Perkins and Kevin Pole   PROPRIETORS: Tony and Wendy Perkins
OPEN: Tue to Sat
CLOSED: 1 week at Christmas
MEALS: 12 to 2, 7 to 9.45
PRICES: £12 (£19)
CARDS: Access, Amex, Visa
SEATS: 90. 6 tables outside. Private parties: 24 main room. Car-park, 60 places. Children welcome. Wheelchair access (1 step). Music

---

Barretts of Princess Street

27 Princess Street, Plymouth PL1 2EX   COOKING 1
PLYMOUTH (0752) 221177   COST £17–£25

Stephen Barrett is a Plymouth character: chef, wine enthusiast, journalist, raconteur, lover of jazz. Visitors may encounter all of these in one man when eating in the basement café/restaurant behind the Theatre Royal. It makes a strenuous effort to be a city centre utility: open all day, a range of prices, 'one dish' meals for the not so hungry or impecunious. Many people enjoy the atmosphere, with metallic topped tables, black bentwood chairs and crisp image chiming well with the broad ebullience of the proprietor. The speciality is fish, strongly supported by 'Devon' meats, that is, game or local lamb, and organic produce which is now highlighted on the menu. Thus an offering of daily dishes might be asparagus, fresh crab, local smoked sea trout and scrambled eggs, a 'ragout of today's seafood' or haunch of Tiverton venison. The cooking, like the man, is ebullient: full of good ideas and often satisfactory. The wine list is a rolling selection of a couple of dozen bottles, each described

with notes and none expensive. House wines: £6.50. CELLARMAN'S
CHOICE: Pinot Blanc 1985, Jekel, £13.95; Côtes de Roussillon 1988, de
Villeneuve, £7.95. Sensibly, Stephen Barrett cares primarily about taste in
wine, not breeding on the label.

CHEF: Stephen Barrett   PROPRIETORS: Stephen Barrett and Geoffrey Rogers
OPEN: Mon to Sat
MEALS: 10.30am to 10.30pm
PRICES: £15 (£21), Set L £10.95 (£17)
CARDS: Access, Visa
SEATS: 50. 6 tables outside. Private parties: 50 main room. Car-park, 35 places. Vegetarian
meals. Children's helpings. Music. Air-conditioned

Chez Nous

13 Frankfort Gate, Plymouth PL1 1QA   COOKING 4
PLYMOUTH (0752) 266793   COST £30–£54

Not much of post-war Plymouth is exciting to the eye, though the trees of
Frankfort Gate make a stab at neighbourhood planning and a habitat for a
multitude of pigeons. Chez Nous closes its eyes to this world outside and
visitors may indeed think themselves in France. The rudimentary surroundings
have seen some uplift lately but the menu is still in illegible French on a
blackboard – take opera glasses or ask Suzanne Marchal to interpret. She will
do this and serve the rest of the meal with gentle, undemonstrative humour.
Jacques, meanwhile, beavers away in a tiny kitchen crammed with cooking
equipment (but no microwave) and produces food of simple yet refined
immediacy. The style is obviously as French as can be, vegetables (charged
extra) being the main concession to English preferences. It is not the French
often met in currently fancy restaurants that layers several flavours in almost
bewildering profusion. Nor is it a markedly herbed or garden cooking style.
Dishes commented on this year include a rich onion soup; a salad of pickled
herring on warm new potatoes; three slices of foie gras on a bed of cabbage
with a pungent wine sauce; a mousse of chicken livers; fresh snails in garlic
butter; scallops with a ginger sauce; a plate of salmon, brill, John Dory,
scallops and red mullet with a saffron sauce, big enough to sink even the
fisherman; venison of extreme tenderness in port sauce; veal with morels or
sweetbreads with girolles; or confit of duck on summer cabbage with pine
kernels. Success relies on first-rate materials and when they are, the harmony
of dishes is very great. Desserts are predictable in the modern form and rarely,
like the rest of the menu, involve pastry. The wine list has a supplement of
small parcels. Both are French only. There are some nice mature clarets and the
selection of bottles is from serious makers. However, prices zoom with
old-fashioned mark-ups. House wines are from £8. CELLARMAN'S
CHOICE: Ch. Chasse-Spleen 1982, £24.80; Clos de la Roche 1981,
Rousseau, £30.70.

*See the inside of the front cover for an explanation of the 1 to 5 rating system recognising
cooking standards.*

CHEF: Jacques Marchal   PROPRIETORS: Suzanne and Jacques Marchal
OPEN: Tue to Sat
CLOSED: first 3 weeks Feb and Sept, bank hols
MEALS: 12.30 to 2, 7 to 10.30
PRICES: £32 (£45), Set L and D £21.50 (£30)
CARDS: Access, Amex, Diners, Visa
SEATS: 30. Private parties: 30 main room. Children welcome. Wheelchair access (also WC). Music. Air-conditioned

Yang Cheng

30A Western Approach, Plymouth PL1 1TQ	COOKING 1
PLYMOUTH (0752) 660170	COST £10–£29

The restaurant is in a row of shops on the inner ring road. The decor is subdued with only a flash of bright green bamboo wallpaper adding a touch of colour. The food is the main attraction. Old-style Cantonese influences show up in the dozen dim-sum and in the small selection of one-plate rice, noodle and soup dishes. Crispy fried wan-tun, glossy dark-skinned roast duck, and Singapore vermicelli noodles have all been praised. Otherwise the menu deals in lemon chicken ('a revelation'), juicy prawns with garlic, and squid with black-bean sauce. The consensus is that the food outshines its competitors in the city. Service is unobtrusive, but as crisp as the young manager's suit. Great Wall Chinese wine is worth investigating. House Spanish: £5.50.

CHEF: K.Y Wong   PROPRIETORS: M.Y Wong and K.S.L. Wong
OPEN: Tue to Sun, exc Sun D
MEALS: 12 to 2.30 (3 Sun), 6 to 11
PRICES: £14 (£24), Set L £5.15 (£10) to £5.70 (£10), Set D £10 (£15) to £16 (£22)
CARDS: Access, Visa
SEATS: 70. Private parties: 70 main room. Vegetarian meals. Children welcome. Music. Air-conditioned

---

POLPERRO Cornwall	map 1

Kitchen

The Coombes, Polperro PL13 2RQ	COOKING 1
POLPERRO (0503) 72780	COST £20–£37

All pinks and pine is this cottage-like restaurant on the road down to the harbour, and it has a serious attitude towards fresh lobster and crab. Ian and Vanessa Bateson treat good ingredients carefully, and often in a novel and wholesome way. Set menus, now reduced to 'Kitchen', 'Lobster' and 'Vegetarian', and with fewer choices than last year, share a list of first courses and desserts. Old favourites such as cashew-nut and cheese pâté, and duck with blueberry and Drambuie sauce are often found. Nut roasts or loafs might be brazil or cashew-nut with sweet pepper or Dijon mustard sauce. Local lobster in filo pastry with a well-executed wine and lobster sauce is, like the more-ish home-made bread, a justifiable fixture. Desserts that have enticed are bread-and-butter pudding or banoffi pie. The reasonably priced list of around

30 wines includes Rocks Elderflower. House French is £6.70. CELLARMAN'S CHOICE: Ch. Lemoine Lafon Rochet 1987, £10.30.

CHEFS/PROPRIETORS: Ian and Vanessa Bateson
OPEN: all week D, exc Tue; Fri and Sat only in winter
MEALS: 6.30 to 9.30
PRICES: Set Vegetarian D £14 (£20), Set Kitchen D £16.50 (£23), Set Lobster D £24 (£31)
CARDS: Access, Visa
SEATS: 24. Private parties: 12 main room. Vegetarian meals. Children welcome. Wheelchair access. Music

---

POOL IN WHARFEDALE West Yorkshire   map 5

▲ *Pool Court* ♥

Pool Bank, Pool in Wharfedale LS21 1EH   COOKING 3
LEEDS (0532) 842288   COST £22–£52

Long experience has given the Gills an eye for detail and skill in training. Unanimous praise is heard for the tact and efficiency of the staff and their ability to make a celebration memorable, and for the solid worth and luxury of fixtures and fittings. The work of the kitchen fits in well with this. Details are thought out beforehand: petits fours are impressive, cheese biscuits properly made, ancillaries as they should be. The formula of dining has also had thought. It is possible to have a sensationally cheap three-course set meal (£10, no deviation allowed); vegetarians are given their due; the four-course meal, priced by choice of main course, allows plenty of options and no supplements – even for the popular and well-reported 'assiette du chef' as a dessert. The palate is informed by alcohol, mushrooms and vegetables as the main determinants of flavour. Herbs or spices are not often deployed as the front line. To that extent, the kitchen is traditional. Otherwise there are many signs of a concern for lighter sauces and there is welcome relief from overburdening with fruit or sweet-sour combinations. Dishes that show the outer perimeters of the repertoire include calf's liver roasted in the piece with a herb and watercress topping; chicken with stir-fried vegetables and a soy and ginger sauce; osso buco; a pigeon and rabbit terrine with herbs and vegetables and a truffle *jus*; oysters with salmon roe, spinach and a Sauternes jelly. Reports have concentrated on the consistency of the production: first courses such as chargrilled sea trout with 'spaghetti' of vegetables and a light sauce of virgin oil and fish stock; mussels and scallops with lightly smoked bacon on fresh pasta with a saffron sauce; second courses such as a pea and mint soup that erred on the thin side and a chicken terrine with a salad accompaniment. Main dishes prompted no cavil save that the herb *farce* to a breast of guinea-fowl was too strong, but a duck breast with calvados sauce (Aylesbury, not Barbary or Gressingham) came with a good spinach timbale filled with the leg meat. A nougatine ice-cream in a brandy-snap case was enthusiastically judged the best of good deserts, including passion-fruit parfait and layers of white chocolate mousse separated by wafers of dark chocolate with a raspberry coulis. Good growers and decent vintages give confidence that disappointments are unlikely from the balanced wine list, even if prices are high. Relief can be found on the page of 'everyday wines,' all priced at £7.95. From classics such as Ch. Kirwan

425

1983 to unknowns such as La Grola 1986 from Allegrini, the choice reflects robust and serious drinking.

CHEF: David Watson   PROPRIETOR: Michael W.K. Gill
OPEN: Tue to Sat, D only (L by arrangement for parties of 10 or more)
CLOSED: 2 weeks Jul to Aug, 2 weeks at Christmas
MEALS: 7 to 10
PRICES: Set D £10 (£22) to £29.50 (£43). Service of 10% for large private parties
CARDS: Access, Amex, Diners, Visa
SEATS: 65. Private parties: 30 private room. Car-park, 65 places. Vegetarian meals.
Children's helpings. Smart dress preferred. No cigars/pipes in dining-room. Wheelchair access. Air-conditioned
ACCOMMODATION: 6 rooms, all with bath/shower. B&B £70 to £120. Garden. TV. Phone
[*Which? Hotel Guide*]

POUGHILL   Cornwall   map 1

▲ *Reeds*

Poughill EX23 9EL   COOKING 3
BUDE (0288) 352841   COST £28

You can see the sea from Margaret Jackson's airy guest-house and repose in her large pleasant garden. Another reason to stay here is her excellent dinners, to which she welcomes friends of guests as well. In fact, she's a welcoming sort of person, and continues to voice rapturous enthusiasm for what she calls 'a very personal project.' She keeps standards up, too. As ingredients become available in this distant corner of Cornwall, her repertoire expands. Because there's no choice, you will be consulted beforehand about preference and special requirements. The season also dictates what's to be served. Vegetables are home grown and independent suppliers are tapped for local fish and meats. In autumn, a tomato ice-cream starter with prawns and avocado rated as much for its rich flavour as its novelty value. In early summer, a light and bubbly tomato charlotte with cream, breadcrumbs and fresh herbs, and sole wrapped around smoked salmon in cream and fresh mushroom sauce were intelligently judged and tasted fine. There have been raves, too, for the stuffed quail pie, a pungent, herb and sausage-flavoured concoction covered with red wine and mushrooms. Simpler fare – salmon poached in fish stock with lime juice, chives and tarragon, for instance – succeeds, too. Vegetables are carefully treated to conserve flavour as well as texture. Portions are hefty. And oh, those puds! Wickedly rich was the chocolate mousse, tart and refreshing the compote of plums in red wine with a redcurrant jelly and Japanese almond meringue giving perfect sweetness as counterpoint. Local and imported cheeses, the fourth course, are exemplary. The same cheeses feature in a cheese and fruit lunch by arrangement – 'whatever is in the fridge', says the amicable and accommodating Margaret Jackson. The wine list is more extensive than a small guest-house would suggest. There are more than a few half-bottles. House Duboeuf: £6.50. No tipping.

The Guide *relies on feedback from its readers. Especially welcome are reports on new restaurants appearing in the book for the first time.*

CHEF/PROPRIETOR: Margaret Jackson
OPEN: Fri to Mon, D only
CLOSED: 25 Dec
MEALS: 8
PRICES: Set D £19.50 (£23). Service inc
SEATS: 10. Private parties: 10 main room. Car-park, 10 places. No children under 16. Smart dress preferred. One sitting
ACCOMMODATION: 3 rooms, all with bath/shower. B&B £37.50 to £65. Deposit: £10
No children under 16. Garden. Scenic. Doors close at midnight. Confirm by noon
[*Which? Hotel Guide*]

POULTON-LE-FYLDE Lancashire   map 5

▲ *River House* ♀

Skippool Creek
Thornton-le-Fylde FY5 5LF   COOKING 3
POULTON-LE-FYLDE (0253) 883497   COST £43

Skippool Creek is a good place for a small hotel: isolated yet with sufficient variety of landscape as well as human activity among the yachts and jetties, not to mention all the birds. The River House is like its owners: different and characterful. Antiques are everywhere. It is not like a hotel, even being compared to a Victorian church – and about as draughty to one party facing a cold winter's evening. Bill Scott has never had much truck with nouvelle cuisine, though his repertoire is not devoid of modern influences; the twin poles of his cooking are fresh produce and generous treatment. The *carte* numbers about 10 dishes in each course with extras recited, particularly the fish – perhaps sole or turbot from Fleetwood. Salmon in several guises is a feature: served with a bordelaise sauce as a first course; cured according to the River House recipe, then cold-smoked at Fleetwood or en papillote with a chive sauce. Meats are substantial prime cuts, often roasted, often rare: venison with a game sauce; veal with tomato and basil sauce; lamb with a mint sauce; hare and pigeon. Desserts do not let up on quantity: crème brûlée is helped by a compote of oranges; chocolate mousse comes in a threesome of dark, milk and white in cake form. The Beluga caviare starter is priced for a splurge. Incidentals are well thought out: walnut bread and good butter, home-made biscuits for the cheese, three sorts of coffee and 10 sorts of tea plus infusions, home-made chocolates. The wine list shows certain gaps in information about growers and even years but there is much choice, and some happy pickings among the bin-ends. Prices are fair. Clarets are worth a look, offering mature ones from excellent properties. The Italians are also interesting as well as four Bandols from Dom. Tempier and a couple of Swiss wines for variety. House wine: £10.

All details are as accurate as possible at the time of going to press, but chefs and owners often change, and it is wise to check by telephone before making a special journey. Many readers have been disappointed when set-price bargain meals are no longer available. Ask when booking.

CHEFS/PROPRIETORS: Bill and Carole Scott
OPEN: Mon to Sat, exc Sat L
MEALS: 12 to 2, 7.30 to 9.30
PRICES: £26 (£36)
CARDS: Access, Visa
SEATS: 40. Private parties: 40 main room. Car-park, 20 places. Vegetarian meals. Children's helpings. Music
ACCOMMODATION: 3 rooms, all with bath/shower. B&B £50 to £100. Baby facilities. Pets welcome. Garden. TV. Phone. Scenic [*Which? Hotel Guide*]

POWBURN Northumberland   map 7

▲ *Breamish House*

Powburn NE66 4LL   COOKING 2
POWBURN (066 578) 266   COST £17–29

Substance, seclusion and simple comfort are the principal virtues of this classical house in a treed garden, the Cheviots away to the north. The cooking shares in at least two of these qualities: 'a good balance between gastronomy and simplicity,' is one observation. The menu affords small choice and the evidence is that relative convention is favoured in dishes such as eggs with curried mayonnaise, trout with almond butter and roast beef followed by a dessert trolley with, one summer night, chocolate roulade and fruit salad among the offerings. Yet the tastes, even if discreet, are fairly handled and local materials are given a showing. This understated approach may yield the dividends of good soups, enjoyable vegetables, a fair range of British cheeses and enlivening dishes like tomatoes and prawns *en cocotte* or halibut, prawns and a simple butter sauce. On the other hand, it may descend to dullness. Hospitality is pleasing, though with few frills. The wine list has a number of alternate vintages but is otherwise a fair selection of largely French wines at very acceptable prices. House French is £7.25. CELLARMAN'S CHOICE: Sancerre, Clos du Roc 1988, £11.25; Ch. La Tour de By 1982, £16.50.

CHEFS: Patricia Portus and Doreen Johnson   PROPRIETORS: Doreen and Alan Johnson
OPEN: all week, D only and Sun L
CLOSED: Jan
MEALS: 12.30 for 1, 7.30 for 8
PRICES: Set Sun L £11.75 (£17), Set D £18.50 (£24)
SEATS: 30. Private parties: 22 main room. Car-park, 30 places. No children under 12. Smart dress preferred. No smoking in dining-rooms. Wheelchair access (also unisex WC). One sitting
ACCOMMODATION: 11 rooms, all with bath/shower. B&B £41 to £62.50. Deposit: £20 per person. No children under 12. Garden. TV. Phone. Scenic. Doors close at midnight. Confirm by 6 [*Which? Hotel Guide*]

The Guide *office can quickly spot when a restaurateur is encouraging customers to write recommending inclusion - and sadly, several restaurants have been doing this in 1990. Such reports do not further a restaurant's cause. Please tell us if a restaurateur invites you to write to the* Guide.

POWERSTOCK Dorset   map 2

▲ *Three Horseshoes*

Powerstock DT6 3TF
POWERSTOCK (030 885) 328   COOKING 1
4m NE of Bridport   COST £14—£37

This pub with a thatched-roof bar has developed into a restaurant over the
years. Pat Ferguson has restricted the restaurant hours since the last *Guide* to
ensure reliable performance. Indeed there have been very mixed reports this
year, stemming both from quality and price. The supplies of fresh fish and the
cooking of simple fish dishes are satisfactory, none the less. At very busy times
service may be slow. The wine list, though short, offers a good and fairly priced
selection. House wine: £6.

CHEF: Pat Ferguson   PROPRIETORS: Pat and Diana Ferguson
OPEN: Tue to Sun, exc Sun D
MEALS: 12 to 2 (3 Sun), 7 to 11
PRICES: £24 (£31), Set L £8.50 (£14) to £12.50 (£18), Set D £16.50 (£23) to £22.50 (£30)
CARDS: Access, Amex, Visa
SEATS: 60. 12 tables outside. Private parties: 60 main room, 12 and 20 private rooms. Car-
park, 30 places. Vegetarian meals. Children's helpings. Smart dress preferred. No smoking
in dining-room. Wheelchair access (also WC)
ACCOMMODATION: 4 rooms, 2 with bath/shower. B&B £20 to £50. Deposit: one night. Pets
welcome. Garden. Scenic. Doors close at midnight. Confirm by 6.30

PRESTBURY Cheshire   map 5

▲ *White House*

New Road, Prestbury SK10 4DG   COOKING 2
PRESTBURY (0625) 829376   COST £16—£38

The house is a converted farmhouse, now in the centre of the village, with a
conservatory extension. Ryland Wakeham's long menu has dishes starred for
'spa cuisine', low in fats, cream and alcohol for reducing waistlines and eating
healthily. It also has a strong suit in fish, brought from Brixham in South
Devon, not from Fleetwood. There is an affection for fruit, for example scallops
with mango, melon and mange-tout in a sesame oil dressing or duckling with
summer berries and kirsch, and for vegetable sauces, as used in a vegetable
sausage on a broad bean sauce or a trout mousse with a smoked salmon and
courgette sauce. Mixing various media results in complicated restaurant
cookery. Chicken, for example, appears only with scallops or lobster on a
summer menu. Desserts may undo the good effected by 'spa cuisine' if
profiteroles or sticky toffee pudding are consumed in preference to the warm
nectarine and caramel tart with zinfandel sabayon, or light terrine of Belgian
chocolate and mint with cherries. The large plate of petits fours with good
coffee will be yet another undoing. The wine list leans heavily on négoçiants'
wines and information on growers and vintages is sparse. House wine is £8 a
litre. More reports, please.

429

CHEF: Ryland Wakeham   PROPRIETORS: Ryland and Judith Wakeham
OPEN: Tue to Sun
CLOSED: first week Jan and Aug
MEALS: 12 to 2, 7 to 10
PRICES: £23 (£32), Set L £9.50 (£16) to £11.50 (£18)
CARDS: Access, Amex, Diners, Visa
SEATS: 75. 2 tables outside. Private parties: 70 main room, 20 and 40 private rooms. Car-park, 16 places. Vegetarian meals alc. Children's helpings. Smart dress preferred. Wheelchair access (also M amd F WC). Music
ACCOMMODATION: 8 rooms, all with bath/shower. Rooms for disabled. B&B £65 to £108. Deposit: 20%. No children under 12. Garden. Sauna. TV. Phone. Doors close at midnight. Confirm by noon day before

---

PRESTON Lancashire   map 5

Auctioneer

ADT, Walton Summit, Bamber Bridge,
Preston PR5 8AA   COOKING 1
PRESTON (0772) 324870   COST £13−£23

In this unusual location just 100 yards from the motorway, surrounded by a motor auction ring and in industrial buildings, the restaurant exemplifies the good and bad of British catering. The forceful and cheery personality of Nigel Brookes is to be admired, just as is his commitment to fair prices. The serving of paella with chips and potato cake, or breaded plaice that seemed no better than frozen can hardly be admired. On the plus side again are kidneys with button onions and a brown sauce; mushroom pancakes with lots of mushrooms, light pancakes and not too heavy a cream sauce; a surprising looking 'claret chicken' where the breasts are stuffed with cheese mixed with red wine and served with a red wine sauce; or 'coloured lamb' where the lamb is cooked with capsicums of three different colours and served with a redcurrant-based sauce. These have been praised for their robust vigour, if not subtlety − in fact, on the minus side, they are about as subtle as the very large chips that come with most main courses. Puddings appear to be bought in and coffee is not always the best. There is a children's menu and the set-price lunch usually includes two roasts. Bar snacks are also available at lunchtime on weekdays, from £1.55 to £5.95. Wines are basic with house wines at £6.95 a litre.

CHEF: Nigel Brookes   PROPRIETORS: Nigel and Elizabeth Brookes
OPEN: Mon to Sun L, exc Tue and Sat; Fri and Sat D
MEALS: 12 to 2.30, 7 to 10
PRICES: £13 (£19), Set L £7.95 (£13)
CARDS: Access, Visa
SEATS: 100. Private parties: 100 main room. Car-park, 500 places. Vegetarian meals. Children's helpings. Music. Air-conditioned

---

The 1992 Guide will be published before Christmas 1991. Reports on meals are most welcome at any time of the year, but are extremely valuable in the spring. Send them to The Good Food Guide, *FREEPOST, 2 Marylebone Road, London NW1 1YN. No stamp is needed if posted in the UK.*

Stane Street Hollow

Codmore Hill, Pulborough RH20 1BG	COOKING 3
PULBOROUGH (079 82) 2819	COST £14–£27

Places that are described as 'just like home' occasionally strike dread into the heart of the casual visitor. However, René and Ann Kaiser have so warm a consideration for their guests, their restaurant is decorated so artlessly, and the food has such generous aromas and flavours that the description has positive accuracy. The classically inspired menu, changing each month, has continuity: smoked meats and fish are a strong point, as are a number of Swiss or German specialities, such as Badische schnecken suppe (chicken and snail soup) or Kasseler mit weinbirnen (home-smoked loin of pork with peas and a red wine sauce). Flavours are robust, even in the scallops with a white wine sauce and the once traditional accompaniment of plain boiled rice, but more so in another constant dish, the leg of smoked duck stuffed with pork, duck liver, garlic and herb sausage, sauced sometimes with madeira, at others with white wine spiked with gherkins. Desserts are no use to slimmers: a meringue swan filled with strawberry mousse and a fine layer of cream encrusted with 'feathers' of sliced berries showed careful use of sugar and an ability to make yielding meringue; 'assiette René' gives a chance to play the field. Pastry and baking skills are well deployed. Details could be improved: the bread, the butter, the coffee and, it has been whispered, even the vegetables on the occasional night. As everyone leaves, they are shown the door by the Kaisers with as much consideration and regret at departure as they were welcomed at the outset. Just like home indeed. The wine list is mainly French, though there are two from Switzerland and half a dozen from Germany. A glass of German wine is sometimes offered, to take with dessert. No-one could complain at the prices, in this department, as in any other. Alsaces from Zind-Humbrecht are worth a look, and Ch. Rahoul makes a welcome appearance. The gems are Barolo from Ceretto and Ch. Fombrauge 1983. House French: £8 litre. CELLARMAN'S CHOICE: Muscat 1987, Zind-Humbrecht, £13.75; Chorey-lès-Beaune 1984, £12.45.

CHEF: René Kaiser PROPRIETORS: René and Ann Kaiser
OPEN: Wed to Sat, exc Sat L
CLOSED: 2 weeks May and Oct, 24 to 26 Dec, 31 Dec and 1 Jan, one week Feb
MEALS: 12.30 to 1.15, 7.30 to 9.15
PRICES: £19 (£27), Set L £7.25 (£14)
SEATS: 35. Private parties: 24 main room, 16 private room. Car-park, 14 places. Children's helpings. No smoking in dining-room

'We paid £100 for two, there were five other people in the dining-room, and the waiters still couldn't remember which of us ordered what.' On inspecting in Berkshire

See the inside of the front cover for an explanation of the 1 to 5 rating system recognising cooking standards.

RAMSBOTTOM   Greater Manchester   map 5

Village Restaurant 🍾

16 Market Place, Ramsbottom BL0 9HT   COOKING 3
RAMSBOTTOM (070 682) 5070   COST £37

'Lucky Ramsbottom. The Village Restaurant feels like a national treasure.' So
begins a report of a meal which highlights many of the special attributes that
mark out the operation. The move next door to what was the wine bar is now
complete so that 'we are no longer ashamed of the toilets or the kitchen.' It has
changed neither the mood nor the formula: a daily set menu, at one sitting, that
takes in four courses without choice before the cheese and sweet stage, where
choice comes in. It constitutes tremendous value and shows absolute integrity
as to ingredients as well as skill in cooking. Here is a spring meal, with
comments from two independent parties: smoked trout pâté that 'was gentle'
and a tomato and onion salad 'with a piercing vinaigrette'; then nettle soup of
'wonderful taste and texture.' 'While we ate our soup Mr Johnson delivered a
panegyric on the nettle. The soup was rich and thick, apparently made without
stock, but with plenty of cream, rather in the manner of a classic French
watercress soup.' Steamed halibut with lengthwise slices of banana and
toasted almonds but no sauce came next; it was excellent quality though too
many almonds obstructed appreciation of the admirable combination of
banana with fish. The turkey breasts were 'of impeccable moistness and
flavour' with an emulsified sauce of Dijon mustard and fugitive orange. To one
side was a small quantity of dark meat, cubed and casseroled with cider and
tarragon. 'Ample demonstration of the meat's versatility;' 'brilliant, we got a
free second helping.' A huge oval platter of vegetables comes with the meat:
cauliflower and coriander, spinach and cabbage with raisins (unstoned) and
sour cream, 'a wonderful combination', swede with pine kernels, plain carrots,
leeks and mashed potato. Six unpasteurised British cheeses showed what we
can do: 'Tottington goats' left the French standing,' 'mature Lancashire was
notable.' Four desserts are offered: 'I had all four': chocolate angel cake, fruit
salad of guava, passion-fruit, mango and pineapple, rhubarb and ginger amber
that could have done with a 'little sugar' according to one, but was
'refreshingly tart' for another, and crème brûlée. Coffee comes with a plate of
chocolates. This meal gets much approbation, differences of opinion surfacing
over bulk (one reader had seconds of everything) and seasoning (Ros Hunter
likes neither salt nor sugar). It should be stressed how enveloping, enjoyable
and singular an experience these evenings are found. The great wine list
notwithstanding, most people elect to drink Chris Johnson's choice of wines
by the glass through the meal. He happily lectures on their conjunction with
the food, as one reader reports: 'with the halibut, an inspired choice of 1988
Wiederhirn Pinot Gris; we are enjoined to make a soup of the fish, banana, nuts
and wine in one mouthful. Mr Johnson makes a series of rapid, noisy,
masticating actions to encourage us.' Chris Johnson might have done well at
Hyde Park Corner. There is also a certain theatre of the kitchen's relations with
front of house. Dinner is long, planned to finish around midnight; some find it
too long, most do not. 'I counted an hour and a quarter between halibut and
turkey: good for the digestion, but accompanied by uncomfortable shifting in
one's chair.' One reason for extended timing is 'concentration', understandable

and accepted, and sheer quantity. Quite a lot of food may pass one's lips. This is not, perhaps, a place to visit too frequently. If bad luck strikes, several points of similarity may emerge. One person who went in July and then a month later found three of the four puddings were the same. But the experience is so remarkable that it should be full for years and thus enforce a period between bookings. A note about taking children: 'our style only suits very sophisticated children', the owners say. The wine list is just as distinctive as the food. The 'short' list is of 150 wines, arranged by grape type. The 'long' list is a cellar book, geographically divided, of 1000 bins. Each is full of notes, the long list marked where items are not yet ready to drink. Chris Johnson notes that the long list is read in instalments by regulars. It would be superogatory to mention many particulars. He will fill in all the details. Spain and Italy are well covered, with good starts made in the New World but the major glories are in the French stock. He has a motto on the front, 'Life is too short to drink cheap wines' which is fair warning that the stock is aristocratic. Therefore, although prices are not greedy, most of the wines cost quite a lot from the merchants in the first instance. Orange juice is fresh. Lillet is in the bar list though not yet Suze, the ideal aperient.

CHEF: Ros Hunter PROPRIETORS: R.C.P.L. Ltd
OPEN: Wed to Sat, D only (Tue by arrangement)
MEALS: 8 for 8.30
PRICES: Set D £23 (£31)
CARDS: Access, Visa
SEATS: 20. Private parties: 12 main room. Children welcome. Smart dress preferred. No smoking in dining-room. Music. One sitting

---

REDLYNCH Wiltshire   map 2

▲ Langley Wood

Hamptworth Road, Redlynch SP5 2PB   COOKING 1
ROMSEY (0794) 390348   COST £15−£26

This is the personal fief of David and Sylvia Rosen and almost all readers comment on the good value they offer. 'The surroundings are pleasantly unpretentious,' notes one report. The manor is surrounded by acres of woodland and David is adept at building log fires. 'Where are the staff?' cried one reader who saw only David Rosen during the length of his stay. 'He does not stand on ceremony,' said another. All are agreed that, while the necessities are well provided, it is not a hotel in conventional terms. Yet the dining-room functions smoothly and well, one pair of hands or no. Back in the kitchen, Sylvia Rosen is an inventive cook within the framework of a short *carte*. Good reports have come of rabbit in red wine sauce with prunes, and fillet of beef steak with cold curried apricot sauce. Vegetables are praised almost unanimously for their variety. There is more than a nod towards vegetarians with walnut-stuffed aubergines as a first-course and leek roulade as a main dish for instance. If meat can be served with a fruit, it will be as a rule. Desserts such as orange fool, summer pudding and chocolate truffle cake have been rated higher than a trifle with little fruit. House vin de pays is still £5. The rest of the list is creditable and mainly French. Bedrooms are described as 'spacious, simple and very good value' by one, as 'basic' by another.

CHEF: Sylvia Rosen   PROPRIETORS: David and Sylvia Rosen
OPEN: Wed to Sat, D only and Sun L
MEALS: 12.45 to 2, 7.30 to 11
PRICES: £16 (£22), Set Sun L £11 (£15)
CARDS: Access, Amex, Diners, Visa
SEATS: 30. Private parties: 65 main room. Car-park, 25 places. Vegetarian meals. Children's helpings. No cigars/pipes in dining-room. Wheelchair access (also WC). Music
ACCOMMODATION: 3 rooms. B&B £15 to £30. Baby facilities. Pets welcome. Afternoon teas. Garden. Scenic

---

RICHMOND Surrey   map 3

Chez Max

291 Sandycombe Road,
Richmond TW9 3LU   COOKING 3
081-940 3590   COST £31−£55

This little restaurant on a back road from Kew to Richmond has been lovingly furnished to replicate some ideal France. It is very uncomfortable and very crowded. The barely legible menu is in a syntactically strange, abbreviated French. It is set-price but there are numerous supplements and in the end, the price is high. Run by twin brothers, one in the kitchen and one front of house, the experience of eating Chez Max, or Chez Marc, can be surprising for the unprepared. Max will come and explain the menu for you; though anglophone, he is francophone for customers, and he does it in Franglais: 'Quenelles de homard with sauce de seafood' might be an example. Although at first sight it may appear to be an old-fashioned *bistrot à vins*, the drift of the menu is towards top-quality produce cooked in old-fashioned ways. There are not many mousses but an amazing quantity of rich offal, wine and cream. Some aspects of the place sometimes obtrude too much on people's enjoyment: smokers (though no pipes), discomfort, a determined ritual to the meal (menu explanation, then nibbles, then the food, no choice for dessert). A certain chaos to the service irritates some while entrancing others because it does seem well meant. The final bill may take the shine off that, though. The food is excellent until chaos extends to the kitchen; then disaster may strike. A soupe paysanne in which the garlic must have wafted as far as Kew pagoda and which was heavy with ham and vegetables; côte de boeuf done on the grill; rabbit in white wine; sauté of foie gras on spinach with a sweet wine sauce; veal kidneys *en chemise*; fillet of beef with green peppercorns; chicken and lobster, sauce Nantua; and squab with cloves of garlic are some dishes that celebrate old France – sometimes main dishes are given headings: 'Plat du jour lyonnaise, tradition, bressane,' etc. The end of the meal is cheese, then a tarte Tatin, a sorbet and a chocolate mousse, perhaps some cherries: no choice, sometimes good, sometimes scrag end. Coffee is strong. Generosity marks the Renzlands' spirit, in the cooking and the serving, but they have now found it has to be paid for. Many wish the bills were not so high, and that the form, the content and the price were more in harmony. The wine list is also out of sync in that it is aristocratic and dear. It is wise not to order from it unless you know what you are in for. The wines are good to very good, but sloppily treated. To be fair, there are daily specials at £8.50 and house wine is £12.50. This place is for the hungry, the converted and the francophile: they will love it and smile; others may sometimes scowl.

CHEFS: Marc and Max Renzland   PROPRIETORS: Marc and Max Renzland
OPEN: Tue to Sun
CLOSED: 25 and 26 Dec
MEALS: 12.30 to 2.30, 7.30 to 10.30 (9.30 Sun)
PRICES: Set L £19.50 (£31) to £22.50 (£36), Set D £26.50 (£39) to £32.50 (£46).
Service 12.5%
CARDS: Access, Amex, Visa
SEATS: 38. Private parties: 30 main room. Children's helpings (L only). No children under 8. No pipes in dining-room. Wheelchair access. Air-conditioned

---

RICHMOND   North Yorkshire   map 7

▲ *Howe Villa*

Whitcliffe Mill, Richmond DL10 4TJ   COOKING 2
RICHMOND (0748) 850055   COST £15–£20

It is not far from Richmond centre, but be warned that the route is circuitous. Take the Leyburn and Reeth road and turn left at the Tyre Service Station; follow the signs for Richmond Cleaners and Howe Villa. A local correspondent remarked: 'Nothing changes here, unless it's for the better. Anita Berry's cooking never varies; her standards are high.' The rather tacky approach of light industry and a caravan park is put behind you once through the gates. Serenity reigns; the well-proportioned facade gives courage; the pleasant decoration is a happy frame for the view of the river Swale from the dining-room. Cooking has no frills but the ingredients are delightfully fresh and presented generously and properly. There is no choice for the main course, which may be a roast joint but is often something like noisettes of lamb with a filo parcel filled with spinach; breast of chicken with a madeira sauce; or ham with Cumberland sauce. Vegetables are fresh, crunchy and 'a huge helping.' There is a choice of three for the first course and for dessert. Thereafter comes a cheeseboard (local of course) and coffee for the all-in price. For one happy couple these alternatives spanned a salmon pancake with a well-made hollandaise and platter of fresh fruits with melon and a lemon sorbet to begin, then a hazelnut gateau with home-made vanilla ice-cream and an Alsace apple tart to finish. Good bread is made by Anita Berry – who may also answer the front door with one hand while whipping a roulade mixture with the other – and she serves nice canapés with a complimentary apéritif. She also waits at table as well as cooking the meal. Her question, when returning our questionnaire, 'Why aren't there 25 hours in a day?' was evidently not rhetorical. The Villa is not licensed (hence the complimentary aperitif) and does not charge corkage. This is a place that should be treasured.

'*Bad luck struck a few weeks ago when the chef injured his back* en pleine wonton *and had to be stretched out.*' **From a reader**

CHEF: Anita Berry   PROPRIETORS: Tom and Anita Berry
OPEN: all week, D only
CLOSED: Dec to end Feb
MEALS: 7.30 to 8
PRICES: Set D £15 to £17. Service inc
SEATS: 12. Private parties: 12 main room. Car-park. Children's helpings by arrangement.
No children under 8. No smoking in dining-room
ACCOMMODATION: 4 rooms, all with bath/shower. D,B&B from £65. Deposit: £20.
No children under 8. Garden. TV. Scenic. Doors close at 11.30. Confirm by 6.30
[Which? Hotel Guide]

RIDGEWAY Derbyshire   map 5

Old Vicarage 🍷

Ridgeway Moor, Ridgeway S12 3XW
SHEFFIELD (0742) 475814
off A616, on B6054 nearly opposite   COOKING 4
village church   COST £32–£51

It is not an easy place to find. The tentacles of Sheffield obscure one's sense of
direction. Make for Ridgeway church. The house itself, its gardens looking out
to open fields, is furnished discreetly with none of the excessive ruching and
rigging of some country houses. Rather, it is on a domestic scale with warm
cream paint, comfortable sofas, good pictures and myriad flowers. There is a
conservatory as well as the main dining-room and the huge, efficient stove
dispels any draughts thence. Sadly, Peter Bramley died late in 1989, which
must have been a great blow to a settled family partnership. Tessa Bramley, his
widow, continues as chef, while their son, Andrew, runs the front of house and
the wine list. She is a fine cook. She has absorbed the technical lessons and
shifts in tastes and flavours propagated by the neo-classical chefs of the last 10
years, such as Blanc, Ladenis and Mosimann, and grafted them to a strong
sense of English and domestic cookery. To this is joined Andrew Bramley's
ideas of how to run a restaurant: great attention to detail, fine appointments, an
English style that stops short of stuffy. It makes 'a satisfying symbiosis of
country house and accomplished cookery in the modern style.' A great point is
made of the priority of supplies and of mentioning suppliers – like the new
source of farmyard chickens and geese from Ford Farm, Ridgeway, noted this
year by Andrew Bramley – and of home cultivation where possible – to which
end the Bramleys' large and productive garden. This shines through the short
menu of five or six choices in each course as well as the constant small touches
on the food itself: a blossom here, leaf there, somehow stopping short of being
precious. These varied strands are seen in dishes such as terrine of chicken,
offal and foie gras with apple and geranium jelly; fillet of lamb with mint and
garlic and tortellini of devilled kidneys; or saddle of wild rabbit roasted with
herbs, its legs made into a rabbit pie, and served with mulled pears. It also
shows in the good range of vegetables, each with its own small touch, again
imagination without excess. This cooking is usually assured, strong on game
and wild meats – which occasionally have their attendant problems of
toughness – but very good, too, on the extras that make a modern meal:
baking, home-made chocolates, interesting appetisers. The skill extends to

desserts as well; the baked chocolate pudding still gets raptures, but miniature fruit tartlets with crème pâtissière show the skill in pastry as did the shortbread layered with orange segments and orange cream on an orange custard, or the hazelnut and strawberry roulade, or a variation of hazelnut roulade with little heaps of mango on a coffee sauce, 'an amazing amalgam of flavours'. The clothing of the waitresses in Victorian skirts imparts a certain theatricality to the service, which is in fact chatty and informed. Andrew Bramley will tell you the origins of ingredients to the last detail and will be just as knowledgeable about his fine wine list. This, a roll-call of the great and the good, is clearly presented and, thankfully, lacks the portentous notes favoured by so many lesser restaurants. With such careful selection from all the major regions of France and a well chosen set of Spanish wines, is it greedy to ask for the same attention to be given to Italy and the Antipodes? As we went to press, the Bramleys were planning to open for lunch too, Tuesday to Saturday, with much the same menu as at dinner.

CHEF: Tessa Bramley   PROPRIETORS: Tessa Bramley and Andrew Bramley
OPEN: Tue to Sat
MEALS: 12.15 to 2.30, 7 to 10
PRICES: £21 (£32) to £31 (£43)
SEATS: 50. Private parties: 30 main room, 30 private room. Car-park, 30 places. Vegetarian meals by arrangement. No children under 12. Smart dress preferred. No smoking in dining-room

---

RIPLEY Surrey   map 3

Michels ♀

| 13 High Street, Ripley GU23 6AQ | COOKING 2 |
| GUILDFORD (0483) 224777 | COST £25–£44 |

Erik Michel once admitted to be inspired by Frédy Girardet. His cooking in this brick house, now light and attractive where once it was all heavy maroons and patterned carpets, has always shown the influence of high fashion: a preoccupation with display and a fascination for melding as many potential flavours in a dish as possible. In previous years, there were mousses a-million on the menu; wherever you turned, something had one on top or inside. That has faded from the set-price menu of maybe half-a-dozen choices and, although there are still plenty of tastes knocking around on the plate, the approach is gutsier. Two years ago, chicken was stuffed with a chicken mousse, foie gras and vegetables. Last year it came filled with langoustines. This year it contains merely watercress and chives, though a foie gras accompaniment has reappeared. Lamb used to have an envelope of tarragon mousse, now it has just a strong mushroom sauce. The conversion is not total, for many dishes are still characterised by complicated balances. A dish of poached salmon had a strong chanterelle sauce and an accompaniment of carrot 'spaghetti' cooked with garlic and lemon, but at the same meal a more homogeneous partridge with lentils and leeks struck a more robust and fitting note. The intentions are clear. It is not as clear whether they are achieved to the same standard every night. Desserts have overtones of fashion about them, too. 'Three citrus fruits' consists of a lemon tart, an orange soufflé and a lime sorbet. Service may have some

437

hiccups, but you will be consoled with crudités while waiting. Be consoled, too, by the wine list which, while not long, contains some good choices from very fashionable growers. Wine prices are not high for Surrey though it is easy to run up an overall bill for £100 for two in the evening (lunch is cheaper). House wine: £8. CELLARMAN'S CHOICE: Ch. la Cardonne 1982, £16.95; Côtes du Rhône 1984, Guigal, £10.95.

CHEF: Erik Michel   PROPRIETORS: Erik and Karen Michel
OPEN: Tue to Sun, exc Sat L and Sun D
MEALS: 12.30 to 2, 7.30 to 9.15 (9.45 Sat)
PRICES: Set L £16.50 (£25) to £20 (£29), Set D £16.50 (£25) to £28 (£37)
CARDS: Access, Amex, Diners, Visa
SEATS: 45. Children welcome

RIPPONDEN   West Yorkshire   map 5

Over the Bridge

Millfold, Ripponden HX6 4DJ   COOKING 2
HALIFAX (0422) 823722   COST £29

Go up the outside steps to a bar before going down a floor to the restaurant in this conversion of a weaving shed or weavers' cottages. Tastes are quite assertive on a set-price menu of half a dozen choices with a soup course in second position. Typical of the cooking are salmon fishcakes with caper sauce; mushrooms with pesto; gingered scallops with orange hollandaise; chicken with spices and honey. Fruit and modern pickles, as in a spinach and lemon mousse with an apple relish, seem to figure less prominently than hitherto. Occasionally the aim may seem more ambitious than the reality, the food becoming pretentious or over-fussy, but in general the cooking is competent and the service pleasant. The wine list has some fair bottles, some very fair prices and a good range for every taste. Ch. Haut-Bailly, Théo Faller, Brokenback Vineyard, Dry Creek and Abel Garnier are good names anywhere. House wine: £7 and £8.95. CELLARMAN'S CHOICE: Ch. Musar 1982, £11.75; Marlborough, Stoneleigh Sauvignon Blanc 1988, £11.25.

CHEFS: Sue Tyer and Lindsay Barratt   PROPRIETOR: Ian H. Beaumont (Dales Hotels)
OPEN: Mon to Sat D
CLOSED: bank hols
MEALS: 7.30 to 9.30
PRICES: Set D £18.50 (£24)
CARDS: Access, Amex, Visa
SEATS: 48. Private parties: 25 main room. Car-park, 50 places. No children under 12. Wheelchair access (1 step)

'Accompanying vegetables tend to be a bit hit and miss, both in choice and in preparation, eg, overcooked red cabbage and green beans, which do not complement or compliment King prawns with wild mushrooms.' On eating in the Isle of Man

The Guide *is totally independent, accepts no free hospitality, and survives on the number of copies sold each year.*

ROADE Northamptonshire — map 3

Roadhouse Restaurant

16-18 High Street Roade NN7 2NW
ROADE (0604) 863372

COOKING 3
COST £18−£29

The Kewleys run a cosy country restaurant in two open-plan rooms with a small bar straight ahead as you walk in. 'Chris Kewley continues to improve in the kitchen,' writes one reader in form-teacher mood,' 'each time we've been we've felt this.' The menu does not so much evolve as revolve around a core of favourite dishes. Asparagus arrives in pastry with a herb butter sauce; moules marinière is 'excellent and fresh;' gravlax is properly home-cured; rack of lamb with herbs and garlic is served with a compote of haricot beans, bacon and tomato; breast of roast guinea-fowl comes with a casserole of the leg meat. Ingredients are sound, fresh and sometimes local, and simple dishes can delight with both flavour and texture, as in a soup of cabbage, bacon and salami or breast of chicken stuffed with leeks and wrapped in bacon with a piquant herb sauce. There are generous bowls of vegetables. The saucing can be rich − beurre blanc is a trademark − as can puddings such as chocolate marquise. Butter and cream can mount during a meal to send the calories off the graph. The *Guide* asked all restaurateurs, 'Do you see your restaurant as a place where customers can eat healthily?' The Kewleys replied to the effect that many people prefer rich dishes when they come out to eat: 'most customers regard it as an occasional treat.' Take-up of the lighter dishes, say the Kewleys, is less than encouraging and red meat is simply more popular than fish as a main course. Reports bear this out, with nominations for veal in madeira sauce, pheasant with redcurrant sauce, veal kidney and sweetbreads, and rack of lamb outnumbering those for fish. Favourite puddings include raspberry tart and pancake filled with caramelised pears and Cointreau-flavoured custard. Wines are not tackled with quite the same enthusiam as the food but some care has gone into the selection and bottles are fairly priced. The list is varied and includes some good Australians and Italians. House French: £8. It must be one of the few lists in the area on which clarets and burgundies do not outnumber bottles from other regions, a happy characteristic. CELLARMAN'S CHOICE: Yalumba Chardonnay Signature 1986, £13.95; Viña Alorta 1983, Reserva Rioja, £12.60 and consider 1983 Ch. Ormes de Pez and Echézeaux from Mongeard-Mugneret.

CHEF: Christopher Kewley   PROPRIETORS: Christopher and Susan Kewley
OPEN: Tue to Sat, exc Sat L
MEALS: 12.30 to 1.45, 7 to 12
PRICES: £19 (£24), Set L £13 (£18). Service inc
CARDS: Access, Visa
SEATS: 32. Private parties: 40 main room. Car-park, 15 places. Children's helpings. Smart dress preferred

All details are as accurate as possible at the time of going to press, but chefs and owners often change, and it is wise to check by telephone before making a special journey. Many readers have been disappointed when set-price bargain meals are no longer available. Ask when booking.

ROCHFORD Essex map 3

▲ *Renoufs*

1 South Street, Rochford SS4 1BL COOKING 1
SOUTHEND (0702) 544393 COST £34

Renoufs is dominated by Derek Renouf; he is large enough to be inescapably visible and must constitute a living recommendation of his cooking. This, over a long menu, is conventional in its restriction to prime cuts and prime fish but has shown some reduction in its dependence on foie gras, moving on to mushrooms and herbs. The speciality of the house is three versions of pressed duck, that from Rouen being admittedly 'rich', and it is. Although this may not please those who have become used to a lighter style, there is no gainsaying that Derek Renouf knows the techniques of cooking: from onion soup through grills to a lemon mousse, light and zestful, from the five-tiered trolley. There are also days when the cooking seriously misses its mark: 'heavy handed', 'over-rich', 'over salted'. The wine list takes in a mixed bunch of claret vintages, but the off-years can yield bargains on a lucky strike. There is a wide range from classic French regions as well as special showcase sections on Dom. de la Romanée-Conti, Ch. Gilette, Duboeuf and others. House wine from France is £8.40.

CHEF/PROPRIETOR: Derek Renouf
OPEN: all week, exc Sat L and Mon and Sun D
CLOSED: first 3 weeks Jan, last week June, first week July
MEALS: 12 to 1.45, 7 to 8.30 (9.30 Fri and Sat)
PRICES: £21 (£28). Service inc
CARDS: Access, Amex, Diners, Visa
SEATS: 100. Private parties: 70 main room. Vegetarian meals. Children welcome.
Wheelchair access (also WC). Music. Air-conditioned
ACCOMMODATION: 24 rooms, all with bath/shower. Rooms for disabled. B&B £54 to £72.
Baby facilities. Pets welcome. Garden. Air-conditioning. TV. Phone [*Which? Hotel Guide*]

ROMSEY Hampshire map 2

Old Manor House ▮

21 Palmerston Street, Romsey SO5 18GF COOKING 4
ROMSEY (0794) 517353 COST £23–£50

It is surprising what people notice about restaurants. In the new crop of reports on the Old Manor House, everyone mentions the basket of breads offered and cut for each table – walnut, onion and raisin, pain de campagne and more – and the synchronised dome lifting. They don't forget the food, but observation of the one colours their views of the other. They detect a serious effort to elaborate service and presentation in this well-restored half-timbered house, doubtless once standing among closes and fields but now fully in town. Some feel this has put the prices up too high, particularly the cheaper set-price lunch menus (though by London standards they are not dear), and made the place more of a 'temple' than it was. Restaurants go through these cycles of change, sometimes barely noticing it themselves, but it should also be recorded that the bulk of opinion is favourable. The repertoire displayed by the menus indicates

Mauro Bregoli's Italian origins, for instance: bresaola made at home; arista de maiale, home-smoked fillet of pork; at least one fresh pasta dish; and an enjoyment of meats such as hare, venison and kid. Yet French modern cooking shows his wish to be part of the neo-classical pan-European mainstream: brill with celeriac and Sauternes sauce; langoustines with artichoke hearts with a chive sauce; foie gras à la Normande. This also means that the meal starts with an appetiser, perhaps a pike quenelle, that it may involve an intermediate sorbet and a remarkable choice of cheese from Olivier, and that there is a full-blooded wine-list. The kitchen is thoroughly self-supporting, as it has to be to maintain these standards: those breads; those cured and smoked meats; the ceps gathered by the staff and dried in the kitchen to give year-round supplies; the huntin', shootin', and fishin' side of Mauro Bregoli, hunter-gatherer-in-chief for his customers. A meal in the winter began with foie gras (at a stiff supplement) pan-fried and just caramelised, with a fan of apple slices cooked with calvados; ceps were served with snails in a pastry case in a red wine sauce permeated wholly with the essence of mushrooms; mallard breast was fanned out, accompanied by a rather under-done leg and a peach wrapped in filo pastry, the sauce a clean balance of fruit, acid, and spices; partridge, plain roasted with bacon, was served on a potato galette with a compote of cabbage and showed the kitchen's skill both in choosing and cooking game. Desserts ranged from tarte Tatin on an orange custard swirled with chocolate and crème brûlée with honey and saffron to good and varied sorbets. England may be Mauro Bregoli's adopted country but French wines, and especially Bordeaux, seem to have part of his heart with 300 fine clarets and not a duff vintage among them. Who can complain that Burgundy has only 100 plus the whites, and Italy has but two pages of magnificent wines including several 'super-Tuscans'? House wines, including Bandol from Mas de la Rouvière and Alsace from Kuentz-Bas, show equal care and a sensitivity to the customer who is not prepared to read through 30 pages of nearly 900 wines! House French £8. CELLARMAN'S CHOICE: Pinot Blanc d'Alsace 1988, £12.50; Ch. Tillède 1985, £14. The sommelier is 'charmingly knowledgeable about the wines'.

CHEF/PROPRIETOR: Mauro Bregoli
OPEN: Tue to Sun, exc Sun D
CLOSED: 24 Dec to 2 Jan, last 3 weeks Aug
MEALS: 12 to 2, 7 to 9.30
PRICES: Set L £14.50 (£23) to £21.50 (£31), £33.50 (£42)
CARDS: Access, Visa
SEATS: 45. 6 tables outside. Private parties: 12 main room, 24 private room. Car-park, 12 places. Children welcome. Smart dress preferred. No cigars/pipes in dining-room

RUGBY Warwickshire   map 5

▲ Grosvenor Hotel

Clifton Road, Rugby CV21 3QQ   COOKING 1
RUGBY (0788) 535686   COST £19–£34

Richard Johnson is a chef who enjoys elaboration, often elaborately described on the menu. He sometimes tests the limit of orthodoxy. Avocado pear with poached egg and béarnaise sauce sounds wrong, yet was enjoyed by the customer who reported it. Bets are hedged by offering plain grilled meats and fish in parallel to the more extreme. It sounds more fantastic than it is. Most ingredients sit happily together, even if breast of chicken filled with soft fruits and poached with an orange and vanilla sauce sounds like dessert in another guise. Service can be very slow, in the dining-room and from the kitchen. The wine list continues the prose, even getting in an 'erotic' for the Sauternes. Notes apart, it is a fair range, many from the reliable merchant Thorman Hunt, at firm prices. House French: £7.50: CELLARMAN'S CHOICE: Pouilly Fumé 1988, Dom. Thibault-André, £17.30; Ch. Roudier, Montagne-St-Emilion 1985, £16.05.

CHEF: Richard Johnson   PROPRIETORS: J. Hall and J. Hawes
OPEN: all week, exc Sat L
MEALS: 12 to 2, 7 to 10
PRICES: £20 (£28), Set L £11.85 (£19)
CARDS: Access, Amex, Diners, Visa
SEATS: 42. Private parties: 40 private room. Car-park, 40 places. Children welcome. Smart dress preferred. No pipes in dining-room. Music
ACCOMMODATION: 22 rooms, all with bath/shower. B&B £55 to £85. Deposit: £20. Baby facilities. Afternoon teas. Garden. TV. Phone

---

RYE   East Sussex   map 3

Landgate Bistro ♥

5–6 Landgate, Rye TN31 7LH   COOKING 3
RYE (0797) 222829   COST £22

About a hundred yards down the hill from the historic Landgate – Rye's protection in the past – the modest shop-front, fresh looking decor and casual atmosphere suggest a neighbourhood bistro. The remarkable little restaurant is much more than that. Its strength lies partly in the quality of ingredients and the attention to details: fresh fish from the south-coast ports, a full range of salad leaves from Park Hill Produce, Appledore, and 'the very best real loaf' baked in-house. The menu now features some new dishes, such as poached turbot with watercress sauce and jugged hare, but perennials continue to get votes. Squid stewed with white wine, tomato and garlic, and perfectly balanced leek and Roquefort tart are firm favourites, and there is praise for wild duck breast, sliced 'impressively thin' on a port and orange sauce; fish stew; and pigeon breasts sauté with stock and red wine sauce. Almond and apple tart is sufficiently rich not to need the little jug of cream provided, while chocolate marquise and summer pudding have both been good. All this comes at prices that make it exceptional value for money. 'Tipping is unnecessary and discouraged.' Like the menu, the wine list has developed; everything is chosen with care and purpose; the run of bourgeois clarets at very reasonable prices sets the tone. House French: £6.50. CELLARMAN'S CHOICE: Lirac, Les Queyrades, Dom. André Mejan 1985, £13.90.

'We have to insist on bookings for dinner as we have to know how many bread rolls to cook for the meal and how many vegetables to prepare.' A Welsh restaurateur, explaining policy

---

CHEF: Toni Ferguson-Lees   PROPRIETORS: Nick Parkin and Toni Ferguson-Lees
OPEN: Tue to Sat, D only
MEALS: 7 to 9.30
PRICES: £14 (£18). Service inc
CARDS: Access, Amex, Diners, Visa
SEATS: 34. Children's helpings. Music

SAFFRON WALDEN Essex   map 3

Old Hoops

15 King Street, Saffron Walden CB10 1HE   COOKING 1
SAFFRON WALDEN (0799) 22813   COST £24

Souvenir menus from dozens of other restaurants decorate the dark green walls
of the first floor dining-room. Mismatched chairs and starched linen allied to
doting service contribute to a sense of comfort and well-being. The menu
changes frequently, but stays within a fairly constant repertoire with slightly
more elaborate offerings at dinner-time. There is also a vegetarian menu.
Dishes that have been endorsed include the long-running 'musselcress soup' (a
mixture of watercress, potatoes and mussels, finished with cream); the lamb
dijonnaise; an excellent herb and onion omelette 'just melting in the centre';
and good floating islands for dessert. Vegetables are generous, simple and
decent. There is a short wine list, adequate and unexciting but all very fairly
priced. The menu states that there is no service charge. House French: £8.25

CHEF: Ray Morrison   PROPRIETORS: Don Irwin and Ray Morrison
OPEN: Tue to Sat
CLOSED: 2 weeks in summer
MEALS: 12 to 2.30, 7 to 10
PRICES: £13 (£20) Service inc
CARDS: Access, Amex, Diners, Visa
SEATS: 40. Private parties: 40 main room. Children's helpings. Music

---

ST KEYNE Cornwall   map 1

▲ *Well House* ♥

St Keyne PL14 4RN
LISKEARD (0579) 42001   COOKING 3
on B3254, 3m S of Liskeard   COST £27–£40

'There is no sign of flagging in the standard of service or attention in the hotel
or restaurant, nor of a decline in the excellent cooking. The Well House
manages to be a fine hotel and restaurant, not a good restaurant with a few
rooms thrown in. As a result, one's morning tea and (home-made) biscuits are,
in their way, as good as dinner.' That was one couple's judgement, but
endorsed by others, including a mention for the packed lunch. St Keyne, barely
a village, is to the south of Liskeard, and the Well House is a consequence of
that first wave of retirement homes built by old colonials and veterans in
Victoria's reign. Though by no means grand, it is highly polished thanks to
Nicholas Wainford's serious attention to decoration. David Pope has remained

443

in the kitchen and produces two menus – as well as high tea for children under 8 – for the cool, modern dining-room: a no-choice meal of five courses and coffee that changes every day, and a short set-price meal of up to five options at each course that changes monthly. Cooking is assured and modern: duck and wild mushroom mousse is wrapped in duck meat and served with a quince compote; soups of mange-tout, or game, or crab and lobster that doesn't stint on the shellfish; layered puff pastry, pigeon and broad beans scented with sage; squab on cabbage with a chicken liver and bacon sauce; a plate of fish with baby vegetables and a chive hollandaise; tiny joints of beef, lamb and pork served lightly with mixed vegetables. Flavours are well handled, quantities are generous, techniques up-to-date. Good purchasing shows in the materials, not least for the cheeseboard, and the kitchen also enjoys baking: breakfast brioche, biscuits here and there, walnut and rosemary bread to go with the cheese, accurate pastry. Desserts will usually include at least one pastry item, perhaps pecan pie or a prune and armagnac tart. Nicholas Wainford superintends everything but the kitchen in a punctilious way. The bottom line on credit card vouchers is always filled in so tipping is truly optional. His attention to the bar and the wine list have borne fruit. Zingy cocktails, 'Martinis not bettered by the Carlyle in New York', may give strength for later exertions, but the wines that accompany the food are also well chosen and offer a fair enough range for anyone. Prices are not excessive, nor did they increase between mid-1989 and mid-1990. The list is dominated by France and has best length in claret with some 1970s and 1966s worth investigating. There are excellent growers from Burgundy and just a baker's dozen of half-bottles (excluding Champagne and sweet wines). House wine: £7.

CHEF: David Pope   PROPRIETOR: Nicholas Wainford
OPEN: Tue to Sun
MEALS: 12.30 to 2, 7.30 to 9
PRICES: Set L £21 (£27), Set D £27.50 (£34)
CARDS: Access, Amex, Visa
SEATS: 36. 5 tables outside. Private parties: 40 main room. Car-park, 24 places. No children under 8. Smart dress preferred. Wheelchair access (1 step)
ACCOMMODATION: 7 rooms, all with bath/shower. B&B £60 to £80. Deposit: £25 per person per night. Baby facilities. Pets welcome. Afternoon teas. Garden. Swimming-pool. Tennis. TV. Phone. Scenic [*Which? Hotel Guide*]

ST LEONARD'S East Sussex   map 3

Röser's ▮

64 Eversfield Place
St Leonard's-on-Sea TN37 6DB   COOKING 3
HASTINGS (0424) 712218   COST £21–£36

Gerald Röser is a serious chef cooking modern classical food in an unlikely situation. Visitors not only get canapés, but an appetiser as well – smoked salmon and noodles perhaps. The raw material is carefully sought out, from speciality vegetables and salads to fish from the boats. In this, Gerald Röser has energetic and time-consuming help from his wife Jenny who works for the kitchen as much as front-of-house. There is no lack of luxury ingredients: caviare, morels, cheese from Olivier, Belgian chocolate. The restaurant is of dark wood panelling, antlers, copper and a stuffed pheasant (not edible) but with good napery and incidentals. As you go through the hall, view the kitchen: well staffed, clean and impressive. Menus are now all fixed price, a substantially cheaper one operating at lunch. The cooking is as up to date as any, with dishes from a summer menu like 'cappuccino' of vegetable soup, a frothy job with a cream topping; avocado, mango and prawn salad with a yoghurt dressing; scallops with lentils and green coriander; monkfish on shredded fennel with a star anise sauce; or a mille-feuille of apples with a butterscotch sauce. Pike makes a regular showing, as in a pike mousse with smoked salmon sauce and Beluga caviare. Flavours have been reported as intense in splendid duck breast with madeira sauce; an excellent dill and mustard mayonnaise with gravlax, where the fish itself was saved by its accompaniment; a tournedos topped with a mousse of foie gras and a rich madeira sauce reduced to the correct point – that is, short of either tar or salt. An 'indulgence' of Cointreau showed skill with mousses, whether sweet or savoury, as did an asparagus mousse served with fresh spears. The food is not cheap – 'nor should it be,' may be the response – so that survival among the English seaside attractions of Hastings and St Leonards must owe much to the Rösers' faith in their capacities. The same might be said of the wine list: remarkably long, very good and sometimes pricy on the better bottles. The depth is good, more than a dozen Chablis from the best people; some really good clarets with good affordable ones as well as first growths, and from decent years; plenty of halves; a wide and enticing German section and vintage ports including 1963 Warre's by the glass.

CHEF: Gerald Röser   PROPRIETORS: Gerald and Jenny Röser
OPEN: Tue to Sat, exc Sat L
MEALS: 12 to 2, 7 to 10
PRICES: Set L £14.95 (£21) and £24.50 (£30), Set D £24.50 (£30). Service inc
CARDS: Access, Amex, Diners, Visa
SEATS: 40. Private parties: 20 main room, 40 private room. Children welcome. No pipes in dining-room. Wheelchair access (2 steps). Music

---

ST MARGARET'S AT CLIFFE   Kent   map 3

▲ Wallett's Court

West Cliffe,
St Margaret's at Cliffe CT15 6EW
DOVER (0304) 852424

COOKING 2
COST £22–£35

Anyone delayed from crossing the Channel, arriving back in England after a long continental rush to the French ports, or merely wishing to explore this corner of Kent would be well advised to stay the night at this amalgam of every architectural style from the Middle Ages to the eighteenth century, lovingly restored by Chris and Lea Oakley. The rooms are good value, though gone are the days when they cost no more and were no more than a seaside boarding house. The formula of an inexpensive, short, set-price menu in the week, crowned by a five course gourmet meal on Saturdays, continues and the choice has been increased. Chris Oakley's cooking has always surprised the stranger for its enthusiasm and skill. 'I'm visiting Wallett's Court again this evening with my millionaire button-manufacturer student from Germany, and I'm sure he'll be delighted,' wrote one returnee who, this year, will notice more work done on the grounds and an expansion of hotel facilities. But for all the growth and the serious training, the Court retains, or perhaps nurtures, a country simplicity. Good reports have been had of a 'huntsman's platter' of smoked duck, pork terrine and bacon with Cumberland sauce; fettucine with prawns and Pernod; mussels with Martini and fresh herbs; salmon with a basil and tomato sauce; turbot with a crab and mustard sauce; roast leg of lamb spiked with mint and nasturtium; and desserts of meringue with pineapple or blackcurrants, many mousses, or cream confections like raspberry syllabub. The Oakleys make much of their supplies: Kentish lamb, Folkestone fish, Hebridean salmon. They even intend to rear their own beef in the paddock. Although the wine list has lengthened the selection of wines is weighted too strongly in favour of négociants to command great confidence, but prices are fair. CELLARMAN'S CHOICE: Savigny-lès-Beaune, premier cru, Les Rouvrettes 1984, £16.50.

CHEF: Chris Oakley   PROPRIETORS: Chris and Lea Oakley
OPEN: Tue to Sat, D only
MEALS: 7 to 9
PRICES: Set D £16 (£22) to £23 (£29)
CARDS: Access, Visa
SEATS: 50. Private parties: 30 main room, Car-park, 26 places. Children's helpings
ACCOMMODATION: 12 rooms, all with bath/shower. B&B £40 to £60. Baby facilities.
Garden. Snooker. TV. Scenic. Doors close at midnight. Confirm by 5 [*Which? Hotel Guide*]

ST MARTIN'S   Isles of Scilly   map 1

▲ *St Martin's Hotel*

St Martin's TR25 0QW   COOKING 1
SCILLONIA (0720) 22092   COST £11–£35

The population of the island is 84 and the way to get there is by launch. Once the jetty is negotiated, there is the hotel. Completed in 1989, it is a masterpiece of 'old fogey' design that, predictably, gets an illustration in the Prince of Wales's book on how to build without noticing the join. Reports of the cooking are less uniform than of the decoration: 'it must have formed its own blip in Laura Ashley's profit figures.' One of the difficulties is maintaining a skilled staff in so remote a location. That said, among some predictably 'hotel' food, the fresh fish produced by Martin Ault is very satisfactory and the view from the dining-room is sensational. There is a good, concise, though not cheap, wine list with Comte Lafond Sancerre and Ch. Lyonnat from St Emilion, as well as Acacia and Dry Creek from California. Curiously, vintages are not shown, which is a pity. House wine: £6.50.

The text of entries is based on unsolicited reports sent in by readers, backed up by inspections conducted anonymously. The factual details under the text are from questionnaires the Guide *sends to all restaurants that feature in the book.*

CHEFS: Martin Ault and Mhcima Licg PROPRIETOR: Robert Francis
OPEN: all week
MEALS: 12 to 1.45, 7.15 to 9
PRICES: £23 (£29), Set L £6.50 (£11), Set D £17.50 (£21). Service inc
CARDS: Access, Amex, Diners, Visa
SEATS: 80. 6 tables outside. Private parties: 80 main room; 2, 12 and 20 private rooms.
Children's helpings 5.30 to 6pm. Smart dress preferred. Music
ACCOMMODATION: 24 rooms, all with bath/shower. Rooms for disabled. B&B £55 to £150.
Deposit: 20%. Baby facilities. Pets in certain rooms only at £4 a day. Afternoon teas.
Garden. Swimming-pool. Fishing. Snooker. TV. Phone. Scenic. Confirm by 6
[*Which? Hotel Guide*]]

ST MICHAEL'S ON WYRE Lancashire   map 5

Mallards

Garstang Road,
St Michael's on Wyre PR3 0TE   COOKING 1
ST MICHAELS (099 58) 661   COST £13–£30

Back in the *Guide* after a year's enforced leave. Recent reports extol thoughtful,
well-executed dishes and a particularly warm atmosphere. Ann Steel helps
create this while husband John is creating in the kitchen, never to appear.
Drinks in the bar are served with nuts and stuffed olives. 'You are left in peace
to study the menu and the wine list. You are led eventually to a table in a room
with rough plaster walls hung with plates'. Says John Steel, 'There is an
abundant supply of mallard, fish is fresh from Fleetwood and most of the
vegetables are grown locally.' Duck breast marinated in soy sauce and served
on a sauce of orange and grapefruit juice and ginger was 'pink as ordered and
tender; the skin had a pleasant burnt flavour.' Also recommended was quail
coated in coarse-grain mustard and butter and lightly grilled. Vegetable
portions are over-generous. 'Service is good, if perhaps a little inconspicuous.'
Sunday lunch is a four-course meal and excellent value. The adequate wine list
is fairly priced. House French is £6.25. CELLARMAN'S CHOICE: Morgon, Henri
Chavy 1987, £10.80; Seppelt Gold Label Chardonnay 1988, £11.25.

CHEF: John Steel PROPRIETORS: John and Ann Steel
OPEN: Mon to Sat, D only and Sun L
CLOSED: 2 weeks Aug, 1 week Jan
MEALS: 12 to 2.30, 7 to 9.30 (10 Sat)
PRICES: £18 (£25), Set Sun L £8.50 (£13)
CARDS: Access, Visa
SEATS: 24. Private parties: 36 main room. Car-park, 20 places. Children's helpings.
No smoking while others are eating. Wheelchair access. Music

Prices quoted in the Guide *are based on information supplied by restaurateurs. The figure
in brackets below an entry is the average for a three-course meal with service, coffee and
half a bottle of house wine, as calculated by computer. The prices quoted at the top of an
entry represent a range, from the lowest average meal price to the highest; the latter is
inflated by 20 per cent to take account of the fact that very few people eat an average meal,
and also that prices are likely to rise during the year of the* Guide

Harper's

7 Ox Row, The Market Square,
Salisbury SP1 1EU
SALISBURY (0722) 333118

COOKING 1
COST £10–£25

'Real food is our speciality', say the Harpers, and few visitors to their honest restaurant would argue with that. From the windows of the upstairs dining-room there are good views of the coming and goings in the Square, but it seldom distracts from the food. The emphasis is on local produce: New Forest venison goes into a pie with burgundy and grapes; Poole plaice is grilled with herb butter. The fish soup and haddock with lemon and caper sauce have also been praised. Vegetarians get a decent deal, with anything from gazpacho and creamy mushroom tart to nut loaf with fresh basil and tomato sauce. Everyone enthuses about the home-made bread-and-butter pudding, prepared with double cream. The 'Shopper's Special' lunch is a bargain. The philosophy of quality and good value extends to the carefully selected wine list which gives good spread, both geographic and economic. House French: £8.50. Beer drinkers should look for the locally brewed Bishop's Tipple. CELLARMAN'S CHOICE: Tokay, Pinot Gris, Cuvée Jean Baptiste Adam 1983, £11.50.

CHEFS: Adrian Harper and Julie West   PROPRIETORS: Adrian and Ann Harper
OPEN: Mon to Sat
CLOSED: 25 and 26 Dec
MEALS: 12 to 2, 6.30 to 10 (10.30 Sat)
PRICES: L £13 (£19), D £14 (£21), Set L £4.30 (£10) to £6.70 (£12), Set D £13.50 (£21)
CARDS: Access, Diners, Visa
SEATS: 60. Private parties: 60 main room. Car-park. Vegetarian meals. Children's helpings. Music. Air-conditioned

Lanterna

33 Queen Street, Scarborough YO11 1HQ
SCARBOROUGH (0723) 363616

COOKING 2
COST £25

'We had dinner here last month: the biggest, juiciest mussels in a wine and garlic sauce I've ever had in England. The Italian cooking has some authenticity; the cannelloni passed with flying colours. We had to try hard to drink the house wine.' Here is a taverna, small and crowded but 'so friendly' and informal. It constitutes a fixed point to one reader's New Year visits to Scarborough where he is still greeted like an old friend. The menu does not go in for those 'everything-bar-the-kitchen-sink' listings of many trattoria, and the Areccos serve excellent meat balls (polpette) with tomato sauce; pollo pizzaiola served with saffron rice; and decent zabaglione. There is a short and inexpensive wine list, half of it Italian, with scanty details of growers and vineyards. House Italian is £8 a litre.

CHEF: G. Arecco PROPRIETORS: Mr and Mrs G. Arecco
OPEN: Tue to Sat, D only
MEALS: 7 to 9.30
PRICES: £14 (£21)
CARDS: Access, Visa
SEATS: 36. Private parties: 36 main room. Vegetarian meals. No children under 5.
Wheelchair access. Music

SCUNTHORPE Humberside   map 6

Giovanni's

44 Oswald Road, Scunthorpe DN15 7PQ   COOKING 1
SCUNTHORPE (0724) 281169   COST £17

Glass-topped tables, tiled floor, good cheerful service and a menu that goes on
from year to year offering nearly two dozen pasta dishes, acceptable pizza, a
few steaks and daily extras on a blackboard. Above all the value is excellent,
with price increases kept way below the rate of inflation. House Italian:
£6.20 a litre.

CHEF: Giuseppe Catalano PROPRIETORS: Giovanni and Angela Catalano
OPEN: Mon to Sat
MEALS: 12 to 2, 6 to 11 (11.30 Fri and Sat)
PRICES: £10 (£14). Service inc
CARDS: Access, Visa
SEATS: 90. 6 tables outside. Private parties: 100 main room. Car-park, 10 places. Vegetarian
meals. Children's helpings. Wheelchair access (also WC). Music

---

SEAFORD East Sussex   map 3

Quincy's

42 High Street, Seaford BN25 1PL   COOKING 2
SEAFORD (0323) 895490   COST £20–£31

Seaford is a seaside resort town with suburban stability and, in its tiny hub,
Ian and Dawn Dowding's still newish restaurant. Recent books by Raymond
Blanc and Nico Ladenis share the shelf with several decades of old *Good Food
Guides*. You might therefore reckon on some clever and modern cooking here.
Instead, the set menu, priced for two and three courses, settles in territory that
might have been considered daringly mid-Channel in the seventies but today
is middle-of-the-road franglais. Some imbalance has been noted: boozy sauces;
a penchant for tarts and croustades; fish as five of the eight starters, for instance.
But vegetarians get more than a look-in and, although overly strong or vague
flavours crop up now and again, Ian Dowding's cooking is for the most part
sound. Dinners are not expensive and are spiced along the way with good
home-made extras such as taramosalata, warm bread rolls and mint chocolate
petits fours. Crab mousse has been complimented, but the taste of breadcrumbs
ruled a mussel-stuffed smoked salmon mousse and there was too much
bickering among other ingredients. Simpler has been the calf's liver with port
and raisin sauce, though a little less of the overpowering stock flavour

would please more. Sweets play it safe with slight deviations from the classics. Profiteroles might be paired with strawberries and cream. More adventurous was a chocolate soufflé with Amaretto ice-cream, which was even textured and well flavoured. Nearly half of the more than 60 wines cost less than £10, and there are better than token non-French options. Lamblin House white or red is £5.75. CELLARMAN'S CHOICE: Breaky Bottom 1989, £9.85. There is good service from Dawn Dowding and bright, well-informed staff. In keeping with the cottage theme, and to compensate for limited space, tables are closely packed. Smokers are divided between the two dining-rooms on request, so on occasion there may be a completely non-smoking gathering.

CHEF: Ian Dowding PROPRIETORS: Ian and Dawn Dowding
OPEN: Tue to Sat, D only
CLOSED: First 2 weeks Sept
MEALS: 7.15 to 10
PRICES: Set D £13.95 (£20) to £19.95(£26)
CARDS: Access, Visa
SEATS: 32. Private parties: 20 main room. Vegetarian meals. Children's helpings on request. Children welcome. Music

---

SEAVIEW Isle of Wight   map 2

▲ Seaview Hotel

The High Street, Seaview PO34 5EX   COOKING 1
SEAVIEW (0983) 612711   COST £28

Seaview is a little village sporting a fleet of a hundred dinghies, and the hotel has as good a grandstand view of their water-borne frolics as any. The clientele divides between holidaying or visiting couples and families and locals (or quasi-locals) happy to use the bar for refreshment before another bout on the briny. This makes for a busy and energetic atmosphere; indeed the dining-room can at times get unacceptably full. It is all dealt with amicably by the Haywards; readers say it works better when their supervision is close. Criticisms have concentrated on a harshness of flavouring in the sauces that tends to overpower the main ingredient. Even something as simple as fresh plaice comes 'swimming in butter'. The menu has a certain continuity from year to year, but pride of place is accorded fish: potted shrimps (more butter than shrimp); crab ramekin; moules marinière; pike and leek terrine; sea bream; sole; and a mixture of shellfish with a basil sauce. For all the unequal performances, people do enjoy staying here: the holiday mood is infectious and treatment of young people is civilised. Breakfast is no great shakes; the orange juice 'is fresh, it says so on the carton'. It is perhaps a pity that there is no competition on the eating-out scene: it might do everyone a good turn. The wine list is as fairly priced as the rest of the operation. Burgundies include a lot of Louis Latours, the Sancerre is Paul Millérioux and there is a Seaview Cabernet Sauvignon from South Australia. House wines from Corney and Barrow are £6.50.

▮ denotes an outstanding wine cellar; ▯ denotes a good wine list, worth travelling for. See the Introduction for a fuller explanation.

CHEFS: Charles Bartlet PROPRIETORS: Nicola and Nicholas Hayward
OPEN: all week, exc Sun D
MEALS: 12 to 1.45, 7.30 to 9.30
PRICES: £16 (£23)
CARDS: Access, Amex, Visa
SEATS: 30. 10 tables outside. Private parties: 30 main room, 20 private room. Car-park, 12
places. Vegetarian meals. Children's helpings. No children under 3. Smart dress preferred.
No smoking in dining-room. Wheelchair access
ACCOMMODATION: 16 rooms, all with bath/shower. B&B £33 to £56. Baby facilities. Pets
welcome. Afternoon teas. Fishing. TV. Scenic. Doors close at midnight [*Which? Hotel Guide*]

SHEFFIELD South Yorkshire   map 5

Greenhead House

84 Burncross Road, Chapeltown,
Sheffield S30 4SF
SHEFFIELD (0742) 469004

COOKING 2
COST £27–£40

Book a month in advance for popular nights in this renovated stone cottage just
on the outskirts of Sheffield. It shows professionalism, from the hedgehog
butters with peppercorn eyes and good bread to the petits fours at the end. The
pattern is a monthly changing menu of four courses: one of them a no-choice
soup, the others with four alternatives. The city may not be far away but
indoors the style is country – and the herbs come from the garden. The cooking
is anything but countrified, however, and dishes draw on all of Europe as well
as modern thinking for inspiration. As well as herbs, used to good effect in
soups, Neil Allen employs a few luxuries, such as foie gras, wild mushrooms
and truffles, used as components of dishes rather than the centrepiece. Diners
are also likely to find lobster on the menu, with fresh basil and orange, and
asparagus as a vegetable. Desserts continue this vein of sophistication,
although there is no fear of including a crumble or hot pudding on occasion,
and pride enough in local materials to offer a good British cheeseboard. 'It is a
restaurant which I am confident will give a good meal to visiting foreign
businessmen.' The wine list, though short, is quite adequate for the task in
hand. House wine: £8.55.

CHEFS: Neil Allen and Christine Roberts PROPRIETORS: Neil and Anne Allen
OPEN: Tue to Sat, D only
CLOSED: first 2 weeks May, first 2 weeks Sept, 24 to 31 Dec
MEALS: 7.15 to 9
PRICES: Set D £20 (£27) to £25.75 (£33)
CARDS: Access, Amex, Visa
SEATS: 32. Private parties: 32 main room. Car-park, 14 places. Children welcome.
Wheelchair access

---

*All details are as accurate as possible at the time of going to press, but chefs and owners
often change, and it is wise to check by telephone before making a special journey. Many
readers have been disappointed when set-price bargain meals are no longer available. Ask
when booking.*

▲ Henfrey's Restaurant, Charnwood Hotel

10 Sharrow Lane, Sheffield S11 8AA	COOKING 2
SHEFFIELD (0742) 589411	COST £40

While some Sheffield restaurants close down for lack of business, the Charnwood goes from strength to strength. A major attraction is the building, an eighteenth-century house once owned by the master cutler after whom the restaurant is named, which lends country-house ambience in a run-down part of town. The Kings have been successful hoteliers, although hitherto the food has been thought overdressed. Now, however, here comes local boy made good: Wayne Bosworth, once chef at Odette's in London (see entry) and trained in prestigious kitchens. Although his cooking, too, has always been on the fussy side, recent reports suggest that he is tending towards the more substantial and simpler. The restaurant is full-dress formal: bread delivered with tongs, very solicitous service, yet a lively enough atmosphere for all that. The *carte* is not cheap. It represents Wayne Bosworth's own brand of mainstream modern British cooking with a lot of sweet-sour combinations, pickles and relishes, and flavourings that depend on more than just herbs. A summer meal started with a medallion of salmon with chive butter sauce and woodpigeon with a blueberry sauce. There were several elements of ornament and taste in these compositions: pink peppercorns, spring onion, and tiny mushrooms with the salmon; chestnut purée, blueberries, a poached and fanned pear with the pigeon. Save for toughness in the bird, the execution and taste combinations were very satisfactory. Main courses were rosettes of lamb topped with a tarragon mousse, and calf's liver with apple, spring onion and madeira sauce; vegetables were a fashionable pot-pourri, well soaked in butter. 'It was well cooked, combinations and contrasts were interesting and imaginative, the diced vegetables and fruit added balance and the food looked good on the plate.' Fresh fruit terrine with a cream and mango sauce, and an apple and toffee biscuit mille-feuille, were satisfactory desserts. Other desserts might include hot prune and armagnac tart and bread-and-butter pudding. Reports suggest that the potential may be great, but that performance could be more even and the tendency to overload dishes with elements may need to be curbed. There were plans afoot for a brasserie as the *Guide* went to press. The wine list is a good range of bottles from France and elsewhere. Some decent properties are featured, including Deiss's Alsaces, Ch. des Tours Brouilly, oak-aged Muscadet from Chéreau, Perrin's Côtes du Rhône, or Dry Creek's Chardonnay. The smaller regions receive more attention than Burgundy. House wine: £7.95 and £8.95.

The 1992 Guide will be published before Christmas 1991. Reports on meals are most welcome at any time of the year, but are extremely valuable in the spring. Send them to The Good Food Guide, FREEPOST, 2 Marylebone Road, London NW1 1YN. *No stamp is needed if post in the UK.*

The Guide is totally independent, accepts no free hospitality, and survives on the number of copies sold each year.

CHEF: Wayne Bosworth   PROPRIETORS: Chris and Val King
OPEN: Tue to Sat, D only
MEALS: 7.30 to 10
PRICES: £21 (£33)
CARDS: Access, Amex, Diners, Visa
SEATS: 26. Private parties: 25 main room, 80 private room. Car-park, 29 places. Children's
helpings on request. Smart dress preferred. No smoking in dining-room. Wheelchair access
(also WC). Music. Air-conditioned
ACCOMMODATION: 26 rooms, all with bath/shower. Rooms for disabled. B&B £71 to £120.
Baby facilities. Afternoon teas. Air-conditioning. TV. Phone

Nirmal

193 Glossop Road, Sheffield S10 2GW	COOKING 1
SHEFFIELD (0742) 724054	COST £19–£25

Nirmal Gupta is one of the few female Asian chefs in the country, and her
revamped restaurant is still supported by a strong local following. There are
shades of home-cooking in her style, and a few unexpected ideas appear among
the tandooris and curry-house staples. Paneer not only comes with peas or
spinach, but is used to stuff nan bread. Potato chops is a name given to potatoes
stuffed with lentils and onions, and topped with almonds; these are a
speciality. Other specials are chalked up on the blackboard. The restaurant's
list of vegetables and vegetarian dishes is expanding, and a different dhal is
served each day. Some readers have complained about slow service and
overcrowding at peak times. House wine from Paul Masson is £7.50; otherwise
drink Kingfisher, Tiger beer or Grolsch.

CHEF: Nirmal Gupta   PROPRIETOR: P.L. Gupta
OPEN: all week, exc Sun L
MEALS: 12 to 2.30, 6 to 12 (1am Fri and Sat)
PRICES: £11 (£21), Set D £12.50 (£19) to £14.50 (£21). Service 10%
CARDS: Access, Amex, Visa
SEATS: 90. Private parties: 30 main room, 60 private room. Vegetarian meals. Children
welcome. Wheelchair access (also WC). Music

SHEPTON MALLET Somerset	map 2

Blostin's

29 Waterloo Road,	
Shepton Mallet BA4 5HH	COOKING 2
SHEPTON MALLET (0749) 343648	COST £17–£29

This small restaurant attracts enough regulars to keep Lynne Reed busy
orchestrating a bustling dining-room. After five years, her husband Nick is still
adapting his assured repertoire. 'The range of local supplies seems to increase
year by year,' he says, and local goodies find their way on to either a two-or
three-course menu as duck terrine with toasted brioche and chutney, rack of
lamb roasted with herbs and served with ratatouille or fillet of pork with sage
mousse. Familiar yet different. Portions are not 'overwhelming'. The wine list

is concise and prices are very generous. House French is £5.50. CELLARMAN'S CHOICE: Ch. La Jaubertie, Reserve Red 1986, £9.95; Ch. La Jaubertie, Sauvignon Blanc 1988, £8.95.

CHEF: Nick Reed   PROPRIETORS: Nick and Lynne Reed
OPEN: Tue to Sat, D only (L by arrangement)
MEALS: 7 to 9.30 (10 Sat)
PRICES: £18 (£24), Set D £11.95 (£17) to £12.95 (£18)
CARDS: Access, Visa
SEATS: 32. Private parties: 30 main room. Children's helpings. Wheelchair access. Music

---

SHERBORNE Dorset   map 2

▲ Pheasants

24 Greenhill, Sherborne DT9 4EW   COOKING 1
SHERBORNE (0935) 815252   COST £13–£29

The meal on both the *carte* and the cheaper, shorter, set-price lunch menu is divided into 'introduction', 'continuation' and 'conclusion' – and salmon and monkfish have a 'dalliance' under a cabbage leaf. This may strike dread into lovers of food that tastes of itself, as might a main course of monkfish enclosing strips of beefsteak wrapped in bacon and served with a redcurrant sauce. That it can be eaten at all is a triumph of cookery. The three-storey house at the top of Sherborne's main street used to be council offices, though no council worker would recognise the pinks and greys of the small bar and the domestic-scale dining-rooms. The high pressure imagery of the menu is kept up with enthusiasm by Andrew Overhill but it does not disguise fair cooking by Michael Voyce of dishes such as a crab and mussel soup of vivifying flavour; a smoked salmon and smoked halibut roulade that managed to keep each taste distinct; spinach and oyster soup; fillet of beef in a puff pastry lattice with a mushroom *farce* and sticky port sauce; sea bream with vermouth; lamb with apricots; or desserts like honey and apricot bavarois; double chocolate truffle cake (more truffles with the coffee); and coconut mousse with a rum custard. Gestures such as mashed potatoes encased in a filo parcel and a raw apple fanned to one side of a fillet steak with port sauce are eccentricities of the age we cook in. These need controlling so that the main business at hand is mastered. The short wine list has a few Australian bottles (including Wolf Blass) but is essentially French. Prices are fair. House Duboeuf is £7.50.

CHEF: Michael Voyce   PROPRIETORS: Andrew and Michelle Overhill
OPEN: Tue to Sun, exc Sun D
CLOSED: 2 weeks mid-Jan
MEALS: 12 to 2, 6.30 to 10 (earlier or later hours can be arranged)
PRICES: £17 (£24), Set L £7.95 (£13) to £9.95 (£15)
CARDS: Access, Visa
SEATS: 40. Private parties: 28 main room. Car-park, 10 places. Vegetarian meals. Children's helpings on request. No cigars/pipes in dining-room. Wheelchair access. Music
ACCOMMODATION: 2 rooms. B&B £25 to £30. Doors close at midnight. Confirm by 6

The Guide *always appreciates hearing about changes of chef or owner.*

L'Ortolan ☠

The Old Vicarage, Church Lane,
Shinfield RG2 9BY   COOKING 5
READING (0734) 883783   COST £40–£70

In front of the rectory is a 'water feature', firmly 1989 to the building's 1847.
Although this is a country house, it does not pretend to the grandeur of a
mansion. The bar sitting-room is small, indeed too small to hold every party
before the meal on a busy Saturday night, but there is space enough in the pair
of linked dining-rooms and conservatory, even if a few tables are more
cramped than the bill would warrant. John Burton-Race continues to present
food of great sophistication. It is marked by a harmony of flavours, not usually
given strong accent but, on good days, a soaring euphony. That there have been
bad days seems a fact of the last year. The second half has been better than the
first. The menu offers eight dishes in each course, supplemented by a half-
dozen specialities of mainly fish. It comes at a set-price with some supplements
among the specialities. Just reading the menu brings out the characteristics of
the style: many mousses and many meats. Veal kidney is filled with a
sweetbread *farce* and wrapped with an escalope; guinea-fowl breast is served
with an 'andouillette' of its leg bound with pig's trotter; squab is wrapped in a
mousse of its liver and foie gras; lamb has a mousse topping of ham,
sweetbread and foie gras. This complexity is handled in such a way that the
result is not impossibly rich. Foie gras and truffles make their presence forcibly
unavoidable. There is a countervailing side to the cooking that injects earthy
flavours and intensity so that the whole does not topple into brainless and
bland display. *Tête de veau* is refined yet robust, then there is the dish of potato
galettes fried crisp in olive oil, served with slices of gutsy smoked French
sausage, *andouille de Vire*, just-cooked quail eggs and a sour cream sauce; or
scallops are served in a salad with mixed winter leaves, toasted hazelnuts and
slices of Jerusalem artichokes. 'The scallops were golden and slightly crisp, but
pure curd white inside, sweet and firm to the bite. With the salad and
artichokes, it was a wonderful combination of colours, textures and tastes.' His
style seems one of the least influenced by the Mediterranean, but his 'bourride
façon Ortolan' is well loved and consists of monkfish, sea bass, scallop, red
mullet and turbot in a very creamy shellfish sauce heavily flavoured with
saffron and served with a stinging rouille. The complexity comes through in
dishes like the feuilleté of sweetbreads served as a first course. The case of puff-
pastry is lined with a leek mousse, topped by a slice of sweetbread; more slices
of the offal are then laid on a light veal stock sauce, lightened with vegetable
stock, butter and lemon juice. They alternate with piles of chanterelles and
broad beans. Vegetables have not yet been integrated into the main courses as
in many places this year, in that they are still served on a separate side plate.
However, they are often carefully matched to the dish served. Roast teal with
armagnac and orange sauce was served with bobby beans, celeriac strips
lightly bound with a butter sauce, a broccoli floret with a hint of orange sauce, a
baby beetroot and game chips; fillet of lamb came with four turned roast
potatoes, beans and a ratatouille mould of layers of aubergine, tomato and
courgettes flavoured with cardamom. For a stiff £7.25, the cheese selection is

unpasteurised, ripe and extensive. Neither biscuits nor bread is home made. A meal at L'Ortolan never goes into diminuendo: the desserts are as good as the first courses. Pastry work is generally first-rate. A hot chocolate soufflé comes with a chocolate sauce and a plate of chocolate sorbet and vanilla ice-cream. Gilding the lily? Some would say so, yet it is very good. Orange nougat is surrounded by passion-fruit ice-cream served on a bed of mango, wild strawberries and passion-fruit: 'this is what I always thought expensive eating would be about, a range of different and intense flavours exploding in the mouth one after the other.' A favourite is the chocolate saucepan filled with dark chocolate, white chocolate cream and dark pitted cherries, with a pool of vanilla and kirsch sauce and cherry coulis. Coffee, sometimes not enough of it, comes with usually excellent petits fours and chocolates from a pirate's treasure chest, itself in chocolate. Service can run on smooth tracks; there are enough staff to make sure it does. However, if Christine Burton-Race is not there to explain, information can be less than full, and there have been nights of sad disarray. It may come down to training. The same may be said of wine service: some good, some poor. At these prices, people have understandably objected. The wine list is a good one, at high prices. These are slightly moderated if choice is restricted to the first page of French regional wines and the good sections of half-bottles for each region. However, the dice sometimes seem loaded against judicious spending, as one party found most of the bottles under £18 seemed to be out of stock. The list, bar the final page of *vins d'autres continents*, is resolutely French. Its glories are the red burgundies, though for those with a few hundred pounds, there is a Cheval Blanc 1947 or Lafite 1953. CELLARMAN'S CHOICE: Gers, Vin Sauvage Blanc de Blancs, Méthode Champenoise, £17.50; Gard, Syrah Primaire 1989, Berthier, £15.45.

CHEF: John Burton-Race   PROPRIETORS: John and Christine Burton-Race
OPEN: Tue to Sun, exc Sun D
CLOSED: last 2 weeks Feb and last 2 weeks Aug
MEALS: 12.15 to 2.15, 7.15 to 10.30
PRICES: Set L £26 (£40) to £46 (£61), Set D £44 (£59)
CARDS: Access, Amex, Visa
SEATS: 60. Private parties: 40 main room, 32 private room. Car-park, 15 places. Children's helpings. Wheelchair access (2 steps)

SHIPTON-UNDER-WYCHWOOD Oxfordshire   map 2

▲ *Lamb Inn*

Shipton-under-Wychwood OX7 6DQ   COOKING 1
SHIPTON (0993) 830465   COST £17–£26

A traditional Cotswold inn – beams, stone walls, polished floors and oak furniture – in a village that itself has elements of the picturesque. The Wainwrights have been superseded by the Valentas but George Benham remains. He wields the ladle over a traditional, set-price menu of dishes such as salmon, duck, guinea-fowl with mushroom cream sauce, or roast lamb with rosemary. Chance visitors, arriving on St Valentine's day, found the welcome friendly and the cooking sound. So did a couple retreating from Cheltenham

races who commented on the generous portions, fair value and the Hook
Norton ale. House wine is £6.50.

CHEF: George Benham PROPRIETORS: Vivien and Luciano Valenta
OPEN: Mon to Sat D, Sun L
CLOSED: Mon in winter
MEALS: 12.30 to 1.45, 7.30 to 9
PRICES: Set Sun L £11.50 (£17), Set D £16.50 (£22)
CARDS: Access, Amex, Visa
SEATS: 30. 8 tables outside. Private parties: 36 main room. Car-park, 30 places. No children
under 14. No smoking in dining-room. Wheelchair access (1 step)
ACCOMMODATION: 5 rooms, all with bath/shower. B&B £48 to £58 double only. Deposit:
£20. No children under 14. Garden. TV. Doors close at 11

SISSINGHURST Kent   map 3

Rankins

The Street, Sissinghurst TN17 2JA   COOKING 2
CRANBROOK (0580) 713964   COST £22–£32

There is not a lot in Sissinghurst, gardens apart, and this beamed dining-room
with spindle-backed chairs and hunting-scene curtains is opposite the post
office and general stores. Hugh Rankin cooks and Leonora Rankin looks after
the customers, when responsibilities of family don't intrude. The Sunday lunch
menu is shorter than the dinners on four weekday nights. These consist of
fewer than half a dozen options, priced according to the main course chosen.
Cooking is not the 'Olde Englishe' you might expect from deep, tourist, Kent
but includes up-to-the-minute mixtures such as a salad of roasted red peppers
with capers, anchovies and hard-boiled eggs; a ceviche of cod and prawns with
a mustard mayonnaise; salmon with capers and a mustard sauce; and a pair of
roast quail with mushroom stuffing. There are times when first and main
courses seem repetitious, thus restricting choice. Tradition revives on Sundays
when a roast is offered. Vegetables have not always pleased, reportedly dully
flavoured and overcooked. Normally the desserts are well liked, although one
reader was struck by their lack of flavour and generosity: more sponge than
fudge, for example. However, the range is good and shows nice ideas, such as a
'terrine of jellied orange fillets' with an orange custard. Readers sometimes
express surprise at the *Guide's* failure to locate more good country restaurants
near London. Just look, for example, at the map of Bedfordshire and Herts. But
a nice, and earnest, place like Rankins is often sparsely occupied, right in the
middle of the richest county in the country. The wine list is short and sweet and
unambitious, but offers decent wines at fair prices. Do not expect much choice,
there are two halves of red (both Beaujolais) and only five halves of dry white
wines. House French: £7.30.

CHEF: Hugh Rankin PROPRIETORS: Hugh and Leonora Rankin
OPEN: Wed to Sat, D only, and Sun L
MEALS: 12.30 to 1.30, 7.30 to 9
PRICES: Set Sun L £16.50 (£22) to £19 (£24), Set D £19.50 (£25) to £22 (£27) Service inc
CARDS: Access, Visa
SEATS: 30. Private parties: 10 main room, 24 private room. Children's helpings (Sun L
only). No children under 8. Smart dress preferred. No smoking till coffee served. Music

SLAIDBURN Lancashire   map 5

▲ *Parrock Head Hotel*

Slaidburn BB7 3AH   COOKING 1
SLAIDBURN (020 06) 614   COST £25

While waiting for their dinner, two guests watched a neighbouring farmer call at Richard and Vicky Umbers' country hotel to discuss a dog (not theirs, of course) and his sheep. Parrock Head used to be a farm as well – as if the long, low whitewashed buildings (surprisingly modernised with plate-glass windows but still traditional within) did not proclaim their origins a mile off. The Umbers are much in evidence at the front of the house and the kitchen team continues to produce food based on local ingredients (duck from a nearby farm, free-range chicken) with some modern touches like filo purses, carrots tied in *fasces*, or a two-pepper sauce with halibut. All this is carried off with a fair degree of success: an excellent tomato and herb chutney with potted chicken and tarragon; fillet of pork with a mushroom stuffing and madeira sauce; generous quantities of vegetables. 'The food is good home-made stuff – delicious fresh soups and huge portions of tender meat in light sauces.' Not everybody has concurred about the tender, though generosity is always praised and 'light' sauces may as often mean they are a trifle bland as not overbearing. The coffee is very good cafetière. House wine: £5.75.

CHEFS: Vicky Umbers and Steven Hill   PROPRIETORS: Vicky and Richard Umbers
OPEN: all week, D only
MEALS: 7 to 8.15
PRICES: £16 (£21)
CARDS: Amex, Access, Visa
SEATS: 32. Car-park, 20 places. Children's helpings. No smoking. Wheelchair access
ACCOMMODATION: 9 rooms, all with bath/shower. Rooms for disabled. B&B £47 to £80.
Baby facilities. Pets allowed in garden. Afternoon teas. TV. Phone. Scenic. Doors close at
11.30 [*Which? Hotel Guide*]

SOURTON Devon   map 1

▲ *Collaven Manor Hotel*

Sourton, Okehampton, EX20 4HH   COOKING 1
BRIDESTOWE (083 786) 522   COST £17–£41

The long stone house, punctuated by dormers and a double-storeyed porch, is pure Devon – fifteenth-century at that. Some of the beamed rooms are fine though never grandiose. There are two dining-rooms, each serving a set-price menu, but the Hamilton room is fancier and dearer than the Inglenook. Actually, both have the same chef, both use fair ingredients, and the interpretation put on 'modern' and 'elaborate' results in combinations such as avocado, grapefruit and prawns with a hollandaise. Notwithstanding, presentation and cooking is not excessively ornate and flavours were in fact enjoyable in a meal that began with squid and scallops on a deep yellow vermouth sauce studded with green shards of leek, and went on to beef wrapped in bacon on a smoked trout sauce. The beef was accurately cooked. The 'English cheese selection' stretched to Brie and Cambozola. Pavlova was fine with an orange coulis that counteracted any tendency to overpower by sweetness. Some of the country cooking – pork chop; veal Holstein; gammon with fried egg – is fitting to the situation and fair value. There is an acceptable short wine list though choices below £12 are limited. The unexpected page of Italians offer some relief. House wine: £6.95.

CHEF: Ian Mottram PROPRIETORS: C.L. and J.B.L. Buckley
OPEN: all week
CLOSED: 2 weeks Jan
MEALS: 12 to 1.45, 7.30 to 9.30
PRICES: Set L £9.95 (£17) to £10.95 (£18), Set D £13.95 (£21) to £25.95 (£34)
CARDS: Access, Visa
SEATS: 30. Private parties: 20 main room, 20 private room. Car-park, 20 places. No children under 12. Smart dress preferred
ACCOMMODATION: 9 rooms, all with bath/shower. B&B £50 to £77. No children under 12. Garden. TV. Phone. Scenic. Doors close at midnight. Confirm by 4 [*Which? Hotel Guide*]

SOUTHAMPTON Hampshire   map 2

Kuti's

70 London Road, Southampton SO1 2AJ   COOKING 1
SOUTHAMPTON (0703) 221585 and 333473   COST £10–£24

A place, perhaps, to use when awaiting a cross-channel ferry. The decoration and style of it, however, indicate more than mere utility and it is justifiably popular, not least for a bargain buffet lunch. Bhel puri and Bangladeshi dishes are often the best from the unchanging menu, though the standard of the Gujerati thali very much disappointed one less-than-happy reader. House wine is £5.85 but there is Kingfisher or Golden Eagle beer or you can have chaas, a more liquid lassi.

CHEFS: Anjab Ali and Kuti Miah PROPRIETOR: Kuti Miah
OPEN: all week
CLOSED: 25 Dec
MEALS: 12 to 2.15, 6 to 11.30
PRICES: £10 (£18), Set L £6.50 (£10) to £10 (£14), Set D £9.50 (£14) to £15 (£20). Service 10%
CARDS: Access, Amex, Visa
SEATS: 66. Private parties: 30 main room. Car-park, 10 places. Vegetarian meals. Children welcome. Smart dress preferred. Wheelchair access (also WC). Music. Air-conditioned

---

SOUTHEND-ON-SEA Essex   map 3

Alvaro's

32–34 St Helen's Road, Westcliff-on-Sea,
Southend SS0 7LB   COOKING 1
SOUTHEND (0702) 335840   COST £32

Alvaro's is a Portuguese restaurant that lives a dual life: Portuguese specialities on one hand, steaks in profusion on the other. There are a pair of dining-rooms that could once have been a tea shop but now have an emphatic Portuguese overlay from a hundred pottery cockerels and colourful plates and copperware brought back from regular visits to the home country. The menu runs for page after page, but in fact lists the same basics with different finishes: steak a dozen ways, sole likewise, and so on. The dishes that gain approval are the cataplanas, the espetadas, the earthy cabbage and potato soups and fresh fish such as sardines, sole fried with banana Madeiran style, or a fish casserole. Desserts are from a trolley and include rich Portuguese custards, and there are plenty of flambé pancakes and fruits. The wine list continues this ability to be all things to all people. On one page the Niersteiners and Mouton Cadet, on the other a score of Portuguese wines including three vinho verdes and half a dozen Dãos. The bar has plenty of Portuguese spirits, vintage ports and Portuguese beer. House wine: £6.75 per litre.

CHEFS: José Rodrigues, Carlos Barreto and Martin Stace   PROPRIETORS: Alvaro and Joyce Rodrigues, José Rodrigues
OPEN: Tue to Sun, exc Sat L and Sun L
CLOSED: 2 weeks at Christmas and New Year, 3 weeks June
MEALS: 12 to 2, 7 to 10.30 (6.30 to 10 Sun, 7 to 11 Fri and Sat)
PRICES: £18 (£27). Service 10%
CARDS: Access, Visa
SEATS: 55. Children's helpings. Smart dress preferred. Wheelchair access. Music

Slassor's

145 Eastern Esplanade,
Southend SS1 2YD   COOKING 1
SOUTHEND (0702) 614880   COST £25

The sea is there, behind the sea wall. The restaurant hums on regardless. The Slassors have been in the *Guide*, in one guise or another, for more years than they may care to remember, and it is perhaps for old fashioned values that their enterprise gets the support it does. Fish is the most popular ingredient, often a good range of it, weather permitting. The choice included sea bream, monkfish, salmon and sole on one day. As many meat dishes are on offer, the daily variations to the standard menu being chalked on a blackboard. Black pudding with apple and calvados; leg of lamb steaks with herbs and garlic; veal stuffed with smoked salmon and served with a dill sauce, or pigeon breasts with blackberry sauce, are just some of the meat options and indicate that Leslie Slassor has moved with gustatory times in his recipes. Desserts are a late-childhood roll-call of banana bliss, crème de menthe sundae, raspberry meringue cake and coffee kahlua sundae, among a dozen or more keys to saccharine paradise. The restaurant is unlicensed, popular, and not dear.

CHEF: Leslie Slassor   PROPRIETORS: Margaret and Leslie Slassor
OPEN: Mon to Sat, exc Mon L
MEALS: 12 to 2, 7 to 9.30
PRICES: £16 (£21). Unlicensed, but bring your own: corkage 75p
CARDS: Access, Visa
SEATS: 22. Private parties: 30 main room. Children's helpings. Music

'This is a designer restaurant with inadequate content – all suit, no man, as my favourite calypso has it.' On inspecting in London

SOUTH MOLTON Devon   map 1

▲ *Whitechapel Manor*

South Molton EX36 3EG   COOKING 3
SOUTH MOLTON (076 95) 2554 and 3377   COST £27–52

The extension of the North Devon Link Road may open up this region to more
visitors: good for the Shaplands, bad for lovers of isolation. Whitechapel
Manor is on a road to nowhere. That such a pot of gold may exist for those who
chase the rainbow to its end is encouraging. A seventeenth-century manor
house, it has been decorated with great aplomb. The original features – a
Jacobean screen, early eighteenth-century wainscot and painted decoration –
are thrown into relief and it contrives 'to be both grandiose and intimate.' Some
of the latter quality is due to the Shaplands' sense of hospitality, complete but
not pressing. We remarked in the last *Guide* that it would be terrible if Thierry
Lepretre-Granet left Whitechapel, but at least two visitors have commented
that their meals on 'chef's night off' were as good as any of the others. The
menu continues in the same mould: a choice of six dishes at each course at a set
price that is much cheaper at lunchtime. A hike of 35 per cent in twelve months
heralds that Devon is getting more expensive than London. The kitchen has
strong local foundations even though judicious use is made of London
suppliers. The Shaplands were farmers before they became hoteliers and
supply lines show this. They have benefitted from the proximity of Ann Petch's
Heal Farm for the supply of beef, lamb and pork reared on sane principles.
There is also no skimping on basics: bread, pastry and oatmeal biscuits are all
first rate. Readers are struck by the refinement of the cooking in dishes such as
sea bass served with delicate, just cooked, fennel and green olives with a
sabayon sauce; or mousseline of scallops and courgettes, together with lightly
fried scallops on a caviare butter sauce. By contrast, two main courses – best
end of lamb with a spicy aubergine purée and red pepper coulis, and salmon
with tomato and olive oil sauce – were much punchier, indeed may have been
overpowered by their sauces. 'The chef seemed to be trying a Provençal
approach this week.' The intermediate cheese course, with a mix of south-
western and French, is enjoyed for itself and for the oatmeal biscuits; but
plaudits are often reserved for the sweets. 'An apple tart that most restaurants
would give a fancy name to but would not have the ability to reproduce the fine
pastry and ethereal flavour'; sorbets of passion-fruit, apple and raspberry with
fresh fruits; raspberry mille-feuille, 'heaven on earth'; a brilliant yoghurt
mousse of delicate flavour that could hardly carry the strong citrus sauce. The
wine list is long enough for most but stops well short of the encyclopaedic. It is
an even-handed choice, though with small sections on the New World. The
price range is kindly and the French material is not drowned by expensive
aristocrats, even though mark-ups are not especially low.

The Guide *office can quickly spot when a restaurateur is encouraging customers to write
recommending inclusion and sadly, several restaurants have been doing this in 1990.
Such reports do not further a restaurant's cause. Please tell us if a restaurateur invites you
to write to the* Guide.

CHEF: Thierry Lepretre-Granet   PROPRIETORS: John and Patricia Shapland
OPEN: all week
MEALS: 12 to 2, 7 to 9
PRICES: Set L £20 (£27), Set D £34.50 (£43). Service inc
CARDS: Access, Visa
SEATS: 20. Car-park, 40 places. No children under 10. No smoking in dining-room
ACCOMMODATION: 10 rooms, all with bath/shower. B&B £55 to £75. Deposit: 20%.
Afternoon teas. Garden. TV. Phone. Scenic. Doors close at midnight [*Which? Hotel Guide*]

SOUTHWOLD Suffolk   map 6

▲ *Swan Hotel* ♥

Market Place, Southwold IP18 6EG	COOKING 2
SOUTHWOLD (0502) 722186	COST £15–£32

The two bay windows dominate the market place. The hotel has been
refurbished with considerable style down to the last floorboard, – rugged bar,
country-house drawing-room, dining-room with long curtains, tall
upholstered chairs and deep-pile carpets. Staff are committed to the Loftus
(Simon Loftus, of the wine merchants Adnams, is managing director) way of
doing things, ably headed by Dudley Clarke. The cooking gets more
ambivalent reports. It is not as expensive as many newly renovated hotels, and
a serious attempt is made to offer a fair price range. There are three menus at
each meal: the Swan lunch or dinner, English classics and a menu of the day.
There is a strain of tradition in the repertoire: smoked haddock with a Cheddar
cheese and parsley sauce in the Swan dinner; deep-fried Dover sole with
tartare sauce in the English classics. Some object to the mobilisation of luxuries
to elevate cooking to *haute cuisine,* particularly as many errors are detected in the
dearest as in the cheapest menu. However, good reports of foie gras on brioche;
smoked wild boar with mustard sauce; well-trimmed lamb with a light
redcurrant sauce; and saddle of rabbit with red wine and juniper sauce show
that all is not impossible. The wine list is a careful, well-spread selection from
all the world's producers. It is not an encyclopaedia – which might be expected
from the wine merchant connection – but the makers are exemplary: Joubert
from Beaujolais, Machard de Gramont's Nuits-St-Georges, Ch. St Pierre
Sevaïstre in St Julien, Fernandez' Pesquera and many more. The price range
makes it affordable for all, with interest and dependability at every level.
House wines start at £5.10.

CHEF: John Olerenshaw   PROPRIETORS: Sole Bay Hotels
OPEN: all week
MEALS: 12 to 2, 7 to 9.30
PRICES: Set L £9.95 (£13) to £17.50 (£22), Set D £14.95 (£19) to £21.95 (£27)
CARDS: Access, Amex, Visa
SEATS: 96. Private parties: 44 and 50 private rooms. Car-park, 50 places. Children's
helpings. Smart dress preferred. No smoking in dining-room. Wheelchair access (also WC)
ACCOMMODATION: 45 rooms, all with bath/shower. Rooms for disabled. Lift. B&B £35 to
£110. Deposit: £10 per person. Baby facilities. Pets welcome in garden rooms only.
Afternoon teas. Garden. TV. Phone. Scenic. Doors close at midnight. Confirm 6 days ahead
[*Which? Hotel Guide*]

▲ *Bridgefield House* ♥

Spark Bridge, Ulverston LA12 8DA
LOWICK BRIDGE (022 985) 239
4m N of Ulverston, off A5084 on back   COOKING 2
road leading to Coniston   COST £30

The solid brick house sits behind wrought iron gates, the scene of constant improvements by Rosemary and David Glister who provide five bedrooms to stay in all the year round and a long set meal for both non-residents and residents. Turn up promptly, though, and let any special dietary needs be known in advance. Rosemary Glister doesn't cook until she's seen the white of guests' eyes. Meals steer a passage from a choice of three first courses through soup, main dish and sorbet to choices offered once again for dessert and a pair of savouries, though many find they've reached port before they get to that last tack. Cooking is careful and without needless elaboration yet there are sufficient ideas to give point to eating out: smoked mackerel pâté with fresh figs and salad; potted pike; asparagus soup with sesame toasts; leek and potato soup with an accompanying croissant; salmon poached with white wine and ginger; gammon poached in lager with a damson and port sauce; interesting vegetables, such as red onion with pine kernels or cauliflower with turmeric; plum fool with rosemary shortbread or papaya in a passion-fruit syllabub. There have been moments when the food has lacked the edge of excitement, but normally it shows the benefit of a single person's taste and skill. Residents eat for slightly less than non-residents. David Glister gives meals the right pace and cheer as well as guidance on the long list of wines. He must also have been studying auction records, for price rises among the older bottles are occasionally ferocious, even if justifiable. The length means there is something for everybody, including lovers of Australasian wines. Burgundies are dominated by Latour and other shippers while the Rhônes afford a very wide choice. CELLARMAN'S CHOICE: Orvieto Classico, Vigneto Torricella 1988, £8.59; Rioja Contino Reserva 1984, £11.80.

CHEF: Rosemary Glister   PROPRIETORS: David and Rosemary Glister
OPEN: all week, D only
MEALS: 7.30 for 8
PRICES: Set D £20 (£25)
CARDS: Access, Visa
SEATS: 20. Private parties: 24 main room. Car-park, 10 places. Children's helpings. Smart dress preferred. No smoking in dining-room. One sitting
ACCOMMODATION: 5 rooms, all with bath/shower. B&B £33 per person. Deposit: £20. Baby facilities. Pets welcome. Garden. Scenic. Confirm by 3

Several sharp operators have tried to extort money from restaurateurs on the promise of an entry in a guide book that has never appeared. The Good Food Guide *makes no charge for inclusion and does not offer certificates of any kind.*

Restaurateurs justifiably resent no-shows. If you quote a credit card number when booking, you may be liable for the restaurant's lost profit margin if you don't turn up. Always phone to cancel.

▲ McCoy's

The Tontine, Staddlebridge DL6 3JB   COOKING 4
EAST HARLSEY (060 982) 671   COST £26–£55

'I hope it's not shaken to the ground by HGVs or smashed into by a number 9 bus,' observed one who would like to preserve the Tontine in aspic. Built as an inn it sits, a fairly handsome Georgian house with a small front garden and a giant stable block, right beside the A19. To reach it if travelling north, you have to describe a loop over the dual carriageway. To call the decoration idiosyncratic is an understatement. The exterior frays at the edges, a strange 1960s porch being the main entry from the stable side. Within, the preliminary rooms are sepia brown and 1930s; a lot of it looks straight out of the seedy auction room or put together by a demented DIY carpenter keen on blockboard and woodstain. The main sitting-room has more zing and style, thanks to wallpaper and the shape and scale of the room itself. The dining-room, too, was originally of fine proportions though these are obscured by giant parasols over the centre tables and are barely visible at night because of atmospheric lighting. It is, however, a pleasant place to eat. People enjoy the incessant music, starting with 1930s and 1940s collectors' items and progressing to 1990s singers as the evening wears on. The tables are well set and well spaced, and the service is so enthusiastic, without oppression, that it is discerning and comforting at once. The long menu, about 10 choices at each course, shows intense affection for foie gras, truffles and lobster. It is difficult to avoid them. The repertoire is not fast moving, though given some variety by daily fish and game in season: one autumn night turbot with a tapénade and meat juices, lobster with caviare butter and grouse with bilberries. The choices, however, are very enticing and the execution assured. Basics, such as pasta and pastry, are first rate, as could be seen immediately from an amuse-gueule of a cheese custard tart with a stunningly light crust, or from a ravioli of langoustine, lemon and truffle with a slightly bitter lobster sauce. This pasta and its filling were as tender and full flavoured as any eaten in the year. Other first courses that have met with approval are a hot salad of artichokes, sweetbreads, girolles and a madeira sauce; smoked salmon with a cream mousse of celery, cucumber and truffle juice; and wild mushrooms in a tart with a Muscadet sauce. For main courses, duck is offered rouennaise, with shallots and Toulouse sausage, or with a stuffed spiced peach and red wine sauce. Although the peach is good, neither its stuffing nor spicing are always in evidence, but the sauce has good balance, helping consumption of the well-trimmed breast and over-fat thigh. Vegetables are not exciting. The kitchen enjoys treating fish in a substantial fashion: bass with a red wine and madeira sauce; turbot with meat juices, with make-believe scales fashioned from courgettes. The cooking is not overpowered by these luxuries nor made silly by modishness; quantities and balance are well judged. It is possible to eat more here than in many places. The dessert list is also full of old favourites, good enough to encourage further experiment. Choc-o-bloc Stanley, a rich, wildly large slice of fondant with sponge fingers soaked in Tia Maria and a coffee sauce, manages so exact a pay-off between the sugar of the chocolate, the slight crunch in the sponge, and the bitterness of the sauce that it might be eaten to infinity. Crêpes San Lorenzo, filled with vanilla cream, Amaretti and Grand Marnier, is another old favourite; mille-feuille of strawberries shows the skill in pastry again. The wine list, arranged by taste rather than the map, is a challenging mixture of old and New World producers. Though the classification may help the unknowledgeable, the detailed sequence within each section seems to have no financial or other order and sometimes no clue as to a wine's origin. As prices range widely (£30.50 for Cloudy Bay Chardonnay 1988 well over the odds but CVNE Imperial Reserva 1983 at £15.50 a snip), it needs to be read carefully. However, there are many growers that should be noted, not least Marcel Deiss's Pinot Noir, Nobilo's Pinotage, de Bartoli's Bukkaram Moscato, Vernay's Condrieu, or Puiatti's Sauvignon. They are switched on enough to have, if not spell correctly, several of the best new Italian makers. Prices are in keeping with those of the restaurant with little under £13. There is a Pétrus 1981 for any who can afford it. The practice of opening the bottle before showing it is not liked by some people. The Tontine has rooms (double-glazed against the traffic) and a good breakfast in the most normal room in the house. There is also a bistro in the basement. This is as popular as, if not more so than, the main restaurant. It makes few concessions to comfort and the loud music and the crowds means it is not quiet, but the food is good and fair value. Seafood pancakes; giant slices of rough pâté; black pudding (French); pork fillet with mushroom and walnut sauce; an excessively rich halibut with dill and green pepper sauce; a properly substantial osso buco with new potatoes and a salad are some of the dishes noted. The service is usually, though not always, complimented for the same open friendliness and enthusiasm as upstairs.

CHEFS: Tom and Eugene McCoy   PROPRIETORS: Peter, Tom and Eugene McCoy
OPEN: restaurant Tue to Sat, D only; bistro all week, L and D
CLOSED: 25 and 26 Dec
MEALS: bistro 12 to 2, restaurant and bistro 7 to 10
PRICES: restaurant £32 (£46), bistro £17 (£26)
CARDS: Amex, Access, Diners, Visa
SEATS: 115. Private parties: 70 main room (restaurant), 60 (bistro), 25 private room. Car-park, 60 places. Vegetarian meals. Children's helpings. Music. Air-conditioned
ACCOMMODATION: 6 rooms, all with bath/shower. B&B £69 to £89. Baby facilities. Pets welcome. Garden. Air-conditioning. TV. Phone. Scenic. Doors close at 2am
[Which? Hotel Guide]

STAFFORD Staffordshire	map 5

Curry Kuteer

31 Greengate Street, Stafford ST16 2HY	COOKING 1
STAFFORD (0785) 53279	COST £10–£38

New chef Mohammed Salim Ullah continues the policy of cooking a menu that ranges over the sub-continent, while all around him the restaurant is a maelstrom of redecoration. People still attest to the quality of the karai dishes, cooked and served in a sizzling skillet which are first cousins to the baltis of Birmingham. The pati shapta – a pancake sweetmeat – is also mentioned. House Spanish: £6.90.

CHEF: Mohammed Salim Ullah PROPRIETOR: Shah A. Quayum
OPEN: all week
MEALS: 12 to 2, 6 to 12
PRICES: £9 (£16), Set L £4.95 (£10) to £8 (£13), Set D £10.95 (£16) to £26 (£32)
CARDS: Access, Amex, Diners, Visa
SEATS: 85. Private parties: 50 main room, 60 private room. Car-park, 8 places. Vegetarian meals. Children's helpings. No children under 4. Smart dress preferred. No-smoking area. Wheelchair access (2 steps). Music

---

STAMFORD Lincolnshire   map 6

▲ *George* 🍴

71 St Martin's, Stamford PE9 2LB   COOKING 1
STAMFORD (0780) 55171   COST £37

The George has been many things to many people for a long time – since its days as a coaching-inn and stop for travellers on the Great North Road through Stamford. It continues the tradition with a restaurant and a more informal garden lounge. The first runs a long seasonal menu mixing a roast meat trolley – a silver wagon, no less – with trendy prawn mousse with a raspberry and walnut vinaigrette, or veal with a pear-flavoured sauce. The second is characterised by light foods, some with a Mediterranean tilt, Italian wines, and a pleasant easy-going approach. The scallops with a ginger sauce; large ravioli of wild mushrooms; beef from the trolley (with a tendency to being too cooked); partridge on a bed of cabbage; and calf's liver with a lemon sauce have been endorsed, as have the Cheddar, Stilton, Brie and the trolley of desserts. The greater economy in the garden lounge has been spoiled by very mixed performance. The wine list, as in all Poste Hotels, is a model of selection, range and economy. There is generous provision beyond Europe and a strong collection of Italians. It certainly makes a stop on the way North mandatory, even if it be just overnight to sleep off the effects. Half-bottles are never ignored and bin-ends give a happy hunting ground for bargains.

CHEF: Chris Pitman PROPRIETORS: Poste Hotels Ltd
OPEN: all week
MEALS: 12.30 to 2.30, 7.30 to 10.30
PRICES: £21 (£31)
CARDS: Access, Amex, Diners, Visa
SEATS: 85. 20 tables outside. Private parties: 90 main room, 16,22, and 30, private rooms. Car-park, 150 places. Vegetarian meals. Children's helpings. Smart dress preferred. Wheelchair access (also unisex WC)
ACCOMMODATION: 47 rooms, all with bath/shower. B&B £64 to £140. Baby facilities. Pets welcome. Afternoon teas. Garden. TV. Phone. Scenic. Confirm by 6 [*Which? Hotel Guide*]

The text of entries is based on unsolicited reports sent in by readers, backed up by inspections conducted anonymously. The factual details under the text are from questionnaires the Guide sends to all restaurants that feature in the book.

All letters to the Guide are acknowledged with an update on latest sales, closures, chef changes and so on.

Olivers

Cripps Corner, nr Staple Cross TN32 5RY
STAPLE CROSS (058 083) 387, changes to
(0580) 830387 in winter 1990/91

COOKING 2
COST £21–£31

Cripps Corner is on the road from Hastings to Hawkhurst just south-west of
Staple Cross, and Olivers stands clean and bright, ploughing its own furrow of
kitchen self-sufficiency in a part of the world where too many things come from
the catering pack. There is a party that says the flock wallpaper and other
aspects of the decoration of the first-floor restaurant are at odds with the
ambitions of Gary Oliver's cooking. Menus are set price, a choice of four dishes
at each course. Special events sometimes intrude on the even progression of the
months, so in the summer there was, for instance, a 'fish week' when only fish
was offered. There is an oriental streak now running through the recipes –
perhaps in homage to Mrs Oliver's origins – evinced by dishes such as steamed
Chinese dumplings of prawn and squid with a sherry sauce; duck with plums
and pine nuts; or medallions of lamb with a crab curry mouse. Vegetables
show the same tendency: a mixture of leek and mushroom spiced perhaps with
soy and star anise, or broccoli with sesame. Cooking is often assured: in a
venison pâté in a crust where the smooth pâté surrounded a central core of
meat, the pastry was good and the gamey flavour set off the cubed jelly on the
side; in a rolled pancake of smoked salmon and sour cream with a cream and
chive sauce; good tasting if somewhat firm breast of duck with raisins; and in
decent execution of nice ideas like escalope of veal with young nettles and
hazelnuts. The cooking is not without its drawbacks: not a lot of salt is used
(some would say that's good) and flavours have been described as indistinct,
while others dishes were thought too simply finished for the intentions of the
kitchen. Desserts end the meal on a high point: a passion-fruit delice; exotic
fruits set in a light vanilla mousse on a tartlet; a very good hot sultana sponge
pudding on an apple custard, are some mentioned. Petits fours show the same
enthusiasm found in the nibbles and the breads but if you ask for fresh orange
juice, you may get a bottle. This place is good value for the area and deserves
support for its genuine intentions.. The wine list is extremely short and French,
save for three local wines. Prices are fair and the bottles nicely chosen. There
are no halves. House French is £6.

CHEF: Gary Oliver   PROPRIETOR: Albert and Gary Oliver
OPEN: Wed to Sun
CLOSED: first 3 weeks Jan
MEALS: 12 to 1.30, 7 to 9.30
PRICES: Set L £14.75 (£21), Set D £18.75 (£26)
CARDS: Access, Visa
SEATS: 36. Private parties: 45 main room, 18 private room. Car-park, 20 places. No children
under 5. Music

*See the inside of the front cover for an explanation of the 1 to 5 rating system recognising
cooking standards.*

STOKE-BY-NAYLAND Suffolk

map 3

▲ *Angel Inn*

Stoke-by-Nayland CO6 4SA
COLCHESTER (0206) 263245

COOKING 2
COST £31

A series of interconnected rooms, with plenty of log fires, beams and deep sofas, make up the pub side of this small hotel which occupies a series of renovated cottages and related buildings. Opinion seems divided between recommending the bar food, written up each day on a blackboard, or the restaurant. Dishes may be interchangeable, and fresh fish daily in both places is given its due: halibut, sole, lemon sole, lobster, scallops, bream and codling are some noted. The bar, of course, is cheaper. There is a weakness for fruit combinations, as in duck with apricots, liver with raspberries or prawns with melon and grapes, but also every sign that real effort is made. Thus a dressed crab is offered with a mayonnaise, a vinaigrette for the salad and a well-herbed yoghurt dressing – and this is bar food. The bar also deals in steak and kidney pie and liver and onions, whereas the restaurant offers a warm salad of smoked pigeon and deep-fried parcels of Brie, Stilton and Camembert with cranberries, walnuts and apple. Criticisms revolve around the time it may take to get the food and the occasionally amateur service. The restaurant wine list is short and adequate. It is also very reasonably priced. Bar tables cannot be reserved: rather like 'Pay and Display' parking, you find a table and then order your food. House French :£6.50.

CHEF: Mark Johnson PROPRIETORS: Richard Wright and Peter Smith
OPEN: Tue to Sun, exc Tue L and Sun D
CLOSED: 25 and 26 Dec
MEALS: 12 to 2, 6.30 to 9
PRICES: £19 (£26)
CARDS: Access, Amex, Diners, Visa
SEATS: 40. Private parties: 26 main room. Car-park, 20 places. Vegetarian meals. Wheelchair access (also WC)
ACCOMMODATION: 6 rooms, all with bath/shower. Rooms for disabled. B&B £35 to £45. Garden. TV. Phone. Doors close at 11.30 [*Which? Hotel Guide*]

STON EASTON Somerset

map 2

▲ *Ston Easton Park* ♟

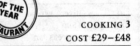

Ston Easton BA3 4DF
CHEWTON MENDIP (076 121) 631

COOKING 3
COST £29–£48

Ston Easton is one of the grandest hotels in the countryside. Its bare facade, Georgian austerity itself, gives little hint of the splendours within. Some understanding of the potential for abashment by 20-feet ceilings, glorious plasterwork and acres of flooring has been shown by the Smedleys, for their and their staff's attitude is one of relaxed friendliness, offering comfort where otherwise there might be coldness. The architecture changes gear in the dining-room, which remains grand but modern. It has views of the park and stream; for Ston Easton is nothing if not a house in context. The kitchen reflects this as well, with first-class vegetables from the walled garden – at the end of which some guests can enjoy the alternative eighteenth-century dream by hiring the gardener's cottage. A set menu of half a dozen choices per course at dinner (shorter at lunchtime) is a sensible compromise between tradition and adventure. It does not indulge in any new wave peasantry, but it borrows a little from country-house colleagues – for instance, a dish of scallops with lentils and coriander – and it makes fair play with luxury, regularly including lobster and foie gras. It is light in touch, some say light in seasoning, too, and except for a certain fondness for fruit, is not set on pushing back the frontiers of taste. There is a simple sub-menu, perhaps for long-stay guests. A summer meal showed well in a first course of galantine of chicken filled with duck liver pâté on a redcurrant sauce feathered with cream that might have been reminiscent of a sweet presentation, and a layered terrine of monkfish and mushrooms with a cold vermouth cream sauce. The fruit tendency reappeared in a chargrilled guinea-fowl, again with a redcurrant sauce, topped with pineapple and wild strawberries. Against the odds, this was approved, mainly because of the condition of the poultry, though the grilled lobster dish, accompanied in more orthodox style by a basil butter, was of equal quality. Ston Easton Tulip is a standard by now: a tuile basket, good sorbets, plenty of exotic fruit. Cheese, British and Irish, is well kept and enhanced by young celery from the garden. The meal will begin with a chef's complimentary dish, maybe a sliver of foie gras. This may put in the shade the other ancillaries of the meal. Solid country-house cooking is offered, and if it may occasionally seem less remarkable than the house itself, it should none the less enable the guest to eat and sleep in stately style. The food is backed up by an excellent wine list, the prices of which are less plutocratic than might be feared. Some effort has been made to offer a choice at the lower end, there are plenty of halves, and it takes an even view of the world's wine production. The clarets are the longest suit, going back to 1929, but maturity is not ignored in burgundies, Rhônes, or even in Hock and Mosel where the 1971s make a welcome appearance. House wine is £9.50. CELLARMAN'S CHOICE: Gigondas 1967, Jaboulet, £39; Edward Sheldon Champagne Rosé 1983, £27.

CHEF: Mark Harrington   PROPRIETORS: Peter and Christine Smedley
OPEN: all week
MEALS: 12.30 to 2, 7.30 to 9.30 (10 Fri and Sat)
PRICES: Set L £21.50 (£29), Set D £32 (£40)
CARDS: Access, Amex, Diners, Visa
SEATS: 40. 8 tables outside. Private parties: 40 main room, 14 and 22 private rooms. Carpark, 40 places. Vegetarian meals. Children's helpings. No children under 12. Smart dress preferred. No cigars/pipes in dining-room. Wheelchair access
ACCOMMODATION: 21 rooms, all with bath/shower. B&B £75 to £115. No children under 12. Pets welcome. Afternoon teas. Garden. Snooker. TV. Phone. Scenic. Doors close at midnight. Confirm by 6 [Which? Hotel Guide]

All details are as accurate as possible at the time of going to press, but chefs and owners often change, and it is wise to check by telephone before making a special journey. Many readers have been disappointed when set-price bargain meals are no longer available. Ask when booking.

See the inside of the front cover for an explanation of the 1 to 5 rating system recognising cooking standards.

Mr Underhill's ♟

Stonham IP14 5DW
STOWMARKET (0449) 711206   COOKING 3
on A140, 300 yards S of junction with A1120   COST £26–£44

Mr Underhill's has fully justified our flagging it 'County Restaurant of the Year' in 1990. Christopher Bradley is an accomplished cook and Judy Bradley skilful in the front of house. Their restaurant, strongly coloured, boldly furnished, appallingly sited for the innocent motorist, displays visual taste as invigorating as the oral sort that comes winging off the hob. Menus are fixed no-choice affairs. However, consultation before arrival is extensive, so 'no-choice' is a relative term. What convinced one visitor of the class of the place was the quality of the ancillaries, save the bread. Before the meal two tartlets of fragile shortcrust contained diced ham, cream cheese spiked with horseradish and a chive flower on top. Butter was excellent; the coffee was 'the best I've ever had, really, with a touch of cinnamon to the flavour and powerful aroma'; petits fours included truffles encased in hard chocolate, strawberries in fondant and a brandy-snap, all of tip-top judgement. Such things colour one's perception of a meal, but the centre to this frame was of like achievement. Simple recipes are faultlessly executed: carrot and orange soup, served chilled; asparagus piled like logs for making a fire, topped with diced tomato (with, for once, real taste), sauced with a frothy, well-balanced beurre blanc; breast of Landais chicken with a thin, clean tasting tarragon and tomato sauce; a gratin of courgettes, timed exactly; new potatoes with earthy flavour; cheeses from Androuët; then a choice of dessert (the only choice), of which a cinnamon parfait with vanilla sauce, its flavours intense and as advertised, gave a creamy finish to what had already been a fairly rich and dairy-laden meal. No meal will be exactly as this was, though the repertoire will have fixed points – thus the soup has been a favourite as long as the restaurant has been open – but others agree the balance of dishes may edge towards the rich and others have observed a tendency to overcook poultry, which was the only fault with the chicken described here. The wine list that accompanies all this is also evidence of experience and enthusiasm. There are adequate half-bottles, prices are fair, the range is acceptable to most pockets, and attention is given to New World, Italian and Spanish growers. There are some interesting items, from Mâcon la Roche Vineuse, Guigal's Côte Rôtie La Mouline 1978, to Wirra-Wirra in Australia or Duckhorn's Merlot from Napa. House wine: £7.95 and £8.75. CELLARMAN'S CHOICE: Pinot Blanc 1988, Ch. D'Orschwihr, £9.75; Collioure, Cuvée les Piloums 1984, £13.95.

CHEF: Christopher Bradley   PROPRIETORS: Christopher and Judy Bradley
OPEN: Tue to Sat, D only (L by arrangement)
MEALS: 7.30 to 8.45
PRICES: Set L £20 (£26) to £25 (£32), Set D £25.40 (£32) to £29.50 (£37)
CARD: Access, Visa
SEATS: 30. Private parties: 30 main room, 16 private room. Car-park, 12 places. Vegetarian meals. Children's helpings (with prior notice). Smoking after meal. Wheelchair access (also WC)

STONOR Oxfordshire	map 2

Stonor Arms

Stonor RG9 6HE	COOKING 2
TURVILLE HEATH (049 163) 345	COST £25–£42

This erstwhile pub retains its licence but locals supping at the bar are
outnumbered by visitors coming to eat in the restaurant or try the simpler and
cheaper à la carte bar meals in the conservatory. There is a local who avers that
whenever flooded or stranded by power failure, 'then the Stonor Arms for me',
but he too is an eater not a drinker. The welcome he would receive is warm,
competent in the case of Anne Frost, the wife of the chef, and enthusiastic if not
always informed in the case of the young staff. Accounts of meals have varied
greatly, though the consensus tends to be that Home Counties prices should
deliver more adventurous, more flavoured food. Materials are generally
approved – the fish is good, for example – but tastes lack emphasis and
technique lacks finish. Dishes that have been approved include a fillet of fresh-
tasting John Dory (though the crab sauce was deemed too mild); often a good
roast beef at Sunday lunch; venison with a poivrade sauce; breast of guinea-
fowl with endives and a mustard sauce; a wing of skate with black butter.
Desserts are applauded for the regular appearance of hot puddings which,
when not too sweet, can be satisfying, and pastry work may also be
satisfactory. The discreetly restored rooms, with a wealth of bare wood and
some good watercolours on the walls, gleam from polish on the tables and the
silverware. They make a pleasant locale for an evening in the country. Clarets –
all highly priced, some good – head the wine list. Pass these by and the
mark-up favours the lesser but soundly selected bottles: Givry from
Lespinasse, the excellent Pouilly-Fuissé of Michel Forest, Trimbach's Riesling.
There is much enthusiasm for the Loire, less for Italy, and a good page of
French country wines. California and Australia are robust. A page of half-
bottles is commendable but highlights the voracious mark-up policy.

CHEF: Stephen Frost PROPRIETORS: Stonor Hotels Ltd
OPEN: restaurant Mon to Sat and Sun L; bar all week
MEALS: 12 to 1.45, 7 to 9.30
PRICES: £17 (£25), Set L £18.95 (£25) to £19.95 (£26), Set D £26.75 (£34) to £27.75 (£35)
CARDS: Access, Amex, Visa
SEATS: 40. 6 tables outside. Private parties: 22 main room. Car-park, 30 places. Children's
helpings. Smart dress preferred. No cigars/pipes in dining-room. Wheelchair access. Music
ACCOMMODATION: 9 rooms, all with bath/shower. Rooms for disabled. B&B £80 to £135.
Garden. TV. Phone

STORRINGTON West Sussex	map 2

▲ *Abingworth Hall*

Thakeham Road, Storrington RH20 3EF	COOKING 2
WEST CHILTINGTON (0798) 813636	COST £21–£43

The Hall has ancient origins but took its present form in 1910. The Bulmans
have restored it to immaculate condition over the last seven years, the last
addition being the conservatory, with views over lake and velveteen lawns,

471

where snacks and light lunches are served. At dinner a four-course set-price menu with choices is offered in tandem with a *carte*, some of the dishes being virtually interchangeable. In all, it makes for a fair range of choice (there's a three-course set lunch, too). The kitchen's approach, though described as 'nouvelle', is mainstream country-house in style: field mushrooms with glazed goats' cheese; salade gourmande; duck pâté with Cumberland sauce; turbot with lobster and chive sauce; duck with apple and calvados sauce; ending perhaps with a hot soufflé or crème brûlée. Cooking is sound in the main, and efforts are made with home production of breads and preserves. The Bulmans have a good sense of hospitality. Burgundies have the benefit of good growers, Juillot and Vincent among them, and a fair range of price. Clarets are limited but otherwise the wine list offers many decent bottles at around £12 or under. House wine: £7.50.

CHEF: Peter Cannon   PROPRIETORS: Philip and Pauline Bulman
OPEN: all week
MEALS: 12.30 to 2, 7.15 to 9
PRICES: £27 (£36), Set L £15 (£21), Set D £25 (£32)
CARDS: Amex, Access, Carte Blanche, Diners, Visa
SEATS: 54. Private parties: 54 main room. Car-park, 40 places. Children welcome. No smoking in conservatory. Smart dress preferred. Wheelchair access (4 steps; also WC)
ACCOMMODATION: 21 rooms, all with bath/shower. B&B £58 to £135. Deposit: £10. No children under 10. Garden. Swimming-pool. Tennis. TV. Phone. Scenic. Doors close at 11

▲ *Manleys*

Manleys Hill, Storrington RH20 4BT
STORRINGTON (0903) 742331

COOKING 4
COST £25–£49

The small Queen Anne house at the foot of the South Downs has two interconnecting dining-rooms that achieve a high degree of luxury beneath their beamed ceilings. This is carried through to the service, which is cast in as classic a mould as Karl Löderer's cooking. He is a serious exponent of European high cuisine, influenced by the French, of course, but also by the Austro-Hungarian example. He manages to graft these antecedents on to an awareness of modern tastes so that a menu may contain scallops with a squid-ink sauce and tagliatelle of vegetables; fillet steak 'Rubens', with a mushroom duxelle, tomato and hollandaise; and the Austrian dish of veal stuffed with kidney served with spätzli. Fish cookery is complex and is the area that shows most original invention. Reports have stressed the excellence of salmon layered in filo with a langoustine sauce as first course, or the sole fillets with asparagus and vegetables seasoned with a lemon confit. Meat, too, has its supporters: venison Baden-Baden; rack of lamb with herbs and paprika potatoes, joining the flavours of Romney marsh, Provence and Hungary in one dish; or duck, first marinated to give it edge to fight the fat, then grilled and served with cabbage spiked with ginger. Portions are more than generous, but space should be left for the Salzburger Nockerln or other desserts which show the hand of an adept at pastry work. There is a serious wine list, dominated by the best of France but with some price relief from the New World. House wine: £10.80. 'We arrived in rather bad humour due to a delayed meeting but our meal restored our equanimity'. Thus should restaurants contribute to happiness.

CHEF/PROPRIETOR: Karl Löderer
OPEN: Tue to Sun, exc Sun D
CLOSED: first two weeks Jan, last week Aug and first week Sept
MEALS: 12 to 2, 7 to 9.15 (10 Sat)
PRICES: £29 (£41), Set L £17.60 (£25)
CARDS: Access, Amex, Diners, Visa
SEATS: 48. Private parties: 36 main room, 22 private room. Car-park. Children's helpings on request. No children under 7. Smart dress preferred. No cigars/pipes in dining-room. Wheelchair access (also WC)
ACCOMMODATION: 1 double room, with bath/shower. B&B £55 to £87. TV. Phone. Scenic

---

STOURPORT-ON-SEVERN Hereford & Worcester   map 5

Severn Tandoori

11 Bridge Street,
Stourport-on-Severn DY13 8UX   COOKING 1
STOURPORT (029 93) 3090   COST £16−£28

The restaurant shares an owner and a nearly identical menu with Stafford's Curry Kuteer (see entry). It is keen to establish a smart modern interior, 'a conservationist's nightmare − a completely gutted Georgian town house.' The emphasis is on the tandoor oven. Reports over the years, while often agreeing that it is a useful local resource, have also registered some lapses. Drink lassi or Asti Martini.

CHEF: A. Audud   PROPRIETOR: S. A. Quayum, M. Miah, A. Audud, Z. Ali and M. Meah
OPEN: all week
MEALS: 12 to 2, 6 to 11.30
PRICES: £9 (£19), Set L and D £11 (£16) to £17 (£23)
CARDS: Access, Amex, Diners, Visa
SEATS: 70. Private parties: 70 main room, 70 private room. Vegetarian meals. Children's helpings (weekend D only). No children under 4. Wheelchair access (also WC). Music

---

STOW-ON-THE-WOLD Gloucestershire   map 2

Epicurean

1 Park Street, Stow-on-the-Wold
GL54 1AQ   COOKING 3
COTSWOLD (0451) 31613   COST £23−£53

Epicurus, who crops up as a spotlit bust on the menu cover and even on the candlesticks, held that 'the highest good is pleasure and the world is a series of fortuitous combinations of atoms.' So says Patrick McDonald, chef/proprietor of this restaurant in a good Cotswold house that mixes bare limestone with a slate and 'custard' colour scheme: a decorator's version of the raw and the cooked. Some might counter that Epicurus did not equate luxury with pleasure but they would recognise elements of his atomistic philosophy in mix and match recipes that combine, in a very short menu, chicken with lobster and scallops with foie gras, and offers a 'ratatouille' sauce that is not a liquid refulgent with the glorious colours and aroma of that Provençal dish, but

473

almost of pure cream with tiny dice of sweet peppers in three colours. It is apparent from this that the food is modern; it is also skilled and people have enjoyed it. A steamed chicken and lobster sausage is briefly chargrilled for flavour and cut open to reveal the two elements separated by spinach leaves. (Spinach seems to be viewed, as in a lot of other places, 'as a substance separating different layers' – more atomism!) The lobster was more precisely timed than the chicken but both materials were of good quality. The sauce was proclaimed as white truffles, chervil and butter. The eater maintained the truffle flavour was indeterminate, the chervil was chives and the chicken stock base was excellent. The overall impact of the dish flanked by undercooked but good fettucini and nearly raw asparagus, was harmonious enough to convince a reluctant diner. Other dishes show a wish to compose chords of taste and the style, as evinced by that sausage, is rarely cacophonous. Patrick McDonald has not been seduced by the wilder strains of English novelty, but rather by the neo-classical tunes of the Anglo-French moderns. As yet, the base notes of strong taste are modulated, so the impact of a dish may be unclear. The *carte* has four or five dishes at each stage, and there is a set-price seven-course wonder where the amuse-gueule counts as a course, and a cheaper set-price lunch. Desserts also follow the path of atomisation or hoping for unity out of dissonance. Thus in his version of hot hazelnut soufflé with caramel ice-cream, the main plate is occupied by the ice-cream – not caramel but vanilla with caramel sauce – and the soufflé, slightly leathery, comes on a side plate. Coffee may be weak but the petits fours are good, as are the breads and butter. The informed service is under the control of Mrs McDonald, although one party had a waitress who said, 'There you go,' as she delivered each item. The French wine waiter has been very difficult to understand but the list is clear, short and not over-priced, although relentless application of a percentage mark-up favours the more modest bottles. House French: Ch. Lyonnat, St Emilion, £14.75, and Quincy, Dom. Mardon, £13.50.

CHEF: Patrick McDonald   PROPRIETORS: Partick and Claire McDonald
OPEN: Tue to Sun, exc Sun D
MEALS: 12.30 to 2.30, 7.30 to 11.30
PRICES: £34 (£44), Set L £16.50 (£23), Set D £26 (£33). Service inc
CARDS: Access, Amex, Diners, Visa
SEATS: 30. Private parties: 18 private room. Vegetarian meals. Children's helpings.
No children under 7. Wheelchair access (also WC). Air-conditioned

---

STRATFORD UPON AVON Warwickshire   map 2

Sir Toby's

8 Church Street,
Stratford upon Avon CV37 6HB   COOKING 1
STRATFORD UPON AVON (0789) 68822   COST £28

This tiny restaurant of two beamed rooms is conveniently placed, and dinner helpfully timed, for the theatres. So one theatre-lover popped in between a matinée of *Pericles* and an evening performance of *All's Well*. The Watkins, who continue to cook and serve the food, were able to discourse on the plays as well as the food. Over the years the menu has changed greatly. Where once Joanna

Watkins would offer ham and spinach pancake with a cream cheese sauce, now she makes a sorrel, spinach and ham roulade with walnuts. The Watkins have their own smoker and smoke pork for grilled cutlet with apple and calvados, and salmon. The popular bresaola is also home made. The menu seems long for so small a restaurant, but the materials are fresh, with a fair showing of fish dishes. Pancakes do occur, filled with seafood as a starter, for instance. The prawn and ginger bisque first course – 'easily the best course' – required a finger bowl after the prawns. The Orient has made an impression on Joanna Watkins as she expands her repertoire: coconut cheese sauce with stuffed peppers; a dish of spiced braised squid; and fresh ginger and monkfish. The puddings are firmly and expansively creamy or English: trifle, bread-and-butter pudding with apricots; meringues and brandy snaps filled with cream. Carl Watkins can keep the unruly in their place. To a request for chips, 'There is no frier here, sir; this is a *real* food restaurant,' was the dignified answer. Two dozen wines are not overpriced. House wine: £6.

CHEF: Joanna Watkins   PROPRIETORS: Carl and Joanna Watkins
OPEN: Mon to Sat, D only (L by arrangement)
MEALS: 5.30 to 9.30
PRICES: £17 (£23)
CARDS: Access, Amex, Visa
SEATS: 40. 4 tables outside. Private parties: 34 main room, 20 private room. Vegetarian meals. No pipes in dining-room. Children's helpings. Wheelchair access (1 step). Music. Air-conditioned

---

STROUD Gloucestershire   map 2

Oakes

169 Slad Road, Stroud GL5 1RG
STROUD (0453) 759950   COOKING 4
on B4070, ¹/₂m from Stroud   COST £19–£47

Defenders of Slad have protested at our description in the last edition. Oakes is not in suburban Slad, merely on the road to it. The locale remains slightly dispiriting but the small house, set a few yards back from the road, is charming and the welcome will overcome any misgivings. Chris Oakes does not often mention foie gras, wild mushrooms or fancy shellfish on his menus. This is good but not showy cookery, even if not averse to a little artful arrangement. It can be likened to the setting and the service. The setting is not deluxe but comfortable; the service is not formal, but usually effective, the exception being when staff are not yet adequately trained. The mood is well suited to a place that wishes to identify with local supporters but may come as unexpected to those who think very fine cooking only happens in temples of gastronomy. The seemingly small choice of food is also deceptive. The Oakes compose three menus - and a fourth for lunch - at differing prices, each offering two dishes, normally one fish, one meat, per course. Menus may be mixed as the diner fancies, which increases the range still further but makes costing a meal a little speculative. With no luxury ingredients, the menus read quietly. That may be the impact of the food itself: exact execution enhanced by restrained saucing and composition. The sauces were the chief point of one summer lunch, spoiled only by finding the same one occurring on two of the menus. Tender chicken livers were thrown into relief by herbs and a dark shallot sauce; a warm onion tart, on moderate pastry, was brought to life by smoked ham and an aromatic tomato sauce; ragout of seafood, with the taste of each fish quite distinguishable, came with a tarragon cream sauce. Conspicuous by their absence are the strong flavours of the neo-Italian school, though there are indications of fashion-following – of an innocent nature – in the seaweed served with monkfish with a red wine and shallot sauce, and in the perennial rösti, found in this instance under very well reported venison with a madeira sauce. Brill with spinach and asparagus with a lemon sauce was the third main course served at this meal. It had begun with ravioli of oysters and scallops in a chive cream sauce and finished with hot rhubarb soufflé with a honey cream, and apple in puff pastry with fresh dates. One reader enjoyed Sunday lunch, always reasonably priced, commenting 'our most favourite ever', particularly for the mixed hors d'oeuvre of ratatouille, warmed goats' cheese, red pepper purée, a chicken liver parfait and a small cream cheese tart; the roast saddle of lamb with rosemary sauce and lentil purée; and bread-and-butter pudding with an apricot glaze. 'A more serious wine list would help,' he went on to observe and, though the existing list has no faults of pricing or individual choice, it does look as if it has received less attention than the food. This may be wise – there is no easier way of losing money than getting priorities the wrong way round – but many may wish for a more adventurous exploration. House wine from Lamblin: £6.30. CELLARMAN'S CHOICE: Pouilly Blanc Fumé 1988, Denis Gaudry £11.65; Brouilly 1988, Thévenin, £10.40. Old Spot from Uley Brewery is also available.

CHEF: Christopher Oakes   PROPRIETORS: Christopher and Caroline Oakes and Nowell and Jean Scott
OPEN: Tue to Sun, exc Sun D
MEALS: 12.30 to 1.45, 7.30 to 9.30
PRICES: Set L £14.50 (£19) to £32 (£39), Sun L £18.50 (£24), Set D £28 (£34) to £32 (£39)
CARDS: Access, Visa
SEATS: 30. Private parties: 30 main room. Car-park, 12 places. Children's helpings.
Wheelchair access

STUCKTON Hampshire   map 2

Three Lions

Stuckton Road, Stuckton SP6 2HF
FORDINGBRIDGE (0425) 652489   COOKING 3
1m off A338 at Fordingbridge   COST £18–£37

'This cooking is of outstanding quality' was the parting comment of an old and valued contributor to the *Guide*. Karl-Hermann and June Wadsack run a pub that has not turned its back on its origins even while producing first class food: this is why such places are so important to the future of British catering. Unlike restaurants, they have none of the pretentiousness that makes all but a few so removed from day to day life. The Wadsacks were once brewery tenants here, but his true background is classical cooking. He was chef at Chewton Glen and this grounding emerges as soon as the blackboard menu is studied. The interior may not be to everybody's taste: plain wood furniture, green flock paper on wall and ceiling, embroidered pictures, certificates, bold patterned carpet, and objects *everywhere* crowd out a sense of design. To others, this is part of its attraction. The upgrading of the glassware and table settings has not altered the priority, which is still wholly on the cooking. There are no nibbles and only a few petits fours. Bread and vegetables are extra. This stripped-down approach is almost necessary in a place that serves such a wide variety of meals, from snacks to full dinners, at one and the same time. Chef Wadsack's professional skills come out in extracting flavours, in his use of beneficent technology such as a steam oven, which produces vegetables 'having so much flavour I felt I'd never tasted them before' (this from a 100-dinners-a-year correspondent), and knowledge of technical tricks like the wrapping and keeping of meat for just long enough to make it both perfectly tender and full of taste. Such was the breast of guinea-fowl with pine kernels, grapes and wild rice, prompting the comment that 'I had not realised before how interesting this bird can be, and how juicy.' The ability, then, should be recognised, after which value the range. Seven or eight fish, game in profusion, hearty dishes such as steak and kidney or leg of lamb braised with port and herbs, haute cuisine in magret of duck with pink peppercorns, German influence in haunch of venison Baden-Baden with home-made noodles, or mega-snacks of avocado and seafood jambalaya, fresh oysters, asparagus or mussels marinière. Only the scale of business engendered by popularity can keep all this fresh, and it does. June Wadsack is in charge of service, which is amiable, honest and no-nonsense, and of the wine list, which is a fitting complement to the food. It has a much wider remit than France, although claret is the best section. Germany, Rhône and Alsace run close seconds for interest. Prices are acceptable. Note some of the Pomerols and St Emilions among the clarets, Rolly-Gassmann's Alsaces and Balthasar Ress from the Rheingau. Dessert wines, many in halves, should be studied early to fit into a good drinking plan. One reader compared this place to Franco Taruschio's Walnut Tree Inn (see entry, Llandewi Skirrid, Wales) for its long menu, matter-of-factness, and concentration on taste. In some ways, Karl-Hermann Wadsack is where the Walnut Tree used to be, particularly in serving substantial hearty food (and large portions), but they share a catholic approach to the cuisines of the world, a love of fish, and a disregard of major-league comforts. Desserts are not a big matter, but the hot pudding is invariably good.

CHEF: Karl-Hermann Wadsack   PROPRIETORS: Karl-Hermann and June Wadsack
OPEN: Tue to Sat
CLOSED: 2 weeks July to Aug, 23 Dec to 3 Jan
MEALS: 12.15 to 1.30, 7.15 to 9 (9.30 Sat)
PRICES: L £13 (£18), D £19 (£31). Service charge of 10% on parties of 6 or more
CARDS: Access, Visa
SEATS: 55. Private parties: 45 main room. Car-park, 40 places. No children under 14.
Wheelchair access

▮ *denotes an outstanding wine cellar;* ♟ *denotes a good wine list, worth travelling for.*
See the Introduction for a fuller explanation.

▲ *Plumber Manor*

Sturminster Newton DT10 2AF	COOKING 2
STURMINSTER NEWTON (0258) 72507	COST £31

Plumber Manor excites loyalty, perhaps because it's been in the Prideaux-Brune family since the early seventeenth century. Now, just as they coped with earlier revolutions and upheavals, the family has adjusted to modernity by converting house and barns to rooms and restaurant. Shooters may be seen in the autumn, and hunters are offered free stabling, straw and water, so life has not moved too fast. Loyalty is won by the peace and comfort (sports enthusiasts notwithstanding), and the combination of the solicitous care of Richard Prideaux-Brune, the 'well-cooked but never fancy' food and the atmosphere that produces 'the country-house style to perfection', according to one connoisseur of such things. The cognoscenti of food would say the offerings from two set-price menus combine ancient and modern quite cannily – beef Wellington and pigeon breast with strawberry vinegar – finishing strongly with a traditional English sweets trolley on which meringues get the highest vote. Complicated cooking is not the intention and the materials, especially the meat, are sound and the technique is up to the task even if not the acme of delicacy. The wine list is admirable in its provision of half-bottles. It leans quite heavily on Avery's of Bristol. House French: £7. CELLARMAN'S CHOICE: Ch. Latour St Bonnet 1983, £16; Montagny premier cru 1987, Bernard Michel, £15.

CHEFS: Brian Prideaux-Brune and Mrs S. Baker   PROPRIETORS: Richard, Alison, and Brian Prideaux-Brune
OPEN: all week, D only; L for parties by arrangement
MEALS: 7.30 to 9.30
PRICES: Set D £17 (£21) to £22 (£26). Service inc. Licensed, also bring your own: corkage £4
SEATS: 60. Private parties: 40 main room, 12 and 22 private rooms. Car-park, 20 places. Vegetarian meals. Children welcome. Smart dress preferred. No cigars/ pipes in dining-room. Wheelchair access
ACCOMMODATION: 16 rooms, all with bath/shower. Rooms for disabled. B&B £50 to £100. No children under 12. Garden. Tennis. TV. Phone. Scenic [*Which? Hotel Guide*]

Mabey's Brasserie

47 Gainsborough Street,	
Sudbury CO10 7SS	COOKING 3
SUDBURY (0787) 74298	COST £20

Is the fact that Robert Mabey has swapped his baseball cap for a chef's toque significant? It seems not. 'We love the atmosphere here – if not the ventilation. The welcome from Jo Cheesman and the staff is as fresh and unpretentious as the cuisine. Sure, the pine furniture (benches and screens) are wobbly from use and not every seat provides a view of Mabey's technique in the open kitchen but the small discomforts are accepted with good humour by customers for the value and candour as well as imagination and competence of the cooking.' The

menu is on a blackboard and should be closely studied (if you can see it).
Garlic bread with fresh herbs; roast prawns with a Chinese dipping sauce; a
salad of smoked goose and bacon; home-cured gravlax; duck with cream and
green peppercorns or with an excellent onion sauce; skate with ginger butter;
chocolate crème brûlée; apple strudel with vanilla ice-cream; or rich chocolate
and raisin parfait are some things singled out through the year. Chips fanatics
still enjoy them here – 'the skin-on factor takes some of the guilt out of it.'
Coffee is not always great and may be served with semi-skimmed milk but the
buttery fudge was compensation for some. There is a real attempt to offer high-
grade food in an accessible form. Occasional slips may occur, but they are fewer
than recorded last year. The wine list is short, but not trying to top up turnover
in the way adopted by some apparently cheap places. House wines from £5.95.

CHEF: Robert Mabey   PROPRIETORS: Robert Mabey and Johanna Cheesman
OPEN: Tue to Sat
MEALS: 12 to 2, 7 to 10
PRICES: £14 (£20)
CARDS: Access, Visa
SEATS: 35. Private parties: 40 main room. Vegetarian meals. Children's helpings.
Wheelchair access (2 steps)

SURBITON Surrey   map 3

Chez Max

85 Maple Road, Surbiton KT6 4AW   COOKING 3
081-399 2365   COST £24–£41

Max Markarian may have been here for years, but locals are still discovering
him. In the newly decorated and enlarged dining-room, plants soften sharp
angles, colours are cool, yet the feel is warm. The kitchen works some bright
modern ideas into the repertoire without straying into quirky or cumbersome
contortions, but success is largely built around accepted notions and
ingredients: crab and pistachio terrine with green pepper sauce; chicken
quenelles in pastry with lime sauce; squid with tomato and tarragon
vinaigrette; rosette of lamb with roasted shallots and madeira sauce. Cooking
invites drooling superlatives: salmon and asparagus mousse with watercress
sauce or cheese mousse on a base of spinach, are 'absolutely delicious';
scallops, wild mushrooms, spring onions and melon are piled into a pastry case
and 'cooked to perfection'. The upbeat mood continues into puddings of
strawberry meringue, chocolate truffle cake, and exotic fresh fruit salad with
sorbet. Portions are generous, service is generally friendly, the menu is written
quite unnecessarily in two languages, and wines (all French save the port and
two Germans) are well chosen. The list, however, is light on details of growers
and origins. If the whole list were as cannily chosen as the clarets, it would be
an impressive short selection, with prices not high in many instances. House
wine is £8.75.

All entries in the Guide *are rewritten every year, not least because restaurant standards
fluctuate. Don't trust an out of date* Guide.

CHEF: Max Markarian   PROPRIETORS: Mr and Mrs Max Markarian
OPEN: Tue to Sat, exc Sat L
MEALS: 12.30 to 2, 7.30 to 10
PRICES: £19 (£28), Set L £17 (£24), Set D £17.60 (£26) to £24.55 (34). Minimum £12.50.
Service 12.5%
CARDS: Access, Amex, Diners, Visa
SEATS: 45. Private parties: 45 main room. No children under 7. No pipes in dining-room

---

TAUNTON Somerset   map 2

▲ Castle Hotel ♥

Castle Green, Taunton TA1 1NF   COOKING 4
TAUNTON (0823) 272671   COST £17–£64

Stories of an impending sale surface and sink with regularity, just as the
departure of Gary Rhodes is presaged but not yet effected. Best ring before
going. The Castle presents two faces to the world on several counts. There is the
service, often complimented but also often condemned, be it on the hotel side
or in the restaurant. Then there is the output of the kitchen itself. On one hand,
lunch is on a British theme and very fairly priced; on the other, dinner is
emphatically haute cuisine, all luxury and punishingly dear. Lunch gets
constant praise. A typical meal from a short menu 'restored our faith in English
cooking', with Cullen skink; a mixed salad of chicken, quails' eggs, avocado
and saladings; roast leg of lamb; braised ox-tail; pear crumble and chocolate
sauce. There is a daily roast and one dish from Gary Rhodes's 'traditional
repertoire'. The execution of this menu has become very consistent in the last
years and combines pure taste with refined but not twee presentation. Dinner
is very different. There is a *carte* of six dishes in each course supplemented by a
set menu. The chef is a good housekeeper. Over a weekend there was red
mullet on Friday, red mullet sauce on Saturday and red mullet soup on Sunday.
This may go beyond careful husbanding when a menu has some sort of
mushroom in every main course save one, a fillet of sea bass with fennel,
pepper and an olive and coriander dressing. His approach leads to firm tastes,
witness turbot served on a bed of vegetables and wild mushrooms cooked in
goose fat with ginger or a first course of duck confit with a cassoulet. Most
dishes are not pale affairs of white flesh and delicate sauces. A fish soup is of
red mullet, foie gras is served with a black pudding, oysters with a risotto, so
the potentially rich and bland are given punch. Technical capacity is also clear:
'the best crème brûlée I have eaten,' 'rich and robust ox-tail,' properly trimmed
and expertly cooked, sauces that are deep yet not overpowering. This luxurious
and spacious restaurant needs a wine list to match. It is indubitably long and
offers a very wide price range, starting at £5.55. Its best section is claret, with
depth and breadth; the best run is St Julien. French provinces are not
especially strong, though there is a goodly collection of Jaboulet which
monopolises the Rhône. Burgundies are drawn from conservative sources and
so miss out on many of the more exciting growers and recent vintages. The
Australian and Californian choice is good and there are extras from Italy,
Greece and a run of Torres from Spain. 'A slightly miscellaneous list,' was the
verdict of one who has taken on board the new developments both in wine

making and in importing into this country. Suppliers are declared against each wine and this confirms the absence of smaller, excellent merchants who have proliferated in recent years. CELLARMAN'S CHOICE: Ch. La Fleur Gazin 1982, £18.80; Chablis, Montée de Tonnerre 1987, Louis Michel, £17.70.

CHEF: Gary Rhodes   PROPRIETORS: The Chapman family
OPEN: all week
MEALS: 12.30 to 2, 7.30 to 9 (9.30 Fri and Sat)
PRICES: £44 (£53), Set L £12.50 (£17) to £13.90 (£18), Set D £24.50 (£32) to £31 (£39)
CARDS: Access, Amex, Diners, Visa
SEATS: 110. Private parties: 65 main room, 50 and 110 private rooms. Car-park, 40 places. Vegetarian meals. Children's helpings (with prior notice). Smart dress preferred. Wheelchair access (also WC). One sitting
ACCOMMODATION: 35 rooms, all with bath/shower. Rooms for disabled. Lift. B&B £75 to £125. Baby facilities. Pets welcome. Afternoon teas. Garden. TV. Phone. Doors close at midnight. Confirm by 6

TAVISTOCK Devon   map 1

▲ *Stannary*

Mary Tavy PL19 9QB   COOKING 1
MARY TAVY (0822) 810897/8   COST £25

'A totally vegetarian restaurant which aims to show that "animal-friendly" cuisine can be exciting,' is how the owners describe their work in this former truck shop to a tin mine on the Tavistock-Okehampton Road. The relatively bare Dartmoor stone exterior belies the riot of Victoriana, sage-green paintwork and plants within. A glance at the menu reveals the aim: it carries codes to signify gluten-free, vegan, yeast-and mushroom-free or mustard-free food. Even the wine list is marked up for vegans where possible. This concern sits uneasily with the tolerance of smoking, though this is confined to the lounge area. The menu is creative, with original dishes of which some are very successful. Fruit forms an important part of the repertoire while salt is totally absent and sugar barely tolerated. A tomato and mango soup illustrates the use of fruit to impart a difference to a hackneyed recipe; though insufficient for distinctiveness. A herb and nut pâté on pumpernickel was adorned with kiwi, grapes, ugli, Asian pear, carrot and radish, all in prime condition. Lemon gave the pâté the accent that might otherwise have been gained by use of salt. The speciality of the house is mushrooms stuffed with a moist *farce* of pine kernels, rolled in crumbs before frying. A blue cheese sauce is poured over them and a salad accompanies. These were very successful. Heavier were the vegetarian rissoles, mainly sweetcorn and potato, on a light cheese sauce. These needed further depth of seasoning. Surprisingly, the vegetables cooked for the main courses have not always been very creative. Some opine that more than chopping up and boiling needs to be done to swede and turnip, fresh though they tasted. Sweets may include a sponge pudding, or a syllabub given variety by a passion-fruit purée. The restaurant is not especially cheap but the service is genial and the cooking has potential to convert the meat eater. The two dozen wines are moderately priced and chosen with organic viticulture to the fore, including respectable bottles such as Chaumont's Givry, Bossard's Muscadet, Frey Vineyard's Zinfandel, and Guerrieri-Rizzardi's Soave. Newquay Real

Steam Bitter or Inch's scrumpy might also be good choices. House
wines: £5.90.

CHEF: Alison Fife   PROPRIETORS: Michael Cook and Alison Fife
OPEN: all week, D only (by arrangement in winter)
MEALS: 7 to 9
PRICES: £15 (£21). Minimum £10
CARDS: Access, Visa
SEATS: 20. 3 tables outside. Private parties: 25 main room. Car-park, 20 places. Vegetarian
meals. Children welcome. No smoking in dining-room. Music. Air-conditioned
ACCOMMODATION: 3 rooms. B&B £13.50 to £30. Deposit: 20%. No children under 12.
Afternoon teas (in summer). Garden. TV

TEFFONT EVIAS Wiltshire   map 2

▲ *Howard's House Hotel*

Teffont Evias SP3 5RJ   COOKING 2
SALISBURY (0722) 716392   COST £21–£29

The village name is an odd one for Wiltshire, deriving from the medieval
Herefordshire family of Ewyas. The manor owns the village, including the
ornate, high-spired church and the grey-stone Tudor buildings. Howard's
House takes its name from Catherine Howard, one of Henry VIII's ill-fated
spouses, who lived here. The present owners, Paul Firmin and Jonathan Ford,
ran the Garden Room at Tisbury before taking over in 1989, bringing in legions
of builders and gardeners to rescue the place from its derelict state. Bold floral
designs and soft green colour schemes echo the Tisbury restaurant, and the
garden is a delight with its lily pond. Paul Firmin's trademarks are good sauces
and a generous use of fragrant herbs, spices and fruits in savoury dishes. His
short menu is modern, although flavours can be a shade timid and some of the
details can seem 'satisfactory rather than revolutionary'. Even so, there has
been praise for warm salad of sauté scallops with an oily, lime-flavoured
dressing; and a good home-made apricot and passion-fruit tartlet with crisp
buttery pastry and a sauce of pure passion-fruit juice without the seeds. Main
courses have ranged from medallions of venison with spring cabbage, bacon
and poivrade sauce to supreme of turbot with spring vegetables and ginger
butter sauce. Most sweets are modern versions of the classics: Pavlova has
taken wild strawberries on board; chocolate mousse has become 'white', with
mango purée and a summer fruit garnish. Cheeses are from Androuët of Paris.
Service is civilised and very English. The wine list of some 80 bottles displays
intelligence in selection and consideration for the customer; with much decent
drinking around £10, a good solid middle band, and a few above £20, this is an
unintimidating list. There are half-bottles, too, but rather thinly provided in
the classic areas.

---

*'Correction to my last report – the pillars in the dining-room are not polystyrene but plaster
– I tapped them.'* A reader

*The Guide is totally independent, accepts no free hospitality, and survives on the number
of copies sold each year.*

CHEF: Paul Firmin PROPRIETORS: Paul Firmin and Jonathan Ford
OPEN: all week, D only and Sun L
CLOSED: one week late Sept, 2 weeks Feb, 24 to 31 Dec
MEALS: 12.30 to 2, 7.30 to 10
PRICES: Set Sun L £13.95 (£19), Set D £21 (£27) to £23 (£29)
CARDS: Access, Amex, Visa
SEATS: 40. 4 tables outside. Private parties: 40 main room, 20 private room. Car-park, 35 places. Children's helpings (Sun L only). No cigars/pipes in dining-room. Wheelchair access (also WC). Music
ACCOMMODATION: 8 rooms, all with bath/shower. Rooms for disabled. B&B £65 to £80. Baby facilities. Pets welcome. Afternoon teas. Garden. TV. Phone. Scenic

---

TETBURY Gloucestershire map 2

▲ *Calcot Manor* 🍷

Beverston, Tetbury GL8 8YJ
LEIGHTERTON (0666) 890391 COOKING 3
on A4135, 3m W of Tetbury COST £16–£43

The Cotswolds must contain the greatest concentration of polished dining tables and silver domes in England, but Calcot Manor, under the enthusiastic direction of the Ball family, rises above the frequent inanities of the form. The bedrooms are luxuriously equipped and the bar and a pair of dining-rooms impressed one reader as 'homely but grand, with a jolly atmosphere'. She was therefore put out by such display as butter sculpted into roses, domes still lifted in unison (though without needless theatre) and long explanations of the chef's complementary dish at the start of the meal. This still disconcerts people taken unawares: 'Where's the first course I ordered, then?' Ramon Farthing's cooking, conspicuously modern though it is, seems to please visitors for its accurate invention. At dinner there is a set-price *carte* of five dishes in each of three courses, plus cheese and coffee with a complimentary confection. At lunch there is an undisclosed chef's surprise meal and two short menus; one is no-choice and very inexpensive. That the cooking is modern is apparent from the sauces and vehicles: warm vinaigrette, clarified wine infusion, a casserole of shallots, lentils and potato. That it is quite complex in presentation is shown in dishes such as breast of chicken filled with a truffle mousse, on rösti potato with roasted root vegetables and a light chicken sauce, or pigeon with creamed herb potatoes, glazed apple slices, pan-fried chicken livers and a caramelised game sauce. That it is successful is seen in one account of a meal consisting of brothy mussel soup with a dish of fried noodles; boned quail stuffed with wild mushrooms and a fruit-laden sauce; fillet of brill with pastry scales on a ginger sauce; lamb noisettes with lentil sauce; 'innovative' vegetables of a cauliflower and mushroom purée, courgettes *à la ficelle* with slivers of apple, beans and potato gratin. Cheeses followed, English and Irish. Then desserts included a trio of English sweets on a plate: bread-and-butter pudding, rhubarb crumble and sherry trifle – 'Don't be misled by the prosaic names; these were fine examples beyond the normal genre' – and a plate of apples, – 'a celebration of the fruit in steamed pudding, parfait, tart, mousse and sorbet, each an ambassador of a different variety of the fruit.' The wine list is certainly an adequate partner to the food. A few old red burgundies, even some mature whites, a group from Oregon and Washington states, and a useful slate of Provençal wines contribute to an interesting small list. Prices are not a bargain but there are some very good brandies to absorb when the bill is finally presented. House wine is £8.45. CELLARMAN'S CHOICE: Menetou Salon, St Ceols 1987, £15.80; Collioure Blanc, Dom. de Mas 1986, £21.30. No service charge is made or expected, say the Balls, though no mention of this policy is made on the menus.

CHEF: Ramon Farthing   PROPRIETORS: Brian and Barbara Ball
OPEN: all week, exc Sun D
MEALS: 12.15 to 1.45, 7.30 to 9.30
PRICES: Set L £12 (£16), to £25 (£29), Set D £25 (£29) to £32 (£36). Service inc
CARDS: Access, Amex, Diners, Visa
SEATS: 45. Private parties: 48 main room, 12 private room. Car-park, 75 places. Vegetarian meals on light menu. Children's helpings (L only). Smart dress preferred. No smoking in dining-room. Wheelchair access (also unisex WC).
ACCOMMODATION: 13 rooms, all with bath/shower. Rooms for disabled. B&B £80 to £130. No children under 12. Afternoon teas. Garden. Swimming-pool. TV. Phone. Scenic. Doors close at midnight. Confirm by 6 or by arrangement [Which? Hotel Guide]

THORNBURY Avon   map 2

▲ Thornbury Castle 🍴

Castle Street, Thornbury BS12 1HH   COOKING 3
THORNBURY (0454) 418511   COST £23–£40

Amid scenes of dereliction – for inconvenient decapitation meant the Duke of Buckingham never finished his glorious castle – lies a hotel of super-luxury. Maurice Taylor has never stopped making improvements, though modernising plans may sometimes be inhibited by regard for historic monument. On a chill night in summer, a visitor noted with pleasure the giant log fire, the mood reinforced by cascades of candles, wood panelling to the 10-foot mark and dark paintings looming from the upper reaches. The dining-room, by contrast, relies on octagonal form for interest, details made spare by the defensive origins of the great tower in which it is sited. A reading of the menu may prompt the thought that Thornbury has remained stuck in a 'new British' time warp: 'paupiette of chicken filled with an apricot and basil stuffing presented on a shallot and Pernod reduction' does not inspire confidence and may worry the hearts of those who prefer lighter eating. The reality, however, is more encouraging. Derek Hamlen's cooking is more restrained in taste than description. A meal that included fish soup nîmoise; a hot salad of pigeon breasts with a blanket of melting cheese; a beef tournedos on rösti potatoes with caramelised onions and a light wine sauce; rack of lamb coated with mint with a sweetish madeira sauce; hot orange and passion-fruit soufflé; hot butterscotch pudding; and a grand selection of largely west country cheeses was judged satisfactory. The preliminaries were especially enjoyable, from olives with aperitifs to kebabs of beef and other hot canapés, and the bread was well baked. Errors of seasoning or flavouring, in each case too light, were apparent in the fish soup and the hot soufflé (which the readers were sure was apple). Others have recorded decent cooking with only occasional gross error. Lunch is a menu of half a dozen choices at each course and is fairly priced;

dinner sees a longer choice, the price set according to the number of courses taken. There are Thornbury Castle favourites that recur from meal to meal, including home-smoked salmon, devilled crab, salmon with saffron sauce and treacle tart. Some people have reflected that portions are small. Service is always professional, though doubt might be cast by the couple who commented that their Beaujolais was warm only to be told that the cellar was a long way away. Perhaps it was a joke. The wine list is good. Its chief curiosity is that Thornbury is the only hotel-restaurant to have its own vineyard (Müller-Thurgau), although vinification is left to others. Its second attraction is the list of fine old wines in the private cellar: a remarkable collection at prices that allow some experiment. The main run of the list is all right too: good range, fair selection of halves, plenty below £14 a bottle. A virtual absence of Italians (due to the restaurant's possibly outdated views) is compensated by other sections worth particular attention, including the Beaujolais, Spain, some fair Hocks and Moselles (though without note of makers), and a long list of ports. House wine: £8.50 and £9. The menu ends with the note: 'You are entitled to good service – gratuities are not expected.'

CHEF: Derek Hamlen   PROPRIETOR: Maurice Taylor
OPEN: all week
MEALS: 12 to 2, 7 to 9.30 (9 Sun)
PRICES: Set L £16.50 (£23), Set D £22.50 (£29) to £26.50 (£33). Service inc
CARDS: Access, Amex, Carte Blanche, Diners, Visa
SEATS: 60. Private parties: 25 main room. Car-park, 30 places. Vegetarian meals. No children under 12. Smart dress preferred
ACCOMMODATION: 18 rooms, all with bath/shower. B&B £68 to £180. No children under 12. Afternoon teas. Garden. TV. Phone. Scenic [*Which? Hotel Guide*]

THORNTON-CLEVELEYS Lancashire   map 5

▲ *Victorian House*

Trunnah Road,
Thornton Cleveleys FY5 4HF
CLEVELEYS (0253) 860619

COOKING 2
COST £14–£26

This one-time convent is opposite the church at the Thornton end of Thornton-Cleveleys. Not everyone finds it easily, so ask for directions. Ring the bell and the door will often be answered by Mme Guérin in 'a long black satin dress and stunning green shoes', 'a white evening gown' or some other Victorian costume. This is but preface to a wonder world of Victoriana, from the dress of the staff to the suggestive prints in the lavatory. Mme Guérin's welcome impresses by its warmth and suavity. The dining-room has lace table-cloths, 'advancing clutter', fretwork radiator masks, balloon-back chairs – but serves twentieth- not nineteenth-century food. The menu is long for the scale of business and dinner comes at a set price for four courses with only the odd supplement. Lunch is *à la carte*. Vegetarians may find regular dining tedious inasmuch as the dish for them, a pavé of hazel-nuts and brown rice, seems to go on from year to year. Others, too, will find a relatively unchanging framework, though surface variations occur from month to month. Some things have pleased mightily: a salmon roulade with a mushroom mousse filling on a rich

485

cream sauce; a smoked ham, pea and lettuce soup 'suggesting that the North of England is unrivalled soup territory', and a first course salad with a subtle vinaigrette. Not all has been praise, however, and on a bad night, readers have wondered if the place should be supported at all. It seems capable of tremendous ups and downs in the span of a single meal. Satisfaction with a roast loin of lamb with garlic stuffing, which could have been better trimmed, may be set against sauces described as 'black potions' or 'grey glue'. A good range of British cheeses is complemented by a refreshing kiwi and orange salad with orange sorbet or passion-fruit bavarois with raspberry coulis but a leaden apple tart and poor coffee did not end a meal well. People do enjoy the setting, though on a quiet night the attentions of the waitresses may seem a little close. The music too can be worrisome. One reader remarked on how a tape recorder in an adjoining room is turned up to high volume ('giving the impression of rowdy neighbours') and plays Mike Sammes Singers followed by Grieg. That the policy is unchanging is seen in the succession on another night of Mike Sammes, Mozart, Dvorak, and Grieg (with five minutes' silence between movements one and two). The wine list holds good bottles at very fair prices indeed. The clarets are from interesting properties (Palmer, Gloria, Lagrange, La Lagune, and Canon) and some good years: even the 1980 listed, as the heart sinks for that unpropitious year, proves to be a Palmer, one of the few successes. Burgundies also have some nice growers and négociants, though details are light. House French: £7.50. CELLARMAN'S CHOICE: Mâcon-Clessé 1988, J. Dépagneux, £11.50.

CHEF: Didier Guérin PROPRIETORS: Louise and Didier Guérin
OPEN: Mon to Sat, exc Mon L
CLOSED: last week Jan, first week Feb
MEALS: 12 to 2, 7 to 9.30
PRICES: £9 (£14), Set D £16.50 (£22). Service inc
CARDS: Access, Visa
SEATS: 40. 4 tables outside. Private parties: 40 main room. Car-park, 20 places. Vegetarian meals. No children under 6. Smart dress preferred. Music
ACCOMMODATION: 3 rooms, all with bath/shower. B&B £37.50 to £55. Deposit: £10. No children under 6. Pets welcome. Garden. TV. Phone. Scenic. Confirm by 6
[Which? Hotel Guide]

THRESHFIELD North Yorkshire   map 7

Old Hall

Threshfield BD23 5HB   COOKING 1
SKIPTON (0756) 752441   COST £17

A refurbished roadside pub with gleaming brass, dark stained wood panelling and a restaurant to one side is given a domestic touch with a display of teapots and cups. Success has brought further extension into a conservatory but the blackboard menu still offers a world tour in 15 items: from ratatouille to Chinese-style chicken wings; from chicken satay and sag ghost to Yorkshire lamb with rosemary. Good fish such as scampi in chilli and tomato sauce, plump marinated herrings or monkfish fried with garlic is supported by decent bread, lots of garnish, standard vegetables and value for money. A tiny wine list, with house wine starting at £4.95, is supported by Timothy Taylor's and Guest's beer and Combes Farmhouse cider.

CHEFS: Carl Gilbert and Rachel Mawer PROPRIETOR: Ian Taylor
OPEN: all week, exc Mon Jan to May
MEALS: 11.30 am to 2, 6.30 to 9.30
PRICES: £9 (£14)
SEATS: 80. 4 tables outside. Private parties: 35 main room. Car-park, 30 places. Vegetarian meals. Children's helpings. Wheelchair access (also WC). Music

---

TIDEFORD Cornwall   map 1

Heskyn Mill

Tideford PL12 5JS   COOKING 1
LANDRAKE (0752) 851481   COST £30

In a declivity just off the main road from Plymouth into Cornwall stands this water mill, the machinery still intact – armchairs, tables, vases of flowers and life in general adapting to its picturesque presence. The business of dining occurs on a floor above the entrance and reception hall. There is a simple *carte* supplemented by a more interesting list of specials that may change every few weeks. The repertoire remains steady from year to year: quail with oatmeal stuffing; quail's eggs with a prawn dip; chicken livers with bacon and garlic croûtons; guinea-fowl Rossini; lamb with lime and chive sauce. Fish is offered as a daily extra. Ice-creams are still enjoyed, as is the marquise, for dessert. Elaborate presentation can be a feature, but one reader commented that the less fancy dishes tasted better. Vegetables are many and varied. The wine list is a sound selection from all major regions. Clarets are perhaps the longest suit and Spain is particularly impressive. House wine: £6.75.

CHEFS: F.A. Eden and J. Baird PROPRIETORS: F. and S.M.L. Eden
OPEN: Tue to Sat
MEALS: 12 to 1.45, 7 to 10
PRICES: £17 (£24)
CARDS: Access, Amex, Visa
SEATS: 60. 6 tables outside. Private parties: 50 main room. Car-park, 25 places. Vegetarian meals. Children's helpings. Music

---

TORQUAY Devon   map 1

▲ Mulberry Room

1 Scarborough Road, Torquay TQ2 5UJ   COOKING 2
TORQUAY (0803) 213639   COST £9–£22

Lesley Cooper hardly conforms to the image of a seaside hotelier but her guest-house is a model of its kind. On the ground floor is a two-roomed café, prettily decorated, a great table of cakes and cream greeting the expectant arrival. Morning coffee and afternoon tea join lunch on five days, but dinner is offered on Saturday only. The blackboard menu is the main seat of action: iced port and mushroom soup; mushrooms à l'arménienne; fillet of bream, sauce messine; chicken stuffed with prunes and apricots with a sloe gin sauce; rhubarb fool; and lemon meringue pie are some of the dishes, all cooked with verve and enthusiasm. Saturday dinner consists of a choice of four items at each course and will always include a vegetarian dish. It can be taken as a set-price extravaganza fleshed out with sorbets, cheese and coffee, or à la carte. Sunday lunch is mostly to do with a roast, though choice is there still. Torquay needs 20 places of this standard. The wine list is short but cheap; house Vacqueyras is £5.50.

CHEF/PROPRIETOR: Lesley Cooper
OPEN: Wed to Sun L, Sat D
MEALS: 12.15 to 2.30, 7.30 to 9.30
PRICES: £11 (£14), Set L £6.35 (£9) to £7.50 (£10), Set D £14.50 (£17) to £15.50 (£18)
SEATS: 30. 2 tables outside. Private parties: 40 main room. Vegetarian meals. Children's helpings. Wheelchair access (also WC). Music
ACCOMMODATION: 3 rooms. B&B £10.50 to £31. Deposit: 10%. Children welcome. Afternoon teas. TV. Doors close at dusk. Confirm by 9.30

Remy's

3 Croft Road, Torquay TQ2 5VN
TORQUAY (0803) 292359

COOKING 2
COST £26

Remy Bopp, who hails from Alsace, continues to improve the comfort of his customers – the number of seats is reduced this year to give more space – while ploughing his own furrow of wholesome French cooking. Set in a quiet part of the town, where Saturday night crowds do not roam the streets, the restaurant is a haven of serious purposes, baking its bread, making its ice-creams, buying good raw materials, which makes it a happy find for the visitor and none too expensive at that. M. Bopp's three proclaimed specialities are sweet: a vacherin, an almond tart with chocolate sauce and a carrot and almond cake with vanilla sauce, but his first courses of chicken with pasta and shallot cream sauce or lamb's kidney with Meaux mustard and main courses of chicken with tarragon or rack of lamb are reliable too. The wine list is a fairly chosen French range – what else – with house wines at £6, and prices generally reasonable.

CHEF/PROPRIETOR: Remy Bopp
OPEN: Tue to Sat, D only
CLOSED: 2 weeks in Aug
MEALS: 7.15 to 9.30
PRICES: Set D £16.85 (£22). Minimum £16.85. Service inc
CARDS: Access, Amex, Visa
SEATS: 32. Private parties: 32 main room, 32 private room. Children's helpings Smart dress preferred. No-smoking area. Music

---

Consumers' Association is planning to publish Out to Eat, *a new guide to budget eating out in restaurants, pubs, cafés, brasseries and so on. Please send reports and recommendations to Out to Eat, FREEPOST, 2 Marylebone Road, London NW1 1YN.*

map 1

▲ New Inn

Tresco TR24 0QQ   COOKING 1
SCILLONIA (0720) 22844   COST £15–£25

Light, air and balmy warmth are some of the charms of these islands but food
can be more difficult. The New Inn gives as energetic an answer to the problem
as anywhere in the archipelago. The dining-room has been opened up to
provide more space between tables, and there are now two sittings for dinner.
Non-meat eaters are provided with grilled local mullet, roast monkfish, whole
baked sole stuffed with crab and Cornish Yarg, or plaice with green capsicum
butter, and a vegetarian dish of the day is usually on offer. A sorbet or soup (ox-
tail with herb croûton or turnip and dumpling) precedes main courses, which
may run to braised pheasant or loin of pork with yoghurt and rosemary. Ice-
creams, chocolate gateau, and a variation of the bread-and-butter pudding
theme round things off. Wines are varied and reasonably priced, and half-
bottles are not neglected. House French: £5.40.

CHEF: Graham Shone   PROPRIETORS: Christopher and Lesley Hopkin
OPEN: all week, D only
CLOSED: 2 weeks Dec
MEALS: 7 to 9
PRICES: Set D £10.50 (£15) to £15.95 (£21)
SEATS: 30. Private parties: 30 main room. Vegetarian meals. Children welcome for
early D only
ACCOMMODATION: 12 rooms, 10 with bath/shower. D, B&B £29 to £49 per person.
Deposit: £30. Baby facilities. Afternoon teas. Garden. Swimming-pool. TV. Phone. Scenic

---

TRURO   Cornwall   map 1

▲ Alverton Manor

Tregolls Road, Truro TR1 1XQ   COOKING 2
TRURO (0872) 76633   COST £14–£28

A new chef and front of house management have ushered in the summer season
of Cornwall's still most luxurious hotel, set above Truro's centre in a former
convent that was once a bishop's palace. Drapes and drapery have not been
stinted in the redecoration and locals speak warmly of it as a refuge during
hectic shopping expeditions, appreciating its comfort and the facility of an
outdoor lunch on fine days. Christopher Musgrave has not moderated the
modern style of his predecessor and offers such dishes such as ratatouille and
leek terrine with virgin oil; a warm seafood mousse with a thyme butter sauce;
loin of lamb with a timbale of courgettes and roast garlic; or salmon with
creamed potatoes and a red wine sauce. The wine list steadfastly refuses to list
vintages, simply claiming the bottle will be shown before uncorking and the
best vintage available will be supplied. This may just work for Muscadet, but
not for claret. Prices vary from year to year, depending on the vintage. House
wine: £8.25. More reports, please.

CHEF: Christopher Musgrave PROPRIETORS: Mr and Mrs J.J. Costelloe
OPEN: all week
MEALS: 12.15 to 1.45, 7.15 to 9.45
PRICES: £17 (£23), Set L £7.95 (£14) to £15.95 (£22), Set D £11.95 (£18). Service inc
CARDS: Access, Amex, Diners, Visa
SEATS: 50. 3 tables outside. Private parties: 35 main room, 25 and 35 private rooms. Car-park, 70 places. No children under 12. Smart dress preferred. No smoking during meals. Wheelchair access (also WC). Music
ACCOMMODATION: 25 rooms, all with bath/shower. Rooms for disabled. Lift. B&B £67 to £90. No children under 12. Afternoon teas. Garden. Snooker. TV. Phone. Scenic
[*Which? Hotel Guide*]

TUNBRIDGE WELLS Kent   map 3

Cheevers

56 High Street, Tunbridge Wells TN1 1XF   COOKING 2
TUNBRIDGE WELLS (0892) 545524   COST £29

'The inside is too stark,' says one reader, 'but quite excusable with one's head down over such good cooking.' Priorities are kept in mind by this restaurant behind a shop front on the main street: the food, the effective service, a short yet adequate wine list; clean but not overworked surroundings; a sound base of economic self-sufficiency that allows the charges to be affordable. Tim Cheevers is an alumnus of Blakes Hotel (see entry, London) which is a sure indication of a modern style, though the wilder shores of invention are kept beyond the horizon. A meal that contained an intense tomato and orange soup; mussel ravioli; gammon with lentils; a subtle dish of mallard with wild mushrooms and a mousse made from the legs and liver; coconut and rum tart with good pastry and a decent modern lemon tart shows the drift of the cookery. Other dishes approved included a crab mousse enveloped in spinach leaves; terrine of quail and pigeon with toasted brioche; duck roasted with spring onions and ginger; rack of lamb with a mint and almond crust; and puddings such as a two-chocolate parfait and rhubarb crumble. At lunchtime the menu is à la carte but in the evenings the cost is fixed. The half-dozen choices in each course may show variations between the meals, but the repertoire overall evolves quite slowly. The wine list is not more than three dozen long and is an adequate choice from largely classic zones. It is hard to perceive any logic to its arrangement, so read it all to find what is needed. House Lamblin is £6.50. CELLARMAN'S CHOICE: Mâcon, la Roche Vineuse 1987, £14; St Nicolas de Bourgueil 1988, Vallée, £12.50. There is no service charge and 'tips are not expected.'

CHEF: T.J. Cheevers PROPRIETORS: T.J. Cheevers, M.J. Miles and P.D. Tambini
OPEN: Tue to Sat
MEALS: 12.30 to 2, 7.30 to 10.30
PRICES: £17 (£24), Set D £19 (£24)
CARDS: Access, Visa
SEATS: 36. Private parties: 16 main room. Children welcome. No cigars/pipes in dining-room. Wheelchair access

Sankey's Seafood at the Gate

The Gate, 39 Mount Ephraim,
Tunbridge Wells TN4 8AA   COOKING 1
TUNBRIDGE WELLS (0892) 511422   COST £37

This year's reports for Guy Sankey's town centre restaurant are divided. 'He has
the goods but not the flavour', exclaimed one dissatisfied diner. The freshness
of the seafood is applauded, and the simplest dishes are probably the best bets
off the reasonably priced *carte*: baby scallops grilled with garlic and
breadcrumbs, or deep-trawled Greenland prawns with homemade
mayonnaise, for instance. The seafood plate contains the works, and smoked
salmon is wild. Desserts include lemon and ginger crunch and real sherry trifle.
The mostly French wine list, on the back of the menu, is well chosen.
Alternative drinks include cidre bouché, natural French ale and a tart German
Weisse beer. House French: £7.50. Plans to create an informal wine bar
downstairs and make the upstairs more formal haven't yet been realised, so the
dining-room still has bare tables in front and covered ones at the back.

CHEF: Eleutorio Lizzi   PROPRIETOR: Guy Sankey
OPEN: Mon to Sat
MEALS: 12 to 2, 7 to 10
PRICES: £26 (£31). Service inc
CARD: Access, Visa
SEATS: 60. 6 tables outside. Private parties: 8 main room, 30 private room. Children's
helpings on request. No cigars-pipes in dining-room

Thackeray's House ♥

85 London Road,
Tunbridge Wells TN1 1EA   COOKING 3
TUNBRIDGE WELLS (0892) 511921   COST £22−£43

A reader whose day trip to France was delayed by industrial action decided on
lunch here instead. 'We were unlikely to have done better in France,' was the
verdict. Here was a house truly inhabited by Thackeray; he might have
regretted that Bruce Wass was not his cook, though the Wass approach to food
is neither so conservative as the characters in Thackeray's historical novels, nor
as would meet the orthodoxy of the Conservative Club that is next door on
London Road. This year the fixed-price dinner has yielded to an à la carte
choice. As prices increase, the fixed-price system becomes more restrictive, in
theory if not in fact. The house has not been changed too much structurally, so
dining-rooms remain separate and customers are not thrown into one daunting
space. Service is good; 'we were not in the slightest hassled to leave at 3.45,
and that after we had turned up half an hour late.' The cooking is professional
in that it is skilled and pays attention to flavour and materials. Tastes are as
modern as anywhere in London − pesto, lentils, bresaola and olive oil featured
on a recent menu − but there is also use of herbs in a fresher and more
thoroughgoing way than in places who drown them out with alcohol or
reduction. Dishes that have given pleasure include a salad of Arbroath
smokies; a soup in the manner of a bouillabaisse; a salad of confit of duck, pine
kernels and quails' eggs; guinea-fowl with lentils and tarragon; rack of lamb

with pesto, or served on one occasion with spinach and stir-fry vegetables. British and Irish cheeses are from James of Beckenham. Good desserts have included apricot, walnut and ginger pudding with toffee sauce; apricots and mascarpone with mango sauce – though this was thought too light in taste by one reader; or a chocolate and griotte cherry loaf with vanilla sauce. There are periodic gourmet evenings which do not seem to have a special theme, just good food and good wine at an all-in price. Downstairs is a bistro version of the main restaurant providing good food in the same vein but at lower prices. A consciousness of price and value, never easy in places like this where corners are not cut, is apparent from the wines where, a dozen carefully chosen bottles at under £12 head the lists. Thereafter quality and prices rise steeply. Good growers abound – Lassaret and Forest in Burgundy, Sorrel on the Rhône, Teruzzi e Puthod from San Gimignano and a good spread from Rioja. Bruce Wass has been persuaded that California is OK – he now lists 10, from Mondavi to Phelps. Australia and New Zealand are less favoured. There are many good spirits and dessert wines.

CHEF/PROPRIETOR: Bruce Wass
OPEN: Tue to Sat
CLOSED: 1 week at Christmas
MEALS: 12.30 to 2.30, 7 to 10
PRICES: £29 (£36), Set L £14.90 (£22) to £16.85 (£24). Service inc
CARDS: Access, Visa
SEATS: 35. Private parties: 40 main room. Children's helpings

---

TWICKENHAM Greater London map 3

Cézanne

68 Richmond Road, Twickenham TW1 3BE COOKING 3
081-892 3526 COST £28

'I like it as much for what it is not as for what it is. It is not plushy or pretentious, and it does not describe its food in phoney French or flowery English,' said one reader. To others, the white tablecloths, wooden floor and occasional Cézanne reproduction are too plain a canvas for the fine cooking. The *carte*, with half a dozen choices at each stage, avoids the rich and heavy, and might take in scallops marinated with lime juice and ginger with yoghurt and vegetable julienne, breast of corn-fed chicken with saffron, and lemon mousse with raspberry sauce. Good have been green vegetable soup, guinea-fowl with oyster mushrooms, and vegetarian pasta with pine kernels and a herby sauce. The madeira and rosemary sauce with best end of lamb could have been more vibrant, and the balance in a coconut and banana ice-cream was out a shade. Kumquat and apricot crumble was an excellent concoction, however. Service is competent and friendly. The mainly French wine list is from the minimalist school: 40 unembellished entries and sensible prices. House wine: £8.
CELLARMAN'S CHOICE: Wente Brothers Chardonnay and Cabernet Sauvignon, £11.50; Trimbach Riesling 1985, £12.50.

See the back of the Guide *for an index of restaurants listed.*

CHEF: Tim Jefferson   PROPRIETORS: Tim and Philippa Jefferson
OPEN: Mon to Sat, exc Sat L
CLOSED: bank hols
MEALS: 12.30 to 2, 7 to 10.30 (11 Fri and Sat)
PRICES: £16 (£23)
CARDS: Access, Amex, Visa
SEATS: 38. Private parties: 40 main room. Vegetarian meals. Children's helpings. Wheelchair access. Music

McClements

12 The Green, Twickenham TW2 5AA	COOKING 3
081-755 0176	COST £21–£38

Estate agents would call the two-up, two-down house 'bijou'. What is striking is the technical skill of the cookery and its presentation, 'like sculptures on a bare landscape'. A lunch from a very short menu that none the less had aching gaps – 'no morels today', nor scallops – included a smoked ham mousse of perfect texture and well-balanced taste with an intense meat-glaze sauce. A better beginning, filled out with decent home-made bread and fresh butter, could not be imagined. The main course of fillet steak lacked the proclaimed morels but the sauce again showed full mastery of stocks and reductions. It also displayed meat of less than fillet quality and very small quantity. Other experiences might mirror this with recommendations for Dublin Bay prawns with a green peppercorn sauce; fine home-made black pudding, crisp but moist, in a light pastry shell; succulent lobster and asparagus salad; and 'the tenderest lamb we've ever eaten' with a charlotte of aubergines. Because John McClement produces everything himself, with virtually no help in the kitchen, delays may occur. Emotions, too, can run high. Reports comment on unevenness, notwithstanding the evident ability – sign again of the need for more help. Portions are small, while prices stay high. An inspector said in the early days of the restaurant, 'One to watch.' John McClement still is.

CHEF/PROPRIETOR: John McClement
OPEN: Tue to Sat, exc Sat L
MEALS: noon to 2.30, 7 to 10.30
PRICES: £26 (£32), Set L £15 (£21). Service 10%
CARDS: Access, Amex, Visa
SEATS: 24. Private parties: 20 main room, 15 private room. Vegetarian meals. No children under 3. Smart dress preferred. Wheelchair access (also WC). Music. One sitting

---

Prices quoted in the Guide *are based on information supplied by restaurateurs. The figure in brackets below an entry is the average for a three-course meal with service, coffee and half a bottle of house wine, as calculated by computer. The prices quoted at the top of an entry represent a range, from the lowest average meal price to the highest; the latter is inflated by 20 per cent to take account of the fact that very few people eat an average meal, and also that prices are likely to rise during the year of the* Guide.

UCKFIELD   East Sussex   map 3

▲ Horsted Place

Little Horsted TN22 5TS
UCKFIELD (0825) 75581   COOKING 2
2m S of Uckfield, on A26   COST £25–£51

Horsted Place looks to the new 'saviour' of country-house hotels: golf. Across
three farms are being sculpted two 18-hole wonders, complete with
clubhouses and a new hotel. From all this, the ultimate beneficiary is insulated
by 23 acres of landscaping. In this exceptional early Victorian Gothic pile with
a very well decorated interior and links with the architect A.W.N. Pugin, only
one room will be designated a 'golf lounge'. Visitors may continue to visit for
the food and the role-playing country-house style for which they will pay
prices at the top end of the norm. Chef Allan Garth, who at the time of our last
edition was at New Hall, Sutton Coldfield, joined at the beginning of 1990.
Both he, and Horsted Place, need a period of consolidation, though more upset
is due as more seats for dining are scheduled. First indications are that the
cooking does not rise above the modern country-house style but is competently
done, with surprising exceptions. Warm salad of scallops with sesame seeds
was generous, under-cooked, and nicely dressed; venison on a turnip rösti was
again ample, the meat good and well timed, but the rösti boring and ineffective
and the port sauce poor; vegetables are just adequate; a poor charlotte of kirsch
ended the meal. One inspector asked whether rösti was about to displace gratin
dauphinois, which she calls 'GFG potatoes', as the potato cliché of the decade.
They certainly might, and they are usually as badly made as all those gratins
we are forced to consume every year. 'When I remember gloriously moist,
creamy, aromatic plates of potatoes, and think of the dry, creamless, badly
chosen, badly baked and prissy little cut-outs of gratin that we so often get
now, I despair.' Cooking has not necessarily improved for all our self-
satisfaction. Sunday lunch is deemed a good meal for which to visit Horsted.
Approach the wine list with discretion. Taittinger Comtes de Champagne 1982,
available wholesale at about £40 including VAT, is listed at £140. That's quite a
mark-up. Not everything is as depressing as this and there is a good range,
including some new country wines. The list is longest in claret, but stay with
Italy or Australia.

CHEF: Allan Garth   PROPRIETORS: Granfel Hotels
OPEN: all week
CLOSED: first 10 days of Jan
MEALS: 12.30 to 2, 7.30 to 9.15
PRICES: Set L £14.50 (£25) to £18 (£28), Set D £27 (£38) to £30 (£42)
CARDS: Access, Amex, Diners, Visa
SEATS: 36. 10 tables outside. Private parties: 36 main room, 18 and 24 private rooms.
Car-park, 30 places. No children under 7. Smart dress preferred. No smoking. Wheelchair
access (also WC)
ACCOMMODATION: 17 rooms, all with bath/shower. Rooms for disabled. Lift. B&B £110 to
£295. No children under 7. Afternoon teas. Garden. Swimming-pool. Tennis. Golf. TV.
Phone. Scenic. Doors close at 11. Confirm by 9 pm

map 7

▲ *Sharrow Bay*

Howtown Road, Ullswater CA10 2LZ
POOLEY BRIDGE (076 84) 86301 and 86483
2m from Pooley Bridge on E side of lake,
signposted Howtown and Martindale

COOKING 4
COST £24–£48

'I noticed that many of the guests were on the large side but, interestingly, the staff are thin.' The explanation may lie in the constant attention devoted to the guests by those etiolated members of staff. No hotel, no restaurant, makes its customers feel as important, as special, as does Sharrow Bay. Its owners, Francis Coulson and Brian Sack, now guiding it through its forty-second season, 'have a kind avuncular manner, smiling down at you over the top of their spectacles, which all their young waiters seem to copy'. On the eastern shore of Ullswater sits this house of soft grey stone, built about 1840, with low-angled roofs and broad eaves giving it a continental look. A few hundred yards down the road is Bank House, which acts as annexe. Only breakfasts are served in its remarkable dining-room. The interior of Sharrow Bay is fabled for its gewgaws, pictures and bibelots: so packed full of them, indeed, that for once the exclusion of children is understandable if not estimable. One inveterate diner of 23 years reports his delight at finally spending a night and sampling the breakfast, which lived up to expectations. The slight excess of it all extends to the lavatories – 'gentlemen seem to emerge smelling of Cacharel', and women are amazed by the automatic dispensing of a plastic lavatory seat protector. More important is the food, served all week long in a dining-room that will afford fine views of sun, rain or wind on water if no more unusual matter obtrudes. The set-price menus are long (slightly shorter at lunch) and give choices at the first, main and dessert courses. In between there is a no-choice fish course, then a sorbet; at the end, cheese (at dinner) and coffee come included in the price. Now the reason for large guests is apparent. It would be wrong to categorise the cooking as conservative: roast saddle of rabbit with fresh noodles and a light mustard sauce, with the legs of the rabbit braised in their own juices and herbs, could figure in the most avant-garde of south-eastern restaurants. However, elements of the traditional are allowed to survive and indeed prosper: avocado and prawns, consommé, omelettes, cold cuts and hot puddings. Certain elements of the style are also unchanging: a fair quantity of butter and cream is the most significant aspect of this. For some, it is just too much and those of lighter appetites are advised to walk hard before setting to. The range of the kitchen is so great that it would be easy to skate over its production without identifying subtlety and skill. Thus a meal earlier this year by an inspector began with mussels and monkfish in a white wine reduction with tarragon and vegetables. It was served in a little copper pan, the fish tasted fresh and was enhanced by the sauce: juices, wine, cream, tarragon, a little lemon at the end and correct seasoning. Simple, but exactly performed. The vegetables, celery, carrots and a trace of onion, were enough to add a fresh neutrality to the unctuous reduction. To follow was the no-choice fish course, Aberdeen brill with a white wine and chive cream sauce and soufflé suissesse. The fillet was wrapped round slices of Florence fennel, placed in the middle of a small pool of sauce with a small soufflé 'sandcastled' to one side. The cumulative effect was substantial, but made palatable by the sauce which, though reminiscent of the preceding course, had sufficient bite and distinction to negate criticism on that score. A buttery leaf of puff pastry seems to have merely added to the bliss. The sorbet was nectarine. The breather was necessary. The main dish was leg of lamb 'English style'. In the event this was overcooked, though still of fine flavour. Meat is often cooked longer than Southerners' habits have prepared them for. It came with a lamb gravy – always very fine – a pile of hot vegetables that had been part of the initial pot-roast, some mint sauce (made, our reader would swear, with malt vinegar) and an onion sauce tartlet, the pastry as crisp and sweet as could be. Vegetables were of a mixed standard. Carrots were overcooked and a mite tired; spring greens came with walnuts and sultanas with a little cumin; mange-tout were very good, as were the new potatoes. A dish of rösti was handed round, but our reader was unable to oblige the donor. The sweet course was brandy angel cream: a light brandy mousse with a thin layer of strawberry coulis across the top of the glass in which it was served. Coffee was cafetière and chocolates and truffles kept the good things coming to the end. Were others dissentient, this meal might not have warranted such detail, but its qualities seem archetypal. In the course of the last year, the team of chefs, still headed by Johnnie Martin and Colin Akrigg, has been joined by Colin White, who worked here 25 years ago before branching out as a restaurateur in his own right. Whether his presence will cause a shift in style is as yet unknown, but the strengths of the kitchen – wonderful pastry work, fine puddings, sympathetic treatment of good materials – are quite capable of absorbing a different approach without self-destruction. It must be hoped that he will release Francis Coulson from too much pressure of work. After 42 seasons, one may reasonably expect a supervisory role. A separate 'Before and after' wine list shows more enthusiasm than the main one. There are many marvellous Garvey sherries by the glass and dessert wines in abundance, many in halves and also by the glass. The main list is rather overpriced and largely from the big négociants. It lacks the commitment of the menu. One warning: the restaurant is closed for lunch on some Mondays, so check first.

CHEFS: Johnnie Martin, Colin Akrigg, Colin White, Philip Wilson, Chris Bond and Gillian Glennie PROPRIETORS: Francis Coulson and Brian Sack
OPEN: all week
CLOSED: Dec, Jan and Feb
MEALS: 1 to 1.45, 8 to 8.45
PRICES: Set L £19 (£24) to £23 (£28), Set D £35 (£40). Service inc
SEATS: 65. Private parties: 10 main room. Car-park, 30 places. No children under 13. Smart dress preferred. No smoking. Wheelchair access
ACCOMMODATION: 29 rooms, 25 with bath/shower. Rooms for disabled. D, B&B £68 to £136. No children under 13. Afternoon teas. Garden. TV. Phone. Scenic. Doors close at midnight. Confirm by 10am [*Which? Hotel Guide*]

All details are as accurate as possible at the time of going to press, but chefs and owners often change, and it is wise to check by telephone before making a special journey. Many readers have been disappointed when set-price bargain meals are no longer available. Ask when booking.

Bay Horse Inn and Bistro

Canal Foot, Ulverston LA12 9EL
ULVERSTON (0229) 53972

COOKING 3
COST £17–£30

'The Glaxo factory is the ghastly marker' for progress towards this unpretentious restaurant with very good food. It calls itself 'Inn and Bistro' advisedly, even after refurbishment during the winter. The food is by no means bistro, but for some, the view out is better than the vision in. The positive angle is given by the Londoner who had a bar lunch: 'Leek and potato soup, an unusual dark green with a thick, almost mushroom, texture; melon and Cumbrian air-dried ham with a tartlet of damson cheese; sirloin steak (hung for four weeks) served with salad and walnut oil dressing; sticky toffee pudding and cheese followed. It was delightful'. Some bar food! The restaurant, most tables allowing sight of the fast moving tide, offers a rapid-change menu with a cheaper, short set-price meal at lunchtimes. The style of cooking, in like manner to mentor John Tovey's at Miller Howe (see entry, Windermere), is a free adaptation of English eclecticism in the 1960s. Emphasis is laid on the central ingredient and reinforced by inventive accompaniments. When they gell, the consequence is satisfying to both appetite and tastebuds. A poached fillet of sea trout comes with strips of salsify, asparagus tips and a white wine and chive sauce: 'a dish like this starts you wondering why other places serve such mundane food.' Breast of duck is marinated in white wine, lime juice and juniper, then stuffed with apple and sage, wrapped in more Cumbrian ham and served fried on a spring onion, thyme and madeira sauce. This may sound complicated but it hangs together. Accompaniments sometimes lift the centrepiece higher than it might otherwise have reached. A venison and chestnut terrine, containing stuffed olives and pistachio, was slightly friable but galvanised by its apple and ginger jelly and the skilful salad to partner it. Vegetables have also earned praise: mange-tout – 'the best' – carrots and ginger, and good new potatoes came with one reader's already top-notch main dish. Desserts such as strawberry and angelica mousse or an orange crème caramel on a strawberry brandy purée end the meal softly, unless a diner takes good cheeses with home-made soda bread or biscuits. The prices charged for this food make it the more appreciated, and complimentary coffee is a further attraction. Service is always cheerful but sometimes not organised: 'I'm only just back from Tenerife' is no excuse for ignorance. Wines come in two lists, one Old, one New World. Robert Lyons shows great enthusiasm for the second, which is well presented. There is a wine suggestion on each menu and take-up of the New World wines is very general. Their value is enjoyed. House wine: £7.95. CELLARMAN'S CHOICE: Brookfield, Hawkes Bay Chardonnay 1988, £15.75; Orlando, St Hugo Cabernet Sauvignon 1986, £14.75

The text of entries is based on unsolicited reports sent in by readers, backed up by inspections conducted anonymously. The factual details under the text are from questionnaires the Guide *sends to all restaurants that feature in the book.*

CHEF: Robert Lyons   PROPRIETORS: Robert Lyons and John J. Tovey
OPEN: Mon to Sat, exc Mon L
MEALS: 12 to 1.30, 7 to 9
PRICES: £18 (£25), Set L £11.50 (£17). Minimum £7.50. Service 10%
CARDS: Access, Visa
SEATS: 30. 3 tables outside. Private parties: 20 main room. No children under 12. Smart
dress preferred. No smoking in dining-room. Wheelchair access (1 step; also unisex WC).
Music. Air-conditioned

UNDERBARROW Cumbria   map 7

Tullythwaite House

Underbarrow LA8 8BB   COOKING 2
CROSTHWAITE (044 88) 397   COST £18–£32

This country has no shortage of beauty spots, and the Greenwoods' Lakeland
slate home has bagged one that's both isolated and elevated. It's a pity, then,
that you can no longer stay here. Non-residents have gladly ventured up from
cosmopolitan Windermere, however, and judging by reports, the food still
warrants the trek. There's one sitting and a small choice of first and main
courses on the fixed-price menu. Some combinations are bold, some just
interesting. The quality of ingredients, now including home-grown herbs and
salads, remains high. First courses at a Saturday dinner in spring included
mushroom eclairs with oyster mushrooms and tomato coulis, and avocado and
grapefruit with sesame seeds. Summer courgette soup with rosemary pleased
one reader, seafood lasagne another. Main courses are rarely straightforward,
for example roast lamb with date and almond stuffing and redcurrant sauce or
duck breast with oranges and chicory in a gin and lime sauce. English cheeses
may follow tangy plum, apple and mint flan, say. Service is as accomplished
and precisely judged as the food. The wine list has grown to 100 bottles, with a
larger representation of halves. House French: £5.95 and £6.60. CELLARMAN'S
CHOICE: Beaune premier cru 1986, Drouhin, £25.50; Delegats Proprietor's
Reserve Chardonnay 1987, £15.95.

CHEF: Janet Greenwood   PROPRIETORS: Michael and Janet Greenwood
OPEN: Wed to Sat, D only and Sun L
CLOSED: Feb
MEALS: 12.30 for 1, 7 for 7.30 or 7.30 for 8 (by arrangement)
PRICES: Set Sun L £13.50 (£18), Set D £21.50 (£27)
CARDS: Access, Visa
SEATS: 16. Private parties: 16 main room. Car-park, 14 places. No children under 12. Smart
dress preferred. No smoking in dining-room. One sitting

---

*'We enjoyed it all, but I don't think we would pay our own money to visit again. This is
not going to worry them. God only knows how many times they were turning the tables
over in an evening.'* On inspecting in London

Consumers' Association is planning to publish Out to Eat, *a new guide to budget eating
out in restaurants, pubs, cafés, brasseries and so on. Please send reports and
recommendations to Out to Eat, FREEPOST, 2 Marylebone Road, London NW1 1YN.*

UPPINGHAM Leicestershire   map 6

▲ *Lake Isle* 🍷

16 High Street East, Uppingham LE15 9PZ   COOKING 1
UPPINGHAM (0572) 822951   COST £15–£34

An inspector wrote that the Whitfields have 'created a charming town-house
hotel where their English affection for French wines and French country style
is expressed in the short daily *prix fixe* menu and long, far from everyday wine
list. Beechwood chairs and pine kitchen tables are comfortably spaced in the
green-painted dining-room looking out on to the High Street. A diplomatically
worded note to smokers on each table as well as high ceilings and good
ventilation contribute to comfort.' The cooking is resolutely French, as is the
short menu with up to five courses. It does not pretend to more than it can
achieve, which is refreshing, but there are times when the approximate results
have caused disappointment. Goujons of fish and tartare sauce 'might have
come from a pub basket' but blackberry and bilberry sauce with pork fillet was
'simple yet well defined.' There is a certain affection for flesh and fruit
combinations that is English rather than French. Satisfaction, however, has
been noted for broccoli soup; melon with melon sorbet; pork with orange and
walnut stuffing; chicken stuffed with spinach; a pot-au-feu; and guinea-fowl
with a deliciously tangy winterberry sauce. Sometimes the sauces have outrun
the meats, casting too strong a shadow on the primary taste. Desserts can yield
good ices, something substantial (a rhubarb crumble was not a success, but
sticky toffee pudding and chocolate rum cake were), or perhaps a crème brûlée
making ill-advised use of strawberries. Coffee is good, bread is substantial
wholemeal made on the premises. The wine list is the star of the party. Some
would come for bread, cold cuts and the wine alone. Prices are generous
without idiocy, half-bottles abound, growers are sound and occasionally more
than that, and the scant notice accorded the rest of the world is forgivable
for the generous offering of halves. House French: £7.25, CELLARMAN'S
CHOICE: Montagny premier cru, Les Coères 1987, £12.

CHEF: David Whitfield   PROPRIETORS: David and Claire Whitfield
OPEN: All week, exc Mon L and Sun D
MEALS: 12 to 2, 7 to 10
PRICES: Set L £9.50 (£15) to £10.75 (£16), Set D £16.50 (£22) to £20 (£28)
CARDS: Access, Amex, Diners, Visa
SEATS: 35. Private parties: 40 main room, 12 private room. Children's helpings.
Wheelchair access
ACCOMMODATION: 11 rooms, all with bath/shower. B&B £36 to £60. Pets welcome. TV.
Phone. Doors close at midnight. Confirm by 6

---

*Restaurateurs justifiably resent no-shows. If you quote a credit card number when
booking, you may be liable for the restaurant's lost profit margin if you don't turn up.
Always phone to cancel.*

*Several sharp operators have tried to extort money from restaurateurs on the promise of an
entry in a guide book that has never appeared. The Good Food Guide makes no charge
for inclusion and does not offer certificates of any kind.*

WADHURST East Sussex   map 3

▲ *Spindlewood Hotel*

Wallcrouch, Wadhurst TN5 7JG
TICEHURST (0580) 200430
on B2099, between Wadhurst and   COOKING 1
Ticehurst   COST £26

This late Victorian house with a good setting in gardens, ponds and woodland
is 'old fashioned' rather than 'antique'. The service may be anything but that
and the owners themselves are characterful hosts. It is a popular spot for family
reunions, pleasing, at least in part, a wide age-range with food that can be
better than expected. Materials are satisfactory, including fish from Billingsgate
and the south coast, and meals are less expensive than sometimes encountered
in more fanciful country houses. Reports have expressed satisfaction with
marinated salmon with an avocado mousse; chicken and crab in a pastry case;
breast of guinea-fowl with mushrooms; baked salmon; ginger soufflé with
coffee and vanilla sauce; and a duet of liqueur parfaits with a red fruit coulis.
There is a short, largely French wine list of five dozen options. Natter's Sancerre
and Juillot's Mercurey show that there is real quality among the growers.
House Mâcon is £6.50. CELLARMAN'S CHOICE: Côtes du Rhône, J. Molière,
1985 (organic), £9.20

CHEF: Harvey Lee Aram   PROPRIETOR: R. V. Fitzsimmons
OPEN: all week, exc L Mon bank hols
CLOSED: 4 days at Christmas
MEALS: 12.15 to 1.30, 7.15 to 9
PRICES: £16 (£22), Set L and D £17 (£22)
CARDS: Access, Amex, Visa
SEATS: 40. Private parties: 50 main room, 18 private room. Car-park, 60 places. Vegetarian
meals. Children's helpings. No cigars/pipes in dining room. Music
ACCOMMODATION: 9 rooms, all with bath/shower. B&B £45.50 to £77. Baby facilities.
Garden. TV. Phone. Doors close at midnight. Confirm by 6

WALBERSWICK Suffolk   map 6

Mary's

Manor House, Walberswick IP18 6UT   COOKING 1
SOUTHWOLD (0502) 723243   COST £11–£18

Seaside eating is often like this. The sea blocks off one end of the street, tables
are plastic-topped, nets and prints are draped over the walls, families come to
eat, and the cooking is unpretentious. The Jelliffs rely on locally landed fish –
slip soles, plaice, cod – and grill or fry it. Simple, well cooked and very fresh, it
is music to many ears. Fisherman's Pot and Seafood Thermidor combine
shellfish and white fish in sauces with cheesy potatoes to good effect. Smoked
ling roe or smoked haddock in cheese sauce are more conventional first courses
than baked banana with Stilton cream. If some dressings appear to be bottled,
and croquette potatoes or an odd pudding seems bought in, it does not affect
the excellent fish. Vegetarians are indulged regularly at lunchtimes with such
as leek croustade, or pasta with ratatouille (order ahead for dinner or 'it would

be of necessity very simple'). There are menus for lunch, dinner, morning coffee, afternoon tea and high tea, as well as a list of daily specials which will include the most recent catch. Rob Jelliff could probably get a part as a brisk, bright-eyed and amusingly sardonic Sherlock Holmes if he gave up supervising the service. The modest list of mainly decent wines has reasonable mark-ups. House wine: £4.90 and £5.25.

CHEFS: Felicity Jelliff and Mark Bracey PROPRIETORS: Felicity and Rob Jelliff
OPEN: Tue to Sun L, Fri and Sat D
CLOSED: Mon to Thur Nov to Easter
MEALS: 12 to 2, 7.15 to 9
PRICES: £8 (£11), Set L £4 (£7), to £9(£12), Set D £12.25 (£15). Service inc
SEATS: 45. 10 tables outside. Private parties: 25 main room; 20 and 25 private rooms. Car-park, 20 places. Vegetarian meals L. Children's helpings. No smoking in dining-room. Wheelchair access (2 steps; also unisex WC). Music

---

WARWICK Warwickshire   map 2

Fanshawe's

22 Market Place
Warwick CV34 4SL   COOKING 1
WARWICK (0926) 410590   COST £30

David Fanshawe made his name as chef at the Restaurant Diment in Kenilworth before moving to this converted shop in Warwick's market place. Outside there are window boxes full of flowers; inside it is cottage-like with chintzy curtains. The tables are close set. Susan Fanshawe is an efficient hostess and helps to create a thoroughly pleasant informal atmosphere. 'It operates above the unsatisfactory British norm,' says one reader, 'and as such should be recommended as widely as possible.' A basic repertoire of familiar favourites, such as good chicken liver pâté and steak and kidney pie is backed up by a regularly changing selection of more adventurous dishes. Mushrooms stuffed with crab pâté served on a bed of crisp vegetables; tandoori-style chicken in puff pastry; and beef fillet with green peppercorn sauce have all been positively reported. Sweets such as chocolate marquise and apricot ice-cream are made on the premises. There are separate menus for vegetarians and young children, who may also get half portions from the main menu. The flexibility of the operation extends to the short lunch menu, which provides useful snacks and sandwiches as well as a few more meal-like dishes such as cold poached salmon or duck and orange pie. Portions are immense, making a full three-course meal heavy going for some finely tuned appetites. The wine list is commendably short, well chosen and unpretentious. House French is £5.60.

CHEF: David Fanshawe PROPRIETORS: David and Susan Fanshawe
OPEN: Tue to Sat
CLOSED: 2 weeks Oct
MEALS: 11.30 to 2, 6 to 10
PRICES: £17 (£25)
CARDS: Access, Amex, Visa
SEATS: 35. Private parties: 38 main room. Vegetarian meals. Children's helpings till 7.30pm. Wheelchair access (1 step). Music

WATERHOUSES Staffordshire

map 5

▲ *Old Beams* ♟

Waterhouses ST10 3HW
WATERHOUSES (0538) 308254

COOKING 3
COST £22–£35

The village, on the Leek to Ashbourne Road, is so called because it was a water stop for horses in coaching days. Sad reflection, then, on the state of our nation that a customer's request for tap water was declined as it was 'not fit to drink', and a French mineral water offered in its place, at a charge. Old Beams is a restaurant with rooms: 'The hand-made Heal's bed makes for an excellent sleep but it is probably Nigel Wallis's cooking and Ann's hospitality that cause me to make a second report of a visit here.' So wrote one who had enjoyed a game terrine accompanied by a winter leaf salad laced with pine kernels and sunflower seeds, followed by a complementary sorbet as prelude to a main course of brill, bass, salmon, mullet and bream in a herb butter sauce. Vegetables included dauphinois potatoes, fish notwithstanding, turnips, carrots, beans, mange-tout: 'first-class ingredients, judiciously cooked in a simple style, what more could you want?' The cheeseboard finished this meal and is always impressive. That, and the fish, are good signs of the state of supplies even in unpropitious regions – doubtless with some hard work on the part of Nigel Wallis. There is a *carte* at dinner, which is satisfactorily short and shows a decent appreciation of the markets. At lunch there is a set-price menu of four or five courses that is keenly priced indeed. The cooking is ambitious, more the credit therefore that it should be called 'judicious'. As if there were not enough species in that rendezvous of fish mentioned (and the oyster that topped it all was not), think of the lamb dish that includes rack, liver and kidney, or the trio of venison that has the cutlet baked in pastry, the haunch roasted and a steamed roulade of trimmings, all on a port wine sauce. Other dishes have included at a Sunday lunch (also fairly priced) goose breast on a bed of salad leaves, grilled lamb with a yoghurt and tarragon sauce, a marvellous Stilton, then a plum pudding; scallops and bacon in a salad; breast of wild duck exactly cooked; hare with a burgundy sauce; and puddings such as Grand Marnier soufflé and a tart with vanilla ice-cream surrounded by raspberries anointed with a sabayon. Some have witnessed a laxity of detail and service at busy times but generally the running of the restaurant is in safe hands. Apart from a few weak bottles, the wine selection is admirable. The 'Favourite Dozen' exemplifies the care which has gone into the list, which is refreshingly broad in its range. Although the number of half-bottles is small they are chosen to give a good spread of price. Big names are well represented, so also are interesting bottles: Cornas 1982 from Clape, a 1970 Gigondas of Jaboulet, fine Sancerre from Gitton and a 1976 Gran Reserva Protos from the Duero. It is sensible to ask advice. House French: £10.85 and £11.05.
CELLARMAN'S CHOICE: Vega de La Reine Blanco 1985, £10.50; Chianti Classico 1986, Podere il Palazziano, £13.25.

See the inside of the front cover for an explanation of the 1 to 5 rating system recognising cooking standards.

CHEF: Nigel J. Wallis PROPRIETORS: Nigel J. and Ann Wallis
OPEN: Tue to Sun, exc Sat L and Sun D
MEALS: 12 to 2, 7 to 10
PRICES: £22 (£29), Set L £12.25 (£22)
CARDS: Access, Amex, Diners, Visa
SEATS: 20. Car-park, 18 places. No children under 4. Wheelchair access (also WC). Music
ACCOMMODATION: 6 rooms, all with bath/shower. Rooms for disabled. B&B £50 to £85.
Deposit: £35. Garden. Tennis. TV. Phone. Scenic. Doors close at midnight. Confirm 48
hours ahead [*Which? Hotel Guide*]

WATH-IN-NIDDERDALE North Yorkshire   map 7

▲ *Sportsman's Arms*

Wath-in-Nidderdale HG3 5PP   COOKING 3
HARROGATE (0423) 711306   COST £18–£32

Three buildings in one make a complex succession of public rooms that
culminate in a large and popular restaurant. It is done out in a style far removed
from the pub it was (and remains, though in a minor key). The cooking, too, is
more serious than pub pies and meats though it retains its sense of place –
Dales lamb, east coast lobster, cream from the farm next door – while
branching out to farther shores for recipes and inspiration. Dishes on the *carte*
offer half a dozen choices, and the shorter set-price menu includes a half-bottle
of wine and coffee. There are some interesting combinations: banana and sauce
Robert with chicken; pork with an onion, garlic and ginger sauce, slightly
curried, or with beetroot, gherkin and onion; duck with figs and orange. The
emphasis is on cream and butter, and sometimes on fruit. Fish, however, is
very good: mussels, scallops, salmon, sole, trout are well handled and
plentiful. Traditional food is not ignored: black pudding with apple and
mushroom sauce and the Sunday lunch roast with good Yorkshire pudding
have been well received. Booking should be well in advance. All speak of the
generous portions and good foundations to the cooking. Cheeses and the end of
the meal keep up the standard: summer pudding is perennial, there is often a
flan or tart, dairy products and fruit are used to good effect. Watch for excellent
north country cheeses. There are few complaints. The wine list has a fair spread
over the globe; its longest section is claret; it does not levy too high a profit and
includes respectable names. Half-bottles there are, but unevenly grouped.
House wines, four of them, are £7.50.

CHEF/PROPRIETOR: J.R. Carter
OPEN: all week, exc Sun D
MEALS: 12 to 1.45, 7 to 10
PRICES: £19 (£27), Set D £15.90 (£18)
CARDS: Access, Amex, Diners, Visa
SEATS: 45. 6 tables outside. Private parties: 60 main room. Car-park, 50 places. Vegetarian
meals. Children's helpings. Wheelchair access (also WC)
ACCOMMODATION: 6 rooms, 2 with bath/shower. B&B £27 to £45. Baby facilities. Pets
welcome. Garden. Fishing. TV. Scenic [*Which? Hotel Guide*]

The Guide always appreciates hearing about changes of chef or owner.

WATLINGTON Oxfordshire   map 2

▲ *Well House*

34–40 High Street, Watlington OX9 5PY   COOKING 1
WATLINGTON (049 161) 3333   COST £19–£30

The well is in the small bar of this economical conversion from a medieval
brick and flint house, usefully sited in relation to Oxford, Reading, Heathrow
and London. Patricia Crawford cooks quite gently and carefully. Meals may
consist of marinated new salmon; mushroom tart with a béarnaise; carrot and
orange soup; haddock pancake Mornay; steak, mushroom and oyster pie, or
roast beef for Sunday lunch. Sometimes the food is a mite bland, but many of
the recipes are well-tried English country classics: salmon in pastry with
ginger and currants; banoffi pie; crème brûlée. A certain coolness in handling
customers evaporates with the warmth of acquaintance, which makes it a place
enjoyed by regulars. The wine list shows enterprise. Clarets, especially
bourgeois growths, are well chosen, other regions perhaps a little less so. Prices
are fair; the moves beyond France are sound and show the stirrings of a very
good list. House French: £6.50. CELLARMAN'S CHOICE: Ch. Léoville-Barton
1976, £31.30.

CHEFS: Patricia Crawford and Lisa Bauma   PROPRIETORS: Patricia and Alan Crawford
OPEN: Tue to Sun, exc Sat L and Sun D
MEALS: 12.30 to 2, 7 to 9.15 (9.30 Sat)
PRICES: £18 (£25), Set L and D £14.90 (£19). Service inc
CARDS: Access, Amex, Diners, Visa
SEATS: 40. 4 tables outside. Private parties: 45 main room. Car-park, 15 places. Children's
helpings. Smart dress preferred. Wheelchair access (3 steps)
ACCOMMODATION: 9 rooms, all with bath/shower. Rooms for disabled. B&B £30 to £53.50.
Baby facilities. Afternoon teas. TV. Phone. Scenic. Doors close at 11.30. Confirm by 6
[*Which? Hotel Guide*]

WELLS-NEXT-THE-SEA Norfolk   map 6

Moorings

COUNTY
OF THE
YEAR
RESTAURANT

6 Freeman Street,
Wells-next-the-Sea NR23 1BA
FAKENHAM (0328) 710949   COOKING 3
                                                        COST £16–£25

'Neighbourhood restaurant' is an abused term, and sometimes more appealing
to blasé livers-on-the-town than occasional visitors who actively want
circumstance and theatre. The Moorings will provide circumstance by the
flavour and immediacy of the cooking, and theatre from the open kitchen and
press of people (book early in high season). But the restaurant with its white
paint, white cloths, excellent paintings and crafts (many for sale), is never
pompous nor above itself. The menu, inexpensive by any measure, takes in a
lot of dishes, with fish the prime subject: three sorts of smoked fish, cured
salmon, crab, oysters, Dover sole, lobster, skate, sea trout, cockles, mullet,
dabs, and smoked cod's roe were on offer one evening. All these are locally
caught or processed, and it shows. The Phillips are locked into a strong
network of supplies, always more obvious in waterfront places but feasible for

every country restaurant in the UK. Cooking is not elaborate – no sugar cages or foie gras laid over tired fish – but flavours and textures are considered. Cockle pie is a casserole of cockles and cream, the smooth emollience of the one contrasting with the resilient bounce of the cockles and the crunch of the crumb topping. The cooking style is emphatic in its use of flavourings: a shrimp and anchovy sauce; red wine herb butter with plain flat fish; tomato, garlic and capers with mullet; Mediterranean and Middle Eastern tastes with vegetarian dishes such as aubergine purée or kofta with tahini cream. Some readers find the finished dishes simpler or more approximate than they expected but never impugn the materials: the smoked and cured fish get constant reaction whether for the generous gravlax with vibrant mustard sauce, or the smoked fish 'Russian salad' where three sorts of fish are mixed with apple, beetroot and potatoes. The menu changes frequently, though the repertoire is finite, so many old favourites run and run; it all depends on supplies. Abiding perennials include spicy fish soup; pork brawn; taramosalata; cockle pie; 'stockfish' marmite; pigeon with red wine, port and cream; Greek style meat-balls; and puddings such as open apple tart or a trifle, together with a good and lively range of British cheeses. One person remarked last year, 'it is the scene of most family celebrations, get-togethers, whatever. Carla Phillips is almost faultless as a hostess, mingling with friends after cooking, telling recipes.' Service can go awry, being sometimes too fast, or too slow, but it is never grudging. Bernard Phillips reports that they have allocated three tables (10 places) under an extractor fan for smokers. 'Smoking causes me more problems than anything else. Most of our customers are non-smokers and most smokers obey a polite notice to refrain until others have finished. A few don't. Once a neighbouring table was told to hurry up so that the smokers could start. We hope the restricted area will work, but it will involve asking every booking which area is preferred.' Precede your meal with a 'hedgerow' kir made with cider and then look to the wine list, which deserves notice for the efforts that have gone into buying, in France as well as from merchants here, and for low prices. It is an interesting and enthusiastic list, making a virtue of avoiding expensive heavyweights, yet picking quality growers. Note the Alsaces from Runner, Ovid's Tears sweet wine from Romania, an organic Puligny Montrachet and Ch. Laurou, a rosé from south-western France. Eight house wines are all French and all £5.60. CELLARMAN'S CHOICE: Matua Valley, Sauvignon 1988, £12.85.

CHEFS: Carla Phillips and Jane Lee   PROPRIETORS: Bernard and Carla Phillips
OPEN: all week, exc Tues and Weds and Thur L
CLOSED: 4 to 22 June, 29 Nov to 14 Dec, 24 to 27 Dec
MEALS: 12.30 to 2, 7.30 to 9
PRICES: Set L £11 (£16) to £15 (£21), Set D £14.50 (£20)
SEATS: 40. Private parties: 40 main room. Vegetarian meals. Children's helpings. Wheelchair access

All details are as accurate as possible at the time of going to press, but chefs and owners often change, and it is wise to check by telephone before making a special journey. Many readers have been disappointed when set-price bargain meals are no longer available. Ask when booking.

▲ Heath Lodge

Danesbury Park Road, Welwyn AL6 9SN   COOKING 3
STEVENAGE (0438) 840000   COST £41

The menu describes a main course as no more than 'A Combination of Guinea-Fowl.' 'What does the combination of guinea-fowl consist of?' 'It's a bird.' 'Can you elaborate?' 'I'll go and ask.' On returning from the kitchen: 'It's different parts of guinea-fowl combined.' In the event the dish was a large white plate with a light stock sauce over the whole. In the centre was a pile of thin-cut apple with a drumstick to the right, six roundels of breast meat at the bottom and a helping of thigh to the left. At the top was a mound of spinach flanked by two turned roast potatoes and segments of mandarin oranges and grapefruit. This tasted excellent: the sauce was correct, the meat moist and full of flavour, the tang of fruit gave life and variety, the spinach and potatoes were as they should be. So Heath Lodge, a new restaurant that missed full entry in the last *Guide* owing to changes in staff, has a chef who knows his stuff. Neither the menu, which might do for a vaguely interesting grill room, nor the locale, which seems pitched for sales conferences and a few holes of golf, would lead one to think it. Nor would the service. Dishes that have met with approval, like the guinea-fowl, include a game consommé; ravioli of wild mushrooms with a cream sauce; lettuce hearts with anchovies, croûtons and Parmesan with olive oil; braised duck with prunes and potatoes and a red wine sauce; an apple tart and cinnamon ice-cream; hot praline soufflé with a vanilla ice-cream. Stuart Busby worked at Tante Claire (see entry, London) and his background shows through. If the hotel is not submerged by its environment, it may be a beacon of light for miles about. Special requests for varying meal times will receive attention. The wine list is not cheap but has some top-drawer sources such as Leflaive, Latour and Drouhin for burgundies. It is not yet too long. House Muscadet and Côtes du Rhône are £9.75.

CHEF: Stuart Busby   PROPRIETORS: Heath Lodge 1965 Limited
OPEN: all week
MEALS: 12.30 to 2, 7 to 9.30
PRICES: £26 (£34). Minimum £7.95. Service inc
CARDS: Access, Amex, Diners, Visa
SEATS: 40. Private parties: 120 main room, 40 private room. Car-park, 100 places.
No children under 10, exc private functions by arrangement. Smart dress preferred.
Wheelchair access (1 step; also unisex WC). Air-conditioned
ACCOMMODATION: 47 rooms, all with bath/shower. Rooms for disabled. B&B £72 to £150.
Deposit: £20. No children under 10. Baby facilities. Pets welcome in certain rooms.
Afternoon teas. Garden. Sauna. Air-conditioning in public rooms. TV. Phone. Scenic.
Confirm 48 hours ahead

▮ *denotes an outstanding wine cellar;* ♟ *denotes a good wine list, worth travelling for.*
See the Introduction for a fuller explanation.

▲ *This symbol means accommodation is available.*

▲ *Jule's Cafe*

| Portland Street, Weobley HR4 8SB | COOKING 2 |
| WEOBLEY (0544) 318206 | COST £11–£25 |

Juliet and Julian Whitmarsh pride themselves on their 'greenness'. They have used organic vegetables, naturally-reared meat and free-range eggs for several years and now find that the mood of the times has caught up with them. Their restaurant in the fine timbered building is well supported by locals and gets a good share of tourist trade occupying the booths and oilcloth-covered tables. The serious business centres on the evening menu, which is a global mix of British, Middle Eastern and European. Well reported dishes have included grilled princess scallops with garlic butter; beef, Guinness and pickled walnut pie; stuffed Gressingham duck with orange and clementine sauce; and cassoulet heavy with beans. More space is being devoted to vegetarian dishes such as walnut and mushroom bake with orange sauce and kumquats. Enthusiasm colours reports, and what criticism is expressed is not about the sound conception of this very catholic repertoire. When selling his cassoulet, Julian Whitmarsh was happy to point out that, 'this is your genuine cassoulet, none of your nonsense,' and, though lacking smoked sausage, it was. Desserts are as whole-hearted as the rest of the cooking: chocolate fudge roulade with chocolate flake ice-cream, 'very rich and sweet but . . . ,' or chilled lemon soufflé with a lemon sorbet; or treacle tart with brown-bread ice-cream are what you may expect. Service is casual but informed – some would say 'take it or leave it, but they do get the customers: it's the food.' A full wine list is expected after the *Guide* went to press, but house wines – organic of course – are £6.50.

CHEFS/PROPRIETORS: Julian and Juliet Whitmarsh
OPEN: Tue to Sun
MEALS: 12 to 2, 7.30 to 10.30
PRICES: L £13 (£18), D £15 (£21), Set D £7 (£11) to £14.95 (£20)
CARDS: Access, Visa
SEATS: 36. Private parties: 30 main room. Vegetarian meals. Children's helpings. Wheelchair access
ACCOMMODATION: 3 rooms, 2 with bath/shower. B&B £18 to £30. Afternoon teas. Scenic. Doors close at 1am. Confirm by 6

Riverside Café and Restaurant

| West Bay, Bridport DT6 4EZ | COOKING 2 |
| BRIDPORT (0308) 22011 | COST £24 |

The sub-post office in another guise, the café and restaurant is a haven of delight in the less than sensational seaside environment of West Bay. The Watsons have been here for years and their aim is simple, 'fresh cooked food at the time of order'. Most of it is fish. It will vary from day to day, and the blackboard reflects supplies, but it is produced on a foundation of wholesome café food that will satisfy all the family, young and old. Fish may be plainly cooked, but made dishes such as 'baked Greek brill' or gurnard with ginger and sweet-and-sour sauce are available as well. The meal may end with substantial puddings: sticky toffee, crumbles, trifle or treacle tart, all genuine. The setting is clean and simple. It is self service unless you book, but then a 10 per cent service charge, though said to be optional, is applied. As mealtimes approach, the quiet yet purposeful air becomes charged with clamour and people. It does get busy. The Watsons are determined to maintain their standards and therefore vary their opening hours, so that they don't get swamped. Telephone before going. There is a basic wine list and a short list of specials. Neither is highly priced and all the bottles are decently chosen. House wine: £7.50 a litre.

CHEFS: Janet Watson, Natalie Green and Pam Townsend PROPRIETORS: Janet and Arthur Watson
OPEN: Tue to Sun, plus Mon in July, Aug, bank hols
CLOSED: Nov to end Feb
MEALS: 10.30 to 3, 6.30 to 8.30 (10.30 to 8.30 Sat and Sun)
PRICES: £14 (£20). Service 10% for waitress service
CARDS: Access, Visa
SEATS: 80. 10 tables outside. Private parties: 70 main room. Children's helpings. Wheelchair access (also WC). Music

---

WEST BEXINGTON Dorset   map 2

▲ *Manor Hotel*

Beach Road, West Bexington DT2 9DF   COOKING 1
BURTON BRADSTOCK (0308) 897616   COST £15–£28

The view on to Chesil Beach is fine, with a conservatory to enjoy the light and avoid the wind. The Manor is all things to all people, in large number: bar meals in the cellar, light lunches, set-price menus in the restaurant, menus for children, holidaymakers and day trippers. The cooking may suffer from sheer weight of number and service may become brisker as the crowds pour in. However, no one objects to the size of portions though some may be daunted by the amount of cream. BSE and its attendant worries have caused greater emphasis on fish, offered as simply cooked daily specials, or in company with elderflower wine (sole), chilli (monkfish), lime hollandaise (salmon) or Thermidor (plaice). The basic cooking is sometimes overwhelmingly sauced or flooded with tastes that should only inform, not crowd out, but the restaurant is useful in the area. The wine list is a good one, though light on some details where continuity is obviously in question. It offers a fair range at fair prices and a good number of half-bottles. House wine is £5.85. CELLARMAN'S CHOICE: Régnié, Ch. du Basty 1988, £11.95; St Véran, Ch. de Leynes 1988, £12.95.

All details are as accurate as possible at the time of going to press, but chefs and owners often change, and it is wise to check by telephone before making a special journey. Many readers have been disappointed when set-price bargain meals are no longer available. Ask when booking.

CHEF: Clive Jobson PROPRIETORS: Richard and Jayne Childs
OPEN: all week
MEALS: 12 to 2, 7 to 10 (10.30 Sat)
PRICES: Set L £10 (£15) to £12.50 (£18), Set D £16.65 (£23)
CARDS: Access, Amex, Diners, Visa
SEATS: 65. 18 tables outside. Private parties: 65 main room, 20 and 50 private rooms. Car-park, 50 places. Vegetarian meals. Children's helpings. Music
ACCOMMODATION: 13 rooms, all with bath/shower. B&B £33 to £56. Deposit: £10. Baby facilities. Garden. TV. Phone. Scenic. Doors close at midnight. Confirm by 6
[Which? Hotel Guide]

WEST MERSEA Essex   map 3

▲ Le Champenois,
Blackwater Hotel

20–22 Church Road,
West Mersea CO5 8QH   COOKING 2
COLCHESTER (0206) 383338   COST £17–£36

Many are those who form a core of long-term support for Monique Chapleo in her ivy-clad hotel created from three cottages, quite close to the church. The impress of Mme Chapleo is strong. 'She slides effortlessly from room to room' and her dual attachment to England and her native country is clearly evident. The lunch menus have an English cast and the comparatively unchanging dinner menus – longer, including dishes such as mushrooms champenois in a garlic cream sauce, duck with port and morello cherries or guinea-fowl with marsala, cream caramel 'always outstanding' – reflect ideas of 'French' cooking of the sixties. Proponents praise the consistency of the cooking and the generosity of the portions; others, however, are disturbed by the sheer length of the menu, wondering how many sorts of meat can be kept in perfect condition awaiting custom. Their reaction is to applaud the fish and some of the simpler dishes. The wine list is a hefty scrapbook of labels which makes selection quite a lengthy job. But effort is rewarded as the selection is sound. Ch. Beychevelle 1978, Barolo 1980 from Borgogno and the bin-ends are worth a look. House French: £7. CELLARMAN'S CHOICE: Pouilly Fumé 1988, Dagueneau £17.80; Côteaux du Lyonnais 1988, Duboeuf £8.40.

CHEF: R. Roudesli PROPRIETOR: Monique Chapleo
OPEN: all week, exc Tue L and Sun D
CLOSED: 3 weeks Jan
MEALS: 12 to 2, 7 to 10
PRICES: £20 (£28), Set L £9.80 (£17) to £13 (£20)
CARDS: Access, Amex
SEATS: 46. 3 tables outside. Private parties: 55 main room, 25 private room. Car-park, 20 places. Children's helpings. Smart dress preferred. Wheelchair access (also WC)
ACCOMMODATION: 7 rooms, 4 with bath/shower. B&B £28 to £60. Deposit: £10. Baby facilities. Pets welcome. Afternoon teas. Garden. TV. Scenic. Doors close at 1am. Confirm by 9 [Which? Hotel Guide]

Report forms are at the back of the book; write a letter if you prefer.

Fantails

The Green, Wetheral CA4 8ET   COOKING 2
CARLISLE (0228) 60239   COST £32

Fantails are doves. They are not served on the menu but there is a dovecote outside this barn conversion at one end of the green in Wetheral, a village on the Eden, its medieval castle and nineteenth-century viaduct among the local sights. A barn, but not barn-like: bay windows give fine views and the space has been intelligently divided into bar and dining-room. Nor is the cooking agricultural. Current favourites include such dishes as a plate of three marinated fishes; a chicken mousseline with a Dunsyre blue cheese filling served on apples with an orange hollandaise; duck with tagliatelle and a white peach sauce; and four vegetarian options on permanent offer. A meal in the summer revealed steady achievement vitiated only by a badly constructed onion, leek and Gruyère soup and small lapses of seasoning. Asparagus soufflé is unmoulded before serving and carried its light flavour well over the vehicle of a cream and Gruyère sauce. There seems to be a fondness for Swiss cheese as it occurs three or four times on the short *carte*. Chicken is sliced and layered with wild mushrooms and spinach, lightly reconstructed on a spinach cream sauce. Cream is well regarded, too, figuring in a number of the sauces. Vegetables are excellent: carefully conceived and accurately cooked. So, too, are desserts such as a chocolate Pithiviers and mango and vanilla terrine. Incidentals are under control as well as essential techniques: fair bread, acceptable fresh nibbles of smoked salmon or fish and herb filled tomato, nice coffee. The wine list has been revamped since the Bowmans took over at the end of the summer in 1989. Prices are very fair and, within the context of six dozen alternatives, the range is apposite. Penfolds, Phelps, Rosemount and Matua Valley make for a strong New World element. House French is £6.95. CELLARMAN'S CHOICE: Ch. du Glana 1985, £17.50; Rosemount Chardonnay 1989, £13.75.

CHEFS: Duncan Todhunter, Cameron Clarke and Peter Bowman
PROPRIETORS: Jennifer and Bob Bowman
OPEN: Mon to Sat
MEALS: 12 to 2, 6.30 to 9.30
PRICES: £20 (£27)
CARD: Access, Visa
SEATS: 75. Private parties: 50 main room, 12 and 25 private rooms. Car-park, 25 places.
Vegetarian meals. Smart dress preferred. No smoking area. Music

WETHERSFIELD Essex   map 3

Dicken's

COUNTY
OF THE
YEAR
RESTAURANT

The Green, Wethersfield CM7 4BS   COOKING 3
GREAT DUNMOW (0371) 850723   COST £17–£35

The premises have been through a number of interpretations of the word 'restaurant', and the carpet survives from the last one. Otherwise, the change couldn't be greater and Essex must live in hope that John and Maria Dicken fulfil the promise of their first year. Then perhaps they could change the carpet. That cooking is the main point of the exercise (not always the case in restaurants) is implied by the display of copper, silver, pewter and old cookery books that greets you upon entry. Progressing further, the dining-room boasts a minstrels' gallery, complete with a few tables. Occupation of the upper level gives undisturbed previews of the food on offer that night. John Dicken previously worked at the Connaught and Longueville Manor on Jersey. This is the first venture on his own and he is, therefore, mindful of value for money: note especially the set-price lunches. This is sophisticated cookery, well executed and nicely served, yet happily free of pretension and flim-flam. Dishes that set the style are a tartlet of poached egg and asparagus coated with a hollandaise or, another day, of asparagus with a coriander hollandaise; strips of skate with slices of avocado and mushrooms in a cream sauce with chives, tomato and coriander; a light soup of scallops and vegetables with saffron; good roast beef at Sunday lunch, with Yorkshire puddings well seasoned with nutmeg; saddle of lamb with mushroom duxelles in a pastry case; chicken with morels, a Frontignan muscat sauce and home-made noodles; a clever fruit terrine layering orange, rhubarb and strawberries; a chocolate tourte consisting of sponge topped with milk and bitter chocolate mousses, served with orange and lemon ice-cream; fine bread-and-butter pudding. Coffee comes with petits fours at dinner; the amuse-gueule starts the meal well; light Granary-style rolls are well crusted though possibly strong flavoured. Faults in execution are small and balance is maintained between artful presentation and over-elaboration. The wine list (some 80 bins) comes from Lay and Wheeler, is intelligently laid out and annotated, and is a careful composition of very good material. Prices are no more than they should be and upper-price margins have been kept down. Half-bottles are more plentiful for whites than reds. House wines start at £6.95. CELLARMAN'S CHOICE: Pouilly Fumé 1988, Dagueneau, £18.50; Savigny-lès-Beaune 1986, Simon Bize, £18.95.

CHEF: W. John Dicken   PROPRIETORS: W. John and Maria Dicken
OPEN: Tue to Sun, exc Sat L and Sun D
MEALS: 12.30 to 2, 7.30 to 9.30
PRICES: £21 (£29), Set L £11.75 (£17) and £12.75 (£18)
CARDS: Access, Visa
SEATS: 45. Private parties: 35 main room, 20 private room. Car-park, 11 places. Children's helpings. Smart dress preferred. Wheelchair access (2 steps; also unisex WC)

WEYBRIDGE Surrey   map 3

Colony

3 Balfour Road, Weybridge KT13 8HE   COOKING 1
WEYBRIDGE (0932) 842766   COST £20–£32

Chilli is favoured by the cooks at the Colony: deep-fried shredded beef, the sizzling dishes and stripped prawns in chilli sauce are good examples. The heat is met again in the several black-bean dishes, for instance one of mussels 'so good we ordered second helpings.' Lighter flavours, in lemon chicken, chicken satay or seaweed with dried fish powdered on the surface are also handled well. Regulars find the welcome friendly and service attentive. Chinese people seem to patronise the Colony in fair proportion, giving comfort that all is as it should be. House wine: £7.

CHEF: Kam Yau Pang PROPRIETOR: Michael Tse
OPEN: all week
MEALS: 12 to 2.30, 6 to 11 (11.30 Fri and Sat)
PRICES: £12 (£23), Set L £13.50 (£20) to £17.50 (£25), Set D £17.50 (£25) to £20 (£27). Minimum £10. Service 12.5%
CARDS: Access, Amex, Diners, Visa
SEATS: 80. Private parties: 70 main room, 20 private room. Children welcome. Music. Air-conditioned

---

WEYMOUTH Dorset   map 2

Perry's

The Harbourside, 4 Trinity Road,
Weymouth DT4 8TJ   COOKING 1
WEYMOUTH (0305) 785799   COST £24

This is a useful resource in a town that deserves better cooking than it has. Perry's outlook is pleasing even if comfort is lacking. The blackboard menu concentrates on fish – not in fingers – and is the place to look rather than the standard menu of garlic mushrooms or vegetable lasagne. Fish is fresh, sometimes cursorily trimmed, but cooked appetisingly, as in halibut with a simple accompaniment of crisp onion and new potatoes in their skins. Monkfish, which needed better skinning, had too many lashings of portugaise sauce. Puddings, too, are fresh on the day and have included a sharp and refreshing raspberry meringue, brandy-snaps with cream and an amateurish grape crème brûlée that was none the less good to eat. Service can be seaside-like but the proprietor knows what she's doing. Coffee may not be brilliant. The wine list doesn't bother with vintages; the prices, for some decent Loires and Alsaces, are fair indeed. House 'Cuvée du patron' is £5.25.

CHEFS: Barbara Perry, Anne Clarke and Darren Walden PROPRIETOR: Barbara Perry
OPEN: all week, exc Sun L
MEALS: 12 to 2.30, 7.30 (7 in summer) to 10.30
PRICES: £14 (£20)
CARDS: Access, Visa
SEATS: 42. 3 tables outside. Private parties: 30 main room. Vegetarian meals. Children's helpings. Wheelchair access (2 steps). Music

---

WHITBY North Yorkshire   map 6A

Magpie Café

14 Pier Road, Whitby YO21 3JN   COOKING 2
WHITBY (0947) 602058   COST £8–£18

A singular Magpie, this, the pick of a bunch of pierside fish and chipperies that is easy to spot by the queues and striking black woodwork. And there are good views of the harbour from window seats. The long menu ranges from crab or lobster salad to fried, poached or grilled flat fish to vegetarian crumble to steak pie to fillet steak. It also caters for restricted diets (weightwatchers now get a separate page) and children. Fish and chips at £3.90 is archetypal, preparation of the potatoes on the premises takes 10 kitchen staff two hours a day. Most intricate of the offerings is cod and prawn Mornay. Made with halibut on request, it brought gasps from a neighbouring table, and the reader who ate it waxes lyrical about the freshness of the fish, the nice tarragon scented cheese sauce browned on top, and the pretty garnishes. 'I think it has got better since I first came to it in 1980 and it would put to shame 90 per cent of more expensive restaurants.' Chutney, jam and coleslaw are home made as are all 30 desserts, such as ginger fudge butter shortbread with cream, hazelnut meringue with strawberries or boozy bananas, and an excellent and authentic sticky toffee pudding. Service comes with a smile. The wine list is skeletal but inexpensive. House wines: £4.50 and £4.95.

CHEFS: Ian Robson and Alison McKenzie-Robson PROPRIETORS: Sheila and Ian McKenzie, Ian Robson and Alison McKenzie-Robson
OPEN: all week
CLOSED: mid-Nov to Mar
MEALS: 11.30 to 6.30
PRICES: £10 (£15), Set L £3.95 (£18) to £9.50 (£14), Set D £5.95 (£10) to £9.50 (£14)
SEATS: 100. Private parties: 50 main room. Vegetarian meals. Children's helpings. No-smoking tables. Air-conditioned

Trenchers

New Quay Road, Whitby YO21 1DH   COOKING 1
WHITBY (0947) 603212   COST £19

From the plasticated benches and menu an unsuspecting visitor could underestimate the quality of the food. The quayside location is apt, and the cod, haddock, plaice and skate obviously fresh. Readers praise these and the service, inexpensive carafe wine, fresh crab cocktail and 'sumptuous' ice-cream. There are also home-made cottage and steak pies, a salad bar, sandwiches and a children's menu. House wine: £7.95 and £8.40 a litre.

CHEFS: Tim Lawrence and Gary Moutrey PROPRIETOR: Terry Foster
OPEN: all week
CLOSED: Christmas to mid-Mar
MEALS: 11 to 9
PRICES: £12 (£16). Service inc
SEATS: 150. Private parties: 150 main room. Vegetarian meals. Children's helpings. Wheelchair access. Music

WHITLEY BAY Tyne & Wear   map 7

Le Provençale

183 Park View, Whitley Bay NE26 3RE   COOKING 1
TYNESIDE (091) 251 3567   COST £12-£31

The great local popularity of Le Provençale is echoed in the words of a visitor: 'It made my Northumbrian holiday; one feels really well looked after, yet lunchtime prices are so reasonable that it is a safer bet than the local pubs.'

Expansion is under way both in the bar and dining-room with acquisition of neighbouring premises. The long menu at night time is not especially provençale, though fish soups and langoustines are done in the style, but salmon is presented à la dieppoise. The strong suits are fresh fish and steaks, and service is consistent. There is a four-course set-price gourmet dinner on Monday and Thursdays. The wine list is very fairly priced with house wine at £6 a litre.

CHEF: Michel Guijarro   PROPRIETORS: Mr and Mrs M. Guijarro
OPEN: Mon to Sat, exc Mon L, Wed L and Sat L
CLOSED: 2 weeks in summer
MEALS: 12 to 2, 7 to 10
PRICES: L £7 (£12), D £18 (£25)
CARDS: Access, Amex, Diners, Visa
SEATS: 52. Private parties: 52 main room. Children's helpings (L only). No children under 7. Wheelchair access (1 step; also WC). Music

---

WICKHAM Hampshire   map 2

▲ Old House

The Square, Wickham PO17 5JG   COOKING 2
WICKHAM (0329) 833049   COST £36

The Old House is as old as 1715 and a handsome addition to the village square. After 20 years in the hands of Richard and Annie Skipwith, the interior of this 12-room hotel has emerged in almost painfully good taste. The dining-room is 'the glory of the house' according to a recent visitor. The roof is supported by heavy beams; French doors open on to a charming garden; tables are highly varnished. Frenchness doesn't stop with the doors and polish: it's there in the menu and in the service – but if the descriptions have to be Gallic, they should also be grammatical. Nicholas Harman's cooking was judged by one reader as 'over-complex – too many unnecessary ingredients'. This might be borne out in *la courgette en fleur* with a lobster and armagnac mousse. Still, 'the sauce really tasted of lobster and the hints of herbs and armagnac were subdued'. To follow might be monkfish grilled and glazed with a topping of coarse mustard and cream, set on a tomato coulis; quail wrapped in bacon and roasted, the cooking juices reduced with a little chicken stock and part finished with Marc de Bourgogne and garnished with grapes; or roasted best end of English lamb served with a tomato and lamb *jus* scented with garden basil, garnished with a dice of ham, mushroom and tomatoes. Vegetables are extra, at high cost; service is haphazard. Enthusiasm for France is shown superficially on the wine list, for good growers and properties are notable for their absence. There is little below £11. House wine: £9.25.

All details are as accurate as possible at the time of going to press, but chefs and owners often change, and it is wise to check by telephone before making a special journey. Many readers have been disappointed when set-price bargain meals are no longer available. Ask when booking.

CHEF: Nicholas Harman   PROPRIETORS: Richard and Annie Skipwith
OPEN: Mon to Sat, exc Mon L and Sat L
CLOSED: 2 weeks July to Aug, 10 days at Christmas, 2 weeks at Easter
MEALS: 12 to 1.45, 7 to 9.30
PRICES: £22 (£30). Service inc
CARDS: Access, Amex, Diners, Visa
SEATS: 35. Private parties: 35 main room, 14 private room. Car-park, 12 places. Children's
helpings. No cigars/pipes in dining-room. Wheelchair access (also WC)
ACCOMMODATION: 12 rooms, all with bath/shower. B&B £70 to £90. Baby facilities.
Garden. TV. Phone. Scenic. Doors close at midnight. Confirm by noon [*Which? Hotel Guide*]

WILLINGTON Co Durham	map 7

Stile

97 High Street, Willington DL5 OPE	COOKING 1
BISHOP AUCKLAND (0388) 746615	COST £22–£28

One recommendation for the place: 'I eat here with friends several times each
year because the host, Mike Boustred, is such good value, cheerful and lively.'
Another enthusiastic recommendation: lashings of plants, conservatories
added to old stone cottages, pine floors and white tablecloths. Comments on
the food are more circumspect, concentrating on the quality of the soups and
vegetables but regretting that the meat can be overcooked and too chewy. The
carte goes on from year to year and any variation occurs in the eight or so daily
specials. These will include two soups (invariable) and composed dishes to
supplement the bare bones of the *carte*, which is strong on beef and prawns.
Two vegetarian choices, for instance spinach and mushroom lasagne or brazil
and cashew loaf, will also figure. The presence of pheasant and partridge on an
April menu makes one wonder about long-term storage. But people write
enthusiastically of their evenings, made more interesting since the beginning
of 1990 by fortnightly French dinners on a set menu. A quirky wine list shows
real enthusiasm; a range of wines from Ch. Tayac, Côtes de Bourg, imported by
the owners, heads an encouraging list of petits châteaux from good vintages.
Details are erratic but wines can be ordered confidently with minimum damage
to the pocket. House wine: £7.25, CELLARMAN'S CHOICE: Ch. Tayac Cuvée
Océane 1989, £7.25 Ch. Tayac Cuvée Réserve 1983, £12.50.

CHEF: Jenny James   PROPRIETORS: Mike Boustred and Jenny James
OPEN: Tue to Sun, D only
MEALS: 7 to 9.45
PRICES: £17 (£23), Set D from £15.75 (£22)
CARDS: Access, Visa
SEATS: 50. Private parties: 34 main room, 18 private room. Car-park, 14 places. Vegetarian
meals. Children's helpings on request. No smoking. Wheelchair access (2 steps). Music

---

*The text of entries is based on unsolicited reports sent in by readers, backed up by
inspections conducted anonymously. The factual details under the text are from
questionnaires the* Guide *sends to all restaurants that feature in the book.*

▲ *White House Hotel* ♟

Williton TA4 4QW   COOKING 3
WILLITON (0984) 32306 and 32777   COST £40

Modest and comfortable, with an atmosphere that can be very low-key, the
hotel-restaurant lies to one side of the main road through Williton. It pleases
for its careful cooking, its good buying and a repertoire of dishes that many
have come to appreciate. These include pork Korean style; Charter pie, a
chicken, onion and parsley shortcrust pie; quail stuffed with apricots, pine
kernels and sultanas; loganberry crème brûlée and strawberry pancakes. 'We
appreciate the informality combined with efficiency,' comments one visitor,
more charitable than those who described the service as almost inattentive on
bad nights. He singles out the first and last courses as his special pleasure,
whether they be the soufflé suissesse or Kay Smith's chocolate praline loaf. The
set-price meal starts with a soup 'good with a rather rough consistency', before
offering a choice of four dishes in each course, with a pause for cheese. Cooking
borrows from the French bourgeois tradition, as in lamb with a garlic cream
sauce, as well as hunting further afield – that Korean pork fillet is baked with
sesame, garlic and soy, then served thin sliced on a salad – or reproducing
English classics. It depends for its success on good materials, such as bread and
cheeses, and has nice touches, such as a vacherin with not just strawberries but
also raspberries, redcurrants, peaches and blackcurrants. Coffee has not always
been good enough though many of the ancillaries are, such as the pissaladière
at the beginning. The wine list is the work of an enthusiast, 'no pompous
sommelier here, but he gives proper treatment to loved bottles.' The balance of
the list has been improved with good New World offerings and value is
maintained by interesting wines from lesser French regions. There is
something of a special line in Bandols. The list of old claret is bound to interest
many, particularly as they are comparatively affordable. Burgundies are
younger but growers like Quillardet, Juillot or Boillot give confidence. There
are plenty of halves. One reader could not fathom why sherries were measured
out as if they were spirits. House wine: £10 and £12. CELLARMAN'S
CHOICE: Crozes Hermitage 1988, Graillot, £13.80; Pouilly Blanc Fumé 1987,
Rolet, £13.50.

CHEFS/PROPRIETORS: Dick and Kay Smith
OPEN: all week, D only
CLOSED: Nov to mid-May
MEALS: 7.30 to 8.30
PRICES: Set D £24 (£33)
SEATS: 26. Private parties: 12 main room. Car-park, 17 places. Children's helpings.
No smoking while others are eating. Wheelchair access
ACCOMMODATION: 12 rooms, 10 with bath/shower. Rooms for disabled. B&B £35 to £70.
Deposit: £25. Baby facilities. Pets welcome. TV. Phone. Doors close at 11.30. Confirm by 6

*'In between first and second courses we were offered, gratis, a strange choice, apple sorbet
or salad leaves with melon and yoghurt. Took both, tried both and left both.'* On
inspecting in Dorset

WINCHCOMBE Gloucestershire

map 2

Corner Cupboard
Dining Room

Corner Cupboard Inn, Gloucester Street,
Winchcombe GL54 5LX
WINCHCOMBE (0242) 602303

COOKING 1
COST £26

On the main road to Cheltenham, not far from the fifteenth-century church whose gargoyles gawp back at the gawping tourists, the restaurant is leased from the Corner Cupboard Inn next door. It is self-contained, tiny, almost secret; impervious to pub noise and free of nicotine. It has rough stone walls, parquet floor, and a stone fireplace that takes up almost an entire wall. Bright, colourful drawings and hand-thrown pottery complete the grotto-like effect. Chris Randle is a 'charming proprietor' who cooks and sometimes welcomes and serves. Her four-course menus have an English bias, reminiscent of home dinner parties inspired by Cordon Bleu recipes. From a small repertoire of sauces comes a stream of frequently changing dishes: lemon hollandaise is served with scallops au gratin or with feuilleté of salmon; madeira sauce with feuilleté of pigeon or with rack of lamb and its ratatouille timbale. The cooking demands quiet skill rather than nervous intensity or bravura: hence warm leek and cream tart, breast of chicken wrapped in spring cabbage and bacon, or baked aromatic lamb fillet with mint and yoghurt sauce. Cheese and puddings are well reported. Thirty wines generally without attribution are very modestly priced. House French: £6.95.

CHEF/PROPRIETOR: Christine Randle
OPEN: Tue to Sat, D only
MEALS: 7.30 to 9
PRICES: Set D £16.95 (£22)
SEATS: 18. Private parties: 18 main room, 18 private room. Car-park, 15 places. No children under 10. No smoking. Wheelchair access (1 step; also WC)

WINDERMERE Cumbria

map 7

▲ Miller Howe

Rayrigg Road, Windermere LA23 1EY
WINDERMERE (096 62) 2536
on A592 between Windermere and Bowness

COOKING 4
COST £44

'Twenty-three years of filling in forms for the *Guide*,' remarks John Tovey, 'and some of the staff have been here for nineteen.' Persistence has its own reward, not least the barrage of letters consequent on our gentle remarks in the last edition. 'Miller Howies' are very loyal. The Edwardian house, with many additions to give usable public space, includes a new Victorian conservatory to cope with overcrowding during the pre-dinner drink period. It sits above gardens plunging down to Windermere itself and Langdale Pike beyond. Both garden and interior show strong tendencies to self-mocking theatricality: statues abound, cute *putti* here, more muscular numbers there, not the usual country-house restraint. The formula of the evening meal served by staff in smart blazers is familiar to many: a fruit or vegetable first course; a soup, normally involving two if not three complementary flavours; a fish dish; a meat main course, usually though not invariably 'an old-fashioned roast with gravy' with several vegetables arrayed in tiny quantities around the centrepiece; then the first choice of the evening, an array of puddings and sweet dishes of which two or three can be had without cavil, three or more with persuasion. Most people will not have room. Coffee and truffles are served in the sitting-rooms or on the terraces. On Saturdays there are two sittings. The first is very early for many and the second may encounter weary staff, though the management required to juggle the numbers from one space to another is by now well developed. Those who are unused to the experience may find the strict timekeeping disconcerting: dinner is 8 for 8.30 and 'when we came down at 8.05 there were no seats available in the lounge'. Hence the new conservatory. There is a symbiotic relationship between John Tovey's writing and teaching, and the dishes served in the restaurant: developed in his own farm kitchen, these last are multiplied tenfold for Miller Howe, then published or broadcast. This makes for a steady flow of new ideas within the all-embracing formula. An autumn meal started with avocado and marinated apple balls with a concassé of tomatoes and curried pastry tartlet with mayonnaise. The soup was cauliflower with grated cheese, toasted almonds and a savoury scone. The fish was a salmon escalope with a chive and Noilly Prat cream sauce with salmon roe, and was succeeded by lamb on a mushroom pâté croûton with greengage purée, rich gravy and fried garlic. Hardly a 'traditional roast' this. Its only drawback was cooling down on the plate before all the flavours were tasted and appreciated. Lemon tart, tipsy trifle, sticky toffee or lemon puddings as well as fruit pies remain enduringly popular. The wine list is especially strong in New World bottles. John Tovey likes their value as well as their style, which stands up to the whirling variety of tastes that are offered in the course of a meal. This kitchen has been an important influence on British cooking in the 1980s. The master himself has inspired many erstwhile amateurs to turn professional and he has enlivened vegetable cookery – sometimes to disconcerting effect in less skilled hands, just as his ideas of combining sweet and savoury tastes have inevitably been coarsened. Correspondents are often surprised at their admiration for the amalgams served at Miller Howe as the combinations seem theoretically unlikely. Compare the style with that of the new-wave Italian school in London, and wonder what will happen to the two streams in the 1990s. House wine is £10.50. The 12.5 per cent service charge is added to the whole bill of hotel guests – accommodation and meals.

CHEF: Gaulton Blackiston   PROPRIETOR: John J. Tovey
OPEN: all week, D only
CLOSED: Dec to Mar
MEALS: 8 for 8.30 (7 and 9.30 Sat)
PRICES: Set D £27 (£37). Service 12.5%
CARDS: Access, Amex, Diners, Visa
SEATS: 70. Private parties: 30 main room. Car-park, 40 places. Vegetarian meals by arrangement. No children under 12. Smart dress preferred. No smoking. Music. Air-conditioned
ACCOMMODATION: 13 rooms, all with bath/shower. D,B&B £85 to £160. No children under 12. Pets welcome. Afternoon teas. Garden. Fishing. Golf. Air-conditioning. TV. Phone. Scenic. Doors close at 11. Confirm by noon [*Which? Hotel Guide*]

Miller Howe Kaff

Lakeland Plastics, Station Precinct
Windermere LA23 1BQ
WINDERMERE (096 62) 2255
behind Windermere station

COOKING 2
COST £16

Lakeland Plastics supplies 'everything for the fridge, freezer and microwave' and a deal else besides, provided it's plastic. The Kaff, an outpost of Miller Howe, aims to bring good food to a wider public than can afford the hotel, and more people than ever are taking advantage of it. A blackboard menu, open kitchen, large crowds of customers and cheerful tables inside and out promote an atmosphere of bustle and anticipation, often justified. Dishes such as celery, orange and apple soup, or tomato and fennel; cheese and herb pâté on a tomato and orange salad; Cumberland sausages with baked potatoes; salmon with a dill sauce; breast of chicken and banana with a herb cream sauce which had been cooked with sufficient precision for the meat to be done yet the banana to retain some bite; crème brûlée with strawberries; or tipsy trifle that lived up to its name show the range and frequent quality. There have been some observations that bread and scones were not of the right texture and that the cooking has been found to miss the mark. In part these faults, the air of disarray on hectic days, and small points like failing to clear the blackboard menu of what is no longer available, are due to popularity and the long queues pressing for food. House wine: £7.

CHEFS: William Tulley and Ian Dutton   PROPRIETOR: John J. Tovey and Ian Dutton
OPEN: Mon to Sat, daytime only
MEALS: 10 to 4
PRICES: £8 (£13). Minimum £3
SEATS: 36. Private parties: 36 main room. Car-park, 60 places. Vegetarian meals. Children welcome. No smoking. Wheelchair access (also unisex WC). Self-service

Roger's

4 High Street, Windermere LA23 1AF
WINDERMERE (096 62) 4954

COOKING 3
COST £26–£34

It may be cramped and people still find the smoking a worry in such circumstances, despite some help from the extractor, but the food is applauded wholeheartedly for its skill, freshness and value. The *carte*, giving six choices at each stage with an intermediate soup course if desired, does not amaze by modernity. What impresses is the precision with which flavourings are deployed in dishes such as a tart of Stilton and asparagus; herb pancakes with lobster; chicken livers with bacon, mushrooms and sultanas with a very rich gravy and flaky pastry; saddle of hare or of rabbit with wild mushrooms; cod with asparagus and mushroom glaze; crisp vegetables; amazing steamed puddings – ginger or almond and amaretto, for instance, with a butterscotch sauce – a good version of brown sugar meringues with bananas and coffee cream, or a triple chocolate terrine with coffee sauce. Alena Pergl-Wilson knows her job when it comes to the wines and represents her husband's intentions in the kitchen with tact and accuracy. On the wine list prices are fair and fairly spread. Selection, though, is uneven, relying too heavily on big

519

names (a lot of Latour) but surprising with little gems like St Joseph from Grippat, the single vineyard Rioja Contino or Ch. Cazil 1975. Ask for recommendations. House French: £7.90 per litre. CELLARMAN'S CHOICE: Ch. la Lagure 1978, £27.65; Puligny Montrachet 1986, Latour £24.90.

CHEF: Roger Pergl-Wilson   PROPRIETORS: Roger and Alena Pergl-Wilson
OPEN: Mon to Sat, D only
MEALS: 7 to 10
PRICES: £16 (£26), Set D £18 (£24) to £23 (£28)
CARDS: Access, Amex, Diners, Visa
SEATS: 42. Private parties: 28 main room, 18 private room. Children's helpings. Wheelchair access. Music

---

WINTERINGHAM Humberside   map 6

▲ *Winteringham Fields*

Winteringham DN15 9PF   COOKING 4
SCUNTHORPE (0724) 733096   COST £20–£42

This converted manor house, dating from the sixteenth-century, is in the centre of the village, close to the Humber. The welcome is charming and courteous as Annie Schwab ushers you into one of the small beamed rooms for a drink. Old chairs and settees, nineteenth-century bric-a-brac, and some higgledy-piggledy period pieces have been collected on merit and assembled, rather than hunted down from a designer's shopping list. The dining-room is bright and modern, but still relaxing; tables are well spaced; the menu is in French (perhaps for the benefit of staff) with English subtitles. Amuse-gueule come in two waves: a first strike with drinks, the second strike at the table. The proximity of water turns out to be a good omen: Grimsby is 30 miles away and fish is one of the highlights. Two inspectors have come away independently with the impression that they have never met such overwhelming freshness anywhere else. There are composed dishes on the menu, such as steamed fillet of cod glazed with oxtail juices and sprinkled with salmon eggs, as well as the day's fish prepared as Germain Schwab sees fit: 'unbelievably flavoursome' scallops in garlic; steamed, firm-textured, rich-flavoured turbot; lobster bisque 'one of the nicest soups I have ever tasted'. Clarity of taste and purpose impress: 'it is as if Schwab is working from a Hubble telescope parked in outer space, while most other restaurateurs attempt to probe the secrets of the universe from their back yard with an old pair of binoculars.' Game is another strong suit, vegetables are unequivocally praised, and the choice and quality of cheeses from Britain, France and Switzerland is outstanding; there is even *tête de moine*, properly shaved. The best way of tackling puddings such as warm marinated banana in banana liqueur with hazelnut cream, fresh strawberries and shortbread (that's all one), or gratin of strawberries in almond and coconut cream served hot with home-made ice cream, may be to take the option of four of them in miniature. Service is rather formal, very professional, and there is staff enough to cope with all needs twice over. The unclear presentation of the wine list obscures some excellent wines such as Vincent's Pouilly Fuissé, decent clarets and bottles from Testug of Switzerland (Germain Schwab is

Swiss). House Bergerac is £8. CELLARMAN'S CHOICE: Twanner 1982, £16; Ch.
Tour Renaissance 1983, £15.50.

CHEFS: Germain Schwab, Mark Midwinter and Paul Orrey   PROPRIETORS: Annie and
Germain Schwab
OPEN: Mon to Sat, exc Mon and Sat L
CLOSED: first 2 weeks Mar and first week Aug
MEALS: 11.30 to 1.30, 7 to 9.30
PRICES: £24 (£30), Set L £13.50 (£20), Set D £24 (£30) to £29 (£35). Service inc
CARDS: Access, Visa
SEATS: 40. Private parties: 14 main room, 10 private room. Car-park, 16 places. Children
welcome. No smoking in dining-room. Smart dress preferred. Wheelchair access (1 step;
also WC). Music. Air-conditioned
ACCOMMODATION: 4 rooms, all with bath/shower. B&B £50 to £85. No children under 12.
No smoking in bedrooms. Garden. TV. Phone. Scenic. Doors close at midnight.
Confirm by 6

WITHERSLACK Cumbria   map 7

▲ *Old Vicarage* ▮

Witherslack LA11 6RS
WITHERSLACK (044 852) 381   COOKING 3
off A590   COST £36

Not 'hushed' at all (*Guide* 1990), but bustling on nights in season, from the pit-
pat of balls on the new tennis court, the extra zip to business from five new
bedrooms in the Orchard House and more staff to help an already solicitous
team. The small touches of hospitality – well equipped bedrooms, tea near the
fire on a cold wet arrival – excite much comment. So, too, does the food, a no-
choice menu served at a single time in a handsome Victorian dining-room. One
meal began with fresh pears stuffed with cheese and herb pâté served with a
tarragon cream sauce and blackcurrant purée: the latter was superfluous,
serving only to mask the good flavours. Spinach soup came next with home-
made bread – soup good, bread nutty and excellent (their baking, and bacon,
make breakfast a pleasure); then chicken in a lemon and herb sauce – the meat
moist and with taste, the sauce finely pointed; vegetables crisp and prettily
presented, a mixture of the simple and the composed, for instance a Moroccan
aubergine casserole or carrot and parsnip pureé with coriander; for dessert a
fresh fruit salad *and* (no question about it) a fine treacle tart that was not
cloyingly sweet – puddings are always remarked upon as the final
extravagance in an already large meal, and as being very fine examples of
British cooking. The final stage is the cheese, a selection of the best British,
with fruit, celery and biscuits. Every night is a new adventure, though the
pattern is identical. Efforts are willingly made to accommodate diet and dislike
within the no-choice formula. But the cooking is not for weaklings. The wine
list is catholic, and takes only the best producers and the better years. Halves
are plentiful, but many diners carry a bottle over two nights. Price bands give
opportunities for cheap drinking as well as dear. There really are no weak
areas, though North America may be due for expansion if they have room. One
visitor was worried that storage was dotted around the house rather than in a
cellar but no one has complained of the wine being out of condition. Eight

bottles are offered by the glass. CELLARMAN'S CHOICE: Chardonnay Rongopai, Te Kanwhata 1988, £15.20, Santenay les Gravières 1986, Leflaive, £20.95, and Jennings' Cumbrian Ales for the thirsty. Roger Burrington-Brown has seemingly taken against young children, having raised the minimum age to 12 years. He remarks that he wishes people would also refrain from smoking in their bedrooms, and expresses vexation at people who do not turn up. No-shows have reached worrying proportions and really do harm isolated businesses like this. Legal considerations apart, doubtless these phantom customers would be the first to pick on the failings of hoteliers.

CHEFS/PROPRIETORS: Roger and Jill Burrington-Brown, Irene and Stanley Reeve
OPEN: all week, D only
CLOSED: 1 week at Christmas
MEALS: 7.30 for 8
PRICES: Set D £23.50 (£30)
CARDS: Access, Amex, Diners, Visa
SEATS: 35. Private parties: 18 main room. Car-park, 25 places. No smoking in dining-room. Music. One sitting
ACCOMMODATION: 13 rooms, all with bath/shower. Rooms for disabled. B&B £50 to £70. No children under 12. Pets welcome by arrangement. Garden. Tennis. TV. Phone. Scenic. Doors close at 11.30. Confirm by 6 [*Which? Hotel Guide*]

WITHYPOOL Somerset   map 1

▲ *Royal Oak*

Withypool TA24 7QP	COOKING 1
EXFORD (064 383) 506 and 507	COST £21–£35

A picture-book pub with bar food and a more formal restaurant offering set-price meals, changed seasonally, and an à la carte that changes very little. The set-price menu offers deep-fried prawn balls, tempura, chicken with lemon and sesame, and mussel risotto, showing a more adventurous side to cooking that also produces several sorts of steak. The bar food can be exceptionally well founded on proper cheeses, local sausages and prawns by the pint. Exmoor and Ushers beer and Hancocks cider share a place with a decent short wine list. This kicks off with house Mouflon d'Or at £6.50.

CHEF: Joanna Lomasney   PROPRIETOR: M.J. Bradley
OPEN: all week
CLOSED: 25 and 26 Dec
MEALS: 12 to 2 (1.30 Sun), 7 to 9
PRICES: £21 (£29), Set L £14.50 (£21), Set D £16 (£23) to £20 (£27)
CARDS: Access, Amex, Diners, Visa
SEATS: 32. 2 tables outside. Private parties: 18 main room. Car-park, 20 places. Vegetarian meals. Children's helpings. No children under 10. Smart dress preferred
ACCOMMODATION: 8 rooms, 6 with bath/shower. B&B £27 to £60. Deposit: £20. No children under 10. Pets welcome. Afternoon teas. Fishing. TV. Phone. Scenic. Doors close at midnight [*Which? Hotel Guide*]

The Guide *is totally independent, accepts no free hospitality, and survives on the number of copies sold each year.*

WOBURN Bedfordshire

map 3

Paris House

Woburn MK17 9QP
WOBURN (0525) 290692
off A4012 1m SE of Woburn in abbey grounds

COOKING 3
COST £23–£48

Fine weather seems to evoke the most favourable impressions. The half-timbered building is set in parkland, with deer and pheasant wandering about. Sitting on the lawn, drinking aperitifs and being fed a succession of elegant pre-prandial morsels is bliss to many. On such days it is cool inside; a nascent air of unreality is encouraged by year-round holly on the wallpaper. The cooking draws murmurs of satisfaction rather than ecstatic whoops of joy. One of the most animated comments has been: 'We eat fish seven days a week at home and my husband's recreation is fishing so we know good salmon when we encounter it. Here it is superbly cooked.' Over the years the menu has moved away from Roux-inspired French to the kind of dishes that might now be found in a cosmopolitan brasserie. Or perhaps it is the latter that have shifted. Either way, the approach produces such dishes as brochette of marinated chicken with spicy peanut sauce; stir-fried fillet of beef with ginger and spring onions; hot filo pastry tarts with creamed leeks and smoked haddock served with a red pepper sauce. There is still a French string to the bow, playing on familiar themes, from fillet of pork charcutière to ragout of fish dieppoise. The kitchen's performance brings applause for judgement, especially with fish; for contrasts, such as the pairing of crisp duck confit with a tart blackcurrant and frisée salad; and for lightness, as in savoury mousses and hot sweet soufflés. Ice-creams decorated with spun sugar have been given standing ovations. More the pity, then, that the relaxation of the no-smoking policy has upset some readers. We have still not been allowed a copy of the wine list, but house Duboeuf red or white is £9.

CHEF/PROPRIETOR: Peter Chandler
OPEN: Tue to Sun, exc Sun D
CLOSED: Feb
MEALS: 12 to 2, 7 to 10
PRICES: Set L £16.50 (£23) to £26.50 (£34), Set D £26.50 (£34) to £32 (£40)
CARDS: Access, Amex, Diners, Visa
SEATS: 52. 3 tables outside. Private parties: 45 main room, 25 private room. Car-park, 25 places. Children's helpings. No children under 12. Smart dress preferred

WOODBRIDGE Suffolk

map 3

Wine Bar 🍷

17 Thoroughfare, Woodbridge IP12 1AA
WOODBRIDGE (039 43) 2557

COOKING 2
COST £19

Prosaic name and inauspicious address notwithstanding, an above-average wine bar. Over a delicatessen and consisting of two casually furnished rooms joined by a corridor with bar, it looks the Woodbridge wine bar norm. But beware of imitations, writes one reader, for out of Sally O'Gorman's tiny kitchen comes inspiration. A first course off the blackboard menu might be boned quail on toast stuffed with lentils and hazelnuts, with a port sauce. Other readers have been impressed by deep-fried herb and sunflower seed choux buns with aubergine and marjoram mousse and avocado vinaigrette as a vegetarian main course in winter, just as cheese potato pancakes with red peppers and walnut oil made a 'fascinating and very enjoyable combination', and a well-balanced smoked salmon and fennel quiche, with fine pastry, came with a dollop of crème fraîche. For pudding, a round of crisp brown meringue is anointed with two large spoonfuls of gooey chocolate mousse and floated on a puddle of tart kumquat sauce. The coffee that followed gave no joy, and some have thought the welcome may lack cheer. There are more than 70 interesting wines, many country French, and Australasia and the United States well represented. More than a dozen come by the glass or quarter bottle. Prices are fair (only the Champagne is over £20 and many are below £10, and the choice is fashionable and worth casting prejudice to the wind for an essay of new styles and makers This is not a 'great names' list. There are brief notes to each bottle. House French: £5.85.

CHEF: Sally O'Gorman   PROPRIETORS: Sally O'Gorman and Richard Lane
OPEN: Tue to Sat
CLOSED: 25 and 26 Dec
MEALS: 12 to 2.30, 7 to 11
PRICES: £11 (£16)
SEATS: 50. Vegetarian meals. No children under 16. Music

WOODSTOCK Oxfordshire   map 2

▲ *Feathers Hotel*

Market Street, Woodstock OX7 1SX   COOKING 3
WOODSTOCK (0993) 812291   COST £28–£54

'Wow! If the *Guide* didn't need more information, that one word would say it all', wrote one inspector who went on to say, 'the kitchen is far, far superior to the type of hotel that the Feathers is.' He didn't know that the Feathers, long a successful experiment in giving good food for fair value, has been taken over by a team that includes Nick Gill, a British chef who made his reputation cooking at Hambleton Hall. The hotel and restaurant is in the throes of refurbishment and expansion, and the kitchen has not yet reached its full potential. Signs are, however, that it might, if Nick Gill's attention can be kept on the task to hand. The formula revolves around a menu of half a dozen choices in each course, fish included. This is offered as a set-price five-course meal at dinner and either three or five courses at lunch. There is also a cheaper lunch menu and flexible arrangements for residents. In the bar, lighter meals are served at midday. What is immediately plain to visitors during the first six months is that the kitchen is striving to deliver more, not less, than is offered on the menu. This reads quite simply: warm salad of duck livers with herbs; a tartlet of quails' eggs and leeks; loin of veal with mustard and tarragon; caramel ice-cream with pastries. A chilled soup of tomatoes and basil arrives as a rich and opulent liquid, with a tomato ice-cream and skinned cherry tomatoes drizzled with virgin oil; pink grapefruit laced with elderflower actually came with an elderflower ice, a simple dish stylishly executed. Balance, within the context of a long meal, is also considered – mussels (substituted by monkfish on one day) reposed in a light fish stock, saffron and cream liquor that carefully kept main course options open. One diner found the main courses did not achieve the dazzle and invention of the first two; this may in part be a question of maintaining appetite. He pointed out how duck with orange and Cointreau, served with carrots, managed to tilt too far towards sweetness. The range of dishes at this stage is quite conservative: veal, duck, beef, baby chicken, spring lamb. It looks like a careful attempt to maintain culinary accessibility, which may explain how and why children seem both welcome and content. In early summer, not much fish apart from wild salmon was available. Conservative, too, is the seasoning; many modern palates would find it heavy on salt throughout. After the meal comes cheese: a few sorts, sometimes advertised as English then arriving as French and Irish, other times only as 'farmhouse', and served with walnut bread. Altogether four sorts of bread rolls have been offered, all good. Desserts return to the form of the earlier dishes: a summer pudding 'was to other summer puddings what Ferraris are to ordinary cars', with a texture of plush velvet and perfect balance of acid and sweet. Display comes into its own with a panoply of fresh fruits served with their own sorbets. Coffee is fine, truffles are outstanding. So are the amuse-gueule of prawns tossed with garlic and coriander, tartlets of salmon hollandaise and quails' egg and bacon. 'The best all-round meal I have had this year', wrote one who did not find the cost out of the way in terms of value, though he did gripe at the 15 per cent 'optional' service charge. The owners point out that this is not levied on accommodation. However, 15 per cent is high, and the practice is antediluvian. Pay the staff or put up the prices to show the *real* cost. It would be better if the service were competent. As it is it is very poorly drilled indeed. The wine list is best for burgundies, from an interesting choice of growers, and clarets, with a set of bourgeois that are not too dear. The arrangement of the meal may ask for more than one sort of wine, which would increase the cost substantially. It helps that there are several decent wines by the glass.

CHEF: Nick Gill   PROPRIETORS: Andrew Leeman, Simon Lowe and Howard Malin
OPEN: all week
MEALS: 12.30 to 2.15, 7 to 9.45
PRICES: £22 (£30), Set L £19.50 (£28) to £34.50 (£45), Set D £26.50 (£36) to £34.50 (£45). Service 15%
CARDS: Access, Amex, Diners, Visa
SEATS: 60. Private parties: 36 main room, 40 private room. Children's helpings. No cigars/pipes in dining-room. Wheelchair access. Music
ACCOMMODATION: 15 rooms, all with bath/shower. B&B £75 to £125. Baby facilities. Pets welcome. Afternoon teas. Garden. Fishing. TV. Phone. Doors close at 11.30. Confirm 2 days ahead

'The bizarre quality of the evening was somewhat enhanced by a private party of thirty or so, the males largely with deerstalkers and false moustaches. Unfortunately(?) they were in a separate dining room!'

The Guide *relies on feedback from its readers. Especially welcome are reports on new restaurants appearing in the book for the first time.*

WOOTTON   Isle Of Wight   map 2

▲ *Lugleys*

Staplers Road,
Wootton Common PO33 4RW   COOKING 3
NEWPORT (0983) 882202   COST £34

Angela Hewitt set up in Lugley Street, Newport, before moving to this remote
little detached house on Wootton Common next door to Butterfly World. Inside
it feels Victorian, a comfortable and pleasing jumble of easy chairs and framed
posters of old masters. The consensus is that Angela Hewitt is now cooking the
best food on the island, which is remarkable because it is still a one-woman
culinary show. She succeeds because she follows the seasons, is loyal to the
market and cares about her raw materials. Lobsters and other fish come from
local waters; spring lamb is raised on the Isle of Soay, grouse is also from
Scotland, and meat is bought from mainland farmers who employ natural
rearing methods and eschew hormones and tenderisers. This translates into a
short, ever-changing menu of three courses with not one but two unexpected –
and complimentary – bonuses in between. A typical meal in February began
with timbale of trout on a seafood sauce studded with freshly shelled mussels,
then the first bonus, a feather light leek terrine in cheese sauce, 'the highlight of
a superb meal'. The unadvertised pineapple and passion-fruit sorbet set the
scene for tender beef fillet glazed with cumin sauce accompanied by wild rice.
To finish there was a beautifully presented apple and marzipan paste tart
sitting on a plate covered one half with cream, one half with red plum sauce. In
May there might be lamb and aubergine charlotte, salmon in sesame pastry
with ginger sauce, and strawberry shortcake with rose-petal ice cream. The
only warning note sounded by readers is that the full meal may outface some
appetites. 'After a filling but delicious asparagus soup followed by an
unexpected but very rich courgette timbale and an equally unexpected melon
sorbet, we were in difficulties with the last half of our beef. The lavender
flower meringue that came with our fresh fruit salad was, to our taste, not so
good an idea.' A warning note by the chef-proprietor is to check open times in
winter. If Sunday lunch is arranged, the set meal costs £12.95. The modest
wine list doesn't keep pace with the food, but prices are low.The
accommodation is self-catering, so breakfast is DIY, though tea, coffee, bread,
butter and honey are provided.

CHEF/PROPRIETOR: Angela E. Hewitt
OPEN: Tue to Sat, D only (Mon and Sun D and L by arrangement)
CLOSED: 4 weeks in winter
MEALS: 7 to 9.30
PRICES: £20 (£28). Minimum £10.95
SEATS: 16. 5 tables outside. Private parties: 16 main room. Car-park, 12 places. No children
under 12. No cigars in dining-room
ACCOMMODATION: Self-contained flat for 3, £25 a night (£30 Aug). No children under 12.
Afternoon teas. TV

▲ *This symbol means accommodation is available.*

WORCESTER   Hereford & Worcester   map 2

Brown's

24 Quay Street, Worcester WR1 2JN   COOKING 2
WORCESTER (0905) 26263   COST £24–£38

There is a lot to absorb both inside and out at this elaborately converted
cornmill with riverside views. It is just below the cathedral and across from the
county cricket ground. Brown's ceilings are a dizzy height; a mezzanine
supported by girders and railings holds the bar. Custard-coloured brick walls
are covered with good modern art. Cooking strives to be simple, healthy and
even experimental. Success does come. At one meal, langoustine and bacon
kebabs with a light curry mayonnaise was 'very good, straightforward, fresh,
excellent flavour combinations, with an impeccable, thick, eggy, subtle,
mayonnaise'. Carré of spring lamb with ham and cucumber was 'really a
modern version of roast lamb and mint sauce: long strips of good ham with five
cutlets roasted, then sliced, and a light sauce.' Simple vegetables are 'almost
consistently accurately timed.' Salads are anointed with walnut oil dressing.
Vinaigrettes are popular: even a warm tomato version with roast guinea-fowl.
Sorbets and ice-creams are home made and a caramel and meringue parfait
showed skill as well as flavour. Staff are young, almost all male, relaxed and
efficient. There are notices on the tables requesting no smoking 'while those
near you are eating'. Someone is nearly always eating in a restaurant, so a
better message would be 'no smoking, please'. The wine list is very French.
Excellent properties abound, especially in Burgundy. Wine mark-ups are
erratic and there are bargains for the knowledgeable. The virtual absence of
anything beyond France prevents a glass award. House French: £6.95 or £7.95.
CELLARMAN'S CHOICE: Menetou Salon 1989, £11; Ch. Haut Marbuzet 1985,
£19. Prices are not low, though the setting and the very fresh materials are some
compensation. A certain disparity of cost and achievement may be felt by those
who want their cooking to appear more svelte.

CHEF: W.R. Tansley and S. Meredith   PROPRIETORS: W.R. and P.M. Tansley
OPEN: all week, exc Sat L and Sun D
CLOSED: bank hols and 1 week at Christmas
MEALS: 12.30 to 1.45 (2 Sun), 7.30 to 9.30
PRICES: Set L £18 (£24), Set D £26 (£32). Service 10%
CARDS: Access, Amex, Diners, Visa
SEATS: 80. Private parties: 80 main room. No children under 10. Wheelchair access (also
unisex WC)

WORLESTON   Cheshire   map 5

▲ Rookery Hall

Worleston, nr Nantwich, CW5 6DQ
NANTWICH (0270) 626866   COOKING 3
on B5074, off A51   COST £27–£72

David Tearle, the general manager, is often on the driveway, welcoming new
arrivals. This keenness for participatory supervision seems to bear results, in
that the Hall may be owned by a group but has commendable steadiness of

staffing and execution. The kitchen, too, produces food that is both of a consistent standard and well-resourced. If its repertoire changes but slowly and if the manner is slightly (but not slavishly) predictable, who should cavil? A meal in the spring included smoked salmon and scrambled egg, the egg timed exactly for the desired creaminess and then laid on a thin layer of spinach set in a pastry case. This protected it, but not the pastry, from promiscuous mingling with a truffled madeira sauce: a nice conceit. A pheasant pâté well laden with strips of breast, the farce studded with vegetables, was served with onion and ginger compote. Main courses of meat showed good buying of lamb and, more remarkably, pork. The latter was roasted with crackling of the right degree and came with a prune and apple accompaniment. The lamb, from Lincolnshire, was on a clear stock sauce, rich without cloying, with orange, carrot and turnips to give it texture and flavour. Cheese is properly kept. A dessert of vanilla seed parfait came with stewed raspberries while a hazelnut bavarois was given point by an Amaretto sauce. Good country-house cooking. Not only is it noticeably cheaper at lunchtime, but also the gentle green fields can then be seen from the now-carpeted dining-room. In the future it may be greens rather than fields, for the intention is to build a golf course – the new panacea for country hotels – and a further 36 bedrooms and conference facilities. Some visitors already regret the marked improvement in decoration and appointment because they fear it presages a certain blandness. The extra bedrooms can only reinforce the tendency, they claim. They may be right and it will be a challenge to prove them wrong. The wine list is long, predominantly French, and includes many fine properties. The sections from other areas are not much more than token but are nevertheless well chosen. Half-bottles are few and prices are, alas, exactly as may be expected. House wine: £14. CELLARMAN'S CHOICE: Aloxe Corton 1982, Latour £29; Cloudy Bay Chardonnay 1987, £27.50.

CHEF: Christopher Phillips   PROPRIETORS: Select Country Hotels plc
OPEN: all week
MEALS: 12.15 to 2.15, 7 to 9.30
PRICES: £37 (£46), Set L £15 (£27), Set D £30 (£44) to £45 (£60)
CARDS: Access, Amex, Diners, Visa
SEATS: 60. Private parties: 40 main room, 20 private room. Car-park, 30 places. No children under 10. Smart dress preferred. No smoking in dining-room. Wheelchair access (also unisex WC)
ACCOMMODATION: 45 rooms, all with bath/shower. Rooms for disabled. Lift. B&B £90 to £140. No children under 10. Afternoon teas. Garden. Tennis. Fishing. TV. Phone. Scenic. Confirm 24 hours ahead [*Which? Hotel Guide*]

WRIGHTINGTON Lancashire   map 5

High Moor

Highmoor Lane, Wrightington WN6 9PS   COOKING 3
APPLEY BRIDGE (025 75) 2364   COST £15–£35

The black and white building, its windows all small leaded panes, is a haven from the Lancashire moor that surrounds it – the privileged will get a window view from their table, sky and hedgerow on a good day, lowering squalls on a bad. 'It has a certain charm, particularly on a cold night after a long journey

through the snow.' The charm may be vitiated for some by closely set small tables. Grumbles through the year of ineffective service have evaporated in the summer's dawning and, though still branded as 'young', it is said to give adequate and happy support to a skilled kitchen. The output has been described as 'simpler, more clean cut than the menu intimated; formal not showy, it is more classical in origin than traditional, the food cooked with confidence and controlled presentation.' Display and modish miniaturisation creep in only at dessert stage. Very good cooking was encountered in a fillet of veal wrapped with bacon served with an escalope of calf's liver and a tarragon gravy where the combination of meats worked well and the gravy was reduced the right degree to provide support without intrusion. Duck with a honey coating, apple pancakes and cider vinegar sauce was also skilled: the pancake filled with apple (a pity an unannounced previous course had been apple and gin sorbet), the duck of extremely high quality, the sauce with tang yet sweetness from the cooking juice. The first course at this meal had included melon with red fruits in an elderflower jelly, 'the only problem was that there was not enough of it', so delicious was it. The serving of fruit at the beginning, rather than the end of a meal has come a long way since the days of grapefuit or melon. It is sometimes inexplicable what qualifies a composition for first or last position in the diner's progress. Melon, red fruits and jelly; gin and apple sorbet; lamb with redcurrant sauce; finishing with cheese and celery hearts will make a nonsense of many earlier taste theories. Periodic infelicities of seasoning – too much salt in stir-fried vegetables served with a ginger and oyster sauce and scallops 'that looked as if they had just tumbled out of the inverted pastry tart' – or execution, as with too-hard meringues or a lacklustre terrine of duck liver, are usually outweighed by satisfaction. Well-liked dishes have included quail with a mushroom stuffing on a bed of foie gras and orange, and loin of lamb with onion and chive purée in a tartlet and a redcurrant sauce. A soup of strawberries and exotic fruits tantalises many, though one was moved to query whether it was not more accurately a 'fruit salad'. The wine list makes a serious effort to give fair choice below £15 in a selection that only nods towards the New World though offering some useful wines from Spain (Jean Léon) and Italy (John Matta). The halves suffer from their usual lack of availability on merchants' shelves. House wines: £7.50 and £8.50.
CELLARMAN'S CHOICE: Ch. Haut-Tuquet 1985, £10.80.

CHEF: James Sines   PROPRIETOR: John Nelson
OPEN: Tue to Sun, exc Sat L and Sun D
MEALS: 12 to 2, 7 to 10
PRICES: £21 (£29), Set Sun L £9.75 (£15). Service 10%
CARDS: Access, Amex, Diners, Visa
SEATS: 95. Private parties: 80 main room. Car-park, 35 places. Children welcome.
Wheelchair access. Music. Air-conditioned

'The food is very nice, but the place is rather over-organised. I made the great mistake of asking for a second roll at dinner.' On eating in Northumberland

Consumers' Association is planning to publish Out to Eat, a new guide to budget eating out in restaurants, pubs, cafés, brasseries and so on. Please send reports and recommendations to Out to Eat, FREEPOST, 2 Marylebone Road, London NW1 1YN.

WYLAM Northumberland	map 7

▲ *Laburnum House*

| Wylam NE41 8AJ | COOKING 2 |
| WYLAM (0661) 852185 | COST £16–£31 |

An eighteenth-century stone building in a pretty village beside the River Tyne. Rowan Mahon and Kenn Elliott have converted the place into a pleasing restaurant with four bedrooms for overnight guests. The dining-room is genteel, with prints on the walls, pale drapes at the windows and cane/wickerwork chairs. Kenn Elliott offers a menu with modern French leanings. Fish shows up well: king prawns with garlic butter; turbot with crab sauce; and fillet of wild salmon with asparagus and lime are typical. Other choices might range from smoked pheasant with a honey and nut dressing to peppered duck breast with raspberries. Desserts are dominated by a big selection of ice-creams and sorbets, plus Normandy crêpes and hot strudel. The short wine list has a few representatives from the New World; growers are often good and prices always fair. House French: £6.25. CELLARMAN'S CHOICE: Cabernet Sauvignon, Beringer 1985, £14.75.

CHEF: Kenn Elliott PROPRIETORS: Rowan Mahon and Kenn Elliott
OPEN: Tue to Sat, D only (L by arrangement)
MEALS: 6.30 to 10
PRICES: £19 (£26), Set D (residents only) £12.50 (£16)
CARDS: Access, Amex, Diners, Visa
SEATS: 40. Private parties: 40 main room. Children's helpings. Wheelchair access (1 step; also WC). Music
ACCOMMODATION: 4 rooms, all with bath/shower. B&B £40 to £50. Children welcome. Pets welcome. TV. Doors close at midnight

WYMONDHAM Norfolk	map 6

Jennings

| Damgate Street, Wymondham NR18 0BQ | COOKING 2 |
| WYMONDHAM (0953) 603533 | COST £27–£36 |

A former shop premises where the feeling is definitely 'country' though avoiding the twee by virtue of a sophisticated menu. This still may need some intensifying of flavours and sharpening of techniques but has brought high praise in general. Approval has come for dishes as various as salmon quenelles; sweetbread and leek terrine; timbale of courgettes with goats' cheese cooked in a filo packet; a fricassee of salmon, scallops and white fish; and breast of duck served with another packet, this time of the leg meat. On the minus side, a pheasant terrine had a port jelly of insufficient character to lend seasoning to the meat, the standard of vegetables has been very uneven, even on a single plate, and Grand Marnier soufflé was barely liquorous. The menu is kept to no more than three choices in each course, with set prices for three or four courses. Sauces are much enjoyed and a fair range is offered even in so small a compass: sorrel with a mille-feuille of crab; Cumberland with rabbit terrine; orange butter with scallop and tagliatelle; chive with fish; crayfish with chicken and kidney, and basil with lamb were produced on a single night. Even on quiet days, the progress through such a meal may be gentle though pleasantly enlivened by Sarah Jennings' service and conversation. She says that 'smoking is not encouraged, but happens occasionally; ardent anti-smokers should ask for our private room when booking, please.' The wine list has grown and has some decent bottles without straining anyone's pocket. Burgundies from Latour, Drouhin and Rottiers-Clothilde, Loires from Saget and Australians from Lindemans are very adequate. There are a dozen halves. House French: £6.20.

CHEF: David Jennings   PROPRIETORS: David and Sarah Jennings
OPEN: Tue to Sat, D only (L by arrangement)
MEALS: 7.30 to 9.30
PRICES: Set D £19.50 (£27) to £22.50 (£30)
CARDS: Access, Amex, Visa
SEATS: 30. Private parties: 18 main room, 12 private room. Vegetarian meals. Children's helpings. Music. Air-conditioned

---

YATTENDON Berkshire   map 2

▲ *Royal Oak* ♥

The Square, Yattendon RG16 0UF   COOKING 3
HERMITAGE (0635) 201325   COST £28–£44

This 'extraordinary village pub, small hotel and kitchen' is often bruited as the shape of British catering to come: it combines all the elements in an economic synergy that can only work to the benefit of consumer and producer. Certainly, the pub customers are happy: Adnam, Wadsworth and Badger beers, a good wine list, food as good as any restaurant in relaxed yet enjoyable conditions, yet very fair prices. A few claim that by being all things to all people, there are infelicities: the lounge, well crowded with sofas and club chairs, is not peaceful enough because of the throng in the wood-panelled, log-fired, pub; the proximity of the kitchen intrudes on the country-formal dining-room; the pub is not sufficiently comfortable for eating. The majority would say this is nit-picking. The choice is yours, so long as you have booked. Turn left for the restaurant, right for the pub. The long menus change every day, offering both sets of customers the same recipes in very similar format, but at a discount in the bar – compensating for the simpler, yet enjoyable service. Richard Smith is still a presence in the kitchen, but his business has grown beyond the stove (see entry for the Beetle and Wedge, Moulsford) and Dominique Orizet does most of the day to day cooking at Yattendon. Materials are usually well chosen; a fishmonger who dined here was impressed by the ingredients as well as the standard of the cooking. He began with a crab and avocado salad, went on to turbot with queen scallops and oysters, 'cooked by a chef who understands how little cooking good fish needs.' Things that get constant recommendation include fish soup; crispy duck salad, 'I had one piece of duck and swooned'; calf's kidney with black pudding in green mustard sauce; salad of smoked chicken, avocado and prawns in a mayonnaise on well-varied greens; halibut with cream and chives; sea bass with tagliatelle and a smoked oyster sauce; lobster salads, even in the bar, perhaps with a tarragon mayonnaise; calf's liver and bacon; salmon with a beurre blanc; duck with apples, cider and brandy;

and a wide range of desserts such as apple crumble, hot lemon soufflé with lemon sauce, and almond parfait with coffee sauce. The failings that occurred at one meal – soggy croûtons, insipid coffee sauce, chewy tuile and sugary fudge – may be of detail rather than conception, though there have been some who, surprisingly, have protested at a 'nouvelle cuisine' tendency in the kitchen. The wine list is excellent for France, especially burgundy, quite poor for Spain, Italy and the New World. The shortage of half-bottles is made up for by charging from a bottle *pro rata*. House wine is Cuvée Georges Blanc at £7.50. CELLARMAN'S CHOICE: Châteauneuf-du-Pape, Dom. du Vieux Télégraphe 1987, £19.50; Tokay Pinot Gris 1985, Trimbach, £11.50.

CHEFS: Richard Smith and Dominique Orizet   PROPRIETORS: Richard and Kate Smith
OPEN: all week (Sun D bar meals only)
MEALS: 12 to 2, 7.30 to 10
PRICES: £28 (£37), Set L and D £19.50 (£28)
CARDS: Access, Amex, Visa
SEATS: 30. 10 tables outside. Private parties: 30 main room; 8 private room. Car-park, 35 places. Children's helpings. No cigars/pipes in dining-room. Wheelchair access
ACCOMMODATION: 5 rooms, all with bath/shower. B&B £50 to £70. Baby facilities. Pets by arrangement. Afternoon teas. Garden. TV. Phone. Scenic. Doors close at 12.30. Confirm by 6
[*Which? Hotel Guide*]

YORK   North Yorkshire   map 5

Kites

13 Grape Lane, York YO1 2HU   COOKING 2
YORK (0904) 641750   COST £17–£22

There is now a bar on the ground floor which opens only at weekends. Otherwise it's still a long pant up several flights to the cheerful pair of rooms (one smoking, one not) with red floorboards, check cloths, modern print curtains and walls painted with kites and birds (which a non-ornithologist took to be cranes). 'Keep Going, It's Worth It' says a sign at half-way – and one reader says, 'It is!' Kites is by no means a vegetarian restaurant, but it accords vegetarians an equal crack of the whip, and the affection shown by non-meat eaters for spices and ingredients such as smetana and tofu is evident throughout the *carte*. A spring meal spread itself through the 10 or so choices at each course: mushrooms came well seasoned with lemon, finished with Parmesan, egg yolks and cream; aubergine was cooked with pesto, mozzarella and garlic; a game terrine was substantially flavoured; the good quality steak with garlic butter was overcooked but the accompanying chips were crisp; lamb's liver was lightly sauced with a sweet Bordeaux wine; the pork fillet came with a substantial paprika and port reduction; 'mish-mash' turned out to be slices of best end of lamb stuffed with herbs, served with tofu and apricot and a cumin and coriander sauce – the lamb was excellent but the dish as a whole too nearly resembled its name. Vegetables cost extra, as do potatoes, but they are decent. Desserts, at this meal, were thought best of all: the banoffi pie was a slice of coffee and banana cream with fresh toffee; an 'upmarket Indian ice' of saffron, cream and fromage frais was stuffed with fruits and nuts and lubricated by a cardamom syrup; a rich chocolate pie; and walnut meringues sandwiched with cream. People who like 'healthy' food seem to have a passion for the most ecstatically substantial puddings. That meal is a good representative: lots of ideas, lots of tastes, occasional misapplications, excellent value. 'The slightly zany atmosphere is conducive to enjoyment and we felt it had been a much better evening than the previous one in a much plusher establishment,' wrote one reader who uses it as a staging post en route to the north. Others disagree. The service sometimes has a tenuous hold on timekeeping and 'zany' or 'casual' is not the ideal for many people. 'When the waitress put on Fauré's *Requiem* (which may have been appropriate for the speed of the service), I baulked and got applause for persuading them to substitute some livelier Mozart. 'Menu prices are discounted by 10 per cent at lunchtime, and the set dinner includes half a bottle of house wine. The wines, supplied by Cachet Wines of York, are excellent: a short list, each bottle carefully chosen, prices extremely fair. If it does not have a Glass Award this year it is because such honours are relative and there is much more competition. House Côtes de Thongue and Gascogne are £6.50. CELLARMAN'S CHOICE: Graves, Ch. Coucheroy 1988, £8.95; Arboles de Castillejo 1983, Bodegas Torres Filoso, £9.50.

CHEFS: Mark Ball and Anne Wilkinson PROPRIETOR: Boo Orman
OPEN: Mon to Sat, D only and Sun L
MEALS: 12 to 2, 6.30 to 10.30 (6 to 11 Sat)
PRICES: £11 (£18), Set D £14.90 (£17)
CARDS: Access, Visa
SEATS: 48. Private parties: 30 main room. Vegetarian meals. Children's helpings.
No smoking in one dining-room. Music

McCoy's at York

17 Skeldergate, York YO1 1DH   COOKING 2
YORK (0904) 612191   COST £29

The reception area in this old riverside wood mill is a storey up from the dimly lit restaurant that makes no effort to hide its structure under a layer of sophistication. This is how it should be, but inhabitants of York question whether the price-quality ratio is not in favour of price. Recent reports have indicated a firm hand in the kitchen, worth the price, though Eugene McCoy can only have an executive role. Good soups; fresh and juicy scallops; a blackcurrant sauce with duck that was not the usual fruit preserve but a real stock sauce spiked with sharp currants, are dishes mentioned. The *carte* is supplemented by daily specials chalked on the blackboard: they both explore a bistro repertoire uninfluenced by London developments among lentils and olive oil, but none the less coming up with enjoyable dishes such as mushrooms baked with a prawn mousse filling; black pudding and apple; fresh pasta with scallops and basil; calf's liver and sage; halibut with wild mushrooms; sticky toffee pudding which 'gave a warm glow for the walk back to the hotel on a cold night;' or less impressive chocolate fudge tarte. Details – foil-wrapped butter in a bowl of ice, cheese served 'fridge-cold' – are on the basic side, and the loud music is deafening. The candlelight may be romantic but it thwarts the solo diner who is anxious to read. A brief but decently selected wine list offering a fair and interesting range. House wine: £7.25.

CHEF: Eugene McCoy   PROPRIETORS: Peter, Thomas and Eugene McCoy
OPEN: Mon to Sat
MEALS: 12 to 2.15, 7 to 10.30
PRICES: £18 (£24)
CARDS: Access, Amex, Diners, Visa
SEATS: 100. Private parties: 100 main room. Vegetarian meals. Children's helpings.
Wheelchair access. Music. Air-conditioned

▲ Middlethorpe Hall ♟

Bishopthorpe Road, York YO2 1QP   COOKING 2
YORK (0904) 641241   COST £18–£49

The house next to the race course is spectacular with gardens stretching out to
the back and a stable court giving extra accommodation to one side. Not only
do private visitors feel like lords and ladies if they have bedrooms in the main
building, but also businesspeople must take on the character of merchant
princes and princesses if they use the full range of meeting rooms that are
cannily offered. The need to address a wide public makes life difficult for the
kitchen and the menu lacks any character, save vague modernity. It is
professionally executed, though. The short *carte*, supplemented by daily set-
price meals, revolves around sole, salmon, duck, fillet and foie gras. Some
dishes, such as lentils and lime butter with the duck or salmon baked on sea
salt with a Pernod and saffron sauce, show the mark of the 1990s. More variety
comes from the daily additions, even if one reader commented on the surfeit of
pastry, albeit very good pastry. Service is stately. The wine list, as in all
Historic House Hotels, is magisterial with a great range in age and origin. It is
particularly generous in its provision of halves. The small selection of country
wines from south-western France appears to have been deleted: otherwise
there is little change since the last *Guide*. House wines: £8.70.

CHEF: Kevin Francksen   PROPRIETORS: Historic House Hotels Ltd
OPEN: all week
MEALS: 12.30 to 1.45, 7.30 to 9.45
PRICES: £30 (£41), Set L £13.90 (£18) to £15.90 (£20), Set D £26.90 (£31). Service inc
CARDS: Access, Amex, Diners, Visa
SEATS: 60. Private parties: 40 main room, 14, 20 and 40 private rooms. Car-park, 70 places.
Vegetarian meals. No children under 8. Smrat dress preferred
ACCOMMODATION: 30 rooms, all with bath/shower. Lift. B&B £89 to £138. No children
under 8. Afternoon teas. Garden. TV. Phone. Scenic [*Which? Hotel Guide*]

19 Grape Lane

19 Grape Lane, York YO1 2HU   COOKING 2
YORK (0904) 636366   COST £14–£35

The restaurant occupying two floors of a small house in this cobbled lane full of
smart shops was unfortunately destroyed by fire at the end of 1989 and took
some months of reconstruction before reopening. Reports, therefore, are rather
sparse but first intelligence is that Michael Fraser and Trajan Drew are cooking
and Gordon and Carolyn Alexander are serving as satisfactorily as before the
misfortune. They offer two set menus, which seem to change but slowly, and a

carte of much greater choice. This has not changed in character from before, though it has in detail: fricassee of wild mushrooms; a trio of cured salmon; a lattice of salmon and turbot in filo with saffron and ginger; saddle of lamb with a rosemary and pine kernel crust; guinea-fowl with leeks and mushrooms. The style is modern standard rather than in any way avant garde. Lunches are especially reasonable. The wine list is also undergoing revision as we go to press but offers a small but adequate range for the scale of the restaurant. House wine: £7.95. CELLARMAN'S CHOICE: Santenay, la Maladière 1986, Girardin, £15.85; Gewürztraminer, Bergheim 1987, Deiss, £14.50. More reports, please.

CHEFS: Michael Fraser and Trajan Drew   PROPRIETORS: Gordon and Carolyn Alexander
OPEN: Tue to Sat
CLOSED: 2 weeks Jan and Sept
MEALS: 12.30 to 1.45, 7.30 to 10.30
PRICES: £21 (£29), Set L £8.50 (£14), Set D £16.50 (£23)
SEATS: 34. Private parties: 20 main room. Children welcome. Wheelchair access
(1 step). Music

Scotland

map 8

Silver Darling

Pocra Quay, Footdee, Aberdeen AB2 1DQ
ABERDEEN (0224) 576229

COOKING 2
COST £18–£36

The restaurant is the first building on the quay at the entrance of the harbour. It stands right at the end of North Pier next door to the pilot round-house. The staff is French with one Scot, 'and his accent is becoming blurred'. As befits the setting, the strength of the kitchen is its sparkling-fresh fish and shellfish, often barbecued Provençal-style by Didier Dejean. Readers have praised the grilled oysters with garlic and shallot butter, the seafood brochette and a mixed grill of turbot, monkfish, Pacific prawns and salmon sauced with beurre nantaise. Away from the grill, baby scallops marinière and la mouclade de Charentes, 'mussels cooked to perfection with cream and herbs', have also impressed. Against this, there have been quibbles about lukewarm, inappropriately nouvelle vegetables and the question of why 'superb' tarte Tatin is served with what seems like synthetic cream foam. The coffee is excellent. A very short wine list has bottles from the major French growing regions, but no hint of the growers. They are expensive, French style, and have a poor range of lower priced bins. Champagne is badly served and greedily charged for; perhaps oil has had a bad effect. House Côtes du Rhône, £8.50.

CHEF: Didier Dejean   PROPRIETORS: Didier Dejean, Norman Faulks and Catherine Wood
OPEN: all week, exc Sat L and Sun L, also Sun D Nov to May
MEALS: 12 to 2, 7 to 10
PRICES: £22 (£30), Set L £11 (£18) to 15 (£22)
CARDS: Access, Amex, Visa
SEATS: 35. Private parties: 35 main room. Car-park. Children welcome. Wheelchair access (1 step; also male and female WC). Music

---

'First was the duck confitt (sic). Now you know what you have left on a duck carcass when its been carved - all the titchy grey bits and chunks of gristle? Give a fair handful to a Kindergarten child and tell them to squeeze into a roly-poly with a touch of wallpaper paste. Cut it into three and - hey presto a first course for three people. Three pieces of curly lettuce , a slosh of very good walnut oil and 'there you go' we were told. We should have done' On eating in Wales

▲ *Atkins at Farleyer House*

Aberfeldy PH15 2JE
ABERFELDY (0887) 20332
from Aberfeldy take B846 to
Kinloch Rannoch for 2m

COOKING 3
COST £27–£46

The tourist, like the English invaders of Scotland, approaches this country-house hotel (owned by English people) across one of General Wade's bridges, built after the '45. Farleyer House was in fact the dower house to Menzies Castle, a mile down the Tay Valley. The scenery is magnificent, the emerald lawns setting off the forested slopes. The house itself has a suburban air, imparted perhaps by the draught-proof plate-glass windows, but it is neat and trim and holds a surprise in the well curtained, colourwashed and carpeted interiors; well warmed too, save for the attic floor. The Atkins have done well since their arrival from Buckinghamshire in 1989, though Bill (Gerald) Atkins will still reminisce about Waddesdon and other Bucks villages. Frances Atkins has oversight of the kitchen and has continued to elaborate her original style, though with more than a nod to local ingredients, in particular fish, game and berries. This style is resolutely British in its pursuit of sweet and sour combinations and bold in attempting partnerships of meats within a single dish. At the same time, it uses most kitchen techniques to good advantage – soups, sauces, ices and baking are strong points – though mousses, for once, seem to figure less in reports than in most 1990s menus. An autumn dinner showed some of these ideas in dishes such as wild mushroom tart with a cheese topping and a warm fig salad; charlotte of grouse with blueberry sauce; parsnip and apple soup; a plate of venison with clove and juniper sauce and breast of duck with a bramble sauce; scallops and wine with dauphinois potatoes and artichoke bottoms. There is a school of thought that this is gilding the lily; that the sauces not only left no room for savoury refreshment of the principal ingredient, but were also too crude (the clove and juniper especially); that salt or seasoning was not carefully adjusted to get the right balance, for instance of parsnip over apple in the soup; that the dauphinois had no garlic and did little to help the scallops; and that an amuse-gueule of mango, avocado and paw-paw with a curry mayonnaise and curls of smoked venison is just in bad taste. Equally, there is a strong body of opinion that the kitchen can do little wrong (except offer the diner poor cutlery). A first course of scallop mousseline, bouchée of mussels, a langoustine with a rouille sauce, and a little brioche on a bed of samphire was 'an extraordinary confluence of taste'. Escalope of pigeon breast offered with crisped duck breast with pistachio nuts and an apple and brandy sauce; scallops with an artichoke gratin; and saddle of lamb rolled in oatmeal and barley and stuffed with a carrot purée have been very well received, as have desserts such as a chocolate marquise with curaçao sauce; a pear-filled brioche with raspberries and a perfect cream sauce soaking into the buttery crust; or a fruit salad of pineapple, fig, raspberries, strawberries and grapes with balls of four different sorbets and a crisp pancake to one side. In contrast, there is also a complete menu of plain foods – the reverse of the coin, so to speak – to which sybarites, tiring of several days of multi-meated extravagance, may retreat. Incidentals are well thought out though the bread may be under-seasoned (thus solid) and the aspic nibbles with drinks made a little far in advance. Breakfasts and afternoon teas for those staying at the house are fair indicators of the quality of dinner or lunch. Bill Atkins has been buying wines from many sources, the list offering something for everyone. Indeed, any list which includes the excellent Bruno Paillard Champagne 1983, Ch. Cissac 1978 and a spread of the Mâconnais from Vincent all at fair prices deserves attention. House French: £8.50. CELLARMAN'S CHOICE: Chablis, premier cru, Fourchaume 1987, £22.50; Santenay 1976, Maufoux, £23.50.

CHEFS: Frances Atkins and Tony Heath   PROPRIETORS: Gerald and Frances Atkins
OPEN: Tue to Sun L, all week D
MEALS: 12.30 to 1.30, 7.30 to 8.30
PRICES: Set L £20 (£27), Set D £30 (£38)
CARDS: Amex, Visa
SEATS: 30. Private parties: 30 main room, 12 private room. Car-park, 14 places. No children under 10. Smart dress preferred. Wheelchair access (also WC). Music
ACCOMMODATION: 12 rooms, all with bath/shower. Rooms for disabled. B&B £65 to £150. Deposit: 20%. No children under 10. Pets welcome. Garden. Fishing. Golf. TV. Phone. Scenic. Doors close at midnight. Confirm by noon day before [*Which? Hotel Guide*]

ABERFOYLE Central   map 8

Braeval Old Mill ♥

By Aberfoyle, Stirling FK8 3UY
ABERFOYLE (087 72) 711
on A81, 1m from Aberfoyle

COOKING 3
COST £19–£35

The Nairns' lovingly renovated watermill stands a mile outside the village against the backdrop of the Menteith Hills. The conversion is skilful and stylish, offsetting the spartan grey flagstone floors with vibrant collages on the walls and colourful decorative touches. Nick Nairn spent a short 'busman's holiday' with Marco Pierre White at Harvey's (see entry, London) at the beginning of 1990, and has been an 'observer' at Peat Inn (see Peat Inn); his cooking continues to improve. He is now progressing confidently – offering artful soufflés as starters and sweets, filling filo pastry baskets with mussels and sea clams, making sauces from marinades. Recommendations have come in for both classic and ambitious modern dishes: game terrine with onion marmalade; red pepper mousse with tomato and basil; fillet of turbot with sorrel sauce; seafood fricassee with saffron and chives. Marinated fillet of lamb might be served on lentil and apricot purée or ranged round a pile of deep-fried leek shreds. Desserts vary from a mixed plate of lemon sweets, including a hot soufflé in a lemon shell, a tart and a sorbet (perhaps 'observed' at Harvey's) to layered raspberry and pear pudding. There are echoes of the Auld Alliance in the plates of French cheeses with oatcakes and fruit. The wine list, just like the cooking, shows every sign of improvement year by year. It is an even-handed choice. France and other regions all get their chance to show their paces at prices that are very acceptable. Nor is there any stinting on halves. Growers are nicely chosen. House wine: £7.50. CELLARMAN'S CHOICE: Ch. Constantin, Graves 1986, £17.95; R.H. Phillips, Semillon 1985, £11.95.

CHEF: Nick Nairn   PROPRIETORS: Nick and Fiona Nairn
OPEN: Tue to Sun, D only and Sun L
CLOSED: 2 weeks Feb, 1 week May to June, 2 weeks Nov
MEALS: 12 to 1.30, 7 to 9.30
PRICES: £21 (£29), Set L £13.95 (£19)
CARDS: Access, Amex, Visa
SEATS: 34. Private parties: 34 main room. Car-park, 16 places. No children under 10.
No cigars/pipes in dining-room. Wheelchair access (1 step; also male and female WC)

ACHILTIBUIE Highland   map 8

▲ *Summer Isles Hotel* ♟

Achiltibuie IV26 2YG
ACHILTIBUIE (085 482) 282   COOKING 2
26m N of Ullapool, last 15m on single-track road   COST £37

'At the tables where a stranger is received, neither plenty nor delicacy is
wanting,' remarked Dr Johnson on his trip round the Western Isles, and as
others travelling the west coast in modern style might occasionally quote. Here,
far down a tongue of land shooting into the Minch, the Irvines themselves
remark, 'There's a marvellous amount of nothing to do' – and they set
themselves the task of feeding large breakfasts and dinners (for all at once) to
guests who walk, watch birds or fish. The five-course dinner includes cheese
and is no-choice. It is explained in detail by Mark Irvine. First is invariably a
soup, served with a loaf of bread: walnut one night, berrymeal the next,
buckwheat and caraway the third. Meat will follow fish, or sometimes the
reverse, then cheese, then a choice of three substantial puddings or an ice. The
formula and location can be intoxicating. 'We stayed three nights; 30 would not
have been long enough.' The air of self-sufficiency, reinforced by the
hydroponicum, which produces post-modern vegetables, the power generated
by solar panels, is occasionally punctured by produce that bears the mark of
slow Scottish supply lines, but Chris Firth-Bernard's cooking usually has a
strong sense of place with dishes of salmon, scallops, squat lobster, venison
and beef. The treatment is not just Highland: spinach and fennel soup comes
with a leek and onion scone; turbot, lemon sole and squat lobsters are cooked
with white wine and tarragon; goose is roast with prunes and a sauce of its
liver; venison comes with bacon and juniper and a port wine gravy. Vegetables
show invention: broccoli with leek and anchovy, beans with walnut oil and
sesame seeds, different sorts of potato each night. The recruitment of kitchen
help may further ensure that standards are kept. Lunch and snacks are
available all day for the peckish in the adjoining café. Mark Irvine is as keen
and helpful about his wine as his cheese. There has been an expansion of New
World bottles to redress the prices of classic French wines, including some
Chilean reds and examples from Australia by Penfolds. As stocks are reduced,
the maturity of burgundies and clarets is getting close to the acceptable
minimum, but they have restrained themselves from increasing the prices of
their fully mature stocks from year to year. It is not, however, a cheap list.
CELLARMAN'S CHOICE: Los Vascos, Cabernet Sauvignon 1987, £10.50;
Savigny, Lavières 1983, Tollot-Beaut, £17.50.

CHEF: Chris Firth-Bernard PROPRIETORS: Mark and Geraldine Irvine
OPEN: all week, D only
CLOSED: mid-Oct to Easter
MEALS: 8
PRICES: Set D £25 (£31). Service inc
SEATS: 28. Private parties: 8 main room. Car-park, 24 places. No children under 8.
No smoking. One sitting
ACCOMMODATION: 13 rooms, 12 with bath/shower. B&B £34 to £70. No children under 8.
Pets welcome. Afternoon teas. Fishing. Scenic. Doors close at 10.30. Confirm by 6 [*Which?*
Hotel Guide]

ANSTRUTHER Fife   map 8

Cellar 🍷

24 East Green, Anstruther KY10 3AA   COOKING 3
ANSTRUTHER (0333) 310378   COST £16–£32

The Cellar takes its food seriously in pleasingly unpretentious surroundings.
You enter via a small courtyard; the tables are treadle bases of old sewing
machines; exposed beams support the low ceiling; the walls remain rough
stone and the floor bare tiles. The fish is supreme. At lunch there is a short and
inexpensive *carte*; at dinner a four-course set-price menu with seven or eight
choices. The majority are fish-based, but there is lamb or a chicken liver pâté,
and a fruit terrine. The food is accurately cooked and treated with discretion.
This is not display cooking nor, in one sense, inspired. It does very well what
all chefs ought to aspire to: complement wonderful raw materials with
methods and accompaniments that allow them to speak with their own voice.
Crayfish and mussel bisque; a small omelette filled with smoked haddock;
turbot and scallops with a Chardonnay sauce; halibut with sauce hollandaise;
langoustines with garlic butter; home-made gravlax; and salmon with
asparagus, wrapped in pastry with a lemon sauce are some of the dishes that
have received repeated mention. It is not a large repertoire but it does not need
to be. A spiced apple strudel, a couple of sauced ice-creams (for example
pineapple with a crème de cacao sauce), or a crème brûlée will round off the
meal. The very lengthy wine list is good value and offers much enjoyment for
comparative drinkers: 20 New World Chardonnays; a dozen Alsace
Gewürztraminers; a dozen Chablis; a dozen Rioja are some of the groups that
may be studied. Other types get little showing. Peter Jukes is an enthusiast
who will take you through the cellar with skill – even if one party found the
wines being served too iced. The properties and growers on show are
exemplary and some consideration has been given to price range, as well as
provision of half-bottles. House Rioja and Muscadet start at £8.50.

CHEF: Peter Jukes PROPRIETORS: Peter and Vivien Jukes
OPEN: Mon to Sat, exc Mon L (Tue to Sat in winter)
CLOSED: 2 weeks at Christmas and New Year, 1 week May
MEALS: 12.30 to 1.30, 7 to 9.30
PRICES: £11 (£16), Set D £25 (£29). Service inc
CARDS: Access, Amex, Visa
SEATS: 32. Private parties: 32 main room. Vegetarian meals by arrangement. No children
under 5. No smoking. Wheelchair access (also WC). Music

AUCHMITHIE Tayside

map 8

But 'n' ben

Auchmithie DD11 5SO	COOKING 1
ARBROATH (0241) 77223	COST £10–£30

A fisherman's cottage, all white, with quarry-tiled floor, houses this simple restaurant serving 'traditional Scottish food' at three meals: lunch, high tea and dinner. It has taken in an extra room to give space for pre-dinner drinks, and tables are given an evening dress of linen and lace; but that does not disguise a real attempt to give value at all stages in the day and to showcase home baking and supplies of fresh fish from Arbroath boats. The fish at lunchtime may come plain with a baked potato and a salad with three dressings, but in the evening is more likely to involve a cream sauce. Arbroath smokies are as good as anyone might want, 'and at ridiculously low prices.' It is small wonder that the London visitors at one lunch polished off two bottles of Champagne, listed at £12.60. However, others have found that changing vintages and labels have not been so well handled: the list needs to be kept more nearly up to date. House wine from Bordeaux is £5.50.

CHEFS: Margaret and Angus Horn PROPRIETORS: Margaret, Iain and Angus Horn
OPEN: all week, exc Tue and Sun D
MEALS: 12 to 2.30, 7.30 to 9.30 (high tea 4 to 6)
PRICES: L £7 (£10), D £12 (£25), tea £5.50. Service inc
CARDS: Access, Amex, Diners, Visa
SEATS: 34. 2 tables outside. Private parties: 40 main room. Car-park, 10 places. Vegetarian meals. Children's helpings. Wheelchair access (also male and female WC)

BALLATER Grampian

map 8

▲ Tullich Lodge

Ballater AB3 5SB	
BALLATER (03397) 55406	COOKING 2
on A93 1m E of Ballater	COST £10–£29

'23rd season' proclaims the wine list – and Hector Macdonald and Neil Bannister have been ploughing their own furrow since opening, compromising little and pursuing their ideas of hospitality and sustenance. 'The proprietors really care, taking active interest in everything, delivering early morning tea, for example,' writes one who has been visiting almost since its inception. The grand Scottish baronial house preserves a Victorian feel, reinforced by the small gilt-edged menu cards that detail the four-course set meal to be served in the panelled dining-room. It is British food: marinated smoked herring with avocado; carrot soup lightly spiced; beef hot-pot with creamy beetroot; gooseberry pie; elderflower wine and cream or Scottish cheeses. Smoking is done in a wardrobe in the garden, 'a real tang of oak smoke, but none of the overdry texture so often found with home-smoking.' Long-cooked dishes are a pleasure: braised ox-tail with potatoes and spring cabbage; home-made haggis, 'not a rough porridgey stodge.' The cooking never falls into the pit of over-decoration or elaboration; some would say it is in its own declivity of

542

understatement. This is a personal enterprise and not all characters will match it. The wine list, about 50 bins, is extremely well chosen and not impossibly priced. It is all French bar a pair each from Germany, Italy and Spain. There are sufficient halves. House wine: £7. CELLARMAN'S CHOICE: Fixin 1986, Mongeard-Mugneret, £17; Mâcon-Clessé, Dom. de la Bongran 1986, £13.

CHEFS: Neil Bannister and Steven Lawson PROPRIETORS: Hector Macdonald and Neil Bannister
OPEN: all week
CLOSED: Dec to end Mar
MEALS: 1, 7.30 to 8.30
PRICES: Set L £6 (£10), Set D £20 (£24). Service inc
CARDS: Access, Amex, Diners, Visa
SEATS: 26. Private parties: 10 main room. Car-park. Vegetarian meals. Children's helpings (L only). Smart dress preferred. No smoking in dining-room. Wheelchair access (also WC)
ACCOMMODATION: 10 rooms, all with bath/shower. B&B £60 to £120. Baby facilities. Pets welcome. Garden. TV. Phone. Scenic. Confirm by 5

BLAIRGOWRIE Tayside   map 8

▲ *Kinloch House Hotel*

Blairgowrie PH10 6SG
ESSENDY (025 084) 237
on A923, 3m W of Blairgowrie

COOKING 2
COST £9–£26

A fine old Scottish country house, with paintings, oak-panelled hall and staircases leading up to the first-floor galleries. Rhododendrons line the drive and cattle graze in the fields nearby. The kitchen specialises in country hotel cooking of the old school with steaks, salmon and game holding centre stage. Some of the more ambitious dishes carry supplements. Visitors have enjoyed the grilled sardines, marinated salmon, whole juicy West Coast lobster and 'the best partridge I have ever had outside my own house, with everything that should accompany it'. Vegetables are freshly cooked and 'uncontrived'. The sweets trolley is usually impressive, although one reporter noted 'meringues the size of footballs and stale chocolate sponge roulade'. David Shentall insists on smart dress – ties are obligatory – but despite this formality, service is friendly and unobstrusive. The wine list is strong on vintage clarets going back to the 1970s. There is a good showing of half-bottles, some notable vintage ports and a whisky drinker's paradise of 134 malts.

CHEF: Bill McNicoll PROPRIETORS: David and Sarah Shentall
OPEN: all week
MEALS: 12.30 to 2, 7 to 9.15
PRICES: Set L £5.50 (£9) to 12.50 (£16), Set D £18.50 (£22). Service inc
CARDS: Access, Amex, Diners, Visa
SEATS: 60. Private parties: 30 main room, 25 and 30 private rooms. Car-park, 40 places. No children under 7. Smart dress preferred. No smoking in dining-room. Wheelchair access (also WC)
ACCOMMODATION: 21 rooms, all with bath/shower. Rooms for disabled. B&B £40.50 to £75. Baby facilities. Pets welcome. Garden. Fishing. Phone. Scenic. Doors close at midnight. Confirm by 6 [*Which? Hotel Guide*]

CAIRNDOW Strathclyde	map 8

Loch Fyne Oyster Bar

Clachan Farm, Cairndow PA26 8BH	COOKING 2
CAIRNDOW (049 96) 217 and 264	COST £19

Smokehouse, produce shop with home delivery service, and café-cum-restaurant with breathtaking views down the loch stand all in one group. Sit inside or out for all-day service and enjoy fresh fish. 'An unexpected delight was the Oyster Bar at the head of the loch. Naturally the *fines claires* were delicious but most impressive was the gigantic plate of langoustines,' reports one who fell on the place by serendipity. There is not a lot of cooking and not much meat, but there is smoked chicken or venison and venison sausages if you have surfeited on fish. Otherwise, take oysters, smoked salmon, gravlax, smoked mackerel, or dressed crab cold, or langoustines, kippers, herring or haddock if needing something hot. Scottish cheeses, home-made bread and shortbread and espresso coffee complete the meal. There is a carefully chosen set of wines and half a dozen trendy beers. The house white got a strong negative from one visitor but the Pouilly Fumé is decent, as is the Manzanilla. Prices, for food and wine, are sensational and the service nearly always cheerful. A branch has been opened in Nottingham (see entry).

CHEF: Greta Cameron   PROPRIETORS: Loch Fyne Oysters Ltd
OPEN: all week
MEALS: 9 to 9
PRICES: £11 (£16)
CARDS: Access, Amex, Visa
SEATS: 80. 10 tables outside. Private parties: 55 main room. Car-park, 80 places. Children's helpings on request. Wheelchair access (also unisex WC)

CANONBIE Dumfries & Galloway	map 8

▲ *Riverside Inn*

Canonbie DG14 0UX	COOKING 2
CANONBIE (038 73) 71512 and 71295	COST £14–£27

Had the Riverside existed in Hadrian's time, perhaps the route of the wall would have shifted to incorporate it. Robert and Susan Phillips have been running this pub/restaurant for several years with much acclaim: the press of business is very great and 'one feels Mrs Phillips has a lot to worry her.' Food is available at the bar as well as in the restaurant for the more formal set-price dinners. The cooking has British substance, although drawing on modern restaurant ideas to give it variety. The bar may invariably offer soup, though many sorts are made through the year, and a range of pâtés. The main courses are very interesting: home-made venison or duck sausages; tripe and onions; beef in beer with fresh pasta; fried lamb's sweetbreads; and puddings like apple and marmalade pie or 'Mother's butterscotch custard bake'. Cheeses, here and in the restaurant, are few in number, farmhouse, British, and good. The restaurant has a slightly different repertoire: char with ginger and spring onions; pheasant with apples and calvados and rowanberry jelly; lamb with a bacon and parsley pudding; always four vegetables, often in some variant way such as carrots tossed in hazelnut oil, artichokes in parsley sauce, or 'Molly Parkin' parsnips. The only observed drawback has been the interpretation of *al dente* as on the hard side. Puddings are still large and sometimes untidy: 'I was glad that others resorted to fingers for their meringue with chocolate sauce, messy but good.' 'Tipping is discouraged.' There are several real ales on weekly rota and the wine list has a good range starting at well under £10. Note Vialard's Haut Médoc, La Vieille Ferme Côtes du Ventoux, Deiss Alsaces, Penfold's Dalwood Shiraz, and the Tinto de Crianza from Bodegas Ribero Duero. House wine is £6.85 and there is a 'wine of the month' offering something off the list at reduced price as well as by the glass.

CHEFS/PROPRIETORS: Robert and Susan Phillips
OPEN: Mon to Sat
CLOSED: 2 weeks Feb and Nov
MEALS: 12 to 2, 7.30 to 8.30
PRICES: Bar L £10 (£14), Set D £17.50 (£23)
CARDS: Access, Visa
SEATS: 28. 4 tables outside. Private parties: 28 main room. Car-park, 25 places. Children's helpings. No smoking in dining-room. Wheelchair access (also WC)
ACCOMMODATION: 6 rooms, all with bath/shower. Rooms for disabled. B&B £40 to £60. Deposit: £15. No children under 10. Garden. Fishing. TV. Scenic. Doors close at 11. Confirm by 5

CRINAN Strathclyde   map 8

▲ *Lock 16 Seafood Restaurant, Crinan Hotel*

Crinan PA31 8SR   COOKING 1
CRINAN (054 683) 261   COST £46

Seafood is landed 50 yards from Nick Ryan's kitchen. It is prepared or cooked and dispatched to the blue-and-white dining-room to be savoured, along with panoramic sea and island views, by an expectant crowd. Simplicity is the watchword, and choice on the five-course set menu is almost non-existent. A summer menu ran thus: Loch Craignish mussels marinière or cantaloupe melon; locally smoked salmon; then the speciality, jumbo prawns from the Gulf of Corryvreckan, sizzling in copper pans with tropical fruit; assorted berries with cream; Stilton with oatcakes and coffee. A winter visitor was content with the formula: 'Even something simple, like roast parsnips, is splendid.' Service is good, though it may be interrupted by the demands of the coastguard, of which Nick Ryan is a member. If the weather is rough and no fresh seafood is available, solace must be sought in the Telford Restaurant in the hotel below. A decent wine list canters through most areas with a few gems on the way; all are fairly priced. House French is £9.50. CELLARMAN'S CHOICE: Chassagne Montrachet, Louis Latour 1987, £29.25.

See the inside of the front cover for an explanation of the 1 to 5 rating system recognising cooking standards.

CHEF: Nick Ryan PROPRIETORS: Nick and Frances Ryan
OPEN: Tue to Sat, D only (L by arrangement)
MEALS: 8
PRICES: Set D £30 (£38)
CARDS: Access, Visa
SEATS: 22. Private parties: 22 main room. Car-park, 30 places. Vegetarian meals. Children
welcome. Smart dress preferred. Wheelchair access (also WC). One sitting
ACCOMMODATION: 22 rooms, all with bath/shower. Rooms for disabled. Lift. B&B £42.50
to £85. Deposit: £50 for first-time guests. Baby facilities. Pets welcome. Afternoon teas.
Garden. Fishing. Phone. Scenic. Doors close at midnight. Confirm by 6 [*Which? Hotel Guide*]

CROMARTY Highland   map 8

Thistles

20 Church Street, Cromarty IV11 8XA   COOKING 2
CROMARTY (038 17) 471   COST £28

Thistles used to be called Le Chardon; the plant is the same. The Wilkinsons
have crossed the country from Arisaig House, settling easily into the
picturesque town and harbour that look over the Scotland of oil and ore. The
restaurant was once a pub, now arranged as a bar with Lloyd Loom chairs,
progressing on to a small dining-room with a cast-iron and tiled fireplace. At
lunch there is a short, light menu at prices that are no more than most cafés,
save on Sundays when David Wilkinson roasts the joint. In the evenings, the
short *carte* offers maybe four alternatives at each stage. The cooking stops short
of wild invention yet is not rooted in ancient practice. Sauces are light and
flavours are clear in such dishes as salmon with cream cheese and watercress
mousse; smoked salmon with chicory and a lemon butter sauce; pork fillet
with white wine, sage and orange; turbot en papillote; a warm gratin of
strawberries and orange; or home-made grape and brandy ice-cream. Soups
have been approved, as in a lettuce soup with depth and decent seasoning, and
the unctuous crème brûlée. The wine list makes a resounding start in a tenure
of less than a year, offering a fair range generously balanced by half-bottles at
reasonable prices. There are already 30-odd bin-ends. The Alsaces from Kuentz
Bas, Stag's Leap Californian Cabernet Sauvignon and Chardonnay and Maby's
Rhônes are some that attract among a choice that stops short of the very best
makers but is more than adequate for the task at hand. House French £7.50.

CHEF: David Wilkinson PROPRIETORS: Alison and David Wilkinson
OPEN: Tue to Sun, exc Sun D (L limited in winter)
MEALS: 12 to 2, 7.30 to 9
PRICES: £17 (£23)
CARDS: Access, Visa
SEATS: 26. Private parties: 30 main room. Vegetarian meals Sat L. Children's helpings.
No smoking

The Guide *office can quickly spot when a restaurateur is encouraging customers to write
recommending inclusion - and sadly, several restaurants have been doing this in 1990.
Such reports do not further a restaurant's cause. Please tell us if a restaurateur invites you
to write to the* Guide.

CUPAR Fife   map 8

Ostlers Close

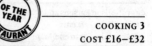

25 Bonnygate, Cupar KY15 4BU   COOKING 3
CUPAR (0334) 55574   COST £16–£32

'Two young enthusiasts establishing a high reputation', is how one reader
summoned up the diligent efforts of Amanda and James Graham. After 10
years in the business their achievement is due precisely to two reasons: they
unite the best local produce in their kitchen – fish from Pittenweem, fruit,
ducks and guinea-fowl from the farms, and game from the estates – and they
create menus that draw on this rich bounty to the fullest effect. Herbs and some
vegetables are organic and from their own garden. Chutneys and jellies are
made from fruits picked in the surrounding countryside. According to James
Graham, who does the cooking, 'We don't purposely avoid heavy use of cream
and butter, but feel we reach a balance that allows other interesting flavours to
come through.' Those flavours may be found in local asparagus served in pastry
on a garden chervil sauce or in roast farm duck on a bed of green lentils with a
coriander sauce. Service is 'informal and friendly'. The wine list is judicious
but lacks detail; it includes quite a few half-bottles. House French is £6.40.

CHEF: James Graham   PROPRIETORS: Amanda and James Graham
OPEN: Tue to Sat
MEALS: 12.15 to 2, 7 to 9.30
PRICES: L £10 (£16), D £20 (£27). Minimum £10
CARDS: Access, Visa
SEATS: 28. Private parties: 20 main room. Children's helpings on request. No children
under 6 at D. No smoking during meals. Wheelchair access (1 step; also WC)

DRUMNADROCHIT Highland   map 8

▲ *Polmaily House Hotel*

Drumnadrochit IV3 6XT   COOKING 2
DRUMNADROCHIT (045 62) 343   COST £20–£30

The drive has been tarmacked and the drawing-room redecorated, but the
personality of the Parsons' country house, a few miles up Glen Urquhart, has
lost none of its comfortable feel. Fresh, local ingredients are the culinary
hallmarks of two set menus, one good value with three courses and no choice
until the dessert, the other running to five courses with a choice of main dish
and discounts for omitting one or two courses. In the spring the menu
comprised cream of prawn, sweet pepper and ginger soup, Kinloch Rannoch
smoked venison with melon, hot mousseline of halibut with mussel sauce,
roast lamb with tomato and garlic (the alternative was baked wild salmon with
sorrel sauce), and apple ice-cream in a meringue basket with blackcurrant
sauce (strawberry meringue vacherin was the other choice). There's more
choice in the drinks department, with nearly a hundred mainly French wines,
many from good years and most with kindly mark-ups. Good names, especially
from Burgundy, give a reliable look to the list and there are many decent half-

bottles. House claret is £6.50. CELLARMAN'S CHOICE: Rouge Homme Coonawarra Chardonnay, £13.95; Raimat Cabernet Sauvignon, £9.75.

CHEFS: Alison Parsons and Barbara Drury   PROPRIETORS: Alison and Nick Parsons
OPEN: all week, D only
CLOSED: mid-Oct to end Mar
MEALS: 7.30 to 9.30
PRICES: Set D £15 (£20) to £20 (£25). Minimum £15. Service inc
CARDS: Access, Visa
SEATS: 30. Private parties: 12 main room. Car-park, 20 places. Vegetarian meals. Children's helpings by arrangement. No smoking in dining-room. Wheelchair access
ACCOMMODATION: 9 rooms, 7 with bath/shower. B&B £35 to £80. Deposit: £25. Baby facilities. Garden. Swimming-pool. Tennis. Scenic. Doors close at midnight. Confirm by 4
[*Which? Hotel Guide*]

DRYBRIDGE Grampian   map 8

Old Monastery

Drybridge AB5 2JB
BUCKIE (0542) 32660   COOKING 1
2m S of junction A98 and A924   COST £31

Dominican monks from Fort Augustus built this spare Gothic complex as a retreat at the beginning of this century. The site is even more remarkable, and the view sensational. Eating is in the chapel, drinking is in the cloisters, now roofed over. The menu includes produce more recognisably Scottish than some of the cooking methods – venison, salmon, scallops, beef are often with garlic and tomato, though rowanberry sauce goes with the venison. Materials can be very good, though quiet times may see them lacking original flavour. Some of the presentation and finish squares with the natural simplicity that best brings out taste. The Grays are willing and forthcoming hosts and, while they continue to make the building less monastic, its austerity is in tune with the landscape. The wine list grows a little each year and remains a good model of a general list with something for everyone, including a fair measure of halves, dessert wines and reasonable prices. There are some bargains among the clarets. House wines start at £5.75.

CHEF: Douglas Gray   PROPRIETORS: Douglas and Maureen Gray
OPEN: Tue to Sat
CLOSED: 2 weeks Nov, 3 weeks Jan
MEALS: 12 to 2, 7 to 9.30 (10 Sat)
PRICES: £19 (£26)
CARDS: Access, Amex, Visa
SEATS: 45. 2 tables outside. Private parties: 45 main room. Car-park, 28 places. Children's helpings. No children under 8. No smoking in dining-room. Wheelchair access

---

The 1992 Guide will be published before Christmas 1991. Reports on meals are most welcome at any time of the year, but are extremely valuable in the spring. Send them to The Good Food Guide, *FREEPOST, 2 Marylebone Road, London NW1 1YN. No stamp is needed if posted in the UK.*

DUNKELD Tayside   map 8

▲ *Kinnaird House*

Kinnaird Estate, By Dunkeld PH8 0LB
BALLINLUIG (079 682) 440   COOKING 4
on B898, 4m NW of Dunkeld   COST £20–£42

A reader suggests purchasing sheet 53 (Blairgowrie) of the Ordnance Survey:
the Tay, he says, is the epicentre of Scottish gastronomy, but all these country
properties are hard to find. He had driven past Kinnaird's discreet gate on the
B898 four times. Both dining-rooms have remarkable views. The main one was
once the drawing-room and has painted landscape panels, chandeliers,
generous tables and appointments. Dinner is a set-price menu of five choices in
each course. The price includes everything, from mineral water to cheese to
coffee and petits fours. The menu states 'service charge is neither included nor
anticipated'. At lunch there is a pair of choices, again for 'a palpable bargain'
set price; the options may be extended by paying a supplement for a dish from
the main menu. Visitors have been uniformly impressed by the accuracy and
finesse of the cooking, which does not go in for redundant trimmings or
outrageous combinations. It is modern in slant, leaning towards neo-classical
French rather than 'granny cuisine' or new-wave Italian, to talk in culinary
clichés. It is prepared to extract flavour from simple foods, hence a carrot
mousse served as an amuse-gueule, and it is not too besotted by luxuries.
Recommendations have included a ragout of seafood with Pernod, tarragon
and cream; a guinea-fowl 'sausage' with wild mushrooms and truffle; apple
and parsnip soup; calf's liver with watercress and tarragon sauce; boned quail
wrapped in bacon on tartlets of creamed leek, with red wine sauce; glazed
pears in caramel cream sauce; hot mango soufflé with mango ice-cream; and a
caramelised prune tart. The kitchens are in the basement so for once the silver
domes have their point. The wine list does no disservice to the food. It is best
for claret and red burgundy, though it does not ignore newer territories or
lesser regions. There is not a lot below £15. House wine: £11 and £12.
CELLARMAN'S CHOICE: Brouilly, Ch. des Tours 1988, £17.20; Muscat d'Alsace
1987, Rolly Gassmann, £18.60. The nine bedrooms have been opened since the
last *Guide*.

CHEF: John Webber   PROPRIETOR: C.C. Ward
OPEN: Tue to Sun, exc Sun D
CLOSED: 25 Dec D
MEALS: 12.30 to 2, 7.30 to 9.15
PRICES: Set L £14.50 (£20) to £18 (£24), Set D £29.50 (£35)
SEATS: 35. Private parties: 25 main room, 25 private room. Car-park, 50 places. No children
under 12. No smoking in dining-room. Wheelchair access (also WC)
ACCOMMODATION: 9 rooms, all with bath/shower. Rooms for disabled. Lift. B&B £95 to
£130. Deposit: 10%. No children under 12. Garden. Tennis. Fishing. Snooker. TV. Phone.
Scenic. Confirm by 6

*County Round-ups, listing additional restaurants that may be worth a visit, are at the back
of the* Guide, *after the Irish section. Reports on Round-up entries are welcome.*

DUNVEGAN Isle of Skye   map 8

Three Chimneys

Colbost, Dunvegan IV55 8ZT
GLENDALE (047 081) 258   COOKING 2
on B884, 4m W of Dunvegan   COST £20–£40

A restaurant located on a single-track road to the north-west tip of Skye may
not seem the ideal place to make your fortune, but the Spears are having a stab
at it and the gathering of tourists to sample Shirley Spear's cooking is a witness
to their reputation. The crofter's cottage is split between two beamed rooms –
pleasantly cool on a hot summer's night – and a tiny wine shop and off-licence
where three people seem a crowd. Lunchtime sees a lighter menu at about half
the cost of dinner with more obviously traditional Scots food: an emphasis on
haddock, oats and crab. Dinner may also have a Scottish tilt, with lots of local
shellfish, but takes on a resolutely metropolitan feel from a determined
combination of meat, fish and fruit which does not always, to some palates,
work to the benefit of the ingredients. A spring menu had pigeon breast with
claret and raspberries, a Skye prawn (langoustine) cocktail with lime and
avocado, hare with prunes, venison with cranberries and halibut with
strawberries. The outside world proclaimed its influence again with baby corn,
the bane of many a vegetable course, appearing with potatoes, mange-tout and
carrots. Cooking is certainly enthusiastic and fresh. Sometimes it has ideas that
would fit a sophisticated picture book but presents them in a homely way with
slip-ups occurring in the balancing of main ingredient and subsidiary flavour.
There are normally three steak dishes, one with home-made mustard, a second
with mushrooms, garlic and 'a hint of orange'. The third, with smoked salmon
sandwiched by a sirloin, is a Skye version of surf and turf. The beef has not
invariably been well-hung. Puddings are on the blackboard and will include
hot ones: marmalade pudding precipitated 'a real danger of being unable to
walk afterwards but was well worth the risk.' People have noticed prices
creeping up and continue to observe that service is reticent and at a gentle pace.
The cooking has to be very good to bring off some of its daring combinations.
The wine list is five dozen nicely chosen items, good Marlboroughs from New
Zealand, C.V.N.E. from Spain as well as some thoroughbred French at
accessible prices. House wines, very carefully chosen, start at £7.45, and are all
available by the glass. CELLARMAN'S CHOICE: Riesling Reserve 1987,
Schlumberger £12.45; Moulin-à-Vent, Dom. de la Bruyère 1987, R. Siffert,
£13.95.

CHEF: Shirley Spear   PROPRIETORS: Eddie and Shirley Spear
OPEN: Mon to Sat, plus Sun D
CLOSED: Nov to end Mar
MEALS: 12.30 to 2, 7 to 9
PRICES: L £13 (£20), D £24 (£33). Minimum £2 L, £12.50 D
CARDS: Access, Visa
SEATS: 35. 2 tables outside. Private parties: 24 main room. Car-park, 30 places. Vegetarian
meals. Children welcome. No smoking. Music

Chinese Home Cooking

21 Argyle Place, EH9 1JJ   COOKING 1
031-229 4404   COST £6−£10

'It must be one of the cheapest restaurants in the *Guide*,' writes one enthusiastic
supporter, 'though it certainly deserves an entry.' The name says it all. This
modest converted shop provides ample sustenance for students and local
inhabitants of Edinburgh's bed-sit land. There's not much decor to speak of but
the food is honest, no-frills home cooking produced with care. The menu may
read like 'items you have loved from your local take-away', but the results are
anything but ordinary. Barbecued spare ribs look as if they have been cut 'from
a mastodon', huge sweet-and-sour prawns are a world away from the usual
tasteless kind; and red-cooked char siu pork comes with plenty of firm fresh
mushrooms. Unlicensed, but there is no corkage charge if you bring your own.

CHEF/PROPRIETOR: Steven Chan
OPEN: all week, D only
MEALS: 5.30 to 11
PRICES: £7 (£8), Set D £5.50 (£6). Unlicensed; bring your own, no corkage
SEATS: 40. Private parties: 30 main room. Children welcome. No-smoking area

Indian Cavalry Club

3 Atholl Place, EH3 8HP   COOKING 1
031-228 3282   COST £11−£30

A stylish restaurant with a lot of pastel drapes, all the staff in para-military
uniforms, and a Tiffin Room for snacks. The menu thoughtfully suggests side
dishes and apposite wines for main selections. The wine list is well above
average for most Indian restaurants. The menu even plays with novelties such
as garlic nan or smoked salmon rice. Portions are not large, so side dishes are
almost inevitable. A meal of East Indian seafood soup, green herb lamb,
tandoori king prawns, garlic nan, lemon rice, mushroom bhaji and aloo gobi
showed no reticence in the use of coriander or garlic, nor in chillies with the
king prawns, though it fell down in the little sawdust-like curls of prawn in
the seafood and in the similarity of spicing in the vegetable dishes. The lamb
was very good. One reader commented that this was food as heavily influenced
by British 'brasserie' concepts as traditional Indian cooking. Another remarked
that vegetarians, though seemingly well served according to the menu, might
find the standards of cooking sadly inconsistent. House French from Ropiteau
is £6.20.

The Guide *office can quickly spot when a restaurateur is encouraging customers to write
recommending inclusion - and sadly, several restaurants have been doing this in 1990.
Such reports do not further a restaurant's cause. Please tell us if a restaurateur invites you
to write to the* Guide.

Report forms are at the back of the book; write a letter if you prefer.

CHEF: Bilquis Chowdhury   PROPRIETORS: Shahid and Bilquis Chowdhury
OPEN: all week
MEALS: 12 to 2.30, 5.30 to 11.30
PRICES: £13 (£21), Set L £5.95 (£11) to £10 (£16), Set D £12.95 (£19) to £18.95 (£25).
Minimum £5
CARDS: Access, Amex, Diners, Visa
SEATS: 63. 16 tables outside. Private parties: 70 main room, 30 and 30 private rooms.
Vegetarian meals. Children's helpings (weekends only). Smart dress preferred.
No-smoking area. Wheelchair access (2 steps; also WC)

Kalpna

2–3 St Patrick Square, EH8 9EZ   COOKING 1
031-667 9890   COST £7–£16

'The word Kalpna means imagination – or rather a combination of imagination
and creation,' says a note on the menu. Most people are entirely won over by
the cooking and its commitment to the vegetarian cuisine of Gujerat, as well as
its fondness for South Indian dishes. Not for nothing did the proprietors choose
an elephant for their logo: 'the message is that you do not have to eat meat to be
big, strong and intelligent.' The immediate attraction of Indian vegetarian food
is its range of flavours: it provides welcome relief from 'the endless succession
of curries' found in most non-vegetarian restaurants. Four set meals or thalis
are a good introduction to the menu, which has a limited choice of snacks and
starters such as bhel pooris, masala dosai and kachori. These set the scene for
main dishes including makni sabji (stir-fried) vegetables with ginger, nuts and
sweet-and-sour sauce; mushroom masala flavoured with coconut, and okra
fried with onions and tomatoes. Aubergines are seasoned with masala spices;
crushed and roasted with yoghurt, cashews and onions; or cooked with
spinach, fenugreek leaves and asafoetida. There's a choice of brown or basmati
rice, done five different ways, and the range of breads is admirable. To finish
there's carrot halva gulab jamun or vegan 'seero', but the star attraction is the
home-made kulfi: vats of boiling milk take three hours to reduce, then are
flavoured with saffron, pistachios and sugar before being frozen. The wine list,
compiled by Wines from Paris of Leith, shows a determination to encourage
Indian food and decent wine to get together. It also includes Indian méthode
champenoise and a gooseberry wine from Scotland, but is mostly French. A
few Italians are well chosen and offered at modest prices. Champagne apart, all
is under £10. House French is £5.50.

CHEF: Ajay Bharatdwaj   PROPRIETORS: M.E. Jogee, Mrs Mehta, E. Barton and
Ajay Bharatdwaj
OPEN: Mon to Sat, exc Sat L
MEALS: 12 to 2.30, 5.30 to 11.30
PRICES: £8 (£13), Set L £3 (£7) to £5 (£9), Set D £6 (£10) to £7.95 (£13). Service 10%
CARDS: Access, Visa
SEATS: 60. Private parties: 40 main room, 30 private room. Vegetarian meals. Children's
helpings. No smoking in dining-room. Wheelchair access. Music

Kelly's

46 West Richmond Street, EH8 9DZ
031-668 3847

COOKING 1
COST £21–£29

Large vases of fresh flowers brighten up this cosy neighbourhood restaurant on a wide street not far from the university. 'There is a not unpleasing touch of amateurism in the ambience.' Jacquie Kelly now runs the kitchen on her own and confines her activities to evening meals. The short fixed-price dinner menu has French regional overtones, and readers have liked the fish soup with rouille, escabeche, and pork fillet with confit of onions and raisins. Some dishes carry a supplement, and there is usually something for vegetarians, such as courgettes gratiné, filled with tomatoes, fennel and Gruyère. Vegetables are fresh and puddings are well made. A well balanced list of around 50 decent wines is informative and reasonably priced. House French: £6.

CHEF: Jacquie Kelly   PROPRIETORS: Jacquie Kelly and Jeff Kelly
OPEN: Tue to Sat, D only
CLOSED: 3 to 25 Sept
MEALS: 6.45 to 9.45
PRICES: Set D £15.50 (£21) to £17.50 (£24)
CARDS: Access, Amex, Visa
SEATS: 32. Private parties: 28 main room. Vegetarian meals. Children's helpings.
No smoking before 9pm. Wheelchair access (1 step; also WC). Music

Loon Fung

2 Warriston Place, EH3 5LE
031-556 1781

COOKING 1
COST £9–£23

Of the two floors of dining, and tables outside if it's fine, downstairs is the shorter straw. The chief qualities of this busy Cantonese restaurant reside in the dim-sum choices and the fresh fish and shellfish. These include mussels or oysters with ginger and spring onion or large fresh pieces of halibut with black-bean sauce. Poultry with lemon sauce has also been enjoyed, and a new speciality this year is chicken with orange and almonds. House French: £7 a litre.

CHEF: Tin Fat Siu   PROPRIETORS: Tin Fat Siu and Sammy Tam
OPEN: all week, exc Sat L and Sun L
CLOSED: 25 Dec, Chinese New Year
MEALS: noon to midnight (1am Fri and Sat)
PRICES: £10 (£18), Set L £5 (£9), Set D £9 (£14) to £13.50 (£19). Service 10%
CARDS: Access, Amex, Visa
SEATS: 75. 14 tables outside. Private parties: 30 main room, 45 private room. Children welcome. Music

All details are as accurate as possible at the time of going to press, but chefs and owners often change, and it is wise to check by telephone before making a special journey. Many readers have been disappointed when set-price bargain meals are no longer available. Ask when booking.

Marché Noir 🍷

2–4 Eyre Place, EH3 5EP
031-558 1608

COOKING 1
COST £14–£30

The Marché serves 'Le Diner' and 'Le Lunch' and the menus are in French. The links between Scotland and France are not sufficiently strong now to free the staff from translating extensively. Two set-price daily menus are offered at each meal. The least expensive seems to give more choice, at least at lunch, which is perhaps why everyone had selected it one day. A choice of charcuterie or smoked salmon, followed by salmon or pheasant, is good for salmon fans but few others. At dinner, however, a good balance of meat and fish is achieved. One meal this summer revealed very satisfactory cooking, even if some of the colours were as 'brown on brown' as the restaurant itself. Thus a black pudding with a dark red wine sauce swirled with cream melded the two components well, the spicy pudding rounded out nicely by the sauce. An avocado mousse of good texture was bland but generously spiked dill cream sharpened it well. In lamb gigot and kidneys with mustard and honey, the sweet honey and sharp mustard did the meat a treat (kidney apart), just as oregano in a tomato sauce for a paupiette of sole enlivened the overcooked fish. It is cooking like this that caused an Edinburgh resident to say that 'the restaurant looks in better shape than hitherto', though some would like a little more care in doing up puddings. The wine list is long and serious, without being highly priced. An order for a white wine that needed 20 minutes to cool, and requests that could not be fulfilled from indicated stock have made some wonder if cellarage is large enough, but the choice of properties – Italian and Spanish as well as French – is very good indeed. Intelligently chosen wines deserve clearer listing than is the case here. House French is £6.75.
CELLARMAN'S CHOICE: Savennières, Dom. de la Bizolière 1987, £11; Ch. St Pierre Sevaistre, 1976, £23.

CHEFS: Patrick Gray, Robert Struthers and Mark-Damien Budworth
PROPRIETORS: Mark-Damien Budworth and Malcolm Duck
OPEN: all week, exc Sat L and Sun L
MEALS: 12 to 2.30, 7 to 10 (10.30 Fri and Sat, 11.30 during Festival; 6.30 to 9.30 Sun)
PRICES: Set L £9 (£14) to £13 (£18), Set D £14.50 (£21) to £19 (£25)
CARDS: Access, Visa
SEATS: 45. Private parties: 45 main room. Vegetarian meals. Children's helpings.
No smoking in dining-room. Wheelchair access (1 step; also female WC). Music

Martins 🍷

70 Rose Street, North Lane, EH2 3DX
031-225 3106

COOKING 3
COST £16–£38

It is the consensus that we underrated Martin and Gay Irons' restaurant in 1990 on two broad counts: the usual finesse of the cooking and the quality of welcome and attention. There is a lot of thought in the enterprise: a consistent effort to use organic and free-range materials, more organic wines, even biodegradable detergents, and staggered booking so that everyone gets proper service without a sense of hurry. One person commented that the owners need encouragement, if only to stop them from being introspective and stuck in a rut.

That seems unlikely currently, as they report the expansion of the kitchen team, the baking of many more sorts of bread and other moves towards culinary self-sufficiency. The cooking was summarised thus: 'although it is modern, it is not silly, seems rooted in the reality of the supplies and likely local clientele. The sauces sound contrived, but anything I've tasted has clear flavours.' Martin's is found in a back passage behind Rose Street; some fear for their wallets but sigh with relief once arrived in the pleasant relaxed bar or light white dining-room 'with fresh flowers, big tables and no music'. Lunch is cheap for a choice of three alternatives; the *carte* at dinner is not much longer. A winter meal included crayfish bisque 'dark, rich and strong in colour and taste': feuilleté of rabbit livers and wild mushrooms, again, quite strong flavours; breast of pheasant in delicate pastry, a sauce of green peppercorns adding piquancy; the same end was achieved by pickled ginger in a watercress sauce for salmon; vegetables played on textures: shredded, whole and puréed; caramel mousse was almost overpowered by a limequat confit; the cheeses, mainly Scottish, have been particularly noted. The 'clear tastes' referred to above perhaps come from an enjoyment of citrus or strong accents to soups and sauces. Beetroot and ginger soup is one instance, pheasant with figs and a lime sauce is another. It is the nouvelle sweet-and-sour theme handled very assuredly. Food has sometimes cooled in its transit on the dumb waiter from the kitchen upstairs. The wine list is extremely good: great makers, fair prices, good range. Note Cape Mentelle, Rolly Gassman, Ch. Chauvin, Dr Florentin, Fernandez, and Wolfspierre Vineyards to start, but there are many more. It is intelligently concise. House wine: £7.95. CELLARMAN'S CHOICE: Chablis, premier cru Côte de Lechet 1986, Defaix, £18.50; Seville Estate Cabernet Sauvignon, Yarra Valley 1986, £19.50.

CHEFS: David McCrae, Andrew Porteous and Forbes Stott
PROPRIETORS: Martin and Gay Irons
OPEN: Tue to Sat, exc Sat L
CLOSED: 4 weeks from 23 Dec
MEALS: 12 to 2, 7 to 10
PRICES: £22 (£32), Set L £9.95 (£16) to £13.95 (£20). Service 10% on parties of 6 or more
CARDS: Access, Visa
SEATS: 28. Private parties: 34 main room, 18 private room. Children's helpings on request. No smoking in dining-room. Wheelchair access (2 steps)

McKirdy's ▼

43 Assembly Street, Leith, EH6 7BQ
031-553 6363

COOKING 1
COST £12–£28

Leith docklands is undergoing its own version of 'waterside yuppification' and it now sports a cluster of competing bistros, bars and restaurants all specialising in seafood. McKirdy's (formerly Oysters) looks like a converted chapel and is marked by a sculpted flying fish outside. Inside it creates different moods. The bar is like an Amsterdam café – all brown colours, wooden blinds, bare floorboards and a baby grand piano spread with the day's newspapers. The dining-room is 'aquarian green'; there are green tiles around the serving area and fans and skylights dominate the ceiling. Designer touches embellish the scene, but the restaurant looks and feels good. The menu is built around fresh fish, cooked lightly and simply in different ways. Grilled lemon sole with lobster butter and sauté fillet salmon with tomato and herb vinaigrette show the style and the quality of the raw materials. Otherwise there is mackerel, halibut, sardines and Dover sole; lobsters are kept in a salt-water tank in the cellar. Oysters, moules marinière, king prawns sauté in walnut oil with lime salad and a prodigious seafood stew packed with good things have all impressed visitors. There are a few equally good carnivorous specialities, such as haggis with neeps and tatties, and excellent juicy venison served on a julienne of vegetables. Blackboard specials supplement the regular menu. Cheeses come from Scotland or Paris, although the staff seem to have difficulty identifying them. Other details, such as the salad dressing, garnishes, delicate sorbets and good coffee are admirable, but the service needs to catch up. Occasionally there is live jazz in the evenings. A no-nonsense, international, 50-strong wine list reinforces the philosophy; with £24 the top price, and that a Barolo, expect much good value – starting with the marvellous Soave from Tadiello for £6.65. House French: £5.95. CELLARMAN'S CHOICE: Ch. la Jaubertie Bergerac 1989, £10.95.

CHEF: Ron Bartlett   PROPRIETORS: Oysters Ltd
OPEN: Tue to Sun, exc Sat L
CLOSED: 25 Dec
MEALS: 12 to 3, 6.30 to 11
PRICES: £17 (£23), Set L £6.95 (£12) to £8.75 (£14)
CARDS: Access, Amex, Diners, Visa
SEATS: 65. Private parties: 100 private room. Vegetarian meals. Children's helpings. No cigars/pipes in dining-room. Wheelchair access (1 step; also WC)

Pierre Victoire

10 Victoria Street, EH1 2HG	COOKING 2
031-225 1721	COST £8–£16

Popularity is inevitable for a place that offers such value and such good food, and it is just as inevitable that acclaim should bring mixed reports. First, to the good, are the prices. Lunch for under £5 cannot be bettered for value. Dinner, from a *carte* of half a dozen dishes in each course and a slate of desserts on the blackboard, is cheap too. The cooking style is full of zip: mussels with coriander and pink peppercorns; oysters baked with red pepper and Pernod; mushrooms in brandy cream with smoked salmon; salmon with raspberries and champagne; pork with crayfish, lemon and thyme. There is as much emphasis on fish as meat. Portions are generous. The roast rib of beef seems nearly always good; the mussels with garlic and Pernod butter come sizzling to the table; crayfish with a fresh ginger and cream sauce had ample flavour and texture; stir-fried lobster with ginger and lime is so good and so cheap that it's best to order in advance. Vegetables can be good and are often generous, but are as frequently an afterthought, or inapt, or cold, or undercooked. So many would-be customers are turned away that those who are not are pleased just to be there. Problems stem from the pressure: noise; cramped tables; discomfort; occasionally ill-informed staff; premises not tremendously clean; the passage of rubbish out, and deliveries in, during meals; 'a persistent drip fell on my hat, occasionally on the next table and on the floor but not on us.' This may connect to the food: duck often seems to respond badly to excess business; the desserts are rarely brilliant, though tarts get good mentions; the kitchen is so crowded and so pressed that errors do occur: there seems to be constant confusion between *homard*, langouste and langoustine. It is worth noting that Pierre Levicky is often seen front-of-house these days, not at the stove. Approach the place with enthusiasm and tolerance, or not at all. Not so many reports come in about the second branch, at 8 Union Street, opposite the Playhouse in Leith (tel. 031-557 8451). The menu is broadly similar; the decoration of the two shops thrown together is 'just adequate'. Here too, the combination of value, decent food and no frills has imparted a lively, glad-to-be-here atmosphere on the crowds that get in. As we went to press, the latest Victoire opening was in Inverness, just opposite the castle (see Round-up section for details). The wine list is as fairly priced as the food, Champagne especially. The notes are cogent and the French stock interesting and adequate for the task. House wine: £4.90 and £5.40 in each branch.

CHEF/PROPRIETOR: Pierre Levicky
OPEN: all week
CLOSED: 2 days at Christmas, 2 days at New Year
MEALS: 12 to 3, 6 to 11
PRICES: £10 (£13), Set L £4.90 (£8). Service inc
CARDS: Access, Visa
SEATS: 65. Private parties: 65 main room. Children's helpings. Wheelchair access (1 step). Music

Shamiana

14 Brougham Street, EH3 9JH
031-228 2265 and 229 5578

COOKING 1
COST £9–£34

Although some have detected changes in the style of cooking in recent months, this smartly decorated restaurant is still among the best in Edinburgh for its North Indian and Kashmiri food. Khalil and Shamime Mansoori have introduced a few alterations in a new menu: some different curries, including dhal gosht of lamb, lentils, fresh herbs and hot spices; Hyder Abadi murgh, which is chicken with nuts and poppyseed with lemon predominating from the marinade; and malai murgh, a much creamier, mild chicken dish. Among desserts, feerni – a pistachio and almond milk rice pudding with strong cardamom and rosewater flavour – is also new. The wine list continues to be excellent although now lacking the helpful indication of what to drink with what. Comments have been varied: one reader felt that dishes had become less chillified, but another said that the spicing was less accurate and, while portions had commendably grown in size, they were oilier. A meal in the spring produced baingan (aubergine) of wonderful texture but underseasoned; okra well spiced though overcooked; excellent dhal with well fried onion, garlic and chillies, and potato koftas with rich sauce spiked perhaps with tamarind and cinnamon. The Makhni chooza, tandoori chicken with coriander in a buttered sauce, has also been highly approved. The Shamiana continues to take its food seriously. Wines are carefully chosen and fairly priced, and house wine is complimentary with the set meals. House French: £5.95. Former partner Moosa Jogee has left to concentrate his efforts on Kalpna (see entry).

557

CHEF/PROPRIETOR: Khalil Mansoori
OPEN: all week, exc Sat L and Sun L
CLOSED: 25 Dec and 1 Jan
MEALS: 12 to 2, 6 to 11.30
PRICES: £11 (£21), Set L £8 (£9) to £15 (£17), Set D £13 (£15) to £25 (£28). Service 12%
CARDS: Access, Amex, Diners, Visa
SEATS: 42. Private parties: 18 main room. Vegetarian meals. Children's helpings.
No cigars/pipes in dining-room. Wheelchair access (1 step). Music

Szechuan House

95 Gilmore Place, EH3 9NU	COOKING 1
031-229 4655	COST £12–£35

The spices that dominate Szechuan cooking are not stinted in this
unostentatious restaurant run by the Lius. Chao-Gang Liu, who cooks, is from
the province though his wife is Cantonese. Service is positively informative
and will guide you through choices such as gong bao pork, pungent 'in a
fermented sort of way' with tender meat, peanut, carrot, onion and mushroom;
Szechuan green beans, tiny green beans with onion and green chillies;
Szechuan aubergine with a voluptuous texture but still pleasantly spicy;
vegetarian chicken, a crisp wrapping of bean curd round yam; a good range of
squid dishes; and fried pork with black-bean sauce, again robustly spiced and
seasoned, fat strips of pork with mainly leek. It is not expensive and, for once,
there is a vegetarian set meal for four with eight dishes plus dessert and coffee.

CHEF: Chao-Gang Liu   PROPRIETORS: Hsueh-Fen and Chao-Gang Liu
OPEN: Tue to Sun
MEALS: 5.30pm to 2am (3am Fri and Sat)
PRICES: £13 (£21), Set D £8.10 (£12) to £23 (£29). Service inc
CARDS: Access, Visa
SEATS: 40. Private parties: 24 main room, 12 private room. Vegetarian meals. Children
welcome. Music

Vintners Room ▼

87 Giles Street, Leith, EH6 6BZ	COOKING 3
031-554 6767	COST £15–£34

Perhaps the best site for a restaurant in Edinburgh, for this is the oldest
commercial building in Scotland still in business. It was almost derelict until
the Scotch Malt Whisky Society bought the premises, converted part into flats
and sold the remainder to an up-and-coming wine merchant and the Vintners
Room. The converted seventeenth-century auction room, complete with an
alcove for the auctioneer, is famous for its ornate Italian plasterwork ceiling
hung with a central candelabra. Tim and Sue Cumming made their name at the
Hole in the Wall in Bath, and many of their signature dishes have moved north
with them. Fish soup, mussels with leeks and saffron sauce, and salmon in
pastry with ginger and currants show the quality of the ingredients and the
skill of the kitchen. Others have praised the boudin noir on a bed of spinach
with mustard sauce, exactly cooked steaks and gigot of lamb with herb sauce.

'Superbly sharp' summer pudding and prune, almond and armagnac tart with 'the best short-crust pastry I have ever eaten' have been notably good sweets. It is possible to eat lightly and informally in the bar, though the prices are high for Edinburgh. People also question the co-existence of bar and restaurant when the style of the one intrudes on the formality of the other. Excellent growers abound on the wine list with Australia getting as careful selection as Burgundy. Prices are fair. The place has improved by leaps and bounds since the last *Guide*. Fourteen good house wines are available by the bottle or glass. House red, Gamay de l'Ardèche 1989, £8. CELLARMAN'S CHOICE: Draytons Chardonnay 1986, £12.

CHEFS: Tim Cumming and William Marsden   PROPRIETORS: Tim and Sue Cumming
OPEN: Mon to Sat
CLOSED: 2 weeks at Christmas
MEALS: 12 to 2.30, 6.30 to 10.30
PRICES: £20 (£28), Set L £8 (£15) to £11 (£18)
CARDS: Access, Amex, Visa
SEATS: 65. Private parties: 40 main room. Car-park, 3 places. Vegetarian meals. Children's helpings. No smoking in dining-room. Wheelchair access (2 steps). Air-conditioned

Waterfront Wine Bar

1C Dock Place, Leith, EH6 6LU	COOKING 1
031-554 7427	COST £18

Refurbishment, a new kitchen and extension of the conservatory have meant that the outside barbecue no longer takes place in this popular wine bar on the Leith dockside, with tables on the quay as well as on a floating pontoon. It is ideal for summer drinking and for simple eating. Regular visits have yielded satisfactory chicken tikka, beef casserole, sauté kidneys and a fish stew with tomato. The chargrill is much in evidence and normally there are oysters and mussels. Trimmings are scant, but prices are low and food is fresh. The wine list is pleasantly cheap and offers a fair choice from France and the rest of the world. It is not as interesting as it could be, given the quality of Edinburgh's wine shippers, but complaints are few, given the prices. There are always some odd parcels for the more adventurous. House wines, of which the white is a Gaillac Perlé, start at £5.50.

CHEFS: Helen Ruthven, Robin Bowie and Barbara Leonard   PROPRIETORS: Helen and Ian Ruthven, Sarah Reid and Robin Bowie
OPEN: Mon to Sat, and Sun L
MEALS: 12 to 2.30 (3 Sat), 6 to 9.30 (10 Fri and Sat)
PRICES: £10 (£15)
SEATS: 110. 19 tables outside. Private parties: 110 main room. Vegetarian meals. No children under 5. Wheelchair access (also WC). Music

---

'I felt that something was not quite right; whether it was my being tempted to defrost the sorbet over the candle or that one of the waitresses was determined to regain ownership of the bread bins she had so deftly placed on our sideplates, I'm not sure.' On dining in West Yorkshire

---

ERISKA Strathclyde   map 8

▲ *Isle of Eriska Hotel*

Eriska PA37 1SD
LEDAIG (063 172) 371   COOKING 2
Off A828, 12m N of Oban   COST £10–£42

The Buchanan-Smith family and assorted animals are well used to guests
trampling over their 250-acre island and making themselves at home in their
well-maintained and comfortable baronial mansion; and they have perfected
the art of laid-back hospitality. None the less, smart dress for dinner is the rule,
and not out of keeping in the newly revamped dining-room. The six-course
menu changes each day, but apart from the dessert trolley, the choice is limited
to alternatives at the first and main course stage. Bread is home made, and
vegetables and herbs are harvested from the garden. The food is modern British
with Scottish innuendos. In spring the following were 'very good': asparagus
with chive butter sauce, cream and pear and watercress soup ('ingredients
clearly identifiable'); a lemon sorbet interlude; and leg of pork, sliced at the
table, with apple purée and calvados sauce. An excellent fresh fruit salad
preceded a savoury. Scottish cheeses plus Stilton, and coffee with petits fours,
bring up the rear. Service has been called 'outstanding' and 'well-trained'.
High tea is served for children under 10 at 6pm, after which the dining-room is
closed to them. A single merchant supplies most of the wine list, resulting in
virtual monopolies – Trimbach in Alsace, Chapoutier on the Rhône and Latour
in Burgundy. But prices are fair and there are plenty of classy clarets.
CELLARMAN'S CHOICE: Ch. Guionne 1985, £9.85; Trimbach Tokay Reserve
1986, £11.65.

CHEFS: Vilas Roberts and Sheena Buchanan-Smith   PROPRIETORS: Robin and Sheena
Buchanan-Smith
OPEN: all week
CLOSED: end Oct to Mar
MEALS: 12.45 to 1.30, 7.30 to 9
PRICES: Set L £5.90 (£10), Set D £30.50 (£35). Service inc
SEATS: 40. Private parties: 10 main room, 12 private room. Car-park, 50 places. Children's
helpings. Children under 10 high tea only. Smart dress preferred. Wheelchair access
(also WC)
ACCOMMODATION: 16 rooms, all with bath/shower. Rooms for disabled. B&B £98 to £126.
Deposit: £50. Baby facilities. Pets welcome. Garden. Tennis. Fishing. TV. Phone. Scenic.
Confirm by noon [*Which? Hotel Guide*]

FORT WILLIAM Highland   map 8

Crannog

Town Pier, Fort William PH33 7NG   COOKING 2
FORT WILLIAM (0397) 3919 and 5589   COST £28

Crannog Scottish Seafoods was set up by a group of fishermen to market their
catch throughout Britain. In 1989 they opened their own restaurant in a
converted bait store overlooking the loch. The original high wooden ceiling has
been retained, and the upstairs women's lavatory – once a Royal Navy look-

out post – now boasts some of the best views in Britain. The place is still finding its feet, but first reports promise a great deal thanks largely to an uncomplicated menu that puts the emphasis on freshness and quality. Langoustines are a speciality, served in huge platefuls with pungent garlic butter, buttery new potatoes in their skins and a 'great mixed salad'. Bouillabaisse makes use of the catch from the boats: one visitor identified mussels, eel, huss and ling in his bowl of richly flavoured stock. Crannog also has its own smokehouse for curing salmon, trout and mussels – and the results are excellent. The menu takes in first courses such as salmon roulade with tomato and pepper coulis, pickled herrings, and crab terrine. Typical main courses are poached sole with lemon sauce, skate with black butter and baked trout with ginger and spring onion. Cranachan laced with whisky is the best-selling dessert. Service is exceptionally friendly. A simple wine list, well provided with half-bottles, suits the food. House white: £6.50.

CHEF: Susan Trowbridge   PROPRIETORS: Crannog Ltd
OPEN: all week (restricted in winter)
CLOSED: Nov
MEALS: 12 to 2.30, 6 to 10
PRICES: £15 (£23)
CARDS: Access, Visa
SEATS: 50. Private parties: 50 main room. Children's helpings. No-smoking area. Wheelchair access (also unisex WC)

▲ Factor's House

Torlundy, Fort William PH33 6SN
FORT WILLIAM (0397) 5767   COOKING 2
3m N of Fort William on A82   COST £25–£34

The name has all the history: it was the estate manager's residence for Inverlochy Castle. Nowadays, however, it is occupied by the son of the castle's proprietor and, in some late twentieth-century version of the servants' mirror of life beyond the green door, operates a 'guest-house with restaurant' to the castle's super-de-luxe catering operation. Peter Hobbs is a geographer and the theme of exploration runs through the decoration of the house – which is on a more domestic scale than a castle – and probably through the minds of most of the guests who will be there for the hills, the water, or flora and fauna. The stomach is usually well cared for, from a daily menu (priced by main-course preference) that encompasses soup and steak every time and a choice of two or three other dishes. The cooking is careful, the food is fresh and flavours are not lacking. Thus a breast of chicken stuffed with cream cheese and herbs was thrown into relief by its excellent sauce of fresh tomato, vinegar, white wine and herbs and a smoked trout salad with avocado and tomato was enlivened by a yoghurt vinaigrette. Steven Doole enjoys cooking fresh pasta and risotto (to take the edge off any outdoor hunger) – and will finish a meal with something of substance too: a walnut tart, perhaps, or a kiwi fruit crème brûlée with an ice, or parfait or cheese as constants. Filter coffee is served either at table or among the guests' clutter in the lounge. People are impressed by the happy balance of informality and propriety of service and hospitality. The wine list is short but properly supplied and there is no attempt to include varieties at silly

561

prices. Ch. Liverson 1983 and CVNE 1981, Riserva show how fair they are.
House French: £9.60 litre.

CHEF: Steven Doole   PROPRIETOR: Peter Hobbs
OPEN: all week, D only (L for residents)
CLOSED: mid-Dec to mid-Jan
MEALS: 7.30 to 9.30
PRICES: Set D £17.50 (£25) to £20.50 (£28)
CARDS: Access, Amex, Diners, Visa
SEATS: 24. Private parties: 24 main room. Car-park, 16 places. Children's helpings.
No children under 8. Wheelchair access (also WC)
ACCOMMODATION: 7 rooms, all with bath/shower. B&B £57.50 to £74. Deposit: 50%.
No children under 8. Garden. Tennis. Fishing. Golf. TV. Phone. Scenic. Doors close at
midnight. Confirm by 6 [*Which? Hotel Guide*]

▲ *Inverlochy Castle*

Fort William PH33 6SN
FORT WILLIAM (0397) 2177
3m N of Fort William on A82   COST £31–£52

This grandest of baronial hotels has appeared in property pages, and chef
Graham Newbould was expected to leave by the end of 1990 as we went to
press. Inverlochy has had a steely reputation for consistency, in management
and cooking, and it is only fair to presume it will win through. Last year's *Guide*
rating was 4; so as not to risk misleading, we omit the mark this year. The
dining-room, dominated by an immense late Victorian sideboard, has been the
scene for subtle blending of English and modern European cooking. Since its
earliest days, simply done roast meats have been pre-eminent. Yet more recent
chefs have balanced this by dishes such as sea bass with sherry vinegar sauce;
wobbly mousselines of scallops; tender ravioli of prawns with truffle sauce or
Gressingham duck with figs. The style has been restrained, the execution
usually accurate. The country-house formula, which the Castle did much to
elaborate, has meant a menu short on choice, though with a supplementary
second course of soup and cheese built in, all at a set price (high). We can only
report that standards appear to be maintained and the expectation is that they
will be. 'There is no service charge, no tipping, and none expected.' Had
we received a copy of the wine list, we would have given awards for
completeness and consideration for those unwilling to afford the classics.
More reports, please.

CHEF: Graham Newbould   PROPRIETOR: Grete Hobbs
OPEN: all week
CLOSED: mid-Nov to mid-Mar
MEALS: 12.30 to 1.45, 7.30 to 9
PRICES: Set L £23 (£31) to £29 (£37), Set D £38 (£43)
CARDS: Access, Visa
SEATS: 36. Private parties: 18 main room. Car-park, 10 places. No children under 10. Smart
dress preferred. No smoking in dining-room
ACCOMMODATION: 16 rooms, all with bath/shower. B&B £121 to £165. Deposit: 50%.
Afternoon teas. Garden. Tennis. Fishing. Snooker. TV. Phone. Scenic. Doors close
at midnight

Café Gandolfi

64 Albion Street, G1 1NY   COOKING 1
041-552 6813   COST £17

Modernism with a good name is the Café, still popular for all-day eating from a
menu kindly to the pocket and accessible to vegetarians and meat eaters alike.
It moves slowly with the times, having added Piedmontese peppers, dates and
ricotta wrapped in Parma ham, and bacon and avocado salad with a warm
vinaigrette to its otherwise unchanging list of starters. These encompass Stilton
in choux puffs, smoked venison, pâté and gravlax. There is a daily hot dish of
more substance to go with other main courses that include cold baked
Cumbrian ham with pease pudding, Finnan haddock and potatoes, or gratin
dauphinois on its own or with smoked venison. One reader commended the
materials used in the kitchen but questioned the consistency of performance.
There are six wines, all decent, offered cheaply by the bottle or the glass, four
good beers and home-made lemonade.

CHEFS: Maggie Clarence and Andrew Bickerstaff   PROPRIETOR: Iain M. Mackenzie
OPEN: Mon to Sat
CLOSED: bank hols
MEALS: 9.30am to 11.30pm
PRICES: £9 (£14). Service of 10% for parties of 6 or more
SEATS: 60. Private parties: 12 main room. Vegetarian meals. Children's helpings.
No children after 8pm. Wheelchair access (2 steps). Music

Colonial India

25 High Street, G1 1LX   COOKING 1
041-552 1923   COST £7−£26

The Raj revisited in central Glasgow: wicker chairs, ceiling fan, military prints,
tiger-hunt mural, easy-listening Muzak, not to mention the solicitous and very
dedicated service. The aim 'to provide the best Indian food in Scotland' is
believable although the range of dishes is fairly standard. There are more fish
dishes than usual and the cooking is above average. Dishes that have pleased
include a delicate gobi chaat of cauliflower in rich, almost sweet-sour sauce,
channa puri in spiced tomato sauce, and a robust, well-sauced mushroom
bhaji. Saffron rice was light and aromatic, sorbets in 'natural skin' are worthy.
Portions are generous, making the value good. The set lunch is available from
noon to 2. Good beer list. An adequate wine list has some good bottles but is
short on information. House wine is £4.90.

CHEF: Tauquir Malik   PROPRIETORS: Tariq Iqbal, Tauqir Malik and Satty Singh
OPEN: all week, exc Sat L
CLOSED: 25 Dec, 1 Jan
MEALS: noon to 11.30 (midnight Fri and Sat)
PRICES: £12 (£22), Set L £3.50 (£7) to £5.90 (£9)
CARDS: Access, Amex, Diners, Visa
SEATS: 45. Private parties: 20 main room. Vegetarian meals. Children's helpings.
Wheelchair access. Music. Air-conditioned

October

128 Drymen Road, Bearsden, G61 3RB
041-942 7272

COOKING 3
COST £14–£32

The modern front will arrest any casual passer-by and alert them to a stylish and interesting enterprise. Should it be possible to sample the food (popular nights are booked far in advance), the presumption will be confirmed. Hugh MacDiarmid once observed that 'The Scots were always devils/For adding rouge to a rose/And whitewash to a lily.' A thousand culinary instances of the failing may be found throughout the country, but not on the whole in Ferrier Richardson's cooking. This is to the point and as described on a menu with plenty of choice. The short lunch menu is a palpable bargain. The cooking is full-blooded modern, market-based, willing to try many strands of culinary tradition: teriyaki sits next to polenta sits next to sun-dried tomato. Thus his gamey pâté will come on the plate with orange and grapefruit sections and a loganberry sauce – firmly of the late twentieth-century taste spectrum – but at the same time he will cook a substantial fish soup, served in a great tureen and given a mark of distinction by a topping of a saffron and herb soufflé. People have spoken well of fine calf's liver and excellent calves' kidneys (such offal is not easy to buy from Glasgow retailers). The kidneys were actually ordered by a 'vegetarian' who wolfed the lot with gusto! A vegetarian dish is normally on the menu, and whether it be carrot and courgette gateau with an onion compote or an exactly spiced mixture of aubergine and courgette, it also has been welcome. So has fish, especially when it is a mixture, as in a tourte of seafood offered one lunchtime, or a good fresh piece of, say, sole topped with a crayfish mousse or salmon with lobster mousse. Invention continues to the dessert stage – people talked happily of the grand plate selection – with nice conceits such as a chocolate terrine with an espresso crème anglaise. Coffee comes with petits fours. October is perhaps Glasgow's most obviously committed restaurant, the owners genuinely trying to improve and aiming high: from the mirrored and cool interior design through the wine list (and bar that stocks Lillet) to the cooking itself. Not every meal is a success; the failings may indicate lack of supervision, with only the occasional lapse of taste. There are still comments about a certain coolness in the welcome and service and about the intrusion of cigar smoke. The wine list is as eclectic as the menu, making a sterling attempt at worldwide coverage in four dozen bins. Prices, as for the food, are fair. The choice of growers is interesting, though few are obvious world leaders. This makes it a list to ask about and discuss. Try the Bandol, Mas de la Rouvière, £13.95.

CHEFS: Ferrier Richardson and George Craig   PROPRIETORS: Ferrier Richardson and Hugh MacShannon
OPEN: all week, exc Sun D
CLOSED: 1 week at Easter, first 2 weeks Aug
MEALS: 12 to 2, 7 to 10
PRICES: £19 (£27), Set L £8.25 (£14) to £9.75 (£16). Service inc
CARDS: Access, Visa
SEATS: 48. Private parties: 52 main room. Children welcome. Wheelchair access (also WC). Music. Air-conditioned

Rogano

11 Exchange Place, G1 3AN
041-248 4055   COST £37

The fine art deco building is worth a visit but currently the restaurant is in flux, hence the removal of the cooking mark. Jim Kerr, once chef at One Devonshire Gardens, took on the kitchens as we went to press. Judging from recent reports, all one can say is that he needed to. It is therefore possible that this will again be a place to enjoy fish that has been freshly bought and freshly cooked. The first move might be to shorten the menu. There has always been a current in favour of the service, although some have found it not very knowledgeable and others that it is too keen to push the wine. The potential is very great. The Café Rogano is also a popular spot, indeed most recently has gained more approval than the main restaurant for its fair steaks and fair value. The wine list is adequate though never cheap. House wine: £6.95.

CHEF: Jim Kerr   PROPRIETORS: Alloa Brewery
OPEN: Mon to Sat
MEALS: 12 to 2.30, 7 to 10.30
PRICES: £20 (£31). Service 10%
CARDS: Access, Amex, Diners, Visa
SEATS: 100. Private parties: 25 main room, 14 private room. Vegetarian meals. Children welcome. Music. Air-conditioned

Triangle ▼

37 Queen Street, G1 3EF   COOKING 2
041-221 8758   COST £13–£30

This is a large set of rooms on the first-floor above Tom Shepherd's Trick Shop. It has been suggested that it was once a snooker hall but now it falls into a broad division between a bar and brasserie and a more spacious, quieter dining-room. Any memory of gaming times is lost beneath table linen, carpet and well-mannered yet enthusiastic staff. Dinner menus give a number of options from a decade of choices at each course, charged according to the number of courses, not by which dishes are eaten. Good notices have included a mousse-terrine of duck; crab in puff pastry parcels; poached oysters on spinach, Rockefeller style; bresaola; venison with redcurrant and juniper berry sauce; beef with wild mushrooms; an irreproachable brioche filled with fruit; and a chocolate bavarois that hovered between delicate and bland. Fish dishes and home-made ravioli have been identified as strengths in the kitchen. Lunch is a relative bargain, and the brasserie is less expensive, too. The contents of the wine list is as stylish as its appearance, including Kreydenweiss Alsaces, Carmenet and Firestone from California, Rion from Burgundy and some modern Italians and French provincial wines. House wine: £7.95.
CELLARMAN'S CHOICE: Rioja, CVNE Imperial 1976, £20.75; Riesling Munchberg 1983, Ostertag, £17.50. Changes of ownership as we go to press may result in other changes, so more reports, please.

Report forms are at the back of the book; write a letter if you prefer.

CHEF: Edward Cooney   PROPRIETORS: Chanceriendon Ltd
OPEN: Mon to Sat
MEALS: 12 to 3, 7 to 11
PRICES: £16 (£25), Set L £7.50 (£13) to £9 (£14)
CARDS: Access, Amex, Diners, Visa
SEATS: 80. Private parties: 100 main room, 50 private room. Vegetarian meals. No children under 14. Music. Air-conditioned

---

Ubiquitous Chip ▮

12 Ashton Lane, G12 8SJ	COOKING 3
041-334 5007	COST £28

'There are no cheap tricks at the Chip' is the rousing peroration of a London Scot who values Ron Clydesdale's cooking and sense of hospitality above all others in Glasgow. The Chip is sometimes called a 'plantarium', such is the profusion of greenery in the warehouse conversion with covered courtyard. It is filled with bare varnished tables and the hum of popularity. Busy as it is, praise is warm for the level of service and the free and easy sense of enjoyment that permeates a visit. The menu is long and has several strengths. It shows evident and single-minded pursuit of good ingredients: fish from Ayr and Oban, pigeon from Perthshire, venison from Inverness, salmon from Loch Lomond. It shows the kitchen's willingness to cook braised dishes, of which ox-tail and silverside are two favourites – a tendency it supported long before the rush back to 'granny food' which, in too many instances, is no more than a ladle of lentils. The chip mixes Scottish and French culinary vernaculars: clapshot, bannocks and haggis are next to duck with apple and cider sauce; langoustines with mayonnaise and game fillets with a walnut vinaigrette. The repertoire manages to look forwards and backwards at once, making it of interest to a wide constituency: 'cod on a bed of clapshot with roasted and chillied red peppers' is an example of this, and merely confirms Ron Clydesdale's long-term objective of teasing Glasgow out of culinary cliché. Execution is often very good indeed: oak-smoked Loch Fyne kipper pâté with yoghurt and dill; monkfish tails with a lightly spiced Sauternes cream sauce on a bed of cracked wheat flavoured with ginger and saffron; shellfish bisque with cream and ginger; dill-marinated haddies with quails' eggs; braised ox-tail, 'not greasy at all with a particularly light gravy'; pheasant with a beer sauce; and venison haggis, 'haggis *nouveau*, very rich and gamey, almost like kofta, topped with sesame seeds, needing the neeps and tatties for balance'. There are, however, failings that vitiate the success of some meals: sauces and renderings that obtrude on the natural flavours, say, of mushrooms and mussels; a cheeseboard that tends to the overripe; some signs that the size of the restaurant overtakes the ability to achieve consistency in all departments. While the accumulation of extras on vegetables, salads and potatoes may end in a fat bill for food, the wine list is a monument to generous pricing. It is also a remarkable collection. It is not an antique list, though 1970s clarets appear in a sufficiency, nor does it stick to France alone: New World, Italy, Germany and Spain are fairly covered. The wine service is intelligent. There is a remarkable list of malts: 'spent ages looking for the ones we had ordered, but came up trumps in the end.' Caledonian 80/- Natural Ale and Furstenburg unpasteurised lager are also available. There are many good bottles under £10. Recommendation from such a list is almost in vain, but note Marquès de Griñon from Castille; Umani Ronche's Le Busche; Valdespino's sherries; Cloudy Bay's wines from New Zealand; Jaboulet's Rhônes (some good mature ones, too); and inexpensive Mas de Daumas Gassac. House wine: £6.50.

CHEF/PROPRIETOR: Ron Clydesdale
OPEN: all week
MEALS: 12 to 2.30 (12.30 to 4 Sun), 5.30 to 11 (6.30 to 11 Sun)
PRICES: £18 (£23). Service inc
CARDS: Access, Amex, Diners, Visa
SEATS: 100. 12 tables outside. Private parties: 60 main room, 40 private room. Vegetarian meals. Children's helpings. Wheelchair access (also male and female WC)

GULLANE Lothian   map 8

La Potinière ▮

Main Street, Gullane EH31 2AA   COOKING 4
GULLANE (0620) 843214   COST £20−£35

Perhaps the biggest news from this village by the sea and the Muirfield golf course is that David and Hilary Brown now provide dinner twice a week, on Friday as well as Saturday. This will please the many who are prepared to book far ahead. The *Guide* always stresses that long forward-planning is necessary to get in. While this is still true for weekends it is less the case for lunches at the beginning of the week. 'We enjoy going here once a year in order to remind ourselves as to what food can really taste like.' Hilary Brown's cooking is infinitely restrained, but never insipid. Meals, which are served at one sitting for all, are no-choice and pursue a consistent pattern. To begin, a soup: a thick tomato and mint cream combining rich, fresh tomato with a cutting edge of mint and subtle undertow of spices. Texture was left slightly rough, and sweetish walnut bread was offered with it. The next course was mousseline of sole and smoked salmon. The sublime was not far distant with this double mousseline: a bombe of faint orange enveloped the vanilla-coloured core of sole. 'The two flavours were in exactly the right ratio, the whole was lifted by a light lemon sauce.' Fish is not inevitable at this stage; a terrine of aubergine with a little ratatouille and virgin oil dressing has been noted as but one variation. The main course was chicken breast with a marmalade served with a gratin dauphinois (a good one) and a salad of green beans, fennel and chicory. The salad gave edge to the caramelised onions that sweetened the chicken. Brie and apples were on the sideboard, and Cheddar for lovers of hard cheese. Desserts have included an apricot parfait, a chocolate parfait in tiny pots, or 'envelopes of the lightest, almond-filled puff pastry arranged on a pool of English custard'. Hilary Brown can bake as well as cook. From the dishes described it will be seen that several kitchen techniques are faultlessly deployed within an apparently simple framework. Tastes are very exact. Repeated visits may involve déjà-vu: the first two courses above, for instance, were encountered in August and again in January. It must have been some relief that on the second date it was not chicken, but turkey, which followed. David Brown masterminds the wine and serving the food. He does this without imposition and at a reasonable pace, though a meal is never abbreviated. The wines are superb and as cheap as they can be for such quality. He stresses that the list, which will take most of the meal to read, is but a starting point, the tip of the cellar's iceberg. His preference is to discuss choice in advance, to tease by conversation some impression of a person's expectations and interest in the remarkable collection on offer. Circumstances may then prompt suggestions of wines not on the list at all. The list does not as yet bother itself much with the 1980s in clarets and red burgundies, and the range of the latter shows not much affection for many new-wave producers, but where else could one drink so many classics for so little? The house wine is from Bouchard at £6.95. The only possible reason for taking it would be lack of time to go through the list.

CHEF: Hilary Brown PROPRIETORS: David and Hilary Brown
OPEN: L Mon, Tue, Thur and Sun; Fri and Sat D
CLOSED: 1 week in June, Oct
MEALS: 1, 8
PRICES: Set L £14.50 (£20) to £15.50 (£21), Set D £22.50 (£29)
SEATS: 32. Private parties: 30 main room. Car-park, 10 places. Children welcome.
No smoking during meals. Wheelchair access. One sitting

HADDINGTON Lothian   map 8

▲ *Browns Hotel*

| 1 West Road, Haddington EH41 3RD | COOKING 2 |
| HADDINGTON (062 082) 2254 | COST £17–£30 |

People have commented that we have been insufficiently precise about Brown's. On the one hand, though a handsome classical house, it is on a domestic rather than a palatial scale. On the other, though busy at weekends, it can be quiet at other times. The decoration is nicely thought out and smart beyond expectations even if the drawing-room is so crowded with soft sofas that on a weekday night it will seem like the *Marie Celeste*, peopled only by ghosts. The very short menu reflects Colin Brown's desire to offer only food in good condition. Cooking is careful and fairly classic. Sauces often use classical sharpness to set off the meat, rather than the fruity acidity that so often plummets into syrupy sweetness in the hands of the unskilled. Duck is served with olives or a very sharp cherry sauce, chateaubriand steak with a sauce Robert. Meals sometimes appear more interested in meat than fish. Buying has been remarked on: good asparagus, well balanced by a lively hollandaise; good vegetables and first-rate potatoes. There may be no choice for dessert, but Sunday lunch yielded a generous apple and blueberry pie with exemplary short-crust as well as a papaya with a mango sauce: a combination that crops up in different versions in other reports. Coffee, petits fours and incidentals match the rest of the meal and Alexander McCallum provides informed and effective service from the bar to the table. The short, mainly French wine list has fair prices. House wines range from £6.25 to £6.75. CELLARMAN'S CHOICE: Menetou Salon, La Charnivolle 1988, £11.90; Ch. La Tour Bayard 1986, £9.30.

CHEF: Colin Brown PROPRIETORS: Colin Brown and Alex McCallum
OPEN: all week, D only and Sun L
MEALS: 12.30 for 1, 7.30 for 8
PRICES: Set L £12.50 (£17) to £14.50 (£20), Set D £19.50 (£25)
CARDS: Amex, Access, Visa
SEATS: 38. Private parties: 38 main room. Car-park, 10 places. Children's helpings.
Wheelchair access (also WC). One sitting
ACCOMMODATION: 6 rooms, 5 with bath/shower. B&B £45 to £59.50. Deposit: £20. Baby
facilities. Garden. TV. Phone. Scenic. Doors close at midnight. Confirm by 6

HAWICK Borders   map 8

Old Forge

Newmill-on-Teviot, nr Hawick TD9 0JU
TEVIOTDALE (045 085) 298   COOKING 1
4m S of Hawick, on A7   COST £15–£20

The anvil is still in the fireplace, the bellows in an alcove. Eight tables, each
with its own storm lantern, are tended by Bill Irving (the wine lover) and
supplied by Margaret Irving (the cook). Home-made Granary-style bread and
butter stamped with a thistle are two early indicators that the blackboard set
menu of four courses may disclose delights. During the week you can choose
three courses for a lower price. The sources of the repertoire are very wide:
hummus; tomato mousse with a dill mayonnaise; vegetable ravioli topped
with goats' cheese; pigeon wrapped in a parcel with pear and tarragon or
casseroled with cider and grapes; good soups, such as lovage and sorrel, tomato
and plum; sticky toffee pudding; semolina pudding with redcurrant sauce.
Local materials crop up with Eyemouth crab and a long list of Scottish cheeses
with oatcakes. Perhaps it is in homage to local preference that plenty of
vegetables – quasi-baked potatoes, celeriac purée with apple, red cabbage and
white cabbage with walnuts and onions – are served with dishes that would
benefit from something different or plainer. The wine list is as surprising as the
cooking – for the location, that is. The prices are extremely fair. Bottles have a
very modern ring to them and many are ultra fashionable. Jobard, Defaix, Rolly
Gassmann, Ridge, João Pires, Cloudy Bay, Dry Creek, Ch. Musar, and Joseph
Phelps are just some from a range that goes way beyond France and keeps well
below £15 for all but a handful. House Chanut is £7.25 a litre. CELLARMAN'S
CHOICE: Cloudy Bay Sauvignon Blanc 1989, £12.95; Ch. Notton 1980, £11.95.

CHEF: Margaret Irving PROPRIETORS: Bill and Margaret Irving
OPEN: Tue to Sat, D only
CLOSED: first 2 weeks May, first 2 weeks Nov
MEALS: 7 to 9.30
PRICES: Set D £10.95 (£15) (Tue to Fri) to £12.95 (£17). Service inc
CARD: Access, Visa
SEATS: 28. Private parties: 30 main room. Car-park, 10 places. Vegetarian meals. Children's
helpings. Wheelchair access

▲ denotes an outstanding wine cellar; ♀ denotes a good wine list, worth travelling for.
See the Introduction for a fuller explanation.

▲ *Culloden House*

Inverness IV1 2NZ
INVERNESS (0463) 790461   COOKING 2
off A96, 3m E of Inverness   COST £30–£44

Turn any corner in this sizeable Georgian pile and you are likely to discover a
cache of weekend kilt-wearers: men and women, highlanders and lowlanders.
There are few settings where they will look more at home sipping malt whisky
supplied from an admirable collection. Bonnie Prince Charlie, himself partial
to kilts and whisky, fought his last battle outside the boundaries of this 40-acre
estate. Surrounding the house are oak and beech trees buffeted by winds from
the nearby Moray Firth. Inside it's a pâtisserie of Adam-style plasterwork.
There is plenty of icing on the dining-room walls and plenty of starched linen
on the polished wood tables. Isolated incidents of food arriving at the tables in
a chilly state have been reported but in a place like this it's a long way to
anywhere, including the kitchen. Lunch is à la carte, dinner a set-price feast.
One course will be sorbet. To start might be smoked haddock and onion soup,
rated by one reader as a highlight of his dinner. Then 'Scottish West Coast
scallops dipped in butter and breadcrumbed and grilled, served with a
pimento and tomato coulis' or 'marinated loin of venison, shallow fried, coated
with a honey and sherry sauce served with a pastry parcel filled with wild rice,
apple and raisins.' Vegetarians get a better than average deal here. One was
'delighted with the availability of genuine vegetarian alternatives, particularly
a wild mushroom crêpe.' The wide variety of Scottish cheeses has also won
praise. One thing that seems certain to be warm is the atmosphere, service and
attention from the laird and his lady, Ian and Marjory McKenzie. Says one
reader, 'the friendliness and helpfulness of the proprietors was remarkable.'
Fine wines abound and halves are plentiful on the wine list which is weighted
to the expensive end. Interest is not lacking under £12, however. House
claret is £9.

CHEF: Michael Simpson   PROPRIETORS: Ian and Marjory McKenzie
OPEN: all week
MEALS: 12.30 to 2, 7 to 9
PRICES: £19 (£30), Set D £27.50 (£37)
CARDS: Access, Amex, Diners, Visa
SEATS: 50. 3 tables outside. Private parties: 50 main room, 25 private room. Car-park, 50
places. Vegetarian meals. Children's helpings. Smart dress preferred. No smoking in
dining-room
ACCOMMODATION: 20 rooms, all with bath/shower. B&B £75 to £140. Deposit: 1 night. Pets
welcome. Afternoon teas. Garden. Sauna. Tennis. Snooker. TV. Phone. Scenic. Doors close
at midnight

---

*The Guide office can quickly spot when a restaurateur is encouraging customers to write
recommending inclusion and sadly, several restaurants have been doing this in 1990.
Such reports do not further a restaurant's cause. Please tell us if a restaurateur invites you
to write to the Guide.*

▲ Dunain Park

Inverness IV3 6JN COOKING 1
INVERNESS (0463) 230512 COST £37

'A country home rather than a country house', if that is not too fine a
distinction, on the road to Fort William. The views are grand and so were the
grounds, but they were in turmoil with building works as the *Guide* went to
press. The house is substantial, with prices more stately than homely, but run
with a human touch in the view of many. The cooking is on show in set-price
dinners which display some enthusiasm for adventurous cooking, with soups
like turnip and pine kernel or courgette and Brie, as well as some skill in
producing good meat and straightforward classics such as asparagus
hollandaise. Too often, however, sensible instincts are crowded out by faulty
technique: a courgette flower is stuffed with uninteresting cheese in a leaden
soufflé, for example. Desserts are often lauded but have also looked decidedly
morning-afterish. A note from the proprietor says that there is a restricted
dinner menu for two weeks in November and February. The wine list is
admirable in its overall selection, even if it implies that the best bottle out of
Portugal is Mateus. Pricing is not ungenerous and halves get a fair showing.
CELLARMAN'S CHOICE: Meursault Rouge 1987, Latour Giraud, £18.50; St
Véran, Les Grandes Bruyères 1988, £13.25.

CHEF: Ann Nicoll PROPRIETORS: Ann and Edward Nicoll
OPEN: all week, D only
MEALS: 7 to 9
PRICES: Set D £22.50 (£31)
CARDS: Access, Amex, Diners, Visa
SEATS: 36. 2 tables outside. Private parties: 6 main room. Car-park, 20 places. Children's
helpings. No smoking in dining-room. Wheelchair access
ACCOMMODATION: 12 rooms, all with bath/shower. Rooms for disabled. B&B £55 to £110.
Deposit: £50. Children welcome. Pets welcome, exc in public rooms. Afternoon teas.
Garden. Swimming-pool. Sauna. TV. Phone. Scenic. Doors close at midnight.
[*Which? Hotel Guide*]

ISLE ORNSAY Isle of Skye map 8

▲ Kinloch Lodge

Isle Ornsay IV43 8QY
ISLE ORNSAY (047 13) 214 and 333 COOKING 2
1m off A851 COST £37

The Lodge, tucked under Ben Breac, is surrounded by trees and garden
overlooking Loch na Dal. It has undergone further remedial work after the
storms of the past two years. The Macdonalds continue to act as unstuffy hosts,
in a house furnished with a certain casual style and handsome furniture. The
dinner gives a choice of two in each course: soup, a roast and a substantial pie
or pudding being almost invariable elements. After the sweet course, a few
whole cheeses and lashings of fruit are on the sideboard for self-service before
retreating for coffee and fudge. The formula may be that of the dinner party but
the genre is pleasing when execution is accurate. Clare Macdonald is conscious

571

of her materials and of the effects, gustatory and ecological, of intensive systems on foodstuffs. The kitchen benefits from this awareness with largely organic vegetables, wild salmon and Highland beef. Approved dishes have included grilled goats' cheese with leeks and walnuts; crab with tomato and garlic mayonnaise; rib of beef béarnaise; leg of lamb with a Reform sauce; apple meringue pie; and brown sugar meringues with rhubarb and ginger. When it is not properly or only adequately done, the downside is that the prices do not show up well in terms of regional competition. 'While the absence of telephones and televisions could assist relaxation, it seems invidious to pay a premium for their absence.' The wine list gives a good range of price and origin as well as a decent number of halves. The classics are the strongest, back through the 1960s and the 1970s for some of the clarets, but Australia and others are not entirely ignored. House wine: £8.

CHEFS: Lady Macdonald, Peter Macpherson and Millie Maclure   PROPRIETORS: Lord and Lady Macdonald
OPEN: all week, D only
CLOSED: 1 Dec to mid-Mar
MEALS: 8
PRICES: Set D £26.50 (£31). Service inc
CARDS: Access, Visa
SEATS: 25. Private parties: 8 main room. Car-park, 25 places. No children under 10. One sitting
ACCOMMODATION: 10 rooms, all with bath/shower. Rooms for disabled. B&B £40 to £80. Deposit: £50. Baby facilities. Pets welcome. Afternoon teas. Garden. Fishing. Scenic. Confirm by 3

KENTALLEN Highland   map 8

▲ Ardsheal House

Kentallen PA38 4BX   COOKING 2
DUROR (063 174) 227   COST £10–£37

Luckily, nothing much changes about the sublime loch-side setting at the end of the bumpy mile and a half drive. The long white house has a mid-eighteenth century birth certificate and appropriate accoutrements of open fires and oak panelling. The Taylors are American, however, so all is not static; there is now a Fax. George Kelso, who took up the ladle in June 1989, has continental leanings (there are new sauce spoons to prove it) and uses good raw materials, many from the hotel garden. One report suggests meals are getting even more nouvelle. Combinations are occasionally inspired, as in mange-tout and ginger soup, the second of six courses on the practically choiceless dinner menu. Other good ideas have been pistachio mousse with a guinea-fowl and game roulade, asparagus and mushroom ravioli with lobster sauce, and apple 'soup' with cinnamon ice-cream. Red snapper, well-known in America, has come to Scotland and is to be found occasionally on Ardsheal's menu. Salad with Stilton comes before dessert which in turn is followed by more cheese (but not Stilton) with a bowl of fresh fruit that one midsummer night contained three kinds of apples, grapes, strawberries, kiwi, passion-fruit, cherries, peaches and two kinds of plums. Lunches are less fancy in conception and price. Quiet efficiency and attention to detail are evident throughout the house, though breakfasts could have more sparkle. The wine list, just topping a hundred labels, scores on several levels: comprehensive scope, many respectable growers and non-greedy prices. House French: £6.50. CELLARMAN'S CHOICE: Hawk Crest Cabernet Sauvignon, 1985, £13.

CHEF: George Kelso   PROPRIETORS: Jane and Robert Taylor
OPEN: all week
CLOSED: 1 Nov to Easter
MEALS: 12.30 to 2, 8.30
PRICES: Set L £6.50 (£10) to £14 (£18), Set D £27.50 (£31). Service inc
CARDS: Access, Amex, Visa
SEATS: 40. Private parties: 38 main room. Car-park, 20 places. Children's helpings. Smart dress preferred. No smoking in dining-room. Wheelchair access (also WC). Music. One sitting at D
ACCOMMODATION: 13 rooms, all with bath/shower. D,B&B £55 to £145. Baby facilities. Pets welcome. Afternoon teas. Garden. Tennis. Snooker. Scenic. Doors close at 12. Confirm by 5.30. [*Which? Hotel Guide*]

KILCHRENAN Strathclyde   map 8

▲ *Taychreggan Hotel*

Kilchrenan PA35 1HQ   COOKING 1
KILCHRENAN (086 63) 211   COST £22–£36

John and Monika Tyrrell's bright white hotel on Loch Awe's northern shore has had a mixed postbag. They aim to please, inflicting neither dress code nor strict timings, and service is widely commended. Recent refurbishments, which include a newly created small dining-room for out-of-season bookings, may not have gone far enough: some shabby elements have still been noted. None the less, it's a comfortable and pleasant place to stay. The loch view and sunny central courtyard remain key features. There is choice on the short set lunch and dinner menu except at the soup and cheese stage. There is interest, too: a trio of vegetable terrines with chervil sauce; tartar of salmon with marinated cucumber; poached turbot with tomato hollandaise; lemon cheesecake and home-made ice-creams were enjoyed. Sometimes too much ambition may be at play – one reader was frankly disappointed by pressed calf's liver with port jelly; ceviche could have been bolder, and a red wine, marrow and onion sauce with a pan-fried fillet of beef less bland. The wine list centres on France, with a look-in by other European and New World producers. Good non-Champagne French bubblies. House wine, Bourgogne Grande Ordinaire, is £10.25.

'There was a recent article in one of the papers about Hotel X becoming "green" etc. The new owners have been in possession about 18 months. The first difficulty was finding the entrance, a small mean one at the side. When we drove up, a cross-looking receptionist came out and asked what we wanted. I asked for a brochure, and was allowed to enter the first hallway only. In fact, she slammed the door in my face. I was left to contemplate the "green" dead things – foxes, birds etc. – stuffed and placed in glass cases. I was given a brochure, and as an afterthought, she told me they were open for Sunday lunch. As there was not a car in sight we declined the offer.' On eating in Gwynedd

---

CHEF: Gail Struthers   PROPRIETORS: John and Monika Tyrrell
OPEN: all week
CLOSED: 28 Oct to 23 Mar
MEALS: 12 to 2.30, 7 to 9
PRICES: Set L £15 (£22), Set D £22.50 (£30)
CARDS: Access, Amex, Diners, Visa
SEATS: 36. 6 tables outside. Car-park, 25 places. Children's helpings. Wheelchair access
(also WC)
ACCOMMODATION: 17 rooms, 15 with bath/shower. D,B&B £45 to £64. Deposit: £50. Baby
facilities. Pets welcome. Afternoon teas. Garden. Fishing. Golf. Snooker. Phone. Scenic.
Doors close at midnight. Confirm by 6. [*Which? Hotel Guide*]

KILFINAN Strathclyde   map 8

▲ *Kilfinan Hotel*

Kilfinan PA21 2AP   COOKING 2
KILFINAN (070 082) 201   COST £22–£29

'All that is best about Scottish fare – with a touch of class,' comments one
reader. 'Beautifully prepared and beautifully presented dishes,' says another.
This old coaching-inn, next to the church and on a single track country lane,
also gets approval for comfort, log fires and personal touches. 'It could hardly
be more isolated, which may explain the excellent value for money.' There are
on average three choices at each stage of the *carte*, and the same on the four-
course set dinners. Home-made soups with home-baked bread ('always a
delight') might be celery made with tasty stock. Leg of lamb might be paired
with yoghurt and mint dressing. Sauces accompanying tender venison have
been singled out – red wine and raspberry, perhaps. Halibut was 'meltingly
good' and vegetables varied and exactly cooked. Cold ham can come wafer
thin. Crème brûlée with cream, melon balls and blackberries, was 'perhaps
overdressed' but other sweets are praised for going lightly on the sugar and the
general approach of the kitchen is one of British reticence – no messed-about
food here. The wine list of around 40 bottles, strongest on clarets, rarely strays
outside France but is priced to please. Good house Sauvignon is £5.50.
CELLARMAN'S CHOICE: Ch. Méaume 1986, £7.75. Service is pleasant. Porridge
for breakfast for some reason requires 24 hours' notice.

CHEF: David Kinnear   PROPRIETOR: N.K.S. Wills
OPEN: all week
MEALS: 12 to 2, 7.30 to 9.30
PRICES: £20 (£24), Set D £19 (£22) Service inc
CARDS: Access, Amex, Diners, Visa
SEATS: 24. 2 tables outside. Private parties: 50 main room. Car-park, 20 places. Children's
helpings. Smart dress preferred. Wheelchair access (also WC). Music
ACCOMMODATION: 11 rooms, 10 with bath/shower. B&B £38.50 to £57. Deposit: 20%.
Baby facilities. Pets welcome. Afternoon teas. Garden. Fishing. TV. Phone. Scenic. Doors
close at 11. [*Which? Hotel Guide*]

---

*Restaurateurs justifiably resent no-shows. If you quote a credit card number when
booking, you may be liable for the restaurant's lost profit margin if you don't turn up.
Always phone to cancel.*

KILLIECRANKIE Tayside   map 8

▲ *Killiecrankie Hotel*

Killiecrankie PH16 5LG   COOKING 2
PITLOCHRY (0796) 3220   COST £24

Though now settled into this former dower house, Colin and Carole Anderson
continue to go out of their way to be good hosts, and even respond to
parenthetical quibblings by the *Guide*. (Supplements on the set menu have
disappeared.) There are four or five choices at stage one and two of the four
course, ever-changing dinner menu, and coffee with mint crisps is included in
the price. Served in the quiet, simple dining-room, the food is appropriate to
the area and seasons, and proves that delicate treatment of raw materials can
produce delicate, memorable flavours. Typical beginnings have been wild
game broth with juniper, dressed crab with chicory and French leaf salad, and a
terrine of shellfish in a lemon jelly. Roast saddle of hare was 'quite the finest I
have ever tasted' and venison, salmon and Angus beef, cooked, for instance,
with a green pepper butter, are of the best quality. Mainly Scottish cheeses
follow the minimum choice of sweets (two), that might be fresh fruit Pavlova
or a lemon mousse filled pancake. Bar meals have people queuing. A short
wine list includes some good names and is as generous in its provision of half-
bottles as it is with prices. House wines start at £5.30.

CHEFS: Paul Booth and Thomas Jamieson   PROPRIETORS: Colin and Carole Anderson
OPEN: all week
CLOSED: mid-Nov to late Feb
MEALS: 12.30 to 2 (bar L), 6.30 to 9.30
PRICES: Set D £17.95 (£20). Service inc
CARDS: Access, Visa
SEATS: 70. Private parties: 20 main room. Car-park, 30 places. Vegetarian meals. Children's
helpings (D only). No children under 5. No smoking in dining-room. Wheelchair access
(also WC)
ACCOMMODATION: 12 rooms, 8 with bath/shower. Rooms for disabled. B&B £21.15 to
£42.30. Pets welcome. Afternoon teas. Garden. Scenic. Doors close at midnight. Confirm by 6
[*Which? Hotel Guide*]

KILMELFORD Strathclyde   map 8

▲ *Cuilfail Hotel*

Kilmelford PA34 4XA   COOKING 1
KILMELFORD (085 22) 274   COST £17

Stopping places are not thick on the ground in these parts and the McFadyens
provide a characterful one in this Victorian hotel with a large garden and
refurbished bedrooms. Much of the food is served in the cheerful bar and bistro
and is sometimes rough and ready. Good soups, good bread, good Youngers
No.3 are the leitmotifs. Vegetarians are given more choice than usual. The daily
menu in the hotel dining-room offers West Coast materials cooked in a direct
manner: salmon with an orange hollandaise; game pie; venison. The bistro
menu is also available in the dining-room. A short wine list has the virtue of
cheapness. House wines: £5.25.

CHEF: Hilary McFadyen   PROPRIETORS: Mr and Mrs J. McFadyen
OPEN: all week
CLOSED: Jan and Feb
MEALS: 12 to 2, 6.30 to 9
PRICES: £9 (£14)
CARDS: Access, Visa
SEATS: 70. 4 tables outside. Private parties: 28 main room. Car-park, 20 places. Vegetarian meals. Children's helpings. No smoking in dining-room. Wheelchair access. Music
ACCOMMODATION: 12 rooms, 7 with bath/shower. B&B £27 to £46. Deposit: 30% or £50. Afternoon teas. Garden. Fishing. Scenic. Doors close at 11.30 [*Which? Hotel Guide*]

KINBUCK Central   map 8

▲ *Cromlix House* ♥

Kinbuck FK15 9JT   COOKING 3
DUNBLANE (0786) 822125   COST £16–£47

The stone house is solidly imposing, built at the turn of the century. The emphasis is on outdoor activities, if only to point up the comfort and warmth that will greet the visitor indoors. Cromlix is enjoyed for the feeling that it is a private home, large though it is – even to having its own chapel. It seems as though Ronald Eden left things as they were – with books in the library and things strewn about – when he migrated to a cottage on the estate so that the hotel conversion could take place. There are three connected dining-rooms and the formula elected for the menu is a six-course set-price dinner without choice. However, there is a list of alternatives at the bottom of the menu so that if the chef's suggestion doesn't suit, some other dish may be chosen. In essence, this makes a choice of three in each course. Quantities are balanced so that complaints of overeating do not surface, yet the meal may be shortened, and the price reduced, if an appetite will not extend. There appears to be an outbreak of colourful prose of late: saddle of red deer nestles on red cabbage; a tuile basket also nestles on a blackcurrant purée; and salmon wrapped in cabbage becomes a pillow that rests on its sauce. It does not signify a radical change in style with the new chef, for the cooking here has always been composed, but language has a way of truth-telling. Dishes that have pleased include quail, pigeon and partridge set in a carefully detailed salad; lobster and scallops with a Meaux mustard dressing and broccoli florets; salmon in pastry with a Chablis butter sauce; oysters, scallops and lobster with a basil sauce; rounds of lamb surrounding a layered construction of potato, aubergine and tomato with a dark rosemary sauce; fillet of beef with a madeira sauce, with a vegetable timbale (some sort of made vegetable accompaniment is common with the main dishes); chocolate coated tuiles filled with passion-fruit mousse; hot almond and caramel soufflé; or a gratin of fruits with kirsch ice-cream, a white wine sabayon and spun sugar six inches high. Desserts and pastries have been especially remarked. Service is as good as it should be, though at Christmas showing signs of inexperience and sometimes described as reserved. To get round the problem of several wines with a long meal, there is a seasonal recommendation of halves and glasses at a fixed price, for example half of Montagny 1988, Latour, followed by half of Jaboulet's Parallèle 45, 1985, finishing with two glasses of Ch. Briette, a Sauternes, or a quarter-bottle of vintage character port. This seems a popular solution. Otherwise there is a long wine list. This has claret as its strongest suit, but also showcases various growers or makers such as Krug, D.R.C, Jaboulet and O. Leflaive. Prices are not as high as may be feared. The rest of the world gets considered, for example Chile, to help with the lower price bands. There are also a dozen petits châteaux to keep claret prices affordable. House wine: £8 and £8.50.

CELLARMAN'S CHOICE: Flora Springs Sauvignon Blanc, 1986 £16.75; Coonawarra, Hungerford Hill Cabernet Sauvignon 1986, £18.75.

CHEF: Simon Burns PROPRIETOR: The Hon. Ronald Eden
OPEN: all week
CLOSED: 2 weeks Feb
MEALS: 12 to 2.30, 7 to 10
PRICES: Set L £12 (£16) to £22 (£26), Set D £22 (£26) to £35 (£39). Service inc
CARDS: Access, Amex, Diners, Visa
SEATS: 60. 4 tables outside. Private parties: 30 main room, 12, 16 and 24 private rooms. Carpark, 30 places. Children's helpings. Children restricted. No smoking in dining-room. Wheelchair access (also WC)
ACCOMMODATION: 14 rooms, all with bath/shower. B&B £95 to £130. Deposit: 50%. Baby facilities. Pets welcome. Afternoon teas. Garden. Tennis. Fishing. TV. Phone. Scenic. Doors close at midnight. Confirm 2 weeks ahead

---

KINGUSSIE Highland   map 8

▲ *The Cross* ▮

25–27 High Street, Kingussie PH21 1HX   COOKING 3
KINGUSSIE (0540) 661762   COST £28–£42

The Hadleys say you can get to Kingussie from Edinburgh in two hours, and slap bang on the main street is this unassuming converted shop with a few bedrooms above. Leave work, stay the night, and be back at the desk the next morning is one game plan – though one party was locked in the house until the Hadleys arrived to prepare breakfast. During the week there are four courses on offer at a fixed price, with soup in second place and three choices at the other stages. On Saturdays the price increases by 25 per cent, the choice is restricted to just first and main courses and the meal explodes to seven courses. Ruth Hadley is a fine natural cook and Tony Hadley is an enthusiastic host and wine lover. The combination works a treat. One reader observed that it was a thoroughly good country restaurant, not a gastronomic temple: 'the soup of red pepper and tomato was pungent and quite outstanding: the lemon sole served hot with a carrot and lime sauce was too insipid to be the only fish course, but the meats returned to form with both pink Highland lamb with a sorrel cream sauce and Gressingham duck served with ceps, ginger and a piquant sauce showing an easy mastery of good materials.' To call it 'country' is not to condemn it to lack of sophistication: calf's liver sliced wafer thin and served with a pear purée, mousseline of local pike, and salmon rillettes all show careful attention to the detail of flavour; soups such as mushroom laced with garlic or fennel or carrot, onion and thyme show enjoyment of both strength and balance. Meats are not served in giant quantity, but then the meal is a slow progression, not a marathon. Game is much enjoyed, particularly the venison

and the hare that are regularly on offer. The cheese at the end of the meal makes a strong local showing, invariably given detailed ancestry by Tony Hadley. These will be a good choice for those with a taste for red wines, but sweettooths are not ignored with chocolate whisky laird, good lemon tart or walnut cheesecake with an orange and cardamom ice-cream. An inescapable companion to eating is the wine list and the host's sheer evangelism in pleading its cause. Prices are even more generous than for the food and the list is both long and good. You can drink a Bulgarian Cabernet Sauvignon for £4.95 or a first growth 1970 (which Tony Hadley has the decency to warn you is still not ready) for £130; whichever, you are not robbed. It is almost invidious to single out any especial strengths, but Australia and New Zealand show much care, the pudding wines cover two pages and the Champagnes are more varied than in any similar place. Italy, however, gets barely a mention. Halves abound and glasses too, so that you can match wine to food on the longer dinners. Hospitality is taken seriously. This may mean that meals are too lengthy when some qualification, small point or interesting aspect is given discussion. It may equally mean the opening up of Champagne at breakfast to celebrate examination success: the memory etched on the brain of one reader.
CELLARMAN'S CHOICE: Buzet 1985, Cuvée Napoléon, £7.95; Cloudy Bay Sauvignon Blanc 1989, £15.85.

CHEF: Ruth Hadley   PROPRIETORS: Tony and Ruth Hadley
OPEN: Tue to Sat, D only
CLOSED: 3 weeks May, first 3 weeks Dec
MEALS: 6.30 to 9.30
PRICES: Set D £23.50 (£28) to £29.30 (£35) Sat
SEATS: 24. Private parties: 18 main room. Vegetarian meals. No children under 12.
No smoking. Wheelchair access
ACCOMMODATION: 3 rooms, all with bath/shower. D,B&B £48 to £110. Deposit: £20.
No children under 12. No smoking in bedrooms. Fishing. Golf

KINROSS Tayside   map 8

▲ Croft Bank House Hotel

Station Road, Kinross KY13 7TG
KINROSS (0577) 63819   COOKING 2
off M90 at Junction 6   COST £32

In this late-Victorian villa sitting on Station Road just off the motorway, it is unexpected to encounter a full-dress menu with dishes such as 'tureen of crustaceans bisque', or 'rendezvous of monkfish, sole, turbot and crayfish meeting in a pastry pot'. The *carte* is quite long for these parts, about seven dishes at each stage, and there is no set-price menu, another exception to the rule. Bill Kerr manages to include a lot of elements in each dish but they are not necessarily at odds so that harmony may reign. Recent examples seem to indicate a certain toning down of the wilder extravagances. Presentation is a strong point and may lift simple items to a higher finesse if you enjoy pastry domes and frills. Dishes that set the style are filo purse of Brie on a red berry coulis with apple, celery and walnuts; roulade of smoked salmon with a lime yoghurt; veal with pink berries and cider sauce; chicken with mango and leek stuffing on an Alsace cream sauce; and pear with mint ice-cream and chocolate sauce. Pastry work is skilled and bread and oatcakes are home made. Service may be variable. The wine list forgets vintages on the 'connoisseur' section, but is an adequate short choice, mainly French, at acceptable prices. House Bouchard is £7.25. CELLARMAN'S CHOICE: Ch. Richelieu, Fronsac 1982, £14.25; Châteauneuf-du-Pape Blanc 1988, Fabre, £15.50.

CHEF: Bill Kerr PROPRIETORS: Bill and Diane Kerr
OPEN: Tue to Sun, exc Sun D
MEALS: 12 to 2, 7 to 9
PRICES: £20 (£27)
CARDS: Access, Visa
SEATS: 44. Private parties: 18 main room, 50 private room. Car-park, 25 places. Children's helpings. Smart dress preferred. Wheelchair access (2 steps). Music
ACCOMMODATION: 4 rooms, all with bath/shower. B&B £30 to £40. TV. Doors close at 11

LINLITHGOW Lothian   map 8

Champany Inn 🍴

Champany Corner, Linlithgow EH49 7LU
PHILPSTOUN (050 683) 4532 and 4388
2m NE of Linlithgow at junction of   COOKING 3
A904 and A803   COST £46

The Davidsons have withdrawn from involvement at Eddleston and Edinburgh. Though there was never a hint that it suffered from diversification, Champany has benefited from the concentration of effort with a new smokehouse and the upgrading of the Chop and Ale House next door. This is a theme restaurant. Beef, lobster, salmon and the charcoal grill is the tune, with variations such as spring lamb, lemon sole or caviare. Every element contributes to this and each is reduced to its stylish essence: raw vegetables are first shown to each table in a great basket for a choice; lobsters are kept live and cleansed in a large tank, not an aquarium plugged in the wall, and they jump about; cheese is Stilton (with home-made oatcakes) and no other, good enough to earn the cheesemakers' award for the best in the UK. Acceptance of self-imposed limitations forces a pursuit of excellence and a New World thoroughness that is sometimes not fully appreciated by home audiences. 'Unimaginative' is a comment that takes no account of the thought expended on the passage of each piece of meat from the pasture to the grill. Somehow the menu manages to stretch over eight pages, a sign of how larger-than-life is every aspect of this restaurant. Concentrate rather on essentials. Beef is aged more than in most kitchens and any butchers. Its colour is never red but the darkest of dull burgundies. It is passed through a marinade and grilled over charcoal. Some may be had with sauces, some without, all in large portions. The alternatives are steamed lobster or steamed or grilled salmon. Many readers agree that the salmon, though farmed, suffers nothing from comparison with the wild. First courses are variations on plain salmon and lobster, gravlax, three soups, oysters, prawns or pâté. Here is the chance to try salmon and beef from the smoke-house. Sweets are no more complicated – crème brûleé, ice-creams, cold soufflés – but they are heartily endorsed. The finely embossed gilt bull that hovers at the corner of each of the many pages of the wine list suggests a robust approach that is more than fulfilled. The first 50 or so pages of burgundies, with names, vintages and prices to astound the strongest, are but an introduction. Cannily chosen Italians, Rhônes and Californians, and winning clarets fill in the picture. Sixty half-bottles finish the list. Length and stock has to be paid for, and the customer certainly does so: the house wines between £8.50 and £10.50 apart, there is little below £15. But spend £25 and be rewarded with such gems as Badia Chianti Classico 1976 or Cornas from Guy de Barjac, among many. Just as with the food, the business of wine is dealt with in style. The caged racks greet the new arrival, machines and accoutrements are there to deal with the most recalcitrant cork and sediment, and the sommelier knows his wine.

CHEFS: David Gibson and Clive Davidson   PROPRIETORS: Clive and Anne Davidson
OPEN: Mon to Sat, exc Sat L
CLOSED: 3 weeks from 24 Dec
MEALS: 12.30 to 2, 7.15 to 10
PRICES: £26 (£38). Minimum £12.50. Service 10%
CARDS: Access, Amex, Diners, Visa
SEATS: 50. 13 tables outside. Private parties: 50 main room. Car-park, 100 places.
No children under 8. Smart dress preferred. Wheelchair access

---

MARKINCH Fife   map 8

▲ Balbirnie House

| Balbirnie Park, Markinch KY7 6NE | COOKING 2 |
| GLENROTHES (0592) 610066 | COST £15−£35 |

Balbirnie Park is 416 acres of landscaped gardens and woodland famous for its rhododendrons. Set in the middle is an ambitiously restored Georgian mansion, plus a craft centre and a new 18-hole golf course. The transformation from country house to hotel has been achieved with no expense spared and the target is clearly the corporate market. Walk down vast corridors through huge rooms to reach the bar, which is a grand room with an enormous coal fire, big comfortable seats and a massive decorative oak table. Everything here is large and plush, but the lavishness is never overstated. The sheer scale and richness of the place spills over into the menu, which tries to please all-comers with its range of elaborately sauced dishes, chargrills and even cold meat salads. An inspection meal in June began impressively with sole and lobster roulade layered with spinach, tiny thin circles of home-cured beef piled on salad leaves with crispy bacon and pecan nuts. The 'intermediate course' which follows defeats its object by being much too substantial. A main course of perfectly cooked duck with peas and wild garlic sauce has been more impressive than chicken breast filled with flavourless prawn and scallop mousse on a dull Noilly Prat sauce. To finish, three-chocolate terrine has been good, but tough choux pastry éclair with a huge banana and copious amounts of cream would have been better suited to a seaside ice-cream parlour. The wine list is ambitious with good growers and properties from around the world. Although it strays into wonders such as Chassagne Montrachet 1985 from Gagnard and a 1983 Vendange Tardive from Hugel, at £36 and £34 respectively, the feet are generally kept firmly on the ground with many decent bottles below £15 and enough, including five French country wines, under £10. Sadly the half-bottle selection is derisory. House wine £8.

CHEF: George Mackay   PROPRIETORS: Balbirnie House Hotel Ltd
OPEN: all week
MEALS: 12.30 to 2, 7 to 9.30
PRICES: Set L £9.50 (£15), Set D £22 (£29)
CARDS: Access, Amex, Diners, Visa
SEATS: 45. Private parties: 60 main room, 16 and 60 private rooms. Car-park, 100 places. Vegetarian meals. Children's helpings. Smart dress preferred. No cigars/pipes in dining-room. Wheelchair access (also unisex WC). Music
ACCOMMODATION: 30 rooms, all with bath/shower. Rooms for disabled. B&B £67.50 to £86. Baby facilities. Pets welcome, exc in public rooms. Afternoon teas. Garden. Golf. Snooker. TV. Scenic. Doors close at midnight. Confirm by 6

MUIR OF ORD Highland   map 8

▲ *Dower House* ▼

| Highfield, Muir of Ord IV6 7XN | COOKING 2 |
| MUIR OF ORD (0463) 870090 | COST £35 |

'A real comer', said one reader about this delightful former dower house, set in pretty gardens and lawns 11 miles north of Inverness. 'Superlative meal well up on the previous standards at Le Chardon' (Mena and Robyn Aitchison's former venture), said another. There is flowered chintz and an abundance of plants and bric-à-brac. The semblance of a private home has been undermined by occasional lapses in the welcome and service, however, and one couple found the atmosphere in the dining-room too hush-hush. But the set lunches and dinners are widely praised for presentation and flavour, including chicory soup; darne of halibut with mustard sauce; and hot strawberries and green peppercorns with vanilla ice-cream. Other dishes enjoyed have been steamed fillet of sole with herbs, and warm pineapple with Tia Maria sauce. Cheeses are local as well as French, supplied by Alan Porter. Not every meal is of uniform excellence: a good pheasant, almond and grape salad was followed by a tasteless courgette and rosemary soup; the main course of pigeon braised with foie gras was 'succulent and pink with a hint of redcurrant in the sauce' but the foie gras had every appearance of being a truffled *bloc de foie gras*, not the real thing. Vegetables were placed on the table and when enquiry was made about the potatoes, the answer was, 'I haven't a clue.' In fact, the dish was an excellent gratin of grated potato. More New World wines are still to come on to the wine list, a compendium of the best of France with a fraction from outside. Overall, prices are not low but enthusiasm for the Loire is manifested in friendly prices. There are lots of half-bottles. House French: £9 and £9.50. Wine service is not invariably proficient. When you book, ask for good directions.

All letters to the Guide *are acknowledged with an update on latest sales, closures, chef changes and so on.*

CHEF: Robyn Aitchison PROPRIETORS: Robyn and Mena Aitchison
OPEN: all week, D only (L by arrangement)
MEALS: 7.30 for 8
PRICES: Set D £22 (£29)
CARDS: Access, Amex, Visa
SEATS: 20. 3 tables outside. Private parties: 20 main room. Car-park, 20 places. Vegetarian
meals. Children's helpings. No smoking in dining-room. Wheelchair access (also WC). One
sitting
ACCOMMODATION: 5 rooms, all with bath/shower. Rooms for disabled. B&B £35 to £70.
Deposit: 20%. Baby facilities. Pets welcome by arrangement. Garden. Fishing. Golf. TV.
Phone. Scenic. Doors close at 11.30. Confirm by 4

NEWTONMORE Highland   map 8

▲ *Ard-Na-Coille Hotel* ▮

Kingussie Road, Newtonmore PH20 1AY   COOKING 3
NEWTONMORE (054 03) 214   COST £28

In an early piece of publicity, this hotel run by refugees from academe – and
who would not flee? – stated, 'Our wine list is modest in comparison to many.'
That is hardly true today. It is best to start reading it at tea if you wish to make a
considered choice. Barry Cottam, for the notes are his, has taken a leaf out of his
friend and neighbour's book at the Cross in Kingussie (see entry), and another
Scottish cellar is born. As the house gets improved piecemeal, the dinners
maintain a constant standard within their format of four courses, with no
choice, served at one time. If guests tire of the fare, there is a reciprocal
arrangement with the Cross for a mutual exchange. Barry Cottam cooks as well
as buying the wine and explaining the excellent cheeses. His style is simple but
very careful. Saddle of venison, boned and well trimmed, was lightly roasted
and came with port and blackberry sauce; pheasant was with a barely sweet
sauce, the aroma of ceps filling the room as they rose off the plate; halibut
'looked like a plate from a book' yet was quite simple, with a curried cream
sauce and a sprinkling of fresh dill. Desserts are often served warm: apricot
tart, lemon mousseline or fresh cherry strudel, for instance. These are signs of a
happy baker who cooks the puddings to time and not early in the morning to
leave the day for other activities. First courses, too, are the sort that are done at
the time – slices of venison liver pan fried with a gin and lime sauce, tomato
flan or Arbroath smokie flan with a warm citrus vinaigrette. Barry Cottam is
self-taught but learning fast. The wine list is worth a journey for itself. If faint
heart cannot face the reading, there is a short list at the front and a wide
selection by the glass, but it is worth persevering for old clarets at very fair
prices (as is everything else): Alsaces from Rolly Gassmann, some fine Italians
including mature Barolos, a great range of Chablis including a 1978 Vaudésir
from Louis Michel, and some first-rate red Rhones. For spirits, try the malts.
The list comments that in 1989 there were many wines at under £10 but people
were loath to buy them. Who would, when faced with such ungrasping riches?
Hence, they have upgraded the quality, and price, of the lesser wines. Even so,
the majority of bottles (and there are ample halves) still cost less than £20.
CELLARMAN'S CHOICE: Cornas 1984, N. Verset, £14.50; Cloudy Bay Sauvignon
1989, £12.50. Tips are 'discouraged'.

CHEF: Barry Cottam PROPRIETORS: Barry Cottam and Nancy Ferrier
OPEN: all week, D only
CLOSED: mid-Nov and Dec
MEALS: 7.45
PRICES: Set D £19.50 (£23). No service charge
SEATS: 18. Private parties: 18 main room. Car-park, 20 places. Children's helpings on
request. No smoking in dining-room. One sitting
ACCOMMODATION: 7 rooms, all with bath/shower. B&B £27.50 to £55. Children welcome.
Baby facilities. Pets by arrangement. Garden. Doors close at 11.30. Confirm by 4
[*Which? Hotel Guide*]

NORTH BERWICK Lothian   map 8

Harding's ♀

2 Station Road, North Berwick EH39 4AU   COOKING 3
NORTH BERWICK (0620) 4737   COST £13—£26

The converted hairdresser's shop close by the railway station is now an
agreeable restaurant with a modern menu and a classy list of antipodean wines.
The dinner menu is short and fixed-price, changing daily and making good use
of local produce. The blackboard might list first courses such as carrot and
tomato soup or warm pheasant terrine with crab-apple jelly. Main courses are
usually sauced: vermouth for steamed fillet of turbot with asparagus and
mussels; sherry and green peppercorn for sauté medallions of hare. To finish
there are sweets, such as hot pear and praline soufflé, or a choice of British and
French cheeses. Lunch is a short *carte* taking in soups, salads and omelettes as
well as dishes such as breast of chicken with rosemary and madeira sauce. The
restaurant is also open for morning coffee with home-made scones, cakes and
jam. With the two Hill-Smith house wines, Australia dominates the list,
supported by New Zealand. It is arranged by maker, which is not necessarily
the most helpful for the unknowledgeable. Cabernet Sauvignon 1982 from
Wolf Blass, vintages of Penfolds Grange Shiraz, and what must be the most
comprehensive set of western Australian wines outside Perth, are among the
dazzling offerings. Prices are fair enough to encourage experiment – it's a pity
there is no accommodation. France gets a good mention on the last page. House
wine: £6.35. CELLARMAN'S CHOICE: Cloudy Bay Sauvignon 1989, £15.20;
Dalwhinnie, Shiraz 1985, £13.80.

CHEF/PROPRIETOR: Christopher Harding
OPEN: Tue to Sat, exc Tue D
MEALS: 12 to 2, 7.30 to 9
PRICES: £8 (£13), Set D £15 (£20) to £16.50 (£22)
SEATS: 24. Private parties: 24 main room. Car-park, 3 places. Children's helpings.
No smoking in dining-room. Wheelchair access (also WC). Music

---

*All details are as accurate as possible at the time of going to press, but chefs and owners
often change, and it is wise to check by telephone before making a special journey. Many
readers have been disappointed when set-price bargain meals are no longer available. Ask
when booking.*

▲ *Knipoch Hotel* 🍾

Oban PA34 4QT

COOKING 2

KILNINVER (085 26) 251

COST £44

The long butter-coloured house seems almost flattened by the woods and hills that rise behind it, but views towards the water that laps a long stone's throw from the front door are magnificent. What's more, the woods are useful for supplies of wood hedgehog to reinforce wild mushrooms bought in from further afield (or chanterelles gathered from across the loch). This information comes from Nicholas Craig's annual progress report: no more smoking of halibut, oysters or mussels because they do not benefit from the process as do salmon and scallops; resumed use of wild mushrooms after their enforced withdrawal in the wake of Chernobyl; concentration on the most successful pickling, of clementines and lemons, for example. It is apparent from this that the Craig family take food seriously and, although not extending their formula beyond a five-course set meal, evidently strive for balance and acceptability within the limitations. Menus do at least tell what is going to happen. Ingredients of sauces and origins of raw materials are spelled out. While this might be tiring on a long *carte*, it makes sense in this context. Not only are materials drawn from the locality as much as possible, but self sufficiency is taken to extremes. There can be few places that roast their own Blue Mountain coffee beans. Variety, for most guests will be there for more than a night, is built in by ensuring that the main course is fish as often as meat, allowing scope for plenty of pâtés and terrines at the second course. Soup is invariably first and a single cheese comes after the main dish. Unexpectedly for Scotland, there is no choice of desserts. Cooking may include modern touches, such as fruit sauces or relishes with the second course, but the centrepiece is normally classically inspired: salmon with a mousseline sauce, duck with a port sauce, or chicken stuffed with mushrooms and pâté and a light wine sauce. The wine list will help you pass a few hours and perhaps gain you a diploma from the Wine and Spirit Education Trust, so full is it of comment and information. However, this does not get in the way of choice which may be hindered only by plenty. Few countries are ignored, with good choices especially from Bulgaria and Chile. The strongest suit is claret, though the mark-ups on them seem more variable. The rest is generally priced very fairly. There are some affordable Vega Sicilia, decent Rhônes and carefully selected Italians. Clarity in presentation is soon shown to be false; where on one page a column lists growers' names, it shows the area on the next. Standardisation would help the informed as well as the uninitiated. Nicholas Craig is really keen on malt whisky and will happily explain its making. House wine: £7.50 and £7.90. 'Tips are discouraged but not refused.'

The text of entries is based on unsolicited reports sent in by readers, backed up by inspections conducted anonymously. The factual details under the text are from questionnaires the Guide *sends to all restaurants that feature in the book.*

CHEFS: Colin and Jenny Craig   PROPRIETORS: The Craig family
OPEN: all week, D only (L by arrangement)
CLOSED: closed from mid-Nov to mid-Feb
MEALS: 7.30 to 9
PRICES: Set D £29.50 (£37)
CARDS: Access, Amex, Diners, Visa
SEATS: 46. Private parties: 24 main room. Car-park, 40 places. Children's helpings
ACCOMMODATION: 18 rooms, all with bath/shower. B&B £49.50 to £99. Baby facilities.
Afternoon teas. Garden. TV. Phone. Scenic. Doors close at 11. Confirm by 6
[Which? Hotel Guide]

PEAT INN Fife   map 8

▲ *Peat Inn* ▮

Peat Inn KY15 5LH   COOKING 5
PEAT INN (033 484) 206   COST £20–£44

Peat Inn the village is over almost before it's begun. At night it can be missed.
So, too, can Peat Inn the restaurant. The old part sits on the road: two storeys
with a bothy. Further back is the modern bungalow where the Wilsons have
guest-rooms, deeply comfortable by all accounts. The unmistakably Scottish
spareness of the surroundings is small warning of the purple carpet and lavish
upholstery of the lounge, nor of the artexed walls, high-backed chairs,
monogrammed china and lavish setting of the three connected rooms that make
up the restaurant. The scale of the building means it can never be grand, but
they make up for it in lots of ways. In his development of Peat Inn, David
Wilson has laid successive layers of polish and display, rather like a plasterer
builds up to the final coat. The inside has nearly gone beyond the vessel that
contains it. Yet out he pops from the kitchen, small, beaming, thinly bearded, a
cloth over a shoulder, wrapped in a work-worn apron, and brings the whole
show down to earth, to a matter of his hands, his craft, his enthusiasm. The
welcome, from Patricia Wilson when she is controlling the front of house, and
from David when he emerges, is palpable. At dinner, a whole table may order a
tasting menu of six courses and coffee; or there is a menu of the day, again set-
price and no-choice; or the *carte* of six or eight options in each course. At lunch
there is a four-course set menu, the price including coffee. This is excellent
value but some are surprised that there is no choice – be warned. Butchers'
meats are used, but not as much as game, poultry and fish. A slate of choices at
one meal included fillet of beef but otherwise consisted of turbot, lobster,
pigeon, duck, quail, hare and venison. The approach is classical, without
undue stress on luxuries – truffles and foie gras are in the minor key. Sauces
are normally alcohol based, mushrooms also figuring prominently. Vegetable
purées are not often found as sauces though warm vinaigrettes do appear. It has
remained a cuisine of the north, neither drawing heavily on Provençal or
Italian inspiration, nor very much on the heady fragrances of the herb garden.
This may be seen in the fish soup: a cream coffee colour, with chewable pieces
of fish in the liquor and a small raft of pastry supporting a nugget of lobster
floating dead centre. It is exceptionally fine in texture and flavour yet has
nothing of the Mediterranean about it. This is a meal that showed off some of
the repertoire: Arbroath smokie flan with a lemon sauce, a house speciality,

more a light cooked custard; breast of pigeon on pastry case with wild mushrooms and a madeira sauce; fillets of lemon sole with a custard-like red pimento sauce; a warm salad of monkfish and scallops sitting on a potato galette with a lemon vinaigrette; saddle of hare in an alcohol-enriched blood sauce; fillet of beef with wild mushrooms and a red wine sauce; wild duck with a thyme sauce; roast grouse, traditionally presented with bread sauce, some roast potatoes, red cabbage under one leg and white under the other, and broccoli; some chaourcé; pineapple and grenadine sorbets; a little pot of chocolate and rosemary; marquise au chocolat with an orange sauce; and a trio of nut desserts, praline ice-cream, nougat and a hazelnut meringue. Apparent were the skills in handling meat and extracting full flavour from fish. Not so positive is the desire to embellish. This may relate to the gradual improvement of the restaurant itself, a manifestation in food terms of 'going up-market'. However, it is neither as stylish as the best practitioners and, worse, gets in the way of the fundamentals. The Arbroath smokie flan sits on a bed of cabbage and pine kernels and is topped by a vermicelli of beetroot and carrot. The cabbage does not contribute to success. Equally, the rösti under the monkfish and scallop salad actually detracts from the clean tastes; the fruit salad surrounding the sorbets is not nearly so impressive as the ices themselves. Tips are neither 'expected nor encouraged'. The wine list is long and clearly laid out, white sheets for whites and pink for reds. The notes are discreet and helpful. The prices are fair: £48 will buy you Krug. There are plenty of halves and a decent worldwide spread, though not much attention to Italy. The New World choice, with the exception of Cabernet Sauvignons from California, is not particularly noteworthy, though Philip Togni's Sauvignon from Napa, or Balgownie Chardonnay from Australia are just two whites that show sure selection. It is predominantly a French list with mouthwatering clarets and burgundies. Age is considered, and the price means it's worth drinking up the scale if you can: Ch. Palmer, Ch. Léoville Las Cases, Ch. Pichon-Lalande, Ch. Ducru-Beaucaillou and others are there in depth. Burgundy makers such as Comte de Vogüé, Rousseau, Dujac, Fèvre, Ampeau and Comte Lafon are excellent and there for half the London prices.

CHEF: David Wilson   PROPRIETORS: David and Patricia Wilson
OPEN: Tue to Sat
CLOSED: 2 weeks Jan and Nov
MEALS: 1 to 2.30, 7 to 9.30
PRICES: £28 (£34), Set L £15.50 (£20), Set D £26 (£30) to £32 (£37). Service inc
CARDS: Amex, Access, Diners, Visa
SEATS: 48. Private parties: 24 main room, 12 private room. Car-park, 24 places. Children's helpings. No smoking during meals. Wheelchair access (also WC)
ACCOMMODATION: 8 rooms, all with bath/shower. Rooms for disabled. B&B £75 to £98. No children under 12. Garden. Fishing. Golf. TV. Phone. Scenic. Confirm by 4

The 1992 Guide will be published before Christmas 1991. Reports on meals are most welcome at any time of the year, but are extremely valuable in the spring. Send them to The Good Food Guide, FREEPOST, 2 Marylebone Road, London NW1 1YN. *No stamp is needed if posted in the UK.*

Report forms are at the back of the book; write a letter if you prefer.

▲ Cringletie House

Eddleston, Peebles EH45 8PL
EDDLESTON (072 13) 233
on A703, 2m N of Peebles

COOKING 1
COST £11–£30

Don't run over the pheasants in the car park, even if you are hungry; there will be food within this Scottish baronial mansion that sprouts turrets and dormers from end to end. The Maguires have been here for 20 years and the new generation has now joined them. Returning guests value the welcome, which mitigates against being over-awed by the grandeur of some of the public rooms. Service has been known to fairly canter through the four-course dinners that allow a choice of four or five dishes, with a single soup separating the first and main courses. The palette of flavours is more eclectic than many Borders establishments: cinnamon with aubergine; coconut and courgette soup; coconut with Dover sole; brambles with duck. On occasion these could be followed through with more commitment and backed up by a more thoroughgoing technique and larder practice (beef, for instance, could have been hung longer). But some nice things have been recorded: excellent vegetables; aubergine sauté with onion, tomato and walnuts carefully spiced with cinnamon; duck that had been skilfully roasted and came with a gin and bramble sauce of good flavour. Desserts are on the sideboard and may appear 'all the same colour (pale beige)' or not in the first flush of intensity and allure. Sieve the shortish wine list for some jewels – a good spread of 1979 clarets including Ch. Chasse Spleen; Dom. du Vieux Télégraphe 1985; Clos du Papillon 1987. House French: £7.80 litre. CELLARMAN'S CHOICE: Médoc, Ch. La Tour St Bonnet 1982, £13.50; St Véran 1986, Jadot, £12.

CHEFS: Aileen Maguire and Sheila McKellar   PROPRIETORS: Mr and Mrs Stanley Maguire
OPEN: all week
CLOSED: Jan and Feb
MEALS: 1 to 1.45, 7.30 to 8.30
PRICES: Set L from £4.50 (£11), Sun L £11.50 (£17), Set D £18 (£25)
CARDS: Access, Visa
SEATS: 56. Private parties: 30 main room. Car-park, 40 places. Vegetarian meals. Children's helpings. No smoking in dining-room
ACCOMMODATION: 13 rooms, all with bath/shower. Lift. B&B £35 to £65. Baby facilities. Pets welcome. Afternoon teas. Garden. Tennis. TV. Phone. Scenic. Doors close at 11. Confirm by 5 [Which? Hotel Guide]

Timothys

24 St John Street, Perth PH1 5SP
PERTH (0738) 26641

COOKING 1
COST £19

Friendly and unassuming, Caroline and Athole Laing have enjoyed long-time success. Menu headings are Danish-inspired – 'snitter', or starters, followed by smørrebrød, or open sandwiches – but that is often the end of the Scandinavian connection. To begin there are 'asparagus roll-ups'. Athole Laing reports that he has a new supplier of asparagus in season who 'delivers freshly cut spears at lunchtime, just ready for service'. Then, it might be 'Sardine shoal', lots of baby sardines with hard-boiled egg and mayonnaise; or 'beef madras', roast beef with potato salad, hard-boiled egg and curry mayonnaise, or 'Russian rubies', home-cooked ham with beetroot and soured cream. You can be sure that there will be a lot of eggs, mayonnaise and soured cream, but these and everything else are of the freshest. More emphasis is now being placed on local Scottish produce, Loch Fyne oysters having recently become favourites. Served unadorned on a bed of crushed ice, they are 'very large, juicy and almost sweet'. The restaurant is also open for morning coffee at 10 and may surprise with hot doughnuts, lemon pancakes or energy bread. The wine list is a fast-moving affair offered at fair prices. Try one of the two iced akvavits. House French is £5.90. CELLARMAN'S CHOICE: Campo Viego Rioja Gran Reserva, 1978, £10.50.

CHEF: Caroline Laing   PROPRIETORS: Caroline and Athole Laing
OPEN: Tue to Sat
CLOSED: 3 weeks in summer
MEALS: 12 to 2.30, 7 to 10.15
PRICES: £11 (£16), Cover charge: 25p after 9.30. Minimum £5 after 9.30
CARDS: Access, Visa
SEATS: 54. Private parties: 20 main room. Vegetarian meals. Children's helpings.
Wheelchair access. Music (D only). Air-conditioned

PORT APPIN Strathclyde   map 8

▲ *Airds Hotel* ▮

Port Appin PA38 4DF   COOKING 4
APPIN (063 173) 236   COST £14–£43

A reader commented: 'Dinners have to be the sort that can be eaten daily for a week. This makes comparison with a restaurant difficult.' Another made her contribution: 'After 12 dinners and 12 breakfasts, every meal faultless.' It is a perspective that the one-time visitor cannot have and may account for one reference to 'dinner-party cooking.' The point may be that Betty Allen's approach is discreet and so avoids the overload common to many cooks. This ultra-refinement of a particular form sits well in the former ferry inn that is Airds. It looks no monument to luxury, though that impression may be dispelled on seeing the furnishings and housekeeping of a very high order. Dinner is a four-course meal, soup at the second, with three or four choices in the others. Guests assemble in the lounge before a single starting time. Recommendations are for many dishes but three categories receive more than the others: the seafood, particularly the prawns from Loch Linnhe; the soups; and the quality of the meats. The venison 'almost dissolved, so tender was it, yet had full game flavour'. The breast of duck 'had a texture almost like liver pâté'. Certainly the meats are treated in a conservative fashion, often roasted, to bring out their essential qualities: venison with a burgundy and juniper sauce; poussin with mushrooms and tarragon; fillet of beef with a classic red sauce. Even veal, roast fillet with a mushroom cream sauce, can be exceptional. Fish is as good in quality as should be expected: Mallaig scallops with a Barsac sauce; a mousseline of scallops with a Champagne and chive sauce; ravioli of seafood with a lobster bisque; turbot with oysters and a Chardonnay sauce have been mentioned with enthusiasm. It will be noted that these are rarely 'made' dishes in the way of fancy chefs, though the techniques used are accurate. Desserts may also have an element of simplicity: 'orange and Grand Marnier terrine was really a jelly'; raspberry and Drambuie ice-cream was just that, in a glass with shortbread on the plate. Normally, the value of this cooking is that it has flavour, from the vegetables to the sauces, though occasions are noted when the flavouring element – coriander in a coriander and carrot soup, or Drambuie in that ice-cream – have been more fugitive than they might have been. As befits a Relais & Châteaux member, the service is good, almost too good for some who like to relax, and rarely subject to indiscretion though youthful. This is on a par with all those supporting elements to the dining-room: fresh bread and croissants, breakfasts, coffee, canapés and petits fours. And, of course, the wine list. This weighty volume is left in the bedroom for a long look before plunging. It is not the prices that will stop a jump headlong into clarets, though they are not give-away; it is the variety of choice, halves as well as wholes. There are great opportunities for comparative drinking if a stay is envisaged: Côte Rôties from Chapoutier, Jaboulet and Guigal; Graves at very fair prices from Pape-Clément, La Mission, Dom. de Chevalier and Haut Brion itself, Chambolle Musignys from Roumier, Latour, de Vogüé and others; or Californian Cabernet Sauvignons from Warren Winiarski, Heitz, Mondavi and Ridge. One couple had wrong vintages on two successive nights, a problem of long lists, long lines of communication, and unobservant wine-waiting, but Eric Allen himself is very knowledgeable and conversant with his stocks. 'Basically a simple small hotel which has advanced to being one of the best in Scotland due to the high standards set by the proprietors.'

CHEFS: Betty Allen, Graeme Allen and Moira Thompson   PROPRIETORS: Eric and Betty Allen
OPEN: all week
MEALS: 12.30 to 1.30, 8 for 8.30
PRICES: Bar L £10 (£14), Set D £28 (£36)
SEATS: 40. Private parties: 40 main room, 8 private room. Car-park, 30 places. Children's helpings. No children under 4. Smart dress preferred. No smoking in dining-room. One sitting
ACCOMMODATION: 14 rooms, all with bath/shower. B&B £60 to £110. Deposit: £75. No children under 4. Afternoon teas. Garden. TV. Phone. Scenic. Doors close at 11.45. Confirm by 4 [Which? Hotel Guide]

PORTPATRICK   Dumfries & Galloway   map 8

▲ Knockinaam Lodge

Portpatrick DG9 9AD   COOKING 3
PORTPATRICK (077 681) 471   COST £22–£38

The blue-grey sea stretches out from the foreshore and visitors to Knockinaam might well be at the end of the earth, were it not for Ireland breaking the line of the horizon. Although isolated – and the principal activities here will be walking, dreaming and warming your socks by the fire – the kitchen is mainlining on European ideas and materials. Even the cheeses are from Philippe Olivier, the butter from Echiré, the foie gras from Delpeyrat. Daniel

Galmiche offers a four-course menu with a choice of two main courses and an alternative of dessert or cheese. It is French, in language and style. For some this is too marked: shocked by a disregard for side dishes of vegetables and no choice of desserts, unlike other Scottish hotels. The style is very assured: the main ingredient dominates, there is no needless decoration, and portions are finely judged so as not to overload. The progression may sound substantial: sole and monkfish on a bed of leeks, then aiguillette of duck with mushrooms, 'so tender a knife was not needed', followed by a main course choice of fish or meat. On occasion the second course may be vegetable based, for instance wild mushroom ravioli with a watercress sauce, but it is rarely if ever soup: another point of distinction from the Scottish norm. The wave of long-cooked as opposed to sauté dishes that has engulfed Europe has also broken here. Thus an autumn meal began in earnest with a piece of turbot roasted with herbs, served with puréed potatoes and turnips. The second course was a small leg of duck braised with lentils, as prelude to either sea bass with mussels or ox-tail presented with young vegetables. Dessert was a greengage feuilleté with a kirsch sabayon. Coffee and petits fours were served afterwards in the lounge. Brill wrapped in spinach beet leaves, with a carrot sauce; sole and monkfish with a light meat sauce and a garlic and parsley purée; rabbit with a beetroot purée and a courgette sauce are examples of light cooking with nice uses of materials around us. It is a pity that reports are not unanimous about consistent standards. The wine list is adequate to the task, though not particularly cheap. Its choice of burgundies is not very adventurous, but some New World reinforcements are bringing fair-priced variety, notably Tim Knapstein's Cabernet/Merlot, Nobilo's Pinotage, and Pirramimma's Chardonnay. Chilean wines are £8.10.

CHEF: Daniel Galmiche PROPRIETORS: Marcel and Corinna Frichot
OPEN: all week
CLOSED: 4 Jan to 14 Mar
MEALS: 12.30 to 2, 7.30 to 9
PRICES: Set L £18 (£22), Set D £28 (£32). Service inc
CARDS: Access, Amex, Diners, Visa
SEATS: 28. Private parties: 40 main room. Car-park, 25 places. No children under 12. Smart dress preferred. No smoking in dining-room. Wheelchair access (1 step; also WC)
ACCOMMODATION: 10 rooms, all with bath/shower. B&B £70 to £170. Deposit: £100. Baby facilities. Pets welcome. Afternoon teas. Garden. TV. Phone. Scenic. Doors close at midnight. Confirm 2 weeks ahead

---

SCONE Tayside   map 8

▲ *Murrayshall Hotel*

Scone PH2 7PH   COOKING 3
SCONE (0738) 51171   COST £21–£52

Drive by the golf course through woodland alive with pigeons, pheasants and rabbits. Bruce Sangster enjoys the quality of supplies here; doubtless you passed some. Murrayshall keeps its reception low key, almost informal. This clearly pays dividends, for business is brisk. The kitchen cooks a single *carte*, five courses long with five or six choices in each course, at a stiff fixed price (though lunch is half the cost). The substantial rise in price since the last *Guide*

is not beneficial to appreciation of the cooking, which is very good. Presentation is a treat as well, not so precious as to be visible, nor so mannered as to delay production and cause cooling of the food. A summer menu promised well, the style interesting without excess, the most wayward dish being veal with langoustine tails on a ginger and shellfish sauce. Meats may be enriched with mousse or stuffing: lamb topped with a tarragon mousse or chicken stuffed with pearl barley and sweetbreads. Combinations of flavour are often well handled: a filo purse is filled with strong goats' cheese, balanced by fruity accompaniment of grapes and apples and infused by aromatic tomato and coriander sauce. In this meal fruit occurred as a side relish in company with a chicken liver parfait with pistachio nuts. It was in the guise of apple and sultana purée – the sultanas soaked in madeira – though the build-up of tastes was less striking. Celeriac spring rolls filled with vegetables seemed to be made of tough pastry, not celeriac, and being burned did not assist delicacy. Too much delicacy, however, vitiated the appeal of a cauliflower, smoked cheese and mustard soup. Balance reasserted itself in a lamb dish with a fragrant herb sauce, the meat benefiting from being left in a marinade of garlic and herbs. Balance was again less apparent in a strong langoustine sauce accompanying bland, tough veal; the announced ginger was hard to detect. Cheese, a good range in prime condition, is very satisfactory. One benefit of a set menu and a multitude of customers is that food is used up before it loses its bloom. The menu makes a distinction between a filo purse (goats' cheese) and a moneybag (pears and bananas). Other sorts of pastry are notable by their absence. Puddings are fresh tasting and direct though of limited range. The price rise may be caused in part by the offering of greater choice – only two at each course previously. It does not seem to reflect a change in style in the kitchen or more use of luxury ingredients, for example. Incidentals are well finished, as they should be, from breads to canapés to cream and truffle chocolates. The wines, which on a busy Saturday night may be served with little ceremony, deserve obeisance. Mature wines figure in many of the sections, especially clarets and burgundies – clarets are the longest suit – and properties are well selected. Half-bottles are numerous. Prices are not always as high as might be feared. House wine from Corney & Barrow is £8.95.
CELLARMAN'S CHOICE: Rully 1988, Faiveley, £15.75; Ch. Coufran 1983, £17.50.

CHEF: Bruce Sangster PROPRIETORS: Macolsen Ltd
OPEN: all week
MEALS: 12 to 1.45, 7 to 9.30
PRICES: Set L £15 (£21) to £17.50 (£24), Set D £35 (£43)
CARDS: Access, Amex, Diners, Visa
SEATS: 60. Private parties: 20 main room, 70 private room. Car-park. Children welcome. Smart dress preferred. No smoking in dining-room. Wheelchair access. Music
ACCOMMODATION: 19 rooms, all with bath/shower. B&B £65 to £105. Deposit: 10%. Pets welcome. Afternoon teas. Garden. Tennis. Golf. TV. Phone. Scenic. Confirm by 6
[Which? Hotel Guide]

The Guide is totally independent, accepts no free hospitality, and survives on the number of copies sold each year.

SCOTLAND

STEWARTON Strathclyde   map 8

▲ *Chapeltoun House* ♥

Stewarton KA3 3ED
STEWARTON (0560) 82696
2m from Stewarton, on B769 towards   COOKING 2
Irvine   COST £21–£36

The industrialist who built Chapeltoun at the very beginning of this century
liked things solid. It is a heavy place, not lightened by the strong, dark colours
of much of its decoration and furnishings – stained and polished wood
bulking large. The outside is architecturally rather more satisfying. During
1989 Kevin McGillivray came to take charge of the kitchen, having worked
previously at Craigendarroch Hotel and Country Club at Ballater. The kitchen
is not nervous of elaboration: salmon layered with a sole and scampi mousse
with a yellow pepper coulis; loin of lamb with a mousse of parsley and corn
seeds on a redcurrant glaze; even avocado has a timbale of pink grapefruit. For
all this, the details are considered and the standard has proved acceptable.
Desserts have hitherto been confined to rather creamy affairs set out on a table
for self-service. This feature is preserved but has been added to: a hot pudding
(though at an unjustified supplement to the fixed price) and a composed iced
dessert. On the wine list the claret section is longer than any other and includes
a fair amount from the second half of the 1970s. Otherwise it is an orthodox
French list with some reinforcement from outside, including Chianti Castell' in
Villa, Inglenook and Simi Cabernet Sauvignons and Hardy's Cabernet/Shiraz.
House wines start at £7.50. CELLARMAN'S CHOICE: Meursault les Perriers 1982,
Grivault, £30.50; Ch. Haut Madrac, Haut Médoc 1985, £13.10.

CHEF: Kevin McGillivray PROPRIETORS: Colin and Graeme McKenzie
OPEN: all week
MEALS: 12 to 2, 7 to 9.15
PRICES: Set L £15 (£21), Set D £23.50 (£30)
CARDS: Access, Amex, Visa
SEATS: 55. Private parties: 35 main room, 20 and 55 private rooms. Car-park, 50 places.
Vegetarian meals. No children under 12. Smart dress preferred No smoking in dining-
room. Wheelchair access (3 steps; also WC).
ACCOMMODATION: 8 rooms, all with bath/shower. B&B £69 to £109. No children under 12.
Pets by arrangement. Afternoon teas. Garden. Fishing. TV. Phone. Scenic. Doors close
at midnight

SWINTON Borders   map 8

▲ *Four Seasons,*
Wheatsheaf Hotel

Swinton TD11 3JJ   COOKING 1
SWINTON (089 086) 257   COST £24

An attractive country inn across from a large open green and, for eating, a cut
above the expected. It's often busy, particularly at lunch, but a new sun-
lounge, courtyard and patio ease congestion. Inside, tables are closely packed
and the atmosphere jovial. The à la carte menu favours all- seasons pub fare:

smoked fish brioche with salad, carrot and orange soup, and green figs in brandy are as far fetched as it goes. But if a degree of artistry is lacking, good ingredients and quality craftsmanship have been noted, for instance, in the delicately flavoured and firm-textured smoked salmon or lightly battered mushrooms in garlic mayonnaise. Spinach pancake was light and fresh with a sauce made from good cheese. Beef in real ale hot-pot is a big seller. Desserts have been a let down, with tough profiteroles and tougher meringue. Portions are sized for healthy appetites. Service is hurried and not always personal, but credit card bills are always fully filled in. The wide ranging but short wine list is well chosen and very fairly priced, with much around £10 and a few good, more expensive, bottles. Details are sometimes lacking. House French or Bulgarian is £5.40. CELLARMAN'S CHOICE: Mâcon-Lugny 1988, Mathelin, £8.20; Vina Réal Gran Reserva CVNE, 1981, £10.95.

CHEFS: Alan Reid and George Robertson   PROPRIETORS: Alan and Julie Reid
OPEN: Tue to Sun
CLOSED: 25 Dec, 1 Jan, 2 weeks Feb
MEALS: 11.45 to 2, 7 to 10
PRICES: £13 (£20)
CARDS: Access, Visa
SEATS: 20. Private parties: 20 main room, 28 private rooms. Vegetarian meals. Children's helpings. Smart dress preferred. No cigars/pipes in dining-room. Wheelchair access (1 step; also WC)
ACCOMMODATION: 3 rooms. B&B £20 to £32. Baby facilities. Pets welcome. Garden. TV. Scenic. Doors close at midnight. Confirm by 6

TIRORAN Isle of Mull   map 8

▲ Tiroran House

| Tiroran, Mull PA69 6ES | COOKING 2 |
| TIRORAN (068 15) 232 | COST £13−£35 |

'It is natural, in traversing this gloom of desolation, to inquire whether something may not be done to give nature a more cheerful face,' wrote Dr Johnson of a journey across Mull. One solution, proposed by the Blockeys, is to stay at Tiroran House, a shooting-lodge with water and bare hills to one side, close plantations (which were advocated for the island by Johnson himself) to another. Were the house full of residents, the dining-room would be full as well, so telephone if only a meal is planned. The set-price dinner offered at a single sitting for all contains the option of three first courses and three desserts with a no-choice meat or fish course as a centrepiece. This will often be a roast such as gigot of lamb with a grain mustard sauce and ratatouille, served with purée of carrot and spring cabbage with juniper, or beef Wellington with Jersey royals, courgettes with tomato, and carrots. First courses, of which one is invariably a soup, may include oysters with a lemon butter sauce or, early in the season, gulls' eggs with a garlic mayonnaise. Desserts also have a pattern to them: a hot pudding – syrup and ginger, treacle tart with a melon ice-cream; a cream dessert – iced lemon soufflé or syllabub – and an ice-cream. Cheeses are Scottish, plus Stilton. The cooking is firmly accomplished, with a lightness not always achieved in this repertoire. 'Tips are not accepted,' say the Blockeys. The wine list is a very careful selection with good geographical spread. Much is from Corney & Barrow, which means growers are always respectable, often grand. Prices are very fair indeed and halves there are aplenty. House wine: £7.50. CELLARMAN'S CHOICE: Ch. de Montdespic 1985, £10.50; Ch. des Moines 1983, £13.

CHEF: Sue Blockey   PROPRIETORS: Wing Commander and Mrs Blockey
OPEN: all week, D only (L residents only)
CLOSED: mid-Oct to end May
MEALS: 7 for 7.45
PRICES: Set L £9 (£13), Set D £25 (£29). Service inc
SEATS: 20. Private parties: 8 main room. Car-park, 20 places. No children under 10. Smart dress preferred. No smoking in dining-room. One sitting
ACCOMMODATION: 9 rooms, all with bath/shower. D, B&B £77 to £96. Deposit: £50. No children under 10. Pets by arrangement. Garden. Fishing. Scenic

---

ULLAPOOL Highland   map 8

▲ *Altnaharrie Inn* ♟

Ullapool IV26 2SS   COOKING 5
DUNDONNELL (085 483) 230   COST £53

A report from 1987 gives some perspective to Gunn Eriksen and Fred Brown's achievement: 'Third consecutive year we have visited; goes from strength to strength; but how long can it last?' The answer may be: for much longer than our correspondent imagined, for one of the recent reports says, 'The combination of flavours was so subtle, the ingredients so fresh that one had the impression of a seamless robe. This was enhanced by knowing one had no choice. I did not listen to the recited menu and was left guessing at the ingredients. The nettle and Brie soup was wondrous, a quite sensuous experience, the texture lingering longer than the flavour, but I did have to ask what was in it. No such problem with the lobster, the wood-pigeon and a very melting lemon and pistachio tart. The French cheeses seem incongruous given the emphasis on local ingredients in the other courses.' It bears repetition that Altnaharrie is isolated, reached by boat from Ullapool: 'The launch ride and the wait on the cold pier beforehand were rather grim. It brings one from reality to fairyland then back again,' wrote one who made the trip in the off-season. It explains why the terms are for dinner, bed and breakfast. Comfort, however, envelops the body once arrived. You will not want for much, though a reader who brought elderly parents advises lodging the less than athletic in the main house rather than a satellite. Gunn Eriksen's cooking is never simple, but nor does it fall into the error of being ornate. It uses flavours, often growing right outside the door (nettles, elderflower, hawthorn), to a purpose. 'We had elderflower soup; ravioli of lobster, scallops and langoustines in a Champagne sauce; wood-pigeon with liver and kidneys en croûte; cheese; and then tried all three sweets: rhubarb tart – the name just doesn't do it justice – oatcakes with honey ice-cream and warm chocolate cake,' reported one bowled over by the experience last summer. A meal with points in common was reported by another couple: 'Rich and creamy nettle and Brie soup, terrific; ravioli of prawns and lobster were garnished with a lobster claw, samphire, rings of red pepper, dill sprigs and finished with a Champagne butter sauce; very good wholemeal bread; pigeon breast was accompanied by a puff pastry package of pigeon livers and chopped leg meat wrapped with a layer of lettuce, in a sauce of redcurrants and the juice from the cooking. A few redcurrants added a dash of colour. One could taste a hint of ginger in the lettuce package, setting off the richness of the meat. Vegetables were finely grated cabbage, mange-tout and new potatoes sliced and buttered (unfortunately cold).' Common elements within the repertoire are seen in a meal that began with a 'soup' of langoustine and squat lobster with a mousseline of scallops wrapped in a lettuce leaf; went on to the meat dish of the day, layers of foie-gras and asparagus on a bed of potato galette, with a light veal stock sauce and a sorrel and mustard sauce. The main course was salmon stuffed with crab, leek and ginger with a Champagne butter sauce. Desserts, always three, were cranberry cake, baked banana with an orange sauce and a pastry basket of strawberries, raspberries and blueberries with ice-cream and two coulis. Although a few have been defeated by the scale of the meal, the accuracy of technique and seasoning may well leave the majority gasping for more – stay another day. The inhibited may find on one day that 'the sociable disposition of 12 like-minded, enthusiastic diners' is too much for them; equally, the others have said 'one has to whisper an awful lot for fear of interfering with other people's conversations.' No reports, though, question the effectiveness of housekeeping, hospitality or breakfasts. The wine list, a purist remarked, could be even better to match the food, but it is not bad, nor is it impossibly priced. Maturity is considered in both burgundy and claret, by far the strongest sections, but Fred Brown does not have the encyclopaedic approach. Every effort to supply decent halves is made. Restaurant guides are forced to select and then compare the best – a nonsense really, for how can one compare Gunn Eriksen's work to that of a chef turning out 150 meals a day, year in year out? However *on the plate* comparisons will be made, and many there are who say this woman is among the best.

CHEF: Gunn Eriksen   PROPRIETORS: Fred Brown and Gunn Eriksen
OPEN: all week, D only
CLOSED: late Oct to Easter
MEALS: 7.45
PRICES: Set D £40 (£44). Service inc
SEATS: 14. Private parties: 14 main room. Car-park, 20 places. Vegetarian meals. Children's helpings (D only). No children under 10. No smoking in dining-room. One sitting
ACCOMMODATION: 8 rooms, all with bath/shower. D,B&B £79 double only. Deposit: £75. No children under 10. Pets by arrangement. Garden. Fishing. Scenic. Confirm by 4
[*Which? Hotel Guide*]

▲ Morefield Motel

Ullapool IV26 2TH	COOKING 1
ULLAPOOL (0854) 2161	COST £8–£27

The dining-room is more elaborate than the pub, which is as fundamental as most in the north of Scotland. The shining value is the fish, which is fresh as fresh can be – the Motel has a share in a trawler to guarantee its supplies. Order simple dishes as the sauces do not improve things. Persevere on this line and be repaid by remarkable food. Do not deviate. The wine list is perfunctory but includes Frascati, Graves and Muscadet under £5. It is not offered automatically, observed a visitor, because few people seem to buy wine north of Inverness. House wine: £5.50.

CHEF: Gary Quinn PROPRIETORS: David Smyrl and David Courtney Marsh
OPEN: all week
MEALS: 12 to 2, 6 to 9.30
PRICES: £15 (£18), Set L £4 (£8) to £9 (£13), Set D £6.50 (£11) to £17.50 (£22)
CARDS: Access, Amex, Visa
SEATS: 106. 6 tables outside. Private parties: 40 main room. Car-park, 35 places. Children's helpings. No-smoking area. Wheelchair access (also WC). Music
ACCOMMODATION: 11 rooms, all with bath/shower. Rooms for disabled. B&B £20 to £35. Deposit: 10%. Baby facilities. Afternoon teas. Garden. Fishing. Scenic. Doors close at midnight. Confirm by 6

WALLS Shetland   map 8

▲ Burrastow House

Walls ZE2 9PB
WALLS (059 571) 307   COOKING 2
3m W of Walls   COST £11−£22

The setting is remote, so this eighteenth-century house is a true haven of peace to which congenial informality is added. Ann Prior and Bo Simmons have plundered local auctions for furniture and fittings, which contribute much to the atmosphere of well-lived-in domesticity. Peat fires burn in the panelled dining-room. Each partner takes turns in the kitchen, week by week. Their raw materials are local or home-grown, from the smoked salmon and Shetland lamb to the garden vegetables, but their inspiration is global. Rillettes of goose from France, the classic Scandinavian egg and anchovy dish, Jansen's Temptation, and Chinese-influenced salmon with ginger and spring onion share the stage with Arbroath smokies or thoroughly English spiced beef with mustard sauce. There is no problem for vegetarians. Reporters praise the soups served with home-made nut and herb bread, the rich puddings and the ewe's cheese made with milk from the animal tethered in the garden. The reasonably priced wine list has an increasing number of organic and biodynamic offerings, and there is organic Avalon cider as well as Orkney Raven ale on draught. House wine (organic) is £5. CELLARMAN'S CHOICE: Bourgogne Irancy 1985, Luc Sorin, £12.

CHEFS/PROPRIETORS: Ann Prior and Bo Simmons
OPEN: all week, exc Tue (residents only); L by arrangement Oct to Apr
CLOSED: Jan and Feb
MEALS: 12.30 to 2.30, 7.30 to 9
PRICES: L £8 (£11), Set D £15 (£18). Service inc
SEATS: 20. Private parties: 16 main room. Car-park, 5 places. Vegetarian meals. Children's helpings. No smoking in dining room. Music
ACCOMMODATION: 3 rooms, 2 with bath/shower. D,B&B £36 to £62. Baby facilities. Pets welcome. Afternoon teas. Garden. Fishing. Scenic. Doors close at 9. Confirm by 6 or by arrangement [*Which? Hotel Guide*]

map 8

▲ *Knockie Lodge*

Whitebridge IV1 2UP
GORTHLECK (045 63) 276   COOKING 2
on B862, 8m N of Fort Augustus   COST £31

Stunning views and good local walks are part of the attractions of this country house. The kitchen succeeds because it offers fresh seasonal Scottish produce – including beef, salmon and vegetables – cooked with care and a lack of elaboration. In the elegant dining-room, that philosophy extends to the properly trained, personable staff. The four-course menu (plus cheese and coffee) has no choice until the sweets. One excellent meal began with goujons of haddock with tartare sauce followed by pea and mint soup. The centrepiece is invariably a roast – anything from beef fillet with chanterelles and a pastry cup of béarnaise, to duck generously sliced with a citrus sauce pointed up with slices of oranges and grapefruit. Sweets such as black cherry and almond tart are served with a jug of thick Scottish cream. Light bar lunches are no longer offered and the Milwards stress that non-residents must telephone ahead to see if dinner is available. It won't be if all the guest rooms are occupied. Seventy wines offer adequate range and value. House French: £6.50. CELLARMAN'S CHOICE: St Amour, Clos des Billards 1986, £11; Villa Montes Sauvignon Blanc, Chile 1989, £7.50.

CHEF: Chris Freeman PROPRIETORS: Brenda and Ian Milward
OPEN: all week, D only
CLOSED: end Oct to end Apr
MEALS: 8
PRICES: Set D £20 (£26)
CARDS: Access, Amex, Visa
SEATS: 22. Private parties: 12 main room. Car-park, 30 places. No children under 10. Smart dress preferred. One sitting
ACCOMMODATION: 10 rooms, all with bath/shower. D,B&B £65 to £144. Deposit: £50. No children under 10. Pets welcome. Garden. Fishing. Snooker. Scenic [*Which? Hotel Guide*]

Wales

Hive on the Quay

Cadwgan Place, Aberaeron SA46 0BT   COOKING 1
ABERAERON (0545) 570445   COST £15

This summertime café/restaurant overlooking the harbour is more than 15
years old. The café opens for the long season, but the restaurant for the high
season only. Self-service and light snack meals rule until 6 o'clock when
waitresses take over. Here is a place that aims to serve genuine food to all the
family. The name comes from the honey farm once occupying the premises;
apiarists can still gaze at observation hives and visit the honey shop. It is also
the home of the 'original' honey ice-cream, now extended into a range of
yoghurt and honey ices with passion-fruit and strawberry flavours. The
evening menus are supplemented by daily specials on the blackboard; there
may be a greater emphasis on fish this year because 'we now have a resident
fisherman.' The sort of food served is typified by grilled mackerel with parsley
sauce, broad beans and new potatoes; crab tartlets with a mixed salad and new
potatoes; a hot-pot of organic vegetables and salad; Aberaeron Prize Sausages
with spicy red cabbage, baked potatoes and sour cream; lots of ice-cream ideas
for sweets, fresh raspberry Bakewell tart or other fruit tarts. Genuine, with a
concern for freshness and proper origins, this place is excellent value. We can
do no more than quote Margaret Holgate's letter to us on two subjects, with
which we agree. 'Children will never learn unless they see how other children
fit happily into adult territory. We sometimes think we qualify for an
educational grant. With regard to modern cooking, the copycat syndrome has
trickled down to the detriment of simpler provincial cooking. Restaurants
think it is smart for their not-so-accomplished chefs to ape the great ones with
excruciatingly affected recipes, everything stuffed to death and tasting of
nothing in particular. Surely visitors to this country want to taste real food
flavours, not silly concoctions.' The two wines available are organic.

CHEF: John Bromley   PROPRIETORS: Margaret and Sarah Holgate
OPEN: all week
CLOSED: end of Sept to spring bank hol
MEALS: 12 to 2, 6 to 9
PRICES: £9 (£13). Service 10% at D
SEATS: 55. 2 tables outside. Vegetarian meals. Children's helpings. Wheelchair access.
Self-service at L

Old Coffee Shop

13 New Street, Aberdovey LL35 OEH   COOKING 1
ABERDOVEY (065 472) 652   COST £12

The coffee is far from old and the street isn't new. Otherwise, the tidy and homely, much-loved café near the sea is unenigmatic and reliable. It's also very inexpensive, and the cooked lunches and all-day snacks taste genuinely of their ingredients. Cream of watercress soup with home-made brown rolls had a true flavour. The set Sunday lunch might be roast chicken ('best flavour I've had for some time') with home-made sage and onion stuffing that was chunky and crisp. Large, creamy strawberry Pavlova had 'about half a pound of strawberries'. Unlicensed, but corkage is low if you bring your own wine.

CHEF: Susan Griffiths   PROPRIETORS: Alan and Susan Griffiths
OPEN: Tue to Sun, daytime only
MEALS: 10 to 5.30 (L 12 to 3)
PRICES: £9 (£10). Minimum £1.75 at L. Unlicensed, but bring your own: corkage £1.50
SEATS: 30. Private parties: 30 main room. Vegetarian meals. Children's helpings.
No-smoking area

▲ Penhelig Arms Hotel ♟

Aberdovey LL35 0LT   COOKING 1
ABERDOVEY (065 472) 215   COST £12–£22

The Hughes have spent the year removing bench seating and generally smartening up this habourside inn that offers a daytime menu in the bar or dining-room and a set-price dinner menu in the restaurant alone. Sunday lunch, virtually half the price, remains a constant bargain. The lunch cooking runs from soups and sandwiches to more ambitious cod gratin or mildly curried chicken. The dinner is where Sally Hughes shows her mettle. The ideas range from current – smoked duck with melon, orange and ginger salad or Barbary duck with a raspberry demi-glace sauce – to the happily conventional such as rack of lamb or grilled Dover sole. Good, fresh materials, especially the fish and meat, remain fair value, and there is a certain studied simplicity so as not to crowd out flavours. Ideas are there in a coral hollandaise with salmon; redcurrant and Sauternes sauce with duck; prawns and mushrooms with chilli; or hazelnut shortcake with cream cheese and blackcurrants. People applaud the value, the cheerful informal service, and the commitment to fresh food. Robert Hughes is a wine enthusiast, but not a magpie. His list, long enough but not overweighty, is chosen from good modern growers such as Goyard (Mâcon), Olek (Chinon), Lurton (Graves) and Prum (Mosel). The list opens its arms to the wider world, considers the half-bottle drinker, and features wines 'of the month' to give a chance to show bargains and the less familiar. Prices are very reasonable. It is a model of what might be done by all smaller restaurants trying to serve the local community as well as the wider world. House wine: £6.50. CELLARMAN'S CHOICE: Paul Berthelot Champagne, N.V., £16.50; Brown Bros Chardonnay, King Valley 1987, £13.75.

CHEFS: Sally Hughes and Jane Howkins   PROPRIETORS: Robert and Sally Hughes
OPEN: all week
MEALS: 12 to 2, 7 to 9
PRICES: £8 (£13), Set L £7.50 (£12), Set D £13.50 (£18). Service inc
CARDS: Access, Visa
SEATS: 42. Private parties: 24 main room. Car-park, 12 places. Vegetarian meals by arrangement. Children's helpings. Music
ACCOMMODATION: 11 rooms, all with bath/shower. B&B £27 to £60. Deposit: £10. Pets welcome. Afternoon teas. TV. Scenic. Doors close at midnight. Confirm by 6

ABERSOCH Gwynedd   map 4

▲ *Porth Tocyn Hotel*

Abersoch LL53 7BU	COOKING 2
ABERSOCH (075 881) 2966	COST £17–£30

More than 30 years on, this family-run hotel still receives enthusiastic praise. Its magnificent setting overlooking Cardigan Bay must rank as one of the finest of any seaside hotel in Britain. The cooking never seems to pall: 'We had dinner on three successive evenings and any one of the meals, if from a new restaurant, would have sent the press into every kind of hype!' Another couple stayed for seven nights and 'ate like Trojans.' The Fletcher-Brewers continue with what they call 'the dinner party style' although the kitchen has evolved over the years. A daily changing five-course dinner menu features starters such as smoked duck and sweet pepper quiche. Then a soup precedes main courses ranging from roast leg of Welsh lamb with mint and Islay whisky sauce to glazed poussin with honey, grapes and sesame seeds. Vegetables are imaginative, local cheeses are well kept, and there are some praiseworthy sweets such as queen of puddings. Recommended dishes have included walnut roulade with lobster; veal with ginger and spring onion sauce; and baked sea bass with a 'delicate' curry sauce. At lunchtime there are snacks and light meals, and on Sunday a buffet. The wine list rather lacks ambition and might be improved with wider buying. There is surprisingly little under £10, but there are some halves. House French: £7.50.

CHEFS: E. L. Fletcher-Brewer and Sue Bower   PROPRIETORS: The Fletcher-Brewer family
OPEN: all week
MEALS: 12.30 to 2, 7.30 to 9.30
PRICES: Set Sun L £11.50 (£17), Set D £13.50 (£19) to £19 (£25)
CARD: Access
SEATS: 60. 12 tables outside. Private parties: 60 main room. Car-park, 60 places. Children's helpings with prior notice. No children under 7 at D. Smart dress preferred. Wheelchair access (1 step; also WC)
ACCOMMODATION: 17 rooms, all with bath/shower. Rooms for disabled. B&B £33 to £78. Deposit: £40. Baby facilities. Pets welcome but not in public rooms. Afternoon teas. Garden. Swimming-pool. Tennis. TV. Phone. Scenic. Doors close at midnight
[*Which? Hotel Guide*]

'The ingredients are delicious, magnificent, brilliant, but whenever the chef starts to add sauces and accompaniments he seems to have a sledgehammer touch.' On eating in Scotland

---

▲ Riverside Hotel

Abersoch LL53 7HW	COOKING 1
ABERSOCH (075 881) 2419 and 2818	COST £15–£28

The hotel, set between the harbour and the river, stretches long and low from its four-storey beginning. Riverside's business is that of holidaymakers – for a weekend perhaps, but often for a fortnight – and the daily changing menus are composed with variety as well as freshness and simplicity in view. Lunch is served only in the bar. At dinner a set-price menu of half a dozen choices is served in the terrazzo-floored restaurant reached by a spiral staircase. The raffia-backed chairs, bright napkins and polished tabletops combine with plain white paintwork to project an image of a holiday restaurant in Majorca. The food, however, is clearly British in first courses such as smoked salmon and avocado with a walnut dressing, garlic mushrooms or baked banana with a curry mayonnaise; main dishes such as lemon sole with prawns, chicken stuffed with apricots with a Grand Marnier sauce; or desserts along the lines of ginger meringues with rhubarb sauce, morello cherry trifle or crème caramel. Vegetables are fresh; bread is home-made. It is a sound family hotel, with a conscience about what it cooks and all the qualities that may imply. 'I have been staying here over the past 20 years and the standards have improved year by year.' There is a short wine list of some three dozen. For reliability, though, select from the additional two pages supplied by Haughton Fine Wines, reasonably priced and excellent. House wine: £8 per litre.

CHEFS/PROPRIETORS: John and Wendy Bakewell
OPEN: all week
CLOSED: Nov to Mar
MEALS: 12 to 2, 7.30 to 9.30
PRICES: bar L £9 (£15), restaurant Set D £18.50 (£23)
CARDS: Access, Visa
SEATS: 34. Private parties: 34 main room. Car-park, 30 places. No children under 5. Smart dress preferred. No smoking in dining-room. Music
ACCOMMODATION: 12 rooms, all with bath/shower. B&B £39.25 to £58.50. Deposit: £30 per person. Baby facilities. Afternoon teas. Garden. Swimming-pool. TV. Phone. Scenic. Doors close at midnight. Confirm by 4

BEAUMARIS Gwynedd   map 4

▲ Ye Olde Bulls Head Inn ♥

Castle Street, Beaumaris	
Anglesey LL58 8AP	COOKING 3
BEAUMARIS (0248) 810329	COST £28

Ye Olde it is. Parts of this landmark coaching-inn – whose courtyard claims to have the largest single-hinged door in Britain – were built in 1617 and still look it. Reporting on the Bull's Head seems to be as much about renovation as about food. Owners Keith Rothwell and David Robertson pay attention to detail on both scores. The recently refurbished bar, the heart of this hotel-restaurant, has had its leatherette seating replaced with the real thing. Bar snacks are moderately priced. The dining-room menu is not short on choice:

there are half a dozen first courses, the same number of main courses and a supplementary daily selection which emphasises the quantity and quality of local produce, especially fish. A warm salad of duck, pine nuts and walnut oil elicited the verdict of 'tasty, tender and not too much of it.' Main courses range from fresh local grilled dover sole to steamed chicken breast with a filling of spring vegetable mousse served with a saffron sauce. One reader judged the cooking of Keith Rothwell, now helped by Anthony Murphy, to be even better than before in terms of quality, imagination and execution. 'Sauces were varied and superb.' This might mean orange butter to go with poached fillet of sea bass or rich port to accompany pan-fried calf's liver. The approach is thorough and diligent. 'The fresh mango crème brûlée was the first genuine crème brûlée I've had away from home for years.' Cheeses are Welsh and service is friendly. Wines, chosen very carefully are from Australia and California as well as France and are from reliable and varied suppliers. Prices are very fair. Here is another place that avoids a flat mark-up across the range and cuts its margins to the bone on more expensive bottles. House claret is £7.50, not up since the last *Guide*. CELLARMAN'S CHOICE: Ch. Calon Ségur 1966, £35.50, Hautes Côtes de Nuits 1985, Alain Verdet £15.50; Cloudy Bay Chardonnay 1989, £14.95.

CHEFS: Keith Rothwell and Anthony Murphy   PROPRIETORS: Rothwell & Robertson Ltd
OPEN: all week
MEALS: 12 to 2.30, 7.30 to 9.30
PRICES: £16 (£23)
CARDS: Access, Visa
SEATS: 70. Private parties: 70 main room, 40 private room. Car-park, 15 places. Children's helpings. No children under 14
ACCOMMODATION: 11 rooms, all with bath/shower. B&B £32.50 to £55. Baby facilities. Phone. Scenic. Doors close at 1am. Confirm by 6 [*Which? Hotel Guide*]

BROAD HAVEN Dyfed   map 4

▲ *Druidstone Hotel*

Broad Haven SA62 3NE   COOKING 1
BROAD HAVEN (0437) 781221   COST £19

'A wonderful place for a summer evening, having dinner and watching the sun dip into the sea,' writes one enthusiastic reader. Another has been coming back for many years and says that her children and grandchildren thoroughly enjoy the place. It is very much a family hotel, personally run by Rod and Jane Bell, with the added attractions of 'overpowering' views and plenty to occupy the time. 'We like natural food, ale, people, gardens and animals,' say the Bells. Chris Tancock now runs the kitchen and has added some exotic overtones to the menu: Indonesian chicken, spicy Moroccan eggplant, and pork fillets with yoghurt and mint dip are typical dishes. Jane Bell still cooks on Sundays and Mondays and Rod Bell still makes the terrines and pâtés. The output of the herb garden shows in gazpacho, asparagus with ham and lavender mousse, and lamb chops with elderflower and hyssop sauce. There is plenty of alcohol in the ice-creams and 'tipsy' baked bananas. Bar meals have become so popular that the Bells have introduced a club and supper licence so that they can look after residents in the dining-room with even more comfort. The wine list is adequate, fairly priced, and includes a few organics. House French: £5.

CHEF: Chris Tancock   PROPRIETORS: Rod and Jane Bell
OPEN: all week
MEALS: 12.30 to 2.30, 7.30 to 10
PRICES: £11 (£16)
CARDS: Amex, Visa
SEATS: 40. 8 tables outside. Private parties: 36 main room, 12 private room. Car-park, 40
places. Children's helpings. Wheelchair access (also WC)
ACCOMMODATION: 9 rooms. Rooms for disabled. B&B £21 to £42. Deposit: £15. Baby
facilities. Pets welcome. Afternoon teas. Garden. Scenic. Doors close at midnight

---

CAERNARFON Gwynedd   map 4

Y Bistro Bach

4 Y Maes, Caernarfon LL55 2NF   COOKING 1
CAERNARFON (0286) 673075   COST £19

A cheap and cheerful bistro, but one with serious intent to produce Welsh
cooking as convincing as that found in the original, fancier, Y Bistro in
Llanberis (see entry). The food, listed bilingually on the long but constantly
changing *carte*, taps local produce if not always Welsh recipe books. Good bets
are baked leek and ham with cheese sauce, deep-fried Glamorgan sausages
with onion croquettes, Welsh burger made with local lamb, and local gammon
with fresh pineapple. Brown sugar meringues with cream and crushed
hazelnuts was one of five dessert choices on a set Sunday lunch in summer.
There are about five teas and six wines. House wine: £6.

CHEFS: Nerys Roberts and Graham Ward   PROPRIETORS: Danny and Nerys Roberts
OPEN: all week (all week L and Fri and Sat D in winter)
MEALS: 12 to 3, 6 to 8.30
PRICES: £10 (£16)
CARDS: Access, Visa
SEATS: 60. Private parties: 36 main room. Vegetarian meals. Children welcome

---

CARDIFF South Glamorgan   map 4

Armless Dragon

97 Wyvern Road, Cathays, Cardiff CF2 4BG   COOKING 2
CARDIFF (0222) 382357   COST £26

'It took us four attempts to find a date with a vacant table – David Richards and
his team evidently go from strength to strength. Elsewhere, gastronomic
excursions may lead inevitably to indigestible combinations but the Armless
Dragon has its food rooted in healthy reality.' Windows filled with greenery
shut out the terraces of Wyvern Road; the beige dining-room has pictures for
sale from a gallery and rock music for 'quiet' times – turned off as people arrive
in number. There is a fixed duplicated menu, short and to the point,
supplemented by white boards toted round the restaurant listing the day's
specials. The range of dishes in the repertoire is wide and there is an obvious
delight in distant countries and their flavourings: fish 'Barbados' or 'Oriental';
crispy winglets with five spices. The essence of the cooking is European

bourgeois dishes: steak, kidney and oyster pudding; lamb paloise; rabbit with leeks and bacon. It is balanced by a vegetarian line of long practice as well as invention. A meal took in red pimento stuffed with lamb and cracked wheat, with minted yoghurt to one side; escabeche of eight anchovies pickled in a mango and tamarind sauce, 'almost a marmalade'; scallops with samphire, in sauce and stir fried; lamb, duck and lentil hot-pot with cumin, cardamom, coconut and tamarind, served with 'risi bisi', 'rich in flavour, balanced in digestive impact; stir-fried vegetables that were a model'; Hunza apricots and cashew-nut cream. A note of dissent reported a complaint handled 'with poor grace'. The wine list is short in length, short on detail, cheap and good. House wine: £5.90. CELLARMAN'S CHOICE: Brouilly, Les Jarrons 1986, £9.80; Thomas Mitchell Fumé Blanc, £9.50.

CHEFS: David Richards and Debbie Coleman   PROPRIETOR: David Richards
OPEN: Mon to Sat, exc Sat L
CLOSED: bank hol Mon, Christmas to New Year
MEALS: 12.30 to 2.15, 7.30 to 10.30 (11 Sat)
PRICES: £16 (£22)
CARDS: Access, Amex, Diners, Visa
SEATS: 50. Private parties: 50 main room. Vegetarian meals. Children welcome. Wheelchair access. Music

Bo Zan

78 Albany Road, Roath,
Cardiff CF2 3RS   COOKING 1
CARDIFF (0222) 493617   COST £16−£25

Szechuan specialities dominate the 80-dish menu in this suburban restaurant. The food overshadows the decor. Classic dishes such as crispy aromatic duck, mo po du fu (minced beef with bean curd in a hot sauce), and shredded pork with Szechuan pickled radish, share the bill with sesame prawn toasts, steamed scallops with garlic and black-bean sauce, and fashionable sizzling specialities. Hot and spicy dishes are marked on the menu with an asterisk. The dining-room has doubled in size and prices have risen. Saké is a better bet than the basic wine list.

CHEF: Kim-Lam Fung   PROPRIETORS: Kim-Lam and Emma Fung
OPEN: all week, exc Sun and Mon L
MEALS: 12 to 1.45, 6 to 11.30 (11.45 Sat)
PRICES: £12 (£21), Set L and D £10.50 (£16) to £15.50 (£21). Minimum £7
CARDS: Access, Amex, Diners, Visa
SEATS: 60. Private parties: 35 main room, 25 private room. Vegetarian meals. Children's helpings L and early D. Wheelchair access (1 step). Music

'My principal objection was to the service. One knows this is not a silver service establishment, but I am not in my first flush of youth and my father is nearly 70. To be constantly called ''you two'' was grating! ''What can I get for you two? How are you two then?'' ''Unimpressed'', would have been my answer. It became a toss-up as to whether one wanted to get the waitress's attention or not.' On inspecting in Devon

La Brasserie

60 St Mary Street, Cardiff CF1 1FE	COOKING 1
CARDIFF (0222) 372164	COST £21

The French arm of Benigno Martinez' cluster of lively city eating places (see also Champers and Le Monde). Chargrilled meats, brochettes and fish are the mainstays, backed up by snails and frog's legs, baked mussels and oysters. Specialities cast the net further afield for honeyed crispy duck, suckling pig and venison. Expect a crowd and plenty of noise. The carefully selected wines cover the major French growing regions at fair prices. House wine: £5.25 and £6.95.

CHEF: Franco Peligno   PROPRIETOR: Benigno Martinez
OPEN: Mon to Sat
MEALS: 12 to 2.30, 7 to 12.15am
PRICES: £12 (£18)
CARDS: Access, Amex, Diners, Visa
SEATS: 75. Private parties: 75 main room. Vegetarian meals. Children welcome. Smart dress preferred. Music

Le Cassoulet

5 Romilly Crescent, Canton,	
Cardiff CF1 9NP	COOKING 2
CARDIFF (0222) 221905	COST £31

After a walk of three miles, a reader was still able to write that his 'faith in French cooking in South Wales' was restored by a winter lunch at Le Cassoulet. Gilbert Viader has worked in Glamorgan for some years, so knows the market potential for his brand of French cooking. This is neither bourgeois nor regional (save for the cassoulet), but a satisfactory rendering of Franglais standards: lamb with basil, chicken with Pernod, duck with blackcurrant, marinated salmon, prawns and garlic or a salade composée. This is offered as a *carte* of eight choices in each course at night, abbreviated for lunch onto a blackboard menu. Readers comment that it gives good value, offers 'an excellent robust experience' with service that is 'extraordinarily attentive yet not once intrusive.' More 'authentic' dishes may occur as lunchtime or daily specials; this is where the fish will be found, and perhaps beef *onglet* with shallots or something truly from the bourgeois repertoire. Vegetables, though not always matching the main dish, may at least avoid the little pile of plain green beans: thus one day a stuffed tomato, dauphinois potatoes and cabbage finished with bacon. The cassoulet itself is enjoyed and regional identity is reinforced at the end of the meal by a list of a dozen armagnacs. The wine list is short and best on south-western French bottles. House wine is £5.95.
CELLARMAN'S CHOICE: Dom. de Durand, Côtes du Frontonnais, £8.95.

CHEF: Gilbert Viader   PROPRIETORS: Gilbert and Claire Viader
OPEN: Tue to Sat, exc Sat L
MEALS: 12 to 2, 7 to 10
PRICES: £19 (£26)
CARDS: Access, Visa
SEATS: 35. Private parties: 35 main room. Children welcome. Wheelchair access. Music

Champers

61 St Mary Street, Cardiff CF1 1FE   COOKING 1
CARDIFF (0222) 373363   COST £19

The strengths of this bodega-style Spanish wine bar are its magnificent vintage
reserva Riojas and its chargrilled meats. Steaks, kebabs, ribs, and pork chops
are backed up by fresh fish, veal and pollo al ajillo. People looking for finesse
comment, 'the food seems to rely on the notion that lots of large chunks of meat
must be good.' Mixed salads, garlic bread and cheeses are the sidelines.
Portions are massive, prices realistic and service fast, to the point of being
peremptory. You are expected to help yourself where appropriate. Reminder:
no desserts. House red £5.95.

CHEFS: Paul Griffiths and Antonio Louis   PROPRIETOR: Benigno Martinez
OPEN: all week, exc Sun L
MEALS: 12 to 2.30, 7 to 12.15
PRICES: £9 (£16)
CARDS: Access, Amex, Diners, Visa
SEATS: 70. Private parties: 6 main room, 70 private room. Children welcome. Music

La Chaumière

44 Cardiff Road, Llandaff,
Cardiff CF5 2DP   COOKING 1
CARDIFF (0222) 555319   COST £17—£31

Younger new owners are aiming to revitalise this small restaurant over a
betting shop (no connection) near Llandaff cathedral. The style, a modern
mixture, has nothing to do with the name, which has shades of French
peasantry. Reports speak well of veal and pistachio terrine with apricot and
brandy chutney; marinated salmon with yoghurt and lime dressing; pigeon
with port sauce; good beef; lamb steaks with spicy peach sauce; raspberry
meringues or ginger and strawberry cheesecake. Sunday lunch is half-price for
children. House wine is £6.75. More reports, please.

CHEF: Karen Duncan   PROPRIETORS: Karen Duncan and Rory Garvey
OPEN: Tue to Sun, exc Sat L and Sun D
MEALS: 12.15 to 2, 7.15 to 10
PRICES: £19 (£26), Set L £11.95 (£17) to £14.95 (£20)
CARDS: Access, Amex
SEATS: 32. Private parties: 35 main room. Car-park, 15 places. Children's helpings (Sun L
only). Smart dress preferred. No smoking during meals

De Courcey's

Tyla Morris House, Church Road, Pentyrch,
Cardiff CF4 8QN   COOKING 1
CARDIFF (0222) 892232   COST £16—£32

This Scandinavian wooden house was imported lock, stock and barrel in 1892.
They were not to know that the M4, kept out only by thick double-glazing,
would run so close. The inside is barely Scandinavian save for all that

607

varnished wood, as layer upon layer of drapery and carpeting has hoisted it to luxury. Reports have not been so consistent for the long set-price menu – which carries supplements for smoked salmon and beef – that aims to preserve the art of the flambé dish for the denizens of Cardiff. That aside, the approach takes in dishes such as crab and prawn salad with mango and basil; smoked chicken sausage with a marmalade of onions; swordfish with a lime vinaigrette; duck with green peppercorns and elderberry wine; Black Forest roulade; and poached pear with honey ice-cream. Details of execution may be missing, and service may be untrained below, learning the ropes, though cheerfully relaxed at the top. Wines include a few from Spain and Italy; otherwise the list is French, generally dear and rather unevenly annotated. House wine: £7.75. CELLARMAN'S CHOICE: Ch. la Grave Singalier 1982, £14.75; Corton Charlemagne 1985, Voarick, £58.25. More reports, please.

CHEF: David Leeworthy   PROPRIETORS: Thilo and Patricia Thielmann
OPEN: Tue to Sun, exc Sat L and Sun D
MEALS: 12.30 to 2, 7.30 to 10
PRICES: Set L £12.50 (£16), Set D £23.50 (£27). Service inc
CARDS: Access, Amex, Diners, Visa
SEATS: 50. 20 tables outside. Private parties: 14 and 50 private rooms. Car-park, 30 places.
Vegetarian meals. Children welcome. Smart dress preferred. Wheelchair access (3 steps)

Indian Ocean

290 North Road, Gabalfa,
Cardiff CF4 3BN   COOKING 1
CARDIFF (0222) 621152 and 621349   COST £16–£24

Pleasant surroundings in pinks and blues have always given this tandoori house a smart aura, reinforced by a cocktail list that includes 'Raja's Ransom' and 'Elephant's Trunk'. The tandoori meats are sufficiently marinated yet freshly and quickly cooked so as to remain moist, with a good balance between the spices and the taste of the meat itself. There is a fair range of other dishes including butter chicken cooked with butter and cream, and lamb pasanda made with good-quality meat and not almondy like many. Drink Kingfisher lager.

CHEF: Abdul Kadir   PROPRIETORS: Abdul Muhim and Abdul Kadir
OPEN: all week
CLOSED: 25 Dec
MEALS: 12.15 to 2.30, 6.15 to 11.30
PRICES: £12 (£20), Set L and D £11.95 (£16). Service 10%
CARDS: Access, Amex, Diners, Visa
SEATS: 60. Private parties: 50 main room, 8 private room. Vegetarian meals. Children welcome. Smart dress preferred. Wheelchair access (1 step; also WC). Music.
Air-conditioned

The Guide *office can quickly spot when a restaurateur is encouraging customers to write recommending inclusion and sadly, several restaurants have been doing this in 1990. Such reports do not further a restaurant's cause. Please tell us if a restaurateur invites you to write to the* Guide.

Le Monde

60 St Mary Street, Cardiff CF1 1FE
CARDIFF (0222) 387376

COOKING 1
COST £23

One of the trio of restaurants specialising in grills and fish run by Benigno
Martinez. It is on the first floor above La Brasserie – Champers is next door.
Fish soup is more Spanish than French, squid is fresh and crisply deep fried.
These may serve as two first courses out of eight or nine, all fish, to a meal that
can take in up to ten fish from the grill, bought by weight, or straightforward
meats. The meats come on cast-iron plates with baked or chipped potatoes and
perhaps a salad from a bar. There are no desserts but cheese is to be had before
strong coffee. The new chef has been a Welsh Chef of the Year. The formula is
carried through with style and the materials are excellent. Wines are well
chosen. House wine: £5.25 and £5.95.

CHEF: Andrew Jones   PROPRIETOR: Benigno Martinez
OPEN: Mon to Sat
CLOSED: 25 Dec, 1 Jan
MEALS: 12 to 3, 7 to 12.15
PRICES: £12 (£19)
CARDS: Access, Amex, Diners, Visa
SEATS: 86. Private parties: 80 main room. No children under 10. Smart dress preferred.
Music. Air-conditioned

Noble House

9–11 St David's House,
Wood Street, Cardiff CF1 1ER
CARDIFF (0222) 388430 and 388317

COOKING 1
COST £12–£37

A harpist performs every night except Saturday amid the plush decor of this
Chinese restaurant. The short menu centres on Peking and Szechuan favourites
from sesame prawn toasts and hot-and-sour soup to crispy shredded beef and
Peking duck. It also makes a whistle-stop tour of the Orient, taking in
Indonesian mee-goreng noodles, sum thum from Thailand, Vietnamese
chicken with lemon grass and mint, and garlic lamb with peanuts and chilli
from Tibet. Vegetables and vegetarian dishes are positively reported: who
could resist the seductively named 'Enchantment of the cucumber'? Sunday
lunch is a buffet. House French: £5.90.

CHEF: D. Tang   PROPRIETORS: Charlen Ltd
OPEN: all week
MEALS: 12 to 2.30 (3 Sun), 6 to 11.30 (6.30 to 11 Sun)
PRICES: £12 (£21), Set L from £8 (£12) to £25 (£31), Set D £14 (£19) to £25 (£31).
Service 10%
CARDS: Access, Amex, Diners, Visa
SEATS: 80. Private parties: 80 main room. Vegetarian meals. Children's helpings (Sun
only). Wheelchair access (also WC)

Salvatore

14 Romilly Crescent, Canton,
Cardiff CF1 9NR
CARDIFF (0222) 372768

COOKING 1
COST £28

As in so many Italian restaurants, the welcome is noted in reports to the *Guide*. Another feature enjoyed is the procession of daily specials before the order is taken, which here supplement an already long menu. Readers suggest that the simpler the cooking, the better. Thus a veal chop pan-fried in butter and finished with white wine, and fried fillets of fresh mullet were more appreciated than tomaxelle, escalopes filled with Parma ham, herbs, pine kernels and garlic cooked with a rather crude tomato sauce. Pasta is not a feature but antipasto is. Laverbread with cockles and bacon, and duck with apples and orange may serve as reminders that the Italian community has long been resident in South Wales, and that the chef is English. Vegetables are not brilliant. Among desserts, Amaretti soaked in black coffee and liqueur, then enrobed in chocolate, are much enjoyed. The wine list has a page of unannotated Italians, and the rest is French. House wine: £6.50. CELLARMAN'S CHOICE: Brunello di Montalcino 1984, Villa Banfi, £18.95.

CHEF: Robert Deacon PROPRIETOR: Elizabeth Talfan Colayera
OPEN: Tue to Sat, exc Sat L
CLOSED: 2 weeks in summer
MEALS: 12.30 to 2, 7.30 to 10
PRICES: £16 (£23)
CARDS: Access, Amex, Diners, Visa
SEATS: 50. Private parties: 50 main room. Children's helpings. Wheelchair access. Music

Tandoor Ghar

134 Whitchurch Road, Cardiff CF4 3LJ
CARDIFF (0222) 615746

COOKING 2
COST £23

Shamsul Khan's restaurant is singular in its explicit endorsement of organic vegetables, no colourings or additives, and in its open kitchen for the world to watch the preparation. As the chef is able to converse with diners, dishes may be adjusted to the customer's wishes. Shamsul Khan is also prepared to cook prearranged meals using materials (especially fish) and recipes not on the menu. As the best Indian cookery is often 'home' cookery, such an opportunity to sidestep the limitations of menu planning needs to be encouraged. The strong point of the restaurant lies in vegetables and rice: the samosas have lightness, variety and succulence, and rice is available as lime rice, onion rice and lentil rice – khichuri bhoona. Other recommendations have been dolma (cauliflower in a special lentil sauce, deep-fried), sobjy bhajee, and a vegetable thali. The restaurant was once a Greek taverna and still shows signs of its previous occupants in the Artexed walls, blue curtains and carpet. There is a good range of Indian sweets, though they are bought in. Main dishes are half-price for children. Wines start at £7.50.

CHEF: Shamsul Khan PROPRIETORS: Shamsul and Tahmina Khan
OPEN: Mon to Sat, D only and Sun L
CLOSED: 25 and 26 Dec
MEALS: 12 to 2.30, 6 to 12 (1am Fri and Sat)
PRICES: £11 (£19)
CARDS: Access, Amex, Diners, Visa
SEATS: 40. Private parties: 50 main room. Vegetarian meals. Children's helpings.
No-smoking area. Wheelchair access (1 step; also WC). Music

CHIRK Clwyd   map 4

▲ *Starlings Castle*

Bronygarth, nr Chirk, SY10 7NU
OSWESTRY (0691) 72464   COOKING 2
5m NW Oswestry   COST £26

Enclosed by rhododendrons and conifers, this is 'not so much a castle but a solid sandstone eighteenth-century farmhouse' to quote Antony Pitt's own description. His own history encompasses Popjoys, Homewood Park, the Priory and the Beaujolais in and around Bath since 1973. These less peopled hills are his new parish, and not easy to find: get bearings from Oswestry. It is isolated; the hotel sits on its own shoulder of mountain looking on to the Glynn valley. Bedrooms in the first season are at old-fashioned prices. The daily menu is not set price, but it might as well be as each dish within a course costs the same, except lobster. The style is more direct than the area is used to, more in tune with London fashion. Chicken, pork and spinach sausage with spiced lentils; lambs' tongues with a blue cheese dressing; rabbit with red peppers, tomatoes and garlic; plaice and grey mullet with coconut, coriander and chilli; or fromage blanc with strawberries, all might be found somewhere south of Camden Passage. First reports of the light brown bread and farmhouse butter; grey mullet with mint and butter sauce; best end of lamb with spiced apricots and aubergine; delice of blackcurrants and white and dark chocolate mousse show that his touch is accurate and tastes are lively. The Tanners list is short and not dear, though locals like lower margins than metropolitans expect. House wines start at £6. It is early days yet and the style will doubtless settle to its new location. More reports, please.

CHEF: Antony Pitt PROPRIETORS: Antony and Jools Pitt
OPEN: all week D, and Sun L (other days by arrangement)
MEALS: 12 to 2.30, 7 to 9.30 (10 Fri and Sat)
PRICES: £16 (£22)
CARDS: Access, Visa
SEATS: 30. Private parties: 30 main room, 30 private room. Car-park, 25 places. Vegetarian meals. Children's helpings. No cigars/pipes in dining-room. Wheelchair access (also WC)
ACCOMMODATION: 8 rooms. B&B £12 to £24. Baby facilities. Pets welcome. Garden. TV.
Scenic

Restaurateurs justifiably resent no-shows. If you quote a credit card number when booking, you may be liable for the restaurant's lost profit margin if you don't turn up. Always phone to cancel.

DINAS Dyfed

map 4

Rose Cottage

Dinas SA42 0XD
DINAS CROSS (034 86) 301

COOKING 1
COST £23

The cottage at the end of a terrace by the main road from Newport to Fishguard was once a pub. Its owners, Olwen and Gareth Thomas, formerly cooked at the Freemasons' Arms in Newport, where they had a strong following. By all accounts, the crowds have followed them here, which means: book up on Saturdays, come on time, and expect occasional glitches under pressure. Drinks and orders are taken in the extension that acts as entrance and bar, before three steps down to the restaurant itself: three steps from chintz and leather easy chairs to black beams and white plaster, though a burgundy colour scheme unites both zones. The Thomases aim to cook local produce in ways that draw on the last two decades of tastemaking in Britain (raspberry and green pepper sauce with salmon) and on those wider influences opened up by travel, immigration and television. Hence, on one early spring evening, the menu offered lamb kebabs, chicken moghlai and cannelloni with spinach and almonds alongside onion soup, avocado with cream cheese, and grapefruit with spiced sherry. In the winter, supply lines fail or are stretched too taut, and the cooking may draw on different sources from those of summer. Then, good fresh fish, local vegetables and soft fruit are readily available for dishes such as sewin with spring onion and cucumber sauce or strawberry Pavlova. The wine list is short, not expensive, nicely chosen and supplied by Haughton Fine Wines, which is no bad thing. Gareth Thomas does tasting sessions, attracting good support, so he knows his stock. Chardonnay from David Wynn, Ch. Flotis and the reliably excellent Muscat de Frontignan, Ch. de la Peyrade, are good examples from a seemingly low-key selection. There are several house wines, all French and some organic, and an organic rosé. CELLARMAN'S CHOICE: Bordeaux Supérieur, Ch. Coursou 1987, £7.50; Soave Classico Superiore 1988, Rizzardi, £7.50, both organic.

CHEFS/PROPRIETORS: Olwen and Gareth Thomas
OPEN: Tue to Sat D, Sun L
CLOSED: Tues Oct to May
MEALS: 12.30 to 1.30, 7 to 9.30
PRICES: £13 (£19)
SEATS: 30. Private parties: 30 main room. Car-park, 15 places. Vegetarian meals. Children's helpings. Wheelchair access (also WC)

DINAS MAWDDWY Gwynedd

map 4

Old Station Coffee Shop

Dinas Mawddwy SY20 9LS
DINAS MAWDDWY (065 04) 338

COOKING 1
COST £8

The gabled station building, equipped with a wooden verandah for eating out of doors when weather permits, has been providing holiday visitors with wholesome vegetarian lunches and snacks all day for many years. 'It fulfils all the basic rules: fresh produce, freshly cooked, tasting delicious.' Three stand-you-up-again soups of carrot, coriander and orange, parsnip and apple, and spiced mixed vegetable were the choice one day in spring. Excellent bread and good baking. Substantial snack dishes like cauliflower cheese, juicy pizza, mushroom flan or vegetarian cottage pie is food that might encourage the most disconsolate that the day's outing was worth it. French house wine is 80p by the glass.

CHEF/PROPRIETOR: Eileen M.A. Minter
OPEN: all week, daytime only
CLOSED: mid-Nov to mid-Mar, exc 1 week from 27 Dec
MEALS: 9.30 to 5
PRICES: £4 (£7). Service inc
SEATS: 36. 9 tables outside. Private parties: 16 main room. Car-park. Vegetarian meals. Children's helpings. No smoking. Wheelchair access (also unisex WC). Self-service

---

DOLGELLAU Gwynedd   map 4

▲ *Dolmelynllyn Hall*

Ganllwyd, Dolgellau LL40 2HP
GANLLWYD (034 140) 273
4m N of Dolgellau

COOKING 2
COST £25

'South Snowdonia and mid Wales have all that the Lake District can offer, with fewer people and less traffic,' claims Jonathan Barkwith. Cader Idris is not far away, and there are views down the Mawddach Valley from the hotel and its three acres of formal gardens. The atmosphere is country rather than country house. If the building rambles, it is perhaps because the sixteenth-century foundation was extended during the eighteenth century, and again during the nineteenth. Joanna Barkwith of this father and daughter team offers intelligent and reflective cooking that fits well with the quiet rural style. Traditional British ideas are freshened up, as when deep-fried venison sausages in a light beer batter are served with an orange sauce, or laverbread roulade comes with smoked salmon, cucumber and a sharp lime dressing. The five courses permit little choice, but a wise kitchen does not stretch its resources unnecessarily. Soup or a water ice constitute the second course, and British cheeses bring up the rear. Here is flavoursome cooking, Aga-based, with precision where necessary and due regard for texture. Asparagus soufflé omelette is light, sweetcorn soup smooth. The overall effect of dishes such as medallions of pork with apricots, or guinea-fowl with a cream and apple brandy sauce, is to elicit all-encompassing praise rather than detailed analysis – which perhaps is the proper response to good food. Desserts are as traditional as Dolly's bread-and-butter pudding, or hot sticky toffee pudding with butterscotch ice-cream and caramel sauce. Coffee is not so good. Service is courtesy itself. Wines, over a hundred, are predominantly European; reliance on mundane négociants makes for monotony in places, but where the bigger names are avoided, there is good value.

CHEF: Joanna Barkwith   PROPRIETORS: Jonathan Barkwith and Joanna Barkwith
OPEN: all week, D only
CLOSED: Dec to end Feb
MEALS: 7.30 to 8.30
PRICES: Set D £15.95 (£21)
CARDS: Access, Amex, Visa
SEATS: 24. Private parties: 44 main room. Car-park, 25 places. Vegetarian meals on request.
No children under 8. Smart dress preferred. No smoking in dining-room. Wheelchair access
(2 steps)
ACCOMMODATION: 11 rooms, all with bath/shower. B&B £34 to £68. Deposit: £25. No
children under 10, exc by arrangement. Pets welcome in certain rooms. Afternoon teas.
Garden. Fishing. TV. Phone. Scenic. Confirm by 6

Dylanwad Da

2 Smithfield Street, Dolgellau LL40 1BS	COOKING 2
DOLGELLAU (0341) 422870	COST £20

'Dylanwad Da' means 'A Good Influence' – and this is what one inspector
called the bi-lingual owner, Dylan Rowlands, after his take-over from La Petite
Auberge. He goes into semi-pragmatic hibernation during the winter, but
bounces back at full tilt in time for the summer holidays. The inexpensive *carte*
offers seven main courses: two beef steaks, a vegetarian dish, one each of fish,
lamb, chicken and pork. Fruit figures, as in 'Paradise lamb' stuffed with mango
and served with a mango sauce, and also a mild cream curried pork with
banana. Two other dishes have a tomato sauce base: stuffed vine leaves and
chicken pasta. A further pair, salmon and fillet steak, are finished with a cream
sauce. This substantial cooking, with not much truck given to fancies but with
every attention to taste, would seem to accord with the unpretentious
appearance of the bistro and the 1960s image of the name to non-Welsh
speakers. This image is reinforced by the 'smiles and helpfulness' as well as the
evident care of the staff, who make up for any misgivings at their apparent
casualness. Desserts keep up the quantities and are enjoyed for the richness of
chocolate velvet creme pie, the sweetness of meringue swans with double
cream and a blackcurrant sauce or the good home-made ice-cream. Save for the
Pommery Champagne, no wine costs more than the £11.90 for a Pouilly Fumé.
There are a score of options, including Ch. Musar from the Lebanon, a Chilean
Cabernet Sauvignon from Ortiz Hermanos, and a wood-aged Semillon from
Quelltaler Estate in Australia. House French is £5.95.

CHEF/PROPRIETOR: Dylan Rowlands
OPEN: D only; all week July, Aug, Sept; Thur to Sat in winter; Tue to Sat from Whitsun
CLOSED: Feb to mid-Mar
MEALS: 7 to 9.30
PRICES: £12 (£17)
SEATS: 30. Private parties: 30 main room. Vegetarian meals. Children's helpings. Music

---

Consumers' Association is planning to publish Out to Eat, *a new guide to budget eating
out in restaurants, pubs, cafés, brasseries and so on. Please send reports and
recommendations to Out to Eat, FREEPOST, 2 Marylebone Road, London NW1 1YN.*

EGLWYSFACH Powys   map 4

▲ *Ynyshir Hall*

Eglwysfach SY20 8TA   COOKING 1
GLANDYFI (065 474) 209   COST £19–£26

The Reens have been owners for over a year and have initiated extensive
redecorations to this long low house: flagstones in the hall, a fire in the bar and
an elegantly furnished small dining-room. New owners but same chef, for
David Dressler remains from at least two previous changes of ownership. His
cooking has a light touch and a good sense of flavouring, shown in dishes like
fresh sardines in vine leaves with a lemon dressing; lamb roasted with honey,
ginger and cardamom; pork in pastry with a lavender perfumed sauce; or
pigeons pot-roasted with blackcurrants and brandy. Welsh cheeses are an apt
choice in a place that values local produce and grows a fair head of vegetables
in the garden. Rob Reen is a painter whose work hangs on the walls in the
public rooms; maybe preoccupation with his next work encourages a cool
approach to customers. However, the spate of reports after the change here has
been very positive, even if a Sunday lunch showed up an absent or unthinking
team. The wine list is a short selection, extending this year to Australia, at not
impossible prices. House wine from France is £7. CELLARMAN'S CHOICE: Blue
Pyrenees Estate Cabernet Sauvignon 1984, £15.25; Peterson's Hunter Valley
Chardonnay 1987, £15.

CHEF: David Dressler   PROPRIETORS: Joan and Rob Reen
OPEN: all week
MEALS: 12 to 1, 7 to 8.30
PRICES: Set L and D £15 (£19) to £17 (£22). Service inc
CARDS: Access, Amex, Diners, Visa
SEATS: 24. Private parties: 30 main room. Car-park, 15 places. Children's helpings on
request. No smoking in dining-room
ACCOMMODATION: 9 rooms, all with bath/shower. Rooms for disabled. B&B £35 to £70.
Deposit: 10%. Baby facilities. Pets welcome. Afternoon teas. Garden. Fishing. TV. Phone.
Scenic (*Which? Hotel Guide*)

FISHGUARD Dyfed   map 4

Farmhouse Kitchen

Glendower Square, Goodwick,
Fishguard SA64 0BP   COOKING 2
FISHGUARD (0348) 873282   COST £7–£19

The only visible animals are a pair of Bengal finches and the public car park in
the rear is hardly a field. None the less the dresser, plants, pottery, coarse-
weave carpeting and rocking chair inside, in the 'tiniest bar area in Wales', give
their own rustic feel. The Harveys offer good value and honest cooking, which
accounts for the restaurant being full much of the time, both in the basement
dining-room and the one by the front door. The food is not complicated:
mushrooms with grain mustard; 'Abbot's Favourite Supper', a slice of ham on
Granary-style bread with cheese, mayonnaise and a sliced pear; melon in port;
leg of lamb steak with gooseberry sauce; pork with a mustard cream sauce; a

choice of vegetarian dishes, such as country lentil crumble or mushroom and nut fettuccine; and acceptable bought-in desserts such as chocolate fudge cake or cheesecakes. Set-priced lunches are even better value with discounts for OAPs during the week. Cooking is careful, though the odd dish has been blander than it might have been. Service is eminently good- tempered, even at the end of the evening – and the day starts early with fresh sandwiches for morning customers. Two dozen wines, mostly in single figures. House French: £4.50.

CHEF: Barbara Harvey   PROPRIETORS: Norman and Barbara Harvey
OPEN: Tue to Sun; also Mon D June to Sept
MEALS: 12 to 2, 7 to 9.30
PRICES: £12 (£16), Set L £3.65 (£7) to £5.80 (£10)
SEATS: 38. Private parties: 24 main room, 24 private room. Vegetarian meals. Children's helpings. No-smoking area on request. Wheelchair access. Music

---

GLANWYDDEN Gwynedd   map 4

Queen's Head

Glanwydden LL31 9JP   COOKING 1
LLANDUDNO (0492) 46570   COST £19

The severest criticism this last year was that butter came in packets. Most comments corroborate past verdicts: the food in this village centre inn is not only proper pub food, straight up and freshly cooked, but good food. 'It does what it sets out to do, with style.' You're likely to see local seafood on the à la carte lunch and dinner menu – dressed crab, for instance, or green lip mussels with warm anchovy butter. Mushroom and broccoli soup 'tasted of just that.' Grilled trout fillet and poached salmon steak were endorsed for perfect timing, and vegetables have been singled out, in one case (turnips), by a young visitor. A dish of Welsh lamb with plum sauce put the Queen's Head into the regional finals of a pub food competition, with some reason. 'Lovely' desserts, which might be a very alcoholic chocolate brandy trifle, cherry Bakewell and fresh fruit Pavlova, are often creamy. A slightly longer menu now includes ewe's milk ice-cream, variously flavoured. The short but far from stodgy wine list has seen some organic additions, including the house red, a 1986 Côteaux de Languedoc, at £6.65. House white is £6.60. CELLARMAN'S CHOICE: Côteaux d'Aix en Provence, Les Baux, Mas de Gourgonnier 1988, £7.65.

CHEF/PROPRIETOR: Robert F.W. Cureton
OPEN: all week
MEALS: 12 to 2.15, 6.30 (7 Sun) to 9
PRICES: £11 (£16)
CARDS: Access, Visa
SEATS: 120. 12 tables outside. Private parties: 26 main room. Car-park, 25 places. Vegetarian meals. No children under 7. Music

---

Several sharp operators have tried to extort money from restaurateurs on the promise of an entry in a guide book that has never appeared. The Good Food Guide *makes no charge for inclusion and does not offer certificates of any kind.*

▲ *Cemlyn* ♟

High Street, Harlech LL46 2YA   COOKING 3
HARLECH (0766) 780425   COST £19–£26

Even in the rain – if the windows haven't misted up – the view of the castle
standing majestic against Tremadoc Bay will afford solace to those finding
themselves on the western edge of Britain. Ken Goody's cooking, and his bluff
yet modest welcome to customers old and new, is another reason for making
for Harlech. 'Between us, we have eaten at 88 restaurants in the past year. At a
guess, we would not choose to revisit 70 of them and only eight are definite
"must returns". The Cemlyn heads that list.' This is not only a sobering
reflection on British restaurants in general, it also epitomises the loyalty that
the Cemlyn (Welsh for frog) inspires. The format the chef/owner works to is a
menu of eight first courses, five main dishes and a half dozen desserts plus a
preliminary course of soup. You may select a four-course dinner at one price, a
two-course at another, or eat cheese as an extra for a tiny supplement. Prices are
stunningly low for anyone used to the commercial rigours of Thatcherite
Britain. Quantities are substantial: the light-of-frame may think it wise to stay
with two courses. Not that Ken Goody's cooking is over-rich, though cream
figures, for the raw material, especially the fish, is allowed to shine through.
The soup course is one that still excites comment: 'pea with tarragon was
superb, creamy, flush with tarragon'; gazpacho 'full of peppers and full of
flavour'; vegetable and chicken 'a mini-meal in itself, shredded chicken,
cucumber, courgette, broccoli and, we thought, a touch of melted soft cheese.'
But flavour does rule paramount here: pork with Roquefort and almond sauce;
Persian chicken with a delicate sauce of almond, sultanas and yoghurt, served
with banana and tomato chutney; duck with sage and onion purée and a peach
purée; or salmon with saffron and Champagne sauce are some of the main
dishes. Vegetables, one regular avers, have departed from last year's health
faddist's parboiled and plain and returned to more interesting cooked
mixtures: a cream-laden dauphinoise, peppery parsnips, a purée of swede and
so on. Cheese is mainly local, with foreigners occasionally allowed, and has
been noticed to suffer from lack of customer support. Desserts tend to more
substance: mud pie, Gâteau St-Honoré, a roulade, pecan pie, Pavlova. This has
all the virtues of home cooking: immediacy, robustness where suitable,
candour and an insouciance about arrangement and pictures on the plate. But
the skill is as professional as anywhere. The wine list keeps hold of financial
reality while offering some very good bottles (halves as well) from all regions
of the world. The interest of the list exceeds the bounds of this entry but note
the organic wine from Verdet, and the passe-tout-grains from Jayer in red
burgundies; the nice Loire selection; the Brunello de Montalcino from Tenuta
Carpazo; and the Martinborough wines from New Zealand. CELLARMAN'S
CHOICE: Riesling Reserve 1985, Gassman, £11; Morgon, 1988 M. Gutty, £11.
Ken Goody celebrated his sixtieth birthday in 1990. He says that this entitles
him to cut-price rail travel but no pension. Harlech will be a lesser place if he
buys a one-way ticket.

CHEF/PROPRIETOR: Ken Goody
OPEN: all week, D only, L by prior arrangement
CLOSED: Jan to Easter
MEALS: 7 to 9.30
PRICES: Set D £13 (£19) to £16 (£22). Minimum £13
CARDS: Access, Visa
SEATS: 42. 3 tables outside. Private parties: 40 main room, 10 private room. Children's helpings. No smoking in 1 dining-room. Wheelchair access (also WC)
ACCOMMODATION: 2 rooms, 1 with bath/shower. B&B £18 to £30. No children under 8. Golf. TV. Scenic. Doors close at midnight. Confirm by 6

HAVERFORDWEST Dyfed

map 4

Jemima's

Nash Grove, Freystrop,
Haverfordwest SA62 4HB
HAVERFORDWEST (0437) 891109
S of Haverfordwest, on the Burton Road

COOKING 2
COST £23

This converted house on what is known as Puddleduck Hill has been stylishly decorated – Laura Ashley colours and printed fabrics, green in the bar, pink in the restaurant, with floor-length cloths on the tables. The bread is fresh home-baked, the vegetables and herbs come mostly from the garden behind the house and the fish is from Milford Haven. Readers have remarked that the cooking is of 'real quality though the feel may be unpretentious'. What better than fresh salmon with sorrel and cream and garden vegetables, if they are done as they ought to be? The menu changes daily and keeps its options short – a sign, to any sensible person, that the cook cares for freshness. Soups; melon with a 'wild' sorbet, perhaps blackcurrant leaf or elderflower; wild boar pâté; home-cured gravlax make up the first courses. Main courses have overtones of French country cooking as interpreted in Britain – chicken with tarragon; ham with madeira sauce; pancakes with spinach and cheese. The cooking is nicely informed by the garden: borage dumplings with pork or geranium ice-cream are instances. 'I haven't had such good value for a long time,' wrote one who appreciated Ann Owston's real efforts not to rely on a freezer to make a caterer's lot an easier one. The wine list is sensationally cheap, with Bollinger at £18.20. It may have only two dozen items and details of growers may be sketchy, but it is drawn from good sources and shows every sign of being a decent choice. House wine: £6. CELLARMAN'S CHOICE: Stoneleigh Sauvignon Blanc 1988, £10; Peter Lehmann Shiraz Cabernet 1985, £8.30.

CHEF: Ann Owston   PROPRIETORS: Ann Owston, Wendy and April Connelly
OPEN: Tue to Sat, D only
MEALS: 7 to 9
PRICES: Set D £13.50 (£19)
CARDS: Access, Visa
SEATS: 20. Private parties: 26 main room. Car-park, 10 places. Children welcome.
No smoking in dining-room

LALESTON Mid Glamorgan   map 4

Great House

High Street, Laleston CF32 0HP   COOKING 1
BRIDGEND (0656) 657644   COST £15−£30

The Bonds converted this commanding seventeenth-century house into a
restaurant. The dining-room is an impressive space of uncluttered white. Large
fireplaces, though filled with gas logs rather than the real thing, dominate it
and the Leicester Room upstairs, used for parties. The *carte* is supplemented by
various set-price meals, and a salad bar at lunchtime is a praiseworthy attempt
to be all things to as many people as possible. The overly full descriptions on
the menu give nearly enough detail to cook from, if you need to do loin of pork
with Malibu. The kitchen's approach is not tied to any one style; it may take in
mushrooms with Stilton and port wine; filo parcels of pork and bacon on a
provençal sauce; salmon and turbot wrapped in a cabbage leaf on a lobster
sauce; or steak stuffed with garlic. Cheeses are often Welsh and the trolley of
sweet things may have cream, chocolate and strawberries in abundance. The
wine list is noteworthy for the cheapness of its house Champagne. Other house
wine: £6.

CHEFS: Steven Mudd, Norma Bond and Darren McNulty   PROPRIETORS: Stephen and
Norma Bond
OPEN: Tue to Sun, exc Sat L and Sun D
MEALS: 12 to 2, 6.30 to 9.30 (9.45 Sat)
PRICES: £18 (£25), Set L £10.25 (£15), Set D £16.25 (£21)
CARDS: Access, Diners, Visa
SEATS: 120. 3 tables outside. Private parties: 80 main room, 40 private room. Car-park, 30
places. Children's helpings. Wheelchair access (2 steps; also WC). Music

---

LLANBERIS Gwynedd   map 4

Y Bistro

43−45 High Street, Llanberis LL55 4EU   COOKING 2
LLANBERIS (0286) 871278   COST £22−£30

The Roberts' original bistro has a suburban parlour-like bar and coffee room
and a pleasant, spacious dining-room. Their second, more basic Y Bistro Bach,
is in Caernarfon (see entry). Three- or four-course set dinners offer a decent
choice of principally Welsh-inspired dishes. Deep-fried local goats' cheese is
served on a rhubarb and ginger sauce. Pigeon breasts might come with a grainy
mustard, redcurrant and soured cream sauce. Ingredients and cooking are often
high-quality as, for instance, in a foil-baked Dover sole with chopped spring
onions and white wine. Grilled sirloin steak, with a mushroom and bacon
filling and fresh tomato and herb sauce, was 'overcooked in the old style', but
the side plate of assorted vegetables was 'positively excellent'. Green salads
can be less than impressive, and the cheeseboard has sometimes been past its
prime and over-chilled, but coffee rates well. The 80-strong wine list tours the
world reliably and at modest cost to the customer. House wine: £6.25.
CELLARMAN'S CHOICE: Ch. Tour de Moulin 1983, £11; Moillard Beaune-
Grèves 1986, £16.50.

CHEF: Nerys Roberts   PROPRIETORS: Danny and Nerys Roberts
OPEN: Tue to Sat, D only
CLOSED: Christmas week
MEALS: 7 to 9.30
PRICES: Set D £17 (£22) to £20 (£25)
CARDS: Access, Visa
SEATS: 48. Private parties: 36 main room, 20 private room. Vegetarian meals. Children welcome. Smart dress preferred. Wheelchair access (2 steps). Music. Air-conditioned

---

LLANDEWI SKIRRID Gwent   map 4

Walnut Tree Inn ▮

Llandewi Skirrid NP7 8AW
ABERGAVENNY (0873) 2797   COOKING 4
on B4521, 2m NE of Abergavenny   COST £43

'We left with a glow of well-being; the love of our fellow men would have lasted all weekend had we not run into a 10-mile tailback on the motorway.' So ends a report on eating in this country pub that is devoted to serving remarkable food in restaurant, bistro and bar. Bookings are taken for the first, but not the others. The food is the same in each. This is outlined on a scrappy duplicated sheet of card: about 15 first courses and main dishes, more than that of desserts. Fish is given greater priority than meat and, although the restaurant is inland, is generally in good condition. The repertoire changes slowly. It revolves around Italian food, neo-classical restaurant cooking and not a little influence from the orient. Meats display less range and excitement, though not less skill, than the fish, available in a large number of species: proven by the plateau de fruits de mer (cold) or the Italian seafood platter (hot). The best bet, we were advised, is to arrive early, grab a table and a menu, order a Punt è Mes, and study hard while nibbling on deep-fried triangles with ham and mozzarella filling and a generous sprinkling of Parmesan. This creates the right aura. Go on perhaps to trenette con pesto; goujonettes of sole with a Thai dip, 'hot and prickly'; crispy crab pancake 'tightly filled with fresh crab'; salad of saddle of rabbit with bacon and pine kernels, good though one person felt the rabbit lacked substantial flavour; rack of lamb with artichoke, a sensational combination, 'seven cutlets trimmed of all fat with the bones standing proudly round artichoke bottoms, a trace of garlic, a light sauce'; rabbit roast with coriander served with a salad topped by a mustard mayonnaise; brodetto, 'gloriously presented in a terracotta dish, rich, fragrant, generous'; fillets of fish, though the silver bream was very bony, with a balsamic vinegar dressing; vegetables that sometimes leave a lot to be desired; desserts such as pears layered with cream between shortbread, a trio of chocolate – ice-cream, marquise and white chocolate mousse – chestnut pavé or good ice-creams. The qualities of this cooking are its immediacy, its directness of flavour and pure skill. A fellow caterer observed that the menu offered two dozen varieties of fish embodied in some 15 different dishes and at least 10 different cooking techniques. None of this is done in much comfort. The best area is the restaurant, but tables are small and require rearrangement if the orders are for shellfish platters. Decoration is not a priority. Service is not grand hotel. Wine service may be less than satisfactory. Yet prices are as high as anywhere: even Londoners can be surprised by them. For this, of course, you may get, 'the best tasting lasagne outside Italy'. Prices respond to the market and no one is constrained to eat more than they need, unlike full-dress restaurants. More telling, in any attempt to place the cooking, is that the Walnut Tree pioneered a new form for eating out, but others have learned from and overtaken it. On a bad day, and it has to be said that they exist, there is some truth in this. However, much of this argument revolves around form, not content. The wine list is a fine collection of old claret, classics, Italians and Rhônes. The Walnut Tree is one of its kind, and it is the ludicrous urge to classify, rate and pigeon-hole that makes for trouble.

CHEFS: Franco Taruschio and Nigel Ramsbottom   PROPRIETORS: Franco and Ann Taruschio
OPEN: Tue to Sat
CLOSED: 12 to 24 Feb
MEALS: 12 to 2.30, 7.15 to 10
PRICES: £27 (£36)
SEATS: 80. 5 tables outside. Private parties: 30 main room. Car-park, 60 places. Children's helpings. Wheelchair access (also WC). Air-conditioned

---

LLANDRILLO   Clwyd   map 4

▲ *Tyddyn Llan*

Llandrillo LL21 0ST
LLANDRILLO (049 084) 264
on B4401 at end of village;   COOKING 2
turn off A5 at Corwen   COST £14−£21

Smooth lawns surround this Georgian house of stone, setting up a resonance of a quiet oasis among mountains, rivers and the great outdoors. Inside all is light, comfort and elegance, reinforced this year by a new dining-room of pleasing proportions. There is no sign of the Kindreds resting on their laurels. Having evolved a satisfactory formula of good cooking and bedrooms for visitors and holidaymakers, they have tilted the emphasis towards the restaurant side of things by improving amenities, and widening the scope of the wine list. The chef, David Barrett, used to cook at the Buttonhole in Ruthin, a restaurant that quickly gained a strong local following, and Tyddyn Llan seems to attract local people as much as the English in search of space and quiet. The kitchen has taken on a new edge of professionalism, welcome for the most part although some have noticed a desire to gild the lily on the plate by over-elaboration. The set-price menu offers five choices at each course with a welcome emphasis on local materials (salmon, lamb, beef, cheese), cooked in a straightforward yet sophisticated manner. The lily gets gilded with garnishes and little accompaniments. Excellent reports have been given of exactly timed and trimmed asparagus with hollandaise; kidneys wrapped in bacon served on a bed of mushrooms with a madeira sauce; a filo parcel of fish mousseline with a lobster sauce; and grilled fillet of salmon with a little tartlet of creamed leeks and a dill sauce; a roast duck with apple and prune stuffing and blackcurrant sauce. Timing is good and the balance of certain ingredients well thought out, for example the still crisp apples in the stuffing for the duck counteracted the bird's richness to a nicety. Vegetables showed equal skill and the cheeses have given much pleasure, as indeed have the bread, coffee and other incidentals. One dinner proceeded without fault until the dessert stage, when judgement seems to have lapsed, but this is the exception. The Kindreds succeed in making people feel relaxed and welcome; the fact that the food is not overpriced helps jolly everyone along. On the wine list, Ch. Cissac 1983 is one of the most expensive but the majority are below £15. Menetou Salon 'Le Petit Clos', the Martinborough Pinot Noir and the Rongopai Sauvignon Blanc show a refreshing departure from the mainstream. House French: £7.50.

CELLARMAN'S CHOICE: Graves, Clos la Maurasse 1983, £12.65; Chardonnay, Milawa 1986, Brown Bros., £15.

CHEFS: Bridget Kindred and David Barrett   PROPRIETORS: Peter and Bridget Kindred
OPEN: all week D, Sun L, snacks L Wed to Sat
MEALS: 12.30 to 2, 7 to 9.30
PRICES: Set Sun L £10.50 (£17), Set D £17 (£24) to £19 (£27)
CARDS: Access, Visa
SEATS: 35. Private parties: 45 main room. Car-park, 25 places. Vegetarian meals. Children's helpings. Smart dress preferred. Wheelchair access. Music
ACCOMMODATION: 10 rooms, all with bath/shower. B&B £40.50 to £67. Deposit: 15%. Baby facilities. Afternoon teas. Garden. Fishing. Phone. Scenic. Doors close at midnight. Confirm by 6 [*Which? Hotel Guide*]

LLANDUDNO Gwynedd   map 4

▲ *Bodysgallen Hall* ♟

Deganwy, Llandudno LL30 1RS
DEGANWY (0492) 584466
from A55 join new A470 and follow   COOKING 3
Llandudno signpost, hotel 1m on R   COST £17–£36

This imposing but not formal house incorporates stones from every century since the middle ages. The oldest is the topmost: the medieval tower, which affords views of the Menai Strait. The main elevations are seventeenth century, but there were many Victorian improvements and redecoration of the interior. This century contributed restoration by courtesy of Historic House Hotels. The house, with good formal gardens, is a great place to visit, even if the car-park seems particularly distant during a Welsh deluge. Outings from Merseyside for Sunday lunch are popular both for the locale and for the outstanding value. At night, the price goes up and the menu length increases. This length was given as a demerit by a couple whose meal disappointed them by lack of flavour, overcooked vegetables and poor pheasant. This they put down to a restaurant of this size trying to serve 11 starters and 9 main courses. It is worth noting that three or four years ago the kitchen was content to produce fewer alternatives, especially at the first course. Martin James is generally a consistent cook producing hotel food which is ace on presentation but light tasting; he uses prime cuts and cooks no stews. The menu does not have a strong personality and in this may be likened to Middlethorpe Hall (see entry, York) and Hartwell House (see entry, Aylesbury), sister hotels in the group. It may be pressure of conference and international business that imposes a common language of 'international' cooking of vague modernity. The repertoire may include hot potted shrimps with saladings; Carmarthen ham and exotic fruits; avocado with prawns, smoked salmon and an orange sauce; duck with blackcurrants; chicken with tarragon; red fish with samphire; mille-feuille of raspberries with a lemon sauce; grapefruit and Campari sorbet with banana and lime; or strawberry bavarois with caramelised strawberries. The service is appreciated for its enthusiasm and constant motivation. The dishes outlined above do not have much regional identity, though the kitchen has always encouraged local producers and does serve excellent Welsh and British cheese. The wine list's strongest suit is claret with a run of Ch. Gruaud Larose and a flight of petits châteaux, all under £15. The geographical spread is fairly even, not forgetting Wales, and there is a fair deal on half-bottles. Prices are not low but there is some effort to give a price range for all pockets. 'Tips are not encouraged.'

CHEF: Martin James   PROPRIETORS: Historic House Hotels
OPEN: all week
MEALS: 12.30 to 2, 7.30 to 9.30
PRICES: Set L £12.60 (£17), Set D £25 (£30). Service inc
CARDS: Access, Amex, Diners, Visa
SEATS: 40. Private parties: 48 main room, 2 private room. Car-park, 50 places. No children under 8. Smart dress preferred. No cigars/pipes in dining-room. Music
ACCOMMODATION: 28 rooms, all with bath/shower. B&B £95 to £125. No children under 8. Pets welcome in cottages. Afternoon teas. Garden. Tennis. TV. Phone. Scenic. Confirm by 5
[*Which? Hotel Guide*]

▲ St Tudno Hotel

North Parade, Llandudno LL30 2LP   COOKING 2
LLANDUDNO (0492) 874411   COST £16—£37

The Blands' quality of welcome and their professionalism as hoteliers in a classic seaside site, well decorated and comfortable, has been well spoken of, though they have had many changes of staff. Currently David Harding is in charge of the kitchen. He has been successful at Bodysgallen Hall and Craigside Manor over previous years. The combination of à la carte and set-price menus means that a bewildering number of dishes are on offer at any one time. This may account for a winter report of disappointing food: immediacy and freshness are difficult to maintain over so wide a range. More recent accounts have been encouraging: avocado with a tomato and Pernod mayonnaise; good asparagus; fillet of salmon with cucumber and sorrel sauce; breast of duck with a plum sauce; breast of chicken with wild mushrooms and asparagus; Grand Marnier parfait with a kiwi-fruit sauce; and pears in red wine have been competently executed. A good range of Welsh cheeses are also appreciated. Service is smooth, friendly and attentive, and tipping is not encouraged. There is an adequate wine list; house wines start at £7.20. More reports, please.

The Guide *office can quickly spot when a restaurateur is encouraging customers to write recommending inclusion - and sadly, several restaurants have been doing this in 1990. Such reports do not further a restaurant's cause. Please tell us if a restaurateur invites you to write to the* Guide.

CHEF: David Harding   PROPRIETORS: Martin and Janette Bland
OPEN: all week
CLOSED: 2 weeks from New Year
MEALS: 12.30 to 1.45, 6.45 to 9.30 (9 Sun)
PRICES: £22 (£31), Set L £10.50 (£16), Set D £20.95 (£27). Minimum £10
CARDS: Access, Amex, Visa
SEATS: 60. Private parties: 45 main room. Car-park, 4 places. Vegetarian meals. Children's
helpings. No children under 5 at D. Smart dress preferred. No smoking in dining-room.
Wheelchair access. Air-conditioned
ACCOMMODATION: 21 rooms, all with bath/shower. Rooms for disabled. Lift. B&B £52.50
to £75. Deposit: 1 night's cost. Baby facilities. Afternoon teas. Swimming-pool. TV. Phone.
Scenic. Doors close at midnight [*Which? Hotel Guide*]

LLANDYBIE Dyfed   map 4

Cobblers

3 Church Street, Llandybie SA18 3HZ   COOKING 1
LLANDYBIE (0269) 850540   COST £14–£23

The pink and white corner house near the church accommodates diners on two
floors, the ground floor being used mostly at lunchtimes. Margaret Rees lays
emphasis on her locality: menus are in Welsh with English subtitles; materials
are given their provenance, which may often be her garden; she has often won
'Taste of Wales' awards. For all that, the tilt of cooking is not historical
revivalism: brill with rhubarb and elderberry sauce; loin of lamb with an
elderflower and Champagne sauce; a purée of mushrooms with garlic; lentil
and pea casserole with French mustard sauce all show modern preoccupations,
albeit firmly set in context. Her outlook is not parochial: special menus, for
instance celebrating the 'French connection', are sound exercises in bourgeois
cookery. The herb garden and the hedgerow are often featured, particularly in
salads of many elements and decorative features such as nasturtiums and
borage flowers, or as central ingredients to sauces and desserts. The menu,
changed seasonally, with a longer-term buttress of grills, and snacks for lunch,
may be very simple: a soup, a salad, a terrine and a vegetable dish as first
course; a fish and three meats as main courses; a greater range of puddings after
good local cheese and home-made biscuits. The herb bread is also home made.
Cooking may be inconsistent and the condition of some ingredients may
depend on business. This fluctuates to the frustration of both the restaurant and
the customers, as shown by the London visitor who found the place shut after
confirming that it would be open. The wine list is short, inexpensive and well
balanced. House Bulgarian: £5.

CHEF: Margaret Rees   PROPRIETORS: Hywel and Margaret Rees
OPEN: Tue to Sat, exc Thur L
MEALS: 12 to 1.30, 7 to 9.30
PRICES: £11 (£14), Set D £16.50 (£19).
CARDS: Access, Visa
SEATS: 40. Private parties: 40 main room, 20 private room. Car-park. Vegetarian meals.
Children's helpings. Wheelchair access (2 steps; also WC). Music

LLANGOLLEN Clwyd

map 4

▲ *Gales* ❢

18 Bridge Street, Llangollen LL20 8PF
LLANGOLLEN (0978) 860089 and 861427

COOKING 1
COST £14

Richard and Gillie Gale's wine bar plus B&B in the town centre is known for
its affordable food and carefully selected wines at equally affordable prices.
The enthusiast's 'fine wine list' is a treat. Inside is all oak-panelling and church
pews with a blackboard menu of soups, salads, quiches and cheeses. These are
backed up with hot specials along the lines of French country-style lamb.
Home-made ice-creams and cheesecakes to finish. House wine: £5.95.

CHEFS: Gillie Gale, John Gosling and Jenny Johnson   PROPRIETORS: Richard and
Gillie Gale
OPEN: Mon to Sat
CLOSED: Christmas to New Year
MEALS: 12 to 2, 6 to 10.15
PRICES: £7 (£12)
CARDS: Access, Visa
SEATS: 50. 6 tables outside. Private parties: 8 and 12 private rooms. Children welcome.
Wheelchair access. Music
ACCOMMODATION: 8 rooms, all with bath/shower. B&B £25 to £40. Deposit: £20. Baby
facilities. TV. Phone. Scenic. Confirm by 5 (*Which? Hotel Guide*)

LLANRWST Gwynedd

map 4

▲ *Meadowsweet Hotel* ▮

Station Road, Llanrwst LL26 0DS
LLANRWST (0492) 640732

COOKING 2
COST £17–£44

This small hotel is a conversion of terraced villas into a popular restaurant and
rooms that vary from good to adequate. As we went to press, John Evans
dropped the small *carte* to concentrate on the daily set-price menu with a choice
of three or more at each stage plus a cheese course. Menus are not adventurous,
nor are they of the steak-house variety, but the impression of mainstream
modern British cooking, happily free of wild fruit or sweet-sour combinations,
is confirmed in the eating. A party that sampled everything on one menu found
a consistency of achievement let down only by the 'Welsh farmhouse' cheeses,
of which the Evans are enthusiasts. 'Tired morsels of worn-out ends' was one
verdict. However, this is not always the case. Terrine of chicken and cheese; a
seafood Thermidor as a first course that consisted of a pastry boat filled with
fish and a mustard sauce; cauliflower soup with a Stilton crust; salmon with a
prawn and chive hollandaise; guinea-fowl with cider, cream and wild
mushrooms; duck with tomato sauce and brandied cherries; Amaretto ice-
cream and butterscotch sauce; and brandy-snaps coated in chocolate and filled
with chocolate mousse were some of the dishes that night. The cooking has an
eye on digestibility, so methods are free of otiose fats and enrichments. Service
is sometimes off-hand, sometimes slow but often enjoyable and welcoming.
The wine list is very long indeed. While strong on France, particularly clarets,
it has Italian, Spanish and Australasian sections and an especially good (for the

625

UK) German choice. California remains a little scanty, but no one will notice, given the wealth of alternatives. There is a mixture of growers represented, some very good indeed, others who perhaps lead the second division, but length is a useful defence against criticism of that sort. House French: £7.30 a litre. CELLARMAN'S CHOICE: Gewürztraminer 1987, SIPP, £11.75; St Joseph, La Grande Pompée 1985, Jaboulet, £14.50.

CHEF: John Evans PROPRIETORS: John and Joy Evans
OPEN: all week, D only
MEALS: 6.30 to 9.30
PRICES: £21 (£30), Set L £9.95 (£17), Set D £19.75 (£28) to £27.50 (£37)
CARDS: Access, Visa
SEATS: 36. Private parties: 50 main room. Car-park, 10 places. Children's helpings. Smart dress preferred. No smoking in dining-room. Music
ACCOMMODATION: 10 rooms, all with bath/shower. B&B £35 to £70. Deposit: £5. Baby facilities. Pets welcome. TV. Phone. Scenic. Doors close at midnight. Confirm by 6.30

LLANSANFFRAID GLAN CONWY Gwynedd   map 4

▲ Old Rectory

Llansanffraid Glan Conwy LL28 5LF   COOKING 3
LLANDUDNO (0492) 580611   COST £37

Suburbia falls away from the first-gear driveway and large gardens frame spectacular views of mountains and the Conwy estuary. The Vaughans have created a very particular recipe for entertainment, combining guest-rooms and communal dining with very good cooking. It is open to the outside world, though prior booking is essential, and visitors willingly suspend freedom on entry. Arrive by 7.30, appreciate the good furnishings, choose aperitifs, listen to a harpist at 7.45 for 12 to 15 minutes, then go into dinner. Residents sit at a long handsomely set table, others take their places as in any other restaurant. Dinner is no-choice and displays much skill. A first- course terrine of leeks in an avocado cream surrounded by a wreath of pickled walnuts and diced chilled jelly: texture contrasts and piquant counterpoints of taste gave class to a simple dish. The second course was pretty: a filo basket embraced half a boned quail stuffed with a *farce* of chicken. The dark quail had strength, was firm to bite and had character enough to balance the sweet smoothness of the chicken. The main course of turbot was presented on a white wine sauce with shallots and dark strands of samphire. A crayfish gave a slash of colour, vegetables some simple crunch. Dessert did give a choice: chocolate roulade with raspberries or orange cheesecake with kiwi-fruit. The roulade was ineffably light. Ten Welsh and Border cheeses preceded coffee with fudge and chocolate-dipped strawberries. For those so inclined, home-made fruit ice-creams or sorbets are alternatives always available. Small wonder foreign visitors are guided here by various publications. The total ban on smoking should be noted. The wine list is not over priced. House wines are £9.90.

Consumers' Association is planning to publish Out to Eat, *a new guide to budget eating out in restaurants, pubs, cafés, brasseries and so on. Please send reports and recommendations to Out to Eat, FREEPOST, 2 Marylebone Road, London NW1 1YN.*

CHEF: Wendy Vaughan   PROPRIETORS: Michael and Wendy Vaughan
OPEN: all week, D only
CLOSED: 7 Dec to 1 Feb
MEALS: 7.30 for 8
PRICES: Set D £22 (£31)
CARDS: Access, Visa
SEATS: 16. Car-park, 10 places. Vegetarian meals. No children under 12. Smart dress preferred. No smoking
ACCOMMODATION: 4 rooms, all with bath/shower. B&B £69.50 to £122. No children under 12. No smoking. Garden. TV. Phone. Scenic [*Which? Hotel Guide*]

MATHRY Dyfed   map 4

Ann FitzGerald's Farmhouse Kitchen

Mawbs Fawr, Mathry SA62 5JB   COOKING 2
CROESGOCH (0348) 831347   COST £14–£25

It speaks of popularity that there were a score of diners midweek at the fag-end of the season in this Welsh longhouse reached only by the most exiguous of tracks. Watch out for the signpost. Increasing business and investment in building have resulted in concentration on the restaurant side at the expense of the pasties and baked foods for casual visitors, though Ann FitzGerald will still cook carry-outs for those who telephone in advance. A very long menu is remarkable in its range of fish and meats for this part of the world, and it is buttressed by short fixed-price meals giving three choices save on Sunday, when the roast joint is it. Generosity is a byword, from the initial plate of herbed biscuits, mussels and salmon, to the giant cheeseboard left for the customer to attack, and the unlimited coffee and sometimes sugary fudge. Being so near the coast, there is much fish and shellfish on offer, such as Mediterranean fish soup with a blistering rouille; a lightly curried crab pancake, 'a meal in itself'; oysters with hollandaise; tempura prawns; monkfish and mussel linguine or salmon with a sparkling Loire, dill and butter sauce. Meats, too, get their chance: wild boar; venison; lamb with a crust and a rosemary and red wine sauce; well-basted guinea-fowl with red wine, tarragon and brandy; good roasts on Sunday. Vegetables – two sorts of potatoes, others sometimes too plain, but others made into a self-sufficient dish – are never lacking. There may be a pudding or apple tart cooked to order, or perhaps half a pineapple 'marquise' filled with crushed fruit, cream and kirsch. There have been moments when dishes seem not to work, and when a few of the flavours seemed blander than they need have been, but the general opinion is affirmative. The restaurant has been licensed since the last *Guide* and a short, not expensive list has strong choices from the New World to compensate for the high price of the good French wine. House Bordeaux: £4.50. CELLARMAN'S CHOICE: Moulin de Rousselet 1982, £10; Miguel Torres Sauvignon Blanc 1989, £7.

CHEFS: Lionel and Ann FitzGerald PROPRIETOR: Ann FitzGerald
OPEN: all week
CLOSED: L Christmas to Easter
MEALS: 12 to 2, 7 to 9
PRICES: £16 (£21), Set L £10.50 (£14), Set D £15.50 (£20)
SEATS: 40. 4 tables outside. Private parties: 40 main room. Car-park, 40 places. Vegetarian meals. Children's helpings. No children under 9. Wheelchair access. Music

---

NANTGAREDIG Dyfed
map 4

▲ *Four Seasons,*
Cwmtwrch Farmhouse Hotel

Nantgaredig, SA32 7NY
NANTGAREDIG (026 729) 0238   COOKING 1
on B4310, 1m N of A40, 5m E of Carmarthen   COST £17–£24

Flagstones, bare stone walls, exposed beams, the kitchen visible from the serving area, a woodburning stove: it all sounds like a rural myth, and looks like it as you sit in a conservatory extension gazing at the green hillside beyond. Handsome pottery, decent cloths and pictures contribute to the attractiveness inside. Jenny Willmott and her daughter Emma, complete with Aga, cook a farmhouse sort of menu, starting with multi-grain bread and going on to roast lamb or pork, chicken with a cream sauce, duck, beef, salmon or a vegetarian dish, changing only in detail from month to month. 'Simple but excellent', it is put together with care. Meals that have struck readers as exactly right in context have included melon and Parma ham, fresh made mushroom quiches, roast lamb with port and redcurrant, carved as generous portions off a joint, fillet of beef with white wine cooked more than asked, plain vegetables with good mashed potatoes, and home-made desserts, though on occasion the cheese seemed more supermarket than farmhouse. The wine list is arranged by grape type and is not expensive. It gives few details about makers, but seems to have some acceptable bottles among three dozen bins. House wine: £5.50.
CELLARMAN'S CHOICE: Babich Chardonnay 1984, £11; Ch. de Lastours, Corbières 1986, £7.

CHEFS: Jenny and Emma Willmott PROPRIETORS: Bill and Jenny Willmott
OPEN: Mon to Sat, D only
CLOSED: 2 weeks Mar
MEALS: 7.30 to 9.30
PRICES: Set D £12.50 (£17) to £15.50 (£20)
SEATS: 52. 3 tables outside. Private parties: 42 main room, 10 private room. Car-park, 20 places. No-smoking area. Vegetarian meals. Children's helpings (D only). Smart dress preferred. Wheelchair access (also WC)
ACCOMMODATION: 6 rooms, all with bath/shower. Rooms for disabled. B&B £28 to £36. Deposit: £10. Baby facilities. Pets welcome. Afternoon teas. Garden. Snooker. Scenic. Doors close at midnight. Confirm by 6

The Guide *is totally independent, accepts no free hospitality, and survives on the number of copies sold each year.*

NEWPORT Dyfed map 4

▲ *Cnapan* 🍷

East Street, Newport SA42 OWF — COOKING 1
NEWPORT (0239) 820575 — COST £25

A 'country house for guests' is the extended Lloyd family's way of putting it. Their way of running it is engagingly casual and, in part, why the baby-pink Georgian town house has so many fans. A little confusion in sorting out seating arrangements in the country-style dining-room did not augur well for one couple, but apprehensions lessened with the arrival of fish terrine and broccoli and orange soup with garlic bread. Cooking is of the multi-ingredient sort: Welsh lamb in apricot, brandy and tarragon sauce comes with a savoury flapjack; chicken breast might be stuffed with avocado and cream cheese and wrapped in bacon. This can be grand or it can be an undifferentiated medley of tastes. Eluned Lloyd is vegetarian, one reason that her meatless dishes can stand up and be counted, so mushroom and aubergine buckwheat bake, or a black-eye bean casserole with cheesy pastry hat were virtuous in presentation as well as in interest and flavour. Some of her vegetarian concoctions 'truly made up on the spur of the moment' sound and taste of forward thinking: a three-fold layering of walnut pâté, aubergine and spinach *en croûte* with wine sauce and brandied apricots is not the most intricate. The lunch menu, better value still than dinner, has more classically Welsh specialities such as oat-based flans and onion tart. Coffee is good. The wine list is singled out with an award because of its genuine attempt to choose each bottle for value and flavour. Few of the choices are recondite, but they show forethought. One, Colli Euganei, is brought direct from Italy by a South Wales exile. Six wine merchants and many countries are tapped to give variety and substance to the 40 strong list, but apart from burgundy and Champagne, only a handful of bottles cost over £10. House wine, from the south of France, is £5.95. CELLARMAN'S CHOICE: Ch. St Jean d'Aumières, 1986, Languedoc, £6.95; Marlborough Sauvignon Blanc, Montana, £8.75.

CHEFS: Eluned Lloyd and Judi Cooper PROPRIETORS: Eluned and John Lloyd, Judi and Michael Cooper
OPEN: all week, exc Tue (Fri and Sat D and Sun L only, Nov to Mar)
CLOSED: Feb
MEALS: 12.30 to 2.30, 7.30 to 9
PRICES: £16 (£21)
CARDS: Access, Visa
SEATS: 34. 4 tables outside. Private parties: 36 main room. Car-park, 6 places. Vegetarian meals. Children's helpings. No smoking while others are eating. Wheelchair access (also WC)
ACCOMMODATION: 5 rooms, all with bath/shower. B&B £25 to £40. Deposit: £20. Baby facilities. TV. Scenic. Doors close at midnight. Confirm 3 days ahead [*Which? Hotel Guide*]

See the inside of the front cover for an explanation of the 1 to 5 rating system recognising cooking standards.

The Guide *relies on feedback from its readers. Especially welcome are reports on new restaurants appearing in the book for the first time.*

▲ *Hedleys, Celtic Manor*

Coldra Woods, Newport NP6 2YA COOKING 2
LLANWERN (0633) 413000 COST £22–£42

The modernised nineteenth-century house is set among woods and low hills
giving fine views, except from the dining-room, which overlooks the car park.
Compensation is in the form of space, a giant fireplace and dark oak panelling.
The seigniorial touch carries through to the very proper service and the cooking
by Trefor Jones, Welsh Chef of the Year in 1989. This is modern neo-classical
on a seasonal *carte* of half a dozen choices per course and an extra list of fish
dishes, as well as a daily set-menu that is appreciably cheaper for food that is
often simpler. It makes for a long repertoire, needing a lot of business to keep it
fresh. South Wales is new to the country-house luxury game, so a certain
suspicion of high prices and unnecessary flannel exists, surfacing, for example,
in outrage at high wine prices. For all that, Trefor Jones can cook skilfully as
well as cast a fair list of modern dishes, such as lentil soup with sweetbreads; a
chicken consommé with chervil; best end of lamb with a herb and green
peppercorn crust and a Cassis sauce; or duck with honey and ginger with a filo
parcel of sage and onion. A meal in the winter included a feuilleté of mussels
with chive sauce where the material between the layers of puff was actually
spinach and the mussels were applied externally. They melded into a
satisfactory whole. A charlotte of aubergines and courgettes had its own
spinach wrap and was also arranged nicely in layers, set on a tomato coulis.
This was rich, not improved by a bland olive oil sauce, but good none the less.
A main course of red mullet cooked in a parcel on a bed of fennel and herbs and
served with lots of leaves and vegetable strips lost from being overcooked. This
was not the fate of a veal steak with walnut and caper sauce, nor of the
vegetables which were undercooked to a fault, save the beetroot. The tip-top
hot raspberry soufflé put other desserts in the shade. Unless vegetarians
arrange for their meal in advance, they may be pretty much limited to lasagne.
Private customers, and it must be hoped the place does not only aim at business
trade, may object to extra charges for vegetables tucked away at the bottom of
the daily specials sheet, and the lack of information about tipping except for a
space marked 'Gratuity' on the bill itself. The wine list is adequate but strongly
depends on négociants. There is a good Alsace Riesling from Robert Faller, a
Cabernet Sauvignon from Wolf Blass and a Ch. d'Angludet 1978 among the fair
choices, but none is cheap. House wine: £7.50. CELLARMAN'S CHOICE: Fixin
1986, Faiveley, £21; Gewürztraminer 1986, Sparr, £12.50.

---

*County Round-ups listing additional restaurants that may be worth a visit are at the back
of the* Guide, *after the Irish section. Reports on Round-up entries are welcome.*

*Several sharp operators have tried to extort money from restaurateurs on the promise of an
entry in a guide book that has never appeared. The* Good Food Guide *makes no charge
for inclusion and does not offer certificates of any kind.*

CHEF: Trefor Jones   PROPRIETORS: Raymond and Kay Dawes
OPEN: Mon to Sat, exc Sat L
MEALS: 12 to 2.30, 7 to 10.30
PRICES: £24 (£35), Set L and D £16 (£22) to £20 (£26)
CARDS: Access, Amex, Diners, Visa
SEATS: 60. Private parties: 35 main room, 20, 100 and 200 private rooms. Car-park, 200 places. Children's helpings. Smart dress preferred. No pipes in dining-room and no-smoking area. Wheelchair access. Music
ACCOMMODATION: 75 rooms, all with bath/shower. Lift. B&B £90 to £120. Baby facilities. Afternoon teas. Garden. Swimming-pool. Sauna. Air-conditioning. TV. Phone. Scenic. Confirm by 6

NORTHOP Clwyd   map 4

▲ Soughton Hall

Northop CH7 6AB
NORTHOP (0352 86) 811   COOKING 2
off A5119, Northop to Mold   COST £20–£55

This is a splendiferous nineteenth-century pastiche of early Georgian proportions, Elizabethan details and Islamic folly, in a beautiful part of the country. Inside it's a grand country hotel of rich colour schemes and antiques that are sufficiently solid and flamboyant for the tall intricate ceilings and mullioned windows. The Rodenhurst family stresses informality, but the polished tables in the first-floor 'State' dining-room are set with lead crystal and Royal Doulton, and in the evening a harpist plays. The food is fancy, too, and the two three-course menus are now joined by a seven-course, no-choice menu available from Monday to Thursday. One report of a three-course Sunday lunch singles out a seafood parcel on a pepper and light curry sauce; others wax lyrical about the fruit-based desserts: steamed lemon pudding with intensely flavoured orange and lemon sauce or lemon curd tartlet, for instance, or a raspberry soufflé. Hot, home-made bread and rolls are praised, and service is sound. Niggles have been few; that the coffee is not always hot is perhaps the most serious. The wine list is long with clarets, the safest bet and there is much under £15. House wine: £8.50 and £9.95. CELLARMAN'S CHOICE: Ch. Tour St Christopher 1983, £23; Montagny, Christine Ponsot 1988, £19.50.

CHEF: Malcolm William Warham   PROPRIETORS: John and Rosemary Rodenhurst
OPEN: all week, exc L Mon, Tue and Sat
MEALS: 12 to 2, 7 to 9.30 (10 Sat, 8 Sun)
PRICES: Set L £14 (£20), Set D £19.50 (£28) to £36 (£46)
CARDS: Access, Amex, Visa
SEATS: 50. Private parties: 56 main room, 22 and 50 private room. Car-park, 50 places. No children under 12. Smart dress preferred. No cigars/pipes in dining-room. Wheelchair access
ACCOMMODATION: 12 rooms, all with bath/shower. B&B £80 to £116. Deposit: 25%. No smoking in breakfast room. No children under 12. Afternoon teas. Garden. Tennis. Snooker. TV. Phone. Scenic [Which? Hotel Guide]

The Guide relies on feedback from its readers. Especially welcome are reports on new restaurants appearing in the book for the first time.

PONTFAEN Dyfed   map 4

▲ Gelli Fawr Country House

Pontfaen SA65 9TX   COOKING 1
NEWPORT (0239) 820343   COST £7–£26

Three miles inland from Newport stands this large farmhouse in the Gwaun
valley, run by Frances Roughley and Ann Churcher. Before their take-over, it
used to 'serve chips with everything to the country folk of Pembrokeshire'.
Now, having won a 'Taste of Wales' award, and with Frances Roughley doing
many demonstrations of Welsh cooking, it is set on more serious activity.
Improvements are still in train to remove the vestiges of its previous
incarnation. The cooking is by no means doctrinaire Welsh. A first course of
tempura prawns with a mild sweet-and-sour sauce immediately denies that
description. It is, rather, British eclectic. Substantial vegetable soups are
frequently offered; a loin of pork is stuffed with prunes and a herb forcemeat
and served with rice mixed with prunes and apricots; noisettes of lamb are
presented with little pastry cases of mint and redcurrant jellies; there is a
galaxy of vegetables (six at one meal); and the desserts may run to pears with a
chocolate sauce, bought-in ice-cream or good apple strudel. The most Welsh
touch is the cheeseboard and the Nevern Dairy butter. These come at the outset
of the meal with a whole loaf, made up of layers of white, brown and herbed
doughs with a line of tomato in the middle. Everything is not yet as it may be –
an inspection noted slightly tough meat and undistinguished sauces – but
evidently the spirit is willing. Although it is planned to keep the restaurant
open seven days a week all year the proprietors suggest customers telephone to
check in winter. There are three dozen wines, fairly but lengthily described.
These lean heavily on France, though half a dozen Australians add breadth.
Organic house wine: £5.95.

CHEF: Frances Roughley   PROPRIETORS: Ann Churcher and Frances Roughley
OPEN: all week
MEALS: 12 to 2.30, 7.30 to 10
PRICES: £16 (£22), Set L £2.95 (£7) to £5 (£9). Set D £12.75 (£18) to £15 (£20). Unlicensed,
but bring your own: corkage £1
CARDS: Access, Visa
SEATS: 45. 4 tables outside. Private parties: 70 main room. Car-park. Vegetarian meals.
Children's helpings. Wheelchair access (2 steps; also WC). Air-conditioned
ACCOMMODATION: 10 rooms, 2 with bath/shower. B&B £17.50 to £35. Deposit: 10%. Baby
facilities. Pets welcome. Afternoon teas. Garden. Swimming-pool. Snooker. Scenic

---

Prices quoted in the Guide *are based on information supplied by restaurateurs. The figure
in brackets below an entry is the average for a three-course meal with service, coffee and
half a bottle of house wine, as calculated by computer. The prices quoted at the top of an
entry represent a range, from the lowest average meal price to the highest; the latter is
inflated by 20 per cent to take account of the fact that very few people eat an average meal,
and also that prices are likely to rise during the year of the* Guide

▲ Tregynon Country Farmhouse Hotel

Pontfaen SA65 9TU
NEWPORT (0239) 820531
from junction of B4313/B4329,
take B4313
towards Fishguard; take first R,
and R again for ¹/₂m

COOKING 1
COST £16–£24

The fact that navigational directions fill a page of the hotel's literature indicates the isolation and the owners' desire to instruct. This surfaces again in a wine list where notes exceed the listings by a factor of two. The Farmhouse makes a virtue of dietary problems and cooks meals for every sort of restriction: 'they cope admirably with any requests, keeping medicaments in the fridge, and so on.' Yet for those who are merely looking for good food, bought with an eye to sound agriculture and decent flavour, and cooked in a style informed largely by vegetarianism – a mixture of disparate elements to achieve something 'tasty' – the kitchen may deliver. 'First courses were generally interesting and soups excellent. Vegetables were generously served and lightly cooked. Meat had real old-fashioned taste, the home-smoked gammon especially, and even when it was a mite chewy, lamb for example, it did have flavour. Puddings were good, the ice-creams and sorbets were the favourites.' Typical dishes are a 'banana appetiser' of banana and cucumber tossed with a blend of yoghurt, mayonnaise, lemon juice and sunflower seeds on a bed of lettuce; apple and sweetcorn soup 'with a touch of beetroot'; 'Huntingdon Fidget Pie' of bacon, apples and onions in cider; gammon with pineapple; and desserts such as yoghurt cinnamon cake and those ice-creams, made without eggs. Supplements are in force on most complicated main courses, negating the set-price. Menus change daily and respond to supplies. The wine list has four dozen items and takes 17 closely typed pages to describe them. The notes are useful and interesting and the wines carefully chosen. Prices are very fair indeed. Bruno Paillard Champagne, Lindemann wines from South Australia, Rhônes from La Vieille Ferme and Gaston Beck's Gewürztraminer are just some examples. House wine: £5.95.

CHEFS/PROPRIETORS: Peter Heard and Jane Cox
OPEN: all week, D only
MEALS: 7.30 to 8.45
PRICES: Set D £11 (£16) to £15 (£20)
SEATS: 28. Private parties: 16 main room. Car-park. Vegetarian meals. Children restricted after 7.30pm. No smoking in dining-room. Music
ACCOMMODATION: 8 rooms, all with bath/shower. Rooms for disabled. B&B £18 to £20 per person. Baby facilities. Afternoon teas. Garden. TV. Scenic. Confirm by noon

'Waiting staff are very good; one was, I think, even human. He smiled. Every now and again there is a little gathering of the waiters. Could one say a "wittering of waiters"? This is followed by a predatory prowl by senior waiters. I put my wine glass down, I had just that second finished, and a hand came out and grabbed it. A group of business folk at the next table were getting down to a £10 million deal. They were being rushed as well.'
On inspecting in London

PORTFIELD GATE Dyfed   map 4

▲ *Sutton Lodge*

Portfield Gate SA62 3LU   COOKING 1
HAVERFORDWEST (0437) 68548   COST £24

The early nineteenth-century country house, a mile west of Haverfordwest, has
an upwardly mobile but laid-back style. The set menu created last year to
simplify life during kitchen and dining-room transformations still lives on. It is
four-course and no-choice, but you are encouraged to voice likes and dislikes
when booking. Judicious use of spices and herbs keeps sauces finely tuned,
and the cooking is broad-minded. California comes to Wales with a tomato and
mozzarella salad with balsamic vinegar and sun-dried tomatoes. Other dishes
from closer to home might be French onion soup with cheese croûtons and
roast spring chicken (poussin) stuffed with a mixture of wild and pilau rice,
with white wine and peppercorn sauce. A light white chocolate and blackberry
mousse made an especially good dessert. Service is 'friendly and not pushy.'
The no-nonsense wine list is short and cheap. House French: £5.25.

CHEF: Stanford Moseley   PROPRIETOR: Stapal Hotels Ltd
OPEN: Mon to Sat, D only
CLOSED: Jan and Feb
MEALS: 6.30 to 9
PRICES: Set D £15.50 (£20)
SEATS: 12. Private parties: 10 main room. Car-park, 10 places. No children under 12.
No smoking in dining-room. Music
ACCOMMODATION: 6 rooms, all with bath/shower. B&B £30 to £60. No children under 12.
Pets welcome. TV. Scenic. Doors close at midnight. Confirm by 5 [*Which? Hotel Guide*]

PORTHGAIN Dyfed   map 4

Harbour Lights

Porthgain SA62 5BW   COOKING 3
CROESGOCH (0348) 831549   COST £28

COUNTY
OF THE
YEAR
RESTAURANT

Porthgain once earned its living from fishing and the export of stone and brick.
Now, 'apart from the Sloop pub and Harbour Lights there are only a few
houses', reported one who was drawn by the ruined stone-crushing works but
stayed to enjoy the cooking of the two sisters at the restaurant. They have a sure
sense of taste and do not mess about with 'fine cookery'. Theirs is 'good
cooking' for both vegetarians (one is herself vegetarian) and meat-eaters. 'Good
cooking' does not only mean 'plain', though unadorned food can be had; what
there is, is of prime quality and freshness. This is seen in dishes such as laver
bread with cockles; crab Mornay; prawns with a spiced mayonnaise; brill with
ginger and vermouth; peppered sirloin steak with a brandy sauce; sticky toffee
pudding; 'autumn' pudding; and home-made sorbets. The operation is a family
one: vegetables are grown by Anne Marie Davies's husband and help comes
from parents and in-laws. The wine list is unexpectedly careful. House French
Gamay and Sauvignon Blanc: £6.75.

CHEFS: Anne Marie Davies and Bernadette Barker   PROPRIETOR: Anne Marie Davies
OPEN: all week, D only
CLOSED: Jan and Feb
MEALS: 6.30 to 9.30
PRICES: Set D £17.50 (£23)
CARDS: Access, Visa
SEATS: 40. 6 tables outside. Private parties: 25 main room. Car-park, 100 places. Vegetarian
meals. Children's helpings. Wheelchair access (1 step). Music

---

PORTHKERRY   South Glamorgan   map 4

▲ *Egerton Grey*
Country House Hotel

Porthkerry CF6 9BZ   COOKING 2
RHOOSE (0446) 711666 and 711690   COST £21−£35

There is potential in this handsomely furnished Victorian house set 'yards from
the sea across a country park with a magnificent railway viaduct framing the
view.' The Pitkins have not long been in occupation, but have made their mark
as solicitous hosts. The menu descriptions have displayed signs of floridness: a
fish terrine is 'draped with its own dressing' and 'a gateau of salmon and potato
cake is served with woodland mushrooms swept on red and white wine
sauces'. There are signs, however, that the tendency is moderating. A dessert
chocolate box was once 'filled with a raspberry mousse cascading strawberries
on a pool of its own syrup'. A more recent version is a box of chocolate encasing
a chocolate mousse, set on a vanilla sauce. This is an improvement, says a
reader. Another fanciful over-elaboration was a pillow of puff pastry filled
with leeks, topped with quail breast and 'ribboned with a gazpacho sauce'
which ended up with 'a cream sauce on the leeks, a madeira sauce on the quail
and a gazpacho sauce ribboned over the lot'. Better the home-made and spicy
lamb sausage studded with lentils served with a broad bean and red pepper
salad. Technique as well as reasonable restraint is there in a light salmon
mousse with a shellfish and tarragon sauce, 'pungent with shellfish flavours yet
somehow light'. Main courses have encompassed some good contrasts of
flavour and texture as in sea bass with braised endive and a white wine sauce
and a sandwich of puff pastry, strips of beef, kidneys and field mushrooms
which looked good, 'bar the ubiquitous cherry tomatoes', and has often tasted
as rounded and substantial as it should. Vegetables are profuse but plain.
Desserts include that chocolate box, a clever conceit that lasts but a short while
under marauding spoons, but also poached pears with two sauces, one hot, one
cold, 'though the difference was not perceptible.' The message seems one of
hope, provided the kitchen can control a desire to elaborate which, according to
earlier reports, actually vitiated the ability to cook to time. Residents eat
slightly more cheaply than non-residents. 'The welcome to children depends
on 'how many, what age and time of year. We are open to discussion.' The
sensible and carefully chosen wine list comes from Tanners of Shrewsbury and
allows a fair range of prices and a thin spread over major regions, though not
California. House wine: £8.50.

CHEFS: Paul Whittock and Julian Hutchings   PROPRIETORS: Anthony and Magda Pitkin
OPEN: all week
MEALS: 12 to 1.45, 7 to 9.45
PRICES: Set L and D £24.50 (£29), Set Sun L £14.95 (£21), Service inc
CARDS: Access, Amex, Visa
SEATS: 50. 2 tables outside. Private parties: 35 and 120 (buffet) main room. Car-park, 40
places. Vegetarian meals on request. Children's helpings. Children restricted. No smoking
in dining-room. Wheelchair access (also male and female WC)
ACCOMMODATION: 10 rooms, all with bath/shower. B&B £60 to £75. Deposit: £25. Baby
facilities. Afternoon teas. Garden. Tennis. TV. Phone. Scenic. Doors close at midnight

---

PORTMEIRION Gwynedd   map 4

▲ *Portmeirion Hotel*

Portmeirion LL48 6ET   COOKING 1
PORTHMADOG (0766) 770228   COST £16–£31

See Portmeirion, stay at Portmeirion, experience Portmeirion, even if there are
occasional hiccups of service: 'inexperienced and most certainly
uncommunicative'. Most are agreed that the cooking has steadied through the
year and was happily 'much better than anticipated', though lapses still occur.
Since the fire of 1981 and the subsequent rebuilding, refurnishing and redesign
of the bedrooms and public rooms – still preserving Sir Clough Williams-
Ellis's 'light opera' view of architecture – visitors have been dazzled by the
brilliance. 'You try to sit in the lounge full of mirrors. Well, we tried. It's like
occupying a stage set: you wait for the curtain to rise. You just have to keep
walking.' Walk on to the dining-room: 'views over the estuary, white, gold,
cream, columns, lights at their tops, plants, statues, you name it.' Sheer
exuberance and fantasy. The cooking is not fantastical but it is often sound. The
menu is set price, cheaper at lunch, with a wide choice giving as much weight
to fish as to meat. At a summer meal the gratin of crab and prawns was
generous on crab, innocent of prawns and accurately light on cheese; beef was
of good quality with oyster mushrooms and truffles in a sauce of sufficient
power; chicken with cream and sage was moist-fleshed and properly discreet
on sage; puddings were no great shakes although others have reported an
improvement on last year's reservations in this department. They have also
praised a good selection of mussels, prawns and white fish with white wine
and basil, an excellent beef in pastry and a wide selection of vegetables, though
these are sometimes over-cooked, sometimes under-cooked. Cheese can be
well chosen. The wine list takes in the world but at a price. There are some old
clarets but the straight percentage mark-up makes them unacceptably dear. If
you are prepared to ignore the good Châteauneufs from Beaucastel, organic
Alsaces from Eugene Meyer or other organic French wines dotted through the
list, better value for money may be had from the New World. House French: £8
and £8.50. CELLARMAN'S CHOICE: St Emilion, Vieux Château Carré 1983,
£16.50; Tokay d'Alsace (organic) 1988, Meyer, £14.50. There is no service
charge and tips are not expected or encouraged.

CHEF: Hefin Williams   PROPRIETORS: Portmeirion Ltd
OPEN: all week, exc Mon L
CLOSED: 3 weeks end Jan
MEALS: 12 to 1.45, 7 to 9.30
PRICES: Set L £11.50 (£16) to £12.50 (£17), Set D £19.50 (£24) to £22 (£26)
CARDS: Access, Amex, Diners, Visa
SEATS: 120. 8 tables outside. Private parties: 100 main room, 8 and 30 private rooms. Car-park, 100 places. Children's helpings. Smart dress preferred. No smoking in dining-room. Wheelchair access (also unisex WC). Music
ACCOMMODATION: 34 rooms, all with bath/shower. Rooms for disabled. B&B £61.50 to £88. Deposit: £20. Garden. Swimming-pool. Tennis. Golf. Fishing. TV. Phone. Scenic. Confirm by 6 [*Which? Hotel Guide*]

PWLLHELI Gwynedd   map 4

▲ *Plas Bodegroes* 🍶

Pwllheli, LL53 5TH
PWLLHELI (0758) 612363 and 612510   COOKING 4
on A497, 1m W of Pwllheli   COST £24–£32

The house with a symmetrical front and a veranda skirt sits surrounded by trees, the lawn clipped to a Valentine, echoing the hearts of the cinnamon biscuits served within. A touch sentimental, but there is no escaping the effort and care of Christopher Chown in the kitchen and Gunna a Trodni outside it. This kitchen prides itself on promoting local produce and interpreting it in as modern a way as any in Wales. Hall-marks such as vertical arrangements on the plate, the disposition of single intense flavours in proximity but not as a mélange, and affection for herbs and Mediterranean tastes are often met . This espousal of the local cause is perhaps the more interesting if only because there is difficulty in maintaining its integrity. Christopher Chown relates how local fishermen may not be able to sell in small lots to nearby businesses; so Canadian lobsters suddenly become cheaper than those from Anglesey. Similarly, sea bass has risen from £2.50 a pound to £5.50 in two years, while African bass is offered at £4.50. How can a regional identity be fostered on such a basis? How can price increases be kept within bounds? In national terms, Plas Bodegroes is still not expensive, even with price rises. The menu, of four or five choices in four courses plus cheese, can be taken à la carte or as a set-price extravaganza. On Tuesdays, it's residents only. A meal taken in summer displays some of the techniques. Amuse-gueule given with the menu comprised shingles of smoked chicken and slices of spicy coarse sausage. The first course was guinea-fowl served on a mound of sharp slaw with a piccalilli of red peppers scattered with hazelnuts, 'like a tiny fresh American picnic'. The fish course came as a timbale of lobster encasing sweet chunks of lobster flesh. It was bordered by concentric rings of chervil and armoricaine sauces. The meat dish was grilled fillet of beef with a shallot and herb crust with ox-tail sauce, while another member of the party went on with fish: a monkfish steak with red pepper and fennel, combined white and wild rice and a moat of tarragon sauce. The cheese course was a choice of grilled goats' cheese, a cheeseboard with walnut bread and home-made biscuits, or a mature Colston Bassett Stilton. It was a welcome calm before more multi-storey surprises: cinnamon biscuits layering tart rhubarb and apple and mellow elderflower custard; rich, sweet chocolate mousse (almost marquise) cake in black and white layers with a cherry sauce. Coffee was excellent and the petits fours showed that invention carried on to the end – they included cape gooseberries with pantaloon stripes of chocolate and vanilla. This meal showed the skilful use of single herbs and deployment of strong flavour. Its reporter heard Beethoven string quartets coming from the kitchen, but likened the food more to tumbles of clear Scarlatti. Of the 200 wines, 20 or so are selected as 'appropriate for our food'. This house selection alone would shame many restaurants, not only in its range but also in its mark-ups, which are fair, sensible and always favour the better bottles. Half-bottles are provided generously. Even-handed selection gives Italy as good a showing as Burgundy. The quality throughout is excellent with growers like Mascarello in Piedmont, Phelps in Napa and Huet in Vouvray leaping off the page. At prices that put Dom. de Chevalier 1978 at half that in a south-east country-house hotel – a saving of £30 – the list is not only a joy, but also an affordable one. CELLARMAN'S CHOICE: Tokay Reserve Personelle 1983, Hugel, £18.50; Long Gulley Riesling, Yarra Valley 1987 (Organic), £12.50. 'Tips are not encouraged.'

CHEF: Christopher Chown PROPRIETORS: Christopher Chown and Gunna a Trodni
OPEN: all week, D only, exc Tue (residents only)
CLOSED: 3 Jan to 13 Feb
MEALS: 7 to 9
PRICES: £17 (£24), Set D £20 (£24) to £23 (£27). Service inc
CARDS: Access, Visa
SEATS: 45. Private parties: 60 main room, 18 private room. Car-park, 25 places. Children's helpings. No smoking in dining-room. Wheelchair access (1 step; also WC). Music
ACCOMMODATION: 5 rooms, all with bath/shower. B&B £35 to £110. Deposit: 10%. Baby facilities. Pets welcome. Garden. TV. Phone. Scenic. Confirm by 6 [*Which? Hotel Guide*]

ST BRIDE'S-SUPER-ELY South Glamorgan   map 4

Bardells

St Bride's-super-Ely CF5 6EZ   COOKING 2
PETERSTON-SUPER-ELY (0446) 760534   COST £18–£28

Approached through small country lanes, in a pastoral landscape surprisingly close to Cardiff, the medieval sound of the village name is belied by the modern house in which the Budgen family practise their trade. Its architecture, however, is soft enough for people to mention Lutyens at the same time. Jane Budgen cooks a small set-price menu, sensibly restricted to three choices in each course. (The persistence of small restaurants in offering manifold options every day to minuscule numbers of customers can only undermine faith in their shopping habits; Bardells' restraint does the opposite.) Moules marinière; smoked pigeon with a salad dressed with balsamic vinegar; quail and duck liver parfait; salmon with saffron sauce; guinea-fowl on lentils with orange and lime; lamb with port and herbs; chocolate and rum charlotte; apple tart; coffee and praline ice-cream are examples that show the range. A Sunday lunch showed a nice balance between homely familiarity and skilled composition: chicken liver timbale wrapped in spinach with a mild tomato sauce was followed by lamb with a tangy lemon and herb stuffing and a mint sauce served with plain but good vegetables, then finished with a chocolate mousse as rich as it was fluffy. The experience is made the more enlivening since son-in-law Panikos Antoni runs the front of house. A short wine list is distinguished by its reasonable prices but undistinguished in its apparent lack of half-bottles. The wines have been well and enthusiastically chosen with, for example, Ch. Court les Muts and Dom. de Cauhapé from south west France as indicators that this is very much more than just a Cash and Carry job. House wine: £5.95 and £6.95. CELLARMAN'S CHOICE: Ch. Blaignan 1985, £11.95; Vouvray demi-sec, Ch. de Vaudenuits 1978, £8.95.

CHEFS: Jane Budgen and Lucy Antoni   PROPRIETOR: Jane Budgen
OPEN: Tue to Sat, D and Sun L (other days by arrangement)
MEALS: 12.30 to 1.30, 7.30 to 9
PRICES: Set L £13.50 (£18), Set D £17.50 (£23)
CARDS: Access, Diners, Visa
SEATS: 30. 4 tables outside. Private parties: 30 main room. Vegetarian meals. Children's helpings. No children under 8. No smoking in dining-room. Music

---

SWANSEA   West Glamorgan   map 4

Annie's

56 St Helen's Road, Swansea SA1 4BE   COOKING 1
SWANSEA (0792) 655603   COST £17–£24

Ann Gwilym's pleasant stripped-pine dining-room is just the right setting for some better than average Anglo-French bistro cooking. The range of the menu shows in the recommendations: gravlax with fromage frais and dill; buckwheat pancakes filled with seafood; poached fillets of brill with baby leeks and oyster mushrooms; duck with wine and mushroom sauce. There are hot fruit tarts and sorbets to finish. Welsh farmhouse cheeses such as Llanboidy and organic Pencarreg are served with biscuits and baby pickled vegetables. Young waitresses try hard and mean well; friendliness makes up for any lack of professionalism. Downstairs is a café bar serving a small selection of daily dishes. The wine list from Lay & Wheeler has some decent, reasonably priced drinking, including French country wines. House wine £6.50. CELLARMAN'S CHOICE: Sauvignon du Haut-Poitou, VDQS £8.20.

CHEFS: Ann Gwilym and Stephane Rivier   PROPRIETOR: Ann Gwilym
OPEN: Tue to Sat, D only (plus Mon in summer)
MEALS: 7 to 10.30
PRICES: £16 (£20), Set D £12.80 (£17). Service inc
CARDS: Access, Visa
SEATS: 56. Private parties: 34 main room, 22 private room. Vegetarian meals. Children's helpings on request. Music

---

The text of entries is based on unsolicited reports sent in by readers, backed up by inspections conducted anonymously. The factual details under the text are from questionnaires the Guide *sends to all restaurants that feature in the book.*

La Braseria

28 Wind Street, Swansea SA1 1D2	COOKING 1
SWANSEA (0792) 469683	COST £23

Part of a group with La Brasserie, Champers and Le Monde in Cardiff (see entries), La Braseria shares the same formula of a lot of fish, some simple meats and a grill. The two floors are normally pretty full and can be fairly abrasive, but the quality of the materials is good. Sea bass in rock salt is a speciality but the deeps of the Atlantic and the Indian Oceans also seem to end up on the slab. Fish is priced by weight; salad is the accompaniment. There is a good range of Spanish wines, even Vega Sicilia if you think the ambience is unhurried enough. House wines: £5.65 and £6.25.

CHEF: M. Tercero PROPRIETORS: Benigno Martinez and M.Tercero
OPEN: Mon to Sat
CLOSED: 25 Dec
MEALS: 12 to 2.30, 7 to 12
PRICES: £14 (£19). Service inc
CARDS: Access, Amex, Diners, Visa
SEATS: 200. Private parties: 100 private room. Children welcome. Wheelchair access (also WC). Music. Self-service salad bar

Green Dragon Bistro

Green Dragon Lane, Swansea SA1 1DG	COOKING 2
SWANSEA (0792) 641437	COST £23

Kate Taylor continues cooking a mixture of local and French-inspired dishes for a lunchtime session in this plain restaurant. She can cook not only modern dishes such as duck with cassis, but also old-fashioned braised ox-tail as well – two ends of a spectrum again represented by quenelles of seafood with sauce Nantua, and Irish stew. Some say the fish comes with beurre blanc too often, though it is good. A lunch of rillettes (not sufficiently pounded), pigeon pie and crème brûlée was matched by another of a seafood terrine with a superbly deep sauce, fresh baby haddock simply poached, and fair vegetables. If the Enterprise Allowance could engender more places like this (for that was how Kate Taylor got started), Britain would be a happier place. Wines are carefully chosen, although not always provided with details of growers, with mainly French buttressed by a few Spanish items. Prices throughout are fair to positively low. House wine: £5. CELLARMAN'S CHOICE:Gewürztraminer 1985, Hugel, £10; Ch. Lyonnat 1983, £11.75. In the evenings the premises are used for the Hwyrnos (Welsh night), which aims to replicate a nosen lawen (merry night) with food and Welsh-language entertainment.

CHEF/PROPRIETOR: Kate Taylor
OPEN: Mon to Sat, L only and last Sun of month
MEALS: 12 to 3
PRICES: £14 (£19).
CARDS: Access, Amex, Diners, Visa
SEATS: 50. Private parties: 100 main room. Children's helpings. Wheelchair access (1 step; also WC). Music

Happy Wok

22A St Helen's Road, Swansea SA1 4AP
SWANSEA (0792) 466702 and 460063

COOKING 1
COST £16–£29

Supporters rate this stylish restaurant as the best Chinese venue in Swansea. Good ingredients, lightness and a sense of balance are the hallmarks of the kitchen. Predictably the menu is a Westernised mixed bag, taking in crispy 'seaweed', Peking dumplings, hot Szechuan prawns, duck with mango and the odd-sounding grilled chicken and asparagus rolls with white sauce, as well as the familiar contingent of sizzling dishes. Saké and Chinese liqueurs augment a basic list of 30 wines. House wine: £6.

CHEFS: C.C. Yuen, and K. W. Yuen   PROPRIETORS: I.M. Diu, K.W. Yuen and C.C. Yuen
OPEN: all week
CLOSED: 4 days at Christmas
MEALS: 12 to 2.30, 6.30 to 11.30
PRICES: £15 (£24), Set D £10.50 (£16) to £13.50 (£19). Minimum £6
CARDS: Access, Amex, Diners, Visa
SEATS: 55. Private parties: 60 main room. Children welcome. Smart dress preferred. Music. Air-conditioned

Keenans

82 St Helens Road, Swansea SA1 4BQ
SWANSEA (0792) 644111

COOKING 2
COST £14–£29

Keenans is sandwiched between Joe's Ice Cream Parlour and the Red Fort Tandoori. It looks smart in its greens and pinks and has quickly established a position near the head of the Swansea league. A *carte* of six choices over three courses is leavened at lunch by a shorter and much cheaper menu that all reports applaud as good value. In the eyes of some, lunch also brings out the best in the cooking because it is less involved in display – a fault that has sometimes obscured the flavours of the dinner dishes. The approach is classic, with no excess and some pleasing original ideas. Pigeon is served as a first course with a timbale of cabbage and a peppered redcurrant sauce; sole fillets are wrapped round a salmon mousse, solid but flavourful; rack of lamb is served with a 'basket' of ratatouille and two sauces, one a garlic sabayon that is judged correctly so as not to overpower; calf's liver has been cooked predictably with blackcurrant and more successfully with pink peppercorns; puddings have included a biscuit tube filled with winter fruits and a strawberry cream, a runny crème brûlée and a fine white chocolate mousse with chopped nuts on a dark chocolate sauce, flanked by a tuile basket filled with orange segments. Vegetarians get a separate menu. Service is in need of tightening, for both food and wine. The wine list consists of a sound, short world-wide choice and very fair prices. House wine: £6.75. CELLARMAN'S CHOICE: Pouilly Fumé, Ch. de Tracy 1988, £15; Bourgogne Pinot Noir 1987, Parent, £13.25.

The Guide *is totally independent, accepts no free hospitality, and survives on the number of copies sold each year.*

CHEF: Chris Keenan   PROPRIETORS: Chris and Lynda Keenan
OPEN: Tue to Sat, exc Sat L
CLOSED: 24 Dec to 2 Jan
MEALS: 12.30 to 2, 7 to 10
PRICES: £18 (£24), Set L £7.95 (£14)
CARDS: Access, Visa
SEATS: 26. Private parties: 35 main room, 20 private room. Vegetarian meals. Children welcome. Wheelchair access (1 step). Music

Roots

2 Woodville Road, Mumbles
Swansea SA3 4AD   COOKING 1
SWANSEA (0792) 366006   COST £13

Whether the ecclesiastical touches in the furnishings – a hymn board lists drinks – indicate that vegetarians seek proselytes in South Wales, Roots is thorough in its message of wholefood and organic materials. There are light dishes all day and a more elaborate menu in the evening. Everything save the soya vanilla custard is cooked on the premises, including the bread. Soups have taste; main courses, for instance, an almond roast with onion and red wine sauce, are robustly flavoured; the baking of bread rolls, pizza and cakes (passion-fruit, chocolate roulade) is proficient. Unlicensed, but the corkage is small.

CHEF: Judith Rees   PROPRIETORS: Judith Rees and Andrew Castell
OPEN: Mon to Sat, exc Mon in winter and Tue D
MEALS: 12 to 2.30, 6.30 to 9
PRICES: £8 (£11). Unlicensed, but bring your own: corkage 50p per bottle
SEATS: 38. 1 table outside. Private parties: 50 main room. Vegetarian meals. Children's helpings. No-smoking area. Wheelchair access (1 step). Music

TALSARNAU Gwynedd   map 4

▲ Hotel Maes-y-Neuadd

Talsarnau LL47 6YA
HARLECH (0766) 780200   COOKING 1
off B4573, 1m S of Talsarnau   COST £15–£37

A recurrent nightmare of small hotel owners, who rely as much on the restaurant as rooms for fame if not fortune, is that they will find no chef to work for them or, almost worse, a poor chef. The Slatters and the Horsfalls had a good chef last year in Trevor Pharoah. He has been replaced by Andrew Taylor, and reports are that aspects of the cooking may need tightening up but that time may achieve this. The house is solidly set on a mountainside with views across Cardigan Bay to the Lleyn peninsula; the ascent is steep, but the hospitality is generous and the decorations pleasing. A quantity of refurbishment and rebuilding has gone on through the winter, adding bedrooms and extra dining and meeting spaces. The menu structure has changed. The set-price dinner is restricted to a no-choice five-course meal, there is a short carte, and the range of dishes on offer has been reduced. Lunches continue to be good value. The kitchen is still resolutely 'modern' though the repertoire has less superficial panache. Dishes sampled have included wild mushroom soup; mussels wrapped in sole with a rosemary hollandaise; scallop mousse with a red butter sauce; pancakes with lobster filling and a salad with a kiwi dressing; veal and beef with a tarragon sauce; fillet of beef with foie gras and a madeira sauce; saddle of venison stuffed with apricots; and desserts like passion fruit charlotte; whisky-soaked prunes wrapped in almond paste and baked in filo pastry; bread-and-butter pudding on a cinnamon sauce. Cheeses may not be very exciting in dead of winter. Bread comes as tiny rolls of varying hues. Although the ideas are fine – no grotesque mixing-and-matching – execution is still uncertain. Meats have been found wanting; fish not always in best condition; dishes have not been as described on the menu. The construction programme may have unsettled more than just the fabric of the building. Service, however, is not in question: 'unremittingly cheerful' is the usual, though not invariable, comment. The wine list is not cheap but offers a fair range with some nice bottles from the likes of Trimbach, Jaboulet and Firestone. It might benefit from more careful research among leading growers rather than relying so heavily on négociants. House wines from Chandesais and Christine Ponsot are £6.60. CELLARMAN'S CHOICE: Tokay Pinot Gris Réserve 1985, Trimbach, £15.40; Ch. Pape Clément 1978, £30.

CHEF: Andrew Taylor   PROPRIETORS: Michael and June Slatter, Malcolm and Olive Horsfall
OPEN: all week
CLOSED: 9 to 19 Dec
MEALS: 12.15 to 1.45, 7.30 to 9.15
PRICES: £23 (£31), Set L £11.50 (£15) to £12.50 (£16), Set D £21 (£24). Service inc set L and D
CARDS: Access, Amex, Diners, Visa
SEATS: 46. Private parties: 50 main room, 16 private room. Car-park, 50 places. Children's helpings. No children under 7. No smoking in dining-room. Wheelchair access
ACCOMMODATION: 16 rooms, all with bath/shower. Rooms for disabled. B&B £36 to £105. Deposit: £40. No children under 7. Pets welcome. Afternoon teas. Garden. TV. Phone. Scenic. Doors close at midnight. Confirm by 5 [Which? Hotel Guide]

TALYLLYN Gwynedd   map 4

▲ *Minffordd Hotel*

Talyllyn LL36 9AJ
CORRIS (0654) 761665
at junction of A487 and B4405   COOKING 2
                                                                                      COST £22

'The nearest town of any size is Shrewsbury, 63 miles away,' commented Bernard Pickles when explaining that this former roadside inn operates principally as a hotel with meals for its guests. Space is limited, so non-residents should telephone rather than just arrive. The house has grown over centuries: sloping ceilings, heavy beams and a dining-room with see-through partitions are some sort of concrete lesson in vernacular architecture. Once, marooned travellers might have taken refuge here; today, the customer is more likely to be seeking peace, clean air and long walks. Jonathan Pickles cooks a short menu, changed daily, well suited to these activities: good materials, honestly if robustly treated on the formula of a soup, a fruity or a made dish for a beginning; a meat or a fish for the main course; then a board of substantial puddings – take two if you like – to precede the Welsh cheeses and coffee. The set price has remained very fair. Soups continue to be enjoyed and the kitchen makes a good sweet pie. Tipping is unnecessary as 'our service is freely and willingly given.' A short wine list offers decent bottles at generous prices. House wine: £6.90. CELLARMAN'S CHOICE: Tamburlaine Vineyard Chardonnay, Hunter Valley 1988, £12.60; Ch. Cissac 1982, £18.95.

CHEF: Jonathan Pickles   PROPRIETORS: Bernard and Jessica Pickles
OPEN: Tue to Sat, D only
CLOSED: Jan and Feb
MEALS: 7.30 to 8.30
PRICES: Set D £14.25 (£18). Service inc
CARDS: Access, Diners, Visa
SEATS: 28. Private parties: 28 main room. Car-park, 12 places. Vegetarian meals. Children's helpings. No children under 3. Smart dress preferred. No smoking in dining-room. Wheelchair access
ACCOMMODATION: 6 rooms, all with bath/shower. B&B £44 to £68. No children under 3. Garden. Phone. Scenic. Doors close at 11. Confirm by 6 [Which? Hotel Guide]

THREE COCKS   Powys   map 4

▲ Three Cocks Hotel

Three Cocks LD3 0SL
GLASBURY (049 74) 215   COOKING 2
on A438 between Brecon and Hay-on-Wye   COST £22–£30

The hotel is pure British heritage. As the brochure puts it, this fifteenth-century stone built hostelry is 'complete with a cobbled forecourt, mounting blocks, ivy-clad walls, worn steps, cracked doorways, great oak beams and log fires'. The cooking, however, takes its cue from across the channel. Mrs Winstone is Belgian and that country provides much of the culinary inspiration. There's a north-European generosity about the food, with tureens of soup brought to the table and second helpings of meat and vegetables freely offered. This year's postbag has yielded a healthy cluster of reports and the list of recommended dishes takes in salmon and crab mousse with tomato coulis; huge platefuls of raw Ardennes ham with honey-pickled onions; fricassee of lobster with noodles; and guinea-fowl with tomato and tarragon sauce. Duck with apricot and mustard sauce is liked by everyone and there are no complaints about the eight little parcels of accompanying vegetables. This kitchen uses a lot of cream, although strawberries soaked in lemon juice may provide some light relief. The short, adequate and fairly priced wine list includes English Bodenham and Welsh Crofton, and – appropriately – there are eight Belgian beers on offer. House wine from Georges Duboeuf, £7.50.

All details are as accurate as possible at the time of going to press, but chefs and owners often change, and it is wise to check by telephone before making a special journey. Many readers have been disappointed when set-price bargain meals are no longer available. Ask when booking.

CHEF: M.E. Winstone PROPRIETORS: Mr and Mrs Winstone
OPEN: Wed to Mon, exc Sun L
CLOSED: Dec and Jan
MEALS: 12 to 1.30, 7 to 9
PRICES: £20 (£25), Set L and D £18 (£22). Service inc
CARDS: Access, Visa
SEATS: 35. Private parties: 35 main room. Car-park, 30 places. Children welcome. Smart
dress preferred. Music
ACCOMMODATION: 7 rooms, all with bath/shower. B&B £36 to £48. Baby facilities. Garden.
Scenic. Doors close at midnight. Confirm by 5 [*Which? Hotel Guide*]

TREFRIW Gwynedd   map 4

Chandler's

Trefriw LL27 0JH   COOKING 2
LLANRWST (0492) 640991   COST £23

The outside of this old ship's chandler says roadside caff, and the school desks,
benches and polished slate floor mimic a schoolroom, but Adam Rattenbury's
dinners, made from fresh local ingredients, have little in common with either.
His bistro-style *carte* of half a dozen first and second courses draws on modern
British but shows invention. There are frequent reappearances because they
continue to please: hot goats' cheese salad with sage dressing was
recommended by readers in 1988 and 1990. Chicken livers with grapes is an
old favourite. Roulades and hazelnut and passion-fruit are almost as popular as
the iced white chocolate and Cointreau mousse. Devilled lamb kidneys with
mushrooms and pan-fried lamb sweetbreads with smoked bacon and madeira
sauce are recent innovations. A first course of deep-fried monkfish with apple
sauce was true to top form, according to one report. This also singled out a
vegetarian speciality, a parsnip and cashew bake with mushroom and sherry
sauce. Fresh fish and vegetables have had a happy reception, too. Service is
casual but efficient and friendly, and prices are commendably low. The wine
list of around 40 mostly non-French bottles is haphazard in organisation but
good in value and sensibly and carefully chosen. A supplementary list changes
often (and may include bargains such as Ch. Hanteillan at only £10.75), and
has more than a token number of rosés and half-bottles. House French: £6.45.
CELLARMAN'S CHOICE: Montana Sauvignon Chenin, £8.15; Rioja Berberana
Gran Reserva 1978, £12.95.

CHEF: Adam Rattenbury PROPRIETORS: Adam and Penny Rattenbury and Tim Kirton
OPEN: Tue to Sat, D only
MEALS: 7 to 10
PRICES: £13 (£19)
CARDS: Access, Visa
SEATS: 36. Private parties: 36 main room. Car-park, 10 places. Vegetarian meals. Children
welcome. No smoking. Music

---

*Restaurateurs justifiably resent no-shows. If you quote a credit card number when
booking, you may be liable for the restaurant's lost profit margin if you don't turn up.
Always phone to cancel.*

WALES

TRELLECH Gwent   map 4

Village Green

Trellech NP6 4PA   COOKING 1
MONMOUTH (0600) 860119   COST £15–£31

Colin Sparks has left but Bob Evans, who has long experience of cooking from
his time as landlord of the Bridge Inn at Llangwm, joins Jonathan Badham in
the kitchen. Regulars from across the border claim that this restaurant and
brasserie, itself a former pub, offers fair value and adaptable cooking from
either menu. This may not be exactly normal pub fare – the example of the
nearby Walnut Tree (see Llandewi Skirrid) must weigh heavily – but ranges
from smoked pigeon with a peanut oil dressing and toasted pine kernels to
seafood lasagne or kashmiri beef. Jane Evans looks after sweet dishes like soft
fruit tartlets or banoffi pie. Whoever is cooking the vegetables, however, may
have the mistaken idea that *al dente* means raw. The short wine list has house
wine at £5.95.

CHEFS: Jonathan Badham and Bob Evans   PROPRIETORS: Bob and Jane Evans
OPEN: Tue to Sun, exc Sun D
CLOSED: 25 and 26 Dec
MEALS: 12 to 2, 7 to 9.45
PRICES: £19 (£26), Set L £11 (£15). Licensed, also bring your own: corkage £3.50
CARDS: Access, Visa
SEATS: 50. Private parties: 10 main room; 10 and 18 private rooms. Car-park, 14 places.
Vegetarian meals. Children's helpings. No children under 5. Smart dress preferred. No
pipes in dining-room. Wheelchair access (1 step; also WC). Music

WELSHPOOL Powys   map 4

▲ *Edderton Hall*

Forden SY21 8RZ   COOKING 1
FORDEN (093876) 339 and 410   COST £14–£26

The political prints in the bar may have to do with Warren Hawksley's own
background, and he certainly has a politician's tact in dealing enthusiastically
with visitors to this double bow-fronted Georgian house. It stands clean and
white at the top of a hill with panoramas to distant hilltops. This exterior gives
no clue to the idiosyncratic tented room, with a ceiling mirror, that is used for
meetings and private parties. Evelyn Hawksley's cooking won her a 'Taste of
Wales' prize in 1989 so it demonstrates some specific regional dishes such as
'Welsh over Welsh with Welsh as well'. This is a shortbread with vanilla ice-
cream that is studded with sultanas soaked in Welsh whisky and liberally
sauced with Merlin cream liqueur. She developed it for the competition she
won. Welsh lamb with fresh mint and port is another local dish, but the
tendency is not 'historical Welsh'. It is, rather, a modern style that depends
especially on good garden produce. A meal taken in the summer showed the
excellence of the vegetables, in vegetable soups as well, and a robust approach
to cooking that may sometimes lack finish. A fixed-price menu, not expensive,
gives a choice of four dishes in each course that may include first courses such
as pigeon breasts with walnuts and elderflower or avocado and tomato salad

646

with samphire, olives and anchovies; main courses of salmon with dill sauce or chicken in filo with baby corn, peppers and girolles; and desserts that often include a steamed hot pudding as well as two whole cheeses on the sideboard with great stems of celery ad lib, or rhubarb jelly with gooseberry, elderflower and strawberry purée representing the fruit tendency. Although children's helpings are available at dinner, the Hawksleys say: 'If possible we prefer small children to have tea and are happy to provide it.' The short wine list from Tanners is generously provided with half-bottles and supplemented by a mixed bag of auction purchases by Warren Hawksley. House French: £6.55. Although there is a grand piano in the dining-room, Chopin's Minute Waltz came from an amplifier – and seemed to take half a minute.

CHEF: Evelyn Hawksley   PROPRIETORS: Evelyn and Warren Hawksley
OPEN: all week D only (L by arrangement)
MEALS: 12 to 2, 7.30 to 9.30
PRICES: Set L £8.50 (£14), Set D £16.95 (£22)
CARDS: Access, Amex, Diners, Visa
SEATS: 34. Private parties: 25 main room, 65 private room. Car-park, 45 places. Children's helpings. Smart dress preferred. Wheelchair access (1 step; also unisex WC). Music
ACCOMMODATION: 8 rooms, all with bath/shower. B&B £22 to £55. Pets welcome. Afternoon teas. Fishing. TV. Phone. Scenic. Confirm by 1pm

Isle of Man

Rafters

9 Duke Street, Douglas	COOKING 1
DOUGLAS (0624) 72344	COST £17

Set among the rafters of the Peter Luis department store is this daytime restaurant with big sloping ceilings, windows looking out on to the street and a feeling of light and air even when things are running full steam ahead. The basic all-day menu is supplemented by specials that often please for freshness and taste – moules marinière, a gratin of tomatoes and basil, and simple lamb cutlets are instances – but a fluffy large omelette with cheese and onion shows that not all the energies are spent on dreaming up daily variations. A place as busy as this is bound to pick up mixed comments, but the standard is high for the area. A no-smoking zone has been introduced but first reports imply that its enforcement will not be easy. Wines change according to what's available at the shops. House wine: £6.50.

CHEF/PROPRIETOR: Stephen John Whitehead
OPEN: Mon to Sat, daytime only
MEALS: 10 to 5.30 (L 12 to 2.30)
PRICES: £9 (£14)
SEATS: 56. Vegetarian meals. Children's helpings. Wheelchair access (also WC). Music

---

Woodford's

King Edward Road, Onchan	COOKING 2
DOUGLAS (0624) 675626	COST £18–£44

This restaurant, opened by Kevin Woodford, TV's Reluctant Cook, and racehorse owners Robert and Susan Sangster, occupies the former premises of Boncompte's, now at Douglas (see entry). It is thus assured of a wall of window looking out over Douglas Bay. The Isle of Man seems to exist in a catering time warp so that even Woodford's, a restaurant intended to be in the forefront of fashion, has a menu design that might have been created in the

1940s and offers dishes from earlier periods still. These are mixed with dishes in more modern vein, such as 'a trilogy of wild mushrooms in filo parcels' or 'oriental marinated fillet of beef served on a nest of bamboo shoots'. For all that, Kevin Woodford is an enthusiastic host and islanders have reacted enthusiastically to cooking reportedly more stylish than hitherto practised. They have also warmed to the 'clublike' atmosphere. A first course of queenies with bacon and wild mushrooms were 'the fleshiest and tastiest in years of eating queenies'. A main course was lamb with onions, mango and oyster mushrooms in a trellis of pastry, served on yet more wild mushrooms; eight vegetables – eight – came at a stiff extra £3.25. Summer pudding or terrine of two chocolates are examples of desserts, and bread-and-butter pudding with a whisky and honey cream has also been recommended. The wine list is priced so high that they must be needing to recoup the extra cost of transport to the island, but house wine is £8.95. CELLARMAN'S CHOICE: Leroy d'Avernay 1978, £16.20; Lindeman's Gold Medal Chardonnay Padthaway 1987, £26.50.

CHEF: Alan Coxon   PROPRIETORS: Kevin Woodford, and Robert and Susan Sangster
OPEN: Tue to Sun, exc Sat L and Sun D
MEALS: 12.30 to 2.30, 7.30 to 9.30
PRICES: £24 (£37), Set L £10.25 (£18)
CARDS: Access, Amex, Diners, Visa
SEATS: 90. 3 tables outside. Private parties: 90 main room. Car-park, 12 places. Vegetarian meals. Children's helpings on request. Smart dress preferred. Wheelchair access (1 step)

Channel Islands

ROZEL Jersey   map 1

Granite Corner

Rozel Harbour, Rozel   COOKING 3
JERSEY (0534) 63590   COST £32–£42

Jean-Luc Robin is serious; his winter holidays were spent in the kitchens of
the Waterside Inn and the Connaught Hotel (see entries, Bray and London); he
buys vegetable seeds in France and supplies them to a grower, he even has his
own lobster pots. Whereas the *carte* used to change seasonally, it now works to
the markets, being rewritten every day. There are two sides to the cooking. The
first is Jersey oriented: island asparagus, lobster en feuilleté and local fish. The
second is about the Périgord: foie gras, confit and truffles are shipped to him
regularly and he runs a Périgourdine menu in parallel with the daily *carte*.
Gradual improvements are being made to the tiny cottage dining-room and the
kitchen staff is expanding, so it is hoped that the Robins can retain their
genuine enthusiasm and not be worn down to the generally depressing Island
norm. There was a preponderance of mousses on an autumn visit according to
one report: a chicken timbale, a courgette mousse on top of rack of lamb, and
desserts that were all airy in one way or another, for instance, blackcurrant
bavarois or mocha mousse with pear sauce. However, the chief attraction is the
exact fish cookery: a rendezvous with saffron sauce; sea bass with asparagus; or
a warm terrine of turbot, bass and salmon with sorrel sauce are examples.
Prices now include service, and 'we do not encourage tipping.' The bottom line
on credit card forms has always been and continues to be closed. A short wine
list includes some fine growers but does not pursue the south-west French
connection though the collection of armagnacs does. Beaujolais, Mâcon Blanc
or Chinon can be had for less than the house Spanish, which is £9.50.

CHEF: Jean-Luc Robin PROPRIETORS: Jean-Luc and Louise Robin
OPEN: Mon to Sat, D only
CLOSED: 2 weeks at Christmas
MEALS: 7.45 to 9
PRICES: £26 (£32), Set D £28 (£35). Service inc
CARDS: Access, Amex, Diners, Visa
SEATS: 24. Private parties: 24 main room. No children under 12. Smart dress preferred

▲ *Longueville Manor*

St Saviour   COOKING 3
JERSEY (0534) 25501   COST £20–£43

'Whereas most country-house hotels have moderately priced antiques scattered around, this place has the *real* thing, from the sterling silver on the sideboard to the Royal Doulton in the lounge,' wrote one who was impressed by this rambling country manor in a sylvan setting on an island where riches are more likely *nouveaux* than antique. If the dining-room has panelling of the darkest of oak, blackened by age and craft, the cooking – this year in the hands of a new chef, who spent a year as sous-chef at Hambleton Hall (see entry, Hambleton) – is of the most modern in looks and construction. 'I had to dismantle the dish before eating it,' was the comment on a seriously vertical arrangement of turbot with spinach and langoustine tortellini standing four inches high. Money and taste have combined to produce good flavours and accurate cooking in dishes such as a terrine of lobster with baby leeks, beans and yellow and red peppers where the *farce* was so light and yet true-tasting that the vehicle was as enjoyable as its passengers. Simple crab, though dressed as if for a May Ball, shows a respect for raw materials, to be eaten without too much intrusion of art. Grilled duck is laid on a confit of onion laced with orange zest and a mixture of vegetables and supported by a gutsy stock sauce; it exemplifies a willingness to handle strong flavours. These are from a *carte* of half a dozen options, supported by a long *menu dégustation*, a set-price vegetarian menu which shows balance and invention and, at lunchtimes, by a relatively fair-value set-price menu. The good first and main courses have been let down by lacklustre pastry work and desserts. Service is well-trained, photogenic and good. The wine list is acceptable, though not as encyclopaedic as many such places have accustomed us to expect. It takes a less than chauvinist line over French wines and has a few from Italy and Australasia though only Opus One from California. Prices are not low. House Patriarche: £6.50.

CHEF: Andrew Baird   PROPRIETORS: The Lewis family and the Dufty family
OPEN: all week
MEALS: 12.30 to 2, 7.30 to 9.30
PRICES: £31 (£36), Set L £16.50 (£20), Set D £25 (£28). Service inc
CARDS: Access, Amex, Carte Blanche, Diners, Visa
SEATS: 65. 8 tables outside. Private parties: 75 main room, 16 private room. Car-park, 30 places. Vegetarian meals. Smart dress preferred. Wheelchair access (also WC). Air-conditioned
ACCOMMODATION: 33 rooms, all with bath/shower. Lift. B&B £68 to £105. Deposit: £50. No children under 7. Pets welcome. Afternoon teas. Garden. Swimming -pool. TV. Phone. Scenic

Northern Ireland

---

map 9

Woodlands

29 Spa Road, Ballynahinch BT24 8PT	COOKING 1
BALLYNAHINCH (0238) 562650	COST £29

The house is a pleasure: eighteenth-century, the stables tucked around the back, set just beyond Ballynahinch in the quiet of the countryside. Anticipation of the meal ahead is encouraged by the logs burning in the drawing-room fireplace and the discreet attentions of David Sandford while his wife Alison is firmly in charge of the kitchen. The set-price menu is short, perhaps five choices at each stage, but portions are Northern Irish in their generosity. A gratin of mushrooms with garlic; pancakes with smoked haddock and cheese; pork fillet with prunes and apple; pigeon breasts with port and juniper; and large and very creamy sweet dishes are the order of the day. There are nice touches to the cooking that may lift it from the workaday, and people agree that the ambience is gentle and enjoyable. The selection on the short wine list is intelligent and wide ranging, and the prices are very fair. House wine: £6.95.

CHEF: Alison Sandford   PROPRIETORS: Alison and David Sandford
OPEN: Thur to Sat, D only; private parties other times.
MEALS: 7.30 to 9.30
PRICES: Set D £18.50 (£24)
CARD: Access, Visa
SEATS: 45. Private parties: 45 main room, 14 private room. Car-park, 20 places. No cigars/pipes in dining-room.

---

map 9

Nick's Warehouse

35–39 Hill Street, Belfast BT1 2LB	COOKING 2
BELFAST (0232) 439690	COST £19

Drinks and wine bar downstairs, more substantial food upstairs in this new conversion of an old warehouse in the middle of an urban renewal project. The team of Nick and Kathy Price have come in from the outskirts to cater for the city dweller and worker, leaving their former restaurant to Bartjan Brave. The restaurant menu is not long but packs in a fair range of tastes. Chilli and sweet-sour combinations are never far away, for instance in guacamole, fillets of sole with chilli and ginger sauce, or lamb cutlets with port and redcurrantsauce. On the wine bar menu the same tendency can be seen in 'a duo of vegetable terrines, one curried, one not', or Turkish almond dip with pitta bread and a green salad. The happy atmosphere of real enthusiasm for food and no slovenliness fills a gap in Belfast. The wine list and its notes show the same enthusiasm for a good bottle. Very few are priced in double figures, but the fast-changing stock of around three dozen, supplemented by extras for the day or week, is chosen for value and decent drinking. There is a fair range of foreign beers. House wines are from £4.70.

CHEF: Nick Price   PROPRIETORS: Nick and Kathy Price
OPEN: Mon to Fri
MEALS: bar 12 to 3, restaurant 12.30 to 3, 5 to 6.30
PRICES: bar £4 (£8), restaurant £11 (£16)
CARDS: Access, Diners, Visa
SEATS: bar 45, restaurant 50. Private parties: 50 main room. Vegetarian meals. Wheelchair access (1 step; also unisex WC). Air-conditioned.

Strand

| 12 Stranmillis Road, Belfast BT9 5AA | COOKING 1 |
| BELFAST (0232) 682266 | COST £17 |

The long menu in this wine bar/restaurant that continues to draw in the crowds manages a dozen main courses and a like number of first courses. These are drawn from France (duck liver terrine), India (chicken tikka), Hungary (goulash) and that indeterminate repertoire that takes in chilli con carne, baked stuffed mushrooms and leek tart. A good place to eat wholesome food inexpensively. Five dozen wines are no more highly priced than the food and fit the bill to a tee. House wine from Moreau is £4.95.

CHEFS: M. Paine, M. McAuley, Bill Bailey and Terry Monaghan   PROPRIETOR: Anne Turkington
OPEN: all week
MEALS: noon to 11
PRICES: £9 (£14)
CARDS: Access, Amex, Diners, Visa
SEATS: 80. Vegetarian meals. Children welcome. Music. Air-conditioned

| BELLANALECK   Co Fermanagh | map 9 |

Sheelin

Bellanaleck	
FLORENCECOURT (036 582) 232	COOKING 1
4m from Enniskillen	COST £7−£24

The dry mix for Sheelin wheaten bread is exported to America and baking is a principal activity at Bellanaleck. But the Lough is not far away, nor the Marble Arch caves, and the thatched cottage does a busy trade all summer long for teas, high teas, home baking and a salad buffet. The chief qualification for entry in the *Guide* is not the daily menu, which runs along conventional lines, but the Saturday night set menu, when more adventurous and very acceptable cooking takes the stage. There is a five-course extravaganza with the crescendo reserved for the final production: the sweets trolley. The format is constant: a mixed antipasto followed by stuffed pancakes, a sorbet, a choice of meat or fish that may be chicken tandoori style; home-baked ham; Bavarian beef roulade; salmon hollandaise; or pork with an apricot sauce. The reasonable price may be boosted by small supplements for salmon, beef or scampi. The main course is chosen over the phone when booking. No wine costs over £12.60 and some of the bottles are more recognisable than others. House wine: £4.95.

CHEF: Marion Cathcart   PROPRIETOR: Arthur Cathcart
OPEN: all week June to end Aug, Sun L Apr to end Sept only, Fri and Sat D all year
MEALS: 12.30 to 2.30, 7 to 9.30
PRICES: £12 (£17), Set L £3.50 (£7) to £7.50 (£11), Set D £12 (£16) to £16 (£20). Service 10%
CARDS: Access, Amex, Visa
SEATS: 30. Private parties: 24 main room. Car-park, 30 places. Children's helpings.
Wheelchair access

COLERAINE   Co Derry   map 9

▲ *Macduff's*

112 Killeague Road, Blackhill,
Coleraine BT51 4HH   COOKING 1
AGHADOWEY (026 585) 433   COST £25

The Erwins run an enjoyable small hotel with a basement restaurant in this Georgian rectory building, set among decent gardens in a restful farming landscape. Restaurant visitors enter by a separate door, not through the front. Alan Wade's repertoire, presented on a *carte* of about eight choices in each course, is traditionally British in its eclecticism: chicken tikka masala, Latvian pork Stroganoff, supreme of chicken with a herb mousseline, or game in season, such as woodcock. Vegetables are often from the garden and taste like it. First courses are less adventurous: smoked salmon, prawns with Marie Rose sauce, or mushroom and bacon pancakes set the style. This is revisited in desserts such as Athol Brose, hazelnut meringue with fruit, or chocolate roulade. There is a short, balanced, wine list. House Duboeuf: £6

CHEF: Alan Wade   PROPRIETORS: Joseph and Margaret Erwin
OPEN: Tue to Sat, D only
MEALS: 7 to 9.30
PRICES: £13 (£21)
SEATS: 34. Private parties: 34 main room, 16 private room. Car-park, 30 places. No children under 10.
ACCOMMODATION: 6 rooms, 5 with bath/shower. B&B £25 to £45. No children under 10. Garden. Swimming-pool. TV. Scenic. Doors close at 1 am. Confirm by 6

All entries in the Guide *are rewritten every year, not least because restaurant standards fluctuate. Don't trust an out of date* Guide.

KILLINCHY   Co Down

map 9

Iona

18 Kilmood Church Road,
Killinchy BT23 6SB
KILLINCHY (0238) 541472

COOKING 2
COST £16−£34

One reader commented that Bartjan Brave was the best classical chef now working in Northern Ireland, and he has elected to practise his talents on a wider stage. In a series of shuffles in late 1989, Nick Price moved to Belfast, sold his restaurant in Killinchy to Bartjan Brave who moved his stoves and name from Holywood, leaving behind Bistro Iona, with Kees Selles doing the cooking. The new Iona has a series of levels: bar downstairs, split-level dining-room with a balcony for outside dining above. The menu is peppered with wit – 'Magret de pigeon: late-bottled pigeon' – and classical technique is salted with some modern ideas and combinations. Sure technique is displayed in such first courses as salmon with a lemon sauce and pistachios, or mustard cream soup; in main courses such as veal with ginger sauce, spring lamb with red wine and mint, or sole with salmon sauce. Vegetarians get a good deal, for instance, courgettes, spinach and pumpkin seeds with pleurotte mushrooms and a beurre blanc. Desserts are good. The short wine list may have Lafite 1981 at £95 but generally is low-priced, the majority of bottles being under £15. France predominates, but other countries get a look in. Halves are an afterthought. House wine is £7.35. Bistro Iona is at 27 Church Road, Holywood, BT18 9BU, (023 17) 5655. It is unlicensed, takes no bookings and is open for dinner from Tuesday to Sunday with a set-price menu at £9.95 for three courses. More reports, please.

CHEF/PROPRIETOR: Bartjan Brave
OPEN: Wed to Sat, D only; L and D Sun
MEALS: 12.30 to 2.30, 7 to 10.30
PRICES: £17 (£26), Set Sun L £9.50 (£16), Set D £17.95 (£25) to £20.95 (£28)
SEATS: 44. 10 tables outside. Private parties: 44 main room. Vegetarian meals. Children's helpings on request. Music.

PORTRUSH   Co Antrim

map 9

Ramore

The Harbour, Portrush BT56 8DQ
PORTRUSH (0265) 824313

COOKING 2
COST £29

The restaurant is open for dinner but those who wish to take advantage of the fine views over the harbour and West Bay during daylight may take lunch in the wine bar downstairs. George McAlpin is among the best chefs working in the Province, his style of cooking and presentation more emphatically modern than most of his colleagues. A short *carte* encompasses dishes such as filo purses of scallops, spring onion and ginger on a beurre blanc; a cabbage-wrapped timbale of quail spiked with bacon and chervil on a madeira sauce; breast of chicken stuffed with leeks, its boned thigh plumped out with morels, with a vin jaune and truffle sauce; and good fish dishes, the quality of the raw material guaranteed through proximity to boats and the sea. The wine list contains some good makers and properties: Guigal from the Rhône, Lanessan and d'Issan from Bordeaux, Drouhin from Burgundy and Bruno Marcello Cerretto's Barolo. It may be short, but it is very nicely chosen and not highly priced. House Rhône: £6.

CHEF: George McAlpin PROPRIETORS: John and Joy Caithness and George McAlpin
OPEN: bar L Mon to Sat, restaurant D Tue to Sat
CLOSED: last 2 weeks Jan
MEALS: 12.30 to 2.30, 7 to 10
PRICES: £16 (£24)
SEATS: 55. Private parties: 60 main room. Car-park, 8 places. Children welcome. Music.

Republic of Ireland

The following entries are the result of our appeal for more reports in last year's *Guide*. Reporting still falls far short of the numbers and density achieved on the mainland of Britain, but we hope that this list will form solid foundation for further expansion and deepening of our coverage next year. We are grateful to those of you who have helped on this particular aspect, and would appeal to any who are intending a trip to the Republic this year that they bear us in mind. We would like to hear about your experiences.

It is quite clear that the Irish have a great gift for hospitality and, in many cases, an equal one for cooking, whether it be the simple conversion of matchless raw ingredients, more sophisticated modern cookery alive to current tendencies in Europe, or food in the tradition of the Anglo-Irish country-house.

Prices quoted are in Irish punts. As we are still feeling our way, we have not given ratings for cooking as in the rest of the British Isles.

To telephone Dublin numbers, preface the number we have given with a double zero (00). To reach the rest of the Republic from mainland Britain, dial 010 353 followed by the area code and number we have listed dropping, however, the initial zero (0).

ADARE Co Limerick map 9

▲ *Adare Manor*

Adare
LIMERICK **(061) 396566** COST £24−£64

Uncertainties whether this new venture was going to be merely an up-market haven of luxury have for the moment been quieted by the arrival of chef Ian McAndrew from his own venture in Knightsbridge, London. The price is high but it will buy modern cooking of assurance. House French: £12.50.

Prices quoted in the Guide *are based on information supplied by restaurateurs. The figure in brackets below an entry is the average for a three-course meal with service, coffee and half a bottle of house wine, as calculated by computer. The prices quoted at the top of an entry represent a range, from the lowest average meal price to the highest; the latter is inflated by 20 per cent to take account of the fact that very few people eat an average meal, and also that prices are likely to rise during the year of the* Guide.

CHEF: Ian McAndrew PROPRIETORS: Mr and Mrs Tom Kane
OPEN: all week
MEALS: 12.30 to 2.30, 7 to 10
PRICES: £34 (£49), Set L £15 (£24) to £18 (£28), Set D £30 (£42) to £40 (£53). Service 15%
CARDS: Access, Amex, Diners, Visa
SEATS: 70. Private parties: 100 main room, 30, 60, 60 and 150 private rooms. Car-park, 40 places. Vegetarian meals. Children's helpings. Smart dress preferred D. No pipes in dining-room. Wheelchair access (also unisex WC). Music
ACCOMMODATION: 64 rooms, all with bath/shower. Rooms for disabled. Lift. B&B £100.50 to £190.50. Deposit: one night. Baby facilities. Afternoon teas. Garden. Swimming-pool. Sauna. Fishing. Golf. TV. Phone. Scenic. Confirm by 6

Mustard Seed

Main Street, Adare
ADARE (061) 396451   COST £27−£35

Smart surroundings for a kitchen style that is mainly conventional − kidneys with mustard sauce, breadcrumbed breast of chicken stuffed with ham and garlic. There is, however, a modern emphasis with home-made chutneys and pickles; fruit sauces, as in duck with rhubarb and port; exotic fruits and new-wave influences from the garden, as in a brandy-snap basket with Benson strawberries and a camomile cream. House French: £9.25.

CHEFS: Thomas O'Leary and Helen Mullane PROPRIETORS: Daniel and Helen Mullane
OPEN: Tue to Sat, D only
CLOSED: 27 Jan to 27 Feb
MEALS: 7 to 10
PRICES: Set D £19.90 (£27) to £22 (£29)
CARDS: Access, Amex, Diners, Visa
SEATS: 45. 2 tables outside. Private parties: 26 main room, 20 and 26 private rooms. Children's helpings. Vegetarian meals with prior notice. No children under 7. No cigars/pipes in dining-room. Wheelchair access (1 step). Music

BALLINA Co Mayo   map 9

▲ *Mount Falcon Castle*

Ballina
BALLINA (096) 21172   COST £28

A classic old-style country house with simple and wholesome food served to guests seated round one great table. House French: £8.50.

CHEF/PROPRIETOR: Constance Aldridge
OPEN: all week, D only
CLOSED: 3 days at Christmas, Feb to Mar (open for Easter)
MEALS: 8
PRICES: Set D £16.50 (£23). Service 10%
CARDS: Access, Amex, Diners, Visa
SEATS: 22. Private parties: 7 main room. Car-park, 20 places. Vegetarian meals with prior notice. Children's helpings on request. No smoking in dining-room. One sitting
ACCOMMODATION: 10 rooms, all with bath/shower. B&B £37.50 to £75. Deposit: £25. Baby facilities. Pets welcome. Garden. Tennis. Fishing. Scenic. Doors close at midnight. Confirm by 2

BALLYDEHOB   Co Cork   map 9

Annie's

Main Street, Ballydehob
BALLYDEHOB (028) 37292   COST £24–£30

In a warm, friendly, cheerful atmosphere one reader had 'a delicious quick
lunch of fresh scones, soup, excellent mussels and aromatic coffee'. 'Very good
seafood; you can add a dimension to the experience by going across the road to
the Levis sisters' pub, ordering a drink and chatting a bit. Then Annie will
come over and take your order.' The cooking is not elaborate, but the food is
very fresh. House French £9.50.

CHEF/PROPRIETOR: Anne Ferguson
OPEN: Tue to Sat
CLOSED: first 3 weeks Oct, 25 and 26 Dec
MEALS: 12.30 to 2.30, 6.30 to 9.30
PRICES: £17 (£24), Set D £17.50 (£25)
CARDS: Access, Visa
SEATS: 24. Vegetarian meals on request. No cigars in dining-room. Wheelchair access

BALLYLICKEY   Co Cork   map 9

▲ *Seaview House Hotel*

Ballylickey
BANTRY (027) 50073 and 50462   COST £14–£30

The great views from this Victorian manor house live up to the name. A useful
place to stay, with traditional hotel cooking and excellent service. Not for the
culinarily adventurous, but reliable and popular. House wine: £10.50.

CHEF/PROPRIETOR: Kathleen O'Sullivan
OPEN: all week, D only and Sun L
MEALS: 1 to 2, 7 to 9.30
PRICES: £16 (£23), Set Sun L £7.50 (£14) to £9 (£16), Set D £17.50 (£25). Service 10%
CARDS: Access, Amex, Diners, Visa
SEATS: 50. Private parties: 16 main room. Car-park, 30 places. Children's helpings. No
cigars/pipes in dining-room. Wheelchair access (also WC)
ACCOMMODATION: 17 rooms, all with bath/shower. Rooms for disabled. B&B £35 to £70.
Baby facilities. Pets welcome in bedrooms only. Afternoon teas. Garden. TV. Phone. Scenic.
Doors close at midnight. Confirm by 6

BALLYVAUGHAN   Co Clare   map 9

▲ *Gregans Castle*

Ballyvaughan
ENNIS (065) 77005   COST £20–£48

Acceptable cooking, strong on fresh fish and seafood, in a hotel that gets
unreserved endorsement as a beautiful and enjoyable place to stay. House
French: £10.50.

CHEFS: Peter Haden and Olivier Pauloin PROPRIETORS: Peter and Moira Haden
OPEN: all week
CLOSED: end Oct to end Mar
MEALS: 12 to 3, 7 to 8.30
PRICES: bar L £13 (£20), restaurant Set D £20 (£28) to £30 (£40). Service 10% alc, 12.5% set
CARDS: Access, Visa
SEATS: 50. Private parties: 80 main room. Car-park, 20 places. Children's helpings. No
children under 6 at D. No cigars/pipes in dining-room. Wheelchair access (also WC)
ACCOMMODATION: 16 rooms, all with bath/shower. Rooms for disabled. B&B £58 to £100.
Deposit: £50. Children restricted. Baby facilities. Afternoon teas. Garden. Phone. Scenic.
Doors close at 11.30. Confirm by 5

BLACKROCK Co Dublin   map 9

Colin O'Daly's Park Restaurant

40 The Mews, Main Street, Blackrock
DUBLIN (01) 886177   COST £19–£42

Modern cooking with an eye for presentation. Examples of the style are
ribbons of calf's tongue with salade niçoise; cassoulet of guinea-fowl; fresh
fruit scented with mint, cooked *en papillote*. A short menu guarantees the
quality of the supplies and the fixed-price menu at lunch is excellent value.
House wine: £11.

CHEF/PROPRIETOR: Colin O'Daly
OPEN: Mon to Sat, exc Sat L
MEALS: 12.30 to 2, 7.30 to 9.45
PRICES: Set L £12 (£19), Set D £26.50 (£35)
CARDS: Access, Amex, Diners, Visa
SEATS: 70. Private parties: 50 main room, 20 private room. Children's helpings. Smart dress
preferred. No-smoking during meals. Air-conditioned

BORRIS Co Carlow   map 9

▲ Step House

Borris
BORRIS (503) 73401   COST £19–£31

A restaurant with rooms that is expanding with a bistro in the cellar offering
cheaper, plainer food. The restaurant shows European rather than Irish
affiliation in such dishes as smoked salmon roulade with a lobster mousse;
warm oysters with a julienne of vegetables and a beurre blanc; salmon with a
cream oyster sauce; fillet of lamb with mustard and chives. The produce is
firmly of the region. House French £9.50.

'Staff did try hard and even though they locked us out were helpful.' On staying in
Wiltshire

CHEF/PROPRIETOR: Breda Coady
OPEN: restaurant Tue to Sat, D only; bistro Tue to Sun, exc Tue and Wed L
MEALS: 6.30 to 9.30 (11 Sat)
PRICES: restaurant £18 (£26), Set D £17.90 (£26); bistro Set D £12 (£19), Service 10% set
meals in restaurant
CARD: Access, Visa
SEATS: 30 restaurant, 45 bistro. Private parties: 30 main room. Vegetarian meals with prior
notice. Children welcome. No smoking till after dinner. Music
ACCOMMODATION: 4 rooms, all with bath/shower. B&B £20 to £40. Pets welcome.
Afternoon teas. Garden. TV. Scenic. Doors close at 11

CASHEL   Co Tipperary   map 9

Chez Hans

Rockside, Cashel
CASHEL (062) 61177   COST £41

Hans-Peter Matthiä's restaurant is a former church tucked beneath the Rock of
Cashel. It is a memorable location and the restaurant, full of good paintings and
interesting furniture, is also memorable. The menu is fairly settled, classical
and very consistent. Quenelles of turbot and brill were as light as they should
be; veal with a mushroom and lime sauce was very rich. Presentation is a
strong point. House French: £9.95.

CHEF/PROPRIETOR: Hans-Peter Matthiä
OPEN: Tue to Sat, D only
CLOSED: first 3 weeks Jan
MEALS: 6.30 to 10
PRICES: £25 (£34)
SEATS: 60. Private parties: 70 main room. Car-park, 10 places. Vegetarian meals with prior
notice. Children's helpings. No-smoking area. Wheelchair access (also WC). Music

---

CASHEL   Co Galway   map 9

▲ Cashel House Hotel

Cashel
CLIFDEN (095) 31001   COST £23−£43

Far away on the west coast, the kitchen team is split between the French and
the Irish factions. One produces fresh grilled oysters stuffed with vegetables,
fillet of turbot with chive sauce, and gâteau St Honoré; the other smokes its
own salmon, cooks cider baked ham and home-made apple tart. The two sides
of staying in a country house are thus satisfied, and the whole experience is
master-minded by the McEvillys. House French: £11.25.

---

*All details are as accurate as possible at the time of going to press, but chefs and owners
often change, and it is wise to check by telephone before making a special journey. Many
readers have been disappointed when set-price bargain meals are no longer available. Ask
when booking.*

CHEFS: Yves Catiou, Patrick Hernandes and Meta O'Nalley PROPRIETORS: Dermot and Kay McEvilly
OPEN: all week
CLOSED: 15 Nov to 20 Dec
MEALS: 12.30 to 2, 7.30 to 8.45
PRICES: £22 (£36), Set L £15 (£23) to £18 (£26), Set D £23.50 (£33). Service 12.5%
CARDS: Access, Amex, Visa
SEATS: 70. 4 tables outside. Car-park, 40 places. Children's helpings (L and early D). No children under 5. Smart dress preferred. No-smoking area. Wheelchair access (also male and female WC)
ACCOMMODATION: 32 rooms, all with bath/shower. Rooms for disabled. B&B £44 to £88. Deposit: £100. No children under 5. Baby facilities. Afternoon teas. Garden. Tennis. TV. Phone. Scenic

---

CLIFDEN   Co Galway   map 9

O'Grady's

Market Street, Clifden
CLIFDEN (095) 21450 and 21437   COST £14–£31

Excellent fresh fish, as in baked salmon with spinach and nutmeg; roulade of black sole with prawns; poached brill with a ginger sauce. House wine: £9 to £11.

CHEF: Bernard Sinnot   PROPRIETORS: Jack and Marion O'Grady
OPEN: Mon to Sat
CLOSED: 16 to 30 Dec, 12 Jan to 12 Mar
MEALS: 12.30 to 2.30, 6.30 to 10
PRICES: £17 (£26), Set L £7.95 (£14), Set D £15.95 (£22). Minimum £6. Service 10%
CARDS: Access, Amex, Diners, Visa
SEATS: 50. Private parties: 10 main room, 8 private room. Children restricted at D. No-smoking area. Music

---

COLLOONEY   Co Sligo   map 9

▲ Knockmuldowney Restaurant

Markree Castle, Collooney
SLIGO (071) 67800
1m off N4, E of Collooney   COST £13–£30

The castle, featured in Lord Clark's TV series *Civilisation*, has to be seen to be believed. The Coopers are of the family that built it, which may help to make the experience authentic. The prices are lower than many of Ireland's castle hotels for fairly straightforward cooking of a daily menu. House French: £8.90.

The text of entries is based on unsolicited reports sent in by readers, backed up by inspections conducted anonymously. The factual details under the text are from questionnaires the Guide *sends to all restaurants that feature in the book.*

CHEF: Mary Cooper   PROPRIETORS: Charles and Mary Cooper
OPEN: all week
CLOSED: 3 days at Christmas, Feb
MEALS: 1 to 2.30, 7.30 to 9.30
PRICES: Set L £7 (£13) to £10 (£16), Set D £15.50 (£22) to £18.50 (£25)
CARDS: Access, Amex, Diners, Visa
SEATS: 80. Private parties: 60 main room, 25 private room. Car-park, 40 places. Vegetarian meals with prior notice. Children's helpings. No smoking in dining-room
ACCOMMODATION: 15 rooms, all with bath/shower. B&B £39 to £70. Deposit: £20. Pets welcome. Afternoon teas. Garden. Fishing. TV. Phone. Scenic. Doors close at 11.30. Confirm by 5

CONG   Co Mayo   map 9

▲ Connaught Room, Ashford Castle

Cong
CLAREMORRIS (092) 46003   COST £29–£74

The Connaught Room is the flagship restaurant of this enormous castle hotel by the shores of Lough Corrib. Michel Flamme cooks neo-classical French in conditions of extreme luxury. House wine: £14

CHEF: Michel Flamme   PROPRIETORS: Ashford Hotels Ltd
OPEN: all week
CLOSED: Jan and Feb
MEALS: 1 to 2.30, 7 to 9.45
PRICES: £40 (£62), Set L £18 (£29), Set D £32.50 (£45). Service 15%
CARDS: Access, Amex, Diners, Visa
SEATS: 40. Private parties: 40 main room. Car-park, unlimited. No children under 8. Smart dress preferred. No-smoking area. Wheelchair access. Music. Air-conditioned
ACCOMMODATION: 83 rooms, all with bath/shower. Rooms for disabled. Lift. B&B £175 to £210. Deposit: 10%. Baby facilities. Afternoon teas. Garden. Tennis. Fishing. Golf. TV. Phone. Scenic. Doors close at midnight. Confirm by 11am

---

CORK   Co Cork   map 9

▲ Arbutus Lodge

Middle Glanmire Road, Montenotte, Cork
CORK (021) 501237   COST £21–£41

Very fine indeed. A town house, once the residence of the mayors of Cork, now a small hotel with the Ryan family very much in charge. Links with Ireland and its cooking have not been entirely submerged by European influences and wider fame. Bacon and cabbage, Arbutus style; nettle or lovage soups; salmon on a sorrel and nettle sauce are instances of that, just as chargrilled polenta with Mediterranean vegetables or hot oysters with cucumber and herbs go further afield. The wine list is also very fine with some great runs of claret, good Californians and stylish Italians. The burgundies also contain some rarities even if the showing of more go-ahead modern winemakers is not yet very great. Reports comment that the service is less professional than in places of similar stature; this may be because the Ryans wish to maintain the personal touch. House French: £10.50 and £11.75.

CHEFS: Michael Ryan   PROPRIETORS: The Ryan family
OPEN: Mon to Sat
CLOSED: 24 to 29 Dec
MEALS: 1 to 2, 7 to 9.30
PRICES: £25 (£34), Set L £15.25 (£21), Set D £19.25 (£25). Service inc
CARDS: Access, Amex, Diners, Visa
SEATS: 60. 6 tables outside. Private parties: 8 main room, 30 private room. Car-park, 40 places. Vegetarian meals. Children's helpings on request. No smoking in dining-room. Air-conditioned
ACCOMMODATION: 20 rooms, all with bath/shower. B&B £38.50 to £68. Deposit: £20. Baby facilities. Afternoon teas. Garden. Tennis. Air-conditioning. TV. Phone. Scenic

Clifford's

18 Dyke Parade, Mardyke, Cork
MARDYKE (021) 275333   COST £17–£37

Michael Clifford set up on his own in Cork, having gained a matchless reputation at Whites on the Green in Dublin, and in a short time moved into larger premises at the present address. Once a county library, the Georgian interior makes it a fine place to celebrate his version of 'cuisine grandmère'. Breast of chicken with kidney beans in a pearl barley sauce; gateau of Clonakilty black pudding with smoked bacon and potato, mille-feuille of salmon with sorrel and a lemon butter sauce all show enthusiasm for and understanding of taste. The ambience is wonderfully friendly. House French: £11.50.

CHEF/PROPRIETOR: Michael Clifford
OPEN: Mon to Sat, exc Sat L
CLOSED: 1 week Aug, Christmas, bank hols
MEALS: 12.30 to 2.30, 7.30 to 10
PRICES: Set L £10 (£17), Set D £22 (£31)
CARDS: Access, Amex, Diners, Visa
SEATS: 45. Private parties: 50 main room, 20 private room. Children's helpings. Wheelchair access. Air-conditioned

Crawford Gallery, Municipal Art Gallery

Emmet Place, Cork
CORK (021) 274415   COST £13–£26

The café/restaurant in the main art gallery in Cork is an outpost of Ballymaloe House (see entry, Shanagarry). A good place for lunch, particularly for Irish stew and Irish rhubarb cake, and not too expensive for dinner. House French: £8.50.

CHEFS: Myrtle and Fern Allen, Rosie Mcleod PROPRIETORS: Ivan and Myrtle Allen
OPEN: Mon to Sat L and Wed to Fri D
CLOSED: 24 Dec D for 2 weeks
MEALS: 12 to 2.30, 6.30 to 9.30
PRICES: L £7 (£13), D £15 (£22) Minimum £2.50 at L
CARDS: Access, Visa
SEATS: 70. Private parties: 70 main room. Vegetarian meals. Children's helpings. Separate smoking area. Wheelchair access (4 steps). Music

---

DINGLE   Co Kerry   map 9

▲ *Doyle's*

4 John Street, Dingle
TRALEE (066) 51174   COST £29

The place with the reputation in Dingle based on very good, very fresh fish cooked with style. Some examples from a summer menu: crab claws, beurre blanc; haddock with lobster sauce; ray with a gherkin sauce; seafood tartlets with a Champagne sauce. House wines start at £8.50.

CHEF: Stella Doyle   PROPRIETORS: John and Stella Doyle
OPEN: Mon to Sat
CLOSED: mid-Nov to 17 Mar
MEALS: 12.30 to 2.15, 6 to 9
PRICES: £16 (£24). Service 10% D
CARDS: Access, Amex, Diners, Visa
SEATS: 45. Private parties: 28 main room. Vegetarian meals with prior notice. Children's helpings. No-smoking area. Wheelchair access (1 step; also WC)
ACCOMMODATION: 8 rooms, all with bath/shower. Rooms for disabled. B&B £30 to £50. Deposit: £25. TV. Phone. Doors close at 11 weekdays, 9 Sun. Confirm by 6

Half Door

John Street, Dingle
TRALEE (066) 51600   COST £13–£29

A seafood and fish restaurant that runs Doyle's a close second. House French: £8.50.

CHEFS: Diane Flynn and Deirdre Flannery   PROPRIETOR: Mick Casey
OPEN: all week
MEALS: 12.15 to 2.15, 6 to 10
PRICES: £17 (£24), L £9 (£13)
CARDS: Access, Amex, Diners, Visa
SEATS: 48. Private parties: 34 main room, 14 private room. Vegetarian meals. Children's helpings. No-smoking area. Wheelchair access (also WC)

'The proprietor was unfriendly and had forgotten my request for a vegetarian choice which he had said over the phone would be no problem. He then brought a list of 5 or 6 vegetarian main courses which we had been offered over Christmas – so they were still available, in the freezer presumably.' On eating in Norfolk

---

DOUGLAS Co Cork map 9

Lovetts

Churchyard Lane,
off Well Road, Douglas
CORK (021) 294909 and 362204   COST £20–£38

The ground floor of a secluded Georgian house is given over to a restaurant specialising in fish, but not exclusively. Popular with businesses, it can sometimes produce very good meals. Game is also a strong point. House Italian (white) and French (red): £10.50.

CHEF: Manuel Las Heras   PROPRIETORS: Dermod and Margaret Lovett
OPEN: Mon to Sat, exc Sat L
MEALS: 12.30 to 2, 7 to 10
PRICES: £22 (£32), Set L £12.65 (£20), Set D £20 (£28). Service 12.5%
CARDS: Access, Amex, Diners, Visa
SEATS: 40. Private parties: 40 main room, 25 private room. Car-park, 20 places. Vegetarian meals. Children's helpings. No-smoking tables. Wheelchair access (also WC). Music. Air-conditioned

DUBLIN Co Dublin map 9

Café Klara

35 Dawson Street, Dublin 2
DUBLIN (01) 778611   COST £17–£29

Dublin's answer to the brasserie. The cooking, which features quite a lot of pasta dishes, is acceptable and meals are available all day. House French: £9.50.

CHEF: Noel Cusack   PROPRIETORS: Claire and Richard Douglas
OPEN: all week
CLOSED: bank hols
MEALS: noon to 11.30pm (10.30 Sat)
PRICES: £15 (£24), Set L £10.50 (£17), Set D £11 (£17) to £14.50 (£21). Service 10%
CARDS: Access, Visa
SEATS: 100. 3 tables outside. Private parties: 16 main room, 34 private room. Vegetarian meals with prior notice. Children's helpings. No children under 3. No-smoking in half of dining-room

Coq Hardi

35 Pembroke Road,
Ballsbridge, Dublin 4
DUBLIN (01) 689070 and 684130   COST £26–£53

Classical French cooking in a restaurant pre-eminently for the establishment and the world of the world of finance, with prices and standards to match. The classic wine list features clarets with a spectacular run of the 1970 vintage, and most years of Mouton Rothschild on show if not on sale. House French: £14.

CHEFS: John Howard and James O'Sullivan   PROPRIETORS: John and Catherine Howard
OPEN: Mon to Sat, exc Sat L
MEALS: 12.30 to 2.30, 7 to 11
PRICES: £28 (£44), Set L £16 (£26). Service 12.5%
CARDS: Access, Amex, Diners, Visa
SEATS: 50. Private parties: 50 main room, 4, 10 and 20 private rooms. Car-park, 20 places.
Vegetarian meals with prior notice. Children welcome. Smart dress preferred. No-smoking
area. Air-conditioned

Eastern Tandoori

34–35 South William Street, Dublin 2
DUBLIN (01) 710428 and 710506   COST £12–£31

The food is satisfactory and the choice wide enough for all Indian cuisine
fanciers. The service may not be as open and disarming as might be expected in
Ireland. House French: £8.80.

CHEFS: Hendry Paul and Olli Ullah   PROPRIETORS: Mr and Mrs Feroze Khan
OPEN: all week, exc Sun L
MEALS: 12 to 2.30, 6 to 11.30
PRICES: £14 (£26), Set L £6.50 (£12) to £7 (£13), Set D £13.95 (£21) to £15.95 (£23).
Minimum £7.50. Service 12.5%
CARDS: Access, Amex, Diners, Visa
SEATS: 74. Vegetarian meals. Children's helpings. No-smoking area. Wheelchair access (2
steps). Music. Air-conditioned

Kapriol

45 Lower Camden Street, Dublin 2
DUBLIN (01) 751235 and 985496   COST £40

'Dublin's favourite Italian restaurant. Egidia Peruzzi does the cooking and
Giuseppe Peruzzi looks after the front of house. The menu is classic Italian,
uninfluenced by the waves of farmhouse cooking now washing on British
shores. 'A real gem, a wonderful welcome and ambience.' House Italian: £9.50.

CHEF: Egidia Peruzzi   PROPRIETORS: Egidia and Giuseppe Peruzzi
OPEN: Mon to Sat D (L by arrangement for large parties)
CLOSED: bank hols, 3 weeks Aug
MEALS: 7.30 to 12
PRICES: £21 (£33). Service 12.5%
CARDS: Access, Amex, Diners, Visa
SEATS: 30. Private parties: 36 main room. Vegetarian meals. Children's helpings. Children
restricted. Smart dress preferred. No-smoking tables. Wheelchair access (1 step). Music

*All details are as accurate as possible at the time of going to press, but chefs and owners
often change, and it is wise to check by telephone before making a special journey. Many
readers have been disappointed when set-price bargain meals are no longer available. Ask
when booking.*

Locks

1 Windsor Terrace, Portobello, Dublin 8
DUBLIN (01) 543391 and 538352   COST £18–£38

There is a certain Scandinavian influence in the repertoire, so that Irish black pudding is served with a Danish-inspired, but lightened, duck fat and onion sauce. However, modern influences from cookery books and elsewhere are not far away in dishes such as chicken stuffed with crab, served with a lemon sauce. Sound cooking in pleasant surroundings. House French: £10.50.

CHEF: Brian Buckley   PROPRIETORS: Claire and Richard Douglas
OPEN: Mon to Sat, exc Sat L
CLOSED: bank hols, 1 week at Christmas
MEALS: 12.30 to 2, 7.15 to 11
PRICES: £21 (£32), Set L £11.25 (£18), to £12.95 (£20), Set D £17.50 (£25). Service 10%
CARDS: Access, Amex, Diners, Visa
SEATS: 50. Private parties: 15 main room, 8 and 22 private rooms. Vegetarian meals with prior notice. Children's helpings. No-smoking area. Wheelchair access

Patrick Guilbaud

46 James Place, Dublin 2
DUBLIN (01) 764192   COST £24–£49

Offering some of the best food in Ireland, the restaurant is thought still to be improving – not bad after nine years. The style is unreservedly modern. Leek and lemon balm soup served with grilled shallots; bavarois of tomatoes and basil with a cucumber coulis; black pudding, sweetbreads and crubeens with a poivrade sauce; and sweetbreads braised with lemon and coriander are among the signature dishes. House French: £13.

CHEF: Guillaume Le Brun   PROPRIETOR: Patrick Guilbaud
OPEN: Mon to Sat, exc Sat L
CLOSED: bank hols
MEALS: 12.30 to 2.15, 7.30 to 10.15
PRICES: £28 (£41), Set L £14.50 (£24), Set D £25 (£36). Service 15%
CARDS: Access, Amex, Diners, Visa
SEATS: 85. Private parties: 85 main room, 30 private room. Car-park, 6 places. Children's helpings. Smart dress preferred. No-smoking area. Wheelchair access (1 step)

DUN LAOGHAIRE   Co Dublin   map 9

Digby's

5 Windsor Terrace, Dun Laoghaire
DUBLIN (01) 804600 and 809147   COST £19–£47

The well-established restaurant and wine bar has views across the bay and cooking of some finesse. Much of the repertoire is fish: plaice stuffed with crab; charcoal grilled salmon; scallops with ginger, lime and avocado. Game is a feature in winter. House wine: French (red) £9, Italian (white) £11 and £12.

CHEF: Paul Cathcart PROPRIETORS: Paul and Jane Cathcart
OPEN: all week, D only, exc Tue; Sun L only
CLOSED: bank hols
MEALS: 12.30 to 3, 7 to 11
PRICES: £27 (£39), Set L £10.50 (£19), Set D £16.50 (£25). Service 12.5%
CARDS: Access, Amex, Diners, Visa
SEATS: 50. Private parties: 53 main room. Vegetarian meals. Children's helpings (L only).
No-smoking in one-third of dining-room. Music

Restaurant Na Mara

Harbour Road, Dun Laoghaire
DUBLIN (01) 806767and 800509   COST £19—£35

A railway restaurant, owned by Irish Rail in a glorious building overlooking
Dun Laoghaire harbour that was part of the original railway terminal. It
specialises in fish, mainly cooked in classical style. It can be excellent. House
French: £9.

CHEF: Derek Dunne PROPRIETORS: C.I.E. (Irish Transport Company)
OPEN: Mon to Sat
CLOSED: 1 week at Christmas and Easter
MEALS: 12.30 to 2.30, 6.30 to 10.30
PRICES: Set L £12 (£19), Set D £21 (£29). Service 15%
CARDS: Access, Amex, Diners, Visa
SEATS: 75. Private parties: 45 main room, 30 private room. Vegetarian meals. Children
welcome. No-smoking in one-third of dining-room. Wheelchair access (2 steps)

DUNDALK   Co Louth   map 9

Cellars

Backhouse Centre,
Clanbrassil Street, Dundalk
DUNDALK (042) 33745   COST £9—£14

Home cooking with daily menus and a vegetarian emphasis. Bread is home
made. House French: £9 a litre.

CHEFS/PROPRIETORS: Alison and George O'Shea
OPEN: Mon to Fri L, Thur to Sat D
MEALS: 12.30 to 2, 7 to 10
PRICES: L £6 (£12), Set L £2.95 (£9) to £6 (£12), Set D £6 (£12)
SEATS: 150. Private parties: 100 main room, 24 private room. Car-park, 140 places.
Vegetarian meals. Children's helpings. No-smoking area. Music. Air-conditioned

---

The Guide *office can quickly spot when a restaurateur is encouraging customers to write
recommending inclusion - and sadly, several restaurants have been doing this in 1990.
Such reports do not further a restaurant's cause. Please tell us if a restaurateur invites you
to write to the* Guide.

All letters to the Guide *are acknowledged with an update on latest sales, closures, chef
changes and so on.*

DURRUS   Co Cork
map 9

Blairs Cove House

Durrus
BANTRY (027) 61127
COST £19–£34

In a great position above the sea, a simple menu is cooked mainly on a wood-fired grill in the dining-room. Fish is a strong point and the cooking is not elaborate. You help yourself to first courses and desserts and are served the rest of the meal. House French: £9.

CHEF: Sabine De Mey   PROPRIETORS: Philippe and Sabine De Mey
OPEN: Tue to Sat, D only and Sun L
CLOSED: Nov to Feb
MEALS: 1 to 2, 7.30 to 9.30
PRICES: Set Sun L £12 (£19), Set D £20 (£28). Service 10%
CARDS: Access, Amex, Diners, Visa
SEATS: 70. 8 tables outside. Private parties: 35 main room. Car-park, unlimited. Children's helpings. No-smoking area. Wheelchair access. Music

ENNIS   Co Clare
map 9

Cloister

Abbey Street, Ennis
ENNIS (065) 29521
COST £11–£36

The restaurant incorporates three rooms of the former abbey's kitchen and the bar adjoins the cloisters. Acceptable cooking is made the more palatable by fresh seafood and good meats. 'Lunch and dinner times can be arranged to suit individuals,' says the owner. House French: £9.50.

CHEF: Anne Lynch   PROPRIETOR: Rosaleen Spooner
OPEN: all week, exc Sun D in winter
CLOSED: 25 Dec, Good Friday
MEALS: 12 to 13, 6 to 10
PRICES: £21 (£30), Set L £5.50 (£11) to £8.50 (£15), Set D £17 (£24). Minimum £2.50 at L. Service 12.5% at D
CARDS: Access, Amex, Diners, Visa
SEATS: 60. 8 tables outside. Private parties: 50 main room, 25 each in three private rooms. Car-park, 15 places. Children's helpings. No children under 8 after 8pm. Separate smoking area. Wheelchair access. Music. Air-conditioned

HOWTH   Co Dublin
map 9

King Sitric

East Pier, Harbour Road
DUBLIN (01) 325235 and 326729
COST £31

The key words are 'fresh fish'. The restaurant was king of the Dublin region, and though there is now some competition, it still offers very fine fresh fish. The kitchen uses many classic haute cuisine recipes but does not overload with ornament or complexity. House French: £11.

CHEF: Aidan MacManus   PROPRIETORS: Aidan and Joan MacManus
OPEN: Mon to Sat, D only (Sun and L by arrangement)
CLOSED: 10 days each at Christmas and Easter, bank hols
MEALS: 6.30 to 11
PRICES: Set D £18.50 (£26)
CARDS: Access, Amex, Diners, Visa
SEATS: 70. Private parties: 48 main room, 24 private room. Children's helpings. No-smoking in 1 of 2 dining-rooms; no pipes/cigars in either until coffee. Wheelchair access

---

KANTURK   Co Cork   map 9

▲ *Assolas Country House*

Kanturk
KANTURK (029) 50015
signposted from the N72,
NE of Kanturk   COST £30

A lovely house in a remarkable setting close to a river: manicured rusticity. The same might be said of Hazel Bourke's cooking. There is a daily four-course meal with no choice and usually a roast as centrepiece. There is a 'menu of the season' as well, with slightly more choice. Its virtue lies in the materials and the relatively straightforward manner in which they are treated. House French: £9.50.

CHEF: Hazel Bourke   PROPRIETORS: The Bourke family
OPEN: all week, D only
CLOSED: 1 Nov to 16 Mar
MEALS: 7 to 8.30 (8 Sun)
PRICES: Set D £25 (£30). Service inc
CARDS: Access, Amex, Diners, Visa
SEATS: 30. Private parties: 8 main room, 18 private room. Car-park, 20 places. Vegetarian meals. No children under 10. Smart dress preferred. No cigars/pipes in dining-room. Wheelchair access
ACCOMMODATION: 9 rooms, all with bath/shower. B&B £44 to £120. Deposit: £60. Pets welcome. Garden. Tennis. Fishing. Phone. Scenic. Doors close at 11. Confirm by 5

KENMARE   Co Kerry   map 9

Lime Tree

Shelbourne Street, Kenmare
KENMARE (064) 41225   COST £28

An informal cottage-like restaurant that was converted from an old schoolhouse. Pottery is used at table and decent pictures grace the walls. Good are fish soup and potato pancakes with garlic butter, in a marriage of traditions; rather a long menu, but acceptable cooking. House French: £8.80.

All letters to the Guide *are acknowledged with an update on latest sales, closures, chef changes and so on.*

CHEF: Maura Foley   PROPRIETORS: Tom and Maura Foley
OPEN: Mon to Sat, D only
CLOSED: Nov to Easter
MEALS: 6 to 9.30
PRICES: £20 (£28)
CARDS: Access, Amex, Diners, Visa
SEATS: 50. Private parties: 25 main room. Car-park, 20 places. Children's helpings. No-smoking area. Wheelchair access (side entrance). Music

▲ Park Hotel

Kenmare
KILLARNEY (064) 41200   COST £22–£60

'Our ideal guest is over 55 and reading a good book,' is Francis Brennan's tongue-in-cheek reflection that the Park is about service and food rather than tennis courts, saunas and health clubs. It is a place of sensational friendliness and good service. 'My only criticism was at breakfast, when my egg and bacon were overcooked. But it was the waiter who pointed it out to me and asked if I would like another.' A complete refurbishment has improved the bedrooms. The modern cooking does not need a lot doing to it, as reported in confit of duck with red cabbage; timbale of smoked salmon stuffed with crab; shellfish bisque; quail with a celeriac galette and madeira sauce; fillet of veal with mustard sauce. Petits fours are presented in a cardboard model of the hotel. House French: £13.95.

CHEF: Matthew Darcy   PROPRIETOR: Francis Brennan
OPEN: all week
CLOSED: mid-Nov to 23 Dec, 2 Jan to Easter
MEALS: 1 to 2, 7 to 9
PRICES: £34 (£50), Set L £15 (£22), Set D £33 (£40). Service inc set meals
CARD: Access, Visa
SEATS: 90. Private parties: 60 main room, 40 private room. Car-park, 60 places. Vegetarian meals with prior notice. Children's helpings (L and early D at 6pm, only). No children under 6 at D. Smart dress preferred. Wheelchair access (also WC). Music
ACCOMMODATION: 50 rooms, all with bath/shower. Rooms for disabled. Lift. B&B £86 to £180. Afternoon teas. Garden. Tennis. Golf. Snooker. TV. Phone. Scenic. Doors close at 9.30pm. Confirm 24 hours ahead

---

KILKENNY   Co Kilkenny   map 9

▲ Lacken House

Dublin Road, Kilkenny
KILKENNY (056) 61085 and 65611   COST £25–£34

The restaurant is in a Georgian house, where chef/proprietor Eugene McSweeney cooks a short menu in the mainstream Anglo-Irish style. Examples of the dishes include marinated salmon with hot dill potatoes; nettle soup; potato and leek cakes with garden herbs; and stuffed pig's trotters. House Spanish: £10.

CHEF: Eugene McSweeney   PROPRIETORS: Eugene and Breda McSweeney
OPEN: Tue to Sat, D only
CLOSED: 25 Dec
MEALS: 7 to 10
PRICES: £20 (£28), Set D £18 (£25). Service 10%
CARDS: Access, Amex, Diners, Visa
SEATS: 35. Private parties: 40 main room, 10 private room. Car-park, 20 places. Children's
helpings. No-smoking area. Music. Air-conditioned
ACCOMMODATION: 8 rooms, all with bath/shower. B&B £24 to £40. Deposit: £10. Baby
facilities. Garden. TV. Phone. Scenic. Confirm by 6

KINSALE   Co Cork   map 9

▲ *Blue Haven*

3 Pearse Street, Kinsale
CORK (021) 772209   COST £25–£34

A small hotel with a bar, brasserie and restaurant. 'In a town packed with
quality restaurants, this appears to hold its own.' A new chef took over in 1990,
but first reports are encouraging for a fairly conventional modern repertoire.
House French: £9.50.

CHEF: Marius Cleary   PROPRIETORS: Brian and Anne Cronin
OPEN: all week
CLOSED: 25 Dec
MEALS: 12.30 to 3, 7 (6.30 June to Sept) to 10.30
PRICES: £20 (£28), Set D £17.50 (£25). Service 10%
CARDS: Access, Amex, Diners, Visa
SEATS: 70. 7 tables outside. Private parties: 45 main room, 22 private room. Vegetarian
meals. Children's helpings. No-smoking area. Wheelchair access (also male and female
WC). Music. Air-conditioned
ACCOMMODATION: 10 rooms, 7 with bath/shower. Rooms for disabled. B&B £30 to £65.
Deposit: £30. Baby facilities. Afternoon teas. Garden. TV. Phone. Doors close at midnight.
Confirm by 6

LETTERFRACK   Co Galway   map 9

▲ *Rosleague Manor*

Letterfrack
LETTERFRACK (095) 41101   COST £29–£38

A Regency manor overlooking Ballinakill Bay, set in 30 acres of landscaped
gardens. The cooking is low-key country house in a five-course set-price
menu with perhaps four choices; its strongest point is the materials. House
French: £10.

'*As you well know, clergymen invariably only carry two books in their cars, the Bible and
The Good Food Guide.*' A reader from Gloucestershire

CHEF: Paddy Foyle PROPRIETORS: Anne Foyle and Paddy Foyle
OPEN: all week
CLOSED: Nov to Easter
MEALS: 1 to 2.30, 8 to 9.30
PRICES: £20 (£32), Set D £21 (£29)
CARDS: Access, Amex, Visa
SEATS: 70. Private parties: 70 main room. Car-park, 30 places. Vegetarian meals. Children's
helpings. Smart dress preferred. No smoking. Wheelchair access (2 steps; also WC)
ACCOMMODATION: 21 rooms, all with bath/shower. Rooms for disabled. B&B £40 to 90.
Deposit: £25. Baby facilities. Pets welcome. Afternoon teas. Garden. Sauna. Tennis. Phone.
Scenic. Doors close at 12. Confirm by 5

MALLOW Co Cork   map 9

▲ Longueville House

Mallow
MALLOW (022) 47156   COST £21–£44

A beautiful house with a fine Victorian conservatory that may sometimes be
used for picturesque dining. The restaurant is almost better than the hotel.
William O'Callaghan has done his training in good places abroad and it shows
in modern finesse. Timbale of marinated salmon with a cucumber and mint
coulis; terrine of skate, prawns, garden vegetables and a saffron vinaigrette;
tartlet of veal kidneys with shallots and red wine; rabbit with bacon, cabbage
and basil scented sauce; and apple tartlet with calvados ice-cream are dishes
that would not sound out of place anywhere in north-western Europe. House
French: £11.

CHEF: William O'Callaghan PROPRIETORS: The O'Callaghan family
OPEN: all week
CLOSED: 20 Dec to 1 Mar
MEALS: 12.45 to 2, 7 to 9 (9.45 Sat)
PRICES: Set L £14 (£21) to £16 (£24), Set D £26 (£35) to £28 (£37)
CARDS: Access, Amex, Diners, Visa
SEATS: 50. 8 tables outside. Private parties: 16 main room, 16 private room. Car-park, 30
places. Vegetarian meals. Children's helpings. No smoking in dining-room
ACCOMMODATION: 16 rooms, all with bath/shower. B&B £45 to £120. Afternoon teas.
Garden. Fishing. Snooker. TV. Phone. Scenic. Doors close at midnight. Confirm by 6

MAYNOOTH Co Kildare   map 9

▲ Moyglare Manor

Moyglare, Maynooth
DUBLIN (01) 6286351   COST £17–£48

Solid, reliable cooking of a traditional repertoire in an atmosphere of
luxury and antiques. The wine list, too, is aristocratic. House French: £10.95
and £11.50.

▲ *This symbol means accommodation is available.*

CHEF: Jim Cullinane PROPRIETOR: Nora Devlin
OPEN: all week, exc Sat L
CLOSED: 24 to 26 Dec
MEALS: 12.45 to 2.15, 7 to 9.30 (8.30 Sun)
PRICES: £23 (£36), Set L £9.95 (£17) to £16.95 (£25), Set D £18.50 (£27) to £29.95 (£40).
Service 12.5%
CARDS: Access, Amex, Diners, Visa
SEATS: 90. Private parties: 35 main room, 35 private room. Car-park, 100 places. Vegetarian
meals with prior notice. No children under 12. Smart dress preferred. No smoking in
dining-room. Wheelchair access (also WC). Music
ACCOMMODATION: 17 rooms, all with bath/shower. Rooms for disabled. B&B £65 to 100.
Deposit: £50. Garden. Tennis. TV. Phone. Scenic. Doors close at 11.30. Confirm by 6

MIDLETON Co Cork   map 9

Farm Gate

The Coolbawn, Midleton
MIDLETON (021) 632 771   COST £20–£29

A delicatessen and greengrocery come first, then the restaurant, which has an
excellent reputation for fresh food, unpretentiously cooked and reasonably
priced. Máróg O'Brien is a natural cook and seems to have unbounded energy.
'It is wonderful how small local restaurants like this are beginning to pop up
all around Cork,' commented one local supporter. House French: £9.50.

CHEF/PROPRIETOR: Máróg O'Brien
OPEN: Mon to Sat L; Thurs to Sat D
CLOSED: 25 and 26 Dec, Good Friday
MEALS: 12 to 3.30, 7 to 9.45
PRICES: £19 (£24), Set D £15 (£20). Service inc
CARDS: Access, Visa
SEATS: 60. 6 tables outside. Private parties: 60 main room. Vegetarian meals. Children's
helpings. No-smoking area. Wheelchair access (also unisex WC). Music. Air-conditioned

---

MOYCULLEN Co Galway   map 9

Drimcong House

Moycullen
GALWAY (091) 85115 and 85585   COST £26

The cooking is more exciting and more eclectic than most found on the west
coast, for example: lambs' sweetbreads with tabouleh and mint cream sauce;
stir-fried duck with kataif pastry; grilled cod with ratatouille and red pepper
butter sauce. Yet there is no preciousness about it, and presentation is simple
when that is called for. House wine: £8.75.

Consumers' Association is planning to publish Out to Eat, *a new guide to budget eating
out in restaurants, pubs, cafés, brasseries and so on. Please send reports and
recommendations to* Out to Eat, *FREEPOST, 2 Marylebone Road, London NW1 1YN.*

CHEF: Gerard Galvin   PROPRIETORS: Gerard and Marie Galvin
OPEN: Tue to Sat, D only
CLOSED: 25 Dec to Mar
MEALS: 7 to 10.30
PRICES: £14 (£22), Set D £15.95 (£22). Service 10%
CARDS: Access, Amex, Diners, Visa
SEATS: 50. Private parties: 50 main room, 12 private room. Car-park, 40 places.
Vegetarian meals. Children's helpings. Separate smoking area. Wheelchair access
(3 steps; also WC). Music

NEWMARKET-ON-FERGUS   Co Clare   map 9

▲ *Dromoland Castle*

Newmarket-on-Fergus
LIMERICK (061) 71144   COST £27–£60

Another giant castle with a French chef, owned by the same people as Ashford
Castle and within cycling distance of Shannon airport. The dining-room is
wedding-cake gothic and grand. The menu takes in the modish and Irish stew.

CHEF: Jean-Baptiste Molinari   PROPRIETORS: Ashford Hotels Ltd
OPEN: all week
MEALS: 12.30 to 2.30, 7 to 9.30
PRICES: £35 (£50), Set L £17 (£27), Set D £29 (£41). Service 15%
CARDS: Access, Amex, Diners, Visa
SEATS: 90. 4 tables outside. Private parties: 120 main room; 20,60 private rooms. Car-park,
250 places. Vegetarian meals. Children's helpings. Children restricted. Jacket and tie. No-
smoking area. Wheelchair access. Music
ACCOMMODATION: 73 rooms, all with bath/shower. Rooms for disabled. B&B £95 to 340.
Baby facilities. Afternoon teas. Garden. Tennis. Fishing. Golf. Snooker. TV. Phone. Scenic

---

NEWPORT   Co Mayo   map 9

▲ *Newport House*

Newport
NEWPORT (098) 41222   COST £34

Fishing is an important preoccupation of a sizeable fraction of the guests, and of
the chef, with his own smoke-house, a salmon fishery on the estate, and salmon
of all sorts figuring regularly on the menus. The cooking is well considered,
forming a part of that international European style that has respect for
materials, no undue emphasis on strong flavours and tends to be relatively
light. Banoffi pie crops up on this side of the water too. Children can have their
dinner at 6pm. The wine list is good: long on youthful clarets and Rhônes.

---

*Several sharp operators have tried to extort money from restaurateurs on the promise of an
entry in a guide book that has never appeared. The Good Food Guide makes no charge
for inclusion and does not offer certificates of any kind.*

CHEF: John Gavin   PROPRIETORS: Kieran and Thelka Thompson
OPEN: all week
CLOSED: Oct to 12 Mar
MEALS: 12.30 to 2, 7.30 to 9.30
PRICES: Set D £23 (£28)
CARDS: Access, Amex, Diners, Visa
SEATS: 38. Car-park, 40 places. Vegetarian meals with prior notice. Children's helpings. No smoking in dining-room. Wheelchair access (3 steps)
ACCOMMODATION: 19 rooms, all with bath/shower. B&B £48 to £80. Baby facilities. Afternoon teas. Garden. Fishing. Snooker. Phone. Scenic. Confirm by 6

OUGHTERARD Co Galway   map 9

▲ *Currarevagh House*

Oughterard
GALWAY (091) 82313 and 82312
4m NW of Oughterard on Hill of
Doon Lakeshore road   COST £21–£29

The house sits 100 yards from Lough Corrib in the middle of 150 acres of woodland. It is a haven for those who fish, and others can ride, putt or walk. A daily no-choice dinner menu restores the bodies wasted by hours of casting for trout. House French: £7.50.

CHEF: June Hodgson   PROPRIETORS: Harry and June Hodgson
OPEN: all week, D only
CLOSED: Oct to Mar
MEALS: 8
PRICES: Set D from £15.25 (£21) to £18.25 (£24). Service 10%
SEATS: 30. Private parties: 10 main room. Car-park, 40 places. Vegetarian meals with prior notice. Children welcome. Smart dress preferred. No smoking in dining-room. Wheelchair access (2 steps; also unisex WC). One sitting
ACCOMMODATION: 15 rooms, all with bath/shower. Rooms for disabled. B&B £33 to £66. Pets welcome by arrangement. Garden. Tennis. Fishing. Scenic. Doors close at 12.30. Confirm by noon

---

RATHNEW Co Wicklow   map 9

▲ *Hunter's Hotel*

Newrath Bridge, Rathnew
WICKLOW (0404) 40106   COST £16–£29

The hotel has been in the same family for five generations, is a great place to stop for tea after visiting the Usher gardens, and serves good plain food. House French: £8.50.

The Guide *relies on feedback from its readers. Especially welcome are reports on new restaurants appearing in the book for the first time.*

CHEF: John Sutton   PROPRIETOR: Maureen Gelletlie
OPEN: all week
CLOSED: 25 Dec to non-residents
MEALS: 1 to 3, 7.30 to 9.30
PRICES: Set L £10 (£16) to £12 (£18), Set D £16 (£22) to £18 (£24)
CARDS: Access, Amex, Diners, Visa
SEATS: 54. Private parties: 20 main room, 12 private room. Car-park, 30 places. Children's
helpings (L only). Wheelchair access (also WC)
ACCOMMODATION: 18 rooms, 10 with bath/shower. Rooms for disabled. B&B £27.50 to
£55. Baby facilities. Pets welcome by prior arrangement. Afternoon teas. Garden. Fishing.
Phone. Scenic. Doors close at 12.30. Confirm by 6

ROSSNOWLAGH   Co Donegal   map 9

▲ Sand House Hotel

Rossnowlagh
BUNDORAN (072) 517777   COST £16–£30

A large seaside hotel right on the beach of Donegal Bay, open only from Easter
to October. Sound holiday cooking. House French: £9.

CHEF: Liam Quinn   PROPRIETORS: Nin and Mary Britton
OPEN: all week
CLOSED: Oct to Easter
MEALS: 1 to 2, 7 to 9
PRICES: £14 (£24), Set L £10 (£16) to £11 (£17), Set D £16 (£22) to £18.50 (£25)
CARDS: Access, Amex, Diners, Visa
SEATS: 80. Private parties: 60 main room, 75 private room. Car-park, 30 places. Children's
helpings. No children under 8 at D. No-smoking area. Wheelchair access (3 steps)
ACCOMMODATION: 40 rooms, all with bath/shower. B&B £30 to £60 (low season), £40 to
£80 (high season). Deposit: £30. Baby facilities. Pets welcome by arrangement. Afternoon
teas. Garden. Sauna. Tennis. Snooker. Phone. Scenic. Doors close at 11pm. Confirm by 3

SHANAGARRY   Co Cork   map 9

▲ Ballymaloe House

Shanagarry, Midleton
CORK (021) 652531
2m from Cloyne on the
Ballycotton road   COST £18–£36

Famous beyond its borders, this country house spawns hotel, restaurant,
cookery school, TV programmes and cookery books. The root of it, as with so
many Irish country places, was the farm and estate. It is this close link with the
countryside that is the chief strength of the cooking, and the sense of fusion
with the community that makes Irish hospitality so remarkable – and nowhere
better expressed than here. The food is not elaborately modern nor
conventionally country house. There may be a stuffed courgette flower, but
there will also be a roast loin of pork perfumed with herbs and wild garlic.
House French £9.

CHEFS: Myrtle Allen, Paddy Cullinane and Rory O'Connell PROPRIETORS: Ivan and
Myrtle Allen
OPEN: all week
CLOSED: 24 to 26 Dec
MEALS: 1 to 2, 7 to 9.30
PRICES: Set L £11.50 (£18), Set D £23 (£30). Service 10%
CARDS: Access, Amex, Diners, Visa
SEATS: 90. Private parties: 35 main room, 10,18 and 30 private rooms. Car-park, unlimited.
Vegetarian meals. Children's helpings on request (D only). No-smoking in half of
restaurant (separate room). Wheelchair access
ACCOMMODATION: 30 rooms, all with bath/shower. Rooms for disabled. B&B £56 to £75.
Deposit: 50%. Baby facilities. Pets welcome in restricted areas. Garden. Swimming-pool.
Tennis. Golf. Phone. Scenic. Doors close at midnight

WATERFORD   Co Waterford   map 9

Dwyers

8 Mary Street, Waterford
WATERFORD (051) 77478   COST £17–£24

Martin Dwyer worked at the Wife of Bath in Ashford, Kent, and feels he is part
of that post-war British continuum of Elizabeth David, Kenneth Bell and
George Perry-Smith. The restaurant opened in 1989 in a building that was once
a police barracks. It tries to combine a sense of occasion with a lack of
pretension. The food has that certain simplicity that comes from an assured
style and good materials: black pudding and apple pies; mushrooms in
tarragon and cream; salmon with cucumber sauce; noisettes of lamb with
soubise sauce; brown bread ice-cream; French apple tart. House wine: £10
and £10.50.

CHEF/PROPRIETOR: Martin Dwyer
OPEN: Mon to Sat, D only (L by arrangement)
CLOSED: 3 days at Christmas
MEALS: 6 to 10
PRICES: £16 (£24), Set D £10.75 (£17). Service 10% set
CARDS: Access, Visa
SEATS: 42. Private parties: 32 main room, 10 private room. Children's helpings on request.
No-smoking area. Wheelchair access. Music

WICKLOW   Co Wicklow   map 9

▲ Old Rectory

Wicklow
WICKLOW (404) 67048   COST £25–£37

Paul and Linda Saunders make an effort to create a small house-party
atmosphere. He acts as host while guests sip sherry among his fire brigade
memorabilia and other 'personal clutter' in the sitting-room, and she cooks.
Her menu is ecologically aware as well as alive to contemporary food
preferences, for instance vegetarianism. There is one vegetarian dish on the
menu at all times and advance notice will result in a choice. The food is fresh;

the cooking is acceptable; the ambience is relaxing. The wine list has as many Spanish as French bottles. House wine: £10.

CHEF: Linda Saunders   PROPRIETORS: Paul and Linda Saunders
OPEN: all week, D only
CLOSED: mid-Oct to Easter
MEALS: 8
PRICES: £24 (£31), Set D £20 (£25). Service inc
CARDS: Access, Amex, Visa
SEATS: 12. Car-park, 20 places. Vegetarian meals. Children's helpings. No smoking in dining-room. Wheelchair access (3 steps). Music. One sitting
ACCOMMODATION: 5 rooms, all with bath/shower. B&B £34 to £68. Deposit: £10. Baby facilities. Garden. TV. Phone. Scenic. Doors close at midnight. Confirm by 6

YOUGHAL   Co Cork   map 9

Aherne's

163 North Main Street, Youghal
YOUGHAL (024) 92424   COST £17–£37

Standards can fluctuate but, as one inspector put it, 'it is the best pub grub in the area'. Lunch is especially good value. House French: £10.

CHEF: David FitzGibbon   PROPRIETORS: The FitzGibbon family
OPEN: Tue to Sun, exc Sun L (also Mon D in summer)
CLOSED: 4 days at Christmas, Good Friday
MEALS: 12.30 to 2, 6.30 to 9.30
PRICES: £22 (£31), Set L £10.50 (£17). Service 10%. Licensed, also bring your own: corkage £4
CARD: Access, Visa
SEATS: 50. 4 tables outside. Private parties: 40 main room, 30 private room. Car-park, 15 places. No children under 8. Smart dress preferred. No-smoking area. Wheelchair access (also WC). Music

County round-ups

This year we give a revised selection of round-up entries. All the eating places listed below have been recommended by readers but for one reason or another have not graduated to the main listings. They are not places that simply failed at inspection. We hope the list will be especially useful for anyone travelling around the country. All reports on these places would be most welcome.

England

Avon

Bath *Beaujolais* 5a Chapel Row (0225) 423417. Informal French restaurant.
Circus 34 Brock Street (0225) 330208. Friendly, with a large menu, plus dailies on the blackboard.
Sally Lunn's 4 North Parade Passage (0225) 61634. Consistently good café, famous for its buns.
Scoffs 20 Kingsmead Square (0225) 462483. Wholefood café with bakery goods and take away.
Bristol *Arnolfini* Narrow Quay, Prince Street. (0272) 279330. Dockside café bar in the art gallery complex.
Mamma Mia 10a Park Road, Clifton. (0272) 268891. Good-value pizzas.
Millwards 40 Alfred Place, Kingsdown. (0272) 245026. Vegetarian, with a good choice for vegans.
New Inn 86 West Town Road, Backwell. (027 583) 2694. Country pub specialising in fresh fish.
Restaurant du Gourmet 43 Whiteladies Road, Clifton. (0272) 736230. Traditional French, busy at lunchtime.
Oldbury on Severn *Anchor Inn* Oldbury on Severn, nr Thornbury. (0454) 413331. Enterprising pub food; try the Severn Mud Pie.

Bedfordshire

Aspley Guise *Moore Place* The Square, (0908) 282000. The carte is original enough to be exciting, small enough to be believable.
Bedford *Park* 98 Kimbolton Road (0234) 54093. Pub with pretty conservatory and a good selection of English cheeses.

Berkshire

Cookham *Peking Inn* 49 High Street, (0628) 520900. Smart Chinese with good cooking.

Lambourn *Conways* East Garston, nr Great Shefford, (048 839) 275. Professional set menu has a fish course and includes such things as pheasant and wild duck.

Littlewick Green *Warrener* Warren Row, Littlewick Green, nr Wargrave, (062 882) 2803. Expensive French cooking, unashamedly pink surroundings.

Newbury *Elcot Park* (0488) 58100. Fresh ingredients, sometimes too many combined together; well-kept English cheeses.

Pangbourne *Copper Inn* Church Road, (0734) 842244. Good omelettes Arnold Bennett and brioche for breakfast, if staying the night.

Streatley *Swan Diplomat* (0491) 873737. Light modern cooking, making much use of mousses and fromage blanc.

Windsor *The Orangerie* Sir Christopher Wren's House Hotel, Thames Street, (0753) 861354. Restaurant with accommodation; service can be slow.

Buckinghamshire

Amersham *King's Arms* 30 High Street, (0494) 726333. Beautiful 15th-century building; fresh ingredients carefully cooked.
Piazza 16–18 The Broadway (0494) 728367. Friendly new-wave Italian.

Flackwell Heath *Tuptim* Acorn House, Straight Bit, (062 85) 21808. Popular Thai; pancakes, prawns and chilli fish.

Great Missenden *George* 94 High Street, (024 06) 2084. Ambitious pub food, takes in couscous as well as pasta.

High Wycombe *Carrington Restaurant* The Alexandra Hotel, Queen Alexandra Road (0494) 463494. Sophisticated cooking and accommodation.

Taplow *Orangery* Cliveden Estate (0628) 661406. Regulars from all over Bucks come to eat the imaginative vegetarian dishes in this conservatory-housed restaurant.

Cambridgeshire

Cambridge *George Inn* High Street, Babraham, (0223) 832205. Friendly pub with two open fires for winter.
Hobbs Pavilion Park Terrace, (0223) 67480. Pancakes, not cricketers, are the thing.
Shao Tao 72 Regent Street, (0223) 353942. Best Chinese in Cambridge; popular if patchy.

Fowlmere *Chequers Inn* Fowlmere, nr Royston, (076 382) 369. Pleasant pub, the conservatory appeals.

Madingley *Three Horseshoes* 1 High Street, (0954) 210221. Busy pub with ambitious food in restaurant and bar, and a good wine list.

Melbourn *Sheen Mill* Station Road, (0763) 261393. Flamboyant cooking in former mill, now cleared of dust. **Peterborough** *Bistro 29* 29 Bridge Street, (0733) 61996. Variable cooking but good value for money.
Haycock Hotel Wansford-in-England, (0780) 782223. Large country inn with fine wine list and above-average bar and restaurant.

Cheshire

Chester *Fourgate's* 126 Foregate Street, (0244) 315046. Spacious wine bar/restaurant; good herby patés, fresh vegetables.
Franc's 14 Cuppin Street, (0244) 317952. Self-consciously French cooking in a lively atmosphere.
Clutton *Frogg Manor* Fullersmoor, Nantwich Road, (0829) 782280.
Old country-house, hotel and restaurant for traditional English cooking.
Knutsford *Friedlander's* 48 King Street, (0565) 54677. German specialities.
Nantwich *Churche's Mansion* 150 Hospital Street, (0270) 625933. 16th-century surroundings; some things succeed, puddings especially.
Prestbury *Marco Polo* New Road, (0625) 829466. Outside picturesque, inside a simple Italian, one step up from a pizzeria.
Tarporley *Churtons* 55 High Street, (0829) 732483. Wine bar with the emphasis on fresh, local produce; good cooking despite the obsession with cream.
Wilmslow *Stanneylands Hotel* Stanneylands Road, (0625) 525225. Makes gestures towards modernism. Archetypal gourmet food; expensive.

Cornwall

Botallack *Count House* Botallack, St Just, (0736) 788588. Watch the sun go down from the old tin mine atop the cliffs.
Cawsand *Karen's Kitchen* Garrett Street, (0752) 822314. Cosy; fish dishes the speciality.
Constantine *Trengilly Wartha Inn* Nancenoy, Constantine, nr Falmouth, (0326) 40332. Small hotel run by a young and keen team.
Gweek *Mellanoweth* Gweek, Helston, (032 622) 271. Lovingly presented food; locally made ice-creams a draw.
Helford *Shipwright's Arms* (032 623) 235. Authentic friendly pub with a view of the estuary. Generous crab cocktails.
Lostwithiel *Trewithen* 3 Fore Street, (0208) 872373. Consistent Austrian restaurant with a sound wine list.
Mawnan *Nansidwell Country House* Mawnan, nr Falmouth. (03260 250340) Marvellous situation; tastefully furnished; locally produced vegetables and fish a real speciality. Excellent cooked breakfast.
Mullion *Polurrian Hotel* Polurrian Bay, (0326) 240268. On the cliffs above the beach, suiting the more sophisticated sandcastler.
Penzance *Admiral Benbow* 46 Chapel Street, (0736) 63448. Good fresh food and especially fish.
Port Isaac *Slipway* Harbour Front, (0208) 880264. Honest food in charming 16th-century surroundings.
St Agnes Frins *Porthvean* Churchtown, (087 255) 2581. Mostly fish, but also catering for vegetarians, vegans and meat-eaters.

St Keverne *Laden Table* 2 Commercial Road, (0326) 280090. Ambitious cooking using fresh ingredients, friendly welcome.
Saltash *Cotehele Barn* Cotehele House, St Dominic, nr Saltash, (0579) 50652. Vegetarian food at this beautiful medieval manor on the banks of the Tamar.
Truro *Pendower Beach House* Ruan High Lanes, Gerrands Bay, (0872) 501241. Spectacular beach setting for up-and-coming cooking.

Cumbria

Ambleside *Drunken Duck Inn* Barngates, (096 66) 347. Country pub with views over the fells from the garden, home-cooking in the kitchen.
Harvest Vegetarian Compston Road, (053 94) 33151. Competent cooking, puddings especially good.
Bowland Bridge *Masons Arms* Strawberry Bank, Cartmel Fell, (044 88) 486. Real ale, fresh food, take a map.
Dent *Dent Craft Centre* Helmside, (058 75) 400. Good local produce, always a vegetarian choice.
Grange-over-Sands *At Home* Danum House, Main Street, (053 95) 34400. Popular for morning coffee, light lunches and afternoon teas.
Ravenstonedale *Fat Lamb* Crossbank, Ravenstonedale, Kirkby Stephen, (058 73) 242. Cumberland sausages and rum cream; Classic Cumbrian cooking.
Seatoller *Yew Tree Country Restaurant* Seatoller, Borrowdale, Keswick, (059 684) 634. Fills a gap between the touristy and the expensive.
Watermillock *Old Church Hotel* Watermillock, Penrith, (07684) 86204. First-class ingredients stylishly presented.
Water Yeat *Water Yeat* (0229 85) 306. Guest-house; outside diners welcome if there's space. Excellent for the price; good sauces and vegetables, wonderful walnut, date and apple pudding.
County Durham *Barnard Castle* Blagraves House, 30 The Bank, (0833) 37668. Great views from the turrets; black pudding and cheap lunches.
Consett *Pavilion* 2 Station Road, (0207) 503388. Chinese with high standards and good service; vegetable flower-sculpture adorn some dishes.
Durham *And Albert* 17 Hallgarth Street, (091) 384 1919. Home cooking, pleasant atmosphere; savoury crumbles and ice-creams are good.
Romaldkirk *Rose & Crown* nr Barnard Castle, (0833) 50213. Both bar and restaurant meals offer good value; interesting vegetables, striking soup combinations, local Cotherstone cheese.

Derbyshire

Birchover *Druid Inn* Main Street, (062 988) 302. Good local produce, generous portions.
Chapel-en-le-Frith *Brief Encounter* Old Station Masters House, South Station, (0298) 812030. Railway memorabilia sets the theme; a well chosen wine list.
Derby *Boaters* 17 Friargate, (0332) 40581. Honest ingredients cooked and presented simply, in the town centre.
Sarang 14 Peartree Road, (0332) 44815. Indian vegetarian food, lots of choice.
Glossop *Firenze* 54 High Street, (045 786) 1054. Freshly prepared pizzas, from calabrese to calzone.

Hayfield *Kinder Kitchen* 3–5 Church Street, (0663) 747321. Wholefood in an informal atmosphere.
Hope *Poachers Arms* Castleton Road, (0433) 20380. Cosy atmosphere for good pub food.

Devon

Bovey Tracey *Rumbling Tum* 66–68 Fore Street, (0626) 832543. End the hunger pains with imaginative fish cooking.
Doddiscombsleigh *Nobody Inn* (0647) 52394. Local cheeses and good wine list.
Exeter *Café at the Meeting House* 38 South Street, (0392) 410855. Vegetarian café on the site of a Quaker meeting house.
Old Mill 20 High Street, Ide, (0392) 59480. Good ingredients, honest cooking, successful sauces.
Ilfracombe *Angel* 23 Church Street, (0271) 866833. 'The Bovine Revenge', a vegetarian restaurant in an old butcher's shop; choice for vegans and fish eaters.
Kingsteignton *Old Rydon Inn* Rydon Road, (0626) 54626. Careful cooking under thatch.
Lustleigh *Primrose Cottage* (064 77) 365. Pretty setting for lunches and afternoon teas.
Lydford *Castle Inn* (082 282) 242. Up-market pub cooking, beautiful location.
Lynton *Hewitt's* North Walk, (0598) 52293. New chef may do good things.
Modbury *Modbury Pippin* 35 Church Street, (0548) 830765. Small country town restaurant.
North Molton *Sportsman's Inn* Sandyway, North Molton, Exmoor National Park, (064 383) 502. Good-value grills and fresh fish.
Peter Tavy *Peter Tavy Inn* (082 281) 348. Wholefood on the edge of Dartmoor; popular for ploughman's, pies and seafoods.
South Molton *Stumbles Wine Bar* 131 East Street, (076 95) 3683. Rather hit and miss, though decent value.
Torrington *Rebecca's* 8 Potacre Street, (0805) 22113. Sophisticated flavours in pleasant surroundings.

Dorset

Bournemouth *Chez Fred* 10 Seamoor Road, Westbourne, Bournemouth, (0202) 761023. Just the place to satisfy seaside appetites. Fresh fish in the best batter, chips, peas and puddings.
Bridport *George Hotel* Bridport, 4 South Street, (0308) 23187. Homely atmosphere, frequented by artists.
Oborne *Grange* Oborne, nr Sherborne, (0935) 813463. Country setting for fresh ingredients, competently cooked.
Piddletrenthide *Old Bakehouse* Dorchester. (03004) 305. Fresh food, delicate flavours; soups good.
Poole *Barrie's* 292 Sandbanks Road, Lilliput, (0202) 708810. Excellent seafood fresh off the fishing boat.
Warehouse Poole Quay, (0202) 677238. Fish cooking in converted warehouse, frequented by the fashionable.

Weymouth *Hamilton's* 4–5 Brunswick Terrace, (0305) 789544. Despite the basic surroundings, the menu tempts and with some success.

East Sussex

Brighton *English's Oyster Bar* 29–31 East Street, (0273) 27980. Longstanding source for shellfish and fresh fish. Good value.
Haywards 51–52 North Street, (0273) 24261. Ambitious brasserie cooking; the chocolate torte is a house speciality.
Latin In The Lane 10 Kings Road, (0273) 28672. Pasta made on the premises.
Tureen 31 Upper North Street, (0273) 28939. Friendly anglo-french; the seafood pancakes are good.
Hove *Rolling Clock* The Whitehaven Hotel, 34 Wilbury Road, (0273) 731177. Fruit with everything, but none the less one of Brighton's more adventurous menus.
Lewes *Bull House* 92 High Street, (0273) 473936. Exotic combinations among 15th-century beams. A young chef, seeking to make his mark.
Rye *Flushing Inn* 4 Market Street, (0797) 223292. Mostly all fish and shellfish, large portions.
Wilmington *Crossways* Lewes Road, Wilmington, nr Polegate, (032 12) 2455. Fair value, enthusiastic cooking, useful rooms, cheap wines.

Essex

Brentwood *Raffles* 3 South Street, (0277) 234427. Good food and value for table d'hôte.
Burnham-on-Crouch *Contented Sole* 80 High Street, (0621) 782139. Excellent fish.
Castle Hedingham *Old Moot House* Castle Hedingham, Nr Halstead, (0787) 60342. Book for Sunday lunch. Good wines.
Chappel *Swan Inn* (0787) 222353. Simple food but subtle flavours.
Chelmsford *Kings Arms* Main Road, Bromfield, (0245) 440258. Proper home cooking, with patés, soups and duckling. Trifle is a particular success.
Clavering *Cricketers* (079 95) 50442. Delightful surroundings for good-value meals.
Danbury *Anchor* Runsall Green, Danbury, nr Chelmsford, (024 541) 2457. Big portions under the beams of this listed building.
Dedham *Marlborough Head Hotel* Mill Lane, (0206) 323124. Extensive menu; try braised lamb and ratatouille.
Gosfield *Green Man* The Street, Gosfield, Nr Halstead, (0787) 472746. Cold table with imaginative salads; home-made Pavlovas prolong the pleasure.
Maldon *Wheelers* 13 High Street, (0621) 853647. Excellent fish and batter, the incidentals on either side rudimentary.
Witham *Crofters* 25 Maldon Road, (0376) 511068. Has evolved from a simple wine bar into conservatory and garden-room restaurant.
Woodford Green *Pizzeria Bel-Sit* 439 High Road, (081) 504 1164. Recently refurbished; go for the excellent pizzas.

Gloucestershire

Awre *Red Hart Inn* (0594) 510220. Somewhere to take the children and eat al fresco.

Blockley *Crown* High Street, (0386) 700245. Pretty spot for good selection of fresh fish and other pub food.

Chipping Campden *Cotswold House Hotel* The Square, (0386) 840330. Classical pillars, and a live pianist playing the grand three evenings a week.

Coleford *Pikehouse* Berry Hill, (0594) 33010. In the Forest of Dean; simple but satisfying food.

Gloucester *Down To Earth Wholefood Restaurant* 11 The Forum, Eastgate Shopping Centre, (0452) 305832. Vegetarian meals at fair prices.

Lechlade *Colleys Supper Rooms* High Street, (0367) 52218. Banquet meals brought by waitresses in Edwardian dress. Everyone sits down to eat together.

Moreton-in-Marsh *Annie's* 3 Oxford Street, (0608) 51981. English and French country cooking with pretty puddings.

Nailsworth *Tubby's* 28 George Street, (0453) 834802. Huge portions of good-value hot food.

Painswick *St Michael's* Victoria Street, (0452) 812998. Small restaurant and guest-house providing simple home cooking.

South Woodchester *Ram Inn* (045 387) 3329. Good pub food and real ales.

Winchcombe *Gardeners Arms* Alderton, (0242) 620257. Warm and welcoming pub where the landlord's wife takes the orders.

Greater Manchester

Altrincham *Le Bon Viveur* Hare and Hounds Hotel, Woodlane, Timperley, 061-904 0266. French cooking, imaginative puddings.

Manchester *Bella Napoli* 6a Booth Street, 061-236 1537. Unadventurous Italian, but good value.

Royal Oak Hotel 729 Wilmslow Road, Didsbury, 061-445 3152. Outstanding cheeses and bread bring long lunchtime queues; machines and Muzak shunned in favour of theatrical posters.

Sanam Sweet House and Restaurant 169 Wilmslow Road, 061-224 8824. Indian tandoori and takeaway; one of the best of the Rusholme curry houses for value.

Shere Khan 52 Wilmslow Road, 061-256 2624. Outstanding Indian tandoori.

Steak and Kabab 846 Wilmslow Road, Didsbury, 061-445 2552. Busy bistro with beefy and Oriental leanings. Useful for the area.

Tabak 201 Wilmslow Road, 061-257 3890. Indian; the spices are hot.

Wong Chu 63-63a Faulkner Street, 061-236 2346. Cheaper than competitors; excellent salt and pepper ribs and cold roast duck.

Marple *Devonshire Arms* Longhurst Lane, Mellor, nr Marple, 061-427 2563. Eclectic menu takes in impressive soups and local sausages.

La Romantica 13–15 Derby Way, 061-427 7317. Attractive atmosphere for Italian cooking and quality fish.

Rochdale *One Eleven* 111 Yorkshire Street, (0706) 344901. Small bistro open three nights a week.

Sale *Yerevan* 1b Ashton Lane, 061-973 2577. Middle Eastern; Greek wines, good alcoholic brown-bread ice-cream.
Salford *Mark Addy* 7 Stanley Street, 061-832 4080. Pub with good cheeses and hearty portions.
Salford College of Technology Frederick Road, 061-736 6541. Recently graduated from the cheap and cheerful into smart dining. Still cheap, booking necessary.
Stockport *Sawasdee* 12a Churchgate, 061-429 0488. Thai restaurant behind the market.

Hampshire

Hartley Wintney *Mariners* 48 High Street, (025 126) 2273. Good fish and chips.
New Alresford *Old School House* 60 West Street, (0962) 732134. Small and popular restaurant with an elaborate style.
Petersfield *Ship Inn* The Square, South Harting, nr Petersfield, (0730) 825302. Extensive menu of fresh food.
Southampton *Town House* 59 Oxford Street, (0703) 220498. Vegetarian restaurant with some imagination.
Steep *Harrow* (0730) 62685. Excellent pub food.
Winchester *Brann's* 9 Great Minster Street, The Square, (0962) 64004. Wine bar with more expensive restaurant upstairs and good wine list throughout.

Hereford & Worcester

Bewdley *Ile de France* 61 Load Street. (0299) 400040. Unpretentious French restaurant.
Broadway *Dormy House* Willersey Hill, (0386) 852711. Homely atmosphere, relaxed dining.
Goblets Wine Bar Lygon Arms, High Street, (0386) 852255. English country cooking on the lines of casseroled pork in cider with apricots and apples.
Leominster *The Marsh* Eyton, (0568) 3952. Home cooking in a 14th-century building, lovely location.
Ross-on-Wye *Meader's* 1 Copse Cross Street, (0989) 62803. Good-value Hungarian restaurant.
Whitney *Rhydspence Inn* (049 73) 262. Elizabethan country inn, with a long menu.
Woolhope *Butchers Arms* (0432) 77281. Large portions of pub cooking; accommodation.
Worcester *Il Pescatore* 34 Sidbury, (0905) 21444. Fresh Italian cooking.

Hertfordshire

Burnham Green *White Horse* White Horse Lane, (0438 79) 416. Home cooking and a warm welcome, try the puddings.
Cottered *Bell* Cottered, nr Buntingford, (076 381) 269. Old beamed pub with a friendly welcome and high class home cooking.
Hatfield *Salisbury* 15 The Broadway, (070 72) 62220. Sophisticated; savoury dishes have fruity combinations.

Little Wymondley *Redcoats Farmhouse Hotel* Redcoats Green, (0438) 729500.
English cooking, and popular.
Newgate Street *Gable House* (0707) 873899. Well presented food within
comfortable surroundings.
St Albans *Garibaldi Pub* 61 Albert Street, (0727) 55046. Busy pub with
splendid views of the abbey.
Watton-at-Stone *George & Dragon* High Street, (0920) 830285. Thick,
flavoursome soups and good seafood.

Humberside

Barton on Humber *Elio's* 11 Market Place, (0652) 635147. Busy Italian, good
for fresh fish.
Flamborough *Seabirds Inn* Tower Street, (0262) 850242. Charming pub, also
good for fresh fish and ice-cream.
Grimsby *Granary* Haven Mill, Garth Lane, (0472) 46338. Good raw materials,
particularly fish.
Walkington *Manor House* Newbold Road, Northlands, (0482) 881645. Lavish
restaurant with accommodation; extensive dinner menu, expensive wines.

Isle of Wight

Shanklin *Cottage* 8 Eastcliff Road, (0983) 862504. Low prices for good home
cooking; good soups.

Kent

Barham *Old Coach House* Dover Road, (0227) 831218. Honest-to-goodness
French for steaks, shellfish and substantial portions.
Broadstairs *Gourmet* 14 Albion Street, (0843) 601133. French restaurant using
fresh ingredients. Views of the harbour from the back.
Canterbury *George's Brasserie* 71–72 Castle Street, (0227) 65658. Good French
food; friendly service, reasonable price.
Sully's County Hotel, High Street, (0227) 66266. Modern ensembles and
combinations; good vegetables.
Chiddingstone *Castle* (0892) 870247. Pub and restaurant owned by the
National Trust.
Eastry *Coach & Horses* Lower Street, (0304) 611692. Order food a day in
advance for fresh ingredients, well cooked.
Newnham *George Inn* The Street, (0795 89) 237. Decent cooking despite
external appearances - try the game, and the well pudding.

Lancashire

Chorley *Turner's Smithy* Babylon Lane, Heath Charnock, Nr Chorley,
(0257) 480309. Middle-Eastern cooking in a pub.
Cleveleys *Cleveleys* Wholefood and Vegetarian Restaurant, 44 Victoria Road
West, (0253) 865604. Serious vegetarian, with a long dessert list.

Crawshaw Booth *Valley Restaurant* 542 Burnley Road, Crawshawbooth, Rossendale, (0706) 831728. Fresh and often local produce; not trendy but it has its appeal.

Garstang *El Nido* Whinney Brow, (0524) 791254. Italian with sound food, good atmosphere.

Hest Bank *Whitewalls Restaurant* 39 Hatlex Lane, Hest Bank, Nr Morecambe, (0524) 822768. Standard seaside fare, a cut above its local competitors. Friendly atmosphere.

Leicestershire

Ashby-de-la-Zouch *Mews Wine Bar* 8 Mill Lane Mews, (0530) 416683. Long menus using local produce, puddings are heroically British.

Grimston *Olde Stocks* Main Street, (0664) 812255. Good home cooking in a beautiful 17th-century house.

Leicester *Bread and Roses* 70 High Street, (0533) 532448. Falafels and other Middle-Eastern flavours in a wholefood café underneath an alternative bookshop.

Bobby's 154/156 Belgrave Road, (0533) 660106/662448. Indian vegetarian; try the thalis.

Glen Parva Manor The Ford, Little Glen Road, Glen Parva, (0533) 774604/ 774976. Formal restaurant with serious intentions that sometimes succeed.

Loughborough *Angelo's* 65 Woodgate, (0509) 266704. Italian trattoria.

Melton Mowbray *Crown Inn* Debdale Hill, Old Dalby, (0664) 823134. Pretty place with lots of character, doing both bar snacks and restaurant meals.

Stapleford Park Stapleford, (057 284) 522/229. American cooking in a classic country-house hotel and sporting estate; expensive.

Quorn *Quorn Grange* 88 Wood Lane, (0509) 412167. Plush French restaurant with accommodation; great attention to detail.

Stretton *Ram Jam Inn* Great North Road, (0780) 410776. Imaginative modern cooking for motorists. A model for any future Happy Eaters.

Walcote *Black Horse Inn* (04 55) 552684. Pub food with a difference - all the cooking is Thai.

Lincolnshire

Barkston *Barkston House* Barkston, nr Grantham (0400) 50555. Comfortable surroundings, though the food leaves little to chance.

Burgh-le-Marsh *Windmill* 46 High Street, (0754) 810281. Home cooking using fresh ingredients; bread baked on the premises is from flour ground in the windmill.

Gedney Dyke *Chequers* Main Street, (0406) 362666. Country pub and restaurant; home-made quiches, parcels of trout.

Grantham *Kings Hotel* 130 North Parade, (0476) 590800. An orangery/ coffee shop and a restaurant under the same roof; two set meals.

Horncastle *Magpies* 73–75 East Street. (0507) 527004. Good home cooking, that springs no surprises.

Mantles 90 Lawrence Street, (0507) 526726. Seafood in refined surroundings; good value.

Lincoln *Moulin Maison* Clifftop, Ingham, (0522) 730130. French restaurant
newly opened, pleasant ambience, bodes well.
Louth *Ferns* 40 Northgate, (0507) 603209. Fresh ingredients and
unpretentious cooking.
Mr Chips 17–21 Aswell Street, (0507) 603756. Crisply battered fresh fish to eat
in or take away; sweets and sorbets to finish.
Stamford *Exeter Arms* Stamford Road, Easton on the Hill, (0780) 57503.
English cooking with some exotic influences.

Merseyside

Liverpool *Equatorial* 4 Brownlow Hill, (051) 709 5225. Half Thai, half
Singaporean; good range of set banquets.
Eureka 7 Myrtle Parade, off Myrtle Street, (051) 709 7225. Authentic Greek;
good value.
Everyman Bistro 9–11 Hope Street, (051) 708 9545. Popular and good-value
haunt underneath the theatre.
Out to Lunch 6 Tithe Barn Street, (051) 227 1978. Sandwiches made to order.
Ristorante del Secolo 36-40 Stanley Street, (051) 236 4004. Italian offering first
class service.
Southport *Bold Hotel* Lord Street, (0704) 532578. Sophistication at the seaside;
fresh ingredients creatively cooked.
Lotus 177b Liverpool Road, Birkdale, (0704) 67919. Good fish and chips, does
Chinese food too.

Norfolk

Aylsham *Buckinghamshire Arms* Blickling, Nr Aylsham, (0263) 732133. Home-
made stockpot soups, sandwiches; handy for Blickling Hall.
Burnham Market *Captain Sir William Hoste* (0328) 738257. Pub with
picturesque views; seafood the speciality. Forbes, North Street, (0328) 738824.
Imaginative, modern menu in simple, sophisticated surroundings.
Castle Acre *Ostrich Inn* Castle Acre, nr Kings Lynn, (076 075) 5398. Idyllic
location for home-made pizzas and ploughman's.
Fakenham *Crown* Colkirk nr Fakenham, (0328) 862172. Competent cooking;
the Grand Marnier ice-cream packs a punch.
King's Lynn *Tudor Rose* St Nicholas Street, (0553) 762824. Local fish in
luscious sauces.
Norwich *Andersen's* 52 St Giles Street, (0603) 617199. Authentic Danish: fish,
Frikadeller and lagers.
Bedford's Bar & Brasserie 1 Old Post Office Yard, Bedford Street, (0603) 666869.
Fresh ingredients, vaguely nouvelle. Relaxing atmosphere, good choice
of wines.
Green's Seafood 82 Upper St Giles Street, (0603) 623733. Good variety of fresh
fish.
Upper Sheringham *Red Lion Inn* (0263) 825408. Enterprising bar food in
comfortable pine surroundings; fresh crab.
Wereham *Howards Restaurant* School Lane, (0366) 500450. Well chosen
ingredients with a local bias.

Northamptonshire

Crick *Edwards of Crick* The Wharf, (0788) 822517. Wharf conversion by the canal; the cooking tries hard and gets some things right. Good value.
Northampton *Courtyard* Walgrave Road, Holcot, (0604) 781174. Newly opened, doing dinners three nights a week; good food, good choice.
Ristorante Ca'D'Oro 334 Wellingborough Road, (0604) 32660. Italian; home-made pasta and good espresso.
Sun Rise 18 Kingsley Park Terrace, (0604) 711228. Chinese that goes in for sizzling dishes in a big way.
Stoke Bruerne *Bruerne's Lock* The Canalside, (0604) 863654. Waterside dining where presentation counts; comes alive in the evenings.

Northumberland

Berwick-upon-Tweed *Rob Roy* Dock Road, Tweedmouth, (0289) 306428. Fish restaurant also offering steaks.
Corbridge *Flags* 2, 18 Front Street, (0434) 632536. Good for sunday lunch, busy with locals.
Hexham *Black House* Dipton Mill Road, (0434) 604744. Home cooking in large portions, well presented. Not cheap.
Seaton Sluice *Waterford Arms* (091 237) 0450. Huge portions of fresh fish and hearty broths for big appetites.

Nottinghamshire

Bingham *Langar Hall* Langar, nr Bingham, (0949) 60559. Creates the atmosphere of a country-house weekend seven days a week; good fish and puddings.
Yeung Sing 11 Market Street, (0949) 31222. Cantonese cooking, only open evenings.
Nether Langwith *Goff's* 1 Langwith Mill House, (0623) 844137. French cooking in a cosy beamed dining room.
Newark *Gannets* 35 Castlegate, (0636) 702066. Blackboard menu for casseroles and quiches. Old Kings Arms, 19 Kirkgate, (0636) 703416. Wholemeal sandwiches, salads, and hot meals.
Nottingham *Anila's* 23 Goldsmith Street, (0602) 483036. Indian tandoori, good ingredients.
Chung's 984a Woodborough Road, (0602) 604852. Popular Cantonese; the food is fresh, service friendly.
Hotel des Clos Old Lenton Lane, (0602) 866566. New hotel/restaurant on the banks of the Trent, long wine list is entirely French.
Man Ho II 35-37 Pelham Street, (0602) 474729. Chinese with minimalist decor; try the sea bass.
Sonny's 3 Carlton Street, Hockley, (0602) 473041. Set menu has black-bean cakes with crème fraîche, and Créole cod.
Le Tetard 10 Pilcher Gate, (0602) 598253. French cuisine, subtle flavours.

Truffles 43 Broad Street, (0602) 472857. Contemporary cooking in immaculate surroundings; short menu with fish and game in season.
Upton   *Cross Keys* Main Street, (0636) 813269. Good bar food.

Oxfordshire

Abingdon   *Prince of India* 10 Ock Street, (0235) 523033. Indian tandoori and takeaway; pricey but popular.
Adderbury   *Bell Inn* The High Street, Adderbury, nr Banbury, (0295) 810338. Game and good sauces, service amiable.
Burford   *Lamb* Sheep Street, (099 382) 3155. Pub with a good-value buffet piled high with prawns, salmon, meats, salads and quiche.
Goring-on-Thames   *Leatherne Bottel* (0491) 872667. Great riverside location; best to go on fine days and keep orders simple.
Marsh Baldon   *The Seven Stars* (086738) 255. Enterprising bar food in a rural setting.
Oxford   *Gees* 61a Banbury Road, (0865) 58346. Pretty conservatory, though form may be more important than substance.
Stanton Harcourt   *Harcourt Arms* (0865) 881931. Good lunches, excellent black pudding.
Sutton Courtenay   *Fish Inn* (0235) 848242. Above the local standard; good value.

North Yorkshire

Bolton Abbey   *Devonshire Arms* Bolton Abbey, nr Skipton, (075 671) 441. Feast among fine furniture and paintings; Good game salad and puddings.
Harrogate   *Bettys* 1 Parliament Street, (0423) 502746. Traditional teas and light lunches; muffins with smoked salmon please.
La Bergerie 11/13 Mount Parade, (0423) 500089. Intimate atmosphere for feather-light soufflés and fresh fish.
Tiffins on the Stray 11a Regent Parade, (0423) 504041. Vegetarian cooking with lots of choice, though service can be slow.
Helmsley   *Black Swan* Market Place, (0439) 70466. Seasonal menus, colourful and creative presentation, very busy.
Staithes   *Endeavour* 1 High Street, (0947) 840825. Freshness is the thing, local fish predominates.
York   *Bettys* 6–8 St Helen's Square, (0904) 659142. Another branch of the popular tea rooms; this one is busy and high on atmosphere.
Melton's 7 Scarcroft Road, (0904) 634341. Good French; succesful fish dishes.

Shropshire

Ellesmere   *Nightingales* 8 Market Street, (0691 62) 2863. Anglo-French restaurant with competent cooking, if short on atmosphere.
Hopton Wafers   *Crown Inn* (0299) 270372. Good main courses: choose the simple dishes.

Ironbridge *Meadow Inn* Buildwas Road, (095 245) 3193. Good pub grub, taking in bean bakes and vegetable gratin.

Much Wenlock *Wenlock Edge Inn* Hilltop, Wenlock Edge, nr Much Wenlock, (074 636) 403. Proper pies and nursery puddings; have your fortune read at the bar.

Shrewsbury *Barkers* 21 Barker Street, (0743) 232342. Smart wine bar with a wide range of cocktails.

Peach Tree Brasserie 21 Abbey Foregate, (0743) 246600. Cooking with a touch of enterprise; good crab pasties with spinach purée.

Worfield *Old Vicarage Hotel* (074 64) 497. English restaurant with accommodation.

Somerset

Brent Knoll *Goat House* Bristol Road, (0278) 760995. Once a transport café, its sign now reads 'sorry, no lorries'. Instead, find good flans and everything to do with goats.

Shepton Mallet *Bowlish House* Wells Road, (0749) 342022. Handsome architecture, accommodation, fair cooking and good wine list.

Charlton House Hotel Charlton Road, (0749) 342008. Good flavours, eager to please, on its way up.

Waterrow *Hurstone Country Hotel* Waterrow, nr Wiveliscombe, (0984) 23441. Step off the beaten track for simple fare and home-made cheese.

Wellington *Hartleys* 41 High Street, (082 366) 7646. Small and friendly, with fresh seafood banquets.

Wells *Crown* Market Place, (0749) 73457. Pleasing surroundings for decent cooking; try the grilled Wye salmon in a tarragon sauce.

South Yorkshire

Barnsley *Brooklands* Barnsley Road, Dodworth, (0226) 299571. Evolved from a transport café: now home cooking, generous helpings, fresh fish, good wine list.

Sheffield *Bay Tree* 119 Devonshire Street, (0742) 759254. Vegetarian and fish; among the best in the city for a cheap, pleasant lunch.

Fat Cat 23 Alma Street, (0742) 728195. Home cooking, country wines and real ales.

Staffordshire

Abbots Bromley *Royal Oak* Bagot Street, (0283) 840117. Dutch and Indonesian specialities figure on the menu.

Lichfield *Eastern Eye* 19b Bird Street, (0543) 254399. Above-average Indian; good cooking, delicate flavours.

Swinfen Hall Swinfen, nr Lichfield, (0543) 481494. Hotel and restaurant in a listed building; good shellfish, delicate sorbets and desserts.

Thrales 40 Tamworth Street, (0543) 255091. Fresh fish is the thing.

Penkridge *William Harding's House* Mill Street, (078 571) 2955. Quality ingredients include trout, quail and wild pigeon.

Rolleston *Brookhouse Inn* Brookside, (0283) 814188. Restaurant with accommodation; lots of atmosphere, fresh ingredients.

Rugeley *Old Farmhouse* Armitage, (0543) 490353. Decent food, good management, pleasant ambience.

Stoke on Trent *Hanchurch Manor* Hanchurch, (0782) 643030. Country house hotel and restaurant, newly opened, but already changed chefs.

Stone *Granvilles* Granville Square, (0785) 816658. English restaurant with sound ambitions.

Weeford *Old Schoolhouse* (0543) 480009. Anglo-French cooking in elegant surroundings, service can be rushed.

Suffolk

Aldeburgh *Aldeburgh Fish & Chip Shop* 226 High Street, (072 845) 2250. Very fresh fish and good golden chips.

Bury St Edmunds *Beaumonts Health Food Stores* 6 Brent Govel Street, (0284) 706677. Vegetarian café of the varnished pine school; puddings are sumptuous.

Dunwich *Ship Inn* St James's Street, (072 873) 219. Busy, with big conservatory; fish, fish and more fish.

Earl Soham *Victoria Public House & Brewery* (072 882) 758. Friendly, with spicy and filling food; beer brewed on the premises.

Halesworth *Bassetts* 84 London Road, (0986) 873154. Once a bakery, food is nouvelle in type and presentation, though portions are large.

Ipswich *Baipo* 63 Upper Orwell Street, (0473) 218402. Friendly Thai restaurant.

Café Marno 14 St Nicholas Street, (0473) 253106. Relaxed vegetarian venture, tagliatelle and nut roasts are good.

Laxfield *Kings Head* Gorams Mill Lane, (098 683) 395. Pies and sandwiches and sometimes a barbecue when you can choose your own meat and cook it yourself.

Long Melford *Chimneys* Hall Street, (0787) 79806. A new chef at this friendly and ambitious restaurant.

Rede *Plough* Rede, nr Hawkedon, (028 489) 208. Great for garden eating; fresh crab salads, scampi and chips.

Snape *Granary Tearooms* The Maltings, (072 888) 303. Light meals and delicate flavours.

Plough & Sail The Maltings, (072 888) 413. Enterprising food based on seasonal salads; real ales.

Sudbury *Friars* 17 Friars Street, (0787) 72940. French restaurant in weavers' guild-hall that has shown initial promise.

Surrey

Cobham *Cedar House* Mill Road, (0932) 63424. Ambitious and pricey but gets some things right.

Croydon *Kelong* 1b Selsdon Road, South Croydon, (081) 688 0726. Indonesian/Malaysian; full flavours, gigantic portions.

Dorking *Partners West Street* 2–4 West Street, (0306) 882826. Newly opened, once Partners 23 in Sutton, looking a sound prospect.

Godalming *Inn on the Lake* Ockford Road, (048 68) 5575/5576. Expensive, but portions are large.

Guildford *Manor at Newlands* Newlands Corner, (0483) 222624. Good for family Sunday lunches, convenient for Wisley Gardens.

Kingston Upon Thames *Restaurant Gravier* 9 Station Road, Norbiton, (081) 549 5557. Fish and a French style.

Oxted *Coltsford Mill* Mill Lane, Hurst Green, (0883) 713962. A working watermill of the Domesday period; good home cooking.

Richmond *Kim's* 12 Red Lion Street, (081) 948 5777/5779. Indonesian/Malaysian using fresh herbs; good satay and coconut chicken curry.

Kozachok 10 Red Lion Street, (081) 948 2366. Russian cooking to keep out the cold; good dumplings and blinchiki, wide choice of vodkas.

Mrs Beeton's 58 Hill Rise, (081) 940 9561. Old established co-operative, standards vary according to whose turn it is to cook.

Refectory 6 Church Walk, (081) 940 6264. Open for morning coffee, home-cooked lunches and afternoon teas.

Shamley Green *Red Lion* (0483) 892202. Sound cooking, particularly the puddings.

Weybridge *L'Ecluse* 10 Woodham Lane, New Haw, (0932) 858709. Good-value French.

Tyne & Wear

East Boldon *Forsters* 2 St Bedes, Station Road, (091) 519 0929. New opening by chef, Barry Forster (ex-Longueville Manor), luxury ingredients.

Gateshead *Eslington Villa Hotel* 8 Station Road, Low Fell, (091) 487 6017. Home cooking in a landscaped setting.

Ship Eighton Banks, (091) 416 0273. Popular pub food includes a large choice of fresh salads.

Newcastle upon Tyne *Dragon House* 30-32 Stowell Street, (091) 232 0868. Chinese with some imagination; good-value set lunches.

Fisherman's Wharf 15 The Side, (091) 232 1057. Seafood restaurant, rather pedestrian but ingredients are decent.

Red Herring 3-4 Studley Terrace, Fenham, (091) 272 3484. Wholefood café, bakery and shop, with an emphasis on Latin American cooking.

Tandoori Nights 17 Grey Street, (091) 221 0312. Above-average Indian; comfortable surroundings, good value.

North Shields *Chainlocker* Duke Street, New Quay, (091) 258 0147. Simple food from local sources, good cheeseboard.

Warwickshire

Alcester *Rossini* 50 Birmingham Road, (0789) 762764. Italian specialising in fresh fish.

Baginton *Oak* Coventry Road, (0203) 301187. Good home cooking.

Henley in Arden *Le Filbert Cottage* 624 High Street, (056 479) 2700. French; good service, good wine list.

Leamington Spa *Plantagenets* 15 Dormer Place, (0926) 451792. French-style provincial restaurant.

Ryton-on-Dunsmore *Ryton Gardens Café* Henry Doubleday Research Association, National Centre for Organic Gardening, (0203) 303517. Home cooking, selection of organic wines.

Stratford upon Avon *Shepherd's Stratford House Hotel* 18 Sheep Street, (0789) 68233. Michael Quinn has just taken over as chef here. The conservatory dining-room is a very useful pre-theatre amenity.

Warwick *Randolph's* 19/21 Coten End, (0926) 491292. French; huge helpings, unusual combinations.

West Midlands

Birmingham *La Galleria* Paradise Circus, 021-236 1006. Italianate snack bar, handy for a pre-business bite.

Nutters 422 Bearwood Road, Bearwood, 021-420 2528. Friendly vegetarian; spicy flavours, fair prices.

Plaka 204 Lightwoods Road, Warley, 021-429 4862. Good-value Greek.

Thai Paradise Paradise Street, 31 Paradise Circus, 021-643 5523. Basic Thai cooking, opposite the town hall.

Coventry *Brooklands Grange* Holyhead Road, (0203) 601601. Countrified business hotel, quite pricey, but makes much use of fresh market vegetables.

King's Norton *Lombard Room* The Patrick Collection, 180 Lifford Lane, 021-459 9111. Excellent-value lunches, fresh fish daily.

Solihull *Bridgewater Hotel* 2110 Warwick Road, Knowle, (0564) 771177. Lavish interior, competent cooking.

West Sussex

Chichester *Through the Greenhouse* 24 St Pancras, (0243) 531578. Noisy, but good for grills.

Rusper *Ghyll Manor* High Street, (0293) 871571. Light French style, though not nouvelle; good terrines, good coffee.

Storrington *Little Thakeham* Merrywood Lane, (0903) 744416. Lutyens manor house in lovely location, with acceptable cooking, though service lets it down.

West Yorkshire

Bradford *Quiet Greek* 1099 Thornton Road, (0274) 815760. Although not subtle, the Greek cooking here has other virtues; price is one of them.

Elland *Berties Bistro* 7–10 Town Hall Buildings, (0422) 71724. Popular inexpensive bistro with variable output.

Farnley Tyas *Golden Cock* Farnley Tyas, nr Huddersfield, (0484) 663563. Restaurant in a pub.

Huddersfield *Shabab* 37–39 New Street, (0484) 549514. Indian; good chunky curries, disappointing breads.

Ilkley *Bettys* 32–34 The Grove, (0943) 608029. Famous for its teas, light lunches and home-made ice-creams.

Leeds *Bibis Pizzeria* 16 Greek Street, (0532) 430905. Lively place, good cooking, glamorous puddings, no booking.
Hansa 72-74 North Street, (0532) 444408. Indian Gujerati cooking and dhosas beneath a ceiling swathed in fabrics.
Hon Wah 4 The Headrow, (0532) 440750. Agreeable Chinese.
Mandalay 8 Harrison Street, (0532) 446453/446340. Classy interior, live pianist, open tandoor, good pilau rice and kulfi.
Olive Tree Oaklands, Rodley Lane, (0532) 569283. Greek food in pleasant surroundings.
Wentbridge *Wentbridge House* (0977) 620444. Anglo-French – sound ingredients well presented.

Wiltshire

Aldbourne *Raffles* 1 The Green, (0672) 40700. Stick with the simplest dishes for the most success.
Avebury *Stones* High Street, (067 23) 514. Vegetarian cooking from mostly organic produce and local still cider.
Hindon *Grosvenor Arms* High Street, (074 789) 253. Former coaching-inn, good set menu with daily specials, Sunday lunch good value. Lamb Inn, (074 789) 573. Fresh food, no fuss.
Marlborough *Polly Tea Rooms* High Street, (0672) 512146. Home-made cakes and light lunches.
Pitton *Silver Plough* White Hill, (072 272) 266. Pretty location; blackboard dishes are the best bet.
Salisbury *Just Brahms* 68 Castle Street, (0722) 28402. Wine bar with lighter meals in the front room, or the whole works in the main.
Michael Snell Tea Rooms 8 St Thomas's Square, (0722) 336037. Proper cream teas, home-made ice creams, sorbets, lunches.
Woolley Green *Woolley Grange* (02216) 4705. 17th-century manor in a beautiful location. Suave cooking but a new chef as we went to press.

Scotland

Arisaig (Highland) *Arisaig Hotel* (06875) 810/240. Traditional Scottish style, good fish, variable service.
Arisaig House Beasdale, nr Arisaig, (06875) 622. Marvellous position, high luxury and cost, new chef.
Ayr (Strathclyde) *Fairfield House* Fairfield Road, (0292) 267461. Expensive, with the accent on novelty, though some dishes work well.
Carnoustie (Tayside) *Crumbs* Queen Street, (0241) 54044. Café for cheap lunches and home baking.
Edinburgh (Lothian) *Asha Tandoori* 8 West Maitland Street, 031-229 0997. Indian offering rich cooking, striking decor, vegetarian choices.
La Bagatelle 22a Brougham Place, Tollcross, 031-229 0869. French; the set lunches are good value.

The Bamboo Garden 57a Frederick Street, 031-225 2382. Chinese; does curries too. Unusually long wine list.

Café Royal 17 West Register Street, 031-557 4792. Fish restaurant of architectural merit and with continental feel.

Cosmo's 58a North Castle Street, 031-226 6743. Long standing Italian, with the emphasis on seafood.

Doric Wine Bar 15 Market Street, 031-225 1084. Great value for generous helpings: venison and first-rate fish terrine.

Fruitmarket Gallery Café 29 Market Street, 031-225 2383. Popular café, a haven for vegetarians though meat does feature.

Jananti 33a St Stephen Street, 031-226 3675. South American cooking, decor and music. If the menu says 'hot', it means hot!

Modern Art Café Scottish National Gallery, Belford Road, 031-556 8921. Aesthetic surroundings for good soups, substantial salads, Scottish cheeses.

New York Steam Packet 31 North Rose Street, 031-225 4663. American steak and hamburger joint.

Philippine Islands Restaurant 36 Broughton Street, 031-556 8240. Filipino foods, colourful presentation and sweet sauces.

Pukhet-Penang 176 Rose Street, 031-220 0059. Thai restaurant; pleasant if diluted flavours.

Raj 91 Henderson Street, 031-553 3980. Indian, one of the best in the area, cooking not too oily, good seasonings.

Seeds 53 West Nicholson Street, 031-667 8673. Co-operative café for vegetarian food. Very popular, share a table.

Shore Bar 3 The Shore, Leith, 031-553 5080. Inventive fish cooking, friendly.

Singapore Sling 503 Lawnmarket, 031-226 2826. Malaysian cooking, mild flavours, authentic sweets.

Skippers 1a Dock Place, Leith, 031-554 1018. Casual, cheerful, crowded, splendid Orkney oysters and crab terrine.

Gairloch (Highland) *The Old Inn* (0445) 2006. Comfortable accomodation, with fresh local lobster, fish and game on the set dinner menu.

Gattonside (Borders) *Hoebridge Inn* (089 682) 3082. Good-value home cooking, decent starters and sauces.

Glasgow (Strathclyde) *Babbity Bowster* 16/18 Blackfriars Street, 041-552 5055. Some, not all, fresh ingredients, but good value. Some Scottish dishes.

Jimmy's 1–7 Victoria Road, Eglington Toll, 041-423 4820. Exceptional fish and chips restaurant.

One Devonshire Gardens 1 Devonshire Gardens, 041-339 2001. Expensive hotel with flair, expensive food and a new chef as we went to press.

Rab Ha's 83 Hutchson Street, 041-553 1545. Smart decor, go for the fish, or mussels from Loch Sween.

Invergarry (Highland) *Glendale Guest House* Mandally Road, (080 93) 282. Vegetarian cooking of outstanding value. Non residents must book 24 hours in advance for dinner.

Inverness (Highland) *Pierre Victoire* 75 Castle Street, (031) 225 1721. The latest branch of Pierre Levicky's Edinburgh enterprise. French/Scottish flavours and a friendly atmosphere, excellent value.

Kinlochbervie (Highland) *Old School Restaurant* Inshegra (097 182) 383. Home cooking, try the bread-and-butter pudding; admire the views.

Perth (Tayside) *Huntingtower Hotel* (0738) 83771. Fresh ingredients attractively prepared; try the knapsach of seafood – filo pastry with a curried saffron sauce.
St Andrews (Fife) *Brambles* 5 College Street, (0334) 75380. Centrally situated café, popular with students, choice for vegetarians.
Tarbet (Highland) *Tigh-na-Mara* Scourie, By Larig, (0971) 2151. Good plain cooking well presented, in a wild and wonderful setting.
Ullapool (Highland) *Ceilidh Place* 14 West Argyle Street, (0854) 2103. Anglo-French restaurant with accommodation; attentive service.

Wales

Abergavenny (Gwent) *Ant & Rubber Plant* Market Street, (0873) 5905. Small, unpretentious, with blackboard menu; good for soup and garlic bread.
Betws-y-Coed (Gwynedd) *Royal Oak* Hollyhead, (069 02) 219. Good for both formal and informal, good value.
Boncath (Dyfed) *Meigan Fare* Pistyll Meigan, (0239) 841251. Home cooking; good veal, vegetables and puddings.
Borth-y-Gest (Gwynedd) *Blossoms* Ivy Terrace, (Gwynedd) (0766) 513500. Imaginative bistro food.
Brechfa (Dyfed) *Ty Mawr* (0267) 202332. Welsh cooking within stone walls, bread baked on the premises.
Caernarfon (Gwynedd) *Ty'n Rhos* Seion, Llandeiniolen, (0248) 670489. Restaurant with accommodation, open only to residents. Home-made cheese and fresh ingredients.
Cardiff (South Glamorgan) *Orient Rendezvous* 15–23 Westgate Street, (0222) 226901/226904. Chinese and Szechuan; pleasant atmosphere, extensive menu.
Polydores 89 City Road, (0222) 481319. New fancy fish restaurant.
Porto's 40 St Mary Street, (0222) 220060. Portuguese fish restaurant offering tapas throughout the day.
Ristorante Il Padrino 75 St Mary Street, (0222) 222161. Italian with an enterprising menu.
Trillium 40 City Road, (0222) 463665. French restaurant good for fresh fish.
Carmarthen (Dyfed) *Spilman Hotel* Spilman Street, (0267) 237037. New hotel showing promise of inventive cooking and fresh foods.
Chepstow (Gwent) *Royal George* Tintern, nr Chepstow, (029 18) 205. Restaurant with accommodation near the abbey.
Cilgerran (Dyfed) *Castle Kitchen* (0239) 615055. Cosy place for home cooking and a short fixed-price menu.
Cowbridge (South Glamorgan) *Basil's Brasserie* 2 Eastgate, (044 63) 773738. Cheerful but basic, a lot of fish, not many staff.
Harlech (Gwynedd) *Llew Glas* Plas-y-Goits, High Street, (0766) 780700. Bakery, delicatessen, restaurant and café all in one, run by talented chef Trevor Pharoah. May turn out well if taste triumphs over presentation.
Hay-on-Wye (Powys) *Kilvert Court Hotel* (Powys) (0497) 821042. Decent cooking using fresh ingredients.
Lamphey (Dyfed) *Dial Inn* Lamphey, nr Pembroke, (0646) 672426. Good for bar snacks of falafel and fresh local fish.
Llechryd (Dyfed) *Helyg Fach* (023 987) 462. Restaurant popular locally, wine list includes Welsh 'Croffta'.

Maentwrog (Gwynedd) *Grapes Hotel* Main Street, (076 685) 208. Very popular for home cooking.

Mold (Clwyd) *The Sybarite* 33 New Street, (0352) 3814. The weekday set dinner menu is excellent value.

Narberth (Dyfed) *Gregory's* Market Square, (0834) 861511. Restaurant in a converted brewery; silver service, good value.

Newcastle Emlyn (Dyfed) *Y Ffynnon Fach* Newchapel, (0239) 841235. Village pub with Welsh dishes and an adventurous menu.

Rhosneigr (Gwynedd) *Runnelstone's* High Street, Rhosneigr, Anglesey, (0407) 810904. Plain cooking; quality vegetables, nice cheesecake.

Rhyd-Ddu (Gwynedd) *Cwellyn Arms* nr Caernarfon, (076 686) 321. Substantial pub lunches of salads, steaks and pies.

Rossett (Clwyd) *Churton's* Chester Road, (0244) 570163. Wine bar on two levels; appetising flavours.

Southerndown (Mid Glamorgan) *Frolics* Beach Road, (0656) 880127. Classical French food; fresh lobster, good house wine.

Swansea (West Glamorgan) *PA's* 95 Newton Road, Mumbles, (0792) 367723. Wine bar with big blackboard menu; consistent cooking, choice of desserts.
Red Fort 81 St Helens Road, (0792) 48509. Indian tandoori, rather formal, good service.

Isle of Man

Douglas *Bowery* 4 Athol Terrace, Queens Promenade, (0624) 28082. Popular American-style restaurant with good service.
Boncompte's at the Admiral's Hotel Admiral House, Loch Promenade, (0624) 29551. Chef Jaime Boncompte has moved to this hotel with several eating places. Standards seem mixed.

Channel Islands

L'Eree *The Taste of India* Sunset Cottage, Guernsey (0481) 64516. Sophisticated approach in unlikely surroundings; try the tandoori seafood platter.

Gorey *Jersey Pottery Restaurant* Jersey, (0534) 51119. Fish restaurant serving enormous seafood salads.

Rozel *Apple Cottage* Jersey, (0534) 61002. Hearty home cooking, friendly service.

St Helier *La Capannina* 65–67 Halkett Place, Jersey, (0534) 34602. Italian with large portions, home-made desserts.
Central Park 5 Lamotte Street, Snow Hill, Jersey, (0534) 24457. Trendy restaurant in converted warehouse. Burgers, pizzas, potato skins are popular with the young.

St Peters Port *The Chinese Gourmet* Upper Mansell Street, Guernsey (0481) 28457. Chinese with good presentation and seafood.

Café du Moulin Rue de Quanteraine, Guernsey, (0481) 65944. New French restaurant in a converted mill, off to a promising start.

San Lorenzo 42–44 Fountain Street, Guernsey, (0481) 722660. Confident Italian cooking in relaxed surroundings.

Trinity *Red Rose* Oaklands Lodge Hotel, Jersey, (0534) 61735. Good fresh ingredients; trying hard.

Water's Edge Hotel Bouley Bay, Jersey, (0534) 62777. Fresh fish cooking on the harbour.

Northern Ireland

Bangor *Bryansburn* 151 Bryansburn Road, Co Down, (0247) 270173. Popular for home cooking and happy service.

Belfast *Belfast Castle* Antrim Road, Co Antrim, (0232) 370133/776925 Historical setting for ambitious cooking of quality ingredients.

Belle Epoque 103 Great Victoria Street, Co Antrim, (0232) 323244. Popular French; pleasing ambience.

Roscoff 7 Lesley House, Shaftesbury Square, Co Antrim, (0232) 331532. Bistro-style cooking, ultra-modern decor, original combinations.

Bushmills *Auberge de Seneirl* 28 Ballyclough Road, Co Antrim, (0265) 741536. Restaurant with accommodation; sophisticated.

Groomsport *Red Pepper* Main Street, Co Down, (0247) 270097. Good sauces, good puddings, comprehensive wine list.

Hillsborough *Plough* 3 The Square, Co Down, (0846) 682985. Good high teas, cooked to order, booking recommended.

Expensive compared to what?

As the cost of eating out has risen and high interest rates have forced some consumers to trim non-essential expenditure, Good Food Club members have become even more acute in their judgement of what constitutes good value. **Tim Hart** explains the financial equation for proprietors, based on experience at his country-house hotel, Hambleton Hall, and at the lower end of the price scale at his Ram Jam Inn at Stretton, both in Leicestershire.

An invitation to write a piece for *The Good Food Guide* drops through my letter box. I am delighted. Stuffing the longish letter in my pocket I drive to Hambleton day-dreaming. Here is an unrivalled opportunity to indulge some pet theories: for example, to point out that *The Good Food Guide* is ridiculously puritanical in its attitude of mild embarrassment about luxury restaurants. Why is it somehow vulgar to enjoy wonderful curtains, when one eats out, as well as wonderful sauces?

These reveries are cut short. I arrive at Hambleton and re-read the letter with greater care. The theme of my piece, it appears, is to be 'Why my restaurant is so expensive'. This is a frightful set-back to my plans. I consider offering to write instead pieces on 'Why I have got bad breath' and 'My 10 least satisfied customers'. Realising these alternative titles may not have the same appeal for the editor I revert to the original commission, an analysis of the question of price and value relative to luxurious restaurants in general, and my restaurant in particular.

To start by putting the cards on the table, the average cost of a meal for two at Hambleton in 1990 amounted to £100. This figure includes wine, bar drinks, V A T and service, and obscures the fact that a cautious approach to the menu, and the wine list in particular, could result in a bill of around £72.

It is not so long ago that I was a consumer rather than a purveyor of restaurant meals and, it is true, I did boggle somewhat at the size of the bill in the best restaurants of the day. It is almost a truism to say that top restaurants are expensive, but why is there a gap between expectation and reality in this particular sphere? At Marks and Spencer I could, in 1990, buy for £100 a tweed jacket (£80) and a lambswool pullover (£19). This is value. Yet Marks and Spencer made an average profit of £11 on each £100 sale (1989 accounts), whereas I made a measly £5. So huge profit margins are not making my restaurant expensive.

If the Marks and Spencer products represent value, it is because they are of good quality, last for ages, and are fairly priced in relation to competing retailers. We have no fear of submitting to a similar price comparison with our competitors; within the luxury class, they are all equally 'expensive'. Yet expensive compared to what?

Fortunately for Marks and Spencer, most customers do not have the necessary skills to buy the wool, weave the cloth and undertake the final assembly of their own clothing, so the do-it-yourself alternative does not loom large in the public perception.

My situation is quite different. If I place before my clients best-end of lamb, french beans, potatoes and a bottle of wine they can, if they wish, give themselves indigestion by reckoning up the colossal saving that could be made by enjoying the same meal at home. Some of our clients are immensely accomplished cooks and are perfectly capable of investing the necessary time and trouble to produce a meal of Hambleton standards at home.

While that instant price comparison may be natural it does not stand up to closer examination. It is a universal convention of our industry that we only charge for food, drink and (sometimes) service, but we provide, in addition, agreeable surroundings, linen, china, glass, heat and light, flowers, menus and perhaps a garden, and many other hidden extras.

When you compare the cost of dining at home with the cost of a restaurant meal do you count the cost of your flowers at home, the cost of driving to the shops to collect the ingredients, the cost of your own labour, the cost of light and heat, the cost of laundering the table cloth or the cost of replacing the breakages? Of course not. Some of these costs, together with that of servicing your mortgage, will be incurred anyway, whether you eat in or out. But as soon as your buildings and activities form part of a restaurant business all these costs must be recovered under the simple headings of food and drink. If my Sancerre costs £18 and yours costs £7, it's worth remembering what I am throwing in for free.

To underline the fact that I am not merely selling pieces of meat and bottles of wine I, for one, would be happy to charge a flat inclusive dinner charge of, say, £35 to £40 to include basic wine and aperitifs, with a scale of extra charges or supplements for superior wines, caviare or lobster. Judging from the unpopularity of even the cover charge, such a move might be suicidal.

In a country like Britain where property prices are comparatively high, the property element in your restaurant bill could be very substantial. If I took £1 million as a rough estimate of the cost of establishing a mythical version of Hambleton Hall with just a restaurant and no rooms, and if I take £140,000 as an annual average interest charge on that £1 million, this year's restaurant clients would have to pay £8.41 each merely to cover my property interest costs. Turning from that gloomy thought, I now offer a surprising confession. I have never until today made a computation of how much profit or loss my restaurant makes. As it is an integral part of a hotel I have never found it essential to prise the two elements apart, but now I do so for the very first time.

Hambleton Hall restaurant budget 1990

The average dinner spend for two people is taken to be £100 in 1990.

Average income from two customers	£	£	£
Food	64		
Wine	24		
Bar	12		
Total income			100
Less VAT			−13
Cost of food	−22		
Bar cost	−3		
Wine cost	−9		
Credit card commission	−1		
Laundry	−1		
Total variable costs			−36
Wages and salaries	−26		
Staff food, accommodation, welfare, etc.	−3		
Total staff costs			−29
Fixed overheads (Note 1)			−17
Net profit before interest, depreciation and directors' fees			5

Note 1 Fixed overheads include: Rates 94p, maintenance and refurbishment £3.65, cleaning £1.10, china, glass, linen £1.52, energy £1.22, flowers 50p, stationery and printing 73p.

The fact of the matter is, as demonstrated by the table and as I suspected all along, my restaurant will make a loss after interest charges and only exists because my hotel bedrooms (which incidentally would be empty without the restaurant) are relatively more profitable.

Wine mark-ups are an emotive subject and the table shows that at Hambleton clients pay about 2.3 times my cost for a bottle of wine. This multiple is moderated if the wine costs me more than £15, and is slightly higher for the cheaper bottles. In my consumer days in 1971, I recall a splendid and to me expensive meal at the Oasis restaurant at La Napoule in France. We drank a bottle of Chablis. The price of the wine horrified me, being about ten times more than I had recently paid for some Chablis for my cellar at home. The Oasis wine was so good that it made a lasting impression which almost effaced the horror of the price. Looking back on this incident I realise that the Oasis introduced me to the first bottle of great Chablis I had ever drunk. Probably a *grand cru* or a *premier cru*, and emanating from one of a tiny handful of outstanding Chablis growers, this wine bore no resemblance to the rubbish in my own cellar.

I like to think now that the gap between the price of a bottle of wine in a wine merchant's shop and the price in my restaurant is made more tolerable by two features. I buy on slightly more favourable terms and I buy better wine than do most of my clients. My aim with the Hambleton list is to seek out the best Chablis, Sancerre or Pouilly Fumé, to find châteaux and vintages that combine to produce a delicious drink however little-known the label, and to guide the client through the minefield of Burgundian growers so that each wine is outstanding in its class.

I would not like you to gain the impression that my feeble profit performance is simply the result of incompetent management. My friends in the industry with whom notes are compared constantly will confirm that the scenario that the Hambleton figures portray is pretty much the norm in our small and specialised industry. What is more, at our level, the story is very much the same in continental Europe and the USA. If you want to eat in a luxury restaurant with all the trimmings expect to pay £50 per person. At Hambleton you will get about four courses, aperitifs, canapés, wine, home-made bread, coffee, petits fours, VAT and service. You will also get a priceless view, sumptuous surroundings, lovely flowers and the rest. Perhaps you know somewhere where all this is available for £30 or £40? If you do I can only say hang on – I'm coming too.

In addition to the 16,639 clients who we estimate will eat with us at Hambleton in 1990 there are doubtless plenty who have no intention of paying £50 for a meal. Some of them will be seeking top-quality food stripped of the comfort, service and surroundings of a luxury establishment. Armed with the insight derived from my analysis of restaurant costs they will seek out an establishment occupying a low-cost property, with minimal staff levels, offering simple surroundings and delicious uncomplicated food. La Potinière in Gullane in Scotland is a personal favourite of mine and fits the bill perfectly but restaurants of this kind are incredibly rare in the UK, more's the pity.

So, *Good Food Guide*, turn your cannon away from the luxury sector. Our prices if anything are too low, and focus on the real scandal, the dearth of British restaurants providing first-rate food in simple surroundings. It is in this area that France, Germany, Italy and many others knock British catering into a cocked hat.

As it happens I do have some experience of the twilight zone between McDonalds and haute cuisine. Four years ago I bought a very run-down inn of some antiquity situated between Grantham and Stamford on the Great North Road (A1). My aim at the Ram Jam Inn has been to provide an unusually high standard of light meals and snacks, principally to the motorist in the daytime, and in the evenings to function as a brasserie-restaurant for the local community. Three courses cost about £11 (excluding service, which is optional).

My experience at the Ram Jam has thrown considerable light on the problems of running a no-frills, decent-food restaurant in Britain. The first and fundamental problem is to find kitchen staff. I have found it far easier to find talented chefs to work in the more glamorous environment of Hambleton. Indeed, there is doubtless a group of young English chefs evolving who, amazingly enough, are skilled at luxury level but scarcely competent at the more basic level. Part of the blame for the shortage of culinary talent must be attributed to the colleges who are turning out cooks with a veneer of competence but no understanding of what makes food good to eat. Totally untrained in the art of tasting, they are unaware of seasoning, the subtle contrast of crisp and succulent and the details which makes the same recipe succeed or fail in the hands of different practitioners.

My early days at the Ram Jam were devoted to trying to establish my standards in fundamental areas: fresh bread, good vinaigrette, sandwiches carefully seasoned. I had varying degrees of success. McDonalds can doubtless train most chefs to produce their menu accurately. A high degree of mechanisation in the kitchen, food preparation in central manufacturing units, very little menu change and exceptional training skills and resources all make the task more straightforward, but the man who makes the *plat du jour* at the Ram Jam must have a good idea how to eat as well as cook. The final tasting and adjustment will determine whether his casserole is perfect or indifferent.

The second problem is that of finding clients who recognise the right stuff when they get it. My Ram Jam experience has confirmed my suspicion that many British diners have switched off their gustatory sense. It is not that they can't taste – rather that they have never acquired the habit. Herein lies the explanation for the proliferation of elaborate restaurants in Britain and the abuses to which the excellent principles of nouvelle cuisine were subjected in this country. Many restaurant clients need the decorations and the props to draw their attention to the fact that something special has been prepared. A British restaurateur who relies solely upon the freshness of his fish, the clarity of his flavours and the accuracy of his seasoning, might starve.

In France or Italy traditions of excellent home cooking survive more widely throughout society. The baker's wife, or the grocer's daughter, renowned for their Sunday lunch for friends and family, might consider a lifetime of hard graft and a modest living from a decent neighbourhood restaurant an attractive prospect. The typical Brit has more lavish expectations and less sound culinary roots. Outside the ethnic communities, whose restaurants provide almost the only hope of a low-cost meal of quality in this country, we have very few chefs or cooks of the continental type who might be expected to provide our dream restaurant. Similar social considerations underlie the shortage of chefs who might work as their assistants.

Let's return to the country house sector. In *The Good Food Guide 1990* about 20 per cent of all restaurant entries were hotel-restaurants and about half of those outside London, rated 4 or 5, were country hotel-restaurants. This seems strong evidence that much of Britain's best cooking is currently to be found in country hotels and their proliferation over the past 15 years has been good news for culinary standards in the provinces.

To understand why one eats well in so many country hotels, it is worthwhile repeating the exercise carried out above on restaurant profitability for the accommodation side of the business. At Hambleton this exercise shows a trading profit of 24 per cent of turnover for the rooms as compared to five per cent for the restaurant. Before these figures give rise to another article on 'Why my rooms are so expensive', it is important to note that the capital costs of creating the rooms are higher than those associated with the restaurant and my 24 per cent trading profit margin for rooms will be ravaged by interest costs before reaching the bottom line. Even so, the money made in the rooms is subsidising restaurant operations to the benefit of the non-resident restaurant client. The rooms need the restaurant and are often prepared to subsidise its operations.

It may be that some country-house hotels combine luxurious surroundings with pretentious and indifferent food, but we can rely on *The Good Food Guide* to pass over these in silence. On behalf of those of us who are apparently producing excellent food at a highish price I offer a motoring analogy. Does the man who wants to buy a Volkswagen waste his breath complaining to the Rolls-Royce dealer that his motor cars are too expensive? The disease of the mid-priced sector is neither caused by nor related to the health of the luxury sector.

Keeping food cool

As the *Guide* went to press, two pieces of legislation concerning food had just been enacted and were in the process of being implemented – The Food Safety Act and The Food Hygiene (Amendment) Regulations 1990. **Linda Allan**, Under Secretary of The Institution of Environmental Health Officers, believes that the second of these may have considerable impact on restaurant customers and owners, as they specify the temperatures at which certain foods will have to be stored. Here Linda Allan looks at the implications of the amendments for the storage and serving of salads, cheese and sweets.

Many Environmental Health Officers, the officers responsible for inspecting restaurants and other food premises, would regard the introduction of new temperature control regimes, based on current scientific findings, as being the most important change that could be made to food legislation. The changes detailed in the amendments are likely to make a significant impact on the work of the caterer and are specifically aimed at improving food safety.

The main changes proposed relate to the temperature at which food will be required to be stored. Food on display, until now exempt from the provisions of the legislation, comes under the terms of the new law, as do milk, in its various forms, and cream.

The new temperature control requirements are to be implemented in stages. After 1 April 1991, certain foods will have to be kept at 8°C or below; only food in small delivery vans will be exempt, and then only for a year. Broadly, the foods covered by this part of the regulations are some soft cheeses; cooked products containing meat, fish, eggs, dairy ingredients, cereals, pulses or vegetables; cut smoked meats or fish; certain desserts, prepared vegetable salads; cooked pies and sausage rolls; some sandwiches and cream cakes. From 1 April 1993, however, some of these will have to be kept at the lower temperature of 5°C. Foods included in this specification include smoked or cured meat and fish that have been cut or sliced; soft cheese ripened by means of mould or other micro-organisms, for instance Brie, once it has been cut from the whole cheese; cooked products containing meat, fish, eggs (or their substitutes), dairy ingredients, cereals, pulses or vegetables; and finally, sandwiches that contain any of the above, unless they are for sale within 24 hours of preparation.

It would appear that strict compliance with good practice, as given in Government- or Industry-issued Codes of Practice, or as detailed in the regulations, may present a serious conflict of interest for the caterer, since taste may not be permitted to take precedence. That could result in the manufacture and storage of some food being altered, as well as recipes being modified, in order that the rules may be adhered to.

Temperature control is significant in maintaining food safety because it is one way of preventing bacteria from multiplying in sufficient to numbers to cause food poisoning. Since bacteria are living organisms, in order to grow they require warmth, food, moisture and time. Consequently, restricting these conditions limits their ability to replicate, and thus limits the possibility of food poisoning and food spoilage.

The need to ensure that food is maintained in a safe manner has therefore resulted in debate affecting both kitchen and dining areas. For instance, when a sweets trolley is wheeled to your table, do you pause to admire the contents and think how difficult it is to choose what to have, or do you wonder how long the cream gateaux have been sitting in the heat of the restaurant and why the trolley is not refrigerated or even covered?

Ideally, sweets trolleys should be refrigerated, which is technically possible. The new regulations will require cream cakes and desserts that have a pH value above 4.5 to be stored at 8° after 1 April. Thus it is to be expected that trifles, fromage frais, creme caramels and desserts made with whipped cream will have to be refrigerated.

The pH level is a measure of a substance's acidity/alkalinity; the more acidic a substance, the lower its pH value, and the less likely it is to support the growth of bacteria. The use of this measure to differentiate between temperature regimes will require the caterer to question their suppliers, or even the producers, as to the relevant pH levels of products in order to ensure that they follow the correct procedures.

The legislation exempts, however, food that is to be eaten within four hours of preparation. Such products may be stored at ambient temperatures. Food for self-service may also be displayed for up to four hours at room temperature, though it is expected that no more food than is necessary will be displayed. Consequently, surplus desserts and cream should be stored in the kitchen refrigerator and the trolley restocked as required, in order to ensure that food is kept cool. This practice requires skill on the part of the restaurateur, who has to judge whether further portions will be required, and the best time to transfer them.

Several other aspects of restaurant activity may pose problems in the future. Take, for instance, the display of salads. Consumers currently expect more from a salad than mere lettuce, cucumber and tomatoes. Expectations run to combinations of exotic ingredients with equally exotic dressings. If the dressing is acidic, ie has a high volume of vinegar or lemon juice in it, then there are unlikely to be bacterial problems in a salad display. These are more likely to arise if a dressing is cream- or egg-based, since these ingredients can provide an ideal growth medium for bacteria. Hence the need to keep dressings and salads under refrigeration. From 1 April prepared vegetable salads, including those with fruit ingredients, will have to be kept at 8°C. In addition, the display cabinet should be designed to minimise risk of contamination either from customers, staff, or adjacent foodstuffs. Dressings and other foods containing high-risk products should be displayed in small amounts, which can regularly be replaced with new containers from a main supply as they empty. Original containers should certainly not be topped up directly, since this would result in the bottom layer remaining unused all day.

Pâtés and terrines have come under scrutiny following media interest in the prospect of bacterial contamination particularly of the Listeria species, and most especially from *Listeria monocytogenes*. This organism is of particular importance when considering the lower temperatures at which food is to be stored, since it can grow in food at lower temperatures than other bacteria. The problem is compounded by the nature of pâtés and terrines - the small particles of meat have considerable surface areas and trapped available oxygen assists the growth of aerobic bacteria.

The new temperature regulations will require these and similar products to be stored initially at 8C, and at 5 C or below from 1 April 1993. This could well affect their taste, as colder temperatures affect our taste buds, preventing us from savouring the full flavour.

As the amendments exempt food which is intended to be sold within four hours 'from the time of preparation', food cooked to order will not be subject to the regulations. Desserts and any other food prepared in advance will, however, be subject to the new ruling, as the caterer cannot know for certain that they will be sold, or precisely when.

From the restaurateur's and the consumer's point of view, the product that is most likely to be affected by changes to the legislation is cheese. The regulations could see the demise of the cheeseboard sitting out in the dining- room, despite the exemption applying to self-service displays, since cheeseboards are likely to be displayed for more than four hours. In any event, the amount on display should be kept to a minimum.

The new legislation stipulates that soft cheeses which have been ripened by the action of moulds or other micro-organisms, rather than by mechanical means, should be stored at 8°C. Among the cheeses coming under this definition are Brie, Blue Brie, Camembert and soft goats' cheese. The caterer will have to check with the supplier whether a cheese is ripe on delivery, as the requirements apply to cheeses once they have ripened.

After 1 April 1993 any of these cheeses that have been cut or otherwise separated from the whole cheese, will have to kept at 5°C. Thus if a large Brie is cut, its storage temperature will have to be lowered. Ideally, by April 1993 two chilled storage areas should be employed, one run at 5°C and the other at 8°C. To save space and money all cheese could be kept at 5°C, although this would result in some items being kept at a lower temperature than necessary.

The time exemption in the regulations applies only to food which is to be sold within four hours from the time of preparation. Would unwrapping cheese be regarded as preparation? It's doubtful, since no alteration would be made to the cheese. Faced with the prospect of serving customers with chilled cheese, the caterer may have to decide either to cease serving these particular types of cheeses, a situation that would be lamentable, or to adopt different attitudes to the service of cheese. Perhaps in future when taking orders for starters and main courses, the waiter will also ask the customer to make their selection from the chilled cheese display. The cheeses would then be removed at the start of the meal in order to develop them in the interim. Such a compromise would allow the customer to be sure that the cheese have been stored safely in the spirit of the law, while the caterer would be able to serve it having regard to its taste.

Similar procedures would be difficult to adopt for pâtés and terrines, however, as it is unlikely that customers would be willing to accept a long delay prior to their arrival at the table.

The changes introduced in the new regulations should, when they are fully implemented, help further to ensure the safety of the consumer and the survival of the catering industry. As the consumer becomes more knowledgeable, the industry must ensure that high standards are the norm, since it will inevitably be held responsible if things go wrong. While it may be tempting to add a warning such as 'Customers eat this item at their own risk' to dishes such as steak tartare, it really would not be acceptable to either the consumer or the industry. Quality foodstuffs coupled with good practices and adherence to legislation must be the goals.

Be gone, dull cream

'But I *like* cream and butter!' was the disconsolate cry of a chef in those far-off days when *nouvelle cuisine* was a faltering glimmer on the dark horizon of heavy restaurant cookery. It came to us first in the guise of *cuisine minceur*: a health-farm variation worked out by Michael Guérard which travelled faster (through books and magazines) and was the cause of that misapprehension of *nouvelle* as small portions, fromage blanc instead of cream, no sugar and few carbohydrates. Health, it seemed, entered into our calculations for the first time.

No craft has appeared more conservative than cooking yet paradoxically is more subject to the rapid flight of fashion and the dictates of convenience. Yet, whenever there is a hint of criticism, or even constructive suggestion, chefs retreat behind their barricades of old habits and timeworn texts. They will accept revolution from within their ranks but seem to resist it mightily if urged upon them from outside. Thus when we made some comments in the last *Guide* about 'healthy eating', the self-appointed guardians of the old gourmandism were anxious to assert that people liked to feel sick after a restaurant meal, liked to over-indulge like some Ancient Roman epicene, and that chefs 'knew best'.

We have kept a watching brief on the subject in the course of this year: asking restaurateurs their views, reading menus closely, and generally trying to observe how cooking may change. Change it certainly does. There is detectible a new responsiveness to customers' desires and a genuine wish to make food more digestible as well as more interesting. This results, often, in clearer tastes and 'healthier' food.

The shifts of the last three or four years can be encapsulated (and to deal with them in detail would occupy page after page) by the following catch- phrases: 'the Mediterranean diet'; *'cuisine du terroir'*; *'cuisine grand' mère'*; 'west coast cookery'; 'the Pacific rim'; 'new vegetarianism'; and 'green cuisine'. Taken severally or together, they amount to new materials, flavourings, recipes and cooking methods. They have also caused a major change in the composition or balance of the menu.

What are some of the consequences on the plate? In materials, a re-evaluation of olive oil, pasta and bread doughs, southern vegetables, pulses, and cuts of meat that are less than 'prime'. In flavourings, chilli has been accepted as essential (too essential for some); and intense Mediterranean herbs, Thai seasonings and Chinese spices have become lingua franca to many chefs, certainly those near big-city markets. Recipes have moved away from only the fast-cooked towards the long-simmered; and they have absorbed the lesson of balance – that a piece of prime protein needs other, less potent, elements on the plate to throw it into relief, and to relieve the eater. Methods have shown the same radical shift: deep-frying is now uncommon in many restaurants; shallow frying is done in oil rather than in butter; boiling and steaming have been rehabilitated, and, most important of all, char-grilling and charcoal grilling have entered the standard armoury.

These are important developments. Many of them came about because leaders of culinary fashion, especially in France, suggested them, but they were also occasioned by a shift in our own perception (prompted, it is true, by cookery writers and others) of what was appetising. Many of these presumptions, it could be argued, have come to us from the United States whose cooks and writers have acted as both originators of ideas and as filters of trends already existent in Europe: for example, the elevation of 'the Mediterranean diet' into something recognised as good for health as well as palatability.

Taken together, one of the most encouraging outcomes of these changes has been a re-writing of menus to take account of a greater variety of culinary experience: vegetarian dishes, light-cooked salads, many more types of cooking methods and a freeing of sauces from the stranglehold of eggs, butter and cream. Menu composition has absorbed the lesson that not everyone's idea of enjoyment is protein or fat overload. All we ask for is choice and consideration.

This new feeling in the air takes many forms, depending perhaps on the experience of the individual chef. One has suffered a heart-attack himself: 'We refuse to do any deep-frying; meat sauces with the exception of two dishes on the menu, do not contain fresh cream; we cook with olive oil and use extra-virgin cold-pressed for our dressings; we trim our meats rigorously; but we do fall down with our puddings, though summer pudding and crème fraîche or yoghurt may help us turn the tide.' Another has quietly changed his practices: 'We tend to keep the healthy aspect of our cooking low-key, but it doesn't go unnoticed. Regulars spot the slightly un-sweet sweets, the use of olive oil in place of butter and that our pastry is now made with ground almonds or hazelnuts (equal volume of nut to flour/butter).'

Although most small, privately owned, restaurants do not go so far as to signal items on the menu that may be 'low-fat' or otherwise apparently 'healthy' this is a practice that gains ground in corporate chains, especially in big cities, that may be frequented by foreigners – who often care about these things more than we do. It is something that accords well with long menus and a client-base that is constrained to eat regularly outside the home. It is more problematic for a place with maybe a choice of three main dishes and customers who come mainly to celebrate – though, as already noticed, our views of celebration are changing fast.

The other side to this whole question is that of catering for specific diets, be they vegetarian (a large number of people), low cholesterol, gluten-free, no dairy products, and so forth. As restaurateurs have seen more and more of their customers fall into one or more of these categories, so have they stirred themselves to oblige them. The number of vegetarian menus offered in parallel to those for omnivores has risen, in the last twelve months alone, from a handful to a sizeable fistful. In like manner, restaurants are increasingly aware of the need to create dishes for special diets on request; all they want is warning. It would be foolish to assert that everything is coming up roses, but there is definite improvement.

Connoisseurs or victims of institutional catering, from prisons to airlines, have long advocated that a 'special diet' will be a better diet: freshly cooked, more wholesome ingredients, and so forth. Something of the same attitude is detected by chefs who feel, not always without reason, that diet and allergy are used as weapons to get one's own way in the dining-room. (In parenthesis, asking for a variation to a dish on the menu may reveal whether there is a computer and microwave in the kitchen rather than a real chef with raw materials. 'Allergy' often means no more than 'don't like' and 'vegetarian' is a very mobile term. One restaurateur wrote, 'We divide vegetarians into five groups: those who don't eat red meat; any meat; any meat or fish; any meat, fish or dairy produce; and finally macrobiotics. The vast majority of our guests are quite unaware of these categories.' It underlines the wisdom of prior warning and

---

In 1990 we asked 1100 restaurants being considered for *The Good Food Guide*:

a Do you use any kind of symbol on your menus to denote low-fat, low-calorie or dietary-specific dishes of any kind?

b If yes, please give details (on a separate sheet if you prefer)

c If a symbol were available and used by other restaurants, would you be interested in using it?

d If a customer asks you to change a dish – for instance serve fish plain without sauce – do you do so?

e If customers were to request information about the ingredients and/or nutritional content of a dish, would you be able to advise them?

f Do you see your restaurant as a place where customers can eat healthily?

---

discussion and of knowing, and expressing clearly, your requirements.

Healthy eating is all about balance and co-operation. Co-operation, by both sides of the contract in the restaurant, must be insisted on, but on reasonable terms - so that specific demands may be met without stress. Balance is something we might expect as a matter of course: that menus offer variety of methods and materials, just as they offer more than one cut of meat and that individual dishes have something of the same philosophy in their composition.

East meets West

Moving towards a generic South East Asian restaurant?

In the first of two features considering oriental restaurant cooking in Britain, **Sri Owen** wonders whether Thai and Indonesian eating have reached their popularity peak or will move into a new stage, perhaps culminating in chef/owner operations that offer a mix of cuisines, using a spectrum of fresh ingredients to their very best advantage.

It seems to me anyone's guess at the moment which way the ethnic restaurant business in Britain is going to go – its South-East Asian division, anyway. The Thais are doing quite well, popping up in high streets all over the place and seeming to do good business. The Singapore-Malaysian group are doing fairly well, boosting themselves by claiming links with Indonesia; there are very few genuinely Indonesian restaurants, and even fewer Vietnamese and Burmese; when we think of Laos or the Philippines, I know of no representative restaurants in the UK at all, though doubtless I shall be corrected on this (and shall be grateful for it).

Are the successful ethnic restaurants becoming accepted as permanent residents, or do they remain mere gastronomic curiosities? The Chinese and Indians have obviously got their roots well down into British soil, not just in London and the big cities but in little communities far from the metropolis; and they have also penetrated every level of eating out, from the grandest to the most commonplace. In the process, they have made a great many compromises and not everyone will approve of what they have done, but still, here they are; part of the culture. Can one imagine the Thais and Indonesians achieving the same? Or have they already reached their peak or plateau, where they are fated to remain, always a minority interest?

In the Netherlands, Indonesian restaurants and food have penetrated deeply, so deeply that a visitor might almost fancy that the east had colonised the west instead of the other way about – an impression you never get in England. Equally Vietnam, or perhaps I should say Indo-China, has left some mark on the eating habits of the

French. The difference between Dutch Indonesian and French Vietnamese food is that Vietnamese restaurants in France adopt a take-it-or-leave-it attitude that makes few concessions to French tastes or eating habits, whereas in Holland mixed Indo-Dutch cuisine and tradition has developed. You can see the same thing happening in Indonesia itself, where a great many Dutch traditions remain strong, in ice-cream making, in sweet cakes (which Indonesians love), even in cooking and serving main-course staple foods. An obvious example is the so-called *rijsttafel* or banquet, though to my mind it does neither side much credit.

On the face of it, then, an exotic cuisine, depending on the importation of many ingredients and traditions which won't grow naturally in the host country, can only take root and become domesticated if the host country is the former colonial power – and may not do so even then. The exception, of course, is Chinese cuisine, or rather a very limited selection from its vast repertoire. But if my principle holds good outside China, then Thai, Indonesian and Vietnamese food can never expect to achieve popular acceptance or a mass market in Britain. On the other hand, there is nothing to stop them occupying a profitable niche in the restaurant business over here. What should they do to accomplish this, and what can we do, as discerning diners-out, to make sure they flourish?

I am tempted to start with front-of-house management, because after all so much hangs on the customer's first impression of a restaurant, particularly if it represents an unfamiliar tradition; but I shall resist the temptation and go straight through to the kitchen. The chef is a concept still somewhat strange in South-East Asian countries; restaurants have cooks, and in a large kitchen someone will be in charge, but cooking, even of the finest food, is seen as a craft rather than an art. Therefore, one experienced cook is more or less as good as another (this is the theory, anyway), and there is really no room for the notions that a cook can make or break a restaurant, or that cooking can be a creative activity.

At most, the cook may possess secrets that ensure the success of a particular dish – hence you find highly specialised chains of little eating-houses that are well known for their noodles or their fried chicken. I can imagine that some entrepreneur may hit London one day – maybe tomorrow – and establish, say, Javanese *lemper* (glutinous rice) among fast foods, but that would be a totally unpredictable event.

What I think can be foreseen is that the best South East Asian restaurant cooks will metamorphose into chefs, becoming 'names' in their own right and eventually with TV programmes as well. I hope that we shall see more chef-proprietors, who want to please their public rather than their boss (who is often an accountant or a property developer). I hope also to see the development of some system for training chefs, or at least some encouragement for them to keep moving on and learning in the way the best French or English chefs do. This is a matter for the industry rather than for the customers, perhaps, but it needs to be said. The South East Asian restaurant industry, insofar as it has any organisation at all at the moment, isn't organised for the making of good chefs.

It seems to follow that, in Britain at any rate, the small unpretentious restaurant, with the menu chalked up on a board and the owner single-handed in the kitchen, often gives the best value for money. You many not find a 'gourmet meal' (whatever that is) in such a place but you will eat simple food, well cooked, authentic in at least its style and technique and often in its ingredients as well. After all, it is usually agreed that in South-East Asian countries one eats better in a private home than in a restaurant, and a little one-person restaurant – the English equivalent, really, of what in Java we call a *warung*, not much more than a cooked-food stall – is perhaps as close to a private home as you can get.

Another reason why the private home or chef-owned eating-house can produce good food is that the cook goes to market every day. This is not always the case in the big restaurant, at least not in Asian restaurants. I know that Europeans used spices in the past primarily to tenderise tough meat, mask off-flavours and make indifferent food palatable. Asians still use spices, particularly of course chilli, to do these things today, but this has nothing to do with what I may call classic South East Asian cooking, which largely derives from festival dishes served at harvest time, weddings and other special occasions. Then, only the best ingredients would be used. The same need for quality ingredients holds today, especially in meat: cheap cuts are no good. In my experience, even the best butcher needs to have a sharp eye kept on him, and however well-trained he is, I know I will still end up feeding the cat on off-cuts that some Indonesian restaurateurs, I suspect, would regard as perfectly acceptable for their customers and indeed themselves. There is absolutely no danger to health; but the meat is tough, gristly or fatty.

Fish, fruit and vegetables must be chosen and prepared just as rigorously, if not more so, because in most Asian cuisines cooking times are short. Though meat is always cooked through, most vegetables are lightly done – by English standards, anyway.

How far can we expect ethnic restaurant food to be 'authentic'? I often find myself putting this work in quotation marks because it worries me; I am not quite sure what it means. I notice there is a lot of eighteenth-century music being played in concerts nowadays on 'authentic' instruments; but, as someone pointed out, there are no authentic eighteenth-century listeners left. As diners-out we bring to the table palates and eating habits conditioned by a lifetime of experience, and though some of us will always long to go to far- away places and eat exactly what the locals do, the restaurateur's market will always consist of people who demand a certain amount of translation or paraphrase.

This, I suggest, affects presentation more than ingredients or technique. An obvious example is solids, such as tamarind slices and lumps of ginger; these must be removed before the dish leaves the kitchen, or else cut up or shredded so small that they can be eaten without drawing attention to themselves. More generally, there has been, until recently, little attention given in South East Asian countries to making food look attractive.

Ingredients, of course, do matter. Most South-East Asians like chilli pepper, and I put chilli into all the dishes that I cook where chilli is appropriate. But I certainly do not use it in the quantities that I would if I were cooking to please only myself or my Indonesian friends. I would not, therefore, expect an Indonesian restaurant in Europe or America to use authentic amounts of chilli; but I would insist that it should use a little, enough to get the true flavour of the chilli without the hotness.

Asian cooks in exile are always tempted to overdo the flavouring, to use whole lemon grass stems, for example, instead of just the tender inner part, and to let them float around in the pot throughout the cooking process, so that their flavour is completely boiled away, instead of putting them in near the end.

A particular pitfall is the ready-mixed spice package, which may have been flown in fresh from Bangkok this morning but which was still manufactured in a factory according to someone else's idea of what should go into it. Fresh spices vary considerably in the intensity of their perfume and flavour, and the cook needs to be able to assess these separately before they are all crushed or processed into a paste.

Though their languages derive from several quite unrelated language- families, and though their historical experiences, particularly of European colonisers, have been totally different, the South-East Asian countries have a lot in common when they cook and eat. All are tropical or sub-tropical, all regard rice as the most desirable staple food (even if it is beyond the means of most individuals), and all use more or less similar techniques of applying heat to cooking pots. True, the differences between them are as illuminating as the similarities, but they are not differences of kind, only of details.

I hope to see the evolution, not of specifically Thai or Indonesian or Vietnamese restaurants, but of the South East Asian restaurant – with a western-style menu, the meal being served as a sequence of distinct courses. The menu need not be very long, nor need the restaurant itself be large. Indeed, a table d'hote arrangement, with enough choice to ensure that no one has to eat anything they don't actually like, would be the best. The cook can then use his or her knowledge and instinct to produce a combination of dishes that best exploits the materials available.

The cook would also, I suggest, be responsible for doing the shopping and talking to suppliers, on the understanding that the money should go into quality and freshness. If this led to smaller servings, so much the better: they would reflect the common South East Asian attitude to food, that it is to be shared generously with the guest, but it is not to be wasted by giving him more than he can possibly eat – as too often happens now.

Wanted: investment in chefs, not décor

The pink tablecloths and minimalist surroundings of the Indian new wave are still prevalent, but the Indian restaurants that deserve support are cooking high-quality produce without short-cuts, in genuine regional manner. **David Mabey** races their evolution.

Although Britain's first Indian restaurant, Veeraswamy's in London's Regent Street, was opened in 1927 by a well-connected Eurasian, others didn't appear until more than 20 years later. In 1947, British colonial India was divided up into India itself and Pakistan, which became a separate Muslim state. After this many Eurasians emigrated, followed a few years later by Sikhs from the Punjab and Bengali-speakers from Syhlet in the east. Some of them opened restaurants. Legendary London restaurants, such as the Shah in Drummond Street and the Agra in Whitfield Street, were pioneers that pointed the way forward.

The curry-house phenomenon swept across major towns and cities in Britain during the 1960s. The idea caught on because the restaurants had found a winning formula: they offered cheap food and plenty of it, they stayed open after the pubs had closed, they were tolerant of all-comers and they were casual. 'Going for a curry' became a part of British social life and the 'standard' menu of anglicised dishes with invented names like Madras and Malaya entered the popular vocabulary. In fact the cooking style, with its permutations of chicken, meat and prawns, with rice, vegetables and bread, was largely a legacy from the nineteenth century, when Syhleti seamen held a virtual monopoly as cooks on Indian ships that docked at British ports. Their all-purpose menus proved a perfect prototype for the food in the first British dockside restaurants.

In 1971, East Pakistan became an independent state called Bangladesh, separated from the rest of Pakistan by parts of Northern India. And in 1972, the dictator Idi Amin expelled thousands of Asian families from Uganda, in a purge. Many of them, originally from the Punjab and Gujaret, came to Britain, following an earlier wave of immigrants from Kenya in 1968. These political events change the complexion of Indian restaurants in Britain. Curry houses flourished and close-knit Asian communities started to appear in many major cities.

In fact the term 'Indian restaurant' is as much a misnomer as the umbrella word 'curry'. Pat Chapman of The Curry Club reckons that only 15 per cent of these establishments are owned and run by Indians. The vast majority are from Pakistan and Bangladesh. Now there are more than 1.2 million Asians living in Britain, and there are restaurants and cafés across the land, from Cornish villages to the Yorkshire Dales.

With such proliferation it is difficult to spot the good from the indifferent. The benchmarks of a good Indian restaurant kitchen should be no different from any other: cooking based on fresh ingredients (including spices and herbs, as well as vegetables, meat and fish), a sense of balance, plenty of variation and no short-cuts. Cooks should be able to give their own signature to dishes and menus should offer a range of styles from different regions. Above all, the restaurant should be consistent. This is virtually impossible to judge from one meal. New Indian restaurants are notorious for putting on a fine show for about three months and then – once they have a following – going into a downhill slide. Prices go up, quality plummets. Cooks often move around between restaurants in a neighbourhood. A place that is good on a Saturday evening may be disastrous on Monday, or vice versa. Consistency doesn't imply sameness: instead, there should be consistent *standards* and *quality*. It is often a good sign if dishes taste slightly different from day to day, because that suggests 'cooking to order' and an echo of the virtues of homecooking.

In reality, the picture can be lamentably different. One-dimensional flavours, where chilli heat overpowers everything else, stale-tasting ingredients, dishes swimming in ghee, and re-heating are common complaints. Many Indian homes now have a microwave but its presence in their restaurant kitchens can spell disaster: re-heated rice becomes dry and lumpy; pre-cooked tandoori dishes are brought back to life and given an extra sizzle of vitality with the help of a red hot cast-iron serving platter; samosas and other snacks end up with leathery batter or pastry.

Without doubt, the scourge of many Indian restaurants is the all-purpose curry sauce. More than anything else it has kept most of these places near the bottom of the gastronomic scale. At its worst, the old-style standard menu was a licence to produce different dishes simply by adding different ingredients to a basic sauce – lentils for a dhansak, extra onions for dupiaza, a double dose of chilli powder for anything labelled Madras. Even now, two or three major manufacturers still prop up the kitchens of hundreds of restaurants with commercial curry pastes (including violently dyed crimson tandoori paste), so there's a temptation for cooks to neglect grinding or blending their own spices.

The so-called 'new wave' attempted to put things right. In the late 1970s, Amin Ali made a bid to change the style and image of Indian restaurants in Britain. His progress from waiter to owner of a succession of lavish London establishments – The Red Fort and Jamdani among them – has been well charted. Having set a style based on extravagantly designed interiors, cool service and authentic recipes, he was bound to attract imitators. And before long, heavy pink tablecloths, wicker furniture and bejewelled prints had become as much of a cliché as red flock and 'oil' lamps.

It is a mistake to believe that expensive decor, high prices, a cocktail menu and lavish trappings are pointers to good food. New-wave restaurants often promise more than they deliver and they can easily fall into the same traps as old-style curry houses. There is often more potency, freshness and authenticity in a Bradford café than in a flashily appointed restaurant in London's West End. Another fault of many expensive city restaurants is that they don't move into top gear until the middle of the evening. Go at 6.30 and you may wish you had never entered the door. Waiters can be positively unwelcoming, and you may be paying for food (often with a 15 per cent service charge) that was fresh six hours earlier.

Then there is the matter of deciphering the menu. There are at least 15 major languages in the sub-continent and hundreds of regional dialects. As a result, menu language and spelling can vary from restaurant to restaurant, depending on the owner. It is worth looking for specialities, away from the standard curry house stalwarts. Florid descriptions – 'freshly gathered Himalayan herbs', 'a fragrant preparation of spring chicken' – don't always match the results on the plate. Having said that, even the most forward- looking places are loath to abandon completely their Madras and dhansaks for fear of alienating their customers.

Good Indian restaurants, whether of the old or the new school, score heavily with small but essential details. Apart from using freshly ground spices, authentic recipes and proper ingredients for centrepiece dishes, cooks are showing more care and imagination with side dishes and accompaniments. Pickles, chutneys and relishes are part and parcel of Indian home cooking and this is starting to show in restaurants. Of course, there is still a liking for sweet mango chutney and lime pickle from the catering jar, but home-made items are finding their way on to the table – especially in vegetarian restaurants and neighbourhood cafés.

It's still difficult to find decent Indian breads. Cooks may have mastered the art of slapping 'nan' dough on to the side of a tandoori oven, but other staples are often a travesty. And the more expensive the restaurant, the worse it seems to be. Waiters can mix cocktails, but the kitchens cannot deliver acceptable chapatis. By comparison, quite modest places – where bread is central to the cooking style – can produce superb results. Rice, too, needs proper treatment. More restaurants are producing genuine butter 'pilaus', tinged with saffron for fragrance rather than colour, instead of the bright yellow, boiled rice or the multicolour assortment of artificially dyed grains.

With improved supply lines, vegetables are becoming more interesting Tinda (squash), mustard leaf, karala (bitter melon) and beans and pulses make a welcome change from the ubiquitous peas, overcooked carrots and cauliflower. The same is true of sweets. Indian kulfi, shrikhand, barfi and halwa are ousting vanilla ice-cream and banana fritters.

At its best, Indian cuisine can be complex, subtle, seductive. It has enormous range and depth, and yet there is no restaurant in Britain with the stature to match, say, the best Chinese or Japanese. But there are two hopeful signs that could put Indian cooking on the gastronomic map in a big way. The sheer size of the sub-continent means that there is a rich regional tradition. Until recently, restaurants in Britain had only scratched the surface – virtually all concentrated on North India and Bangladesh – where most of the cooks came from. Now they are beginning to branch out. Some early high-profile attempts to sell the idea of regional cooking were little more than expensive PR exercises, but now genuine regional specialities are offered in restaurants from Birmingham to Edinburgh. A glance at the culinary map of India shows the range of possibilities.

From the Punjab and the North-West Frontier come tandoori dishes cooked on skewers in a charcoal oven. This is also the region where bread rather than rice is the staple. This is the style that has spread from Ami Ali's Red Fort in London to Days of the Raj in Birmingham and the Indian Cavalry Club in Edinburgh. Further north, in Kashmir, there is Balti cooking, where the food is prepared and served in large, flat-bottomed metal dishes cooked to dryness and eaten with big roti or chapatis. The Adil and the Royal Al-Faisal in Sparkbrook, Birmingham cook in this way, but there are also outposts as far away as Cardiff. Gujarat in the west – home of Mahatma Ghandi – is strictly vegetarian and is famous for bhajias, kachori and patra, as well as stews and dishes flavoured with black mustard seed, asafoetida and tamarind. Move south and you will find the roadside and beach snacks of Bombay – especially bhel pooris. Here too are rich, fruity, sweet-and-sour Parsee dishes, influenced by cooking from early Persian settlers.

Further south is the state of Goa, noted for its pomfret and other fish dishes. The Portuguese colonised this region for two centuries and it is the only state where they cook pork – especially in the classic dish called vindaloo, a vinegared pork stew with chillies and potatoes. London's Bombay Brasserie and Jamdani, both high-profile fashionable places, have taken on this style. The Keralan coast has fish and vegetarian dishes, with coconut milk as the frontline flavour, exemplified at Ragam in London.

South Indian vegetarian cooking is similar to that of Gujarat, but it can be intensely hot. This is the home of iddlys, dosa and uttapom, as well as the thali – the complete vegetarian meal consisting of several dishes in small bowls, with perhaps rice, bread, pickles and a sweet. Suruchi in London is a good place to try out this style.

The ceremonial haute cuisine of the sub-continent – Moghul or Muglai cooking – centred on the palaces of Delhi and Hyderabad. There are echoes of this style in some of today's richly spiced, creamy dishes, occasionally adorned with 'vark' – fine leaves of edible silver. The coast of Bengal is also noted for its fish cookery, which goes well beyond the usual king prawns and trout; mustard oil is often used in place of ghee as the essential cooking medium, giving the dishes a distinctive pungency. Chilka House in Rye (whose proprietor was contemplating a move back to Brighton) is influenced by this. In the far north east, the cooking of Assam, is a curious hybrid of classic North Indian with influences from its neighbour China.

Genuine regional cooking needs specially trained chefs. Yet, given the amount of investment currently being ploughed into decor, it should be possible for Indian restaurateurs to procure the services of cooks with the right knowledge and skills. This is clearly a long-term development, but authentic cooking can already be tasted in the cafés and neighbourhood restaurants dotted around many British cities. London still has three main centres: Drummond Street near Euston station, Southall, to the west of London, and the area around Spitalfields and Brick Lane in the East End. In Birmingham, Sparkbrook and Sparkhill dominate; Leicester has Belgrave Road; Manchester's strongest Asian centres are in Rusholme and Wilmslow Road. There are also long-standing communities in many industrialised cities such as Bradford and Sheffield.

The best of these cafés have many advantages. They are invariably good value and can cook specialities to order (although the microwave is widely used for snacks). since they are part of a neighbourhood, they are able to make the best use of local markets, shops and greengrocers for authentic fresh ingredients. And they tend to have a local following – which helps to maintain standards. But don't expect the decor or trappings of a conventional restaurant: many of these establishments are informal meeting places as well as eating places; some close early in the evening, other stay open till the small hours; in many you will be expected to eat with your fingers, although most will provide a fork and spoon if you ask. Quite a number of these cafés have been 'discovered' and are serving customers from way beyond their local neighbourhood. Let us hope they will not become victims of their own success.

What to drink in 1991

No guide such as this can be infallible; poor years produce bargains and pleasant surprises, good years disappointments. Increasingly, the maker of the wine has as much significance as the vintage, not only as technological development enables the canny and the skilled to overcome, at least to minimise, the vagaries of weather but also because the best wine-makers are fearful of a universal bland wine being the result of this technology and are therefore even more painstakingly stamping their individuality on their products. Included here, therefore, are *some* names of makers or properties who are thought especially good – often up and coming rather than well-established. This does not attempt to be complete, but when they appear on a wine list, it may be sign that the restaurant has real interest in recent developments and changing fortunes and has therefore used intelligence in purchasing and selection. Seek advice from the restaurant, especially when wines from generally poor vintages are listed. Countries are listed alphabetically, regions alphabetically within countries. Double starred ** vintages are especially good; single starred * are good.

Argentina

Drink whites as young as possible. Reds up to ten years old can be enjoyed.

Australia

Whites Rhine Riesling – **1988, *1987, not much older unless botrytised. Chardonnay and Semillon – **1988, **1987, **1986, *1985. Older wines if oak-aged or botrytised (Semillon).

Reds *1980–1988. Merlot and Pinot Noir mature faster than Cabernet, Shiraz or Cabernet/Shiraz blends.
MAKERS TO WATCH FOR Balgownie, Cape Mentelle, Coldstream Hills, Evans & Tate, Heggies, Hollicks, Tim Knappstein, Lake's Folly, Peter Lehmann, Geoff Merrill, Michelton, Mosswood, Pewsey Vale.

Bulgaria

Whites Drink young. Chardonnay may age the best, back to 1985.

Reds Drink young unless Cabernet Sauvignon, then *1985, *1983, *1984. Most Bulgarian reds are released by producers only when ready to drink.

Chile

Whites Drink young.

Reds Cabernet Sauvignon ages better, the best vintages are 1981–1985.
MAKERS TO WATCH FOR Canepa, Concha y Toro, Cousiño Macul, Santa Rita, Miguel Torres, Los Vascos, Undurraga.

England and Wales

Drink mostly young, no older than 1985. **1989.
MAKERS TO WATCH FOR Astley, Barton Manor, Breaky Bottom, Bruisyard, Chalkhill, Chiltern Valley, Joyous Garde, New Hall, Penshurst, Pulham, Staplecombe, Three Choirs.

France

Alsace

The best recent vintages have been *1988, **1985 and *1983. Pinot Blanc drinks best young. Some Gewürztraminers age well. Muscat is attractive young, more complex with a few years' bottle age. Riesling and Tokay are good between 4 and 10 years old, even older for Vendange Tardive and Sélection des Grains Nobles wines. Pinot Noir seldom improves after two years.
MAKERS TO WATCH FOR Blanck, Marc Kreydenweiss, Muré, Ostertag, Rolly Gassmann, Schlumberger, Zind Humbrecht, Trimbach.

Beaujolais

Both **1989 and **1988 were fine years. * 1987. Simple Beaujolais or Beaujolais Villages 1989 are drinking well. The *crus* of 1989 especially are not all yet ready though many are now made for quicker maturation. *1987 Villages are fading. 1986 and *1985 are still good for some *crus*. Older vintages will depend for their success on their makers. Moulin-à-Vent commonly lasts the longest.
MAKERS TO WATCH FOR Aujas, Belicard, Braillon, Brun, Descombes, Geoffray, Pâtissier, Pelletier, Sarrau.

Bergerac

Drink whites and rosés young; simple reds within two years, Côtes de Bergerac and Pécharmant **1983, *1985 and *1986 (scarce older bottles might be even better) and sweet Monbazillac five years or older (the best can last 10 years).
PRODUCERS TO WATCH FOR Ch. Court-les-Mûts, Ch. La Jaubertie, Ch. du Treuil de Nailhac, Ch. La Borderie, Ch. Tiregand.

Bordeaux

Red

The wines of Bordeaux span a giant range from ordinary to superfine. Many should be drunk quickly, others may keep a century. There are two broad groupings although variations within them can be very great.

Petits châteaux and crus bourgeois Some properties make wines vastly better
than their humble classification. The districts or appellations include
Bordeaux, Bordeaux Superieur, Côtes de Bourg, Premières Côtes de Bordeaux
and Premières Côtes de Blaye properties in the outlying districts of St Emilion
and Pomerol, Fronsac and the Graves.

The best and most reliable vintage ready for drinking among petits châteaux
is *1986. 1988 and 1987 are patchy and advice should be sought. **1985 is
drinking well. *1983, and **1982 and 1981 are ready, though 1982 may need
more time. 1979 and 1978 are fully ready though St Emilion and Pomerol
wines mature faster than those of the Médoc and the Graves and 1979 may be
fading. Some of the especially good bourgeois, noted for instance in the list
below, will keep for much longer and may be treated as classed growths.
MAKERS TO WATCH FOR This is a most selective list of some châteaux that
always make wine of better quality than their classification implies. It also
includes properties that have recently become fashionable or esteemed for
serious wine-making: Angludet, Beaumont, Bourgneuf-Vayron, Chasse-
Spleen, Cissac, le Crock Fonbadet, Fonréaud, Gloria, Labégorce-Zédé, Patache
d'Aux, Potensac, Siran, Hanteillan.

Classed growths (including St Emilion Grand Cru Classé and Pomerol): *1986
and **1985 are the first years ready to drink for lesser properties and some from
St Emilion and Pomerol. 1984 was not a success in St Emilion or Pomerol;
other communes are not very attractive yet. *1983 is possible from St Emilion
and Pomerol but not for other districts. **1982 is pre-eminent but for the most
part not nearly ready except, again, from St Emilion. 1981 is drinkable for St
Emilion, Pomerol and lesser properties as well as the softer districts like
Graves, St Julien and Margaux. **1979 is a good year for the better châteaux
and many are now at their peak; lesser ones are drying out. **1978 is good.
1977 is best not tried though the best are cheap and drinkable. 1976 is fruity
but may be fading. *1975 is tough for good Médoc and Graves and will not be at
their best for some time, if ever, but St Emilions and Pomerols can drink well.
1975 is often a disappointment. Earlier vintages that can be enjoyable are 1971
(better in St Emilion and Pomerol) although these are now becoming uneven,
**1970 (even now, still tough for the very best growths), *1966 (not very fruity
but classic), 1964 (very fine in St Emilion), 1962 (can still provide good
examples of the best châteaux) and **1961 (be warned that the top ten still have
some way to go although us lesser mortals may find them perfect even now).
Earlier good years are **1959, 1955, **1953, **1949, **1947 and **1945.
MAKERS TO WATCH FOR These are some of the rising stars; it is an arbitrary
but may still have some use when a wine list is unfamiliar: Cantemerle,
Domaine de Chevalier, Couhins-Lurton, Dauzac, Issan, la Lagune, le Pin,
Plince, St-Pierre, Soutard, Tertre-Rôteboeuf.

Dry Whites
Drink them young (especially Bordeaux Blanc and Entre-Deux-Mers), 1988 or
at worst 1987, unless they come from a serious property (mostly in Graves)
with a long history of white wine vinification which also includes a proportion
(if not the entirety) of Sémillon in the cépage and some ageing in wood. Then,
the best of recent vintages are 1987, 1985, 1983. (Top Graves live very much
longer.)

Sweet wines

The Premières Côtes de Bordeaux and St-Croix du Mont may be drunk young, from 1988, 1987, 1986 and 1985, but only the best St-Croix will improve beyond five years. Sauternes and Barsac should be allowed to mature longer than this (good vintages such as 1985 will benefit from 10 years or more), though *1985 is coming round and the light 1984 ready now. **1983 is very fine but the best properties need much longer. Earlier vintages are 1981, *1980, 1979, *1976, *1975 (for the best), *1970. Older vintages include: *1969, *1967, *1955, **1945.

MAKERS TO WATCH FOR Châteaux that have preserved their commitment to great sweet wines include Bastor-Lamontagne, Climens, Coutet, Doisy-Daëne, Guiraud, de Malle, Rabaud-Promis, Rayne-Vigneau, Raymond-Lafon, Rieussec, Sigalas-Rabaud, Suduiraut.

Burgundy

Reds Vintage recommendations are even less reliable for Burgundy than Bordeaux. The maker and his style are essential for success. These are some of the better recent vintages. Côte de Nuits normally matures better, over a longer cycle, than Côte de Beaune and Chalonnais. Drink the simpler wines from *1987 and *1986, but avoid the better growths after *1985 as they are not ready. *1983 was mixed but some are fine; **1982s are now mature; **1980 was best on the Côte de Nuits; **1978 is still drinking wonderfully for the best growths.

GROWERS WHO HAVE BEEN MAKING THEIR MARK There are myriad small growers here and this is only a note of a few whose name have caught the British eye of approval in recent years: Robert Ampeau, Simon Bize, Dujac, Jean Grivot, Jayer, Olivier Leflaive, Domaine Parent, Daniel Rion, Armand Rousseau, Jean Trapet, Alain Verdet, Michel Voarick, Chopin, Juillot.

Whites Drink Mâcon from the most recent vintage and Mâcon Villages (including the good villages Lugny, Viré, Clessé) from **1988, **1987, *1986, and *1985. The best of the recent vintages for the Côte d'Or and Chablis are *1987, **1986, **1985 and *1983.

GROWERS WHO HAVE BEEN MAKING THEIR MARK René Dauvissat, Jean Durup, William Fèvre, Alain Geoffroy, Henri Laroche, Louis Michel, Louis Pinson, François Raveneau, Philippe Testut, Robert Vocoret, Vincent, Forest, Sauzet.

Buzet, Frontonnais, Gaillac (reds)

Drink Buzet *1987, 1986, **1985, 1983, 1982 or 1978. (Drink Frontonnais and Gaillac young.)

NAMES TO WATCH FOR *Buzet* Ch. des Jonquilles, Ch. de Padèrie, Ch. Sauvagnères;
Frontonnais Ch. Bellevue-la-Forêt, Ch. Flotis;
Gaillac Domaine Jean Cros, Labarthe, Larroze;

Cahors

The lighter style drinks young. The more traditional 'black' wines are good from *1983, *1982 and *1978. **1985 possibly still too young.

NAMES TO WATCH FOR Ch. du Cayrou, Clos de Gamot, Domaine de Gaudou, Domaine de la Pineraie, Domaine de Paillas, Clos Triguedina.

Champagne

The most common vintage in restaurants will still be ***1983**. The best of earlier vintages are ****1982**, ***1981**, ****1979**, ***1978**, ***1975**. Older vintages are an acquired taste.

Loire

Dry whites and rosés Drink the youngest vintage. ****1989** shows promise but ****1988** is still good. Sancerre sometimes has a longer life than expected, developing depth and fruit, as does Savennières or Vouvray, over five years. Pouilly Fumé, Quincy, Reuilly and Menetou Salon last none too long.
MAKERS AND PROPERTIES TO WATCH FOR Bailly, Bizolière, Bossard, Brédif, Dézat, Huet, Poniatowski, Saget, Sauvion, Vatan.

Sweet whites mature as slowly as Sauternes. Young Côteaux du Layon may be drunk from 1986. Best recent vintages for Quarts de Chaume and Bonnezeaux are ***1985**, ***1983**, ***1982**, ***1978**, ***1976**.
NAMES TO WATCH FOR Baumard, Belle Rive, Ch. de Fesles, Renou, Soucherie, Moulin Touchais

Reds Many reds need drinking young, Chinon and Bourgueil and Cabernets ageing the best. They are most susceptible to bad weather because of their northerly situation. Best recent vintages are ****1989**, ***1988**, ***1986**, ****1985**, ***1983**, ***1982**.
MAKERS TO WATCH ARE Caslot-Galbrun, Couly-Dutheil, Lamé-Delille-Boucard, Raffault, Roussier, Vallée.

Rhône

Whites Normally drink young: the best recent vintages are 1988, 1987, 1986, 1985, 1983 and 1978.

Reds In the northern Rhône (Crozes Hermitage, Hermitage, Côte Rôtie, St Joseph and Cornas) Crozes Hermitage is the fastest developer (lasting often no more than five years) and Hermitage and Côte Rôtie the slowest. The best recent vintages are ***1985**, ****1983**, ***1982**, ***1980**, ****1978**.
MAKERS TO WATCH FOR Chapoutier (for white especially), Chave, Clape, Grippat, Guigal, Jaboulet, Sorrel.
In the south (Châteauneuf, Gigondas, Lirac, Côtes du Rhône and many wider appellations) the Côtes du Rhône should be drunk quickly from the current vintage, though some will last from ***1985**. Other good vintages for current drinking are 1986, ****1983**, ***1981**, ***1980** and ****1978**. Châteauneuf is the longest-lasting although fine old Gigondas is a pleasure.
NAMES TO WATCH FOR Domaine de Longue-Toque, Ch. de Beaucastel, Les Cailloux, Chante-Perdrix, Roger Sabon, Guigal, Domaine de Mont-Redon, Ch. Rayas, Domaine de Castel-Oualou, Domaine de Pallières.

Germany

Drink basic wines (QbA) young, none earlier than ***1987**. Earlier vintages that are good for the better wines are ****1985** especially in Rheingau, ***1983** especially Mosel-Saar-Suwer, ***1981**, ****1976** (Spätlese or above), ***1975** (Spätlese or above). Trockenbeerenauslese and Eiswein should not be drunk

from vintages later than 1981 as they are not ready – many will live for decades.
MAKERS TO WATCH FOR Bassermann-Jordan, Deinhard, Diel, Fritz Haag,
Lingenfelder, Balthasar Ress, Schloss Vollrads, Scholl & Hillebrand.

Italy

Whites Drink 1989 from the lighter wines and 1988 or 1986 (1987 was
disappointing for whites) except for senior Chardonnays, where 1985 is
showing well.

Reds Tuscan wines had good years in **1988, 1986, **1985, *1983, **1982, 1978
and 1975. Chiantis are drinking well from 1985, 1986 and 1987, Chianti
Riservas from 1982, 1983**, and 1985. **1982 is the star year, especially for
'super-Tuscans' from top Chianti producers.
Barolos and Barbarescos need time to mature. Younger than 1983 is generally too
young. **1982 and **1978 are the best since *1974 and *1971. Lighter reds
(Dolcetto, Barbera) from 1987 are pleasant now.
MAKERS WHOSE NAMES SHOULD BE NOTED Antinori, Ascheri, Conterno,
Deltetto, Gaja, Isole e Olina, Jermann, Lageder, Mascarello, Schiopetto,
Tiefenbrunner.

New Zealand

Most New Zealand white wines are made for young drinking, although
Chardonnays and Semillons may well last more than four or five years as will
late-harvest (sweet) Rieslings and Muscats. Red wines are too recent a
development for sound advice, although Cabernet Sauvignon will obviously
outlast Merlot and Pinot Noir.
MAKERS TO WATCH FOR Babich, Cloudy Bay, Delegat's, Esk Valley, Matua
Valley, Montana, Nobilo's, Redwood Valley, St Helena, Selaks, Stoneleigh,
Villa Maria

Portugal

Almost all Portuguese white wines should be drunk young but some reds age
well. Older vintages that may be offered from the 1970s are 1971, 1974 and
1978. Most of the 1980s were adequate vintages, 1980, 1982, 1983 and 1985 the
best.
MAKERS WORTH LOOKING FOR Caves Aliança, Quinta da Aveleda, J M da
Fonseca, Adega Cooperativa de Mealhada, João Pires, Caves Velhas, Solar das
Bouças, Quinta do Côtto, Caves Sao João.

Vintage port works to another cycle. The best year for current drinking is
**1966 but much of 1975 is simple and cheap and not a keeper. Some, though
not all, ready from *1970, *1963, *1960, **1955, *1948, **1945.

Spain

Whites Drink quickly unless Chardonnay or white Rioja from the best
producers.

Reds Riojas are not ready (unless not aged in oak – *'sin crianza'*) after the *1985 vintage. Earlier vintages are *1983, **1982, *1981, *1980. Simple Riojas, not Reservas or Gran Reservas, are unreliable if earlier than 1980. Many Ribero del Duero wines need up to ten years and Vega Sicilia even longer. 1982 and 1981 are drinking quite well, however.

MAKERS TO WATCH FOR El Coto, Montecillo, Muga, Chivite, Marqués de Griñon, Raimat, Bodegas Fariña (Toro), Bodegas Los Llanos, Bodegas Ollara, La Rioja Alta, Contino.

United States

California

Whites Drink mostly young, except Chardonnays from **1986 and **1985, and botrytised Rieslings and Gewürztraminers.

Reds Drink vintages earlier than 1987. Zinfandel, Merlot and Pinot Noir are often best before 5–8 years. Cabernet Sauvignon keeps well though old specimens are not common. Best years of the 1980s have been 1986, 1985, 1982, 1980.

MAKERS WHO HAVE RECEIVED ACCLAIM IN RECENT YEARS Au Bon Climat, Carmenet, Frog's Leap, Iron Horse, Jekel, Matanzas Creek, Ridge, Rutherford Hill, Saintsbury, Trefethen, Mark West, William Wheeler.

The humble dozen: decent wines under £10

With the advent of controlled temperature fermentation and stainless steel vats, plus micro-chemists at work in the cellars, poor wines have no right to exist and certainly not on restaurant lists. Yet how often can those of us with neither the knowledge nor the inclination to go straight to the classified clarets feel confident that a bottle under £10 is not going to set the teeth on edge or spark a migraine?

In awarding our 'glass' and 'bottle' symbols to restaurant wine lists (see entries, and the Introduction), the *Guide* has been as concerned with the quality and value of the offerings at the humble end of the list as with the top. A good list will reflect a careful buyer of cheap wines. What, after all, is the wine-loving restaurateur going to sneak off the rack for Sunday lunch? Not the Vosne-Romanée, more likely a decent Valpolicella or Rioja.

On any list you are entitled to expect a full description of the wine: 'Clos de Something' isn't enough. The area of origin, the wine maker and the vintage are essential and for a varietal wine – made from a single grape variety – you'll see the name, 'Chardonnay' or 'Merlot', for example. That level of detail tells you that the compiler of the list has taken some interest and is prepared to give the facts because they matter.

Wherever possible, avoid wines that say 'bottled by . . .', be circumspect about anything that claims nothing more than to be 'bottled in the region of production' and be suspicious of much repetition on a list of one producer's name. This last suggests a lazy restaurateur has bought conveniently from a single merchant or *négociant*. On the other hand don't be embarrassed to order a bottle produced by a large company; good vinification requires investment and if costs are to be kept down, mass production helps; in Spain, Italy and Australia, particularly, some very sound wine is produced on a large scale. And the days of a label just saying *'Réserve du Patron'* or 'Don Juan' are gone.

But perhaps the first, rather than the last, resort in the search for good-value wine should be to ask for a recommendation. If you are feeling bold, ask the restaurant owners what they drank for supper.

We set ourselves the task of compiling a list of good wines that ought to be available on restaurant lists for under £10. After plundering the spring 1990 lists of about a dozen wine merchants for wines costing less than £4 (not including VAT), we applied the

735

mark-up formula common to most restaurants: double the price, add VAT and that's the cost on the table. We came up with the list below. It's not definitive, for we could have selected a hundred other deserving wines just from the lists we chose, but it's a collection of wines with a balance of light and heavy, and an interesting geographical spread. And each bottle is good enough to grace a restaurateur's table, just as much as a customer's.

White wines	In a restaurant, hope to pay approximately
Soave 1989, Tadiello	£5.95
Muscadet de Sèvre et Maine, sur lie 1988, F. Viaud	£8.20
Saumur Blanc 1988, Ch. de Villeneuve	£8.50
Lerida, Chardonnay 1989, Raimat	£8.50
Vernaccia di San Gimignano 1988, Teruzzi e Puthod	£9.10
Bourgogne Aligoté 1987, A. Verdet	£9.10

Red wines	
Vin de Pays de l'Hérault 1985, Dom. de Clairac	£5.90
Chianti Rufina 1987, Selvapiana	£7.70
Valpolicella Classico 1988, Allegrini	£7.70
Bourgueil, 'Cuvée Alouettes' 1987, M. et T. Brocard	£8.60
Ovens Valley, Shiraz 1986, Wynns	£8.80
Toro, Gran Colegiata 1986, Bodegas Farina	£9.50

Your rights in restaurants

A restaurant is legally obliged to provide you with a meal and service which are of a reasonable standard, and a failure to do so may give you the right to sue for breach of contract. Having said this, it is important to remember that the reasonableness or otherwise of both the meal and the service must be judged on the type of restaurant in question.

Dining out should be a pleasurable experience. However, it is as well to be aware of your basic legal rights just in case you find yourself in an awkward situation, like one of these:

You book a table in advance but when you arrive, the manager says there's been a mistake and there's no room.
When you book, you're making a contract with the restaurant and they must give you a table, in reasonable time. If they don't, they're in breach of contract and you can claim a reasonable sum to cover any expenses you had as a result, eg travelling costs.

You go into a restaurant and as you sit and look at the menu, you realise the meal is going to be much more expensive than you thought.
A restaurant must display a menu and a wine list outside, or immediately inside the door – so check the prices before you sit down. Prices shown must be inclusive of VAT. If they aren't, tell the local Trading Standards Officer (see 'The law enforcers').

The restaurant says it doesn't serve children. Can you insist it does so?
No – however unfair it may seem. A restaurant can turn away anyone, without giving a reason, except on grounds of sex, race, colour or ethnic origin.

You only want a cup of coffee but the waiter tells you there's a minimum charge of £3 per person.
A restaurant must display any minimum charge or cover charge outside or immediately inside the door. If no charge is indicated, tell the local Trading Standards Officer. You do not have to pay the charge if it is not displayed. Under a new Code of Practice (see below) menus are supposed to show cover and minimum charges as prominently as any other charges.

The bill comes to quite a bit more than you expected and has had 10% service charge added – do you have to pay this?
As with the minimum charge, the restaurant must display outside or immediately inside the door any service charge to be automatically included in the bill. If it is displayed, you should pay it unless there was something specifically wrong with the service. But if a service charge is not

clearly indicated, you don't have to pay – it's up to you whether to tip and, if you do, by how much.

Restaurants are being asked to follow new rules about how to indicate extra charges on their menus. A Code of Practice, introduced in March 1989 under the Consumer Protection Act, says restaurants should include any compulsory service charges *within* the price for each item (rather than adding a percentage to the total bill). This would make it easier for customers to see at a glance how much they'll have to pay. But they only have to do this 'wherever practicable'. The Code also recommends that restaurants do not suggest optional sums for service or other items, so menus and bills should not say 'We suggest you give an optional 10% gratuity'.

It's not yet clear how much impact the Code will have. It is not legally binding, although if the restaurant is prosecuted, the court will take into account whether it has been followed.

You go into a restaurant because your favourite dish is on the menu. But the waitress says it's 'off' today. Your second choice isn't available either.
A restaurant doesn't have to be able to serve all items on the menu, although it should have most. If you think the restaurant is genuinely trying to mislead people, tell the local Trading Standards Officer.

You order 'fresh fruit salad', yet it's obviously out of a tin.
Under the Trade Descriptions Act, a restaurant must provide food and drink as described on the menu or by the waiter. If you think what you're served doesn't match the description, don't start eating. Complain immediately and ask for something else. You could also tell the local Trading Standards Officer that the restaurant is misleading customers.

Your fish arrives not properly cooked – it's still cold in the middle.
Under the Sale of Goods and Services Act (and under common law in Scotland), restaurants must prepare food with reasonable care and skill. If this does not appear to be the case, do not eat the dish you have been served and complain. If you don't manage to get things put right, you can deduct what you think is a fair sum from the bill (see 'Claiming your rights'). Alternatively, make it clear that you are paying 'under protest', so you can claim compensation later.

You get a nasty stomach upset after eating out at a restaurant. You think the lamb hot-pot was to blame.
If you think your illness is a result of a restaurant meal, tell your doctor and the local Environmental Health Officer (see 'The law enforcers'). The EHO can investigate the incident and may decide to prosecute; under the Food Act, it's a criminal offence for a restaurant to serve food unfit for human consumption. If it can be proved that the restaurant caused your illness – which can be difficult – it could be fined and made to compensate you. In

serious cases, it may be worth getting legal advice about suing the restaurant yourself.

You're kept waiting an hour before the waiter takes your order. When you complain, the waiter is rude to you.
A restaurant must give you a reasonable standard of service. If it doesn't, you can refuse to pay all or part of the service charge, even if it's automatically included in the bill.

The waitress drops a dish and the food goes all over your new suit.
If it's the restaurant's fault that you've had food or drink spilled on you, you can claim the cost of cleaning. If the article of clothing can't be cleaned, you can claim the cost of a new one.

You've come out for a leisurely evening but the waiter has different ideas. He whips dishes away before you've finished eating and then presents you with the bill.
A restaurant must give you reasonable time to finish your meal and have a cup of coffee, bearing in mind the type of restaurant and what time it is. If you think you've been unreasonably rushed, complain and don't pay part or all of the service charge.

The people on the next table are smoking. The smoke's wafting in your direction and is spoiling your meal. Can you get the manager to tell them to stop?
The manager can't insist on people not smoking, unless it's specifically a non-smoking restaurant or a non-smoking area. If it is, smokers could be asked to leave if they don't stop. If it's important to you, check beforehand what the smoking arrangements are.

You're a bit short of cash so you ask if you can pay by credit card. The restaurant says 'no'.
A restaurant doesn't have to accept payment by credit card – or even by cheque – unless it had agreed to do so beforehand, or there's a sign on the door. So check first.

You're paying by credit card. When the waiter gives you the voucher to sign you see the total has been left blank, presumably in the hope you'll add something extra for service. Do you have to pay?
Be careful – you could end up paying for service twice. Check whether service is compulsory and, if it is, whether the charge has already been added to the bill. If it has, then there's no reason why you should add anything extra. We think it's misleading of restaurants to present vouchers in this way when service is already included, although it's not illegal. If the service charge is not compulsory, then it's up to you whether you add any more and, if so, how much.

You give your coat to the waitress to hang up. By the time you leave, it has disappeared.
A restaurant must take reasonable care of your belongings if they're in a

cloakroom. If it doesn't you can claim compensation for any damage or loss. Notices limiting the restaurant's liability are only valid if they're reasonable and prominently displayed. If there's no cloakroom, make sure you ask staff to put your coat or other belongings in a safe place, otherwise you won't be entitled to any compensation.

Claiming your rights

1. Try to sort out your problem on the spot. Ask to speak to the manager, explain what the problem is and say what you want done, for instance, a substitute dish provided. Don't be afraid to make a fuss.
2. If you're not able to come to an agreement with the manager, then you have two options: to deduct a suitable amount from the bill (it's then up to the restaurant to sue you for the balance if it doesn't agree); or to make any payment you're not happy about 'under protest' (put this down in writing when you make the payment). That way you can try to claim it back later by suing under the small claims procedure (see below).
3. If you're still not happy, get advice on your legal position. You can get free advice from Citizens' Advice Bureaux, Law Centres and Consumer Advice Centres. The Trading Standards department of the restaurant's local authority may also be able to help. If you go to a solicitor, check first how much it's likely to cost you. Many solicitors offer a half-hour interview for a fixed fee of £5. Or you can join **Which? Personal Service**, which gives advice and help to individual members (write to Which? Personal Service, Consumers' Association, 2 Marylebone Road, London NW1 4DX for details).
4. When you've found out where you stand, write to the restaurant. Tell them what the problem was and what you want done about it.
5. If you have no success, and think you have a strong case, you can sue under the small claims procedure in the county court. In England, Wales and Northern Ireland, the maximum you can claim is £500. You won't need a solicitor. Just issuing a summons may spur the restaurant into action. In Scotland, claims of under £750 are heard under the small claims procedure of the Sherrif Court.

The law enforcers

The job of enforcing many of the laws affecting restaurants, and which protect consumers' rights, is done not by the police but by officials employed by the local authority. **Environmental Health Officers** enforce food hygiene laws and regulations. They investigate complains by the public. They make routine visits to restaurants – although they're very overstretched. The Institution of Environmental

Health Officers would like all new food premises, such as restaurants setting up in business, to be licensed by their local authority before they start trading. Consumers' Association supports this idea.
Trading Standards Officers enforce the law about factual descriptions of goods and services. They will investigate complaints about false or misleading claims made by restaurants, or misleading indications of prices.

If EHOs or TSOs have enough evidence that restaurants have committed a criminal offence, they can prosecute. If found guilty, restaurants can be fined and you could be awarded compensation.

Restaurants' rights

You book a table for four at a country restaurant. But the car won't start and you decide not to go.
If you book a table at a restaurant, you must turn up in reasonable time. If you don't keep your booking, or are very late, you're in breach of contract and the restaurant could sue you for compensation. Let the restaurant know as soon as possible if you can't make it, so the restaurant can reduce its loss by rebooking the table. Some restaurants have started to take customers' credit card numbers when they book and say that if they don't turn up, a charge will be made. As long as they tell you beforehand, restaurants are within their rights to do this. But the charge should only be reasonable compensation for their loss, not a penalty.

You go out for a meal with relatives but a row develops between feuding members of the family. The manager says the shouting is disturbing other customers and asks you to leave.
You must behave reasonably in a restaurant, otherwise the restaurant can refuse to serve you and ask you to leave.

You can't be bothered to change out of your old gardening clothes before going out for Sunday lunch. The manager refuses to give you a table.
If you are not dressed suitably, the restaurant can refuse to give you a table, even if you've booked.

You've just had the worst meal of your life – it was inedible. Do you have to pay?
You must pay the bill unless you have genuine cause for complaint, in which case you can deduct what you think is a fair amount as compensation. Explain exactly why and, if asked, leave your correct name and address. It's then up to the restaurant to sue you to recover the money. Don't be put off by threats to call the police. They have no right to intervene unless you intended to leave without paying for no genuine reason, or if you caused a violent scene, which could be a criminal offence.

Based on an article that appeared in *Which?* in November 1989.

General lists

The Guide's longest-serving restaurants

Connaught Hotel, W1	38 years	Splinters, Christchurch, Dorset	24 years
Gay Hussar, W1	34 years	Chez Moi, W11	22 years
Porth Tocyn Hotel Abersoch, Gwynedd	34 years	Cleeve House, Bishop's Cleeve, Gloucestershire	22 years
Gravetye Manor, East Grinstead, West Sussex	30 years	Pool Court, Pool in Wharfedale, West Yorkshire	22 years
Sharrow Bay, Ullswater, Cumbria	30 years	Rothay Manor, Ambleside, Cumbria	22 years
Bloom's, E1	28 years	Sundial, Herstmonceux, East Sussex	22 years
Dundas Arms, Kintbury, Berkshire	28 years	At the Sign of the Angel, Lacock, Wiltshire	20 years
Box Tree, Ilkley, West Yorkshire	26 years	Chuen Cheng Ku, W1	20 years
French Partridge, Horton, Northamptonshire	26 years	Le Gavroche, W1	20 years
Walnut Tree Inn, Llandewi Skirrid, Gwent	26 years	Summer Isles Hotel, Achiltibuie, Highland	20 years
Butley-Orford Oysterage, Orford, Suffolk	24 years	Timothys, Perth, Tayside	20 years

London restaurants by cuisine

AFRICAN/CARIBBEAN
Bambaya, N8
Blue Nile, W9
Laurent, NW2

BURMESE
Mandalay, SE10

CHINESE
Chuen Cheng Ku, W1
Dragon Inn, W2
Dragon's Nest, W1
Fung Shing, WC2
Honeymoon, N8
Jade Garden, W1
Ley-On's, W1
Mandarin Kitchen, W2
Mekong, SW1

Ming, W1
Mr Kong, WC2
New World, W1
Poons, WC2
Poons at Whiteleys, W2
Royal China, SW15
Si Chuen, W1
Soong Szechuan, NW3
Zen, SW3
Zen Central, W1
Zen W3, NW3

GREEK
Beotys, WC2
Kalamaras, W2
Nontas, NW1

HUNGARIAN
Gay Hussar, W1

INDIAN
Bombay Brasserie, SW7
Fleet Tandoori, NW3
Ganpath, WC1
Gopal's of Soho, W1
Great Nepalese, NW1
Lal Qila, W1
Ragam, W1
Saheli Brasserie, WC1

INDIAN VEGETARIAN
Diwana Bhel Poori, NW1
Mandeer, W1 Rani, N3
Sabras, NW10
Sree Krishna, SW17
Suruchi, N1
Surya, NW6

INDONESIAN/ STRAITS

Melati, W1
Singapore Garden Mayfair, W1
Singapore Garden Restaurant, NW6

ITALIAN

Carraro's, SW8
Cibo, W14
Eleven Park Walk, SW10
Florians, N8
L'Incontro, SW10
Orso, WC2
Pagu Dinai, SW6
Il Passetto, WC2
Pizzaria Castello, SE1
Pizzaria Condotti, W1
River Café, W6
San Martino, SW3
Santini, SW1
Tiramisu, NW6

JAPANESE

Ikkyu, W1
Miyama, W1
Nakano, SW3
Neshiko, N1
Ninjin, W1
Suntory, SW1
Tatsuso, EC2
Wakaba, NW3

JEWISH

Bloom's, E1

KOREAN

Bu San, N7

MIDDLE EASTERN

Al Hamra, W1
Efes Kebab House, W1
Maroush III, W1
Topkapi, W1

POLISH

Wodka, W8
Zamoyski's, NW3

SPANISH

Galicia, W10
Guernica, W1
Los Remos, W2
Meson Don Felipe, SE1
Rebato's, SW8

SWEDISH

Anna's Place, N1

THAI

Bahn Thai, W1
Bedlington Cafe, W4
Blue Elephant, SW6
Chiang Mai, W1
Khun Akorn, SW3
Sri Siam, W1
Thailand, SE14
Topsy-Tasty, W4
Tui, SW7
Tuk Tuk, N1

London restaurants with tables outside

Al Hamra, W1
Andrew Edmunds, W1
Anna's Place, N1
La Bastide, W1
Blue Nile, W9
Bombay Brasserie, SW7
Le Cadre, N8
Café Flo, NW3
Canal Brasserie, W1
Chanterelle, SW7
Cherry Orchard, E2
Christian's, W4

Connolly's, SW15
La Croisette, SW10
La Dordogne, W4
Eleven Park Walk, SW10
La Fin de la Chasse, N16
Florians, N8
Frith's, W1
Gilbert's, SW7
Greig's, SW13
Joe's Café, SW3
Left Bank, SW10

Lou Pescadou, SW5
Maroush III, W1
Mijanou, SW1
Mon Petit Plaisir, W8
Nichol's, NW6
Nontas, NW1
Soulard, N1
Le Suquet, SW3
Tiramisu, NW6
Tuk Tuk, N1
Zen, SW3

London restaurants open for Saturday lunch

Al Hamra, W1
Andrew Edmunds, W1
Annas's Place, N1
Au Bois St Jean, NW8
Bahn Thai, W1
Bedlington Café, W4
Beotys, WC2
Bibendum, SW3
Blakes Hotel, SW7
Bombay Brasserie, SW7
Bu San, N7
Café Flo, NW3

Capital Hotel, SW3
Le Caprice, SW1
Cavaliers, SW8
Chanterelle, SW7
Chelsea Room, Hyatt Carlton Tower, SW1
Cherry Orchard, E2
Chez Liline, N4
Chiang Mai, W1
Chuen Cheng Ku W1
Cibo, W14
Connaught, W1

Connolly's, SW15
Cork & Bottle, WC2
La Croisette, SW10
Diwana Bhel Poori, NW1
Dragon Inn, W2
Dragon's Nest, W1
Efes Kebab House, W1
Faulkner's, E8
La Fin de la Chasse, N16
Fleet Tandoori, NW3
Florians, N8

Four Seasons, Inn on the Park, W1
Fung Shing, WC3
Galicia, W10
Ganpath, WC1
La Gaulette, W1
Gay Hussar, W1
Gopal's of Soho, W1
Great Nepalese, NW1
Harveys, SW17
Honeymoon, N8
L'Incontro, SW1
Ivy, WC2
Jade Garden, W1
Joe's Café, SW3
Keats, NW3
Kensington Place, W8
Khun Akorn, SW3
Lal Qila, W1
Laurent, NW2
Left Bank, SW10
Ley-On's, W1
Los Remos, W2

Lou Pescadou, SW5
Mandarin Kitchen, W2
Mandeer, W1
Manzi's, WC2
Maroush III, W1
Mekong, SW1 Melati, W1
Ming, W1
Mr Kong, WC2
Nakano, SW3
New World, W1
Ninjin, W1
Nontas, NW1
192, W11
Orso, WC2
Pagu Dinai, SW6
Pizzeria Condotti, W1
Poons, WC2
Poons at Whiteleys, W2
Ragam, W1
River Café, W6
Royal China, SW15
Sabras, NW10
Saheli Brasserie, WC2

St Quentin, SW3
San Martino, SW3
Savoy River Restaurant, WC2
Singapore Garden Mayfair, W1
Singapore Garden Restaurant, NW6
Soong Szechuan Restaurant, NW3
Sree Krishna, SW17
Sud Ouest, SW3
Suntory, SW1 Le Suquet, SW3
Suruchi, N1 Topkapi, W1
Tui, SW7
Upper Street Fish Shop, N1
Wakaba, NW3
Zamoyski's, NW3
Zen, SW3
Zen Central, W1
Zen W3, NW3

London restaurants open for Sunday dinner

Al Hamra, W1
Andrew Edmunds, W1
Au Bois St Jean, NW8
Bahn Thai, W1
Bambaya, N8 Beotys, WC2
Bibendum, SW3
Blakes Hotel, SW7
Blooms, E1
Blue Elephant, SW6
Blue Nile, W9
Bombay Brasserie, SW7
Bu San, N7
Café Flo, NW3
Capital Hotel, SW3
Le Caprice, SW1
Chanterelle, SW7
Chelsea Room, Hyatt Carlton Tower, SW1
Chiang Mai, W1
Chuen Cheng Ku, W1
Connaught Restaurant, W1
Cork & Bottle, WC2
La Croisette, SW10
Diwana Bhel Poori, NW1
La Dordogne, W4
Dragon Inn, W2
Dragon's Nest, W1
Dukes Hotel, SW1
Fleet Tandoori, NW3
Florians, N8
Four Seasons, Inn on the Park, W1

Fung Shing, WC2
Galicia, W10
Ganpath, WC1
Gopal's of Soho, W1
Great Nepalese, NW1
Honeymoon, N8
L'Incontro, SW1
Ivy, WC2
Jade Garden, W1
Kensington Place, W8
Khun Akorn, SW3
Lal Qila, W1
Leith's, W11
Ley-On's, W1
Los Remos, W2
Lou Pescadou, SW5
Mandarin Kitchen, W2
Manzi's, WC2
Maroush III, W1
Mekong, SW1
Melati, W1
Mr Kong, WC2
Nakano, SW3
Neshiko, N1
New World, N1
192, W11
Orso, WC2
Pagu Dinai, SW6
Poons at Whiteleys, W2
Quality Chop House, EC1
Ragam, W1
Rani, N3

Royal China, SW15
Sabras, NW10
St Quentin, SW3
Santini, SW1
Savoy River Restaurant, WC2
7 Pond Street, NW3
Singapore Garden Mayfair, W1
Singapore Garden Restaurant, NW6
Sonny's, SW13
Soong Szechuan Restaurant, NW3
Le Soufflé, Intercontinental Hotel, W1
Sree Krishna, SW17
Sri Siam, W1
Le Suquet, SW3
Suruchi, N1
Surya, NW6
Thailand, SE14
Tiramisu, NW6
Topkapi, W1
Tui, SW7
Turner's, SW3
Wódka, W8
Zen, SW3
Zen Central, W1
Zen W3, NW3

Restaurants with rooms (6 bedrooms or fewer)

England

Abingdon, Thame Lane House
Barnstaple, Lynwood House
Barwick, Little Barwick House
Baslow, Fischer's at Baslow Hall
Birdlip, Kingshead House
Blandford Forum, La Belle Alliance
Bradfield Combust, Bradfield House
Bradford, Restaurant 19, Belvedere Hotel
Brockenhurst, Poussin
Bruton, Claire de Lune
Bury St Edmunds, Kingshott's
Calstock, Danescombe Valley Hotel
Cartmel, Uplands
Cleeve Hill, Redmond's
Clun, Old Post Office
Croyde, Whiteleaf
Dallington, Little Byres
Dent, Stone Close
Diss, Salisbury House
Dorrington, Country Friends
Drewsteignton, Hunts Tor House
Drewsteignton, Old Inn
Dulverton, Ashwick House
East Buckland, Lower Pitt
Exeter, Tudor House
Fletching, Griffin
Glastonbury, Number 3
Harwich, The Pier at Harwich
Hastingleigh, Woodmans Arms
Auberge Haworth, Weavers
Helford, Riverside
Holdenbury, Lynton House
Hopton Castle, Park Cottage
Kintbury, Dundas Arms
Kirkby Lonsdale, Lupton Tower
Knutsford, Belle Epoque
Langho, Northcote Manor
Lavenham, Great House
Leck, Cobwebs
Little Walsingham, Old Bakehouse
Lower Brailes, Feldon House
Lympstone, River House
Manchester, Moss Nook
Montacute, Milk House
Paulerspury, Vine House
Pool in Wharfdale, Pool Court
Poughill, Reeds
Poulton-le-Fylde, River House
Powerstock, Three Horseshoes
Redlynch, Langley Wood
Richmond (N. Yorks), Howe Villa
Sherborne, Pheasants
Shipton-under-Wychwood, Lamb Inn
Spark Bridge, Bridgefield House
Staddlebridge, McCoy's
Stoke-by-Nayland, Angel Inn
Storrington, Manleys
Tavistock, Stannary
Thornton-Cleveleys, Victorian House
Torquay, Mulberry Room
Waterhouses, Old Beams
Wath-in-Nidderdale, Sportsman's Arms
Weobley, Jule's Cafe
Winteringham, Winteringham Fields
Wootton, Lugleys
Wylam, Laburnum House
Yattendon, Royal Oak

Scotland

Canonbie, Riverside Inn
Kingussie, The Cross
Kinross, Croft Bank House Hotel
Muir of Ord, Dower House
Swinton, Four Seasons, Wheatsheaf Hotel
Walls, Burrastow House

Wales

Harlech, Cemlyn
Llansanffraid Glan Conwy, Old Rectory
Nantgaredig, Four Seasons, Cwmtwrch Farmhouse Hotel
Newport, Cnapan
Portfield Gate, Sutton Lodge
Pwllheli, Plas Bodegroes
Talyllyn, Minffordd Hotel

Northern Ireland

Coleraine, Macduff's

Republic of Ireland

Borris, Step House
Wicklow, Old Rectory

The Good Food Club 1990

Many thanks to all the following people who contributed, in one way or another, to this year's Guide…

I.D. Abbatt
R.S.C. Abel-Smith
J.B. Abell
Dr Sidney
　Abrahams
I. Abrahamsen
Dr Michael F.
　a'Brook
John Adams
Miss M.E. Adams
P.D. Adams
Ian Addison
Richard, Marian and
　Zoe Adkin
Eric Adler
Ms A. Affleck
J.R. and J.M. Aisbitt
Mrs L. Ajdukiewicz
E. and J.L. Albarn
N.S. Alcock
Hugh Aldersey-
　Williams
A.W. Aldridge
Gillian M.
　Alexander
Minda and Stanley
　Alexander
Dr and Mrs A.A.
　Alibhai
Mrs M. Allen
Dr A.J. Allen
Ms K.M. Allen
R.G. Allen
Charles Alliott
Peter Alliss
Miss J.V. Allom
David G. Alsar
Mr and Mrs J.G.
　Alston
R. and M.T. Alston
Mr S. Amey
John Amis
R.S. Amsden
Ms Judy Amso

Ms Sue Anderson
Gary Anderson
Geoff Anderson
Prof. J.C. Anderson
Dr M.G. Anderson
Mr and Mrs P.K.
　Anderson
Mrs Margaret
　Anderson
Chris Anderson
L. Andrewes
John R.F. Andrews
Mark Andrews
Gwen and Peter
　Andrews
Mrs M. Angell
Mr and Mrs Kurt
　Angelrath
Michael R. Angus
Mrs Cynthia Archer
Mr and Mrs S.R.
　Archer
Dr J.R. Archibald
Ms J. Archibald
Stephen Arkell
Mr B.J. Armstrong
G.J. Arnold
Ms Carol Arnold
Chris Arthur
Mr M Ashby
David Ashen
Pauline Asher
Mr and Mrs Hubert
　Ashton
L. Aspinall
Mrs Hazel Astley
Mr M.C. Aston
Adrian Aston
Dr P. Aston
Dr Kenneth W.
　Atchley
Mrs M.M. Atherton
Mr W. Atkinson
A.B. Auckland

Pamela E. Austin
N. Auty
Mrs Pamela Avery
Mrs P. Avison
J.L. Awty
H.S. Axton
John and Sue
　Aylward
T.A. Ayres
R.A. Bach
John Bacharach
Dr J.R. Backhurst
Ms Catherine
　Badger
Kenneth Bagnall QC
Sally Bailey
Ian C. Baillie
A.D. Baines
Gino Baio
Ms R Bair
R. Bairamian
J.K. Baker
Miss A.M. Baker
Mrs Julia Baker
Paul and Margaret
　Baker
Mr and Mrs B.
　Baldwin
Richard Balkwill
Mr D.R. Ball
J.C. Ball
William Ballmann
C.D. Bamber
O.W. Bankes
Mrs J.D. Banks
Ms Diana Bannister
Kenneth W. Banta
Mr and Mrs Banwell
Mr K. Barber
Mr and Mrs M.
　Barbour
H.F.H. Barclay
Mrs Carmel
　Bardsley

John A. Barker
Dr D. Barkley
P.J. Barlow
Brigit Barlow
Dr E.D. Barlow
Revd D. Barnes
Mrs K. Barnes
Erica Barnett
Mr and Mrs A.
　Barnett
Mrs K. Barnett
Peter Barnsley
G.J. Barrett
G.P. Bartholomew
M.D. Bartlett
Suzanne Bartlett
J.N. Bartlett
Tony Barton
G.R. Barwick
Mrs E.A. Barwood
Mrs D.L. Basnett
Ms Georgia Bassett
Mr M.J. Batchelor
E.G. Batchelor
E.M. Batchelor
Mr and Mrs J.C.
　Bate
S.R. Bateman
Stanley Bates
T.H. Bates
Col. and Mrs
　Bathurst
Timothy Battle
Dr John R. Batty
Mr W. Batty-Smith
Ms Sian Baverstock
Mr and Mrs T.A.
　Baxter
Muriel Baxter
Robert Baylis and
　Ryta Hulewicz
C.H. Baylis
Conrad Bayliss
H.A. Beadnall

Wanda H. Bean
Philip Bearman
Brian Beasley
K. Beasley
Dr Alan Beaton
Stephen Beaumont
Mrs C Beaumont-
Weeks
Phyllis Becherman
H.H. Beckingsale
Dr John Bedell
Hugh Bedford
F.B. Bedford
Mr and Mrs G.
Bedser
Brian Beedham
A.J. Beer
Mr E.C.M. Begg
Ms Hilary Beggs
John Behle
Mr and Mrs Bell
Mr and Mrs David
Bell
Dr H. Bell
Mrs A. Bellerby
Dr Martin Bellman
Mr and Mrs Paul
Bench
Mrs E. Benford
Mr and Mrs Bennett
Mr G.G. Bennett
A.J.L. Bennett
Paul Bennett
Brian C. Bennett
Elizabeth Bennett
R.D. Bennett
Russell K. Bennett
Mr and Mrs P.
Benny
Mrs Marjorie
Bentham
T.R.F. Bentley
Jon Bentley
S.L. Bentley
William Bentsen
Stephen Beresford
Prof. M.W.
Beresford
Mr and Mrs H.I.
Berkeley
Ruth Berrnard
Mrs Gabriele
Berneck
R.A. Bernstein
Peter Berry
Anita Berry
Mrs S. Berry
Edward A.M. Berry
David Berry
John Berry
Ms Elizabeth Berry
P.E. Berry

J.D. Best
Mr W.J. Best
I.G. Bevan
Ms J.Bewick
Dr D.R. Bickerton
D.R. Bickley
Fred and Vera Biel
F.J.L. Bindon
Keith M. Bingham
E.R. Birch
Mrs S. Bird
C.A.K. Bird
Jackie Bird
Michael D. Bird
Michael J. Bird
William Birtles
Dr Klaus Bischoff
David Bishop
Dr J.M. Bishop
Mr and Mrs B.J.
Blackburn
Mrs V. Blackburn
Graham Blacktop
Sylvia Blades
John Blagden
Mr P.A. Blake
Diana Blake
Charles Blake
M.J. Blakemore
Henry T. Blakeston
M.G. Blanchard
Marilyn Blank
Mrs J.A. Blanks
Mr and Mrs D.E.
Blann
Mr and Mr Blatch
Mrs B. Blewitt
Mary Blewitt
John Blewitt
Mr and Mrs S. Bliss
Ms Ruth Bloom
David Blowers
George Bloy
Jay and Fiona Bluck
David H. Blunt
Alan Blyth
Alan and Doreen
Boden
Paul M. Bogaerts
Linda Bolton
Mr D.R. Bonar
Mrs A. Bond
Richard Bond
A.R. Bond
Lord Bonham-Carter
Brian Bonner
Maurice Bonnor
Mr E. Bonnor-
Maurice
Mrs R.S. Booth
Dr C. Booth

John and Suzanne
Booth
Mr P.J. Bordiss
John W. Borland
G.I. Born
Ms Michelle Borrill
Mrs D. Borton
Janet Boswell
J. A. Boucher
Dr J. Bouffard
Mrs Margaret M.
Boulh
Peter Boulton
B.S. Bourne
Mrs B. Bourne
Mr A.S. Bowell
Mrs I.M. Bowen
Mr A.J. Bowen
C.N. Bowes
I. Bowles
Mr and Mrs D.E.J.
Bowley
Mr and Mrs Ian L.
Boxall
M. Boyce
Simon Boyd
John Boyd
A. Boyes
C.P. Brabban
Roy J. Bradbrook
Wayne W. Bradley
J.G. Bradley
Mrs A. Bradshaw
Rae Bradshaw
Dr and Mrs John
Braithwaite
P.M. Brash
Paul Brassington
K. Brauer
Dr A.M. Braverman
H.G. Brealey
B. Brears
John Brebner
Mrs A.F. Bredin
Joan B. Breen
W.T. Brennan
M.J. Brett
Mr D.H. Brett
Mrs Ann Brett-Jones
H. Brickwood
Lt A. Bridgen RN
David Bridger
Mr T.G. Brierly
J.H. Briggs
B. Brimsmead
Mr and Mrs D.J.
Brine
Mr K.H. Brining
Mr and Mrs J.
Britton
Maurice Broady
Mr and Mrs Brock

Ms B. Brocke
Herr and Frau Hans
Broeske
Miss Chris Brogan
Roy Y. Bromell
G.B. Brook
Keith R. Brook
Dr O.G. Brooke
Cedric Brookes
Garth Brookes
R.S. Brooking
Alan Brooking
Douglas Brooks
Mr M.W.L. Brooks
Stephen Brooks
Dr S.R. Brooks
D.G. Broome
Mrs D. Brotherston
Col. J.M. Browell
Mrs A.C.G. Brown
Graham M. Brown
Lawrence Brown
Barbara Brown
Mrs D. Brown
Dr and Mrs D.G.
Brown
Mrs M. Brown
Ms Jill Brown
Mrs Lillian Brown
I. Brown
Nick Browne
A.C. Brownlow
Mr C.F. Broz
D.W.K. Bruce
M.G. Bruce-Squires
I.S. Brunning
W.H. Bruton
R. Bruton
Mrs Joan Bryan
Terence Bryan
David E.H. Bryan
Ian Bryant
John Bryant
R.K. Bryant
J. Bryant
M Buchanan and Dr
J.H.S. Buchanan
Hugh Buckenham
J.N.G. Buckeridge
Ms Caroline
Buckland
Mr H. Buckle
R.W. Buckle
Richard and Elfie
Buckley
Hans-Joachim Buldt
Mr and Mrs
Geoffrey Bull
C. Bull
Dave Bullen
Mrs Joan Bullock
Mrs Daphne Bullock

Andrew and Sue Crane
Philip Cranmer
Mr J.D. Cranston
Mrs J. Cranswick
T.J. Craven
Patricia Crittenden
Mrs Gloria M. Crocker
Mr T.E. Crompton
Mrs J.H. Crook
Ms Helen Crookston
Peter J. Croome
Miss M. Cropper
Ms Susan Crosbie
R.C. Crosby
David Croser
J.D. Crosland
Rodney Cross
P.R. Cross
G.C. Crossley
B.M. Crowther
T. Crowther QC
Dr S.N. Crutchley
Sir Brian Cubbon
Mrs Cullen
John Culshaw
Frank Cummins
R.T. Cunningham
Dr James Stevens Curl
Steve Currid
A. Currie
Mr and Mrs E.M. Curry
P.L.D. Curry
R.A.J. Curtis
Denis Curtis
David Curtis
Louise Cutler
C.J. Daintree
R.A. Dakin
Dr M.M. Dale
Caroline Dale
Dr W.P. Dallas Ross
Dr V.J. Daniel
D. Danks
L. and P. Darby
David Darley
Wg Cdr K. Dauncey
D.V. Davey
Mr and Mrs P. Davey
Dr T.J. David
E. Davie
A.G. Davies
Jim Davies
Dr John Davies
Gill Davies
Dr R.J. and Mrs K.B. Davies
Sydney G.C. Davies

Roger G. Davies
Dr D.W. Davies
Mrs L.M. Davies
Dr Tim Davies
N.P.A. Davies
A.E.F. Davis
John Davis
Andrew Davis
J.E. Davis
J.R. Davis
Brian Davis
Mr Michael Davis
G.H.A Davis
Martin Davis
Mrs B. Davis
J. Davison
Mrs M. Davison
Dr and Mrs R.P.R. Dawber
Mrs B.A. Dawson
Jenny Dawson-Hodgson
R.K. Day
C. Day
E.N. Day
Basil K. Day
Mrs L.M. Day
J.B. Deby
H.W de Boer
N.R. de Mowbray Jeffrey
N.C. Dee
D. B. T. Deere
John L. De Gurse
N.G. Dekker
Ms Karin De Lange
D.B. Delany
Michael Dempsey
Mr and Mrs M. Dempsey
Kim Dempsey
A.T. Denby
Mr and Mrs Stuart Denney
Dr Thomas H.S. Dent
F.C. de Paula
Ms Kate Derry
David de Saxe
Paul Deschamps
Mrs M.R. de Sousa
Miss I. de Sousa
Judith Dessel
C. Devereux
I.C. Dewey
Charles Dewhurst
Ms Ann W. Dibble
Mark Dicker
Janet and John Dickinson
Mrs G.M. Dickson
Mr S. Dingle

Colin Divall and Karen Hunt
Dave Dixon
Mr and Mrs R.A.E. Dobbs
Christopher Dobie
Mr and Mrs J. Dobris
M.H. Dods
Mr M.R. Dolbear
Peta Dollar
Jean d'Olne
Miss C. Donaughee
Mrs D. Donn
James and Mary Douglas
A.J. Dourleyn
P.B. Dowsett
Jim Doxford
John Drayson
John A. Drew
Garth Drinkwater
Jeff Driver
Stefan Duderstadt
P.Y. Dudgeon
Mrs E.A. Dudley
Ms J.A. Duffin
Mr C. Duggan
R. Duggleby
Mrs J. Dukalski
Ian Duley
Dr and Mrs B. Duncalf
Revd James Duncan
Mrs J. Dundas
John N. Dunham
David and Eileen Dunn
Veronica Dunne
Susan Dunnett
Ray Dunsbier
Denis Durno
Mrs S.F. Durrell-Walsh
James Dutchik
Mr and Mrs N.R. Dutson
Dr and Mrs Dykes
R.T.B. Dykes
R.S. Eades
T.D. Eagling
Mr D. R. Easson
Colin Eastaugh
Dr S. Eden
Roger F. Edgar
Ms Sarah Edington
John Edington
Mr R.W. Edmonds
Mrs B. Edrich
Mr and Mrs K. Edwards
Mrs Juliet Edwards

Mr and Mrs T. Edwards
P.G. Edwards
Ms J.L. Edwards
Dr D.J. Edwards
C.P. Edwards
Mr and Mrs Edwards
Bryan Edwards
Mrs G.M. Eggleston
Mr E. Eisenhandler
Myra and Ray Elderfield
Mrs Hilary Elderfield
Mr J.S. Elliott
Mr L.C. Elliott
Mr I.R. Elliott
L. Elliott
Mr T.A. Elliott
Mrs Peta Elis
D.N. Ellis
Mr D.R. Ellis
Mrs M. Ellis
Roy H. Ellis
Eric Ellsley
C.W. Elston
Nicholas and Victoria Elton
Rod Embley
Mrs J.C. Emmerson
Mike and Anita Emmott
Roger Emmott
D. Enderby
Prof. and Mrs C.E. Engel
R.H. Enslow
Robert Entwistle
Mrs H.R. Erridge
C.G. Erwin
Maurice Escow
Mr and Mrs John Essex
E. Etsen Handler
J.L.D. Evans
Ruth Evans and Juliet Peston
Joy and J.D. Evans
R.W. Evans
Mrs A.J. Evans
J.M.R. Evans
Lord Evans of Claughton
Mr P. Evans
Simon and Rosanagh Evans
Mrs P. Evans
Mrs P.A. Evans
Mrs P.R. Evans
Alan Evers
Mrs R. Ewins

P.M. Eyre
Mr E.G. Eyre
Trevor M. Faber
I. Fair
Mrs Helen Fairley
Mr R.B. Fairweather
Jed Falby
H.C. Fallek
Mrs V. Fama
Mrs C.A. Farmer
Mr R.A. Farrand
Eric F. Farrer
Ms Ann Farrow
Dr M. Faulk
David Faulkner
R.P. Fawcett
Peter Fawcett
G.D. Fearnehough
B. Fehrenbach
Ms P. Feig
Michael Feighery
Mr and Mrs Felstead
D.J. Fenton
Miss S. Fenton
Michelle Ferraton
Paul W. Ferrell
Mrs J. Ferrett
Mr H. Few
S.J. Few
Alan Field
S. Finn
T. Firkins
M.V.C. Firth
Mr M. Firth
Alan Firth
Mr and Mrs D.
  Fisher
Mrs Jean Fisher
Mr I.N. Fishman
Ms Sue Fiske
Mrs J.W. Flack
James and Mary
  Flannery
Clare Fletcher
Mrs Susan Russell
  Flint
V.R. Flint
Derek F. Flitcroft
Ms Eleanor Flood
Mrs V. Fold
Jerry Folkes
D.S. Foord
Mr D.G. Foot
Martyn Ford
Mrs T. Ford
Ms R. Ford
R.A. Ford
Mrs C.K. Forecast
Ms Sally L. Forman
P.J. Forrest
Alan J. Forrest
Mr B.W. Forster

H.P.S. Forster
Mrs Shirley Forsyth
Alan S. Fortune
Roger Forward
Kate Foster
J. Foulston
Mr R.A. Fowler
C. Fowler
Mr R. Fox
Dr Norman France
A.E.J. Francis
Dr G.H.M. Franklin
Howard Franklin
Harold L. Franks
Dr Fraser
R.H. Fraval
Mrs W.A. Fray
John Freebairn
R.W. Freeman
Dr A.G. Freeman
Lindsay and Nick
  Freeman
R. Freeman
Mrs D.J. Freeman
Mrs J. Freeman
P. Freeman
Arthur Freeman
Tony Freeth
Mr and Mrs D.
  French
L.D. Frewin
David Frise
Anthony Froggatt
Helen Froggatt
Prof. Victoria A.
  Fromkin
G.L. Frost
Caroline Frost
Mr and Mrs Froude
Mr G. Froyd
Dr R. Fry
Jonathan Fry
Keith J. Fryer
Mrs Jennifer Full
Mr and Mrs A.
  Fuller
Miss M.N. Fulton
P.R. Fyson
K.F. Gabbertas
Dr and Mrs Roger
  Gadsby
Lt Col. C.S.
  Galbraith
Selwyn Gale
Paul Gallagher
Ms Jane Galt
Mr and Mrs Tony
  Gamble
R. Gamblin
J.H. Gandon
C. Gangsted
R.P. Gapper

Paul Garbett
L. Gardiner
Lawrence Gardiner
Mr E.P. Garner
R.J. Garrard
Amanda Garrett
Patrick Garrett
Clive Garrett
Hazel and Peter
  Garrod
A.E. Gartside
Dr M.S. Gatley
Dr Ian Gavin
Donald M. Gay
H. Geddes
Anthony Gee
Mr and Mrs Paul
  Gentles
E.J. George
K.W. George
H.D. German
Mr R. Gerrard
Mrs P. Gerrard
J.G. Gibbon
Mr and Mrs Austin
  Gibbons
Mrs Jean Gibbs
Mrs J.M. Gibbs
Mrs S. Gibson
Richard J. Gibson
Mrs P.A. Gibson
Mr and Mrs M.C.
  Gibson
Revd Roger Gilbert
Christopher Giles
Mary Giles
Dr Jeremy Gilkes
Phillip Gill
B.S. Gill
Mr and Mrs M. Gill
David I. Gill
Roy Gillard
Basil Gillinson
Ms Susan Gillotti
Tom Gilmore
Ms Sarah Girling
Mrs J. Glasper
Keith Gledhill
Howard Gleek
I.T. Glendenning
Mr Glister
Mrs A.M. Glover
Mrs Joy Glover
K.H. Gluck
A.J. Goater
Peter and Sue
  Godber
Mr and Mrs A.J.
  Goddard
Valerie and Alan
  Golding

Mr and Mrs Michael
  Golding
Arnold Goldman
Joy and Raymond
  Goldman
C.M. Goldsmith
R.W. and Mrs M.E.
  Goldson
Dr J. Goldstein
Michael Goldwater
Mr S.P. Goodacre
John Goodban
Norman Goodchild
Mrs T.A. Goodger
D. Goodger
Mr and Mrs
  Goodison
Mr and Mrs B
  Goodliffe
H.M. Goodman
Peter Goodwin
P. Gordon
Ms Olivia Gordon
David Gordon
M. Gordon-Russell
Jenny Gordon-
  Stables
Brian J. Gordthorpe
J. Gore
D.B. Gorst
Dr J.R. Gosden
D.R. Gosling
Dr C.C.Gosselin
Dr and Mrs K.
  Gough
Mrs Jean Gould
G.K. Gouldman
Michelle Goundry
Mr R.J. Goundry
Mrs Rosalie Gow
Susan Graham
Donald Graham
M. Graham
Valerie Graham
A. Graham
Hugh Graham
Mr and Mrs G.G.
  Grant
Mrs M. Grant
Mrs Patrick Grant
David C. Grant
J.T. Grantley
Mr A.G. Grau
Mrs D.M. Gray
Peter Gray
Rob Gray
P.H. Green and J.
  Thompson
W.G. Green
Colin Green
Lewis Green
Ms S. Green

E. Green
J.C. Green
Mrs M. Green
M.C. Green
M.J. Greenan
Mrs C. Greenbury
N.D.A. Greenstone
Mr. and Mrs K.
  Greenwood
Mr A. Greenwood
Mr J. Greenwood
J. Gregory
Dr P.R. Gregory
Mrs S. Gregory
J.R. and J. Gregory
Mr and Mrs P.V.
  Gregory
C. Greig
Mrs V. Greig
A.K. Grice
John Gridley
Dr A.R. and Mrs
  D.M. Griew
Suzie Griffin
Ms Kristina Griffith
W.T.G. Griffiths
John Alwin Griffiths
W.B. Owen Griffiths
Lt Cdr. R.G.W.
  Griffiths
Mr R.F.B. Grimble
J.W. Grimes
Mr and Mrs Tony
  Grimes
P. Grimsdale
Nigel Grimshaw
Mrs Shirley
  Grimwood
Mr N.M. Grimwood
Don Grisbrook
C.E. Groom
James and Marion
  Grout
Mr R. Grover
Daniel Gruffydd
  Jones
Leif Gudnitz
Mr and Mrs R.K.
  Guelff
W.A. Guerin
Hon. J. Guest
Sally Gugen
Mr B.A. Gunary
Rosalind Gunning
Derek A. Guthrie
Pamela and
  Raymond Guy
Roger Gwynn
C. Hack
Mr and Mrs Hadley
Patrick Hagan

Mr and Mrs John
  Haggar
Mr J. Haines
Mr R. Hainsworth
  and Ms C. Craig
Nicola Hajduk
Dr A.E. Hall
Mr I. Hall
Hazel Hall
Chris Hall
Miss K.J. Hall
Ms Elizabeth Hall
J.P. Hall
Ms Diana Hall Hall
Ms Heather Hallam
G. Hallett
W.J. Hallett
Mrs G. Hallsworth
Mrs Hilary Halpin
Tom Halsall
Mr and Mrs C.J.
  Halsall
R.E. Halstead
G.J. Hamblin
Mr M.V. Hambling
Mrs A.E. Hambly
Malcolm Hamer
Mrs Wendy A.
  Hamilton
F.C.A. Hamilton
Mr D.F. Hamilton
John G. Hamlin
Mary and Ann
  Hamlyn
Ms Kate Hamlyn
J.D. Hammond
Margaretta
  Hammond
Mr H.J. Hamp
Mrs Jose Hampson
Kevin J. Hanafee
M.S. Hancock
S. Hancock
Mrs Lorraine M.
  Handley
Mrs B. Handman
Mr H.G. Hands
Mrs P. Hands
Mr F.G. Hankins
Sir Michael Hanley
Mrs V. Hannam
Revd R.F. Hannay
Mrs G. Hansford
I.R. Hansford
Gilly Harding
Mr and Mrs
  N.B.Harding
Joan Hare
David Harkness
Mr and Mrs James
  Harkness
Mr R.J. Harper

M.J. Harper
L. Harrell
Mr R.W. Harries
W.T.O. Harries
Geoffrey Harris
Raymond Harris
D.T. Harris
Mr and Mrs J. Harris
Mrs R. Harris
Jeremy and Susan
  Harris
Ms Dulcie Harris
M. Harris
Mr and Mrs Harris
Ms Susan Harris
Malcolm Harris
H. Harris
F. Harris-Jones
Anita Harrison
K.G. Harrison
Mrs Annette
  Harrison
P.R. Harrison
J.T. Harrison
Mr and Mrs Blair
  Harrison
Mr and Mrs D.J.
  Harrold
John Harrop
Eric Hart
Mr and Mrs D.J.
  Hart
Ms I. Hart
Miss W. Hart
Ms Laura Hart
Ms Phyllis Harford
Donald Hartog
K.E. Harvey
Dr D. Harvey and
  Mr O.L. Teck
E.H. Harvey
Dr R. Harvey-
  Samuel
P. Harwood
Mr and Mrs I.
  Hassan
Mrs S. Hasseh
Mrs C.A. Hassell
E. Hastings
Simon Havers
Jeremy F. Hawkins
Ms Moni Haworth
Brenda Haydon
Richard Hayes
P. Hayward
Mr J.W. Hayward
Mrs P.L. Hayward
Mr C. Haywood
Peter R. Hazlewood
Mr and Mrs D.J.
  Heacock
D.A. Headley

Greg Heah
Tim Heald
J.D. Healey
A. John Healey
Mrs June Healy
M. Healy
D.J. Heap
Mr and Mrs J. Hearn
Alain Hearn
Frances Heasman
Karen Heaton
Eric Heaton
F. David Heaton
Mr and Mrs J.
  Heaver
Mr and Mrs Heber-
  Percy
J.C. Hedger
Mr H. Heimer
R.G.B. Heller
A. Hemmant
Mr and Mrs M.
  Hemming
K.B. Hemming
Dr W.A. Henderson
Mrs W. A.
  Henderson
Paul Henderson
Mr W.S.D. Hendry
Mr M. Hendy
George W.
  Henshilwood
S.A. Hensman
R.A. Hepher
S.G. Heritage
Philip Herlihy
Dr G. and Dr J.
  Heron
Professor L.J.
  Herrman
Patricia Herrod
Mrs A.L. Hersh
Dr and Mrs
  Herxheimer
Mrs V. Heseltine
Gad Heuman
Mrs G.M. Hewetson
Mrs A.E. Hewitt
Paul and Rosemary
  Hewlett
W.L. Hewlett
D.M. Heyderman
Mrs M.H. Hibbert
E.V. Hibbert
Ms Rosalie Hibbert
Mrs S. Hibbert
Mr D.A. Hickling
Michael S. Hicks
James Hicks
James Higgo
R.P.G. High
F.R. Hilborne

Gordon Hill
Mr M.J. Hill
David Hill
W.G. Hill
Mr H.A.O. Hill
Peter Hill
H.J. Hill
Miles Hill
Wendy Hillary
Mr and Mrs D.W.
  Hills
Ronald and
  Maureen Hinde
Ms Gloria
  Hindhaugh
C. and K. Hindle
Josephine A.
  Hindley
Mr and Mrs R.
  Hinds
Ms Iris Hinds
Mr E.J. Hiram
H. Hirst
G.S. Hislop
Elizabeth Hjort
P. Hoare
Dr Stephen Hoare
J.H. Hobbs
Valerie C. Hobson
Maria Hobson
Ms J. Hobson
W. Hockfield
Mr and Mrs Hodge
Mrs M.R. Hodgson
John Hodson
Dr and Mrs K.
  Hofheinz
Ms Bridget Hogan
Paul Hogarth
P. Hogg
Michael Hoggett
A.C. Holden
A.R.A. Holden
Mrs E.M. Holder
Tony M. Holland
Charles Hollander
Nick Hollis
Mrs P. Holloway
Mr J.F. Holman
Ms Anne Holmes
Mrs M. Holmes
Carolyn Holmes
A.J. Holmes
C.H. Holmes
Rex W. Holroyd
D.A. Holt
F.J. Homer
Paul Honney
Mr A.V. Hopkinson
Lt Col. and Mrs F.T.
  Hopkinson

Ian and Pamela
  Hopley
Mr and Mrs R.H.
  Horncastle
Chris Horner
Mr P.R. Hornsby
Mrs Marily Horton
T.W. Hoskins
Dr Keith Hotten
Revd David
  Houghton
John P. Hoult
Peter Houlton-Jones
Mrs B.M. House
John Howard
Angela Howard
Jan Howarth
Patrick Howarth
Ms Philippa Howell
Mr R.W.F and Dr
  P.J. Howell
Mrs G. Howey
Mrs J.V. Hubbard
David G.T. Hudd
A.M. Hudson
Joan and Peter
  Hudson
Mrs Barbara Huemer
Mrs Vera Huffman
C.J. Huggins
I.W.G. Hughes
Mr C. Hughes
Mr and Mrs Hughes
J.A. Hughes
Dr Louis Hughes
Ian Hughes Smith
Ms M. Huhtala
H. Hull
A.C. Hulse-Wright
David Humphreys
Ms S. Humphries
Sally Hunt
T.V. Hunt
Mr C.J. Hurd
A.G. Hurley
R.G. Hurn
Marvin Hurst
M.J. Hurst
N. Hurst
C.E. Hurt
Ms Sue Hurt
Mrs P.M. Husband
S. Hussain
Sir Michael
  Hutchison
Mike Hutton
Christina Huxtable
Michael Hyde
A. Hyne
Mr T.J. Hypher
Mrs V.A. Iddon
Linden Ife

David N. Ing
Brian Ingram
Mrs Brenda Innes
V.B. Insley
Mrs F. Irving
C.J. Irwin
Dr S.D. Iversen
Mrs L.A. Jack
Dr H.R.S. Jack
R.L. Jackson
Mrs J.J. Jackson
James McG. Jackson
Kate Jackson
H.C. Jackson
Mr and Mrs K.H.
  Jackson
Lt Cdr. Graham
  Jackson
Eric Jaffe
Mrs L. James
G.R. James
Mr B.G.W. Jamieson
P.I. Jamieson
Mr Arthur Jamieson
Edward Jamilly
R.T. Jansen
Mr M.D. Janson
Moira Jarrett
David H. Jarrett
Dr P.N. Jarvis
Michael W. Jarvis
Prof. Barrie Jay
Mrs O. Jeacock
Mr Jeeves
Roland Jefferey
Ms Jill Jefferies
Ronald Jeffery
Mr N.G. Jeffrey
Richard R. Jeffrey
C.M. Jeffries
Julian Jeffs
Debby Jellett
Elgar Jenkins
Richard M. Jenkins
J.C. Jennings
Mrs M.M.G.
  Jennings
Mrs Margaret Jerry
Miss E.N.D. Jervie
D.M. Jessop
B.M. Joce
Dr and Mrs R.T.
  John
J.M. John
Mrs M. Johnson
Mrs J.M. Johnson
Mrs J.K. Johnson
Mrs F.W. Johnson
H.A. and C. Johnson
Mr S.H. Johnston
Dr I.H.D. Johnston
Ian Jones

Mr. and Mrs T.O.
  Jones
Mrs E.C. Jones
Sheilagh Jones
Ms Vicky Jones
J.B. Jones
Suzanne M. Jones
B. Jones
Dr Gill Jones
Mr and Mrs W.
  Morris Jones
Mr N.F. Jones
Canon Ronald Jones
E.H. Jones
Ernest Jones
M.P. Jones
Dr J. Barrie Jones
C.S. Joseph
A.W. Josephy
Peter J.R. Jowitt
M.R. Judd
Mr A.M. Judes
I.R. Judson
Mrs Vivien Jury
Mrs Lesley Kant
Fiona Karlin
L. Katzen
Dr Leon Kaufman
Dr Dina Kaufman
Dr F.C. Kavalier
Ms Ann Kay
G. Kealey
Ms Jane Kearley
Prof. K.M.G. Keddie
Mrs Sheila Keene
Allan Kelly
Mrs Kathleen Kelly
Thomas K. Kelly
Ms Charlotte Kelly
Mr S. Kelly
Mr and Mrs B.G.
  Kemp
Barry and Isobel
  Kempton
Beryl Kendrek
Michael Kenefick
Stephen Kennedy
S.P.L. Kennedy
Air Commodore
  P.A. Kennedy
Michael Kent
W.J. Kent
Frederick N. Kent
Mr R.B. Kenyon
Dr David Kerr
D.F. Kerr
Andrew S. Kettles
J.A. Kewin
John H. Key
Dr Penelope Key
Mathab Khan
J.H. Kilby

753

T. Killelay
K.Y. Kilpatrick
R.J.S. Kimmerling
Ms Diana King
Ronald J. King
A.J. King
Rob and Suzy King
Mrs Lisa King
Sarah King
Stephen King
Paul R. King
Mr and Mrs W.A.
  Kinsman
Dr J. Kirman
Mrs J. Kirton
Janet Kite
Riki Kittel
John Kleeman
Mr and Mrs R. Klein
Robin Knapp
Sylvia Knapp
E.J. Knifton
R.A. Knight
Ms Marion Knight
F.W. Knight
Mrs N. Knoop
Mrs J. Knox
Ms Virginia L. Kolb
S. Koura
Ms Judith Kramer
K.S.S. Krober
C.J. Kuhl
Richard Kunzer
Mr I. Laidlaw-
  Dickson
Miss G. Laing
Maurice Lamb
Christopher
  Lambert
Mr J. Lambert
Miss A.M. Lambert
A.J. Lambert
W. and M. Lamey
Gordon Lammie
Mr J. Lancaster
Mr G.S. Landa
Mrs J. Lane
M.D. Lane
R.C. Lane
Mr R.C. Lang
Jack Lang
J.M. Langer
Mr A.T. Langton
Mrs D. Langton
Mr and Mrs A. Lanzl
Richard C.
  Larkinson
Mr R. Carty
Dr R.D. Last
R.E. Latimer
Ms Anne Laurence
Nicholas Law

H.M.P. Lawford
P. Lawley
Mr and Mrs T.
  Lawmon
D.W. Lawrence
Mrs M.E. Lawrence
Mrs June Lawrence
Tony Lawrence
John H. Lawrence
J. and M. Lawrence
Richard Lawry
Mr. Lawson
R.N. Lay
W.K. Lay
Dr and Mrs R. Leach
R.A.L Leatherdale
David Lea-Wilson
J. Ledbury
Mr and Mrs M.W.
  Ledbury
Dr Vera Lederman
Jean I. Lediard
Stanley Lee
Mrs S. Lee
Mrs B. Lee
Mr and Mrs C.N.
  Lee
Esme Leekie
Anne and James
  Leeming
Robert Lees
David Leibling
Laurie Leigh
P.E. Leigh
Stephen Leinster
Ferrers le Mesurier
A.R. Leon
T.M. Leon
David Leonard
P.L. Leonard
Marjory Lester
John Letman
Ms Ann Levick
Charles Levison
A.S. Levitt
Mr B.P. Levitt
Mr and Mrs Lewin
Nicholas Lewin
W.H. Lewis
Mr D.J.B. Lewis
D.G. Lewis
Ms Leila Lewis
Clare Lewis
Mrs Maggie Lewis
I.T. Lewis
Dr M.G.H. Lewis
Mr C.G. Lewry
Mrs N.K. Leys
Ms Joanna Lidbetter
Harold Lievesley
Mr M.A. Lightfoot
Mrs I.H. Lightman

Peter Lill
David J. Lilly
Helle Linde
Prof. D.V. Lindley
Mr M.M. Lindley
G.R. Lines
J.I. Linley
D.R. and A.J.
  Linnell
Miss E.A. Linton
Joan Lipkin-
  Edwards
Mrs J. Lipman
D.E. Little
B.J. Little
Peter Little
His Hon. Judge I.D.
  Llewellyn Jones
Mrs J.D. Lloyd
Mr J.R. Lloyd
Mr and Mrs S. Lloyd
Robert Lloyd
F.J. Lock
Mrs S. Lockyer
Ms Victoria Logue
Constantine S.
  Loizides
Nigel Lomax
Dr.S Lomax
M.B. Lonergan
Kevin Lonergan
Mr and Mrs W.J.
  Long
Ms Susan Longstaff
Andrew Lonsdale
Ms Susan Loppert
Mr and Mrs Bishop
  Loudon
S.C. Love
A.S. Loveland
Mrs S. Lovell
James Lovely
P.A. and J.B.
  Lowater
H.B. Lowe
Miss C.A. Loy
John L. Lucas
Mrs P.A. Luckly
Robert and Melanie
  Lukies
Patrick Lynch
Mrs Dorothy Lytton
Fred Macaulay
B.E. MacDermott
Mr N. Macdonald
J.M. MacDonald
Alastair Macfarlane
R.B. MacGeachy
Miss J.C. Machin
Mr and Mrs D.B.
  Mack
Dr M. Mack

John S.L. MacKean
C.A. Mackenzie
Ms Shirley A.
  Mackenzie
Mrs B. Mackenzie
Lt Cdr A.G. Maclean
Mr and Mrs
  Maclean
Mr E.W.F. MacLeish
Laurie MacLeod
Mary Maclugash
Mr and Mrs Donald
  Macpherson
Mr G. Macswiney
A.F. Maddocks
Mr and Mrs Kevin
  Magee
Mrs Marlene
  Maguire
Eric Mahoney
Richard D. Mair
Dr James Mair
G.H. Maitland-
  Jones
Mrs P. Makins
Ms E.S. Malec-
  Turner
Frank Maled
Mustafa Malik
Mrs E.J. Malins
Mrs L. Mallett
Mrs I.P. Mallinson
M.R. Mandry
Stuart Manger
E. Manley
Jane Manley
Mr K. Mann
R.K. Mann
Bruce Manning
Mr and Mrs J.
  Manning
Laurence Manning
Peter Mansfield
Mrs Susan
  Mansfield
His Hon. Judge
  Bernard Marder
  QC
Hugh and Cora
  Margey
Jonathan P.
  Margolis
F. Mark
Darryl Marks
Laurence Marks
Mrs Charles Markus
J.P. Marland
L. Marlow
K.G.W. Marsden
Rosemary Marsh
Rowena Marsh
Roger Marshall

James Marshall
John F. Marshall
Mrs A.M. Marshall
Mrs M.G.R. Marshall
Mr and Mrs Roger Marshall
R.F.D. Marshall
Mr and Mrs T.F. Marshall
Tony and Valerie Marshall
Mrs Rosamond Marshall-Smith
Patrick Martensson
Anthony Martin
Christine Martin and Gregory Smith
Mr and Mrs Martin
Mrs J. Martin
J.R. Mascall
A. Mason
Mrs Ruth Mason
Miss P.M. Mason
Christopher Mason-Watts
Ms Patricia I. Massey
Ms Sue Mastriforte
K.G. Mather
Paul Mather
Mr and Mrs H.B. Mathewson
Mr and Mrs Mathias
Mr and Mrs M.R.A. Matthews
Mrs J.S. Maxwell-Hyslop
J. May
Ian May
Mr D. Mayall
Mr and Mrs D. Mayman
W.A.F. McAdam
Mr and Mrs D.G. McAdam
Diana McAndrew
Major M.C.McCabe
A.J. McCall
N.F.J. McCall
Dr Graham McCann
Mrs D.M. McCann
Ms J. McCannon
B. McCarthy
W.J. McClements
Mr and Mrs G.A. McConnell
David McCoy
R.W.J. McCoy
John McCracken
Ms Jennifer McCrea

John McCreasy
Mrs J.M. McDonald
David W. McDonald
Mrs Jean McDonald
Dennis McDonnell
Marcia McDonough
M.J. McErlain
Prof. and Mrs I.D. McFarlane
C.J. McFeeters
Colin McFie
Robin McGhee and Simon Mitchell
Colin and Lilian McGhee
Diana McGowan
Mr and Mrs D.A. McGreavy
Heather McGregor
Lady McGrigor
Mr and Mrs William McGuigan
George F. McInerny
C. McIntyre
Mr and Mrs A.L.G. McKee
Kenneth McKellar
Mr K. Muir McKelvey
Mrs B.D.I. McKenzie
C.W. McKerrow
J.A. McKinnell
Mr and Mrs K.J. McLaren
Mrs Amanda McLaren
John G. McLennan
Peter McLeod
Mrs David McLeod
Karen McMahon
Mr and Mrs T. McMillan
Patrick McNamee
Ms Cathryn McNamee
Ronald S. McNeill
Mrs Moira McNicol
Malcolm McSporran
P. Mead
K. Meader
Philip Meadows
Mr and Mrs E.A. Meager
Joan and Joe Mearns
Mr H.C. Medcalf
Mr and Mrs Tony Mehaffey
Keki D.B. Mehta
Mrs Fiona Mellor
Mrs M.E. Mellor

Peter Mellor
J. Melnyk
David R.V. Mercer
Dr and Mrs A.P. Mercer
Ms Diane Mercer
Major J.B. Merritt
Ms E. Merry
John Messer
Mr I.D. Metherell
Mr E.F.P. Metters
S. Meyler
Jenny Middlemass
Ms Annie Middlemiss
Ian Middleton
W. Middleton
Robin Middleton
R.T. Middleton
Miss P.A. Midwinter
David Millar
Dr and Mrs U. Miller
D. Miller
T.W. Miller-Jones
Gary Millis
Mrs Pauline Mills
Mrs F. Millward
James Milne
M. Milner
D.J. Milner
Luke Milner
Mrs J.M. Milroy
Dr H.G. Mintz
Mohammad Azim Mirza
Martin Mistlin
J. and A.F. Mistry
Robert Mitchell
R. Mitchell
Ashley Mitchell
A.E. Mitchell
Mrs R. Mitchell
Mr and Mrs R.E. Mitchell
Mr and Mrs Moffat
Dr Ainoor Mohamed
Ms Helen Moir
Dr and Mrs A. Moliver
Dr J. Mollon
Dr P.R. Mollson
John Molyneux
W.R. Molyneux
A. Molyneux
Janet Monk
Bob Monkhouse
Mrs N.L. Monks
T.L. Moody
Mrs S. Mookerjee
P.J. Moon

Mr A.J.R. Moon
Eric Moonman
R.D. Moore
Mrs A.S. Moore
Mrs J. Moore
Mrs K. Moore
Mrs M Moore
D.J. Moran
Mr D. Morgan
Rhian Morgan and David Bishop
Howard J. Morgan
Dr B. Morgan
Mr B.M. Morgan
P.A. Morgan
Mrs Len Morland
David Morley and Havovi Todd
F.L. Morrall
Mr F. Morrell
Peter Morrell
D. Morris
Mrs Frances Morris
Ms Aubrey Morris
Jeff Morris
Paul Morris Jones
Mrs W. Morris Jones
A.L. Morrish
Mr J. Morrison and Ms J. Lee
J. Morrison
Mrs P.A. Morrison
A.C. Morrison
T. and M.F. Morrison
George E. Morse
Ralph Mortimer
S. Morton
Mr W.K. Moss
A.W. Moss
A.G. Moss
Mr and Mrs B. Mottershead
Mr and Mrs W.A. Moxon
Ian G. Mucklejohn
Mr and Mrs Barry Muddle
Mrs I.E. Muir
Mrs Suzanne Mulder
Jacqueline Mulhallen
Mr J.M.W. Mullens
Robert Muller
Alan Mullett
Richard Mullineaux
Miss S. Mullins and M. Tungey
A. Mumford
Paul Munday
Ms Annie Munk

A. Munn
Mr P. Munnoch
Mr and Mrs Ken
   Munroe
Deborah Murdoch
David Murdoch
Mr and Mrs
   Raymond
   Murmann
H.A.S. Murray
J. Murray
Mrs G.M. Murray
Mrs M.L. Murray
   Smith
D.P. Murton
D.M. Musitano
Mr M.J. Mylan
Mr S T Naidoo
A.C. Nardini
A.H. Nash
Mrs G. Nash
John Nasmyth
Cdr. and Mrs Barry
   Nation
Mr and Mrs Neal
Mr and Mrs K.
   Neale
Mr D. Neave
Mrs A. Nelson-Iye
John Netherton
Dr and Mrs H.
   Neubauer
Michael Neve
Dr J.M. Newbery
Mrs Laura
   Newcombe
Ken and Jane
   Newell
Charles and Valerie
   Newey
Mr A. Newsham
F.H. Newth
Ms Sandra Newton
A. Nicholas
Tom Nicholls
David Nicholls
Dr C.W. Nicholls
R.A. and P.N.
   Nicholls
Mr H.W. Nichols
R.A. Nicholson
Mr I. H. Nicol
Graham Nicol
Dr A. Nicol
W.E. Nightingale
S. Nisbet
Miss Miriam Nixey
Mr J.B. Nixon
Gianfranco Nobis
David Noble
Geoff Noble
Dr John Nocton

Geoff Normile
J.G. Norris
Ms Alison Northcott
G.E. Nosworthy
Mary B. Notsch
Errol and Ann Nott
Mrs W. Nowell
Mr and Mrs S.R.
   O'Brien
E. O'Casaide
J.B. O'Connor
T.P. O'Hare
Ms Amanda O'Leary
Brendan O'Neill
W.B. O'Neill
Stephen P. O'Rawe
Mr and Mrs D.E.
   O'Sullivan
B.A. O'Sullivan
Ms Lucy Oakley
Charles Oatwig-
   Thain
Graham Oddey
Dr R. Odedra
H.J.M. Offer
Miss Tracy Office
Mr G. Ogilvie-Laing
R.A.L. Ogston
H.N. Olden
Mr and Mrs K.G.
   Oldham
Henry Olejmik
Mrs J.A.L. Oliver
Dr S.N. Oliver
Michael Olpin
Mrs D. Oppenheim
Mr and Mrs M.A.
   Oppenheimer
Mrs E. Orme
Mrs Patricia Orwell
Jonathon F.
   Osborne
Mrs S.E. Osborne
Mr and Mrs R.E.
   Osborne
Ann S. Osborne
T.R. Otley
Mr and Mrs J.R.
   Ovenden
B.T. Overall
George Owen
Walter S. Owen
Mrs D.M. Owen
Mr and Mrs G.R.
   Owen
G. Owens
Philip G. Pacitti
Ms A.M. Pacitti
Meriel Packman
Dr S.D. Page
Brian W. Page
Sue and Geoff Page

Mr and Mrs M.C.
   Paling
William E. Palke
Mr J. Pallot
Michael Y. Palmer
Deborah L. Palser
Mrs J. Pantin
Colin B. Parfitt
Richard Parish
Dr R. Park
Mr W.E. Parker
J.J. Parker
J.R. Parker
John R.J. Parker
Chris Parkin
Ann Parkinson
Martin Parr
Dr C.J. Parsons
T.G. Parsons
Henry Parsons-
   Jones
Harvey Pascoe
Mr and Mrs S.J.
   Passmore
J.D. Patchett
Mrs Rhian Pate
M.H.O. Paterson
Ms Alison Patey
A.J. and H. Patrick
Robert Patten
Dr Anne Paulett
Rosemary Payne
A. and R. Peace
H. Peach
David Pearce
R.J.H. Pearce
Mrs M. Pearlman
John Pearson
H.C.R. Pearson
Mr S.M. Pearson
Dr R.M. Pearson
Mrs C.A. Peberdy
C.J. Peeke
Mr Peel
A.J. Peile
Ms Marianna
   Pencharz
M.C. Pendered
Mr and Mrs P.C.
   Penrose
Adrian Penrose
G.K. Perolls
Mrs D.L. Perrett
F.J. Perring
K. Perry
Michael Perry
Ms Patricia Perry
Mr R.C. Petherick
Mrs M.A. Pettifer
Mr B.W.B. Pettifer
Brian D. Pettit
Anne Phellas

Alicia Gregg Phillips
Spencer Phillips
Mr G.H. Phillips
Mrs I.L. Phillipson
Michael J. Phipps
Mr and Mrs A.
   Pianca
A.M. Pickup
David B. Picton-
   Phillips
Ms Judith Piercey
Mr D.B.E. Pike
J.D. Pilkington
Barry M. Pincus
Geoffrey Piper
Michael Pitel
Hugh Pitt
A.R. Pitt
G.E. Pitts
Mr and Mrs Michael
   Place
Roger Plant
Mr and Mrs T.C.
   Plant
Mrs J. Plante Cleall
Mrs J. Platt
J.H. Plumer
Catherine Plummer
D.M. Pollick
Bruce Poole
P.S.M. Pope
S.J. Popham
Mrs J.M Porter
Rosie Porter
Michael Posner
David Potter
Mr S. Potter
Martin Potter
Dr J.M. Potter
Mr and Mrs A.
   Powell
Mrs C. Powell
Graham Powell
Mr M.J. Pratt
Steven Preece
Mr K.W. Prescot
Mrs J.A. Prescott
Ms Rachel Preston
Ms Sheila Priestner
Dennis Prior
Peter J. Prior
S. Benjamin
   Pritchett-Brown
M.C. Prosser
Mrs S. Proudlove
Gordon W. Provis
Mrs Y. Prynn
Ann and Brian
   Pudner
Mrs S. Pugh
Mrs A. Pulfer
Dr G.P. Pullen

Chris Purchase
Stephen J. Purse
J.C. Purser
Howard Pursey
Angela and Ivor
Quinn
Dr Frank Rackow
Ian and Daniele
Radcliffe
E. Radcliffe
Penny Radford
Christopher Raisin
Mr A. Rampton
Dr and Mrs
Rampton
Mrs W.F.
Ramsbotham
Mrs J. Ramsbottom
Mrs Rosemary
Randall
Colin H. Randell
Dr A.M. Rankin
Robert Ratcliffe
Mrs Pamela Ratoff
Michael Rawling
Mr and Mrs P.A.
Rawlins
Cdr. C.F. Rawnsley
C. Ray
Mr M.A. Rayman
Claire Rayner
Mr G.R. Rayner
Mrs Jo Read
Mr and Mrs David
Reay
Mr Rednall
Mrs Lucie Redway
Dr A.R. Reece
Ms Jane Reed
Alec Reed
Mr R W Reeves
Mrs Rupert Reeves
Mrs R.I. Reeves
Dr W.J. Reeves
Gill Reilly
Mrs A. Reiners
Michael Relton
John Rennison
R.L. Renton
Mrs R.S. Reston
D.N. Reynolds
Mrs K. Reynolds
Jones
Leslie Rhoades
Benjamin Rhodes
V.J. Rice
K.H. Rich
Mr and Mrs B.L.S.
Rich
P.M. Rich
Roy Richards
David Richards

Mrs R.B. Richards
Mrs H. Richards
Mr P. Richards
Mrs G. Richards
Mr C.J. Richardson
D.G. Richardson
M.J. Richardson
Mr F. Richardson
F.G. and S.B. Riches
Mrs J.L. Richmond
Mr and Mrs J.F.
Rickards
Dr and Mrs M. Ridd
Alan Riddle
M.J. Ridgway
H.S. Ridgway
Mr and Mrs D.G.
Ridgwell
Mrs J. Ridley-
Thompson
Mr A.V. Rigby
R. Rigg
N.R. Riley
Gerry Riley
Gordon Ringrose
Mr and Mrs Bryan
Rippin
M. Rippon
Dr B. Ritson
Mrs J. Roach
Ms C.M. Robbins
Ms Linda Roberts
M. Roberts
Miss A.J. Roberts
Mr and Mrs D.
Roberts
Ruth Roberts
P.M. Roberts
Judith S. Roberts
Mr and Mrs John
Robertson
Wendy Robertson
B.C. Robertson
Sheelagh Robertson
L.P. Robertson
Miss A. Robin
Mr and Mrs Mike
Robinson
Mr and Mrs
Robinson
Mr and Mrs D.K.
Robinson
G.L. Robinson
J. Robinson
J.S. Robinson
Ian Robinson
Moira and Dick
Robinson
S.C. Robinson
Mrs P.N. Robinson
Mrs J. Robinson
Ivor Robinson

Mr J. Rochelle
Ms C.J. Rodgers
Mr and Mrs P.N.
Rodgers
Mrs M.E.F. Roe
Leonard Roe
Neil L. Rogall
John A. Rogers
Mr and Mrs R.
Rogers
H.A.E. Rogers
Sir Frank Rogers
Miss E.L. Rogers
D.V. Rogers
B.S. Rooney
Mr D. Rose
Ms C.T. Rose
Dr Eric Rose
Daniel Rose
Jonathan Rose
Dr R. David Rosin
Mr and Mrs G. Ross
Malcolm Ross
Dr D.J. Rostron
R.H. Rowan
Nigel Rowe
Mr J. Rowland
J. Rowland-
Entwistle
Jill Rowley
M.Rowse
Angela M. Royle
Mark Rubin
Mr R.J. Ruffell
J.A. Rumble
John Rumsey
Mr M. Rushton
Mr and Mrs R.E.P.
Russell
Sue Russell
Mrs J. Russell
Alexander B.
Russell
M. Russell
Dr and Mrs J.G.
Russell
Tony Russell
Mr D. Russell
Duncan Rutter
Mr J.S. Rutter
W. Ruxton
R.S. Ryder
Maurice R. Rymill
Miss M. Ruparelia
Michael J. Rysiecki
P. Sachs
Dr Arjun Sahgal
Ron Salmon
D.E. Samuel
Mrs G. Samuels
Ms J. Samulak
Terry Sanderson

Keith Sanderson
Ms A-M. Sands
Mrs J. Sanger
Tony and Mary
Sapsted
Mr and Mrs D.E.
Sarachman-Briggs
Mr S. Sarcar
Vittorio Sartoretto
John W. Savery
Mrs E.B. Sawyer
W.D. Scantlebury
Mr J. Scarisbrick
Mrs S. Scarratt
Herr and Fraulein
Harald Schenk
Tony Schneider
Joyce Schnobrich
Theo P.C. Schofield
Mr R.H. Schofield
Michael Schofield
Alexander
Schouvaloff
Miss J. Schroeder
Peter Schubert
Mr R. Schwarz
Ronald and Anat
Schwarz
Mr P.D. Scott
Mr and Mrs Ian
Scott
K. and D. Scott
Lady Scott
Mrs A. Scott
David Scott
Julian P. Scott
Brian W. Scott
M.J. Scott
C.G.P. Scott-Malden
Miss J.A. Scott-
Malden
M.E. Scourfield
E. Scrannage
R.F. Seaborne
Conrad Seagroatt
Philip Seaman
Peter Searle
D. Seccull
Mr and Mrs N.G.
Sedgwick
Mr and Mrs D. Seel
Ms Gillian Seel
Christian and Hugo
Seely
P.B. Seeman
Mr and Mrs Selby
Professor R. Selden
Mrs J. Seller
Nicholas Selmes
Ms A. Sennett
Dr David and Marlis
Sever

Linda Sewell
Peter M. Seymour
Mrs M. Seymour-
 Smith
Mr and Mrs R.B.
 Shacklock
Kenneth L. Shanks
Ms Rose Shapiro
Dan Shapiro
Mr and Mrs R.
 Sharp
I.G. Sharp
Clifford D. Sharp
Dr J.T.R. Sharrock
Mr and Mrs N.C.
 Shaw
Mr and Mrs C. Shaw
David Shaw
Lester W.K. Shaw
Mike Shea
Mrs C.M. Shearing
B. Sheehan
Mrs Sylvia
 Sheinfield
John Sheinman
Harry Shepherd
P.E. Shepherd
S. Sherwood
P. Sherwood
I. Sherwood-Jones
David Shillitoe
J. Shirley
Matthew Shore
Mrs A. Shorland
James Shorrocks
Michael Shoul
Mrs Hilary Silk
Mrs I. Silva
Harvey Silver
Philip Silver
R. Silverman
Dr and Mrs
 Silverstone
Brian Silverstone
Mrs Deborah J.
 Simmill
R. Simmons and P.
 Carroll
Mr and Mrs
 Simmons
Mr P.H. Simon
Ms Christine
 Simons
Mrs Diana M.
 Simpkins
J.L. Simpson
Mr and Mrs A.
 Simpson
Audrey Simpson
D.A. and B.J.
 Simpson

Mr and Mrs D.
 Simpson
Paul Simpson
Jane Sims
Patricia Sinclair
Mr and Mrs B.
 Sinclair
Ms Anne Sinclair
Tony Sinnott
Mrs Ann Sirkett
S.C. Sixsmith
Ken and Wendy
 Skelton
Ms Jane Skilton
Mr P.R. Slade
Mr D.A. Slade
Nigel Slater
Jonathan W. Slater
Mrs E.S. Slatter
Revd John E. Slegg
Dr T. Smail
Mr B.A. Smart
A. Smart
N.S.L. Smart
M.A.J. Smart
Col. D. Smiley
Alexandra Smith
Mr and Mrs M.W.
 Smith
Wendy Smith
W.M. Smith
Russell Smith
Kenneth E. Smith
Mr D.C. Smith
Stephen Roughton-
 Smith
Mr and Mrs C.L.
 Smith
A. Smith
J.E. Smith
James A. Smith
Mr and Mrs N.L.V.
 Smith
D.A. Smith
Mrs F.M. Smith
Stuart and Gina
 Smith
Ivo Smith
Ms F.M.K. Smith
Ms Helen Smith
Pamela Smith
Mr and Mrs M.Q.
 Smye
Dr G. Smyth
Wendle Snapp
Mr and Mrs John
 Snell
Mrs W. Snowden
M.B. Solomon
Dr B. Solomons
Ian Somerton
S.E. Sondergaard

Michael J. Sookias
Prof. R.R.K. Sorabji
Ms G. Souley
Mr and Mrs Elwyn
 Soutter
Dr D.S. Sowden
Mrs Stephanie
 Sowerby
L.M. Spalton
S.M. Spark
Wg Cdr R.M.
 Sparkes
Ms Alison L.
 Sparkes
David and Ann
 Sparrey
Mr and Mrs Philip
 Spearey
Laila Spence
Mrs V. Spencer
T. Spencer-Andrew
Mr J.F. Spinlove
Mr and Mrs Harris
 A. Sprecher
A.H. Sprey
Jill Springbett
Nicholas Spruyt
Miss S. Squires
Mr M.G. Srivalsan
Sally St Clair
Mr and Mrs G.
 Stacey
Mr and Mrs J.F.
 Stalley
Mr and Mrs R.J.
 Stallwood
Prof. and Mrs K.J.
 Standley
K. Staniland
David and Jackie
 Stanley
John K. Stanley
Sybella Stanley
Mr J.Stanley-Smith
Michael Stark
R.A.J. Starkey
Geoff Stayton
John Stead
Mr and Mrs C.
 Steane
Adrian Stear
D.J. Stedham
Mark A.G. Steeds
G.M. Steel
J.I. Steel
C. Steiger
Mrs G.M. Stein
Mr F.M. Steiner
H. Sternberg
Nikky Sternhell
A.J. Stevens
A. Stevens

J.S. Stevens-Neck
John Stevenson
Alastair Stevenson
Prof. and Mrs J.D.
 Stewart
Mrs F.J. Stewart
Captain and Mrs J.S.
 Stewart
Mrs E.A. Stewart
Dr R.H.M. Stewart
Dr and Mrs J.
 Stewart
A.C. Stoker
Mrs Phillipa J.
 Stone
A.B. Stone
D.W. Stooke
Mr and Mrs C.M.
 Stooke
Mrs M.J. Stowe
Mrs Rosemary
 Stratford
J.W. Straw
Mr G.B. Street
R. Stringer
Prof. W. Stroebe
Ms Louise Stuart
A.R.C. Stuart
Charles Stuart
Mr A.L. Stuart
Douglas Stuart
Bill Stuart
Dr and Mrs J.J.
 Stubbs
Ms Jane Stubbs
Mr E.A. Sturmer
V.K. Subhra
Allyson Sullivan
Mrs K. Summers
Major L.A.
 Summersell
Mr D.J. Sumner
Ms Brit Sundfaer
Dr and Mrs B.
 Surfleet
Malcolm Suss
Vernon Sutcher
Ms Susan J. Sutcliffe
Ms A.M. Sutcliffe
Dr N.S. Sutherland
Graham Sutton
Ms L. Sutton
Mrs I. Sutton
Mrs Stella Sutton
Thomas R. Sutton
A. Sutton
Mrs Margaret Swain
Alan Swain
Tony and Lindy
 Swalwell
David Swift
Mrs Kim Sykes

Alan W. Symes
Ms Brenda Symes
Edith and David
  Symonds
Ms Maxine J.L.
  Symons
R.M. Syrett
Rachel Tackley
Mrs Taggart
Mrs J. Tailford
Cdr Patrick Tailyour
T.G. Talbot
Mr E.E. Tallis
Roger Tame
Mrs G. Tanner
David W. Tanner
Iain Tanquist
N.M. Tapley
L.F.C. Tarrant
Mr J.A. Tarrant
Mr D.W. Tate
Dr P.H. Tattersall
Mrs J. Tavira
Mr A. Taylor
Ms Anna Taylor
T.W. Taylor
Mrs A.C. Taylor
Anthony Taylor
Dr and Mrs P.F.
  Taylor
Mrs Teresa Taylor
Mrs Wendy Taylor
Dr R.J. Taylor
Alan Taylor
George Taylor
Michael J. Taylor
S. Taylor
Mr K. Teasdale
P. Teather
Iain Tenquist
Mrs G. Terry
Ernest Thatcher
Mr B. Theobald
D.O. Thomas
Richard and Carol
  Thomas
Alan Thomas
Mrs V.E. Thomas
R.M. Thomas
J.E. Thomas
Richard Thomas
A.I. Thomas
E.F. Thomas
J.M. Thomas
P.R. and D. Thomas
Oliver Thomas
W.H. Thomas
James Malcolm and
  Jenny Thomas
R.P. Thomas
Mrs P.A. Thomas
Roger Thomas

Ms Jacqueline
  Thompson
W.G. Thompson
S.G. Thompson
Mr and Mrs Peter
  Thompson
Dr C.S. Thomson
Anita Thomson
Mr D.S. Thomson
Mrs J.M. Thomson
Neil Thornber
Mr D. Thornber
Patrick Thorne
A.D. Thorne
Mr M.S. Thornton
G.N. Thornton
Mr and Mrs N.
  Thornton
Miss Tina Thornton
Mr D. Thornton
Peter Thorold
P.W. Thurgood
K. Thurstans
Mr G. Thwaites
T.F. Tiggs
Mr Floyd Timms
Dr J. Timperley
Vera Todd
Mrs Patricia Todd
Revd J. Tolhurst
C.J. Tollett
S.D. Tombett
Neil Tomkinson
Jeremy Tomlinson
Michael Tomlinson
Mr J.E.A. Tonkin
C.G.Toomer
Dr C.J. Torrance
T.D. Tosswill
Martin L. Tovey
Dr M. Townend
A. Townsend
Paul Townsley
Mr G. Tragen
A. Trasi
Jemma and
  Margaret Triance
Dr Michael R.
  Trimble
Prof. E.G. Trimble
Karen Trinder
Alison Trinder
Keith Trobridge
J. Tross
J.R. Trotman
R.J. Trotman
Miss S. Trott
J.L. Tuckey
Fraser Tuddenham
H. Tuit
Mrs S.M. Tunstall
J.A. Turkson

Mr and Mrs Leslie
  Turnberg
John R. Turner
Simon Turner
Charles Turner
Mr and Mrs G.
  Turner
Dr Turner
Simon Turner and
  Caroline Bailey
Mrs Pauline Turner
R. Turner
David Turner
Mr H. Turner
Stuart Turner
Mr B.W.B. Turner
Neil Turner
Mr J.S. Turpin
Mr and Mrs R.D.
  Turvil
Curzon Tussaud
Mr and Mrs R.D.
  Twitchett
John and Gillian
  Tybjerg
Andy Tye and Ms
  Sue Hill
Alan Tye
D.R. Tyler
John Tyrie
Mr I. Tysh
Mr C. J. Uncles
D.N. Underwood
Miss J.P. Urech
Patricia Valentine
Henk and Frances
  Van Heuman
Mr A.C. Vanes
Mr D. Vardy
Mr J Varley
Mr and Mrs Varley
D. Vasudeva
John Vaulkhard
A.C. Verdie
Ms G. Vermeer
A.J.B. Vernon
Anne Vernon
Roger Vielvoye
Mr and Mrs Villa
Mr and Mrs C.A.
  Vinall
Mr and Mrs P.
  Vincent
Amanda Vines and
  Peter Brown
The Hon. Mrs A.M.
  Viney
B.E. Vyner
J.C. Wadams
Mr and Mrs David
  Waddams
John Waddington

Simon Wade
Miss T. Wade
Ms Joan Wagland
Ms G. Wahlstrom
Mrs J. Wainwright
Mrs Sonia Wakely
Tom and Angela
  Walford
Mark Walford
Adam Walford
G. Walker
Mrs P.S. Walker
B.S. Walker
Ian Walker
Mr G.R. Walker
Mr and Mrs Alan
  Walker
Duncan Walker
Mr M.F. Walker
Mrs E. Walker
David Walker
Mr R.P. Walko
William Wall
Mr S.J. Wallace
Mr and Mrs N.E.
  Wallace
R. Wallace
Nick Waller and
  Barbara Gaskell
Mr and Mrs W.
  Waller
Mrs D. Wallin
Francine and Ian
  Walsh
Mr and Mrs D.
  Walter
Mrs P.R. Walters
Jennifer Walwin
Angus H. Wans
A.J.H. Ward
Mrs L. Ward
Mr A.J. Wardrop
Mrs D.S. Warland
Ms Susan R. Warner
Stephen Warr and
  Dr Jane Lolley
Mr and Mrs W.S.
  Warren
David Warren
Dr Warren
Mrs G.M. Warren
John L. Warren
Paul Warren
T.C.T. Warren
C.M. Warrington
Mr R.A. Wartnaby
Toshio Watanabe
N. Waterhouse
Kevin Waterman
L. Waters and P.
  Vanderweele

759

Ms Trudi Wathson-
Ridge
Susan Watkin
W.L.G. Watkins
J.H. Watkins
K. Watkins
A.G. Watson
Allan Watson
Stephen Watson
Mr and Mrs P.
Watson
Miss K. Watson
Mrs T. Wattison-
Ridge
Mr and Mrs E.K.
Watts
Mrs F.T. Wayne
S. Weatherby
Mrs D. Webb
A.E.P. Webb
Dr I. Webb
A.P. Webster
Miss P.M. Webster
Mr John F.N. Wedge
Mrs Ann Weeks
Ms Sally Welbourn
M.D. Welch
C.W. Welch
Ms Ellie Weld
Miss C.S. Wellby
R.J.H. Weller
Dr Frank O. Wells
Mr and Mrs J.E.P.
Wells
Mr R.T. Wells
R.H. Wells
Ms Barbara
Wensworth
M.J. West
C.L. West
R.W. West
J.F.M. West
Christopher West
I.E. West
Ben West
Peter D. West
Mark Western
Ms Lynne Westhead
Sarah Weston
John Weston
Paul Wharton
John E. Whatley
Martin Wheatley
Mrs A.D Whelan

J. Whelans
E. Whitaker
E.H. Whitaker
Mr J.W. Whitaker
Dr D.R. Whitbread
R.A.U. Whitby
Neil White
Terence J. White
E. Clifford White
Mr and Mrs R.
White
N.H. White
Dr J.E.M.
Whitehead
Mr and Mrs J.H.
Whitehead
Katharine
Whitehorn
E.A.O. Whiteman
Mr E.V.M.
Whiteway
Richard O. Whiting
Mr and Mrs L.
Whiting
John Whitley
Paul Whittaker
Ms Susan M.
Whittaker
J.W. Whittaker
Mrs D. Whittle
Kenneth R. Whitton
Mrs L.S. Whitworth
Ms Carole Whyatt
John Whyman
David Wibberly
Miss L. Wickes
B.M. Wicks
Mrs D.L. Widdop
A. Widdup
Mr C.J. Widdup
Gwyneth Wigley
J.B. Wilkin
Edward Wilkin
Paul Willer
G.B.A. Williams
Alun H. Williams
Dr B.D.M. Williams
I. Williams
D.A. Williams
Reginald Williams
Dr M.J. Williams
M. Williams
Mrs J.A. Williams
Mrs J. Williams

Kieran Williams
John Williams
J.M. Williams
Ms Eleanor
Williams
Sandra Williams
Ms Barbara
Williams
David C. Williams
Dr N.J. Williams
Ms Thora
Williamson
J.R. Williamson
Dr J.B.P.
Williamson
Michael Williamson
Stephen Williamson
D.H. Williamson
Mr and Mrs J.
Williamson
Mrs Willson
Gregory Wilsdon
Anthony Wilshaw
Robert Wilson
Mrs A.E. Wilson
David F. Wilson
Peter and Anne
Wilson
Ms Joan Wilson
Miss S. Wilson
Revd. J.L. Wilson
Alan Wilson
Dr J.D. Wilson
Mr D.H. Wilson
Henrietta Wilson
Mr T.M. Wilson
Prof. P.N. Wilson
J. Wilson Bett
Mr T. Wilson Goad
E.P. Wiltshire
Mr A.J. Wingate
J.G.McC. Winslow
Richard S. Winter
L.M. Wise
Alan Wiseman
Mr T. Withers and
Miss H. Cox
Dr D.G. Withers
Mrs Jean Wix
Roger Woddis
K.E.P. Wohl
Dr Kenneth M.
Wolfe
Chas W. Womersley

Mary Wondrausch
Keith P. Wood
Valerie A. Wood
A.J. Wood
Alan Wood
E.A. Wood
G.F.K. Woodhouse
Dr Sheelagh D.
Woods
B.D. Woods-Scawen
Claire P.
Woodwards
Barbara M.
Wooldridge
Jenny Woolf
R.C. Woolgrove
Richard Wootton
Ms Janet Wormell
N.J. Worsley
G.A. Wray
Miss Stephanie
Wray
Christine and
Stephen Wright
Keith Wright
John Wright
Mr G.L. Wright
J. Wright
Mr and Mrs John
Wright
Mrs D. Wright
Alan Wright
Anthony Wright
A.C.H. Wright
Dr and Mrs H.
Wright
Richard Wyatt
Mr and Mrs H.
Wyatt
Trevor Wye
R.A. Wyld
J.A. Yarrow
R.J. Yates
Richard Yates
D. Yeats
Paul Yeoman
D.A. Yerrill
Mohammad Younas
Mrs C. Young
Philip Young
Mr D. Young
P.T. Young
Ms Elizabeth Young
D. Zambia

Alphabetical list of entries

Abbey Green, Chester, Cheshire

Abingworth Hall, Storrington, West Sussex

Adare Manor, Adare, Co. Co. Limerick

Adil, Birmingham, West Midlands

Adlard's, Norwich, Norfolk

Aherne's, Youghal, Co. Cork

Airds Hotel, Port Appin, Strathclyde

Alastair Little, London W1

Alfred's, Louth, Lincolnshire

Al Hamra, London W1

Alouettes, Esher, Surrey

Al San Vincenzo, Cheam, Surrey

Al-Shami, Oxford, Oxfordshire

Altnaharrie Inn, Ullapool, Highland

Alvaro's, Southend-on-Sea, Essex

Alverton Manor, Truro, Cornwall

Andrew Edmunds, London W1

Angel Inn, Hetton, North Yorkshire

Angel Inn, Stoke-by-Nayland, Suffolk

Ann FitzGerald's Farmhouse Kitchen, Mathry, Dyfed

Anna's Place, London N1

Annie's, Ballydehob, Co. Cork

Annie's, Swansea, West Glamorgan

Arbutus Lodge, Cork, Co. Cork

Ard-Na-Coille, Newtonmore, Highland

Ardsheal House, Kentallen, Highland

Ark, Erpingham, Norfolk

Arkle, Chester Grosvenor Hotel, Chester, Cheshire

L'Arlequin, London SW8

Armadillo, Liverpool, Merseyside

Armenian at the Granada Hotel, Manchester, Greater Manchester

Armless Dragon, Cardiff, South Glamorgan

Artistes Gourmands, Nottingham, Nottinghamshire

Arundell Arms, Lifton, Devon

Ashford Castle, Cong, Co. Mayo

Ashwick House, Dulverton, Somerset

Assolas Country House, Kanturk, Co. Cork

Atkins at Farleyer House, Aberfeldy, Tayside

At the Sign of the Angel, Lacock, Wiltshire

Auberge de Provence, London SW1

Au Bois St Jean, London NW8

Auctioneer, Clitheroe, Lancashire

Auctioneer, Preston, Lancashire

Au Jardin des Gourmets, London W1

Austins, Aldeburgh, Suffolk

Aynsome Manor, Cartmel, Cumbria

Ayudhya, Kingston-upon-Thames, Surrey

Bahn Thai, London W1

Balbirnie House, Markinch, Fife

Ballymaloe House, Shanagarry, Co. Cork

Bambaya, London N8

Bardells, St Bride's-super-Ely, South Glamorgan

Barnards, Cosham, Hampshire

Barretts, Glemsford, Suffolk

Barretts, Plymouth, Devon

La Bastide, London W1

Bath Place Hotel, Oxford, Oxfordshire

Baumann's Brasserie, Coggeshall, Essex

Bay Horse, Ulverston, Cumbria

Beadles, Birkenhead, Merseyside

Bedlington Café, London W4

Beetle & Wedge, Moulsford, Oxfordshire

Bell, Aston Clinton, Buckinghamshire

La Belle Alliance, Blandford Forum, Dorset

Belle Epoque, Knutsford, Cheshire

Beotys, London WC2

Le Berger, Bramley, Surrey

Bharat, Bradford, West Yorkshire

Bibendum, London SW3

Billesley Manor, Billesley, Warwickshire

Billy Budd's, Dartmouth, Devon

Bistro Twenty One, Bristol, Avon

Black Bull, Moulton, North Yorkshire

Black Swan, Beckingham, Lincolnshire

Blair's Cove House, Durrus, Co. Cork

Blakes Hotel, London SW7

Blinkers French, Manchester, Greater Manchester

Bloom's, London E1

Blostin's, Shepton Mallet, Somerset

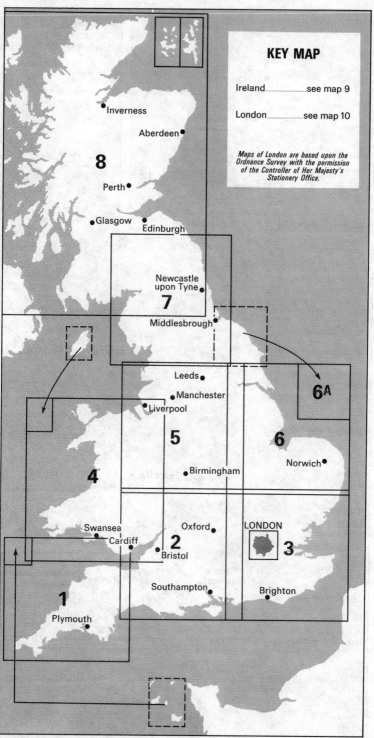

KEY MAP

Ireland .... see map 9

London .... see map 10

Maps of London are based upon the Ordnance Survey with the permission of the Controller of Her Majesty's Stationery Office.

Inverness

Aberdeen

8

Perth

Glasgow

Edinburgh

Newcastle upon Tyne

7

Middlesbrough

Leeds

Manchester

Liverpool

5

6A

6

Birmingham

Norwich

4

Swansea

Cardiff

Oxford

2

LONDON

3

Bristol

Southampton

Brighton

1

Plymouth

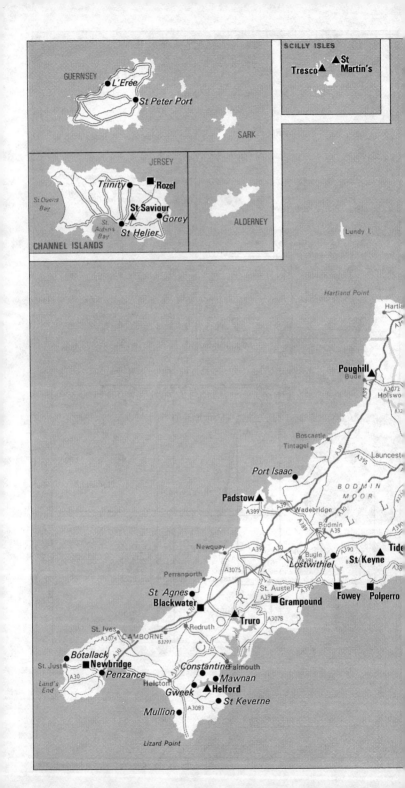

Restaurant ■   **Restaurant with** ▲
       accommodation

● **Round-up entry**

0 Miles   10   20

1

DEVON and CORNWALL

CHANNEL ISLANDS

BRISTOL CHANNEL

Ilfracombe ■

Lynton ●

MINEHEAD ●
Watchet ●

EXMOOR

▲ Croyde

Braunton

Barnstaple ▲

Bideford

Withypool ▲

▲ East Buckland

● North Molton

South Molton

Dulverton ▲

Williton ▲

Langley Marsh ▲

Waterrow

Milverton

Torrington ●

Chulmleigh

Bampton

Wellington ●

Hatherleigh

TIVERTON

Cullompton

M5

Honiton ●

D E V O N

Drewsteignton ▲

Exeter ▲

Sourton ▲

ewdown ▲

Chagford ▲

Lydford ●

Doddiscombsleigh ●

Lympstone ▲

DARTMOOR

Lustleigh ●

Budleigh Salterton ●

Peter Tavy ●

Bovey Tracey ●

Exmouth

Dawlish

▲ Tavistock

Newton Abbot

Kingsteignton ●

Calstock ▲

Buckfastleigh

Babbacombe ■

Torquay ▲

Saltash ●

own Hill

Totnes

PAIGNTON

North Huish ▲

Brixham

Plymouth ■

Modbury ●

Dartmouth ▲

Kingswear

Cawsand ●

int

Kingsbridge ▲

Salcombe

Start Point

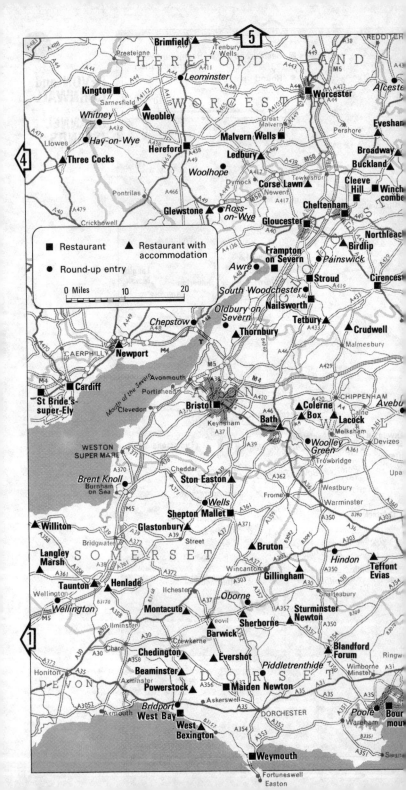

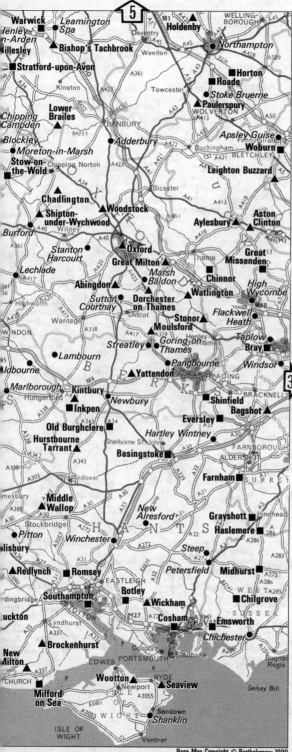

5

3

Warwick
Leamington Spa
Henley-in-Arden
Billesley
Bishop's Tachbrook
Stratford-upon-Avon
Kineton
Chipping Campden
Lower Brailes
Blockley
Moreton-in-Marsh
Stow-on-the-Wold
Chipping Norton
Chadlington
Shipton-under-Wychwood
Burford
Stanton Harcourt
Woodstock
Oxford
Great Milton
Lechlade
Abingdon
Marsh Baldon
Highworth
Sutton Courtnay
Dorchester on Thames
Didcot
Watlington
Chinnor
Wantage
Moulsford
Stonor
SWINDON
Streatley
Goring-on-Thames
Flackwell Heath
Lambourn
Taplow
Bray
Aldbourne
Yattendon
Pangbourne
Windsor
Marlborough
Kintbury
Newbury
Shinfield
READING
BRACKNELL
Hungerford
Inkpen
Bagshot
Old Burghclere
Eversley
Hurstbourne Tarrant
Hartley Wintney
Sherborne St John
FARNBOROUGH
ALDERSHOT
Basingstoke
Farnham
SURREY
Middle Wallop
Stockbridge
Pitton
New Alresford
Grayshott
Hindhead
Haslemere
Salisbury
Winchester
Steep
Redlynch
Romsey
Petersfield
Midhurst
EASTLEIGH
Botley
WEST
SUSSEX
Fordingbridge
Southampton
Wickham
Chilgrove
Ruckton
Lyndhurst
Cosham
Emsworth
Chichester
Brockenhurst
Gosport
PORTSMOUTH
Southsea
New Milton
COWES
Bognor Regis
CHRISTCHURCH
Milford on Sea
Wootton
Newport
RYDE
Seaview
Selsey Bill
ISLE OF WIGHT
Sandown
Shanklin
Ventnor

Holdenby
WELLINGBOROUGH
Daventry
Northampton
Weedon
Horton
Roade
Towcester
Stoke Bruerne
Paulerspury
WOLVERTON
Adderbury
Apsley Guise
Woburn
BANBURY
Buckingham
Fenny Stratford
BLETCHLEY
Bicester
Leighton Buzzard
Aylesbury
Aston Clinton
Witney
Great Missenden
Thame
High Wycombe
Henley-on-Thames

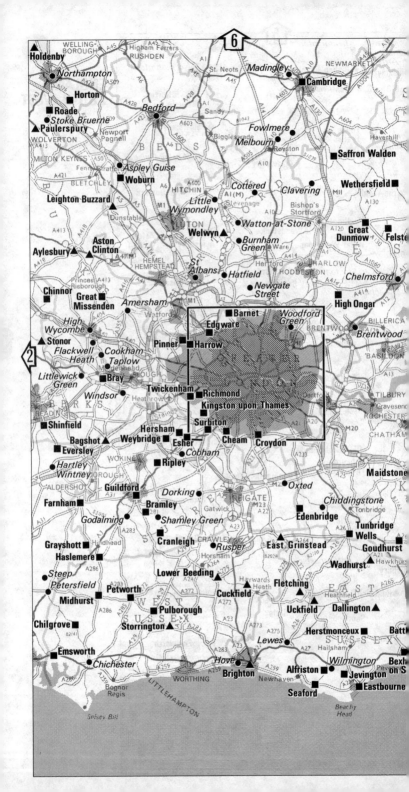

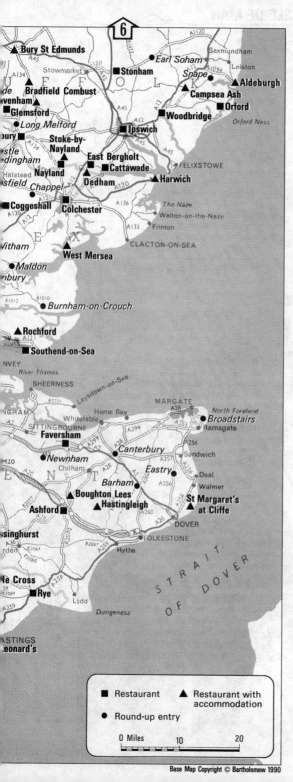

6

3

**ENGLAND:
SOUTH EAST**

▲ Bury St Edmunds
● Earl Soham
■ Stonham
Snape
▲ Aldeburgh
▲ Bradfield Combust
■ Campsea Ash
■ Glemsford
■ Orford
● Long Melford
■ Woodbridge
Stoke-by-Nayland
■ Ipswich
East Bergholt
Nayland
■ Cattawade
Dedham
▲ Harwich
● Chappel
■ Coggeshall
Colchester
West Mersea
● Maldon
● Burnham-on-Crouch
▲ Rochford
■ Southend-on-Sea
Faversham
● Broadstairs
● Newnham
Canterbury
Eastry ●
Barham
▲ Boughton Lees
▲ Hastingleigh
St Margaret's
at Cliffe
Ashford ■
■ Rye

Key	
■ Restaurant	▲ Restaurant with accommodation
● Round-up entry	

0 Miles   10   20

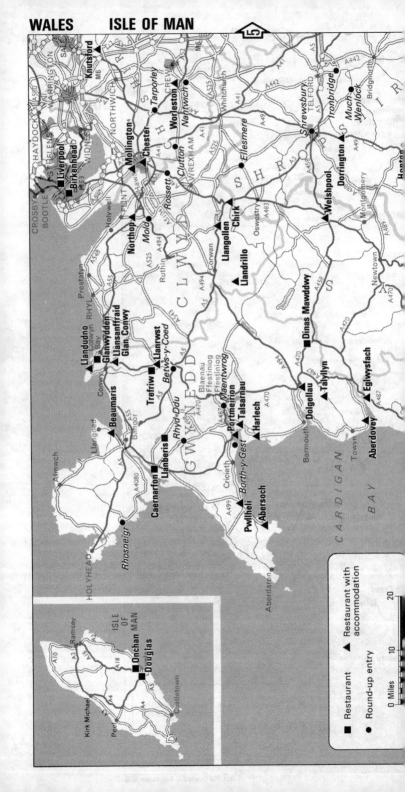

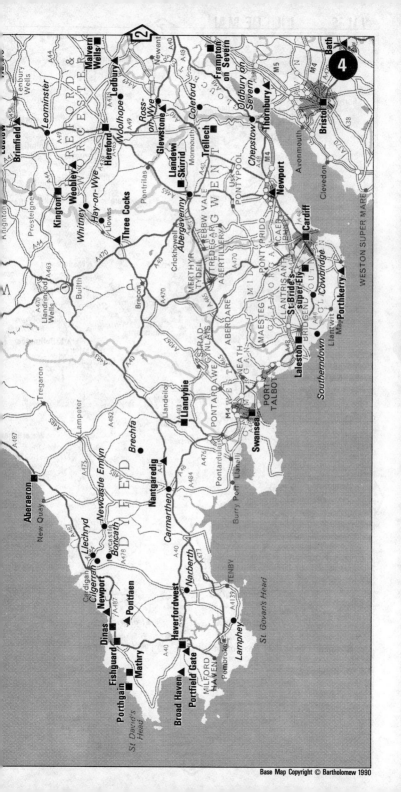

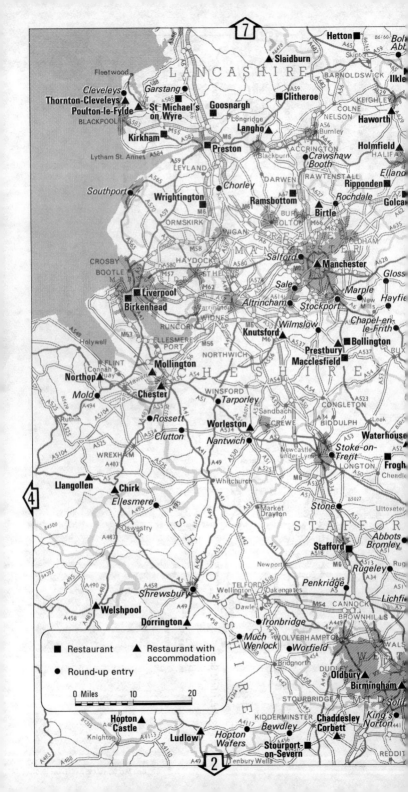

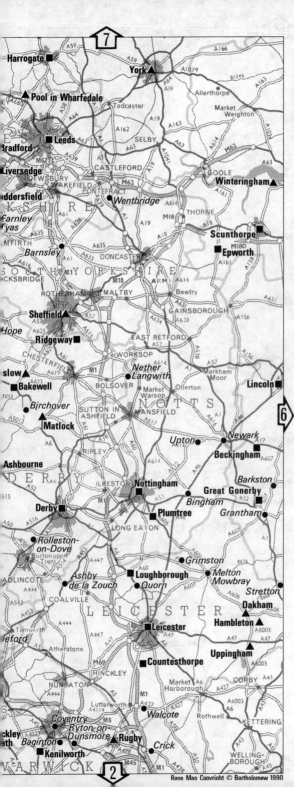

ENGLAND:
MIDLANDS
and
NORTH WEST

Base Map Copyright © Bartholomew 1990

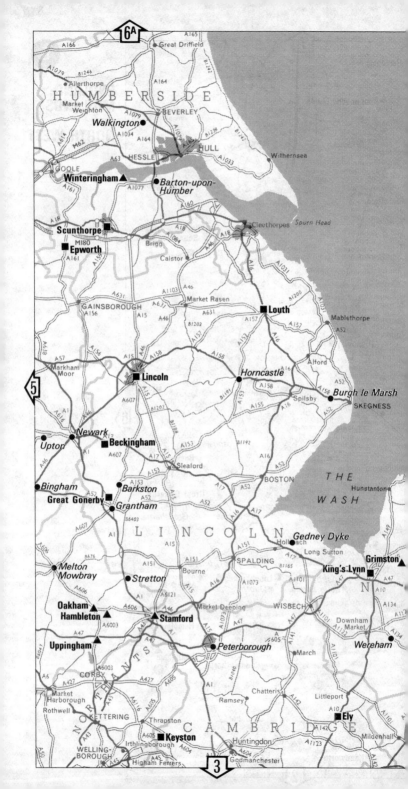

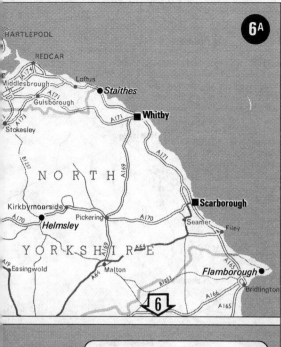

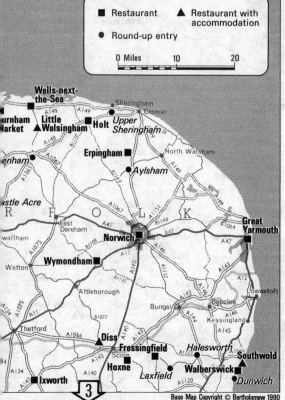

ENGLAND: EAST

6

6ᴬ

Legend:
- ■ Restaurant
- ▲ Restaurant with accommodation
- ● Round-up entry

0 Miles   10   20

Base Map Copyright © Bartholomew 1990

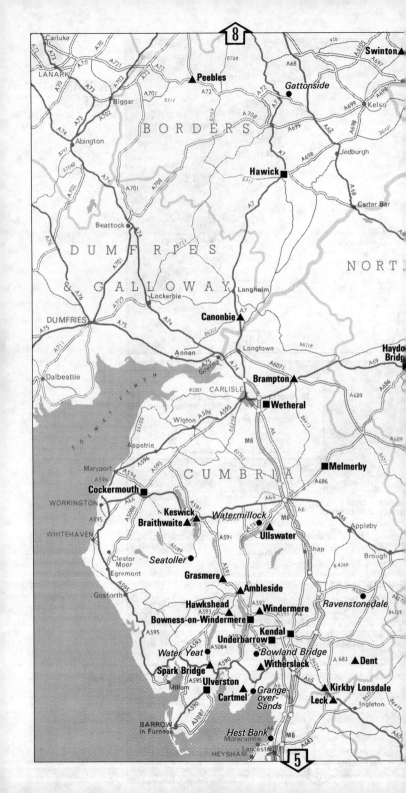

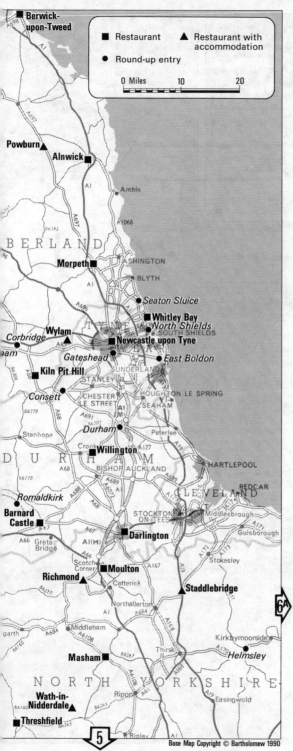

7

ENGLAND: NORTH

Legend:
- ■ Restaurant
- ▲ Restaurant with accommodation
- ● Round-up entry

0 Miles   10   20

■ Berwick-upon-Tweed

▲ Powburn
■ Alnwick

Amble

Corbridge
am

B E R L A N D

■ Morpeth   ASHINGTON
● BLYTH
● *Seaton Sluice*
■ Whitley Bay
North Shields
SOUTH SHIELDS
▲ Wylam   ■ Newcastle upon Tyne
Gateshead   ● *East Boldon*
SUNDERLAND
■ Kiln Pit Hill   STANLEY
Consett   CHESTER LE STREET   HOUGHTON LE SPRING
SEAHAM
Stanhope   *Durham* ●   Peterlee
Crook
■ Willington   H A M
BISHOP AUCKLAND   HARTLEPOOL

D U R H A M

Romaldkirk
REDCAR
C L E V E L A N D
Barnard Castle ■   STOCKTON ON-TEES   Middlesbrough
Greta Bridge   Guisborough
A1(M)   Scotch Corner
■ Darlington
Richmond ▲   ■ Moulton   Stokesley
Catterick
▲ **Staddlebridge**
Northallerton   **6A**
A1
Middleham   Thirsk
garth   Kirkbymoorside
■ **Masham**   *Helmsley*

N O R T H   Y O R K S H I R E

Wath-in-Nidderdale ▲   Ripon   Easingwold
■ **Threshfield**

5   Ripley

SCOTLAND

SCOTLAND

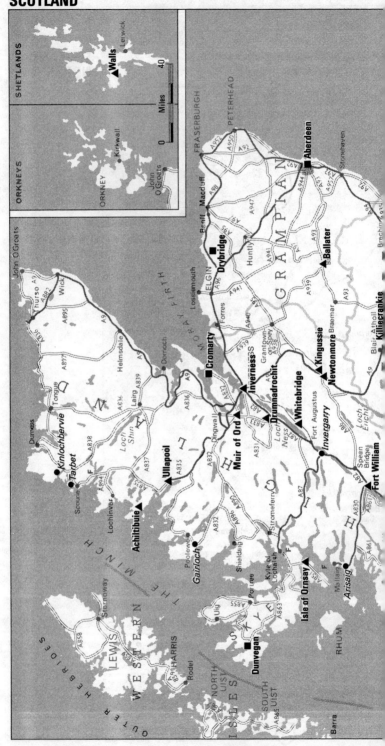

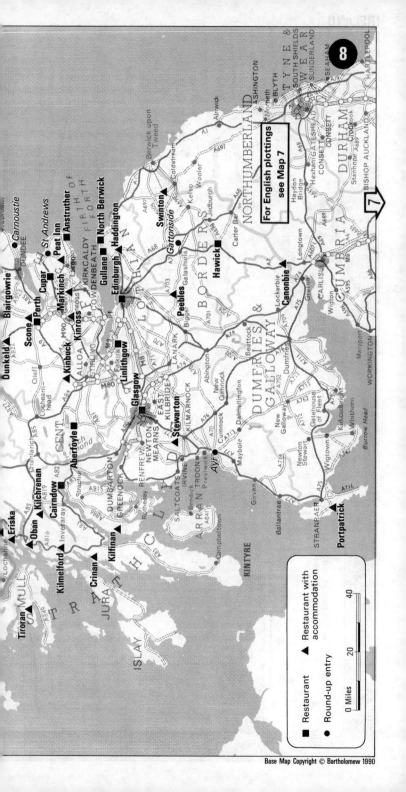

8

For English plottings see Map 7

7

Restaurant ■
Restaurant with accommodation ▲
Round-up entry ●

0 Miles   20   40

Base Map Copyright © Bartholomew 1990

IRELAND

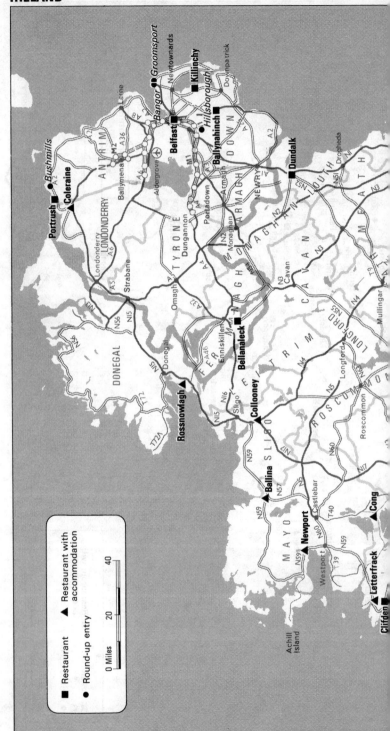

Legend:
- ■ Restaurant
- ▲ Restaurant with accommodation
- ● Round-up entry

0 Miles 20 40

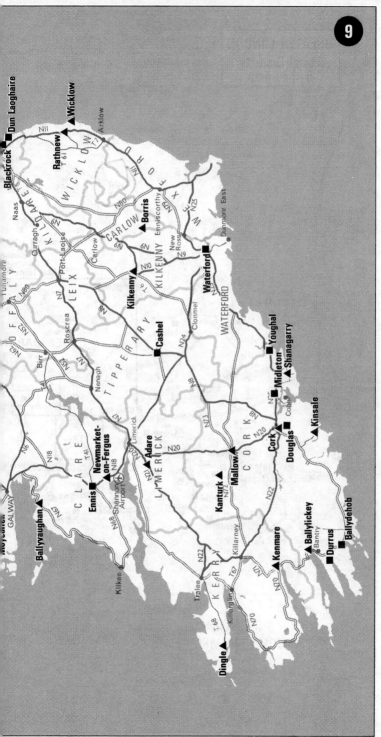

Base Map Copyright © Bartholomew 1990

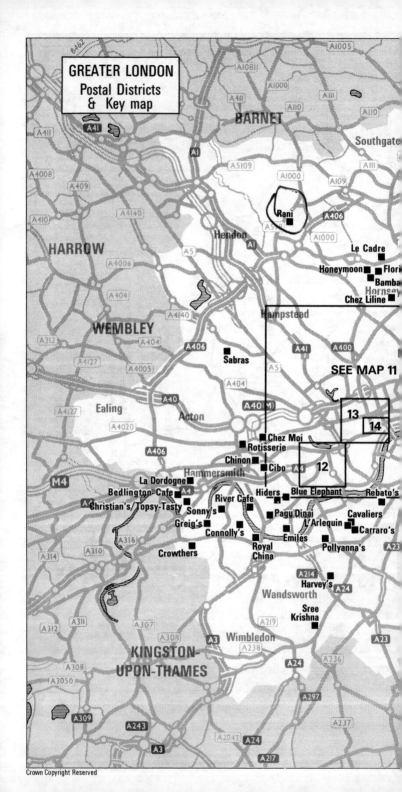

GREATER LONDON
Postal Districts
& Key map

BARNET

Southgate

HARROW

Rani

Hendon

Le Cadre

Honeymoon ■ ■ Flori
■ Bamba
Chez Liline ■

Hornsey

Hampstead

WEMBLEY

■ Sabras

SEE MAP 11

Ealing

Acton

13
14

Chez Moi ■
■ Rotisserie
Chinon ■

12

Cibo ■

Hammersmith

La Dordogne ■
Bedlington Cafe ■
Christian's/Topsy-Tasty

River Cafe ■

Hiders ■

Blue Elephant ■

Rebato's ■

Sonny's ■

■ Pagu Dinai

Cavaliers
■

Greig's ■

Connolly's ■

Royal
China ■

Emiles ■

■ Arlequin

Carraro's
■

Crowthers ■

Pollyanna's ■

Harvey's ■

KINGSTON-
UPON-THAMES

Wandsworth

Sree
Krishna ■

Wimbledon

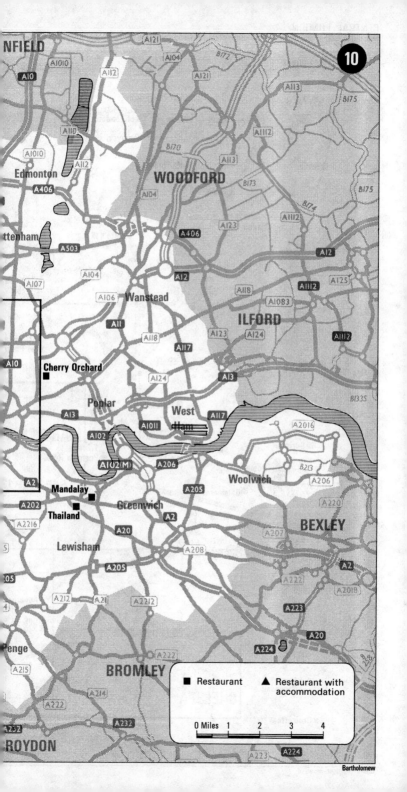

CENTRAL LONGON

CENTRAL LONDON

Child's Hill
■ Laurent
Hampstead Heath
A498
HEATH ST.
A502
GORDON HO. RD.
HIGHGATE
A400

Fortune Green
■ Surya
FINCHLEY

Soong Szechuan
Zen W3 ■ Keats ■
7 Pond St. ■
Gosnel Oak
Fleet Tandoori ■
■ Zamoyski's
MANSFIELD RD.
FORTESS
A502
B511

ROSSLYN HILL
Ken Tow

Cafe Flo ■
A502
MALDEN RD.
B517
CHALK FARM RD.

■ Tiramisu
HAMPSTEAD
IVERSON
B520
SHOOT UP HILL
A5
MILL LA.
B510
W. END LA.
FINE GREE.

■ Wakaba

Singapore Garden Rest. ■ ■ Nichol's
ADELAIDE RD.
BELSIZE
B509
B507

■ Odette's
Primrose Hill
ALBERT RD.
ST.
PA

Au Bois St Jean ■
WELLING-TON
PRINCE ALBERT RD.
A41
A5205
Regents Park
PARK WAY
▲ Nontas
A400
A4201
HAMPS

Kilburn
MAIDA
CAMBRIDGE
B414
B451
B413
AVE
A5

Maida Vale
SHIRLAND
B413
CLIFTON GDNS.
WEST.
WOOD RD.
A5205
Martin's Sta.
PARK RD.
A4
Diwana Bhel Poori

WALTERTON RD.
B414
ELGIN RD.

Canal Brasserie ■
Blue Nile ■
Galicia ■
PADDINGTON
A404
■ Maroush III
Le Muscadet ■
A501
ST. MARYLEBON
A4201

A40 (M)
WESTBOURNE
CHEPSTOW
PK. RD.
■ Surinder
WEST-BOURNE
BISHOPS BR.
PRAED ST.
Los Remos ■
Truffles, Portman Hotel ▲
SEE MAP 13

192 ■
Dragon Inn ■
Leith's ■
Poons at Whiteleys ■
Bayswater
Paddington Sta.
CRAVEN RD.
Kalamaras ■
SUSSEX GDNS.
ROAD
Limited

Mandarin Kitchen ■
PEMBRIDGE
B415
Mayfair

Kensington Place ■
Boyd's ■
■ Clarke's
NOTTING GATE
CHURCH ST.
Kensington Gardens
Hyde Park
PARK LANE
A402

KENSINGTON
Mon Petit Plaisir ■
KENSINGTON HIGH ST.
KNIGHTSBRIDGE
A4
A315
WEST

L'Escargot Dore ■
A315
GLOUCESTER RD.
B325
B319
SLOANE ST.
BELGRAVE SQ.
A302
Auberge Proven ■
Santini ■

CROMWELL RD.
SEE MAP 12
A308
EATON
Ciboure ■
ECCLESTON
Mekong ■

NORTH
WARWICK
B317
EARL'S
A3218
B304 RD.
PIMLICO RD.
WARWICK WAY
Pim
GROSVEN

Lou Pescadou ■
OLD BROMPTON RD.
CHELSEA
A3217
A308

La Croisette ■
LILLIE RD.
A3218
B317
FULHAM RD.
Left Bank ■
KING'S RD.
CHEYNE
OAKLEY ST.
A3217
CHELSEA EMB.
A3212
A3216

Shacklewell

ISLINGTON

Fin de la Chasse ■

Anna's Place ■

Busan ■
Neshiko ■

Soulard ■

Faulkner's ■

Suruchi ■
Tuk Tuk ■
Upper St. Fish Shop ■

SHOREDITCH

Great Nepalese ■

Ganpath ■

FINSBURY

Le Mesurier ■

Quality Chop House ■

Le Cafe du Marche ■

Tatsuso ■

CITY

Bloom's ■

HOLBORN

SEE MAP 14

RSJ ■

Meson Don Felipe ■

SOUTHWARK

Pizzeria Castello ■

LAMBETH

| ■ Restaurant | ▲ Restaurant with accommodation |

0 Mile ½ 1

Bartholomew

CENTRAL LONDON : South-West

Legend:
- ■ Restaurant
- ▲ Restaurant with accommodation

0 Mile   ¼

Restaurants and places marked on map:

- 190 Queensgate
- Wodka
- Launceston Place
- Tui
- St Quentin
- Gilbers
- Bombay Brasserie
- Joe's
- Bibendum
- Hilaire
- Chanterelle
- ▲ Blakes Hotel
- Eleven Park Walk

Streets and places labelled:

- Kensington Gore
- Kensington Rd.
- South
- De Vere Gardens
- Palace Gate
- College of Art
- Royal Albert Hall
- Hyde Park Gate
- Imperial College
- Prince Consort Road
- Royal College of Music
- City & Guilds College
- Princes Gardens
- Ennismore Gardens
- Ennismore Gdns.
- Kensington Gate
- Queen's Gate Ter.
- Gore Rd.
- Petersham Pl.
- Princes Gardens
- Holy Trinity Church
- Elvaston Place
- Imperial Institute Rd.
- Science Museum
- Royal College of Art
- Brompton Oratory
- Queen's Gate Pl.
- Royal College of Science
- Geological Museum
- Cromwell Road
- Natural History Museum
- Cromwell Gardens
- Southwell Gdns
- Grenville Place
- French University College
- Thurloe Place
- Alexander Pl.
- South Ter.
- Ashburn Gdns.
- Ashburn Rd.
- Stanhope Gdns.
- Queensberry Pl.
- Thurloe
- Pelham
- Pelham Street
- Stanhope Gardens
- Harrington Rd.
- South Kensington
- Crescent
- Courtfield Gardens
- Harrington Road
- Clareville Gdns.
- Manson Pl.
- Onslow Square
- Sydney St.
- Pond Place
- Wetherby Gdns.
- Bina Gardens
- Roland Gardens
- Brechin Pl.
- Onslow Gardens
- Sumner Pl.
- Onslow Square
- Old Brompton Road
- Drayton Gardens
- Brompton Hospital
- Royal Cancer Hospital
- Sydney Street
- The Boltons
- Cresswell Place
- Roland Way
- Evelyn Gdns.
- Selwood Ter.
- Neville St.
- South Parade
- Chelsea Hospital for Women
- St. Luke's Hospital
- Little Boltons
- Gilston Road
- Priory Walk
- Thistle Grove
- Elm Park Gardens
- The Vale
- Chelsea Polytechnic
- Tregunter Road
- Redcliffe Rd.
- Seymour
- Callow St.
- Mallord St.
- Mulberry Walk
- Chelsea Square
- Carlyle Square
- Oakley St.
- Fawcett
- Redcliffe
- Hollywood Road
- Eleven Park Walk
- Limerston
- Camera Sq.
- Chelsea Pk. Gdns.
- Paultons
- St. Stephen's Hospital
- King's Rd.
- Globe Pl.
- Upper Cheyne

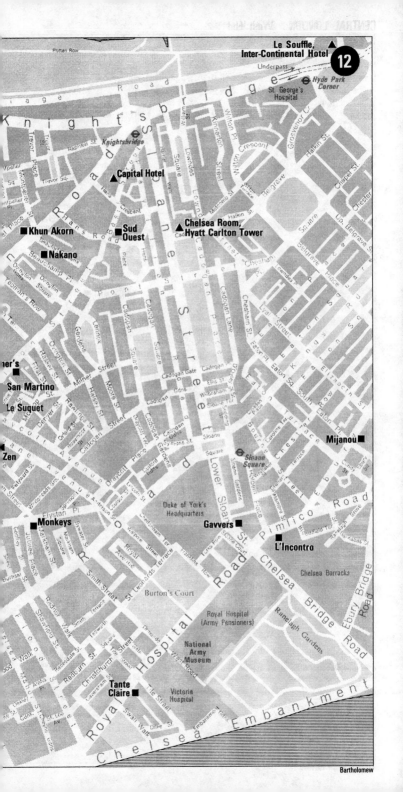

Le Souffle,
Inter-Continental Hotel

12

Potten Row

Underpass

Hyde Park
Corner

St. George's
Hospital

Knightsbridge

▲Capital Hotel

■Khun Akorn

■Sud
Ouest

▲Chelsea Room,
Hyatt Carlton Tower

■Nakano

San Martino

Le Suquet

Mijanou■

Zen

■Monkeys

Gavvers ■

Duke of York's
Headquarters

L'Incontro

Chelsea Barracks

Burton's Court

Royal Hospital
(Army Pensioners)

Ranelagh Gardens

National
Army
Museum

Tante
Claire ■

Victoria
Hospital

Chelsea Embankment

Bartholomew

CENTRAL LONDON: West End

Crown Copyright Reserved

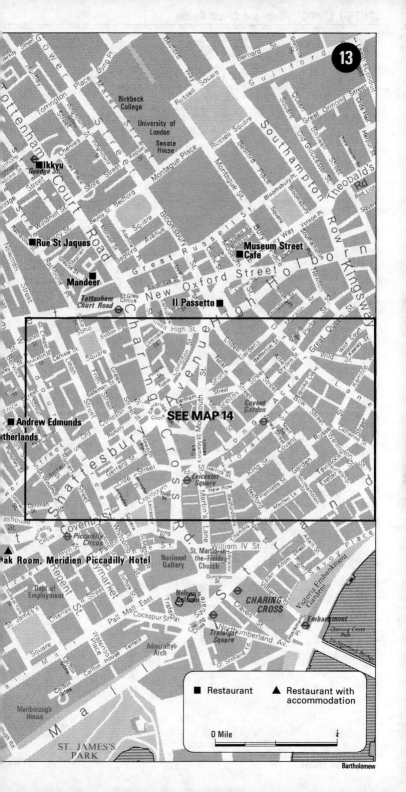

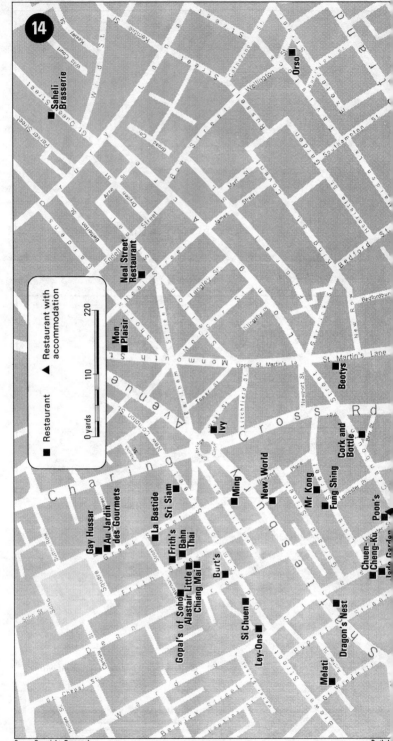

14

Saheli Brasserie

Orso

Neal Street Restaurant

Mon Plaisir

Beotys

Ivy

Cork and Bottle

Ming

New World

Mr Kong

Fung Shing

Poon's

Gay Hussar

Au Jardin des Gourmets

La Bastide

Sri Siam

Frith's

Bahn Thai

Chuen-Cheng-Ku

Jade Garden

Gopal's of Soho

Alastair Little

Chiang Mai

Burt's

Si Chuen

Ley-Ons

Dragon's Nest

Melati

Legend:
■ Restaurant
▲ Restaurant with accommodation

0 yards   110   220

Bartholo

To the Editor *The Good Food Guide*
FREEPOST, 2 Marylebone Road, London NW1 1YN

From my personal experience the following establishment
should/should not be included in the *Guide*.

_____

_____

Telephone_____

I had lunch/dinner/stayed there on _____ 19____

I would rate this establishment _____ out of five.

please continue overleaf

My meal for _____ people cost £ _____ *attach bill where possible*

☐ Please tick if you would like more report forms

I am not connected in any way with management or proprietors.
Name and address (BLOCK CAPITALS)

_____

_____

Signed _____

To the Editor *The Good Food Guide*
FREEPOST, 2 Marylebone Road, London NW1 1YN

From my personal experience the following establishment
should/should not be included in the *Guide*.

_____

_____

Telephone_____

I had lunch/dinner/stayed there on _____ 19____

I would rate this establishment _____ out of five.

please continue overleaf

My meal for _____ people cost £ _____ *attach bill where possible*

☐ Please tick if you would like more report forms

I am not connected in any way with management or proprietors.
Name and address (BLOCK CAPITALS)

_____

_____

Signed _____

Report Form 91

To the Editor *The Good Food Guide*
FREEPOST, 2 Marylebone Road, London NW1 1YN

From my personal experience the following establishment
should/should not be included in the *Guide*.

_____

_____

Telephone_____

I had lunch/dinner/stayed there on _____ 19____

I would rate this establishment _____ out of five.

please continue overleaf

My meal for ____ people cost £ _____ *attach bill where possible*

☐ Please tick if you would like more report forms

I am not connected in any way with management or proprietors.
Name and address (BLOCK CAPITALS)

_____

_____

Signed _____

To the Editor *The Good Food Guide*
FREEPOST, 2 Marylebone Road, London NW1 1YN

From my personal experience the following establishment
should/should not be included in the *Guide*.

_____

_____

                                         Telephone_____

I had lunch/dinner/stayed there on _____ 19____

I would rate this establishment _____ out of five.

please continue overleaf

My meal for ____ people cost £ _____ *attach bill where possible*

☐ Please tick if you would like more report forms

I am not connected in any way with management or proprietors.
Name and address (BLOCK CAPITALS)

_____

_____

Signed _____

To the Editor *The Good Food Guide*
FREEPOST, 2 Marylebone Road, London NW1 1YN

From my personal experience the following establishment
should/should not be included in the *Guide*.

_____

_____

Telephone_____

I had lunch/dinner/stayed there on _____ 19____

I would rate this establishment _____ out of five.

please continue overleaf

My meal for _____ people cost £ _____ *attach bill where possible*

☐ Please tick if you would like more report forms

I am not connected in any way with management or proprietors.
Name and address (BLOCK CAPITALS)

Signed _____

To the Editor *The Good Food Guide*
FREEPOST, 2 Marylebone Road, London NW1 1YN

From my personal experience the following establishment
should/should not be included in the *Guide*.

_____

_____

Telephone_____

I had lunch/dinner/stayed there on _____ 19____

I would rate this establishment _____ out of five.

please continue overleaf

My meal for ＿＿ people cost £ ＿＿＿＿＿＿＿＿ *attach bill where possible*

☐ Please tick if you would like more report forms

I am not connected in any way with management or proprietors.
Name and address (BLOCK CAPITALS)

＿＿＿＿＿＿＿＿＿＿＿＿＿＿＿＿＿＿＿＿＿＿＿＿＿＿＿＿＿＿＿＿＿＿

＿＿＿＿＿＿＿＿＿＿＿＿＿＿＿＿＿＿＿＿＿＿＿＿＿＿＿＿＿＿＿＿＿＿

Signed ＿＿＿＿＿＿＿＿＿＿＿＿＿＿＿＿＿＿＿＿＿＿＿＿＿＿＿＿＿＿＿

To the Editor *The Good Food Guide*
FREEPOST, 2 Marylebone Road, London NW1 1YN

From my personal experience the following establishment
should/should not be included in the *Guide*.

_____

_____

Telephone_____

I had lunch/dinner/stayed there on _____ 19___

I would rate this establishment _____ out of five.

please continue overleaf

My meal for _____ people cost £ _____ *attach bill where possible*

☐ Please tick if you would like more report forms

I am not connected in any way with management or proprietors.
Name and address (BLOCK CAPITALS)

_____

_____

Signed _____

Report Form

To the Editor *The Good Food Guide*
FREEPOST, 2 Marylebone Road, London NW1 1YN

From my personal experience the following establishment
should/should not be included in the *Guide*.

_____

_____

Telephone_____

I had lunch/dinner/stayed there on _____ 19____

I would rate this establishment _____ out of five.

please continue overleaf

My meal for _____ people cost £ _____ *attach bill where possible*

☐ Please tick if you would like more report forms

I am not connected in any way with management or proprietors.
Name and address (BLOCK CAPITALS)

_____

_____

Signed _____

To the Editor *The Good Food Guide*
FREEPOST, 2 Marylebone Road, London NW1 1YN

From my personal experience the following establishment
should/should not be included in the *Guide*.

_____

_____

                                    Telephone_____

I had lunch/dinner/stayed there on _____ 19____

I would rate this establishment _____ out of five.

please continue overleaf

My meal for _____ people cost £ _____ *attach bill where possible*

☐ Please tick if you would like more report forms

I am not connected in any way with management or proprietors.
Name and address (BLOCK CAPITALS)

_____

_____

Signed _____